MAMMALS OF THE WORLD
SECOND EDITION

THE ORIGINAL MATERIAL FOR THESE
BOOKS WAS PREPARED UNDER THE PROJECT
GENERA OF RECENT MAMMALS OF THE WORLD

MAMMALS
OF THE WORLD
SECOND EDITION
VOLUME II

BY ERNEST P. WALKER

FLORENCE WARNICK   SYBIL E. HAMLET
KENNETH I. LANGE   MARY A. DAVIS
HOWARD E. UIBLE   PATRICIA F. WRIGHT

Revision for Second Edition
by
JOHN L. PARADISO

The Original Material for These
Books Was Prepared under the Project
GENERA OF RECENT
MAMMALS OF THE WORLD

THE JOHNS HOPKINS PRESS
BALTIMORE
1968

The Original Material for these
books was prepared under the project
GENERA OF RECENT
MAMMALS OF THE WORLD
begun by the author prior to 1933. The last seven
years and three months of the project were financed by
THE NATIONAL INSTITUTES OF HEALTH under Research Grant 5140
and were sponsored by the New York Zoological Society.

Library of Congress Catalog No. 67-26860

Originally published, 1964
Second Printing, 1965
Second Edition, 1968

CONTENTS

Volume I

Volume II

viii

MAMMALS OF THE WORLD
SECOND EDITION

THE ORIGINAL MATERIAL FOR THESE
BOOKS WAS PREPARED UNDER THE PROJECT
GENERA OF RECENT MAMMALS OF THE WORLD

Order: LAGOMORPHA

Pikas, Rabbits, Hares.

This order contains the family Ochotonidae, the pikas of one genus, and the family Leporidae, the hares and rabbits of nine genera. These lagomorphs occupy a wide variety of habitats on most continents and many of the larger islands, with the exception of Antarctica, Madagascar, and most of the islands southeast of Asia. Members of the family Leporidae inhabit Sumatra and have been introduced on Australia, New Zealand, and other islands.

Lagomorpha was regarded as a suborder of the Rodentia for many years, but few modern zoologists now treat it as such. The origin of these animals is uncertain. Blood tests indicate the phylogenetic distinction of lagomorphs and show no relationship between lagomorphs and rodents. There are some similarities to the various groups of hoofed animals. The geological range of the Lagomorpha is the late Paleocene to the Recent. There is one extinct family.

The members of this order, in the length of the head and body, range from approximately 125 to 750 mm. The hares and rabbits have a short tail and the pikas lack a tail. Adults weigh from 100 to about 4,500 grams. The fur is long, soft, and fine in pikas, and usually thick and soft in rabbits and hares, but it is coarse in some forms. Males do not have a penis bone. The testes are in the scrotum in front of the penis as in the marsupials. In other placental mammals the scrotum is usually located behind the penis.

The internal anatomy is more distinctive than the external characters. The dental formula is: i 2/1, c 0/0, pm 2-3/2, m 2-3/2-3 x 2 = 26 or 28. Lagomorphs, at birth, have three pairs of upper incisors, but the outer one on each side is soon lost. In adults the smaller second upper incisor is located directly behind the first incisor and lacks a cutting edge. The incisors grow throughout life and are completely covered by enamel. The roots of the upper incisors are located in the premaxillary bones of the skull, whereas the lower incisors are of variable length. The cheek teeth are high-crowned and lack roots. In lagomorphs the upper tooth rows are farther apart than the lower tooth rows. The jaw movements of pikas, rabbits, and hares are vertical or transverse.

Pikas are diurnal, colonial, burrowing animals that usually live in rocky areas but sometimes burrow in forests and scrub thickets. Females have four or six mammae.

Rabbits and hares are active mainly in the evening and night. Only a few forms are distinctly colonial. Those species of rabbits that are weak runners generally use burrows for shelters; those rabbits that are strong runners and hares use a grass nest or "form" for shelter. These animals feed on plant material. Females have three, four, or five pairs of mammae.

All members of this order are terrestrial.

Lagomorphs eat only vegetation. Grasses and other herbaceous plants are usually preferred, but when food is scarce, they eat the bark of young trees and shrubs, and even small stems of shrubs. They have a very remarkable provision for obtaining the maximum value from their food. Their fecal material consists of two types: moist pellets which are expelled and are later eaten, and dry pellets which are not eaten. The moist pellets are swallowed with little or no chewing so that most of the food travels through the digestive tract twice. This may be similar to "chewing the cud" in ruminant mammals.

Pika (*Ochotona princeps*), photo by Lloyd G. Ingles.

PIKAS, MOUSE-HARES, RAT-HARES, ROCK CONIES OR RABBITS, WHISTLING HARES; PIPING HARES, LITTLE CHIEF HARES; KORAI-NAICIUSAGI.

THIS FAMILY contains a single Recent genus, *Ochotona*, represented in Asia by 12 species and in North America by 2 species. In the Old World, the range is from southeastern Russia, near the Volga and Urals, through Siberia to Kamchatka and Korea, and southward, east from Iran, Afghanistan, and Turkestan to Mongolia, Tibet, and into the Himalayas. This genus does not occur south of the Himalayas, in eastern and southeastern China, or in southeast Asia, but it does inhabit the northern Japanese island of Hokkaido. In North America, *O. princeps* is present in the Rocky Mountain region in Utah, the Great Basin of New Mexico, and the Sierra Nevada area of California. *O. collaris* occurs in the region of southeastern Alaska and the Yukon. In the southern parts of the range, pikas live high in the mountains to about 373 meters elevation, while in the north they are seen at sea level. The North American species live near and in talus slopes. Some Asian species also live about rocky areas, and others live in forests, shrub thickets, grassy plains, and deserts.

The species of *Ochotona* vary in length from 125 to 300 mm., with most species averaging 200 mm. or less. There is no visible tail. Weight ranges from about 125 to 400 grams (*O. princeps* weighs from 105 to 130 grams). The fur is long, dense, soft, and fine. In most species the general color is a grayish brown, usually darker above than below. One species is reddish in color. Some species have two molts per year; the summer pelage is brighter and more yellowish red, and the winter pelage is grayer. The head is short and blunt; the ears are very short, rounded, and approximately as wide as high. The nostrils can be completely closed. The legs are short, the hind limbs scarcely longer than the forelimbs. Pikas have five fingers and toes. The feet are heavily furred beneath. Females have four or six mammae, and the testes of the males are abdominal, except during the breeding season when they descend into skin folds at the base of the penis.

The dental formula is: i 2/1, c 0/0, pm 3/2, m 2/3 x 2 = 26. The cutting edge of the first upper incisor is V-shaped, and the third upper molar is lacking. The skull is not arched but is rather flattened with a constriction between the orbits.

The warning call is a sharp bark or whistle and is reflected in some of the common names of pikas, such as whistling hare and piping hare. The voice is ventriloquial, and the body jerks forward and upward with each call.

Species which occur in talus areas live among the rocks. Those which occur in plains or desert areas dig burrows. The Japanese pika, for example, is active on top of the snow until the snow is 20 to 30 cm. deep, and then it continues its activity by tunneling under the snow. Conies, with the shortest ears and legs of any lagomorph, have only to drop off a rock into a crevice to hide when an enemy approaches. Other rabbits and hares, with much longer ears and legs, rely primarily or solely on swift running to escape from enemies.

The remarkable custom of curing hay seems to exist throughout this genus. In the late summer, pikas gather grasses, sedges, weeds, and many of the larger flowering and woody plants, sometimes climbing a few meters up trees and out on limbs to cut twigs. The surplus, after feeding, is carried to rocks exposed to the sun to be cured for hay. These piles, which may contain a bushel or more of dry material, are moved constantly to sunny locations. Rock-dwellers store the piles in the shelter of overhanging rocks. Plains-dwellers place the hay at the entrances to their burrows. This stored food is used during the winter when foraging is difficult. Pikas do not hibernate, although they live in regions where winters are long and severe. They have been observed sunning themselves on bright days when the temperature was −17 degrees C. During the warmer months, pikas often bask on exposed rocks with which their color blends. They are active at all hours, particularly in the early morning and evening, and they seem more active on cloudy than on sunny days. Pika calls have also been heard at night. These animals are gregarious, but, at least in O. princeps, one (or possibly two individuals) appears to maintain a small territory where it lives and stores hay. O. princeps advertises ownership of a given territory by an occasional "caack." The forage grounds are communal.

Small, green, ellipsoidal droppings are defecated during the day. The night droppings are black, viscous, and wrapped in a gelatinous substance. This material was eaten by captive O. hyperborea. This habit, common among rabbits, enables them to obtain certain vitamins which would otherwise be lost.

The breeding season appears to be late spring and summer. The gestation period is about 30 days. The litter size varies from two to six, although it is usually three or four. A captive O. princeps female was observed to mate successfully the day after giving birth to a litter. Two or three litters a year are born in a nest of plant material. The young at birth are naked, helpless, and weigh about 9 grams. When one-fourth to one-third adult size, they are weaned. The young of O. hyperborea attain full size in six to seven weeks. The life span is thought to be one to three years.

Parasites found with various species of Ochotona are tapeworms, caecal worms, stomach worms, intestinal nematodes, larval warble flies, ticks, and fleas.

Because of the habitats and geographic areas occupied by most species, these animals rarely come into contact with man's economic activities. O. hyperborea in Japan has been known to damage larch plantings under the snow. This form has also been considered for use as a laboratory animal. It apparently does well in captivity when its vitamin and mineral requirements are met.

The geological range of this family is the late Oligocene to Recent in Europe and Asia, the middle Miocene and the Pleistocene to Recent in North America, and the Miocene in Africa. Remains of an extinct genus, Prolagus, have been recovered from the Pleistocene of France, and Ochotonoides, a fossil member of this family, has been taken from the Pleistocene of China (most abundant in the Choukontein deposits).

The type species of the genus is O. ogotona (Pallas). Pika, Lacepede, 1799, frequently considered as a subgenus, has as the type species O. alpina (Pallas).

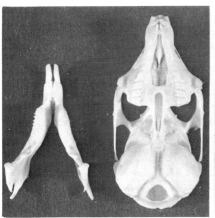 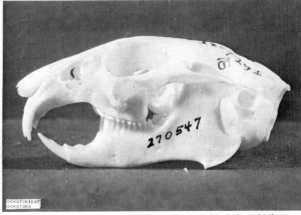

Skull of Pika (Ochotona daurica), in which the second upper incisors can be seen immediately behind the middle two incisors. This arrangement is different from that of most other mammals with second incisors. Photos by P. F. Wright of specimen in U.S. National Museum.

HARES, RABBITS.

THIS FAMILY of 9 genera and approximately 50 species inhabits most of the major land masses and some islands. The natural range does not include the Antarctic region, Madagascar, parts of the Middle East, southern South America, and most oceanic islands. Members of this family have been introduced on Australia and New Zealand and other islands. They are among the most widely introduced mammals. Habitats include forests, shrub-grown areas, grasslands, tundra, and alpine slopes.

Young of rabbits are born naked, blind, and helpless, in a fur-lined nest especially prepared for them, whereas the young hares are born fully haired, with open eyes, and are able to run about a few minutes after birth. Young hares are born in the open, not in a nest. However, the vernacular names "rabbit" and "hare" have been used as though they were synonyms, so they are now often applied to the wrong group. The names "jack rabbit" and "snowshoe rabbit" are applied to hares, and the name "Belgian hare" is applied to a rabbit (*Oryctolagus*). Apart from the larger size and black ear-tips in the hares (this may not be so in all cases), the external differences between the hares and the rabbits are indefinite; the differences are found in the skull. In *Lepus* the palate is short, the postorbital process is broad and triangular, and the sutures of the interparietal bone are fused in the adult. The characteristics are the opposite in *Oryctolagus*.

Female rabbits and hares are usually larger than the males—the reverse is true in most other families of mammals. The members of this family have total lengths of approximately 250 to 760 mm. The tail is short and well furred. Hares are generally larger than rabbits; some weigh as much as 4,500 grams. The pelage is usually thick and soft, but it may also be coarse in some forms. The anal region is nearly naked. If small patches of hair are torn out, new hair soon grows over the area. The coloration ranges through brown, buff, gray, or white. Some forms are striped, and certain northern forms change into a white coat for winter and back to a dark coat for summer.

A sensory pad, normally concealed by hairy folds of skin, is located at the entrance of each nostril, and a Y-shaped naked groove extends from the upper lip to and around the nose. The term "hare-lip," an unusual condition found in man, is derived from this. The ears are relatively smaller in rabbits than in the hares and are longer than wide in all members of the family. The hind limbs are longer than the forelimbs and are usually well adapted for running. All the limbs have five digits, but the first digit is very small. The soles of the feet have hairy cushions. An extensive glandular mass of mammary tissue supplies milk for three to five pairs of mammae. The testes are abdominal but descend during the breeding season.

The dental formula is: i 2/1, c 0/0, pm 3/2, m 3/3 x 2 = 28, except in *Pentalagus* the molars are 2/3. The cutting edge of the first upper incisor is straight, and the incisors are separated from the mouth cavity by lip folds which have a fine velvety covering. The skull is arched and slightly constricted between the orbits. The caecum is the largest part of the digestive tract, having a capacity up to ten times that of the stomach.

Rabbits and hares are active during the evening, usually more active at night than during the day. They feed on plant material and, as far as is known, do not store food as the pikas do. Some rabbits, particularly *Oryctolagus*, associate in groups, whereas hares are usually solitary. Leporids run either a short distance to cover, or over open ground, at speeds of up to 80 km. per hour when in danger. Hares and rabbits are defenseless against predators, but they avoid danger by their keen senses of hearing and smell, nocturnal activity, burrow utilization, and the use of danger signals—rabbits drum with their hind feet. This thumping can be heard by humans at a distance of several feet and can apparently be detected by other hares and rabbits at a considerable distance. Some rabbits, when frightened or captured, emit loud, shrill screams. Those rabbits that are weak runners generally use burrows as shelters; rabbits that are strong runners as well as hares live in a grass nest or "form." Hares sometimes shelter in caves or rock crevices. Males of this family tend to be territorial throughout the year, but the females maintain a territory only during the breeding season.

Pursuit of the opposite sex, flagging of the tail, involuntary urination, caressing, and combat by the males are indications of courtship. Females come into "heat" a number of times during the year and give birth to several litters. Resorption of the developing embryos often occurs. Gestation periods are 28 to 47 days, and hares have longer gestation periods than rabbits. There are usually 2 to 8 young, but often there are more—the maximum is about 15. *Lepus europaeus* utters a bugle-like note to call its young. Puberty is attained in approximately 40 weeks in *Sylvilagus*; however, it may take some species of *Lepus* 2 years to reach this stage of development.

The members of this family are valued as pets, for food, and as fur bearers. They occasionally damage crops and, if present in large numbers, become serious pests and competitors for grazing land.

The geological range of this family is the late Eocene to Recent in North America, the late Oligocene to Recent in Europe, the Oligocene, and Pliocene to Recent in Asia, and the Pleistocene to Recent in Africa and South America. *Hypolagus*, an extinct European and Asian genus of Leporidae, existed during the lower Pleistocene. Fossils are abundant in the Choukontein region of China, where many jaws and even complete skeletons have been found. The modern genus *Lepus* has been found in basal Pleistocene (Villefranchian) deposits in Europe.

Hares and rabbits were important for food and clothing to aborigines who usually caught them in snares. Their thin skins and dense soft fur were well adapted to many uses. Hares and rabbits were, and still are, favorites with sportsmen for hunting. When English immigrants to new lands did not find either hares or rabbits to hunt, they expended considerable effort to transport wild rabbits (*Oryctolagus*) from Europe to Australia and elsewhere as nuclei of breeding stocks to populate the new lands for hunting and other purposes. Sailing ships in the early days often transported rabbits to be released so that they might breed and be a source of food for ships that later might visit the lands where other meat was scarce. The introduction of the animals to Australia, New

Zealand, and other smaller islands was especially unfortunate, for the rabbits were liberated in a land where there were practically no natural enemies and they multiplied rapidly. The results have been extensive destruction of vegetation that has seriously harmed sheep raising in both Australia and New Zealand. This has led to extensive efforts to control the rabbits. Efforts were made to find extensive uses for them, with the result that thousands of skins were exported for use in making felt hats and for fur trimmings on garments. The fur, however, is not of good enough quality to produce the best hats or furs that wear well. The meat was used locally and also frozen and exported. On some of the smaller Pacific islands which were important nesting grounds for such birds as petrels and albatrosses, the rabbits so greatly reduced the vegetation that there was scant cover for the nesting birds and erosion harmed the nesting sites.

On the other hand, rabbits (*Oryctolagus*) have been extensively utilized in many ways. Probably the greatest numbers have been used in medical and other experimental work in laboratories. They have often been given as pets, especially as gifts to children at Easter.

During World War I and II, the raising of rabbits as a food source received great impetus, and many people undertook to raise rabbits in limited space. Thus they were a source for quickly increasing the meat supply for local use.

Through selective breeding during the many years they have been raised in captivity, many breeds have been developed. These range from small to large, white to black, many having varied coloration patterns; and several different types of fur have been developed.

Most people think of hares and rabbits as rodents, but they are sufficiently different in structure to be placed in a separate order with the pikas. There are several differences, but the more easily detected are the lighter structure of the skull and the placing of the second upper incisors behind the first upper incisors. This can easily be observed in the living animal without harming it.

Ryukyu Rabbit (*Pentalagus furnessi*), photo from *List of the Japanese Mammals*, Nagamichi Kuroda.

RYUKYU RABBITS.

Pentalagus furnessi is the only species in the genus and is found only on the Ryukyu Islands, south of Japan.

On the basis of two specimens in the U.S. National Museum, the head and body length ranges from 430 to 510 mm., with a tail about 15 mm. in length. The ear is small to medium, about 45 mm. in length. The fur is thick and woolly. It is dark brown above, becoming more reddish brown on the sides. The underside is a light reddish brown. The claws are unusually long for rabbits (10 to 20 mm.), heavy, and curved.

RED HARES, ROCK HARES; TSOARUS; ROOIHASE.

THESE HARES inhabit the southern part of Africa north through Rhodesia and Tanganyika to Kenya. Authors do not agree at the present time as to the number of species. Ellerman, Morrison-Scott, and Hayman (1953) list three species, Roberts (1951) lists nine, and Allen (1939) lists four species. Members of this genus live principally in rocky areas, usually near crevices to which they retreat when alarmed. They have also been known to live at the edge of dense forests, coming out into open grassy areas to feed at night.

The length of the head and body ranges from about 350 to 500 mm., and the tail is 50 to 100 mm. in length. These hares have short to medium-sized ears, legs much shorter than those of *Lepus*, and short feet provided with short, blunt claws. The fur, including that on the feet, is thick, woolly, and reddish in color. The tail is usually very bushy and is reddish brown to dark brown in color on both surfaces.

In apparent contrast to most other members of the family Leporidae, members of this genus utter vocal calls even though they are not in pain or being restrained. Austin Roberts states in *The Mammals of South Africa* (South Africa, 1951) that when they are alarmed he has "heard them utter a loud startling series of screams when racing away at night." These animals lie secluded during the day, usually between or under large rocks, although some have been observed to hide in vegetation as does *Lepus*. They line these places with their fur, which seems to pull out easily. They sun themselves on boulders in the early

Rock Hares (*Pronolagus rupestris*), photo by James A. Bateman.

morning. In the late afternoon or evening they visit their feeding grounds to feed on grasses and young twigs. If alarmed, they retreat to an observation boulder near their rocky den, into which they can escape if pursued further. These observation boulders are apparently often used, for accumulations of dung nearby provide a conspicuous sign of the animals' presence.

The type species of the genus is *P. crassicaudatus*, Lyon.

Volcano Rabbit (*Romerolagus diazi*), photo by Lloyd G. Ingles.

VOLCANO RABBITS; CONEJITOS, ZACATUCHE, TEPO-RINGO (Mexican names).

THE ONLY species known, *R. diazi*, has an extremely limited geographical distribution and is considered to be a relict form. These little rabbits inhabit elevations between 300 and 3,600 meters high on the slopes of volcanos about 50 km. southeast of Mexico City. This area is only about 40 km. long. The animals are apparently closely associated with two species of tall, coarse "sacatón" grass which grows in dense stands. *Romerolagus* has been described as similar in body form and pelage appearance to a giant, tailless meadow vole (*Microtus*). It is one of the smaller American rabbits, with a head and body length of about 285 to 310 mm. The tail is vestigial. It has short, rounded ears and short hind legs and feet. The upper pelage is grayish brown and black mixed with some yellow hairs. The chin and belly are smoky gray tinged with buff. The feet are buffy yellow. These rabbits prob-ably molt once each year. The skull is similar to that of *Sylvilagus*, except for the lack of an anterior bony projection above the eye socket and some other modifications.

These rabbits are mainly active during the night and twilight hours but sometimes are active by day, especially on cloudy days and during the mating season. They seek the warmth of the sun on cold mornings and after cold, heavy rainstorms. They construct burrows and, unlike most rabbits, maintain well-defined runways through and among the dense tussocks of grass. Apparently they feed on the young shoots of this grass. The droppings are the typical lagomorph ellipsoid, but very small. These little rabbits have a trotting mode of locomotion rather than the hopping motion of a rabbit.

They are hunted by the local Indians for food, despite strict legal protection. When alarmed, their bark sounds somewhat like that of *Ochotona*.

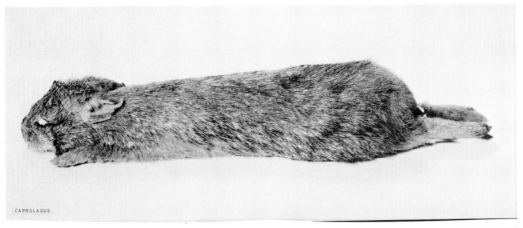

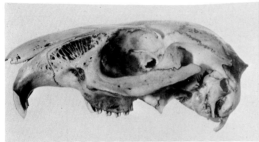 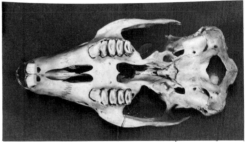

Bristly Rabbit (*Caprolagus hispidus*), photos of skin and ventral view of skull from American Museum of Natural History. Lateral view of skull showing second upper incisors, photo from British Museum (Natural History). (The second upper incisors are lacking in the ventral view of the skull showing only the twin sockets just behind the incisors.)

BRISTLY RABBITS, HARSH-FURRED HARES, ASSAM RABBITS, HISPID HARES; CHOSEN-NOUSAGI.

THIS GENUS has but one species, *C. hispidus*, which occurs in the southern foothills of the Himalayas from Gorakhpur to upper Assam. It does not go into the mountains. It is said to inhabit forest and grassy, bamboo areas.

The hares of this genus have a head and body length of about 475 mm., with a 25 mm. tail, and they weigh about 2,500 grams. The ears are very short and broad, and the eyes are small. The hind legs are short and stout, scarcely exceeding the fore legs in length. The claws are strong, and the teeth are large. The pelage is very unusual, for the outer fur is coarse and bristly. Beneath this there is a shorter, finer underfur. The coloration above is a dark brown, caused by a mixture of black and brownish-white hairs. This color shades to a brownish white on the under parts. The tail is brown on both surfaces, although darker above.

These hares make their own burrows. They are not gregarious but sometimes live in pairs. Their food consists chiefly of roots and bark of trees.

HARES (also erroneously called "Rabbits");
LIÈVRES; HAZEN; HASEN; LIEBRES; JACK "RAB-
BITS."

ABOUT 26 SPECIES have a combined original natural
range that includes most of Eurasia, as far as Sumatra, Java, Formosa, and Japan; most of Africa
except the rain forest of the Congo and the region
along the Gulf of Guinea on the Atlantic coast; and
most of North America south to about the end of
the Mexican plateau, but their distribution is limited
in the eastern half of the United States. They have
been introduced and have become common in some
areas in South America, Australia, New Zealand,
islands off the northwest coast of Africa, and in
some portions of the northeastern United States.

Most of the species live in open grassy areas, but
the varying hare, L. americanus, is generally found in
evergreen forests of northern North America. The
common European hare (L. europaeus) may be found
in both open country (preferably near or on cultivated land) and in woods, usually in deciduous
woods. The blue or mountain hare (L. timidus) even
prefers forested areas to open country. The cape
hare (L. capensis) prefers open country but may
occasionally occur in evergreen forests.

Members of the genus range in head and body
length from about 400 to 700 mm., and in tail length
from 35 to 100 mm. The range in weight is from
1,350 to 7,000 grams. All members of the genus have
long ears and large hind feet. The feet of hares are
well furred, regardless of the climate in which they
live. The usual color is brown or grayish brown
above and a lighter color to white below. The tips
of the ears are black in some of the species, and in
some the upper side of the tail is black. L. nigricollis
of India has a black nape. Some species of Lepus
molt into a white winter pelage, especially those that
live in a snowy winter climate. The time for such
change is governed by the number of hours of daylight. All species that turn white in winter undergo
two molts per year. However, some species that molt
twice do not have a white winter pelage. These usually change from a brown summer pelage to a gray
winter pelage, i.e., L. europaeus. Some species apparently molt only once per year, as those in the subgenus Macrotolagus of western North America,
whereas species in the subgenus Lepus are reported
to molt twice a year.

These hares differ from true rabbits in that they
do not dig or occupy burrows. They spend their
inactive hours hidden in vegetation. Hares are mainly
nocturnal, but some species are active during twilight hours, and some are abroad during the cooler
parts of the day. Individuals that are active in hot,
sunny areas have been observed to habitually rest
in the shade on the north side of shrubs.

Grasses and herbaceous matter are eaten when
available, but twigs and young bark of woody plants
are the staple food when other plants are not available. In isolated cases, hares are reported to have
captured and eaten voles, baby rabbits, and baby
hares.

During the most active part of the mating season,
the males lose their customary caution and are
abroad fighting with other males and pursuing females. Fighting consists of boxing with the fore feet
or kicking with the hind feet. When mating, the females may be quite seriously mauled by their over-
energetic consorts who bite and kick them. Mating
is generally restricted to the milder seasons of the
year, although L. europaeus has been reported to
have bred in every month. In temperate regions two
or three litters are produced by each female during
the spring and summer. Litter size normally varies
from one to seven (three and four seems the average).
In contrast to rabbits, the young are well-furred at
birth, their eyes are open, and they can move about
soon after birth. The young are hidden in several
places in dense vegetation and are visited by the female for nursing. The litter size of L. americanus
increases to eight or ten in periods when the population is increasing rapidly, after a period of very low
population number. The gestation period has been
reported as 36 to 40 days in L. americanus, 41 to 47
in L. californicus, and about 42 days in L. europaeus.

Northern species of Lepus exhibit drastic fluctuations in number which appear to take the form of
cycles of about nine to ten years. They increase to
great abundance and then suddenly decline in numbers. Reasons for the great fluctuation are not definitely known. It is thought that disruption of the
endocrine gland system and various diseases may be
responsible. The most regular cycles of fluctuation
occur among the hares in the northern half of North
America. In some years more than 90 per cent of the
populations of L. californicus in the western United
States die from tularemia. However, this may be an
entirely separate phenomenon.

The various species of Lepus have been used as food
for human beings. Their fur is not durable nor valuable, but it has been used extensively in the manufacture of felt. It is also used for trimming and lining garments and gloves. Hares are eaten extensively
by fur-bearing carnivores, and these are their main
enemies. In addition, they fall prey to the larger
hawks and owls. Those species living near farms or
forest plantations sometimes damage crops and young
trees.

In addition to the scream of fear or injury, hares (L.
europaeus) make a warning noise by grating the teeth
together, as many rodents do when annoyed. This
is taken up by others in the vicinity. When seeking
the young for nursing, female hares call the young
and are answered.

When hares are very abundant, foxes, lynxes,
weasels, and mink increase because of the abundant
food supply, later there is a decline in population
when the hares die off.

The big, long-eared, slender-bodied jack "rabbits"
of western North America are true hares, although
they are regularly called "rabbits." Much of their
range includes regions where vegetation is sparse
(probably due to overgrazing), and on the plains
jack "rabbits" are conspicuous when either running
or sitting up to look about. When crouched against
the ground in the best cover available, they are easily
overlooked. They run rapidly and for greater dis-

A. Arctic Hares (*Lepus arcticus*), photo by A. Pedersen. B. Mountain Hare (*L. timidus*), photo by Kurt Ellstrom.
C. Cape Hare (*L. victoriae*), photo by C. A. Spinage. D. Washington Varying Hare (*L. americanus washingtonii*),
photo by Alex Walker. E. Arctic Hare (*L. arcticus*), very young, photo by A. Pedersen. F. European Hare (*L. europaeus*), photo by A. Pedersen.

657

tances than the rabbits (*Sylvilagus*), which occupy much the same range. Unlike the cottontail and brush rabbits, jack "rabbits" make rather long, high leaps.

The arctic hares are often called snowshoe "rabbits" and the name is appropriate, for the heavily-haired soles of their hind feet give a broad-bearing surface on snow and their tracks look somewhat like miniature snowshoe tracks.

Both of these hares show adaptations for survival under the natural conditions of their environment to a marked degree.

Paleontologically, the genus *Lepus* appears to be young. The oldest remains of a true *Lepus* dates back to the beginning of the Pleistocene.

Lepus, as currently arranged, contains three subgenera, although some mammalogists dispute their validity. They are:

1. *Macrotolagus*, Mearns, 1895, with type species *L. alleni*, Mearns.
2. *Allolagus*, Ognev, 1929, with type species *L. brachyurus* (Temminck).
3. *Bunolagus*, Thomas, 1929, with type species *L. monticularis*, Thomas.

The type species of the genus is *L. timidus*, Linnaeus.

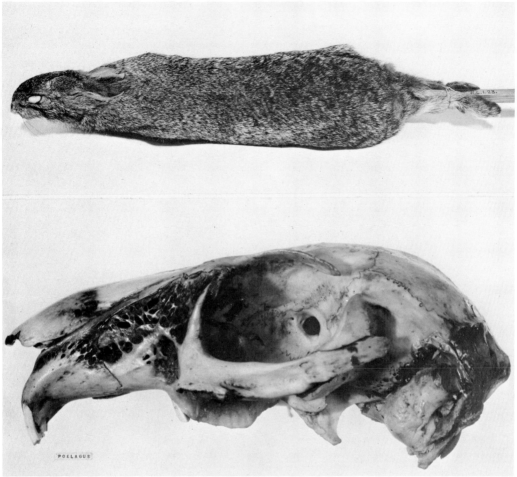

Scrub Hare (*Poëlagus marjorita*), photos from British Museum (Natural History).

SCRUB HARES, UGANDA HARES.

THE RANGE of the one species, *P. marjorita*, is relatively limited: southern Sudan, northeastern Belgian Congo, and northwestern Uganda. It frequents savannah and forest habitats.

The head and body length of these hares is approximately 450 mm., and the tail length is about 50 mm. The weight is about 2,700 gms. The pelage is harsher than that of any other African hare, as the fur is somewhat stiff. The color above is grizzled brown and yellow, becoming more yellow on the sides. The nape is reddish yellow. The tail is brownish yellow above and white below. The under parts are white. Scrub hares have heavier skeletons than *Pronolagus*, and the skulls lack the anterior bony projection over the eye sockets present in *Lepus*. Other distinguishing characteristics are also present. The ears are small, the hind legs are short, and the claws are sharp.

Scrub hares are nocturnal, often seen on the roads at night. While resting, they hide in vegetation. The young are reared in burrows.

Eastern Cottontail Rabbit (*Sylvilagus floridanus*), photo from the New York Zoological Society. Inset: Little Idaho Rabbit (*S. idahoensis*), photo from the American Museum of Natural History through Harold E. Anthony.

COTTONTAILS; TAPETIS, CONEJOS (Sg. *Sylvilagus*), BRUSH RABBITS (Sg. *Microlagus*), TROPICAL FOREST RABBITS (Sg. *Tapeti*), MARSH RABBITS (Sg. *Paludilagus*).

ABOUT 13 SPECIES have a combined range that extends from southern Canada to Argentina and Paraguay. They occupy a great diversity of habitats. Most species prefer open or brushy land or clearings in forested areas. A few frequent forests, swamps, marshes, sand beaches, and desert lands.

The head and body length ranges from about 250 to 450 mm., and the tail length is 25 mm. to 60 mm. The weight varies from about 400 to about 2,300 gms. The smallest is *S. idahoensis*, and the largest is *S. aquaticus*. The ears vary in size among the species but, in general, are of medium length. The tail in the subgenus *Sylvilagus* (= *Microlagus*, Trouessart, 1897) is brown above and white below; hence the vernacular name "cottontail." The underside of the tail in the one species in each of the other two subgenera, *Paludilagus*, Hershkovitz, 1950 and *Tapeti*, Gray, 1867, is dark-colored. The usual color of the various species is grayish brown to reddish brown above. The undersides are usually white or buffy white. The nape is often red, but it may be black. The subgenus *Sylvilagus* molts once a year. None of the members of the genus are known to turn white in the winter.

S. idahoensis is the only species known to construct its own burrows. Other cottontails occupy burrows made by other animals, particularly in the northern part of the range, or they inhabit almost any available shelter. They are active during twilight and night hours and rest in dense vegetation or in burrows during the day. Herbaceous vegetation is preferred, but in winter the bark and twigs of woody vegetation are also eaten. The home range of an individual is usually only a few acres in size. The animals normally follow their own definite routes so that regular trails are maintained. The maximum running speed is about 33 to 40 km. per hour. The breeding season in the northern hemisphere is from February or March to September. From two to seven constitute a litter; four are common. After a gestation period of 26 to 30 days, the young are born naked, blind, and helpless, but they develop rapidly. They are deposited in a nest made in a shallow depression in the earth. This is lined with soft plant fibers and fur plucked from the mother's underside. Three to five litters are produced during the season. In at least some instances the mother does not get into the nest with the little ones but crouches above it, and the babies climb to the top of the nest to nurse. It is likely that this habit is universal as the nest cavity usually appears to be too small to hold the mother, even though there were no young in it with her.

These rabbits are known as game and food species.

In the eastern United States they are rated as the most important game species in many areas because of their abundance. The fur is of almost no value as it is not durable, but it is used in the manufacture of felt. The skin tears very easily. Where they are plentiful in close proximity to croplands, forest plantations, and ornamental shrubs, they sometimes cause damage to such vegetation.

They seldom thrive in captivity unless given unusually good care.

In some portions of their range the local species (*S. aquaticus*) is known as marsh or swamp rabbits because they frequent swampy areas where they enter the water and swim well. The little brush rabbits, *S. idahoensis*, inhabit the other extreme in arid regions.

Although most members of this genus spend most of their time on the surface of the ground, they are adept at finding secluded locations or in sitting so quietly, even when closely approached, that they are often overlooked even by persons who are hunting them. By this trait and their prolificacy they have been able to survive in areas that have been cultivated and thickly populated by man. Indeed, near the center of Washington, D. C. , cottontail rabbits are frequently to be seen in small tracts of vegetation between apartment houses.

Their ability to survive and continue in settled areas makes them a favorite game animal.

Baby cottontails frequently fall into the hands of people who try to raise them but very few survive because the surface on which they are being kept, or the nest, is not kept very clean. Also they do not thrive on whole cows' milk but do better if the milk is diluted, a portion of the cream removed, and egg yolks and vitamins are added.

The type species of the genus is *S. sylvaticus* (Bachman).

Old World Rabbit (*Oryctolagus cuniculus*), photo by Jane Burton. Inset: Baby ten hours old weighing 60 grams—one of a litter of five, photo from U.S. Department of Agriculture.

OLD WORLD RABBITS; DOMESTIC RABBITS; KONY-NEN, LAPINS, KANINCHEN.

THE ORIGINAL RANGE of the one species, *O. cuniculus*, was apparently southwestern Europe and north-western Africa. Through introduction, these rabbits now inhabit many other regions including Great Britain, the Ukraine, New Zealand, Australia, South America, and several portions of the United States. In most of these regions they have become widespread and abundant enough to be pests. They dig burrows in hedgerows and open fields and eat vegetation.

The wild rabbits have a head and body length of 350 to 450 mm., and the tail length is 40 to 70 mm. The weight is from 1,350 to 2,250 gms. The general coloration of the upper parts is a fine mixture of black and light-brown hairs. The ears are the same color except for the black-edged tip. The nape is buff-colored and the collar is dark. The tail is white below and brownish black above. The under parts and inner surface of the legs are buffy white. These animals have long hind legs, long ears, and large eyes. Their feet are well-furred beneath and have large, straight claws.

Unlike most of the other rabbits and hares, they dig burrows in which they live. They are also gre-garious and make their burrows near those of others of their kind so that these "warrens" sometimes occupy more than a hectare of land. Southern re-corded studies of a warren, containing about 150 rabbits, which occupied about 2,023 square meters in an open field. The feeding grounds occupied a surrounding area of about 8,092 square meters. Grasses and other herbaceous plants are preferred food. The bark and twigs of woody plants are also eaten when herbs are not available. These rabbits are essentially nocturnal, coming out of their burrows in the evening and retiring in the early morning. They sometimes bask in the early morning sun at the burrow entrance. The main part of the mating season is from January to June, inclusive. Although mating sometimes occurs at other times of the year, the female is usually not in estrous and pregnancy does not re-sult. After a gestation period of 28 to 33 days, 3 to 9 naked, blind, and helpless young are born in a burrow, newly constructed for the purpose and lined with vege-tation and fur plucked from the mother's under parts. The female is in estrous about 12 hours after birth and may be impregnated again. As many as 6 litters a year are sometimes produced. Abortion frequently occurs, and the phenomenon of resorption of embryos also occurs in this species so that at least 60 per cent of the litters conceived are never born. Although there is a high potential birth rate, studies indicate that the average number of young produced by a fe-male each year is 10 to 11.5. In captivity, at least, they begin producing litters when 4 to 12 months old and continue up to 18 years of age. In the wild their reproductive life generally ends about the sixth year.

Wild rabbits have been extensively used for food, and members of this genus are of great economic importance. Many special strains have been developed, resulting in rabbits which are utilized for a great variety of purposes such as genetic and nutritional studies, laboratory experimental animals, meat, wool, and beauty of coloration. So popular has the raising of rabbits become that numerous clubs and organizations have arisen for the dissemination of information. The American Rabbit Breeders Association recognizes at least 66 breeds and varieties of rabbits. Many of the domesticated forms bear little resemblance to the original wild stock. The coloration ranges from white to black and many mixtures of colors. The fur of some forms is long and unlike that of normal rabbits. The weight of those bred for meat production may be as much as $7\frac{1}{4}$ kg. In some areas, however, rabbits have become pests, especially in areas where they have been introduced. In Australia and some Pacific islands where they have increased so profusely due to the absence of natural predators, they quickly depleted the scant vegetation. In recent years a virus disease, myxomatosis, has been effectively used to exterminate rabbits in some countries, but after outbreaks, a resistance is often built up.

The strain erroneously known as Belgian "hares" belong to this group.

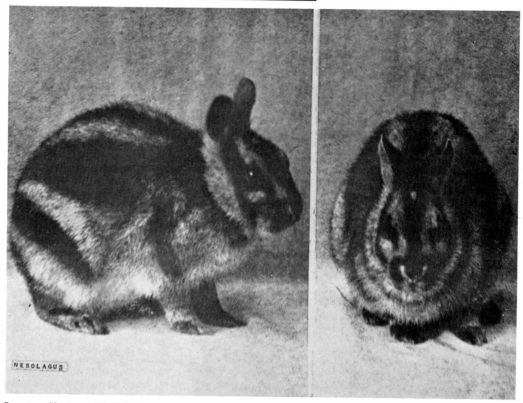

Sumatran Short-eared Rabbit (*Nesolagus netscheri*), photos from *Journal of the Federated Malay States Museum.*

SUMATRAN HARES, SUMATRA SHORT-EARED RAB-
BITS.

Nesolagus, with only one species, *netscheri*, is apparently a rare animal even within its restricted range of the forested mountains of Sumatra.

Sumatran hares are rather small, with a head and body length of about 360 to 400 mm., and an inconspicuous tail measuring about 15 mm. The ears are short. The pelage consists of a soft, dense underfur overlaid by longer, harsher hairs. It has the most definite pattern of any member of the order. The general coloration above is buffy gray on which there are several brown stripes, including a mid-dorsal stripe from snout to tail. Another broad stripe curves from the shoulder upward to the rump region. A third runs from the rump down onto the hind leg. A narrow stripe runs from the shoulder part way down the upper fore leg. In addition, the rump and tail are bright red. The limbs are gray-brown. The underside of the neck is dark brown and the remaining under parts are buffy white.

These rabbits are nocturnal. They feed on succulent stalks and leaves of certain forest undergrowth plants. During the day they rest in burrows on the forest floor. It is believed they use burrows made by other animals, rather than digging their own. They do not seem to be as quick in their movements as the European hare, *Lepus europaeus.*

Apparently they survive in captivity fairly well, as several have been kept for as long as a year. The captives ate cooked rice, young maize, bread, ripe bananas, and sometimes pineapple. They generally refused to eat various cultivated vegetables, roots, and the bark of various trees.

Order: RODENTIA

Squirrels, Chipmunks, Cavies, Chinchillas, Mice, Rats, Gophers, Beavers, Muskrats, Coypus, Voles, Lemmings, Pocket Gophers, "Kangaroo" Rats and Mice, Pocket Mice, Hamsters, Gerbils, Mole Rats, Dormice, Porcupines, Pacas, Hutias.

The rodents comprise 35 families that include 351 genera and 8 extinct families. The distribution of this order is nearly world-wide. Its members have habitats so extensive and so varied that they occupy a large portion of the world's land areas.

Some rodents are specialized for an underground life, many are terrestrial, and still others are largely arboreal. Some species are adapted to progress by leaping, others by running, and still others by climbing, some can glide, and some are adapted for semi-aquatic life.

These animals are remarkably uniform in structural characters. They have four incisors, two above and two below. Canines and anterior premolars are lacking, leaving a space between the incisors and the cheek teeth. The number of teeth does not exceed 22, except in the genus *Heliophobius* which has 28 teeth.

The incisor teeth of rodents grow throughout life. Growth is at the base, and the tooth is a segment of a true circle. Thus the tooth is continuously being pushed out of the end of the jaw; this makes up for the portion worn away by cutting hard materials. The outer surface of the tooth is harder than the inner surface, much like a chisel, so that it is to some extent self-sharpening. There is no nerve in the tooth, except at the growing base.

The grinding or cheek teeth consist mostly of dentine: Enamel forms the outer layer and, in most rodents, it also forms loops or folds in the body of the teeth. These teeth have many peculiar patterns when seen from the grinding surface. The patterns are produced by a combination of soft dentine and hard enamel arranged in various ways—constant for the different groups and therefore valuable to zoologists for classification. In some rodents the molars are rooted and cease growing; in others they are open at the base and grow throughout life. Cement is the third basic substance. This occupies only minor space in a rooted molar, but, in those that are rootless, it fills the space between the folds of enamel. The enamel, harder than dentine and cement, wears less rapidly and forms sharp ridges on the crown of the tooth. The molariform, or cheek teeth, may be either high- or low-crowned. The articulation of the lower jaw with the skull is somewhat loose, permitting considerable rotary motion.

Rodents often grind their incisor teeth together, apparently to keep them in proper condition. If the teeth are not worn down, the tips soon grow past each other and continue to grow in spiral form. The result is that the upper teeth may grow backward and upward, sometimes piercing the roof of the mouth, and the lower teeth may grow upward in front of the nose. This may be due to injury, soft diet, or disease. The space between the incisors and the cheek teeth permits maximum utilization of the gnawing front teeth and the manipulation of food when passed back to the grinding teeth. A fold of velvety or furred skin is present between the incisors and the rest of the mouth.

Some rodents have either internal or external cheek pouches that open near the angle of the mouth. The external pouches are fur-lined, and the animal can turn them wrong side out to clean them. The tongue, which is short and compressed, cannot be protruded beyond the incisors in many genera.

In addition to the dental characters, rodents have other anatomical features in common. The bones of the lower arm, the radius and ulna, are distinct, and the elbow joint permits free motion of the forearm. The hand usually has five fingers, although the thumb may be vestigial or absent; the toes number three to five. Rodents walk on the entire foot or hand. The stomach is variable, ranging from a simple sac to a complex, ruminant-like organ, as in the lemmings. The penis usually has a baculum, and the testes are inguinal or abdominal, in many cases they are inguinal only during the breeding season. Rodents have a generalized rather than a specialized type of brain and placentation.

The tails of members of some families break off readily when the animals are caught by the tail, en-

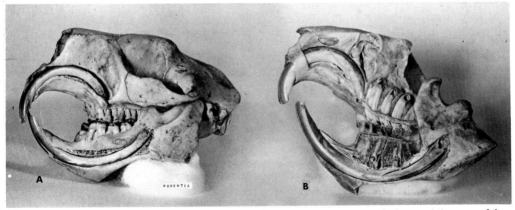

Skulls of rodents with parts of the jaws cut away to expose the entire length of the long incisors and the roots of the cheek teeth. A. Porcupine (*Erethizon dorsatum*), with closed-root molars; B. Beaver (*Castor canadensis*), with open-rooted molars that grow throughout the life of the animal. The incisors of both grow throughout life, as indicated by their open roots. Photos by Howard E. Uible of skulls in U.S. National Museum.

abling them to escape. A partial replacement of the lost portion of the tail then grows again. The skin of the tail may also break readily and slip off beyond the break, leaving the flesh and bone exposed. This also permits escape in some instances. The animal later amputates the exposed portion of the tail with its teeth and the end heals.

Rodents are of great importance to man. Some destroy many insects and weeds. Others, such as the beaver, muskrat, nutria, and chinchilla, are valuable fur animals. Many are used extensively in research, particularly rats, mice, and cavies. At times they become pests by feeding extensively on agricultural crops. Some rodents carry parasites that transmit diseases to which man is susceptible.

Rodents are diverse in form, have a great range, are adaptable and resourceful, and generally exist in abundance in most land areas. They usually have a high birth rate. This permits them to maintain a stable population despite predators and control measures and may insure future survival.

Although this order exceeds all others in variety and actual numbers, the fossil record is comparatively poor. The lack of fossils has caused taxonomists many problems in classification of the higher groups.

It is probable that the teeth of extinct forms may be more common than is generally supposed, for they are inconspicuous and easily overlooked. One worker succeeded in finding even very small teeth by washing soil or sand in a pan (like miners panning for gold).

Mountain Beaver or Sewellel (*Aplodontia rufa*), photo by Ernest P. Walker.

SEWELLELS, "MOUNTAIN BEAVERS."

THIS FAMILY contains only a single Recent genus, *Aplodontia*. The single species, *A. rufa*, inhabits the humid regions of western North America from southern British Columbia south to San Francisco Bay and east to the Cascade and Sierra Nevada mountains. While sometimes found up to 2,200 meters elevation, the greater numbers are found at lower levels. The animals frequent forests and densely vegetated thickets. They burrow in soil which is moderately firm and deep and which has adequate drainage. Most of them live in areas where there is heavy rainfall or along seepages and streams where the ground is usually saturated with water.

Sewellels have a thickset, heavy body with short limbs. They have somewhat the form of a short, heavy-bodied muskrat (*Ondatra*) without a tail and with less sheen to the fur. The eyes and ears are small. All the limbs have five digits; those of the fore feet are fairly long and are used for digging in the earth and for grasping. The length of the head and body is 300 to 460 mm.; the length of the tail is 10 to 25 mm.; the height at the shoulder is approximately 120 mm.; and the weight is 900 to 1,800 grams. The fur is dense and short. The pelage above is rather uniformly grayish or reddish brown, more-or-less grizzled with darker hairs; the coloration beneath is slightly lighter. The coat is composed of sparse guard hairs and thicker underfur. The young are grayer than the adults. Their size, uniform color, and the apparent absence of a tail distinguish them from all other mammals within their range. Females have six mammae. The testes are abdominal, and a baculum is present.

The dental formula is: i 1/1, c 0/0, pm 2/1, m 3/3 x 2 = 22. The cheek teeth grow throughout life. The skull is flattened and greatly widened posteriorly, and the lower jaw is large and powerful.

Sewellels are neither beavers nor particularly mountain-loving animals. They are burrowing mammals which seldom venture more than a few yards from cover. The burrows are close to the surface, 10 to 25 cm. in diameter, and several meters long, with many openings marked by fan-shaped mounds of earth, some of which are plugged. Each adult *Aplodontia* constructs a burrow system, consisting of tunnels which lead from a nest of dried vegetation in the ground under the roots of a tree, a log, or other shelter, toward food supplies or shelters. They are not gregarious; colonies in a given area merely indicate that burrowing and food conditions are suitable to sustain several individuals. The tunnels are cleaned and worked on regularly and, if a tunnel is flooded by rain, sewellels swim in them. During the winter they burrow beneath the snow and sometimes travel on the surface of snow. They do not hibernate, but they do store food in their burrows.

These rodents eat almost any plant material. When deep snow makes it difficult to obtain green food, they will eat bark and small twigs. In winter and summer they climb shrubs and small trees to cut off limbs and twigs, climbing from one branch to another cutting off the branches as they ascend. Although they may let the twigs fall to the ground as they are cut off, they usually carry them back to the ground by descending the tree head first. Sewellels are not very good climbers, but they can go as high as 7 meters. Swordfern fronds and other herbaceous plants are favorites, but lodgepole pine and red and white fir needles are also eaten and stored. These animals drink considerable amounts of water. They are active at any hour of the day or night. Shrill notes and a grating noise, the latter perhaps produced by rubbing the incisors together, have been noted.

The breeding season seems to occur in late winter or early spring and lasts about six weeks. The two to six young (usually two or three) are born about a month later in a nest lined with dry vegetation. They are blind at birth, the eyes open about ten days later. By the end of June the half-grown young are able to

667

leave the den. Most sewellels do not begin breeding until two years of age.

Their burrow systems serve as shelters for other animals — ground squirrels, red squirrels, and rabbits. Sewellels living near cultivated areas sometimes damage crops, and, on occasion, they do damage by tunneling in the walls of drainage ditches.

The proper relative position of these rodents with respect to other rodents is puzzling to zoologists. It appears that they represent a rather primitive type regarding some of their muscular development. So far their ancestry has not been definitely tied in with the ancestry of any other known recent rodent. A family of fossil forms, the Mylagaulidae, has three known genera, *Mylagaulus*, *Ceratogaulus*, and *Epigaulus*, which have been found in the Miocene and Pliocene of North America. The occurrence of fossils of a form closely related to *Aplodontia* in eastern Asia is another one of the many fragments of information that show relationships between Asiatic and American forms of life which probably had relatively unobstructed passage between the two continents in earlier ages over the Bering Sea land bridge.

This is the oldest known group of living rodents; the geological range of the family is from the late Paleocene to the Recent in North America, and the Pliocene in Asia.

The name mountain "beaver" has come into such general use that it will probably persist in our language, although it presents an erroneous picture to persons who are not familiar with their appearance. They are sometimes called "whistlers," but they do not whistle and this name is better applied to marmots (*Marmota*). "Boomer" is also erroneously applied to them.

SQUIRRELS, "FLYING" SQUIRRELS, GROUND SQUIR-
RELS, CHIPMUNKS, MARMOTS, WOODCHUCKS,
PRAIRIE "DOGS."

ABOUT 50 GENERA are included in this family. They
are found in a wide variety of habitats throughout the
world, except the Australian region, Madagascar,
southern South America, and certain desert regions
such as Arabia and Egypt. Squirrels are conspicuous
and known by sight to more people than most other
rodents. Included are arboreal, terrestrial, and burrowing forms.

They range in size from the tropical pygmy squirrels
which weigh less than 10 grams to the marmots which
can weigh as much as 2½ kg. *Ratufa* is the largest
arboreal form.

Squirrels and their relatives have a small upper
premolar which is shed in some forms about the time
they reach maturity; thus, the dental formula is:
i 1/1, c 0/0, pm 1-2/1, m 3/3 x 2 = 20 or 22. The
molariform teeth are rooted, usually low-crowned,
and cuspidate. The upper molariform teeth in sciurids
usually have four transverse ridges, each with a slight
or prominent cusp on the outer border; each lower
molariform tooth generally has a basin-like depression
surrounded by cusps, usually one at each corner.
In the genus of long-nosed squirrels, *Rhinosciurus*, the
incisor teeth are modified into forceps-like structures
for grasping insects, and the molariform teeth are
simple in structure. The skull has well-developed
post-orbital processes, a wide interval between the
orbits, and is never of the type that occurs in burrowing rodents. The eyes are rather large. The legs are
not more than twice the length of the arms, and the
foot has five toes. The tail varies from short to long,
is well-haired, and often bushy with long hairs that
project at almost right angles from the axis of the tail.

The members of this family are diurnal, except
"flying" squirrels which are nocturnal. Almost all
squirrels usually eat nuts, seeds, and other plant
material, but some eat animal food at times. A few
forms seem to be mainly insectivorous.

Tree squirrels, including "flying" squirrels, make their
nests in hollow trees or limbs; if these are not available, they build nests of twigs and leaves. They are
extremely active and agile in the trees, and, if they miss
their hold and fall, they are seldom injured. There is
a record of a Mexican tree squirrel leaping down a
precipice and, as far as could be determined, landing
unhurt on a ledge 180 meters below. Although this
was a forced leap, it illustrates the remarkable ability
of tree squirrels to ease or brake a fall from a great
height. The senior author has seen two tree squirrels
fall at least 15 meters without apparent injury. Most
tree squirrels have a tendency to glide. When tree
squirrels make flying leaps, they extend their legs
widely, broaden and flatten their bodies, and stiffen
and slightly curve their tails. This position presents
the broadest surface possible to the air and partially
neutralizes the force of gravity. The tail, besides
being employed in such maneuvers, is used as a cloak,
and the tree squirrels and most members of this family
wrap it about themselves when resting. Also, it is
often carried over the back especially where danger
threatens and probably misleads or baffles enemies.

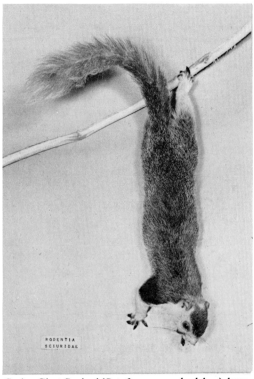

Ceylon Giant Squirrel (*Ratufa macroura dandolena*), hanging by its feet in a pose characteristic of many squirrels.
This gives them an opportunity to use their hands freely
to handle or reach for food or other materials. Photo by
Ernest P. Walker.

"Flying" squirrels are found in both the Old and the
New Worlds. They have a furred gliding membrane
along the sides of the body from the arms to the legs;
in some genera this membrane extends to the neck and
tail. At the outer edge of the wrist the gliding membrane is extended by a rod of cartilage that acts as a
spreader. The membrane contains sheets of muscles
that can be tensed or relaxed at will. The direction of
the glide is controlled by varying the tension of the
membranes and the slant of the tail. These gliders can
even turn at a right angle to avoid a branch. Just
before making contact with the tree trunk where it will
land, a flying squirrel curves its tail upward, so that, in
response, the body turns up, the speed is checked, and
the landing is made facing upward. Some species of
the genus *Petaurista* glide for distances of as much as
65 meters. All glides are made by a strong leap from
an elevation and landings are made at a lower point.

The terrestrial members of this family differ from
the arboreal forms in that they nest in ground burrows,
usually take refuge in burrows when fleeing an enemy,
and feed primarily on low-growing plants. Many of
the terrestrial forms become dormant for varying

periods, in some cases for more than half the year. The breeding season follows shortly after hibernation. Ground squirrels sometimes become so abundant in certain areas that they destroy crops. Their burrows occasionally damage irrigation systems and initiate soil erosion, but these rodents also destroy undesirable weeds and insects.

The oldest known terrestrial squirrels are from the late Miocene, whereas the tree squirrel extends back in time possibly to the Oligocene.

Tree squirrels occasionally emigrate from regions of overpopulation or inadequate food supply, i.e., *Sciurus carolinensis*, native to the eastern United States.

The members of this family have evolved into several different forms and exhibit a wide variety of habits which adapt them to live under a wide range of conditions and to utilize foods that are available. Examples are the prairie "dogs" which are heavy-bodied, short-legged powerful creatures that live mainly on the plains of the western United States far from trees and make their homes in burrows that are sometimes as much as 5½ meters deep. Since these homes are on relatively level ground, they might at times be flooded with water were it not for the fact that these industrious animals maintain volcano shaped mounds around the entrances to the burrows. Prairie "dogs" have developed tolerance of others of their kind to a remarkable degree. They live in large colonies and visit back and forth with their neighbors, with very little evidence of hostility between individuals.

The food of prairie "dogs" is, of course, limited to the grasses and other herbaceous vegetation near their homes, although it is possible they may eat some grasshoppers (*Orthoptera*) and other insects, and possibly some meat of dead animals, but they are not adapted to capturing and killing agile or pugnaceous creatures.

Several other squirrels have adopted a terrestrial life or, at least of necessity, spend much time on or near the ground. Among these are the ground squirrels of several genera of North America, Europe, Asia, and Africa. We are privileged to witness an evolutionary change in some of the African squirrels such as *Xerus*, *Euxerus*, etc. which apparently are descended from tree inhabitants but, due to the gradual dessication of portions of Africa, are now forced to spend much of their lives on or in the ground because the trees are gradually being eliminated in their ranges. In the United States I observed an area of normally good forest which had been burned over, and where a good growth of young conifers had become established, but none were old enough to provide cavities for "flying" squirrels to shelter in. Therefore the squirrels were living in holes in the ground.

The other extreme in form are the "flying" squirrels which are of slender form and have long arms and legs. The tails of some are distinctly flattened from above and below, but some lack this degree of specialization. "Flying" squirrels spend almost their entire time in trees and go down to the ground only when absolutely necessary. Their homes are in hollow trees or other cavities that are available at suitable locations. The "flying" squirrel of the eastern United States, *Glaucomys*, stores its supply of nuts at many different places such as in crevices, knot holes in trees, and almost any place that will hold a nut or two, for all the nuts are not stored in one place. It is also very fond of several kinds of insects.

My pet "flying" squirrels, *Glaucomys volans*, were nervous and restless during storms, which suggests that through the ages tree squirrels have suffered damages to their homes in hollow trees or hollow limbs which were weak and could not withstand the strain of storms. No doubt such worry over storms is common to many tree inhabitants. The attitude of the squirrels was in marked contrast to the ability of some of the burrowing animals to sleep even when being handled. This suggests that the burrowers are so secure in their nests that they are rarely disturbed, so they have become indifferent to, or almost unconscious of, disturbances when they are asleep. Other mammals that are so exposed to danger that they are apparently constantly alert are the hares and rabbits (*Leporidae*), many of which do not go into burrows.

A. (*Sciurus hypopyrrhus*), photo from *Biologia Centrali-Americana, Mammalia*, Edward Alston. B. (*S. kaibabensis*), photo from U.S. National Park Service. C. Eastern Gray Squirrel (*S. carolinensis*), photo by Ernest P. Walker.

TREE SQUIRRELS; EEKHOORNS; ECUREUILS; EICHHÖRNCHEN; ARDILLAS; BIELKI.

THE COMBINED RANGES of about 55 species cover most of Europe, Asia south of the northern limit of trees, Japan, and, in the New World, from southern Canada to northern Argentina. They inhabit deciduous, coniferous, and tropical forests (both humid and arid).

The length of the head and body is 200 to 315 mm., and the length of the tail is about 200 to 310 mm. The weight varies from 200 to 900 grams and may reach as much as 1 kg. The coloration differs greatly among the many forms. The usual colors of the upper parts are gray, grayish brown, blackish brown, and various shades of red. The under parts vary from white through buff and yellow to orange. There are often individuals or whole populations which are much darker than normal, and some are black. Some species have several color types, as *S. granatensis* of South America. The color of the tail is generally similar to that of the upper parts, but it may vary considerably within one species. The tail is always well furred and somewhat flattened in some forms. It is usually about the same length as the head and body, although it may be considerably shorter in some forms. Some species, *S. vulgaris* of Eurasia and *S. aberti* of the western United States, have conspicuous tufts on the ears. There are two molts per year in some, and perhaps all, species, but the tail fur is shed only once yearly. The winter coat is generally slightly different in color from the summer coat. The number of teeth is variable — some species have one and others two premolars in each side of the upper jaw.

Members of the genus utter sounds when alarmed. A sharp bark-like call repeated rapidly is an alarm warning. This is accompanied by vigorous shaking of the tail. These squirrels spend most of their time in the trees and are extremely agile in traveling along the branches. *S. niger*, the fox squirrel of the eastern United States, has a home range of about ten acres, but an individual often travels 1,500 meters from its den. Tree squirrels come down to the ground to forage for food and to bury nuts and acorns. Their periods of greatest activity are in the early morning and late afternoon. They are not known to be nocturnal. Their food consists of various nuts, other seeds, fruit, buds, and young tree shoots. Acorns and hickory nuts are particularly preferred when available. Nuts are opened by a special levering technique of the lower incisors. After some experience, a squirrel can open a nut in a few seconds. Seeds of conifers are eaten by squirrels that inhabit coniferous forests. Mushrooms, insects, bird's eggs, and small birds may also be included in the diet. Feeding shelters are sometimes constructed in trees in the summer. Nests are constructed either in the hollow portion of an old tree for winter use or outside in the fork of a branch for summer use. The nests outside tree hollows are globular and are made of brushwood. Tree squirrels do not hibernate, but in stormy or very cold weather they remain in their nests until it becomes necessary to obtain food. A favored den tree may be used for many years, but the animal always has several other nests where he can escape enemies.

In the better-known species, *S. carolinensis, niger* and *vulgaris*, there are two litters per year. *S. persicus* has been reported to produce two or three litters per year. In the northern hemisphere, mating takes place in January and again in June or July. After mating the male is expelled from the female's territory. Gestation lasts about 44 days in *S. carolinensis* and 38 to 39 days in *S. vulgaris*. In *S. carolinensis*, there are from one to five young (two and three is the average). In *S. vulgaris*, four to ten young have been reported (five to seven is the average). The young are naked and blind when born, weigh less than an ounce, and usually remain in the nest for about six weeks. They have some fur after 14 days and the eyes open about 30 to 32 days after birth (*S. vulgaris*). When the mother leaves the nest, she covers the young with nest material. The females of this genus usually breed within a year of their birth.

Tree squirrels normally do no damage. Under some conditions they may gnaw ears of growing corn and sometimes the bark of trees. *S. carolinensis* of eastern United States has been introduced into Great Britain and South Africa. Due to its abundance, this species has become a pest in these areas, causing damage to trees and crops. Squirrels are favorite game of hunters and their flesh is eaten. Their fur is generally not valuable, but some forms of *S. vulgaris* in the U.S.S.R. have luxuriant winter pelage and are sought for pelts. Squirrels have occasionally become extremely numerous in the United States and have undertaken extensive migrations. Such movements may result from the failure of the nut crop in an area, and have been recorded in northeastern North America for over a century. The gray squirrel, *S. carolinensis*, has been kept in captivity for as long as 15 years.

Some of the nuts and other seeds buried are not utilized for food, so squirrels often are planters of nut bearing trees. The enemies of these squirrels are the pine marten and the goshawk.

This genus has been divided into eight subgenera by many mammalogists:

1. *Sciurus*, Linnaeus, 1758, with type species *S. vulgaris*, Linnaeus.
2. *Guerlinguetus*, Gray, 1821, with type species *S. aestuans*, Linnaeus.
3. *Neosciurus*, Trouessart, 1880, with type species *S. carolinensis*, Gmelin.
4. *Parasciurus*, Trouessart, 1880, with type species *S. niger*, Linnaeus.
5. *Otosciurus*, Nelson, 1899, with type species *S. aberti*, Woodhouse.
6. *Hesperosciurus*, Nelson, 1899, with type species *S. grisens*, Ord.
7. *Tenes*, Thomas, 1909, with type species *S. anomalus*, Güldenstaedt.
8. *Hadrosciurus*, Allen, 1915, with type species *S. flammifer*, Thomas.

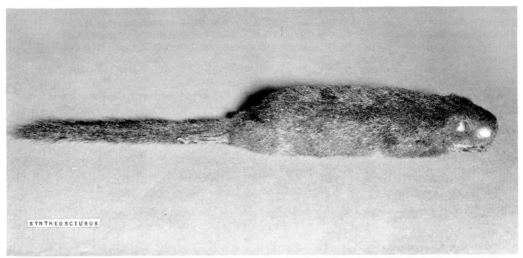

Neotropical Montane Groove-toothed Squirrel (*Syntheosciurus brochus*), photo by B. Elizabeth Horner and Mary Taylor of specimen in Harvard Museum of Comparative Zoology.

NEOTROPICAL MONTANE GROOVE-TOOTHED SQUIRRELS.

THE SPECIES *S. brochus* is known by only two specimens from Boquete (2,150 meters), Chiriquí, Panama, and the species *S. poasensis* is known only from Volcán Poas (2,075 meters), Alajuela, Costa Rica. These squirrels are evidently inhabitants of the higher elevations. Specimens are in the Museum of Comparative Zoology at Harvard University and the American Museum of Natural History.

The length of the head and body is 150 to 170 mm., and the length of the tail is 140 to 150 mm. The upper parts of *S. brochus* are finely mixed olivaceous and dull tawny olive; in *S. poasensis* they are finely mixed cinnamon-buff and black. The under parts of *S. brochus*, especially along the mid-line, are markedly orange-rufous. The upper incisors of *S. brochus* have a longitudinal groove on the front surface, but *S. poasensis* lacks a groove.

In *The Mammals of North America* (New York, 1959), E. Raymond Hall and Keith R. Kelson comment on this group as follows: "Various authors . . . do not accord *Syntheosciurus* generic rank; some retain it as a subgenus. Certainly the characters allegedly diagnostic of the genus scarcely seem to indicate generic rank. Nevertheless, we here retain the group as a genus because the paucity of specimens does not as yet permit a critical analysis of the characters. This group, regardless of its nomenclatural status, seems to occupy a position intermediate between the genus *Sciurus* and the genus *Microsciurus*."

One of the two known specimens of *S. brochus* is a female that was nursing young in April. There are six mammae. This squirrel was unknown to the native hunters who accompanied the collector.

Nothing is known of the natural history of *S. poasensis*.

The type species of the genus is *S. brochus*, Bangs.

Neotropical Dwarf Squirrel (*Microsciurus* sp.), photo from *Biologia Centrali-Americana, Mammalia,* Edward Alston.
Inset: Skull, photo by P. F. Wright of specimen in U.S. National Museum.

Neotropical Dwarf Squirrels, Ardillitas.

Seventeen species are currently recognized. These little squirrels range from southern Nicaragua south through Ecuador to Peru and the Rio Negro in South America. They inhabit wooded areas from the lowlands to dense, fog-shrouded forests at elevations of at least 1,850 meters.

The length of the head and body measures from 120 to 160 mm., and the length of the tail measures from 90 to 150 mm. The texture of the fur varies with the species and with the climate. Lowland forms usually have coarse, short fur, but those that live at higher elevations have dense, longer hair. The color of the upper parts ranges from gray and olive-brown to dark reddish brown; the under parts are lighter in color. One species, *M. alfari,* has two color phases. In one phase the upper parts are dull olive-brown or olive-black, and in the other phase the upper parts are finely mixed ochraceous tawny on black.

The ears are small, rounded, and well-haired. The tail is rather narrow, occasionally much narrowed, and usually considerably shorter than the head and body length. The common name refers to the relatively small size of these squirrels. With the exception of the genus *Sciurillus,* these are the smallest of the American tree squirrels. This group was originally described as a subgenus of *Sciurus.*

The sounds made by one individual were compared to the short squawkings made by chipmunks (*Tamias*). Another individual seemed similar in its behavior (scolding and tail jerking) to North American red squirrels (*Tamiasciurus*). The natural history of the genus *Microsciurus* is little known and is perhaps best summarized by the following remarks of L. E. Miller which are quoted by J. A. Allen: "I have always found *Microsciurus* much rarer than other squirrels, and usually in pairs. They seem to prefer the palm forests that are so abundant on the hillside, where they feed on the various kinds of palm fruits and nuts. They invariably evince considerable curiosity, and can be approached to within a short distance before taking fright and hiding in the palm leaves. They move rapidly and gracefully, making long, daring leaps" ("Review of the South American Sciuridae," *Bull. Amer. Mus. Nat. Hist.,* 1915, vol. 34, p. 189).

The type species of the genus is *M. alfari,* J. A. Allen.

Neotropical Pygmy Squirrel (*Sciurillus pusillus*), photo from *Proc. Zool. Soc. London.*

NEOTROPICAL PYGMY SQUIRRELS; LAS ARDILLAS PIGMEAS; GUERLINGUETOS MINIMOS; CUATIPURUZINHO.

THE SINGLE SPECIES, *S. pusillus*, inhabits the Guianas in South America, southward through the northeastern corner of Brazil to the Amazon River and the Amazon Basin in Peru.

The length of the head and body is 90 to 110 mm., and the length of the tail is about 100 mm. The females are smaller than the males. *S. pusillus* is the smallest squirrel of the Brazilian fauna. The upper parts are grayish brown to brown, and the under parts are usually hazel. Individuals from French Guiana have a reddish head and black outer ear tips.

Little has been recorded regarding the habits or biology of these squirrels, other than that they are arboreal and are extremely agile animals. They live in tall forests on dry ground, in the top of trees. The diet consists of fruits, nuts, bark and resin of trees. The sounds these squirrels make are high, shrill, and penetrating, resembling a cricket call, i.e., "seeek, seeek, seeek." During the mating season (May to August in Amazonian Peru), several males pursue a single female. From limited observations, it appears that June is at least one of the peak reproductive months and that one, usually two, young are born at a time. Specimens are in the American Museum of Natural History, the Field Museum of Natural History, the British Museum (Natural History), and the Departamento de Zoología, São Paulo, Brazil.

CELEBES DWARF SQUIRRELS; BOENTO KETJIL, TENDELANGO.

THREE SPECIES, *P. murinus*, *P. leucomus*, and *P. abstrusus*, inhabit Celebes and small adjacent islands.

The length of the head and body is 100 to 135 mm., and the tail length is 70 to 110 mm. The coloration is brownish or olive above, the hairs of the under parts are usually gray tipped with cinnamon. The skull and dental features separate this genus from other genera of this family, but the genus is very similar to *Sciurillus* of South America.

No information has been found regarding their habits and biology.

Specimens are in the U.S. National Museum, the American Museum of Natural History, the British Museum (Natural History), and the Dresden Museum.

The type species of the genus is *P. murinus* (Schlegel and Müller).

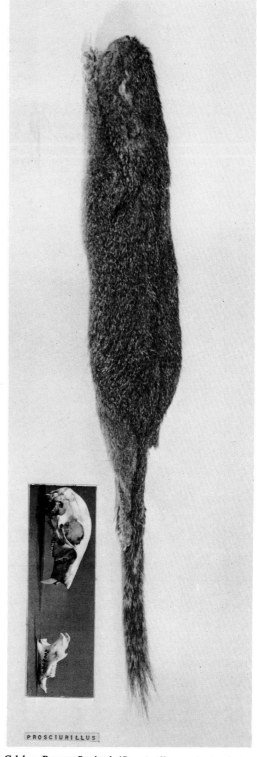

Celebes Pygmy Squirrel (*Prosciurillus murinus*), photos by P. F. Wright of specimen in U.S. National Museum.

Groove-toothed Squirrel (*Rheithrosciurus macrotis*), photo from *Proc. Zool. Soc. London.*

GROOVE-TOOTHED SQUIRRELS; KRAMPU; PAPOEN (native names).

THE SINGLE SPECIES, *R. macrotis*, is one of the few mammals confined to the island of Borneo. Forest is its preferred habitat.

The length of the head and body is 279 to 534 mm., and the length of the tail is 279 to almost 356 mm. The weight is usually 1 to 2 kg. The upper parts of this beautiful squirrel are light chocolate or chestnut-brown. The sides are marked with a buffy or white stripe extending from just back of the shoulder to the flank, and below it is a dark brown stripe. The sides of the face are gray; the fore feet are blackish; the hind feet and the hips are bright brown; and the under parts are white. The tail resembles a plume, the hairs increasing in length toward the tip. The hairs on the upper side of the tail, especially those near the apex, have long gray or white tips that produce a hoary effect. The ears are long, and long stiff hairs grow on the back of the ears that project beyond the ears as conspicuous tufts.

The skull differs in shape from that of most squirrels, it is broader and flatter. The fronts of the broad and rounded incisors are longitudinally marked with seven to ten minute grooves.

Although it has been conjectured that the well-developed tail aids this squirrel in jumping and climbing about trees, subsequent observations indicate that krampus are mainly active on the ground. They are swift runners and carry the tail bent over the back or held straight out when running. They have been observed taking refuge among rocks and feeding on fallen fruits. They have damaged gardens in some areas.

This squirrel sometimes sits upright and practically envelops itself in its bushy tail, the long ears sticking out on each side.

Natives use the tail as an ornament on the sheath of a "parang" (large Malay knife).

677

A. Eastern Red Squirrel (*Tamiasciurus hudsonicus*), photo by Ernest P. Walker. B. Douglas Squirrel (*T. douglasii*) showing tufted ears, photo by Lloyd G. Ingles.

Red Squirrels, Chickarees, Pine Squirrels.

Two species are currently recognized: *T. hudsonicus* ranges from Alaska and Quebec southward, in the Rocky Mountains to New Mexico, and in the Appalachian region to South Carolina; *T. douglasii* ranges from British Columbia south to California. They inhabit deciduous and evergreen forests, and, in the far north, dwarf conifer growth.

The length of the head and body is 165 to 230 mm., and the length of the tail is 90 to 160 mm. They weigh from 141 to 312 grams. The upper parts vary in color from tawny to brownish or olive-brown, appearing more drab in winter. In the summer pelage there is usually a blackish line on the sides, but it often cannot be discerned on adults in winter and on young animals. The under parts are white or nearly so in *T. hudsonicus* and are somewhat rust-colored in *T. douglasii*. The tail is fringed with tawny, yellow, or white.

Red squirrels are attractive, active, vociferous creatures that lend charm to woodlands. Their extensive vocabulary includes chatters, clucks, grunts, and other sounds. The warning call is a "churr-churr" repeated rapidly and drawn out. Although they are tree squirrels, they spend much time on the ground. They can swim fairly well and voluntarily enter water to reach an opposite shore. Occasionally they migrate, but probably they merely travel locally out of an area of inadequate food supply. Red squirrels are active by day and on moonlit nights. They do not hibernate but sometimes stay in their nests for several days during inclement weather.

An individual usually has several nests. These are of three types: (1) a loosely constructed tree nest used mainly during warm weather; (2) a hole in a tree trunk that serves as the winter nest; and (3) an alternative winter nest in the form of a weather-tight structure located in the densest foliage of a tree. Burrows are sometimes constructed under stones or stumps.

Red squirrels eat a wide variety of plant food and occasionally young birds and birds' eggs. Their food consists principally of the seeds from pine and spruce cones. The Douglas pine squirrel cuts and fells the green, unopened cones of several species of coniferous trees in autumn. These are carried or dragged to small streams or to damp places under logs or in hollow stumps where they are accumulated in caches of up to 160 cones or more. The dampness prevents the cones from opening until they are shelled by the squirrels. In the Sierra Nevadas in California, these squirrels have been seen burrowing through 3 or 4 meters of snow to reach the cache.

Ordinarily solitary, chickarees pair for mating in late winter or spring. The gestation period is 36 to 40 days, and the litter size is from 1 to 7, usually 4 to 6. There may be two litters in one year, and females breed within one year of their birth. One captive lived for nine years.

In Pennsylvania there is a popular misconception that red and gray squirrels are enemies and that during fights red squirrels castrate gray squirrels so that reproduction is prevented. Because of this idea, red squirrels are ruthlessly hunted and killed.

The type species of the genus is *T. hudsonicus* (Erxleben).

Asiatic Striped Palm Squirrel (*Funambulus tristriatus*), photo by P. J. Deoras.

ASIATIC STRIPED PALM SQUIRRELS; LENA OR MOOKULA-LENA; ANIL OR SINNA ANIL OR CARU-PU-ANIL (native names).

THESE SQUIRRELS inhabit Ceylon, India, and Baluchistan. Some of the five species—*palmarum, pennanti, tristriatus, layardi,* and *sublineatus*—frequent the open palm growth of lower elevations and others are found in dense forests.

The length of the head and body is from 115 to 178 mm.; the tail length is about the same. The fur is soft and fairly dense. The upper parts range in coloration from a light grayish brown to almost black. The head is grayish or reddish brown, some forms have distinctly reddish heads from December to May. There are usually three stripes on the back, but some species have an additional short faint stripe on the sides below the other stripes. In *F. layardi* the mid-dorsal stripe is much brighter than the outer pale stripes, and in *F. sublineatus* the median stripes are darker than the outer stripes. The stripes in the other three species are all light in color. The under parts of *F. layardi* are deep red, and in all other species they are whitish to rich buffy or light brown. These attractive little squirrels bear a superficial resemblance to the chipmunks of the genera *Eutamias* and *Tamias*.

These squirrels are diurnal. They forage actively on the ground and in trees for seeds, nuts, plant stems, young bark, buds, leaves, flowers, insects, and grubs.

They sometimes eat cocoa pods and the buds and seeds of silk cotton trees (*Ceiba*) which produce kapok; and sometimes they damage twigs used in lac production. They are fond of the nectar of the silky oak (*Grevillea robusta*), and in obtaining it, they become well powdered with the pollen, thus serving as important agents in pollination.

The different species have very different habitats. Some prefer the open palm and scrub growth of the low altitudes, while others frequent the dense jungle and tall trees. The latter are rather rare; they stay in the tree tops or forage on the ground, but little is known of their habits.

Individuals that are found in open country show little fear of man and, if not molested, may live around settlements. If given a little encouragement, they become quite tame.

Usually, several males fight over one female. Breeding takes place in one day, and then the male leaves. From 2 to 4 (usually 3) young are born from 40 to 45 days later. The female suckles the young for about two months, during which time she spurns male attention. Females of this species are sexually mature at six to eight months of age, and there are usually three litters in a year. Most of the females build a globular nest of plant fibers in the trees where the young are born and raised.

The type species of the genus is *F. palmarum* (Linnaeus).

Giant Squirrel (*Ratufa indica*), photo by Ernest P. Walker.

GIANT SQUIRRELS, ROCK SQUIRRELS; DANDOLENA, KALLOE, MALI-ANIL, KARRAT, RASU, KES AN-NALU, TA'RAI, SHINNGAPAW-ANI, SHIN-NIGYI, SHENG, MAMAI, TUPEI-NANDANG, DJALARANG (native names).

THE FOUR SPECIES are distributed as follows: *R. macroura*, Ceylon and southern India; *R. bicolor*, Nepal and Burma through Indo-China and the Malay States to the East Indies; *R. affinis*, the Malay Peninsula and the East Indies; *R. indica*, peninsular India, from Travancore north to Orissa, central Provinces, and Surat.

The length of the head and body ranges from 254 to 457 mm., and the tail is about the same length or longer. The weight is usually 1.5 to 2 kg. but is sometimes as much as 3 kg. These large squirrels are very colorful mammals. The coloration varies widely. Some are shining black above with light yellowish-brown under parts; some are deep red, while others range through dark browns and bays to grays above, without stripes or spots. The under parts are buffy to white. Fading and the growth of new hair in well-defined areas often produce the effect of colored patches on the back that are not true differences in pattern. The ears are short, round, and, in *R. macroura*, tufted. The hand is extremely broad, the inner pad is expanded for gripping, the feet are broad, and the claws are large and powerful.

These squirrels are arboreal, usually going to the ground only to chase another squirrel or to follow a female during the breeding season. They are extremely agile in the trees, making leaps of 6 meters or more, and progressing rapidly through the tree tops. Giant squirrels are solitary or associate in pairs, and they are often wary and keep well hidden in the dense forest vegetation. All have harsh voices of a staccato character, heard when alarmed or angry, but a low "churr" is indicative of pleasure or recognition.

The diet consists of fruit, nuts, the bark of some trees, insects, and birds' eggs. These squirrels do not sit upright with the tail arched over the back while feeding. Instead, they balance themselves with their hind feet on a branch so that their hands are free to manipulate the food. In this position the axis of the body is held at right angles to the support, with the head and forequarters on one side of the branch and the tail as a counterweight on the other side. The very short broad thumb is important in helping to hold food.

Holes in trees are used for shelter. During the breeding season a large nest, about the size of an eagle's nest, is constructed. The young are born and raised in this nest. A gestation period of 28 days has been reported for *R. macroura*, the number of young per litter is one or two, and some observers believe there are several litters a year. An individual has lived in captivity for 16 years.

The type species of the genus is *R. indica* (Erxleben).

681

Oil-palm Squirrel (*Protoxerus stangeri*), photo by George S. Cansdale.

OIL-PALM SQUIRRELS.

TWO SPECIES inhabit Africa: *P. stangeri* ranges from the Gold Coast, including the island of Fernando Po, to Kenya and Angola; and *P. aubinnii* (*Myrsilus aubinnii* of some authors), Liberia and Ashanti.

The length of the head and body is about 228 to 331 mm., and the length of the tail is usually 254 to 382 mm. There is considerable variation in color in the species *P. stangeri*: the upper parts range from tawny olive to almost black, usually the brightest shades are on the back and the paler on the head; the cheeks are whitish or grayish white; the sides are brownish-gray, and the under parts are white to buffy. The tail of *P. stangeri* is sometimes banded with black and white or with black and rufous, or the bands may be inconspicuous. The species *P. aubinnii* tends to have a uniformly grizzled appearance, with a slender black tail. A broad, black band may be present along the middle of the back. These two species are readily distinguished by the amount of hair on the ventral surface of the body: in *P. stangeri* the ventral surface is thinly haired, often almost naked, a rare feature in the order Rodentia, whereas in *P. aubinnii* the belly is well furred. The tail is bushy and often somewhat longer than the head and body. The ears are small and rounded. The pelage is coarse.

Practically nothing has been recorded regarding the natural history of *P. aubinnii*, and that of *P. stangeri* is little known. The natives, however, recognize *P. aubinnii* and call members of this genus bush-cats. They shelter in tree cavities. The members of the species *P. stangeri* are described as active and agile. They are sometimes called the "booming" squirrels because of a booming call that they utter occasionally. When not disturbed, they utter a bird-like twittering call. They feed in trees and on the ground. Seeds, nuts, and fruit are their main diet, and in some regions they feed extensively on the orange-colored nuts of the oil palm which often stains the pelage. They sometimes gnaw fresh ivory tusks and bones and for this reason they have been called ivory eaters; however, it is not unusual for rodents to eat meat and gnaw bones. Nests are built in hollow trees, and there are usually three or four young per litter.

The type species of the genus is *P. stangeri* (Waterhouse).

AFRICAN PALM SQUIRRELS.

TWO SPECIES have been named and described from Africa: *E. wilsoni* from Gabon and the French Cameroons, and *E. ebii* from Ghana and Sierra Leone.

The length of the head and body is usually 254 to 305 mm., and the length of the tail, 280 to 305 mm. The species *E. wilsoni* is mixed rufous and black above, with rufous predominant on the outside of the limbs, and the lower parts are scantily covered with yellow-rufous hairs. There is an abrupt line of demarcation between the sides and the abdomen. The tail of the type specimen has a purplish-red tinge. The species *E. ebii* is rufous over the entire dorsal area, or the head is rufous and the back is buffy. The lower parts of the limbs, the feet, the inside of the limbs, the ears, and the sides of the head are bright red, and the throat, breast, and belly are thinly covered with yellowish-red hairs. The tail of this species is sometimes banded with white.

The general characters of squirrels of this genus are similar to those of *Protoxerus*, but the skull is elongated (with a long muzzle) as in *Funisciurus*. The tail of *Epixerus* is quite bushy and usually longer than the head and body. The belly is thinly haired, often nearly naked, as in *Protoxerus*.

The natural history of these tree squirrels has not been found in our search of published literature.

George Cansdale, who took this picture, states: "As far as I know, the *Epixerus* shown in this picture is the only specimen of this very rare squirrel taken alive and was the first to be taken for very many years. I took it after I had been searching for twelve years."

The type species of the genus is *E. wilsoni* (Du Chaillu).

African Palm Squirrel (*Epixerus ebii*), photo by **George S. Cansdale.**

African Striped Squirrel (*Funisciurus lemniscatus*), photo by F. Petter.

AFRICAN STRIPED SQUIRRELS; GESTREEPTE, EEK-HORINKIES, NGABALENGIZA, BUEN-BEN (native names).

THIS GENUS of 15 species is found in Africa from Sierra Leone and the Ivory Coast eastward to the Congo and Tanganyika, and southward to Angola and South-West Africa. These squirrels occur in palm groves, palm scrub, savannah, and in forests to elevations of at least 2,175 meters.

The head and body length is 135 to 200 mm., and the tail length is 100 to 200 mm. The pelage is soft-furred. Two groups of species may be recognized—one with longitudinal stripes on the back and the other without back stripes. Some of the latter have a whitish stripe on the side. The general color of the upper parts in all species consists of various combinations of red and black, yellowish brown, or olive-brown. The underside is whitish or creamy. The tail is long and thin in some and bushy in others.

These squirrels may be distinguished from *Paraxerus* by the short, rounded ears, four mammae, rather than six, and dental and skull features.

Like most squirrels, they give an alarm or protest call. This is a double "kek-kek," accompanied by a flicking of the tail. They are most active in the early morning and late afternoon, as they rest during the heat of the day. They usually are solitary or associate in pairs. Although arboreal, they come to the ground to forage for food. They feed on seeds, nuts, and fruit, and eat insects and birds' and lizards' eggs at times.

At least one species sometimes makes a domed nest of fibrous material in the undergrowth about 3 meters from the ground, and it has been reported that *F. pyrrhopus* often builds its nest in the axil of a palm frond about 2 meters above the ground.

There are usually two or three young per litter. Young *F. congicus*, just able to run and climb about, have been collected in South-West Africa from March to August.

It is reported that individuals kept in captivity eat various kinds of fruit, nuts, and insects.

The type species of the genus is *F. lemniscatus* (Le Conte).

684

A. East African Bush Squirrel (*Paraxerus* sp.), photo by C. A. Spinage through Wildlife Protection Society of South Africa. B. African Bush Squirrel (*P. antoniae*), photo from *Trans. Zool. Soc. London*.

AFRICAN BUSH SQUIRRELS; BOOMMEERKAT, GOLO-GOLO, KASIDYE, SINDI, KAPALE, KIMHULESI, NHONGOGO, SINDIKULETI (native names).

THE COMBINED RANGES of about 12 species includes areas where there are trees in eastern and southern Africa from the Sudan south to South-West Africa, Bechuanaland, and Zululand. *Tamiscus*, Thomas, 1918 is herein regarded as a subgenus of *Paraxerus*.

The head and body length is usually 153 to 254 mm., and the tail length is about the same. The fur is soft, short, and thick. Among the different species there are a variety of striking color patterns. Members of the subgenus *Tamiscus* usually have a striped pattern, i.e., four black stripes bordering three lighter ones, the general effect being *Tamias*-like. In *Paraxerus*, the color of the upper parts may be speckled yellowish gray tinged with black, blackish brown, green-gray, or brilliant red. The under parts may be dingy white, brown, reddish brown, or bright red. The tail is bushy and may be yellow tinged with black, brown, or reddish brown.

The squirrels of the genus *Paraxerus* are distinguished from those of *Funisciurus* by their high, pointed ears, the presence of six mammae instead of four, and different dental and skull features. These squirrels are distinguished from *Heliosciurus* by the five cheek teeth on each side of the upper jaw and four below, rather than four above and four below as in *Heliosciurus*, and by the narrow, more tapering muzzle.

These animals have been heard to utter an alarm call and also a bird-like twittering. They are reported to be active both day and night but are most frequently seen at dusk. During the middle part of the day, they lie quietly in their nest holes or in deep shade. They are usually found high in the trees, but they also spend much time on the ground foraging for food. When alarmed, they run for a nearby tree and hide by lying flat on a branch. When excited, they whisk the tail about vigorously.

Members of this genus have a varied diet of available seeds and fruits. They also dig bulbs and roots from the ground and eat insects and birds' eggs when obtainable. They live in holes in hollow trees and store seeds and berries in these places.

The only known fact on their reproductive biology is that usually two young are born in each litter. The young are kept in a nest in a tree-hole.

Individuals of the genus *Paraxerus* are hunted and eaten by the natives. In forested areas they are usually plentiful. In captivity they will eat a variety of vegetable food and cooked or raw meat.

The type species of the genus is *P. cepapi* (Smith).

West African Sun Squirrel (*Heliosciurus gambianus*), photo by Ernest P. Walker.

SUN SQUIRRELS; KENDA, KAPALI, LUPALI, KWI-KWI, FOHT, KIPEVEMENDE, IMBELEMENDE, *H. lucifer:* KASINDI (native names).

THE 13 NAMED SPECIES have a combined range in Africa from about 15 degrees north latitude to about 15 degrees south latitude. Habitats range from dense forests to open savannahs.

The length of the head and body is from 153 to 254 mm., and the length of the tail is usually from 153 to 305 mm. The coloration of the single species of the subgenus *Heliosciurus, H. gambianus,* is extremely variable. Above, the pelage is greenish gray, brownish, or black and usually has a whitish- or light yellowish-brown wash; the under parts, including the feet and inside of the legs, range from whitish or yellowish to deep reddish brown. The tail is somewhat darker than the back and has light-colored tips to the hairs, which gives a hoary appearance, or, if the tips are evenly arranged, a distinct crossbanded effect. *H. lucifer* (subgenus *Aethosciurus*) has an attractive color pattern of light-red upper parts with a blackish central dorsal patch. The other species of the subgenus *Aethosciurus* are plainer in color, with mixtures of grays, browns, oranges, and olives, although they may have a greenish appearance.

These squirrels are similar to those of the genus *Sciurus,* the main difference being the structure of the baculum. The front surface of the incisors is orange. It is possible that the species in this genus included in the subgenus *Aethosciurus* eventually may be placed in the genus *Paraxerus.*

Sun squirrels eat seeds, nuts, fruits, insects, and birds' eggs. Their habit of basking in the sun on tree branches probably gives rise to the vernacular name. Much of the color change of the hairs, at least those on the upper parts, is due to sun basking. Sun squirrels are more active in the morning and evening and usually rest during the heat of the day. They run about on the ground as well as in trees. When surprised or alarmed on the ground, they quickly climb a tree trunk on the opposite side from the disturbance and flatten themselves on a limb to avoid detection. Sometimes they go to the tops of the highest trees when startled. They use the holes of trees as shelters and as nests in which to raise their young. Natives often eat these squirrels.

The type species of the genus is *H. gambianus* (Ogilby) = *H. annulatus* (Desmarest)? The subgenus *Aethosciurus,* Thomas, 1916 has *H. poensis* (A. Smith) as type species.

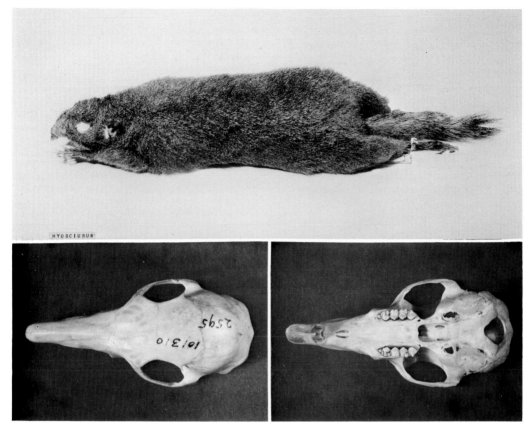

Celebes Long-nosed Squirrel (*Hyosciurus heinrichi*), photos from American Museum of Natural History.

CELEBES LONG-NOSED SQUIRRELS.

THE SINGLE SPECIES, *H. heinrichi,* inhabits the mountains of Celebes. They have been found in the Latimodjong Mountains of southern Celebes at an elevation of 2,300 meters and in northern Celebes at an elevation of 1,700 meters.

This is the largest of the long-nosed squirrels. The length of the head and body measures from about 200 to 240 mm., and the tail length is from 95 to 135 mm. Those from southern Celebes are fuscous, flecked with tawny above and on the sides. Beneath there is an irregular, white, median band, about 30 mm. wide, from the mouth to the belly. The tail is the same color as the upper parts, and the hairs are about 35 mm. in length. The backs of the hands and feet are slightly darker than the body. The squirrels from northern Celebes differ in that the light area is

pale yellowish white and the margins are rather even. There are also cranial differences. The vibrissae are about 35 mm. in length. The fur is thick and soft. The nose is relatively longer than in any of the other long-nosed squirrels (*Dremomys, Menetes, Lariscus,* and *Rhinosciurus*). The tail is short, the feet are long and narrow, and the claws are large.

These squirrels have burrows in the ground and spend much of their time in low vegetation. Mr. Frost, who found this species in the Molengraff Range in central Celebes, believed that they burrow and live underground to some extent. He stated that the natives consider these squirrels to be rats.

No information has been found regarding their habits. The unusual elongation of the front part of the head suggests specialized habits which differ from those of most squirrels.

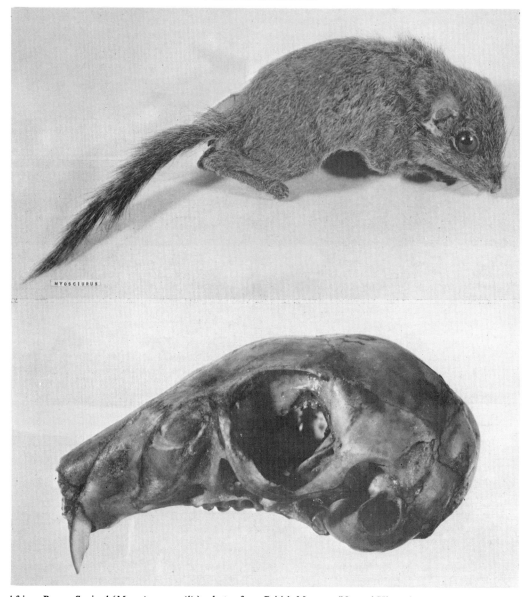

African Pygmy Squirrel (*Myosciurus pumilio*), photos from British Museum (Natural History).

AFRICAN PYGMY SQUIRRELS.

THE SINGLE SPECIES, *M. pumilio*, occurs in the Cameroons and Gabon of western Africa, where the squirrels inhabit the high forest.

For tree squirrels they are extremely small. The head and body length is about 60 to 75 mm. The tail is about 50 mm. in length and is narrow. The pelage is strikingly colorful, with buffy-green upper parts and with an olive-white underside. The edges of the rounded ears are conspicuously white. There is but one premolar on each side of the upper jaw.

The habits and biology of this diminutive tree-dweller have apparently not been recorded. Specimens are in the British Museum (Natural History).

This species is the smallest squirrel in the world. It is so diminutive that it more nearly resembles a small mouse than a true squirrel.

A. Prevost's Squirrel (*Callosciurus prevosti*); B. Finlayson's Squirrel (*C. finlaysoni*); C. Malayan Squirrel (*C. nigrovittatus*); photos by Ernest P. Walker.

BEAUTIFUL SQUIRRELS, TRICOLORED SQUIRRELS; RISANG, KELKUTA, TWAJA, SHIN-NGAPAW or SHIN-NI-GALE, TUPAI (native names).

THIS GENUS of about 20 species is found in southeastern Asia, the East Indies, and Formosa. The species *C. caniceps* has been introduced to Japan. Forests, cultivated areas, and gardens are frequented. *Tomeutes* is herein regarded as a synonym of *Callosciurus*.

The length of the head and body is usually from 127 to 280 mm., the tail is usually from 76 to 254 mm. in length. The weight is normally under 500 grams. The generic name, which means "beautiful squirrels," is appropriate, for these squirrels are among the most brilliantly colored mammals. While the pattern is fairly uniform, the colors are varied. Some are almost pure white or a light cream color with a pinkish or light cinnamon cast at certain seasons; others are various shades of gray tinged with brown and have bright reddish-brown under parts, sometimes with brown feet and white thighs. Still others have a definite tricolored pattern—the top of the head, back, sides, and tail are shining jet black or brownish. The under parts are light to dark reddish brown, and, on each side where the other colors approach each other, there is a pure white line or a narrow line of gray. The species *C. finlaysoni*, as presently understood, may be completely black or completely white, or the under parts may be white, red, or black. If the under parts are red, the whole animal is red or reddish; if they are not red, the root of the tail is pale-colored. Another species, *C. erythraeus*, is usually olivaceous above and a rich red-brown or white below. The extreme variability in color in these squirrels may be illustrated by the following example: in the Chindwin Valley of Burma three races or subspecies of *Callosciurus* have been recorded from the west river bank and eight races have been recognized from the east river bank. *C. caniceps* undergoes a pronounced change in color closely associated with the breeding season.

The fur in this genus is not particularly soft, but it is fairly full; the tail is moderately full in many species but is inclined to be flat as the hairs on the underside are short.

Externally, these squirrels are often indistinguishable from *Sciurus* and *Ratufa*, except that most of them are more brilliantly colored than *Sciurus* and they are smaller than *Ratufa*. The female has four or six mammae.

The habits of these animals seem to be similar to those of other squirrels. They are diurnal, mainly arboreal, and feed on seed, nuts, fruits, buds and flowers, and probably bird and insect eggs. They live in hollow trees and also build leaf and stick nests. The duration of gestation periods is not known, although the number of young in a litter is usually three or four. The Sakais of Malaya call the gray-bellied squirrel (*C. caniceps*) "tupai taratak" because of its alarm call.

Squirrels of the species *C. erythaeus* are sold in large numbers in Formosa to the Chinese, who look upon the presence of such pets as good luck. They are kept in cages similar to the small animal exercise wheels used for laboratory experiments. These wheels revolve freely, even though 200 animals may be enclosed in the cages. The cages are hung in stores, cafes, on porches, and inside houses. Squirrel catching provides a source of income to natives.

The type species of the genus is *C. rafflesii* (Vigors and Horsfield). *Rubrisciurus*, Laurie and Hill, 1954, was erected as a subgenus for the species *C. rubriventer* (Forster).

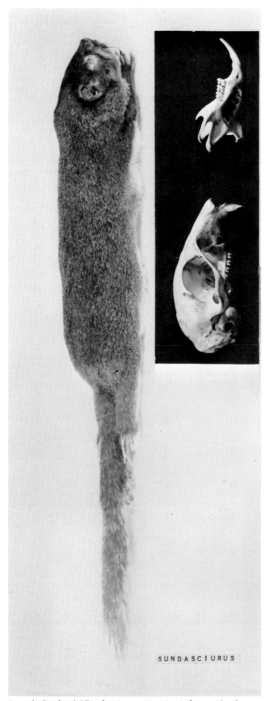

Lowe's Squirrel (*Sundasciurus steerei mindanensis*), photo from *Abh. Zool. Anthrop.-ethn. Mus. Dresden*, "Säugetiere vom Celebes- und Philippinen- Archipel," Adolf B. Meyer. Inset: Skull (*S. lowi*), photo by P. F. Wright of specimen in U.S. National Museum.

LOWE'S SQUIRRELS, HORSETAILED SQUIRRELS.

TWO SPECIES are included in this genus: *S. lowi* found in Borneo, Malay Peninsula, Sumatra, and islands of the Sunda Straits; and *S. hippurus* found in the Malay Peninsula, Sumatra, and Borneo. Moore (1958) erected a subgenus *Aletesciurus* for the species *S. hippurus*. We list only two species for this genus, but many mammalogists include as many as ten species (*S. lowi, S. hippurus, S. pryeri, S. brookei, S. philippinensis, S. steerei, S. juvencus, S. mindanensis, S. samarensis,* and *S. melanogaster*). The determination of the number of valid species must await further research.

The following description applies to *S. lowi*: head and body length, 154 mm., tail, 95 mm. Ears are black-rimmed, under parts and underside of limbs are white to buffy white, and upper parts are dark brownish, quite sleek, finely grizzled with blackish hairs. The tail is obscurely to broadly banded with grizzled orange-brown and black. The long snout has incisors projecting forward. This description applies to *S. hippurus*: head and body length, 255 mm., tail, 275 mm. Ears are rimmed with grayish hairs. Head, shoulders, upper surfaces of limbs, and rump are dark gray; back is dark brown, grizzled with blackish hairs; under parts are bright chestnut. The tail is long-haired and tricolored: basal third brownish above, gray below; median third black, almost glossy; tip dark mahogany brown.

The habits of these squirrels are not well known. Both species are apparently more terrestrial than arboreal, and it is thought that, due to the lengthened rostrum and projecting incisors, their diet includes more insects and other animal food than does that of "normal" squirrels. The habitat is heavy lowland and foothill forests for *S. hippurus* and mountain forests for *S. lowi*.

Asiatic Striped Squirrel (*Tamiops swinhoei*), photo by Robert E. Kuntz.

STRIPED HIMALAYAN and BURMESE SQUIRRELS, ASIATIC STRIPED SQUIRRELS; SWAY; LELAY.

THE COMBINED RANGE of the two species, *T. macclellandi* and *T. swinhoei*, includes southern China, Assam, Burma, Thailand, the Malay States, Indo-China, and a few nearby islands. They inhabit various kinds of forest, including jungles, coniferous growth, and low scrub from sea level to about 1,525 meters in elevation. Some zoologists regard *Tamiops* as a subgenus of *Callosciurus*.

The length of the head and body varies from 100 to 160 mm., and the tail length, from 80 to 115 mm. The weight is from 40 to 85 grams. The tail is usually narrow and shorter than the head and body. Usually there are five dark stripes alternating with light stripes on the back and sides, somewhat like the pattern of the chipmunk *Eutamias*. The general background color above is yellowish brown. The underside is white, pale brown, or bright red. The ears are usually tufted with white, and the tails are slender and rather thinly furred. Apparently there are two molts per year, since the winter and summer coats are somewhat different in color. The female has six mammae. Young have been reported in April. There are two premolars on each side of the upper jaw.

These squirrels are arboreal in habit, living in holes in trees. They are very agile and fast and are able to leap great distances. They have been observed singly and in pairs. They are active during the day, particularly in the early morning. They eat available nuts, fruits, and seeds, and are reported to be partly insectivorous. *T. macclellandi* may damage ripening corn crops in some areas.

These squirrels are easily alarmed, and when frightened they give a short chirp. *T. swinhoei* has a high pitched call like that of a bird.

The type species of the genus is *T. macclellandi* (Horsfield).

Berdmore's Palm Squirrel (*Menetes berdmorei*), photo by Ernest P. Walker.

BERDMORE'S or MULTI-STRIPED PALM SQUIRREL; SHIN-BAYGAYA; QUUAH.

THE SINGLE SPECIES, *M. berdmorei*, is native to Burma, Indo-China, Thailand, the Malay States, and nearby islands from sea level to about 1,225 meters elevation. In some portions of their range, they frequent rocks and stones that are surrounded by thick shrubs. They occur near cultivated areas, in open fields, and in forests.

The length of the head and body is from 177 to 203 mm., and the length of the tail is from 154 to 177 mm. The weight is about 195 grams. The pelage is dense, soft, and full, grayish brown on the back, grayish on the head, light gray on the sides, and whitish to buffy on the under parts. The side stripes, which extend between the back of the shoulders and the front of the thighs, are particularly conspicuous. The upper stripe is a faint black line, below this is a buff line, next a fairly distinct black line, and there is a suggestion of a buffy stripe below. In some sub-species there is a faint mid-dorsal line of black. The tail is relatively full and nearly the same color as the back, or slightly lighter.

As a whole, the appearance of these squirrels is similar to that of a dark *Callospermophilus* with a slightly more bushy tail. The head is sharply pointed, and the incisor teeth are deep orange. The female has six mammae.

Although they are essentially ground squirrels, they are occasionally observed climbing about in clumps of bamboo at short distances from the ground. They spend most of their time on the ground, they may be seen running along railways or up and down slanting or broken bamboo. They are plentiful along the edges of rice fields and in long grass, especially in the early evenings. They are similar to the tree shrews in their movements, hide at the smallest noise, and do not come out again until the danger seems to be passed. It is believed that their habits are similar to those of *Funambulus palmarum*.

Long-nosed Squirrel (*Rhinosciurus laticaudatus*), photo by Lim Boo Liat. Inset: Skull (*R. laticaudatus*), photo by P. F. Wright of specimen in U.S. National Museum.

LONG-NOSED SQUIRRELS.

THE SINGLE SPECIES, *R. laticaudatus*, inhabits the southern portions of the Malay peninsula, Sumatra, Borneo, and adjacent islands at low elevations.

The length of the head and body is from 203 to 242 mm., and the length of the tail is from 95 to 127 mm. The coloration above is reddish brown to blackish brown, buffy on the flanks, and whitish beneath, but sometimes the under parts are the same color as the sides. The short, bushy tail is gray, with white-tipped hairs. The outstanding characteristic of this squirrel is its elongated rostrum which forms the long nose. The general appearance is similar to those species of *Lariscus* that lack dark stripes.

The upper incisors appear to be scarcely functional, but the lower incisors are long and slender. There are two premolars on each side of the upper jaw. All the cheek teeth are unusually large. The tongue is long and remarkably protrusible.

The unusual proportions of the rostrum of these squirrels is related with their diet. Their food consists mainly of large ants, termites, and beetles, but they also eat fruit. In old individuals the teeth are worn down considerably. This is thought to be caused by the dirt and grit taken in with the insect food. Only a few other squirrels have such an adaptation and eat soft animal food regularly, although many squirrels eat some insects and meat occasionally.

Malayan Black-striped Squirrel (*Lariscus insignis*), photo by Ernest P. Walker.

MALAYAN BLACK-STRIPED SQUIRRELS, THREE-STRIPED PALM SQUIRRELS, STRIPED GROUND SQUIRRELS; BUÜT, BOKOL.

THIS GENUS has two species: *L. insignis*, native to the Malay Peninsula, Sumatra, Borneo, Java, and smaller adjacent islands, and *L. hosei*, of Borneo. Although a few subspecies prefer the lowlands, most members of the genus inhabit the mountains from 910 to 1,510 meters elevation. It is said that *L. hosei* frequents the banks of jungle streams.

The head and body length is from 165 to 200 mm., and the tail is 75 to 115 mm. in length. The coloration is of two distinctly different types and patterns, but with intermediate patterns that connect the two extremes. In one, the top of the head and back is dark gray, the sides are brown, the flanks yellowish or reddish, the fore legs grayish, and the belly is white, ivory, or buffy. There is a black stripe along the back from about the shoulders to the rump; another black line, rather high up along each side, separates the gray of the back and the brown of the sides, but this stripe does not reach the shoulders or the flanks. The tail is blackish with the hairs tipped with gray. Contrasting with the distinctly striped forms are some that are a rich chocolate-brown above (mixture of brown and black) that shade gradually to almost white along the middle of the under parts. Stripes are lacking in three forms, and there is no sharp line of demarcation between the colors. Intermediate between those two forms are those with faint stripes and a slight contrast between the color of the dark gray or brown of the back and the lighter gray or brown of the sides. In most cases the fur coat is not dense, and the tail is somewhat flattened. There are three pairs of mammae.

On Sumatra, Java, and Borneo, they are essentially inhabitants of the mountains and are seldom found in trees. They build their nests in the trunks of fallen trees.

For some time the generic name *Laria* was applied to these squirrels; the original describer was under the impression that it was a native name for them. It appears that *laric* is the native word meaning "to run."

According to published reports, *L. insignis* is plentiful, but *L. hosei* is rare.

The type species of the genus is *L. insignis* (Cuvier).

Southeastern Asiatic Squirrel (*Dremomys rufigenis*) (scale in inches), photo by Ernest P. Walker.

ORANGE-BELLIED HIMALAYAN SQUIRRELS, RED-CHEEKED SQUIRRELS; LOKRIA, ZHAMO, KALLI (native names).

THE COMBINED RANGES of about five species embraces Tibet, southern China, Formosa, Nepal, Assam, Manipur, Burma, Thailand, Indo-China, the Malay Peninsula, and Borneo at elevations from sea level to 3,400 meters.

The head and body length is from 165 to 242 mm., and the tail length is 126 to 178 mm. The weight is about 227 grams.

The coloration is generally dull without conspicuous pattern. Some forms are olivaceous above with a slight brownish tone. The upper surface of the tail is almost black, but the tips of the hairs are gray, and the lower surface is bright brown along the median line and edged by almost black. The under parts of the body are white, the sides of the lower and front portions of the head are bright reddish brown, and there is a faint light spot behind the ear. In other forms the general color is rufous-brown above and orange below, with a whitish spot back of the ear and a whitish ring around the eye. Still others are more grayish or more buffy. Some species have a bright chestnut anal patch and a faint dark line down the middle of the back. One species, *D. lokriah*, has a brilliant rufous patch on the outside of the hips. The furry coats are fairly soft and full.

The general form is similar to that of *Sciurus*, except that in *D. rufigenis* the snout is slightly elongated. The female has three pairs of mammae.

These squirrels have been noted in dense forests and seem to spend considerable time on the ground and in trees within 4.5 meters of the ground. They occur with species of *Callosciurus* in some areas.

Apparently the voice of *D. pernyi* has great power and resonance, and *D. lokriah* emits a sharp squeaky chatter, often continuously repeated. Fruits, nuts, plant material, and probably insects are included in the diet.

The type species of the genus is *D. pernyi* (Milne-Edwards).

Père David's Rock Squirrel (*Sciurotamias davidianus*), photo from *Recherches pour Servir à l'Histoire Naturelle des Mammifères*, M. H. Milne-Edwards and M. Alphonse Milne-Edwards.

ROCK SQUIRREL; NCEI-LOU-TSCHU (native name).

THIS GENUS is made up of two species: *S. davidianus*, of northern China and *S. forresti*, of Yunnan in southwestern China. These squirrels inhabit rocky, shrub-clad, mountain cliffs, and avoid dense tree growth. *Rupestes*, Thomas, 1922 is herein regarded as a subgenus, with *S. forresti* as type species.

The length of the head and body is from 194 to 250 mm., and the length of the tail is from 130 to 180 mm. *S. davidianus* has a gray dorsal surface which results from an even mixture of black and pale buffy reddish hairs; the tail and limbs are similarly colored. There is a pale ring around the eyes; the untufted ears are blackish, and the under parts are white. The general coloration of *S. forresti* is grayish brown with an inconspicuous narrow, whitish, lateral line, beneath which is a dark line from the shoulders to the hips. The under parts are pale reddish brown, the flanks reddish, the chest and throat white, and the tail is similar to the back, but is darker near the tip. Many zoologists believe that these squirrels are a connecting link between the pouched chipmunks and the true squirrels. They have small cheek pouches and a slightly lengthened snout. Females have three pairs of mammae. In *S. davidianus* the soles of the feet are densely haired, but in *S. forresti* the soles of the hind feet are almost naked.

Little has been recorded regarding their habits, but apparently they are similar to those of the chipmunks, except that these squirrels do not hibernate. Although members of this genus are able to climb trees, they seldom do so, preferring to travel about rocky terrain, which they do with great agility. They make their homes in deep crevices and between rocks.

Natives report that they enter houses for grain and food. In 1911 Jordan and Rothschild recorded from *S. davidianus* three new species of fleas.

The type species of the genus is *S. davidianus* (Milne-Edwards).

BORNEAN SQUIRRELS, THOMAS PYGMY SQUIRRELS.

THE SINGLE SPECIES, *G. simus*, inhabits Mount Kinabalu in northern Borneo, where a small number of specimens have been taken in forests at an elevation of about 1,200 meters.

The length of the head and body is about 128 mm., and the length of the tail is about 103 mm. The texture of the fur and the coloration of the squirrels of this species closely resemble *Sciurus notatus*; however, the flank stripes of *G. simus* are somewhat broader and more strongly marked than in *S. notatus*. The dorsal surface of the digits, sides of the nose, area around the eyes, and the margins of the ears are buffy yellow; the chest and undersurface are yellowish; and the tip of the tail is black. Externally, there are no outstanding characteristics, but the skull and dentition (large incisors) do differentiate this species.

Nothing is known about the life history of these rare squirrels. Dr. David Johnson, of the United States National Museum, collected one which was running up the bole of a large tree on the forested lower slopes of Mt. Kinabalu.

There are 13 specimens in the British Museum (Natural History) and the U.S. National Museum.

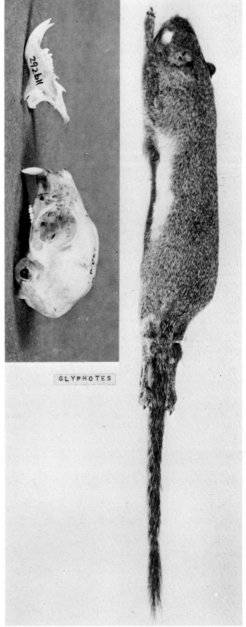

GLYPHOTES

Bornean Squirrel (*Glyphotes simus*), photos by P. F. Wright of specimen in U.S. National Museum.

Black-eared Squirrels (*Nannosciurus melanotis*), photo from *Verhandelingen over de Natuurlijke Geschiedenis aer Nederlandsche Overzeesche Bezittingen door de Leden der Natuurkundige Commissie in Oost-Indie, Zoologie,* C. J. Temminck. Inset: Skull (*N. melanotis*), photo by P. F. Wright of specimen in U.S. National Museum.

BLACK-EARED SQUIRRELS.

THE SINGLE SPECIES which comprises this genus is *N. melanotis* which inhabits Java, Borneo, Sumatra, and some of the smaller adjacent islands. It prefers dense forests from sea level to about 1,650 meters elevation.

These squirrels have a head and body length of from 75 to 115 mm. and a narrow, flat tail which varies in length from 50 to 80 mm. The fur is usually short and soft, often with a velvet-like texture. The coloration of the upper parts varies from grayish to rusty rufous or dark reddish brown. The basal portion of the hairs is gray or slate, and the remainder of the hairs are darker. The under parts are cinnamon-red to gray or buffy, and the sides of the head are light. The tail is usually similar in coloration to the body except that it is darker with occasional bands. There are prominent white facial markings which extend from the nose to behind the ears.

These animals are generally gregarious, two or three of them frequently may be seen together frolicking on the ground, on fallen tree trunks, and occasionally scampering up trees. They utter squeaking noises and shake their tails a great deal. They are diurnal and inquisitive, occasionally coming within close range of man if quick movements are restrained. Although curious, they seldom enter traps, even though they generally carefully explore them from the outside.

Pygmy Squirrel (*Exilisciurus whiteheadi*), photo from *Proc. Zool. Soc. London.*

PYGMY SQUIRRELS.

TWO SPECIES are found on the island of Borneo. *E. exilis* is widespread on the island in heavy forests, while *E. whiteheadi* is known only from the high forests of Mounts Dulit and Kinabalu. Four species, *E. concinnus*, *E. surrutilis*, *E. samaricus*, and *E. luncefordi* live in the Philippines.

The head and body length ranges from 66 to 100 mm. and the tail length, from 50 to 80 mm. The following description applies only to *E. exilis*: The coloration is dark reddish brown on the head and shoulders, shading to grizzled brown on the rump; the under parts are buffy and finely grizzled. The tail is grizzled brown above, and below it is bright rufous mixed with blackish hairs. The ears are almost naked. The following description applies only to *E. whiteheadi*: The upper parts are dark brown, finely grizzled with black; the under parts are paler and more buffy. The tail is dark orange-brown and black, giving an obscurely banded impression. The ears are tufted with very long gray and black hairs; in some specimens these tufts, when laid back, almost reach the rump. *E. whiteheadi* is a heavier-bodied, more robust squirrel than *E. exilis*.

Their habits are very similar to those of *Nannosciurus*.

They were separated generically by Moore to emphasize their very different cranial characters.

The type species of the genus is *E. exilis* (Müller).

Barbary Ground Squirrel (*Atlantoxerus getulus*), photo from *Trab. Mus. Cienc. Madrid*, "Los Mamiferos de Marruecos," Angel Cabrera.

BARBARY GROUND SQUIRRELS.

THE SINGLE SPECIES, *A. getulus*, occurs in Morocco and Algeria in northern Africa. These are the only squirrels that occur in Africa north of the Sahara Desert.

These squirrels are similar to those of the genus *Xerus*, but the fur is not as bristly, although it is short and stiff. There is a prominent white stripe on each flank, and sometimes a stripe down the center of the back. The fur is quite thin on the underside.

There are two premolars in each side of the upper jaw. The upper incisors frequently have traces of a groove.

These squirrels are particularly active in the early morning and late afternoon, but during the middle part of the day they remain in their burrows. Observers report that they are usually found in rocky areas and that they migrate when they overpopulate an area. They eat the fruit and seed of the Argan tree (*Argania sideroxylon*).

A. Ground Squirrel (*Xerus rutilus rufifrons*), photo by C. A. Spinage. B. African Ground Squirrel (*X. [Euxerus]* *erythropus lacustris*), photo by Ernest P. Walker.

AFRICAN GROUND SQUIRRELS, SPINY SQUIRRELS; MARANGEDENGHER, DABERGALI, WAAIERSTERT-MEERKATS (native names).

TWO SPECIES comprise this genus: *X. rutilus*, native to northeastern Africa, and *X. erythropus*, whose range includes the forest region of West Africa and extends eastward into East Africa. *Euxerus*, Thomas, 1909 is herein regarded as a subgenus for the species *X. erythropus*. Some zoologists include *Geosciurus* as a subgenus of *Xerus*, but it is herein treated as a valid genus.

The length of the head and body is from 227 to 305 mm.; the length of the tail is from 184 to 274 mm. *X. rutilus* is the smaller of the two species. The hairy coat is very harsh, underfur is almost entirely lacking, and the guard hairs are short, coarse, crisp and lie close to the body. In both species underfur is lacking. The coloration above is brownish through reddish gray to yellowish gray, and the under parts are buffy to white. *X. erythropus* has a white or buffy stripe on the side, and *X. rutilus* lacks stripes. The markings of the tail vary considerably with age. In immature animals, the light-colored tips to the hairs of the tail almost mask the darker basal part of the hairs. As the animal matures, the light tips are less conspicuous, and the central line of the tail appears as a dark streak. The coat is frequently tinted the color of the soil in which the animal lives, because tiny soil particles adhere to the hairs.

These animals have the body form of typical ground squirrels. In both species the hairs are flattened and grooved longitudinally. The ears are so small that they almost appear to have been bitten off. The orange incisors are not grooved. The claws are long and comparatively straight. Females have two mammae.

These squirrels are most active during daylight; they are terrestrial in their habits, living in burrows which they dig themselves. Although they are always alert, they apparently have little fear of man. They are generally well known throughout their ranges, for they make little attempt to conceal themselves; nevertheless, they are wary and take good care of themselves.

One individual of this genus lived more than six years in the Giza Zoo. Remains of *X. rutilus* have been found as fossils in France.

The type species of the genus is *X. rutilus* (Cretzschmar).

Ground Squirrel (*Geosciurus inauris*), photo by C. A. van Ee, Wildlife Protection Society of South Africa.

SOUTH AFRICAN GROUND SQUIRRELS; GROND-EEKHOORNTJIE, WAAIERSTERTMEERKATS, PHOL-WÁNA, ERUPÚKA-OKAWÁKA, NYANGA, PHOL-WÁNA, KAOKOVELD GROUND SQUIRRELS (native names).

TWO SPECIES comprise this genus: *G. inauris*, native to southern Africa (the southern limit is the vicinity of the Orange River) and *G. princeps*, occupying southwestern Africa and the southwestern section of Angola. *G. inauris* prefers rocky, hilly country, and *G. princeps* is a well-known inhabitant of the open Karoo-Veld. Some taxonomists regard *Geosciurus* as a subgenus of *Xerus*.

The length of the head and body is from 225 to 260 mm., and the length of the somewhat flattened tail is from 200 to 250 mm. The pelage is made up of coarse hair with little underfur. The coloration above is pale reddish brown or grayish brown, lightly sprinkled with black; the stripe on the sides from the shoulders to the haunches is white; the under parts are white; the tail is darker than the body, lightest

along the center. The feet are white. The claws are long, stout, and only slightly curved. The incisors of *G. inauris* are white, but those of *G. princeps* are yellow. There are four to six mammae.

The burrows are from 102 to 153 mm. in diameter and from 1.25 to 1.75 meters in length with several openings which frequently connect with burrows of neighbors. They usually are found in sandy soil. *G. princeps* inhabits rocky areas and utilizes crevices about rocks to a greater extent. Members of this species often live in colonies somewhat like those of the North American prairie dogs. *Geosciurus* behave in a similar manner, also, sitting up to view the surrounding region, visiting among their neighbors, sunning themselves in every conceivable position (including lying on their backs), scolding and chattering if an intruder appears, feeding near the burrows to which they hasten with a peculiar jumping gait and arched tail when alarmed, and cautiously peeping out when safe in the burrow to obtain a last look at the cause of the alarm. They are strictly diurnal, do not hibernate or store up food supplies, and are gregari-

703

ous, living in family groups of 6 to 30 individuals.

From two to six young constitute a litter (four apparently is the average). The young are born in the burrows and become sexually mature in about six months. These squirrels feed mainly on fleshy roots of desert plants that they dig up, but they also eat seeds, a variety of vegetation, and sometimes insect larvae, birds' eggs, young birds, and other meat. Since their habitat is quite arid, they rarely have an opportunity to drink water. Moisture from vegetation and the chemical conversion of starchy foods in their digestive systems is sufficient for their needs.

They are preyed upon by the various carnivores and predatory birds in their range, including the small mongoose (*Myonax*), but, strange to say, reliable observers record apparent harmony among *Geosciurus* and *Suricata* and *Cynictis*, the young sometimes play together.

They tame readily and South African residents often have them about their homes, where they run about like domestic cats (*Felis*).

Farmers often consider these squirrels a nuisance as they sometimes destroy crops. During bubonic plague epidemics, they are said to contract the disease and therefore the Health Department of the Union of South Africa objects to them.

The type species of the genus is *G. capensis* (Kerr) = *G. inauris capensis* as currently arranged.

Long-clawed Ground Squirrel (*Spermophilopsis lepto-dactylus*), photo by F. Petter.

THIN-TOED GROUND SQUIRRELS, LONG-CLAWED GROUND SQUIRRELS.

APPARENTLY THERE IS only one species, *S. leptodactylus*, in this genus of Asiatic ground squirrel. These squirrels inhabit the sandy deserts of Afghanistan, Russian Turkestan, and northern Iran.

The length of the head and body is from about 200 to 280 mm.; the tail length is from 70 to 90 mm. The color of the upper parts is sand-yellow to grayish yellow, and that of the underside is white. The end half of the tail is black below and light above, with a black fringe. There are two molts each year. The summer pelage is rough and bristly, and the winter pelage is long and silky. These animals are unique among the ground squirrels in that they have several pairs of vibrissae on the underside of the body. These vibrissae may serve them when climbing in shrubs. The feet are very thickly furred at all seasons. Another unusual feature is the very long, thick, and powerful claws, more than 10 mm. in length. No genus in the Sciuridae except *Hyosciurus* possesses such well-developed claws.

These ground squirrels live in small family groups in burrows that are usually located in brushy areas. They venture as far as 1,000 meters from the burrow when food is scarce. They are diurnal, and the extent of their activity depends upon the season. In the summer they remain in their burrows during the hot, middle part of the day; in winter, they are out at any time of the day, but they are not often above ground during very cold weather.

They eat the fruits, seeds, bulbs, and herbaceous parts of desert plants and insects.

Mating occurs in February and March, and three to six young are born about April or May.

These animals do not live near cultivated areas, so they are not a menace to farmers. In places where sand-consolidating plantings have been made, they dig out planted seeds and destroy the plants by eating the underground stems.

The skins of these squirrels are marketed in considerable quantity for the fur industry.

Marmot or Woodchuck (*Marmota monax*), photo by Ernest P. Walker.

MARMOTS, WOODCHUCKS; MURMELTIEREN; MAR-MATTES DES ALPS; WHISTLERS; GROUND-HOGS; SIFFLEURS; CHUROK.

THERE ARE ABOUT 16 species whose combined ranges include the mountains of Alaska, most of Canada, most of the United States except the extreme southern parts, western Europe, and most of Asia except in the extreme south. In the southern part of their ranges, these animals usually occur only at higher elevations, but elsewhere they frequent the lowlands as well.

The length of the head and body is from about 300 to 600 mm., and the tail is 100 to 250 mm. in length. The weight is 3 to 7.5 kg. The color of the fur varies considerably among the different species. The upper parts range from bright brownish yellow, dark brown, reddish brown, to a mixture of hairs that are part black and part white. The under parts in some species differ little in color from the upper parts, but in other species there is considerable variation. The under parts range from whitish to dark brown, yellowish gray, or reddish orange. The texture of the fur varies from thin to long and thick, with degrees of coarseness. Climate probably influences the thickness of the pelage. Apparently there is only one molt per year which occurs in the early summer. However, the Olympic marmot (*M. olympus*) changes its color from brown in the spring to yellow by August; this is apparently due to bleaching.

Marmots are active in the daytime and retire into their burrows at nightfall. Their burrows are dug in well-drained soil or among large rocks and often have several entrances. In some species the individuals live in colonies, clans, or coteries, but other species are more solitary. By the end of the summer these animals have become extremely fat, in preparation for a deep hibernation sleep which lasts from September until the end of March. In the northern part of their range, however, the hibernation period lasts as long as eight months. Although keeping mostly to the ground, they occasionally climb into shrubs and trees. They often sit upright on their haunches to watch the surrounding area. Their food consists of herbaceous vegetation and occasionally insects. The alarm call of marmots is a sharp whistle.

They mate in the early spring soon after coming out of hibernation. The gestation period is from 35 to 42 days. From April to July two to nine young (usually four or five) are born in a grass-lined underground den. After about a month, soon after the eyes have opened, they venture forth to feed on herbaceous vegetation. In *M. marmota* the young are very playful and stay in the colony for at least the next year. They are full-grown in two years and are sexually mature in three years. The life span is from 13 to 15 years.

Those species that inhabit areas of intensive cultivation sometimes damage crops. They eat row crops as well as grasses and legumes of the hayfield. The mounds of earth from their burrows can damage some farm machinery. Occasionally livestock injure themselves by stepping into a burrow. The flesh is palatable and regularly used by local residents. The fall pelage is thick and the leather is used to make whiplashes and shoestrings. Some species in western North America and in Asia are sought for fur and flesh. Marmots in some regions have fleas that carry bubonic plague. They also are hosts of ticks that carry Rocky Mountain spotted fever. They have been used in research on the physiology of hibernation. The primary enemy of the European alpine marmot is the golden eagle.

They may be tamed when young and are easily kept in captivity.

The type species of the genus is *M. marmota* (Linnaeus).

Plains Prairie "Dog" (*Cynomys ludovicianus*), photo by Ernest P. Walker.

PRAIRIE "DOGS," BARKING SQUIRRELS; PETITS CHIENS; PRARIEHUNDE; PERROS LIANEROS, PERRITOS.

THE FIVE SPECIES with their four subspecies inhabit most of North and South Dakota, Nebraska, Kansas, Oklahoma, Texas, Montana, Wyoming, Colorado, New Mexico, Utah, Arizona, and a small area in northern Mexico.

They are not dogs but are stout, short-tailed, short-legged, burrowing squirrels which inhabit open plains and plateaus. The length of the head and body of adults is about 300 mm.; the tail is about 87 mm. long; and they weigh from .9 to 1.4 kg. All of the species look much alike, with a grizzled yellow-gray or buffy back and slightly lighter under parts. The tail is somewhat flattened.

Prairie "dogs" show a high degree of social organization. Their "towns," often containing several thousand individuals, are divided into "wards," the boundaries of which are generally determined by the structure of the country. Each ward contains several "coteries"; each coterie is headed by a male that won the coterie by feats of strength, one to four females, and the young of the last two years. When there is quarreling among neighbors about boundaries, the decisions are made by the dominant males and they expel all invaders. All competition within the coterie is regulated or stopped by a strictly hierarchic order.

The burrows vary greatly depending upon local conditions. Usually they are about 150 mm. in diameter and go straight down for 3 to 5 meters to two or three short lateral tunnels in which grass nests are built. There is also a shelf or enlargement within about 900 mm. of the top of the burrow which is used as a listening post or place for passing. The earth from the holes is built up in a volcano-shaped cone which keeps surface water from running down the burrows. The owner of the burrow spends much time maintaining this cone, especially following rains. Prairie "dogs" also keep their visual field open by biting off all tall plants in the area. They feed on herbs and grasses, carrying on a sort of "rotating pasture" which eventually changes the vegetation to fast-growing plants.

Prairie "dogs" are active in the daytime. They are extremely friendly with each other but exhibit a sharp temper when approached by snakes and badgers. They sit upright to see as far as possible and, upon the approach of danger, scurry to their home burrow or the nearest hole. If the danger is not imminent, they sit at the hole or peep out and utter a sharp chirp, which may be likened to a bark, hence the name "prairie dog." Prairie "dogs" have various alarm calls, depending on whether the enemy approaches from the ground or air, a special all-clear signal or territorial call, and a call to the dominant male for help. If the danger appears serious, they disappear into the burrows and remain quiet and out of sight until the more venturesome cautiously peep out to investigate. During severe winter weather, they partially hibernate, but a few days of good weather soon brings them out even in winter.

The gestation period for *C. leucurus* is 28 to 32 days. Two to 10 young are born in March, April, or May. After 33 to 37 days, the eyes open, and in 7 weeks, they are weaned. Prairie "dogs" are full grown in 15 months and sexually mature in three years. At that time, the young males leave the coterie, while the females generally remain.

Because they consume wild grasses and other plants on which domestic livestock feed and because they eat cultivated crops, systematic efforts are made to destroy them, with the result that the large colonies of thousands of individuals which formerly occupied many acres no longer exist. A large colony of these interesting rodents still remains at Devil's Tower National Monument in northeastern Wyoming. They are commonly preyed upon by coyotes, foxes, badgers, large hawks, and eagles.

Leucocrossuromys, Hollister, 1916 has been proposed as a subgenus to include the species *leucurus*, *parvidens*, and *gunnisoni*. The type species of *Cynomys* is *C. ludovicianus* (Ord).

Plains Prairie "Dogs" (*Cynomys ludovicianus*), A. Visiting with their neighbors, a common practice in prairie-dog colonies. B. At the entrance to a burrow in the top of the conical mound of earth that the plains forms maintain with great work and care. Photos by Ernest P. Walker.

A. Thirteen-lined Ground Squirrels (*Citellus tridecemlineatus*), photo by Ernest P. Walker. B. Richardson's Ground Squirrel (*C. richardsonii*), photo by Ralph S. Palmer. C. Arctic Ground Squirrel (*C. undulatus*), photo from U.S. Fish and Wildlife Service.

GROUND SQUIRRELS, GOPHERS, DIGGERS; SOUS-LIKI; ZIESEL; ARDILLAS DE TIERRA; SIESEL, AR-DILLAS TERRICOLAS, CUINIQUIS. (Included are vernaculars used in other countries).

THERE ARE 14 species in the New World whose combined ranges extend from northern Mexico northward throughout the western United States and eastward to Ohio, western and northern Canada, and most of Alaska; seven species inhabit eastern Europe and Asia south to Turkestan and western Mongolia. They prefer a habitat of arid grassy prairies or rocky areas. Some authorities include in this genus the animals treated herein separately under *Ammospermophilus*, *Callospermophilus*, *Otospermophilus*, and *Spermophilopsis*.

The head and body length is 154 to 406 mm.; the length of the tail is 38 to 254 mm.; and the weight of the adults is 85 to 1000 grams. The coloration is of three types. The most common is a grizzled yellowish gray, darkest above, and the upper parts are finely spotted with light buffy, or pale yellowish white. The tail is similar but usually slightly reddish near the center with a darker area at each side of the reddish central line, and the margin is almost the color of the under parts. In another type the general coloration is similar, but the fine spotting is lacking or very faint. The third type is the 13-lined group in which the dark stripes are brownish gray, and the stripes, spots, and under parts are a dull yellowish white. In some forms the guard hairs are fine and soft and the underfur abundant, but in others they are coarse with very

scant underfur. Internal cheek pouches are present.

Ground squirrels are essentially short-legged, adapted to a life on the ground; they dig their own burrows or live about logs, rocks, or such objects as will provide shelter for their nests and food stores. They are active by day, searching for their food of seeds, nuts, roots, bulbs, some plant stems and leaves, mice, insects, birds, and eggs. Quantities of seeds, small soft-shelled nuts, and grain are carried in the cheek pouches to the underground storage chambers.

During the summer they become very fat, and those in the north become dormant. They often go into this sleep while the weather is still quite warm. In the southern part of their range, they are more or less active throughout the year but remain in their burrows during inclement weather or when the green food disappears.

The families are generally large—litters of 2 to 13 are common. The gestation period is 23 to 28 days. Newly born young are naked, blind, and toothless. There is only one litter per year. The life span is about two to five years. They are not strictly gregarious but live in loose colonies, and a large population results if food is sufficient.

They frequently give a twittering or whistling alarm note. They have considerable curiosity and sit upon their haunches or stand upon their hind legs to look over nearby obstructions. They enjoy basking in the sun.

The type species of the genus is *C. citellus* Linnaeus.

Antelope Ground Squirrel (*Ammospermophilus harrisii*), photo by Ernest P. Walker.

ANTELOPE GROUND SQUIRRELS, ANTELOPE SQUIRRELS, ANTELOPE CHIPMUNKS, WHITE-TAILED CHIPMUNKS, ARDILLITAS.

THERE ARE five species: *A. nelsoni, A. insularis, A. interpres, A. leucurus*, and *A. harrisii*, whose combined ranges cover the arid, sparsely vegetated plains and lower mountain slopes of the southwestern United States from western Colorado through Utah, northern Arizona, Nevada, the southern half of California, Baja California, down the Rio Grande Valley through New Mexico to western Texas, and similar terrain in northern Mexico.

The length of the head and body is 140 to 155 mm.; the length of the tail is 55 to 95 mm.; and adults weigh 112 to 142 grams. The background color of the upper parts ranges from a very light grayish brown to a light reddish brown; the side stripe is white bordered by lines of darker shades of the background color. The under parts are white; the top of the flattened tail is darker than the back, but beneath it is nearly white. The hairy coat is scant and coarse. Internal cheek pouches are present.

These are truly "ground-squirrels" that live in burrows they dig and possess few traits of either the squirrels (*Sciurus*) or chipmunks (*Tamias* and *Eutamias*). They are diurnal and are easily seen scampering over rocky slopes in arid canyons and scurrying through the bushy growth on broad, sandy plains. They are active throughout the year, except in the small areas of the higher and colder parts of their range where they become inactive during cold weather, but they do not truly hibernate. They feed on seeds, fruits, plant stems and roots, some insects, and carrion. Food supplies suitable for storage are carried in their cheek pouches and stored in burrows in the ground or under rocks or other shelter.

They have one or two litters per year, from six to eight young in the litter.

Snakes and weasels pursue them into their burrows, and foxes, coyotes, badgers, bobcats, and many kinds of hawks catch them above ground or dig them out.

They are probably the most conspicuous and entertaining mammal in their range, scampering about nervously, tail held straight or arched over the back, and hence they are called antelope chipmunks.

Where irrigation is carried on, these animals sometimes become a nuisance by attacking the crops and burrowing through raised irrigation ditch banks. They are, however, easily controlled.

The type species of the genus is *A. leucurus* (Merriam).

710

Rock Squirrel (*Otospermophilus beecheyi*), photo from U.S. National Park Service.

ROCK SQUIRRELS, CANYON SQUIRRELS.

OF THE FIVE SPECIES which compose this genus, *O. atricapellus*, *O. beecheyi*, and *O. variegatus* have a combined range that extends from central Washington to Baja California and the northern two-thirds of Mexico, and eastward to Colorado and Texas. Two species, *O. annulatus* and *O. adocetus*, inhabit a small area in west-central Mexico. They frequent open, rocky, or wooded hillsides from sea level to about 3,050 meters. *O. beecheyi* is frequently found in the Sierra Nevadas of California at elevations up to 3,000 meters where it lives in clearings in red fir forests.

The head and body length is 177 to 288 mm.; the tail is 138 to 252 mm. in length; and the weight is 500 to 800 grams. The appearance is similar to that of gray squirrels (*Sciurus carolinensis*), but there is a slight mottling or grizzled effect not so pronounced in the gray squirrels. The prevailing color is grayish or brownish gray with small light-gray or whitish spots that produce a mottled or dappled effect. In some parts of its range, *O. variegatus* is largely blackish. The under parts are almost white or yellowish. The tail is slightly flattened and bushy but not so plume-like as the tails of the gray squirrels. The fur is slightly coarse and often thin.

Rock squirrels are diurnal, live in holes in the ground, under logs, rocks, or in crevices in cliffs. Seeds, grains, nuts, acorns, fruits, green vegetation, and sometimes insects and carrion are eaten. They are excellent climbers, particularly about rocks and brush, but they rarely go far up a tree, and if alarmed they immediately seek the ground. They have internal cheek pouches in which they carry food to their burrows.

In those areas of their range where winter is severe or green food is in short supply, they become dormant. Litters of 3 to 15 (usually 7) are born from spring to late summer, after a gestation period of about one month. A second litter is sometimes noted but generally there is a single litter per year. The helpless youngsters are born in an underground nest, which they leave in about eight weeks. The life span is six to eight years.

Rock squirrels are not definitely gregarious, but they are sociable, visit among themselves, and are sometimes so plentiful that they appear to be in colonies. Where plentiful near cultivated areas, they destroy grain, fruit, and plant life and do such damage by digging that it is necessary to control them.

When the bubonic plague was introduced into the vicinity of San Francisco about 1900, the fleas that carried the disease transferred from the rats (*Rattus*) on which they normally lived to the ground squirrels. Consequently, the plague spread into several counties and it became necessary to exterminate the ground squirrels over an area for some time to stamp out the plague. The Hooper Foundation for Medical Research now maintains constant vigilance over the squirrel population to anticipate outbreaks of the disease.

The generic names *Citellus* and *Spermophilus* have often been used for these squirrels.

The type species of the genus is *O. grammurus* (Say) = *O. variegatus grammurus* as currently arranged.

Golden-mantled Ground Squirrels (*Callospermophilus lateralis*), photo from U.S. National Park Service. Inset: Cheek pouches filled, photo by Ernest P. Walker.

GOLDEN-MANTLED GROUND SQUIRRELS.

TWO SPECIES, *C. lateralis* and *C. saturatus*, inhabit the western United States from the Rocky Mountains to the Pacific coast and along the Cascade and Rocky Mountains in Canada. A third species, *C. madrensis*, inhabits the Sierra Madre mountains in Chihuahua, Mexico. These squirrels frequently live in rugged country, among the rocks or about fallen timber in open forested country. Some live in desert mountain ranges, in similar habitat.

The head and body length ranges from about 150 to 225 mm.; the tail is from 50 to 120 mm. in length; and the weight is 170 to 285 grams. Most forms have a longitudinal white or buffy stripe on each side of the back. These are bordered on each side by a black stripe which in some cases may be short or lacking. The upper parts, between the longitudinal stripes, are gray, buff, or cinnamon. Most forms of the genus in summer pelage have chestnut to yellow fur on the head and shoulder region from which the common name is derived. The under parts are whitish. The fur is dense and soft. There is apparently only one molt per year, occurring in June-July.

In addition to a variety of chirping, chittering, and buzzing sounds uttered, golden-mantled ground squirrels have an alarm call which is a shrill, piercing, bird-like whistle. These animals dig short, simple burrows, usually under brush, a stump, or near a rock, about 25 cm. deep and 35 cm. in length. They spend much time resting in the sunshine on logs and rocks. They travel mostly on the ground but occasionally search for food in bushes and trees. They eat some vegetation, seeds, fruits, mushrooms, and some insects. They carry food in their cheek pouches and store it undergound. This is eaten in the spring after they emerge from dormancy and at other times when the food supply is scarce. They are deep hibernators, presumably remaining fast asleep and gaining nourishment from the large fat deposits which they have accumulated by September. They hibernate in their burrows in the fall and are not seen again until the end of March. After awakening from hibernation, mating takes place. Females with four to eight embryos have been found in May, June, and July. The annual litter is two to eight; the young are born in a helpless state, within the protection of the burrow. The gestation period is about one month.

These animals live mostly in areas where there is little agriculture. In those places where they do occur near croplands, they forage in grainfields and carry off grain. They frequently search for food in public campsites and seem to enjoy human companionship. Their burrows may cause erosion on hillsides. These ground squirrels have also been considered as carriers of tularemia and bubonic plague. Weasels, coyotes, bobcats, and red-tailed hawks are known to prey on them.

The type species of the genus is *C. lateralis* (Say). *C. saturatus* is so close to *C. lateralis* in all respects that it is probably better regarded as a now-isolated race of the latter species.

Eastern American Chipmunk (*Tamias striatus*), photo by Ernest P. Walker.

EASTERN AMERICAN CHIPMUNKS, GROUND SQUIRRELS.

A SINGLE SPECIES, *T. striatus*, inhabits most of the eastern United States and southeastern Canada. It has a preference for deciduous forests and bushy areas, especially near broken rocky ground, stone fences, and fallen logs.

These chipmunks are larger than those of the western United States and Asia (*Eutamias*). The length of the head and body is 137 to 186 mm., and the length of the tail is 78 to 113 mm. The weight is 70 to 142 grams. The background color is reddish brown, and there are usually five conspicuous dark stripes alternating with gray or brown; the under parts are white to buffy. The reddish-brown tail is well furred but not bushy. The fur is straight, soft, and fine. The eastern chipmunk resembles the western chipmunk (*Eutamias*), but it is distinguished by its light reddish hindquarters. *Tamias* has two upper premolars, whereas *Eutamias* has four. Openings within the sides of the mouth lead to pouches in which these chipmunks carry food to the storehouse. When filled to capacity, each pouch is almost as large as the animal's head, giving a grotesque appearance. The inside of the cheek pockets is naked but not moist like the mouth.

Chipmunks live in burrows which they construct in the ground, usually under logs, rocks, or in other protected locations. They are active during the daytime. They store up food for the winter; some individuals hibernate, but more often they are in a torpid state during severe weather only to revive and come out when the weather is good. Chipmunks are good climbers but prefer to remain near the ground, where they can scamper rapidly to shelter if danger threatens. In settled regions they frequent fence rows and the edges of woods. Acorns, small nuts, cherry stones, weedseeds, small fruits, wheat, and corn are their principal diet.

Chipmunks are common, but they are rarely so plentiful that they do serious damage to crops. They are easily destroyed if they become a menace. Their skins are used occasionally for furs. They are entertaining little animals and, if encouraged with food and protection, become tame. They make pleasing pets.

Two to eight young are born in a grass-lined section of the burrow about 31 days after mating. Breeding begins in March and continues throughout the summer. It is said that they are weaned in about five weeks but remain with the mother sometimes longer. The life span is about five years, although a captive lived eight years.

The name ground squirrel, sometimes applied to these animals, should not be confused with the ground squirrels of the genera *Callospermophilus* and *Ammospermophilus*. *Callospermophilus* is larger than *Tamias*.

A. Asiatic Chipmunks (*Eutamias sibiricus*), photo by Michi Nomura. B. San Bernardino Chipmunk (*E. speciosus*), photo by Lloyd G. Ingles.

SIBERIAN CHIPMUNKS, WESTERN CHIPMUNKS, LITTLE CHIPMUNKS; BURUNDUK; CHOSEN-SIMA-RISU.

ABOUT 16 SPECIES inhabit most of North America from the central Yukon and southern Mackenzie drainage basins to Baja California and the states of Durango and Sonora in Mexico. Another species, *E. sibiricus*, the Siberian chipmunk, occurs from northern Russia eastward through Siberia and the Far East, Manchuria, Mongolia, northern China, and northern Japan. Habitats occupied by the 17 different forms in the genus include spruce, fir, redwood, and pine forest, sagebrush plains, brush-covered mountains, and dense, temperate-zone rain forest.

Members of the various species range in size from 80 to 160 mm. in head and body length, and from 60 to 140 mm. in tail length. The weight is from 25 to 125 grams. The conspicuous characteristic of the pelage is the five black or black-brown longitudinal back stripes separated by four whitish stripes. The remainder of the upper parts are whitish yellow to sandy yellow in color. The underside is white. The soft and dense fur is slightly woolly in the winter. There are two molts each year, one in the spring and a second in the early fall. The summer pelage is brighter than the grayish winter pelage. Two premolars in each side of the upper jaw serve to differentiate *Eutamias* from *Tamias* which has only one premolar. The narrow ears are erect and are covered with short hairs.

The vocal sounds are generally similar to those of *Tamias*. The alarm call is a sharp chipper. Although *Eutamias* live mostly on the ground, all species climb trees and bushes at times. These chipmunks seek protection in their burrows, in old logs, and in crevices among rocks. They are active during the day. They gather dry food which they carry in their cheek pouches for storage in their underground chambers. During the winter, they retire to their burrows and become torpid, arousing from time to time to feed on the stored caches of seeds. In this respect, they are unlike the ground squirrels (*Callospermophilus*) which burn stored fat during dormancy.

The food of these chipmunks consists of the fruits and seeds of various trees and herbs. The foliage and flowers of some herbs are also eaten, as well as the tender buds of woody plants. Mushrooms, insects, bulbs, and bird's eggs are consumed at times. The one breeding period during the year produces four to eight young in April and May.

Weasels, coyotes, bobcats, goshawks, and the pygmy owls are known to prey on them.

These chipmunks prefer rugged or brush-grown land, but where they occur near agricultural crops, they sometimes do serious damage by eating planted seed and young forest plantings. Fruit trees in certain places have been damaged by these animals in their search for food. The skins of *E. sibiricus* are used to some extent in the fur industry.

The type species of the genus is *E. sibiricus* (Laxmann).

A. Formosan Giant "Flying" Squirrel (*Petaurista grandis*), photo by Ernest P. Walker. B. Yunnan Giant "Flying" Squirrel (*P. alborufus*), photo by J. F. Rock. C. Formosan Giant "Flying" Squirrel (*P. grandis*); D. Formosan White-headed Giant "Flying" Squirrel (*P. lena*); photos by Robert E. Kuntz.

GIANT "FLYING" SQUIRRELS; KORAI-MUSSASABI;
VLIEGANDE EEKHOORNS; GROSSEN FLUGEICH-
HÖRNCHEN. (Included are vernaculars used in
other countries.)

THIS GENUS is composed of five species which have a
combined range that includes most of southern Asia
from the western Himalayas, northeastern China,
Japan, and Formosa, southward to Ceylon, Sumatra,
Java, Borneo, and small adjacent islands. They inhabit dense hillside forests. These squirrels are usually found at 15 to 30 or more meters above the
ground. In central and eastern Taiwan, they have
been observed on the rocky cliffs of deep valleys.
The majority of *Petaurista* occur above 900 meters,
but they have been observed to wander in the spring
(March to April) to lower altitudes. Possibly this is a
migration of short duration, at a time when trees at
the lower altitudes would provide choice leaflets
and flower buds not yet available at higher elevations. On Formosa, the red belly species occurs at
the lower altitudes of 900 to 1,200 meters, and the
white belly species is usually found up to 2,000
meters. This separation is not fixed, however, and
one finds an intermingling of the two species between
1,200 to 1,500 meters elevation.

The length of the head and body is 305 to 585
mm.; the length of the tail is 356 to 635 mm.; and the
weight of adults is 1,138 to 1,362 grams. The soft
fur is fairly long on the back. The coloration ranges
through yellowish gray, bright brown, chestnut, or
black above; the undersurface is yellowish, buffy,
brownish, or white; and the tail is generally the
color of the back. These squirrels have short, broad
heads, complex molars, and a tail which is bushy,
cylindrical, and as long or longer than the head and
body. It is not flat like that of *Glaucomys*. The limbs
are united by broad fur-covered membranes which
extend from the sides of the body to the toes.

These squirrels are arboreal and nocturnal in their
habits; they spend the daylight hours in hollow trees
or branches and become active after dusk. These "flying" squirrels live singly, in pairs, or in family groups.
They travel through the treetops in a squirrel-like
manner, but when a branch or a tree is too distant
to reach by a leap, they go to a high branch and leap
toward their objective, extending the membrane as
they spread the arms forward and out, and the legs
backward and out. At first, the glide is downward
at an angle, but as they approach the objective, they
begin to ascend for the last meter or so before alight-
ing. Some members of this genus have been observed
to glide as far as 450 meters; they seem to have a
basic knowledge of aeronautics, since they may at
times ride on ascending currents of air coming up
deep valleys. In flight the squirrel is actually capable
of banking and, on several occasions, has been observed to make several banks in the course of a single
"flight."

The diet of these squirrels consists of fruits, nuts,
young twigs, tender shoots, leaves, and possibly insects and larvae. In the spring of the year (March-
April) in central Taiwan at approximately 1,800
meters elevation, squirrels have been seen so engorged
with young leaf and flower buds that they probably
could not glide. Squirrels are noticeably fatter or
heavier at this time of the year. The aborigines claim
that they have seen these squirrels in the act of steal-
ing eggs from birds' nests.

Little is known concerning their breeding habits.
The female has six mammae. The aborigines report
that the female usually gives birth to one or occasionally to two young. If they find a squirrel with two
young, they consider it a good omen. The London
Zoo has had them survive in captivity for 13½ years.

While much larger than *Glaucomys*, their habits
are probably similar. These animals are gentle and
timid. *Petaurista* is slaughtered by the hundreds
by the aborigines of Formosa and probably serves
as an important item of food at certain times of the
year.

The type species of the genus is *P. petaurista*
(Pallas).

Large Black "Flying" Squirrel (*Aeromys tephromelas*), photo from *Proc. Zool. Soc. London.*

LARGE BLACK "FLYING" SQUIRRELS.

THE FOUR SPECIES of this genus are distributed as follows: *A. tephromelas*, Penang, Malay Peninsula; *A. phaeomelas*, Borneo; *A. bartelsi*, northern Sumatra; and *A. thomasi*, Baram, Sarawak, and Borneo. They inhabit mature forests or clearings having a stand of a few large trees.

The length of the head and body is 255 to 330 mm., and the length of the tail is 280 to 356 mm. The coloration is dark brown to black above, and the under parts are sparsely covered with grayish-brown hair. At least one form has a reddish cast to its dark coat. The long, slender, round tail is generally the same color as the back. The cheeks lack whiskers, the ears are of moderate size, and the membrane, in addition to being connected between the feet, is continued between the forearms, the neck, the hind legs, and the tail. Members of this genus differ from *Petaurista* mainly in teeth and skull characters.

They are chiefly nocturnal, spending the day curled up asleep in a hole high in a tree and emerging at dusk. They scamper about the treetops during the night foraging for fruits, nuts, leaves, and probably some insects.

Little is known about the habits and general biology of *Aeromys*, but it is believed that the number of young is two to four per litter. The young are born in the mother's nest, where they remain until they have sufficient strength to seek their own food.

They glide like *Glaucomys* and others of the group having gliding membranes.

The type species of the genus is *A. tephromelas* (Günther).

Woolly "Flying" Squirrel (*Eupetaurus cinereus*), photos from *Jour. Bombay Nat. Hist. Soc.*

WOOLLY "FLYING" SQUIRRELS.

THIS GENUS contains a single species, *E. cinereus*, known from only a few skins obtained from local residents. These specimens were taken in Kashmir in the northern portion of India. The extent of their range is not definitely known. They may extend into Tibet or adjacent regions. They apparently prefer a high, mountainous habitat.

The length of the head and body is about 458 mm.; the length of the tail, including the hair, is about 558 mm. The entire body is covered with unusually thick, soft, woolly fur that is dull grayish brown above. The under parts are somewhat lighter. The heavily furred feet are blackish brown. The individual hairs on the dorsal surface are lead gray on the basal half and whitish brown with a dusky ring on the terminal portion. These gliding squirrels are distinguished from *Petaurista* by their longer, more trumpet-shaped muzzle and differ from other members of the family Sciuridae by their high-crowned molars. The tail is cylindrical and the claws are blunt.

Little is known of the habits of this rare animal. It is supposed that they live on or frequent rocky terrain because of the blunt claws and that they may eat mosses and perhaps lichens. The extremely dense fur coat is good protection for the cold weather of the higher altitudes.

Small Japanese "Flying" Squirrel (*Pteromys momonga*), photo by Hajeme Tezuka.

OLD WORLD "FLYING" SQUIRRELS, RUSSIAN "FLYING" SQUIRRELS, SMALL JAPANESE "FLYING" SQUIRRELS; ECUREUILS VOLANTS; FLUGHORNCHEN; VLIEGENDE EEKHOORNS; LITJAGA. (Included are vernaculars used in other countries.)

THIS GENUS contains two species: *P. volans* ranges from Finland eastward across northern Europe and Asia to Siberia, thence southward along the Pacific coast to northern China, Korea, and northern Japan (Hokkaido); *P. momonga* occurs in Japan (Kiushiu, Hondo). This genus inhabits boreal evergreen forests.

The length of the head and body is 120 to 228 mm., and the length of the tail is 108 to 127 mm. The fur is long, thick, and soft. The coloration varies from a light silvery gray to buffy gray above, while the under parts, inner surface of the limbs, and the membrane are buffy white. The tail is usually gray with a dusky tip. The gliding membrane extends from the wrists to the ankles, but there is no membrane between the hind legs and the base of the tail as in *Petaurista*. Although the tail is wide and somewhat flattened, it is not so decidedly flat as in *Glaucomys*. The eyes are large and black.

These animals are strictly nocturnal, silent, and seldom touch the ground. Thus few people suspect their presence in a region, so that they are considered rare in a region where they are often common.

They spend the day in holes in trees or in nests constructed of moss and lichens. The nests are at the junction of a branch and the trunk of a pine or spruce. At dusk the squirrels emerge and begin to scamper about the treetops with exceedingly quick movements. If unable to reach the branch of an adjacent tree in an ordinary leap, they run up to a higher point and leap toward the point they wish to reach. Like *Glaucomys*, they extend their arms and legs, which spreads the gliding membrane so they glide to the desired point. As they near the landing point, they turn upward to check their momentum. They can change direction in flight. Their coloration blends so well with that of tree bark that the animal becomes practically invisible, and it lies so flat that it looks like a slight lump on the bark. The diet consists of nuts, pine seeds, the buds and bark of certain trees, fruit, and probably some insects.

No information has been found regarding the breeding habits of these flying squirrels. The female has eight mammae.

Owls and cats capture them at night—the eagle owl (*Bubo bubo*) is their chief predator.

The type species of the genus is *P. volans* (Linnaeus).

719

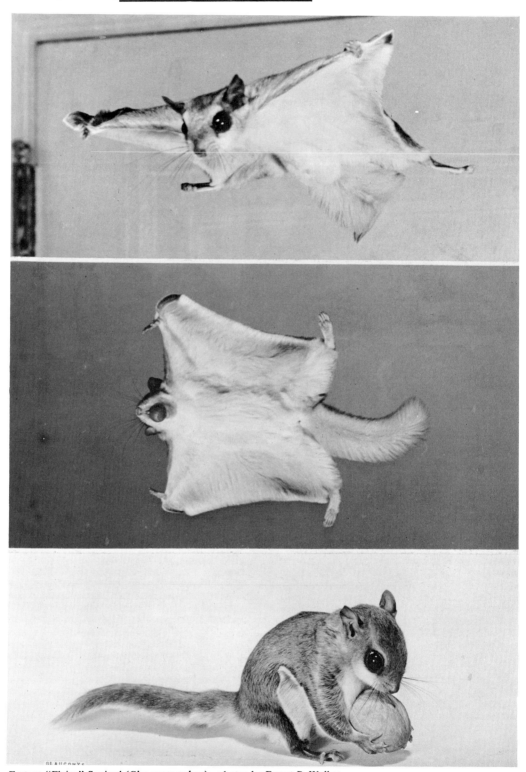

Eastern "Flying" Squirrel (*Glaucomys volans*), photos by Ernest P. Walker.

New World "Flying" Squirrels.

THIS GENUS is composed of two species distributed as follows: *G. volans*, the entire eastern United States and small isolated areas in Mexico and Guatemala; and *G. sabrinus*, parts of southern Alaska southward, including the southern half of eastern Canada, northwest Canada, California, Utah, and Wyoming. These animals are restricted to wooded areas.

The length of the head and body is 216 to 268 mm.; the length of the tail is 90 to 184 mm.; and the weight is 50 to 185 grams. *G. volans* is the smaller of the two species. Their fur, dense, fine, and soft, is gray with varying amounts of a brownish tinge on the upper portions and the tail, while the under parts are whitish or creamy. The arms and legs of flying squirrels are quite long and enclosed in the large, loose skin of the body and gliding membrane. *Glaucomys* is similar in appearance to the "flying" squirrels (*Pteromys*) of northern Europe and parts of Asia.

Members of this genus are exclusively nocturnal. They are somewhat gregarious, except when the females drive the males away before the young are born. For homes they depend primarily on hollow trees and limbs and deserted woodpecker nests. They also take up habitation in attics, in outbuildings, or in boxes constructed for birds. In the spot chosen, a soft nest is constructed of shredded bark, dry leaves, moss, feathers, fur, or other soft material. "Flying" squirrels apparently do not hibernate, but usually remain in their nests during periods of cold, windy, and wet weather.

"Flying" squirrels do not actually fly but glide. They climb to an elevated point and leap out into space, extending their long arms forward and out and their long hind legs backward and out. This stretches the extremely large loose skin of the body so the squirrels can glide as a sheet of paper glides when dropped from a height. The squirrels, however, launch themselves with impetus, for they actually push off from their point of departure. Their tail, flattened like a feather, trails behind. This helps to keep them on course. As they approach their landing point, usually a tree trunk, they change their course to an upward direction by raising the tail. At the same time they also extend the arms and legs forward; this allows the gliding membrane to take a parachute form. It helps to check the glide, and the forward extended legs act as shock absorbers. As soon as they land, they run around to the other side of the tree trunk, thus avoiding an owl or other predator that might be following them. If they wish to make another glide, they race to a higher position and leap again. It is incredible how rapidly they climb and how sure-footed they are. From an elevation of 18 meters they glide about 50 meters at a rate of 22 meters in about 12 seconds. At the start of a glide, they carefully examine the landing spot by leaning far to one side, then far to the other side. In effect, this probably is a triangulation method of measuring distance. Steering is accomplished by raising or lowering the arms and stabilizing is apparently by means of the tail.

They eat acorns and other nuts, bark of twigs, lichens, fungi, fruits, and berries. They are fond of certain insects and some meat and are sometimes caught in baited traps which are set for carnivorous fur bearers. While food is plentiful, they hoard nuts and seeds for use during the winter months.

The southern species breeds in February and continues breeding well into the summer, whereas the northern species breeds in the late winter. Females sometimes and perhaps regularly reproduce when they are about a year old. Some observers have noted that some do not reproduce until about two years of age. Litter size varies from two to six, and the gestation period is about 40 days or perhaps longer. Young are usually born in April or May, but there are many records of births as late as September. At birth they are naked, pink, and blind and weigh from 2 to 3 grams. By the third day, traces of coloration on top of the head, neck, and shoulders indicate growth of hair under the skin. The eyes do not fully open until the babies are about 25 days old. When born, the gliding membrane is well developed and is at least proportional to their size, perhaps relatively larger than it is in the adults. Baby "flying" squirrels nurse for 60 to 70 days and are not vigorous, active, or confident in their activities until that age. A nursing white rat is capable of raising flying squirrels.

Before "flying" squirrels are able to cope with the hazards of great activity in trees and gliding, they must be well developed. "Flying" squirrels are slow in development compared to many terrestrial creatures of similar size.

If subjected to unusual annoyances, a mother will sometimes kill and eat her young.

The type species of the genus is *G. volans* (Linnaeus).

Indo-Malaysian "Flying" Squirrel (*Hylopetes sagitta*), photo by Lim Boo Liat.

INDO-MALAYSIAN or ARROW-TAILED "FLYING" SQUIRRELS, KASHMIR "FLYING" SQUIRRELS; SHIN-PYAN; ENTJANG, MONMON, TJUBUK.

ABOUT SIX SPECIES are included in this genus. They have a combined range from India eastward through Burma, Thailand, Indo-China, the Malay States, Sumatra, Java, Borneo, and small adjacent islands. These animals inhabit areas of partly cleared jungle or mixed temperate forests, often near civilization, from about 150 to about 3,500 meters elevation. *Eoglaucomys*, Howell, 1915 is herein regarded as a subgenus for the species *H. fimbriatus*.

The length of the head and body varies from about 115 to 330 mm., and the length of the tail is 102 to 292 mm. The fur is soft, dense, and moderately long. The coloration of the upper parts of some forms ranges from grayish with a tinge of brownish to yellowish brown, bright reddish brown, glossy brownish black or black, while others are mottled or blotched across the hips and tail. The upper and undersurfaces of the tail are usually similar in color to the back. The under parts are whitish, grayish, or yellowish.

The ears are large and bluntly pointed; the claws are short and blunt; and the flattened tail tapers slightly at the tip.

The members of this genus are generally arboreal and nocturnal. A hollow tree provides a shelter, although natives report that the animals also take possession of discarded *Ratufa* nests. In Java *H. sagitta* sometimes nests in a coconut shell in which other squirrels have gnawed a hole. Sometimes the dried shell remains attached to its stem, or the nest is in a loose shell suspended in the crown of the palm tree. In Malaya, however, *H. sagitta* is said to provide shelter by gnawing openings in shells themselves.

It has been reported that *H. sagitta* glides for distances as far as 135 meters or more. An individual of this species has been observed in an "apparent attempt" at "flight": "... I saw the ... squirrel ... leap from a tree ... at a height of about 10 feet (three meters) and rise through the air with vigorous flapping movements of the skin between the fore and hind feet until it reached a branch about 20 feet (six meters) distant and fully 3 feet (one meter) higher" (W. Adams, "A Flying Squirrel That Really Flew," *Malayan Nature Journal*, Vol. 13, 1958, p. 31).

Some species occasionally feed upon cultivated fruits. Their diet also includes nuts, tender shoots, leaves, and, apparently, insects and small snakes. A captive *H. sagitta* in Java preferred insects such as crickets and locusts but would also eat wood-lice and spiders. It grabbed these insects with the incisors and used its hands to hold the prey. Captives of this same species in Malaya killed and consumed two 255 mm. painted bronze snakes (*Ahaetulla ahaetulla*) which had entered the cage.

H. sagitta in Malaya is reported to have only two young. Female *Hylopetes* have six mammae.

Like the American "flying" squirrels (*Glaucomys*), which they resemble, the Indo-Malaysian "flying" squirrels make fine pets when tamed.

The type species of the genus is *H. everetti* (Thomas).

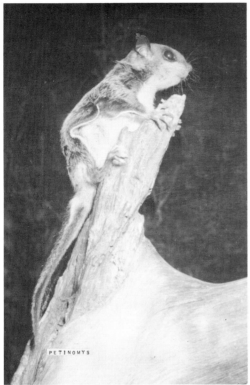

Dwarf "Flying" Squirrel (*Petinomys setosus*), photo by Lim Boo Liat.

DWARF "FLYING" SQUIRRELS.

THIS GENUS is comprised of about eight species which have a combined range from China southward through the Malay States, Tennasserim, Sumatra, Borneo, Java, Ceylon, and southern India. These squirrels inhabit tropical forests to 1,210 meters elevation.

Their general appearance is similar to "flying" squirrels of other genera. The tail is somewhat flattened like a feather, as the hairs on the sides project outward; those beneath the tail are shorter and lie close to the axis, but the hairs on top are not so short, do not lie so close, and make the tail appear bushy.

The length of the head and body is 127 to 406 mm., and the length of the tail is 114 to 292 mm. These animals have a broad, low head with a short muzzle and they differ from other genera in skull characters. The fur is dense above, moderately soft in texture, and thin on the lower surface. The coloration varies widely: the upper parts are brownish through chestnut-rufous to almost black, and the lower parts range from almost white to dark slate. The tail in many of the species is buff but becomes darker toward the tip.

The habits of this genus, though not well known, resemble those of other "flying" squirrels of the southern Asiatic region. They sleep during the day in holes in trees and are active at night when they romp and feed. These squirrels eat nuts, fruits, young twigs, tender shoots and leaves, possibly the bark of certain trees, and perhaps some insects.

No information has been found regarding their breeding habits. The female has four to six mammae instead of eight, the usual number in *Pteromys*.

The type species of the genus is *P. lugens* (Thomas).

Chinese or Groove-toothed "Flying" Squirrel (*Aeretes melanopterus*), photo from *Recherches pour servir á l'Histoire Naturelle des Mammifères*, M. H. Milne-Edwards and M. Alphonse Milne-Edwards.

CHINESE or GROOVE-TOOTHED "FLYING" SQUIRRELS.

THE SINGLE SPECIES, *A. melanopterus*, inhabits the forests of northeastern China.

The length of the head and body is about 305 mm., and the length of the tail is 330 to 356 mm. The short, dense, soft hairs of the back are dull brownish with slate-colored bases; the hairs on the sides of the body have yellowish tips; the under parts are grayish to buffy, except for the throat and the rear portion of the ventral surface which are whitish; the gliding membrane is dark brown; and the head is generally lighter and grayer than the back. The tail is buffy gray with a black tip. These medium-sized "flying" squirrels are distinguished from other members of this family by the structure of the upper incisors which are broad with a vertical groove on the front surface, hence the origin of the common name. The tail is bushy, but distinctly flattened.

Although nothing seems to be recorded concerning the habits of these squirrels, it is possible that their food and perhaps habits differ from those of other related species. This is inferred from the peculiar tooth structure.

Complex-toothed "Flying" Squirrel (*Trogopterus xanthipes*), photo from *Recherches pour servir à l'Histoire Naturelle des Mammifères*, M. H. Milne-Edwards and M. Alphonse Milne-Edwards. Inset: A. Upper molars (top—anterior), B. Lower molars (top—anterior), photos from *The Families and Genera of Living Rodents*, J. R. Ellerman.

COMPLEX-TOOTHED "FLYING" SQUIRRELS.

THE SINGLE SPECIES, *T. xanthipes*, is native to China from southern Tibet, Yünnan, Szechuan, and Shensi to Chihli. Specimens have been taken at 2,150 to 2,750 meters elevation.

The length of the head and body is 267 to 305 mm., and the length of the tail is 267 to 280 mm. These squirrels have a full, dense coat of moderately soft fur; it is not so fine and silky as that of most of the other small "flying" squirrels. The basal part of the fur of the back is lead-colored, whereas the terminal part is chestnut, and a few individual hairs are all black. The muzzle and eye rings are reddish; the tail is gray washed with fulvous; and the under parts and throat are white. These "flying" squirrels exhibit no striking external peculiarities, but long tufts of black hair at the base of each ear are distinctive. The tail is slightly flattened on the underside.

They inhabit forests and are nocturnal. Apparently nothing has been recorded regarding their habits other than that they eat oak leaves.

725

Hairy-footed "Flying" Squirrel (*Belomys pearsoni*), photo of mounted specimen by Robert E. Kuntz.

HAIRY-FOOTED or TUFTED-EARED "FLYING" SQUIRRELS; KELEENSIS.

THE SINGLE SPECIES, *B. pearsoni*, is native to the dense forests of Sikkim, Assam, southern China, Burma, Indo-China, and Taiwan (Formosa).

The length of the head and body is 178 to 203 mm., and the length of the tail is 102 to 153 mm. The fur is fine, soft, and fairly long. The coloration of the top of the head and back is glossy reddish brown. The tips of many of the hairs are black, producing a slightly blackish tone. The gliding membrane is dark brown sparsely washed with reddish; the hands are reddish brown; and the under parts are light reddish to white. There are no cheek whiskers, but the moustachial hairs are long. The feet are covered with long hair which partially conceals the claws. Members of this genus are distinguished from *Pteromys* by their smaller ears and the tufts of long hairs arising from the base of each ear. The dental structure of *Belomys* also differs from that of *Pteromys*.

Almost no information is available regarding the habits and general biology of these squirrels. The scant notes indicate that its habits are similar to those of other southeastern Asia "flying" squirrels.

Dr. Robert E. Kuntz, of the U.S. Naval Medical unit, found them much less common on Taiwan than *Petaurista*. One which he observed on a glide of only about 15 meters landed on a tree branch with considerable impact. This suggested to him that perhaps these squirrels are not such expert gliders as some of the other genera.

Apparently the individuals of this genus are rare, for there are very few records of them in the literature, and these indicate only distribution. The American Museum of Natural History has a mounted specimen.

Günther's or Smoky "Flying" Squirrel (*Pteromyscus pulverulentus*), photo from *Proc. Zool. Soc. London.*

GÜNTHER'S or SMOKY "FLYING" SQUIRRELS.

THE SINGLE SPECIES, *P. pulverulentus*, is native to the Malay States, Sumatra, and Borneo.

The length of the head and body is 254 to 292 mm., and the length of the tail is 216 to 228 mm. The general coloration is brownish black, with a tinge of paler shades from the whitish or yellowish subterminal hair bands; the basal part of individual hairs is gray. The feet are light brown; the chest is yellowish; the pre-anal region is orange; and the under parts are buffy white. The hairs on the sides of the tail are longer than those on the top and bottom so that a slightly flattened effect is produced, but the effect is not so pronounced as in the tails of *Glaucomys*. The tail is somewhat bushy and is pale grayish brown, with blackish hairs at the tips. The members of this genus lack tufts at the base of their small ears which distinguishes them from *Belomys*.

Few specimens have been secured, perhaps indicating that these squirrels are not common, or perhaps indicating only a lack of thorough collecting in their range. No information has been found regarding their habits and life history.

Pygmy "Flying" Squirrels.

There are three species included in this genus: *P. hosei* and *P. emiliae* occur in Borneo, and *P. kinlochii* inhabits the Malay Peninsula. These and *Idiurus* are the smallest of the "flying" squirrels.

The length of the head and body is 70 to 89 mm., and the length of the tail is 2.75 to 4 mm. All species are similarly colored; the upper parts are fawn to pale rufous, and the basal part of the hairs are dark gray; the cheeks are pale buffy; the undersurface is dull white; there is a white spot behind each ear; and the tail is grayish brown with a white tip. The ears are long, narrow, and pointed, and the teeth are not complicated.

There are four mammae. It is believed that a litter consists of two young. The members of this genus are nocturnal and arboreal, but no other information has been found regarding their general biology and life habits.

The type species of the genus is *P. hosei* (Thomas).

Javanese "Flying" Squirrel (*Iomys horsfieldii*), photo by Lim Boo Liat.

JAVANESE or HORSFIELD'S "FLYING" SQUIRRELS.

THE SINGLE SPECIES, *I. horsfieldii*, inhabits the Malay States and the islands of Sumatra, Java, and Borneo, as well as other small nearby islands.

The length of the head and body is 146 to 228 mm., and the length of the tail is 165 to 210 mm. The general coloration is rich rufous-brown, with a scattering of blackish hair bases showing through. The upper surface of the gliding membrane is bright russet; the undersurface of the body is grayish to pale orange; and the tail is brownish above and chestnut beneath. The hairs of the sides of the tail are longer than those on its upper and lower surfaces, so it is flat in cross section. The width of the base of the tail is at least twice that of the tip. The large, broad ears are almost naked.

One observer aroused a pair of these squirrels from a leaf nest (about 280 mm. in diameter) which was built in the top of a small sapling. Both glided to a nearby tree trunk.

These squirrels are supposed to be rare in all areas of their range. Only a few specimens have been taken, and few observations of their habits have been recorded.

POCKET GOPHERS.

THIS FAMILY of 8 genera and approximately 30 species occurs only in North America, from about 54 degrees North latitude in western Canada southward to Panama and from coast to coast in regions where the ground is suited to their needs. Pocket gophers are fossorial and prefer a soil adapted to digging. They do not travel far and occur in localized, isolated areas over much of their range.

Pocket gophers have stout, thickset bodies, with little external evidence of a neck. The legs are short. The tail is generally short, naked, or only sparsely haired and is very sensitive to touch—its end is highly vascular and well supplied with nerves, at least in *Thomomys*. The eyes and ears are small. The well-developed lachrymal glands supply a thick fluid which cleans the cornea, as burrowing mammals frequently get dirt in their eyes. The lips can be closed behind the curved incisors, making it possible for the animal to gnaw dirt without taking any into its mouth. Two long, external, fur-lined pockets apparently are used only in transporting food; they extend from the facial region back to the shoulders. These pouches can be turned inside out for cleaning and are pulled back in place by a special muscle. The powerful forearms are each supplied with five strong digging claws, the third finger being the longest. The looseness and flexibility of the skin and its thickness around the head and throat may be advantageous in fighting, as pocket gophers are very pugnacious. These rodents exhibit significant differences in size, the variations being influenced, at least in part, by sex and by the type of soil they frequent. The length of the head and body is 90 to 300 mm., and length of the tail is 40 to 140 mm.; the males are usually larger than the females. The pelage lacks underfur, and the coloration in the family Geomyidae ranges from black to almost white.

The skull is modified for fossorial life: it is massive, angular, and flattened, with strong and widely flaring zygomatic arches. As in the Heteromyidae, the infra-orbital canal is long, narrow, and sunken within the skull for protection from muscle pressure. The opening to the canal is anterior to the zygomatic arch and lateral to the rostrum. The dental formula is as follows: i 1/1, c 0/0, pm 1/1, m 3/3 x 2 = 20. The premolar, the largest grinding tooth, is 8-shaped. The cheek teeth grow throughout life and their enamel is greatly reduced.

Pocket gophers spend most of their lives underground, although at times they gather food and store it in their burrows. Occasionally they move to other areas. The young leave the nest when about two months old to wander off and establish a new home. In certain parts of the country the older animals may move to moister areas during dry periods. In Canada an individual gopher of the species *Thomomys talpoides* was observed swimming across a river 90 meters wide.

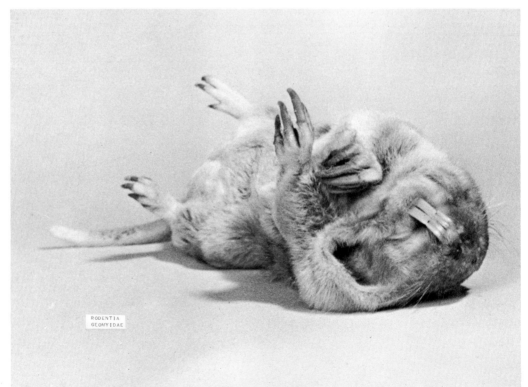

RODENTIA
GEOMYIDAE

Pocket Gopher (*Geomys bursarius*) clearly showing one of the two deep, fur-lined external cheek pouches that are characteristic of the Geomyidae, photo from Colorado State University through Richard S. Miller.

730

Pocket gophers dig two types of tunnels: (1) Long, winding, shallow tunnels which are constructed primarily to obtain food from above (roots and tubers), and (2) deep tunnels for shelter, with chambers for a nest, food storage, and fecal deposits. The burrow systems are often extensive and are usually marked above ground by a series of mounds of earth, the entrances to which are often closed with dirt. The excavated soil is brought to the surface through an inclined lateral tunnel instead of a vertical shaft such as those made by moles, thus the mounds are not conical in shape. Digging is accomplished mainly by the strong foreclaws, but the large upper incisors are used to loosen the soil and rocks and to cut roots. When a considerable amount of loose earth has been accumulated, it is held between the chest and forearms and pushed to the surface. Pocket gophers can run backwards in their burrows almost as fast as they can run forward. They may arch the tail when traveling backward so that the inverted tip is almost in contact with the ground.

The occupied or abandoned burrows of these rodents are used extensively by other animals for shelter or foraging. Of 22 species of terrestrial vertebrates studied in a 110-acre area in the sandhills of Colorado, 15 species regularly inhabited the burrows of pocket gophers (*Thomomys* and *Geomys*).

In *Thomomys talpoides*, two peaks of daily activity were demonstrated, one at dusk and the other after dawn. This species seems to have seasonal peaks of activity, i.e., one in the fall before and after the first snow, and another when the testes are enlarged in late winter. Pocket gophers do not hibernate, although they may become quite inactive during winter in the colder parts of their range. They sometimes travel in the snow. More often, however, they push cores of earth up into tunnels in the snow. These are seen after the snow melts and are known as gopher cores. These animals are solitary during most of the year. When two adults are placed together, they usually fight viciously and emit squeals and hisses. Females have one or several litters per year that consist of 2 to 11 young.

Pocket gophers feed mainly on the underground parts of plants, especially the roots and tubers, but they also cut stems and carry them in their cheek pouches to the storage chambers. Some of their hoard is not eaten, as decayed food is often found in the storerooms when they are excavated.

When the snows melt in meadows inhabited by pocket gophers, rolls or cores of earth cross each other. They are about 50 to 65 mm. in diameter, up to 13 meters long, and lie on the ground in irregular patterns. These rope-like strands of earth are composed of soil that was excavated by the pocket gopher and taken above ground into its tunnels through the snow. The various tunnels were at different levels and ran in several directions. When the snow melts, the earth cores left in the tunnels settle on the ground, thus showing the different directions of the tunnels and their relative levels, but not the actual distances apart vertically.

Geomyids may not be subject to epizootics as they remain solitary most of the year. Their predators are probably weasels, coyotes, badgers, skunks, hawks, owls, and the gopher snake (*Pituophis*).

The very limited range of movements of pocket gophers and the fact that they have been restricted in their ranges to certain valleys or other areas by impassable barriers has resulted in forms which some mammalogists consider sufficiently different from each other to justify placement in separate genera.

The geological range of this family is from the lower Miocene to the Recent of North America.

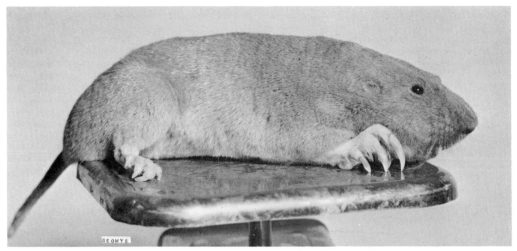

Eastern American Pocket Gopher (*Geomys bursarius*), photo from Colorado State University through Richard S. Miller.

EASTERN AMERICAN POCKET GOPHERS, "SALAMANDERS"; TUZAS.

FOUR SPECIES of this genus, *G. pinetis*, *G. colonus*, *G. fontanelus*, and *G. cumberlandius*, inhabit the coastal plain of Georgia, Alabama, and Florida. The other three species, *G. bursarius*, *G. arenarius*, and *G. personatus*, occur from the Mississippi River to the Rocky Mountains and from the Canadian border to Texas and northeastern Mexico. Pocket gophers prefer loose, sandy soil in open and sparsely wooded areas.

The head and body length ranges from 130 to 240 mm.; the tail is from 50 to 125 mm. in length; and the weight is 300 to 450 grams. The short fur varies in coloration from pale brown to black above; it is usually paler on the underside. The upper incisors each have two grooves on the front surface. The hands are modified for digging, and the tail is used when the animal is running backward in its burrow.

Pocket gophers produce hissing sounds by breathing rapidly when angered. On rare occasions a cry is uttered when they are injured. When strange pocket gophers are placed together they will fight violently. They apparently live alone, each within its own burrow system. They are more active in summer than winter; they do not hibernate.

The food consists chiefly of underground roots, rhizomes, and bulbs; but some eat succulent aboveground vegetation which is easily reached from the burrow or may be pulled down into the tunnel. Food is stored in underground chambers for winter use. Enough water is obtained from moisture in the vegetation, thus they seldom drink.

During the early spring males leave the burrows to seek a female, but after mating they resume their solitary lives. In the southern part of the United States the young are born from February through August, with peaks of reproduction in April, June, and July. The usual number of young is one to three per litter. The gestation period is 18 to 19 days, and the young at birth weigh 2 to 3 grams. More than one litter per year is often produced. The young nurse for about 10 days and stay with the mother for 2 months; sexual maturity is reached in about 3 months.

Whenever *Geomys* occurs in agricultural regions, it is likely to injure crops. Sweet potatoes, sugar cane, peas, and fruit trees are favorite targets. Damage to pasture and forage crops also results when the plants are covered by mounds. Soil erosion on hillsides has been attributed to gopher tunnels. However, pocket gophers provide a useful service as soil builders and improvers because they loosen and aerate the soil and mix organic matter into it. In areas where the soil is suitable for them and the vegetation to their liking, pocket gophers become somewhat abundant. They are easily tamed and kept in captivity.

The type species of the genus is *G. tuza* (Barton) = *G. pinetis* Rafinesque.

Western American Pocket Gopher (*Thomomys bottae mewa*), photo by Ernest P. Walker.

WESTERN POCKET GOPHERS, "MOLES."

THIS GENUS is comprised of six species having a combined range that includes southwestern Canada, most of the western half of the United States, and extends into Baja California and Mexico. Its members inhabit many kinds of soils, from sea level to about 4,000 meters elevation. They live in deserts, prairies, open forests, grasslands, and meadows.

The length of the head and body is 165 to 305 mm.; the length of the tail is 44 to 95 mm.; and the weight is 65 to 545 grams. Males are considerably larger than females. The short, soft, smooth fur is not sharply bicolored, for the under parts are only slightly lighter than the upper parts. The color varies from almost black through gray and brown to almost white. Western pocket gophers have robust bodies, short legs, small eyes and ears, and long front claws. The slightly tapered tail is thinly haired and naked at the tip. Unlike most other genera within this family, their incisors lack frontal grooves.

These burrowing animals spend most of their lives underground; their tunnels are 153 to 1100 mm. under the surface and measure 38 to 76 mm. in diameter. The pattern and length of the tunnel does not follow a definite course. Mounds of earth are thrown out of the burrow in a fan-shaped arrangement at intervals and the openings are carefully plugged from within. Apparently these gophers do not hibernate; even in the coldest areas, evidence of their work appears as the snows melt. They lead solitary lives throughout the year except during the mating season. Their tunnels are interestingly constructed: there are separate chambers in which to store food, raise their young, or eliminate wastes. Their food consists entirely of vegetable matter; they prefer roots, bulbs, and cultivated crops. They also procure a variety of green vegetation from above ground when they come out during the night or on cloudy days, or, more likely, merely pull the stem of the plant down into the burrow after the roots have been eaten off. This vegetation is cut into convenient sizes and pushed into the fur-lined cheek pouches with the front claws so that a large quantity can be carried to a storage or eating place. As these animals do not drink water, they apparently get sufficient moisture from juicy vegetable matter.

Little is known concerning the breeding habits of *Thomomys*. The forms in the north seem to have a more limited breeding season than those of the south. The number of young differs from 3 to 10 among the species, but this variation is not surprising because the number of mammae range from 3 to 7 pairs. The gestation period for *T. bottae* is approximately 19 days. The young are raised in an underground nest, and newborn pocket gophers weigh from 2 to 6 grams and are blind, almost hairless, and helpless. The mother rears the young and, after she has weaned, they begin their typical solitary lives.

An underground existence would seem to render these gophers safe from enemies, but they are preyed upon heavily by hawks and owls that swoop on them in their doorways, and by foxes, badgers, and coyotes that dig them out. Their tunneling is helpful in renovating the soil, but in populated areas they become pests by eating crops, cutting roots, and tunneling through dikes. However, in mountain meadows they perform a valuable service in conserving water and soil. Runoff water from melting snow sinks deep in their burrows. The soil is mixed with humus and vegetation.

The type species of the genus is *T. rufescens*, Wied-Neuwied.

Buller's Pocket Gopher (*Pappogeomys bulleri*), photo by Lloyd G. Ingles.

BULLER'S and ALCORN'S POCKET GOPHERS; TUZAS, TALTUZAS.

IN THIS GENUS are two species: *P. bulleri*, which lives on the slopes of the Volcán de Colima and other nearby ranges and Sierra de Mascota, Jalisco, Mexico, and *P. alcorni*, which inhabits the plain of Guadalajara. This genus lives at 910 to 3,010 meters.

The length of the head and body is 130 to 175 mm., and the length of the tail is 50 to 85 mm. The soft fur has a fine texture. Coloration of the upper parts varies from orange cinnamon to dark brown, but the underparts are lighter. *P. bulleri* has a white nasal patch, whereas the nasal patch of *P. alcorni* is cinnamon or buff. In members of this genus the tail is naked, the claws are similar to those of *Geomys*, and one deep groove on each upper incisor, in the middle of the tooth, is distinctive.

Little is known about the biology of this animal. The gophers do considerable damage to the corn and bean fields. Each Mexican village has its "tucero" who captures the pocket gophers for a price per tail with the aid of a crude but effective dead-fall type trap which drives an arrow through the animal when it comes to plug the entrance to its burrow. The job of the tucero is respected and is passed on from father to son.

The type species of the genus is *P. bulleri* (Thomas).

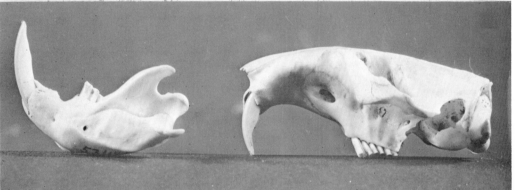

Tuza (*Cratogeomys merriami*), photo by Lloyd G. Ingles. Skull: (*C. fulvescens*), photo by P. F. Wright of specimen in U.S. National Museum.

TUZAS, TALTUZAS.

THERE ARE 12 SPECIES in this genus. *C. castanops* ranges from southern Colorado through parts of Oklahoma, New Mexico, Texas, and south to the state of San Luis Potosí, Mexico. The remaining species inhabit a relatively small area in central Mexico. The elevational range is from sea level to 3,700 meters. Habitats include palm groves in the tropical zone, deserts, and the fir and spruce zone on the high mountains. *Cratogeomys* apparently prefer soils of sandy texture, as they avoid rocky or hard-textured soils.

The length of the head and body is about 140 to 260 mm.; the length of the tail is 60 to 125 mm.; and the weight is 400 to 900 grams. The fur is apparently soft and sleek. The pelage is yellowish, brown, or blackish. The head is sometimes a dull chestnut color. The body in some forms is spotted with white, and the under parts are often white. The single groove of the upper incisor is at the mid-line of the tooth or slightly medial to it.

The mounds of *C. castanops* are 305 to 914 mm. in diameter and about 4.5 meters apart. They are generally placed beneath bushes or cacti. The burrows are deeper than those of *Thomomys* which often occur in the same immediate area. Mounding activities are influenced by rainfall. Few new mounds are constructed during droughts, but after a rain numerous fresh mounds have been observed. Many kinds of vegetation, including desert plants, are eaten. Tuzas eat stalks and joints of prickly pear and spineless cacti roots are chewed in place below the ground level. It is thought that a single litter is produced each year, in May or June. Litter size is one to three.

These animals damage various crops, particularly corn, potatoes, and fruit trees. Tuceros are men employed by farmers to catch these and other rodents on his land at a price per tail.

The type species of the genus is *C. merriami* (Thomas).

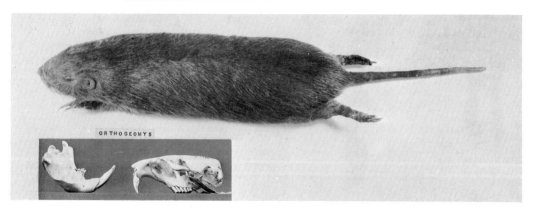

Giant Pocket Gopher (*Orthogeomys grandis scalops*), photos by P. F. Wright of specimen in U.S. National Museum.

GIANT POCKET GOPHERS; TUZAS, TALTUZAS.

THE THREE SPECIES, *O. cuniculus*, *O. pygacanthus*, and *O. grandis*, have a combined range which embraces southern Mexico, Guatemala, El Salvador, and Honduras from sea level to 3,010 meters. They inhabit arid tropical lowlands and oak- and pine-forested slopes of high mountains. Members of this genus are the largest members of the pocket gopher family.

The length of the head and body is 270 to 350 mm., and the length of the tail is 90 to 140 mm. The pelage in most forms is a dull dark brown above and only slightly paler below. The fur on lowland tropical forms is coarse and scanty and that on the high mountain forms is soft and dense. The incisors are either pale yellow or orange on the outer surface and each of the upper incisors has a groove which is located slightly medial to the mid-line. Members of this genus differ from *Heterogeomys* and *Macrogeomys* chiefly in cranial structure.

Earth plugs are used in the main burrows. Giant pocket gophers damage coffee trees in some areas and eat the roots of banana plants to such an extent that the plants may fall to the ground. Natives in some areas regard the meat of these animals as a delicacy.

These gophers, as well as the Mexican species of the other genera, are caught by professional gopher catchers, or "tuceros," who charge the farmer or co-operative a small price for each animal destroyed. Traps, snares, spears, and slingshots are the weapons commonly employed by these men and their small-boy helpers.

The type species of the genus is *O. scalops* (Thomas) = *O. cuniculus scalops* as currently arranged.

Hispid Pocket Gopher (*Heterogeomys hispidus yucatanensis*), photo by Robert T. Hatt. Insets: Skull and jaw (*H. hispidus*), photos by P. F. Wright of specimen in U.S. National Museum.

HISPID POCKET GOPHERS; BA; TALTUZAS.

THE TWO SPECIES, *H. hispidus* and *H. lanius*, range from Tamaulipas in northeastern Mexico south and east to the Yucatan peninsula, Guatemala, and British Honduras. They occur along watercourses in the tropical coastal plain and in the plateau and mountain area to elevations of at least 2,110 meters.

The length of the head and body is 200 to 250 mm.; the length of the tail is 75 to 100 mm.; and the weight ranges from 500 to 800 grams. Pelage color is dark brown above and paler brown below. The fur of *H. hispidus* is generally short and stiff; in subspecies dwelling at higher elevations, the fur is soft and velvety. *H. lanius* has a soft, woolly coat. Molting has been observed in July. The one groove on the upper incisor is medial to the mid-line of the tooth. The feet and tail are nearly naked in some forms.

The burrows are usually shallow and are left open more than those of other genera. These animals often emerge to feed at night and on rainy days. Generally, they pull vegetation into the burrow, with only their head exposed.

The breeding season is thought to be long due to the warm climate in which they occur. Young gophers have been found in early May. They evidently become sexually mature at an early age; females, estimated to be three months old, have been found nursing young.

Sugar cane, corn, and banana and papaya plants are damaged extensively. The natives snare *Heterogeomys* or stab these gophers when they appear at the burrow openings.

The type species of the genus is *H. hispidus* (Le Conte).

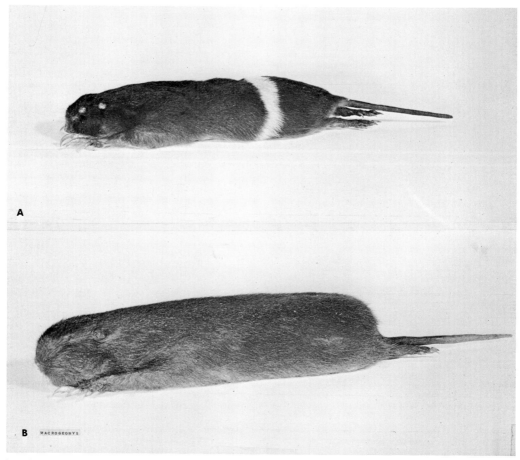

A. Taltuza (*Macrogeomys underwoodi*); B. (*M. dariensis*); photos by Howard E. Uible of specimens in U.S. National Museum.

TALTUZAS.

SIX SPECIES of this genus, *M. heterodus*, *M. cavator*, *M. dariensis*, *M. underwoodi*, *M. cherriei*, and *M. matagalpae*, have a combined range that extends from northern Nicaragua through Costa Rica to eastern Panama and probably into western Colombia. The animals are generally distributed on the slopes of forested mountains where they apparently prefer sugar cane and banana fields as a source of food.

Head and body length ranges from about 100 mm. to 305 mm., and tail length, from 50 mm. to 130 mm. The pelage, which is dark brown to black, may be soft or harsh-furred. One species, *M. underwoodi*, has a white band across the lumbar region. Other species have white markings on the head or rump. The upper incisors are deeply grooved near the inner edge and are orange in front. There are six nipples, one well up on either side of the body behind the fore legs and two on the inside of each thigh (not on the abdomen). There is usually a well-developed, naked nasal pad.

These animals dig their tunnels in the early morning, in the evening, or at night. During the dry season few fresh mounds are thrown up, but during the rainy season much greater tunneling activity takes place. Banana and sugar-cane stalks, as well as other vegetation, are eaten. Sugar-cane stalks are gradually drawn into the burrow as the animal feeds at the basal end.

Reproductive biology, if known, has not been recorded in published literature.

The type species of the genus is *M. heterodus* (Peters).

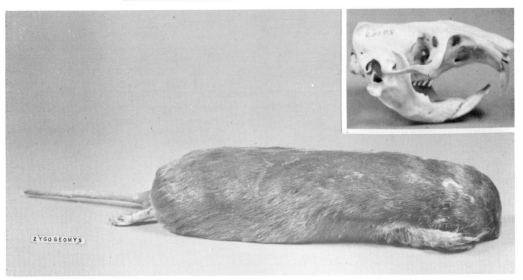

Tuza (*Zygogeomys trichopus*); Inset: Skull; photos by Howard E. Uible of specimen in U.S. National Museum.

TUZAS, TALTUZAS.

THE SINGLE SPECIES, *Z. trichopus*, inhabits the Sierra Madre of Michoacán, Mexico, from Pátzcuaro to Nahuatzín, and is limited to the pine zone between 1,810 and 3,600 meters elevation on the southern part of the tableland of Mexico.

The head and body length is 200 to 250 mm., and the tail is from 90 to 120 mm. in length. Coloration of the upper parts varies from dark gray to seal brown and, in some cases, is finely suffused with rust; the under parts are dark plumbeous washed with fulvous. The upper surface of the hind feet ranges from slate gray to white. An irregular white patch appears on the throat. The tail is entirely naked; the upper surfaces of the feet are densely haired, and there is a conspicuous naked patch at the end of the nose. The upper incisors each have two grooves. E. W. Nelson found *Zygogeomys* plentiful and generally distributed over the wooded mountain slopes except in dense timber, and most numerous about the borders of small, grassy parks. Where the land is cultivated, these rodents damage the corn, wheat, and potatoes.

Nothing more has been recorded concerning their habits and life history.

POCKET MICE (*Perognathus*), KANGAROO MICE (*Microdipodops*), KANGAROO RATS (*Dipodomys*), and SPINY POCKET MICE (*Liomys* and *Heteromys*).

THIS FAMILY of 5 genera and approximately 70 species occurs in southwestern Canada and the western United States and southward through Mexico and Central America to Ecuador, Colombia, and Venezuela. Its habitats include prairies, arid plains, deserts, dry, open forests (*Perognathus*, *Microdipodops*, and *Dipodomys*), brushy or grassy areas, or humid tropical forests (*Liomys* and *Heteromys*). The recognition of four subfamilies is based primarily on the degree of modification that adapts the animals to a jumping mode of progression. Three of these subfamilies have living representatives, namely, the Perognathinae (*Perognathus* and *Microdipodops*), Dipodomyinae (*Dipodomys*), and Heteromyinae (*Liomys* and *Heteromys*). The geological range of the family is the lower Oligocene to Recent in North America and the Recent in South America.

Heteromyid rodents exhibit considerable variation in their external appearance; some genera (*Liomys* and *Heteromys*) are mouse-like in appearance and others are highly modified to travel by jumping (*Dipodomys*). In the latter genus, the hind legs are long and powerful, and the forelimbs are reduced. The tail in all members of the family is long and well-haired. As in the Geomyidae, external fur-lined cheek pouches are present. The animals can turn these pockets inside out to clean them, drawing them back into place by a special muscle. The pelage is soft and velvety to harsh and spiny. The length of the head and body is 55 to 180 mm., and the length of the tail is 45 to 215 mm.

The thin skull is papery in consistency and is not strongly modified for an underground life. The zygomatic arches are slender and thread-like, and the tympanic bullae range from slightly inflated (*Liomys*, *Heteromys*) to greatly extended (*Microdipodops*, *Dipodomys*). As in the Geomyidae, the long, narrow infraorbital canal is sunken within the skull to protect it against muscle pressure, and its opening is anterior to the zygomatic arch and lateral to the rostrum. The nasal bones project beyond the incisors. The jaws are small and weak. The dental formula is as follows: i 1/1, c 0/0, pm 1/1, m 3/3 x 2 = 20. The incisors are thin and compressed. The

cheek teeth do not grow throughout life, except in *Dipodomys*, and the molars have four tubercles.

The members of the family Heteromyidae shelter in self-constructed burrows under bushes, trees, and logs. The entrance may be marked by a mound of earth or it may be identified by a small round hole. The tunnel system, with chambers for storing food and other purposes, often has several openings. At dawn, after returning from their nocturnal forages, many species plug the entrance to the burrow with moist earth, providing a more favorable environment in their diurnal retreat. Heteromyid rodents generally remain in their burrows during cold or wet weather, and pocket mice (*Perognathus*), in particular, may become quite torpid during inclement weather. The members of the genera *Perognathus*, *Liomys*, and *Heteromys* travel on all four limbs, usually assuming a bipedal position while foraging, but the members of the genera *Dipodomys* and *Microdipodops* typically progress only on the hind limbs, with the tail serving as a balancing organ in locomotion and as a prop when standing. The saltatorial habits of these two genera resemble, on a much smaller scale, the jumping proclivities of the kangaroo, hence the common names, kangaroo rats and kangaroo mice.

The diet consists mainly of seeds and vegetation but also includes insects and other invertebrates. Many forms of Heteromyidae store food. Some forms derive all their water from the solid foods they eat and from conversion of some of the food into water within the body. Other species drink very little water. In some species the excretory systems are somewhat modified in order to extract the maximum liquid from the food they eat.

Some members of this family require dusting places during at least part of the year.

The offspring are born in a nest in the burrow. Heteromyids give birth to from one to eight young and have one or several litters a year (usually only one litter in the northern parts of the range).

In *Dipodomys* a gland between the shoulders in both sexes produces an odor which probably helps individual rodents to recognize each other.

The life span in nature may be only a few months because of predators. Natural enemies include coyotes, weasels, badgers, skunks, rattlesnakes, owls, and hawks. In captivity the members of this family are usually gentle and tractable and have lived about eight years.

Forest Spiny Pocket Mouse (*Heteromys desmarestianus crassirostris*) carrying a large palm nut in each of its deep, fur-lined cheek pouches. These are characteristic of the Heteromyidae. Photo by Oliver P. Pearson.

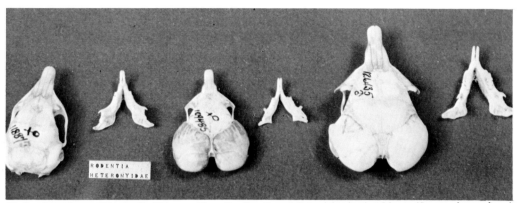

Skulls of members of the family Heteromyidae. Reading from left to right: Pocket Mouse (*Perognathus c. dispar*), Kangaroo Mouse (*Microdipodops megacephalus polionotus*), Kangaroo Rat (*Dipodomys m. merriami*), photo by P. F. Wright of skulls in U.S. National Museum.

Desert Pocket Mice (*Perognathus penicillatus penicillatus*), photo from New York Zoological Society.

POCKET MICE.

THIS GENUS is comprised of about 25 species that have a combined range embracing southwestern Canada and the western half of the United States, southward to Baja California and central Mexico. Most species inhabit low, arid plains and desert country, rarely getting up into the mountains unless there is little rainfall. Sagebrush and bunch-grass habitats are occupied. There seems to be a preference for the denser stands of grass, presumably for the greater amount of cover provided. *Chaetodipus* is herein regarded as a subgenus.

The length of the head and body ranges from 60 to 125 mm., and the length of the tail is 45 to 145 mm. The tail is nearly as long or longer than the head and body. Coloration of the upper paits varies from pale yellow to dark gray, and the under parts are buff to white. Members of the subgenus *Chaetodipus* have a harsh pelage with spiny bristles on the rump, and the soles of the hind feet are naked; members of the other subgenus, *Perognathus*, have a soft pelage with no bristles, and the soles of the hind feet are hairy. The dark-gray pelage of young pocket mice is soft. Apparently one molt takes place in the late summer.

The hind limbs are not much longer than the forelimbs, for these animals, unlike *Dipodomys*, do not run or hop on the hind legs only. Their method of locomotion is similar to other mouse-like animals that also use their fore legs for moving about. The long hind legs advantageously support the animal while it digs in light sand with its fore feet. The fore feet, equipped with long claws, sift the sand for seeds and then place the seeds into the fur-lined, external cheek pouches.

Pocket mice are nocturnal; during the day they remain in their burrows. The several burrow entrances are plugged with earth, presumably to keep the temperature low and the humidity high. The entrances are usually hidden under shrubs. These animals are known to become dormant during inclement weather and to stay inside their burrows.

Their principal food consists of seeds of various desert plants, and small amounts of green vegetation and animal matter are eaten. When insects are available, they are also consumed. These animals do not drink water, as they obtain enough moisture for their needs in the break-down of their food. Their bodies are physiologically adapted to conserve water. Food is stored in small side chambers in their burrows.

Reproduction takes place from April to September. During June and July, breeding activity decreases. There are one or two litters each year consisting of from two to seven young (the usual number is probably four). In *P. californicus* the gestation period is 25 days; in *P. parvus* it is 24 or 25 days.

These animals do not modify the rangeland they inhabit to any great extent. In captivity, they are tractable and may live six years or longer. They can be kept satisfactorily on commercial birdseed.

The type species of the genus is *P. fasciatus*, Wied-Neuwied.

Kangaroo Mouse (*Microdipodops* sp.), photo by B. Elizabeth Horner. Inset: Sole of foot showing heavy hair growth useful as sand shoe, photo by Ernest P. Walker.

KANGAROO MICE, PYGMY KANGAROO RATS.

THE TWO SPECIES of *Microdipodops* are distributed as follows: *M. megacephalus*, the dark kangaroo rat, in southeastern Oregon, most of Nevada, and nearby parts of California and Utah; and *M. pallidus*, the pale kangaroo rat, in west-central Nevada. The elevational range is from 1,210 to 2,000 meters, where they live near shrubs growing around wind-blown sand dunes.

The length of the head and body is 66 to 77 mm.; the tail is 64 to 103 mm. in length; and the weight is 10.2 to 16.8 grams. The upper parts of *M. megacephalus* are brownish to grayish black; the under parts are pale grayish to white, and the terminal end of the tail is blackish. In *M. pallidus* the upper parts are pale creamy buff; the under parts are pure white, and the tail does not have the blackish coloration. The pelage is fairly long, silky, and lax; the tail is not crested or penciled. Fat is stored in the tail and is used as a source of energy during dormancy. A large head has developed due to the great inflation of the audital bullae into paper-thin capsules that encroach onto the upper portion of the sides of the cranium. This inflation is similar to, but greater than, that in any other genus of this family. The hind feet are fringed at the sides with stiff hairs that increase the surface on the fine, soft, sand-like snowshoes; the undersurfaces of the hind feet are well furred. The effect is of a furry animal flattened so much that it is wider than high.

These tiny rodents are restricted in their range and habitat and occur in limited numbers. They are nocturnal, make their burrows in the soft sand with the entrance usually close to a shrub, and feed almost exclusively on seeds, with an occasional supplement of plant leaves and insects.

Many *Microdipodops* live long periods, if not their entire lives, without drinking water. At best, they can obtain only drops of dew or, occasionally, succulent plant tissues. Like many other desert rodents, they can derive sufficient moisture from their food as it is metabolized.

The young of both species are born in burrows in May and June, the litter size is from one to seven, with an average of three to four. There may be two litters per year.

Kangaroo mice move about by leaping with relatively large and powerful hind legs, the tiny fore legs barely touching the ground if used at all. The tail touches the ground only lightly, if at all, and is used as a balancing organ.

These rodents are very sensitive to light. If forced into brightness, they seek the shade or darkest corner and turn their backs to the source of light.

They have been kept successfully in captivity as they are gentle and interesting to study.

The type species of the genus is *M. megacephalus*, Merriam.

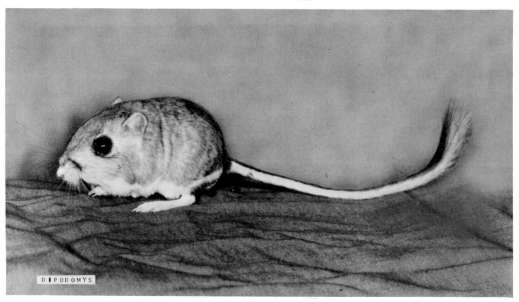

Merriam's Kangaroo Rat (*Dipodomys merriami*), photo by Ernest P. Walker.

KANGAROO RATS.

TWENTY-TWO SPECIES comprise this genus which ranges west of the Missouri River from southwestern Canada to Baja California and south-central Mexico. These animals dwell in arid and semiarid country that is brushy and grassy. They usually prefer fairly open ground which permits an unobstructed view of the surroundings and is best for their rapid method of travel. Well-drained, easily-worked soil is usually also preferred.

The head and body length ranges from 100 to 200 mm., and the tail length is from 100 to 215 mm. The tail is usually longer than the head and body. The weight varies from 35 to 140 grams. The upper parts are pale yellow to dark brown. The underside is white. The tail is usually dark above and below, with white sides. The end of the tail has a tuft of longer hairs. In most species a white band across the thigh region joins the base of the tail. There are distinct facial markings. The hind legs are very long, and the fifth toe on the large hind foot is very small or absent. A prominent, oil-secreting gland is present on the back between the shoulders.

Kangaroo rats rarely utter vocal calls. Thumping or rattling sounds have been heard from the burrow before an animal emerges or if it is disturbed. These animals are active only at night. A bright moon confines them to their burrows, where they also remain during periods of rain or heavy fog. Bathing in dust is apparently necessary for the welfare of kangaroo rats. Captives denied this develop sores on the body and the fur becomes matted from the oily secretions of the gland on the back. They travel by hopping on the hind legs. The fore legs are used only when they travel very short distances. The animals apparently cut down vegetation so that their movement is not impeded. They feed on weeds, seeds, some fruits, leaves, stems, buds, and an occasional insect. Due to the scarcity of foods caused chiefly by drought, most species store food in their burrows. All food and nest materials are transported in the cheek pouches, placed there by the small fore feet, which they also use to empty the pouches by shoving forward from the outside simultaneously. They seldom drink water, for they are able to use water resulting from the chemical breakdown of their food. They conserve moisture by coming out of their burrows at night when the humidity is highest. They have kidneys at least four times as efficient as those of a man and thus need much less water to remove nitrogenous wastes.

Species of kangaroo rats in areas of favorable climate may mate in any month of the year. However, mating activity is low during the winter months. The gestation period is 33 days in *D. merriami*; 32 days in *D. nitratoides*; and 29 days in *D. panamintinus*. Three litters may be produced in a year, consisting of one to five young, but usually two to four. Young kangaroo rats remain in the nest for about six weeks.

Dipodomys living near grain fields may carry away enough seeds to cause some economic loss. Rattlesnakes, kit foxes, and owls are known to prey on them. Kangaroo rats may be successfully kept in captivity under favorable conditions.

The type species of the genus is *D. phillipsii* (Gray).

Spiny Pocket Mouse (*Liomys pictus*), photo by John Eisenberg.

SPINY POCKET MICE.

THIS GENUS is comprised of 11 species that have a combined range in arid and semiarid regions from Sonora, Mexico and extreme southern Texas southward to Panama.

The length of the head and body is 97 to 135 mm., and the length of the tail is 97 to 156 mm. The pelage is generally harsh with stiff, flattened, anteriorly grooved, bristly hairs, interspersed with a few slender, more flexible hairs. The coloration below is white; the upper parts vary from pale mouse gray, bright reddish brown, or dull dark brown to deep glossy black with buffy hairs. A buffy or orange lateral line is present in some species. The tail is generally well haired and frequently sharply bicolored.

In general, *Liomys* differs from *Heteromys* in external appearance; it is larger and exhibits greater spinyness and lighter coloration. Cranial and dental characters are better developed, but the differentiation between the two is not sharp. A specialized spoon-like claw on the second digit of the hind foot may be an adaptation for digging; it also may aid in combing the grooved spines. This development is also present, although to a lesser degree, in the genus *Heteromys*.

The fur-lined cheek pouches open outside the mouth and extend back to about the shoulders. They can be turned "wrong-side-out," cleaned, and pulled back in place by a special muscle. In this family (Heteromyidae), the pouches are used to carry seeds, bits of leaves, grass, and fine fibrous nest material. They are filled by the tiny hands which move so rapidly that the human eye can rarely detect the movements in detail. Seeds and tender herbaceous plants are favorite foods in the wild. *Liomys* is a nocturnal animal and lives in burrows in the ground. The entrances to the burrows are usually located under a log, rock, or bush and are closed when the rodent leaves to search for food.

Two to five, usually four, young are born throughout the year—most births take place in the spring and early summer. The gestation period of *L. pictus* is known to be from 24 to 26 days.

The type species of the genus is *L. alleni* (Coues) = *L. irroratus alleni* as currently arranged.

Forest Spiny Pocket Mouse (*Heteromys anomalus*), photo by Juhani Ojasti.

FOREST SPINY POCKET MICE.

THIS GENUS is comprised of ten species that have a combined range including most of the tropical rain forests from Veracruz, Mexico, to Yucatan and southeastward to southern Panama. Members of this genus live from sea level to about 2,500 meters elevation. *Xylomys*, Merriam, 1902 is herein regarded as a subgenus for the species *H. nelsoni* and *H. oresterus*.

The length of the head and body is 125 to 160 mm., and the length of the tail is 130 to 200 mm. The pelage of the subgenus *Heteromys* contains many stiff bristles or spines and, although the pelage of the subgenus *Xylomys* is harsh, its texture is noticeably softer. Coloration differs among the species; the upper parts vary from brown to mouse gray to blackish, and occasionally a few ochraceous or buffy hairs are scattered throughout. The tail is dusky to brown above and white to tan below. In one species, *H. nigricaudatus*, the tail is blackish throughout. A faint lateral line occasionally separates the coloration above from the white undersurface. These animals are similar to other spiny mice, the principal differences are in dental and cranial structure.

Like many other small rodents, these animals are nocturnal and shy. As a result, their presence is frequently overlooked. They seek refuge in burrows, whose entrances are usually hidden under a bush, rock, log, or other shelter. To add to their inconspicuousness, a mound of earth around the entrance is usually lacking. At dusk these rodents begin their search for seeds, green leaves, twigs, and succulent plants. They occasionally become nuisances near farms and graineries as they not only eat food on the spot but carry off grain in their cheek pouches. Their cache is deposited in their burrows for use when food is scarce. Nuts may also be stored.

Breeding probably takes place throughout the year, although it appears that the young are more numerous in the spring and early summer than at other times. From three to five young are born per litter, but four seems to be the usual number.

The type species of the genus is *H. anomalus* (Thompson).

Beaver (*Castor canadensis*), A. A beaver dam in a small valley in the Rocky Mountain region. The beaver lodge is in the middle distance at the edge of the water, and the considerable area of level land in the bottom of the valley is a beaver meadow formed by the building up of sediment behind beaver dams. Photo by Ernest P. Walker. B. Photo from Zoological Society of London.

BEAVERS; LES CASTORS, BÉVERS; BIBERN; LOS CASTORES; BOBR. (Included are vernaculars used in other countries.)

THIS FAMILY contains a single Recent genus, *Castor*. Two species, *C. fiber* and *C. canadensis*, are recog-nized, although many European taxonomists consider them as only one species. Formerly, beavers inhabi-ted most of the forested regions of the Northern Hemisphere south to the Mediterranean and east through northern Asia to Siberia in the Old World, and in North America from Alaska and Canada south to the Rio Grande. Currently, *C. fiber* exists in a few scattered, small colonies in the Old World, in Germany (the Elbe River), the Rhône Valley in France, Poland, Scandinavia, and Russia. In North America, *C. canadensis* remains in most areas of its range, but in greatly reduced numbers. Beavers prefer waterways having nearby growths of willow, aspen, poplar (cottonwood), birch, and alder.

Beavers are among the largest rodents. They have a thick-set, heavy external form. The length of the head and body is 735 to 1,300 mm.; the tail is 215 to 300 mm. long and 102 to 127 mm. wide. Weight ranges from 9 to 32 kg. (13 kg. average). The unusually dense pelage consists of fine underfur overlaid with coarse guard hairs. The soft, short underfur usually has a slight tinge of lead color; the long, coarse, shiny guard hairs mask and protect the underfur except on the lighter colored under parts where the hairs are not so long or closely set. The coloration of the upper parts is rich glossy brown or yellowish brown, and the under parts are brown to tawny. The tail and feet are black. The small eyes have nictitating membranes; the ears are short and valvular, and the nostrils are valvular. The legs are short and each limb has five-clawed digits. The digits of the enlarged hind feet are webbed, the claws on the second and third toes are split, presumably as an aid to grooming. The paddle-like, broad tail is flattened horizontally, covered with large scales, and mostly naked.

Paired anal scent glands known as castors occur in both sexes, but they are largest in the male. The castors release a pleasant smelling musk which is deposited on piles of stones or mud. These "sign heaps" are probably recognition markers for other beavers. The anal and urogenital orifices open into a common cloaca. A baculum is present.

The dental formula is as follows: i 1/1, c 0/0, pm 1/1, m 3/3 x 2 = 20. The incisors are strongly developed, and the high-crowned cheek teeth have flat grinding surfaces and numerous enamel folds, but they do not grow throughout life. The skull is massive.

Beavers are often thought of as the "engineers" of the animal kingdom because they build complex dams and lodges in streams and lakes. The foundation of a dam consists of mud and stones, then brush and poles are added (with the butt ends facing upstream), and mud, stones, and soggy vegetation are used as plaster on top of the poles. A dam is built higher than the water level and may be kept in repair for years. The impounded water may form ponds many acres in extent. Dams average about 22.75 meters in length but sometimes are more than 600 meters long. Beavers that live in lakes do not build dams except, occasionally, at the outlet of small lakes. Beavers live in dome-shaped lodges of sticks and mud erected in much the same manner as the dam. A given lodge may eventually become more than 1.8 meters high, with a basal diameter of about 12 meters. The shelter has one or more underwater entrances below the ice level and a sleeping platform above the water level. Usually the parents, the young of the previous year, and the most recent litter occupy a lodge; there may be many lodges in a beaver colony. In some areas, especially in larger streams, beavers do not build

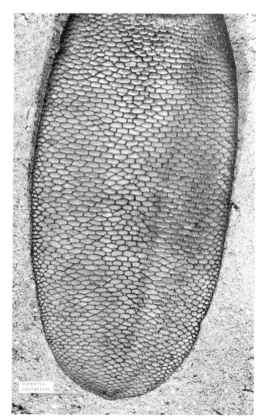

Top view of the webbed hind foot of a beaver (*Castor canadensis*), dorsal view of the broad, flat tail, photos by Karl H. Maslowski.

lodges but dig dens in the banks for shelter. Floods can seriously disrupt a well-situated beaver colony.

The members of a beaver colony generally get along amiably with one another, often working together building dams. However, they sometimes fight during the breeding season. They give warning of danger by slapping the water with the tail as they dive. They rest during the day but come out in the late afternoon when they seek food and begin to work on their dams and lodges. In populated areas, they have been forced to become nocturnal. They are good swimmers and divers. They can store oxygen, use it economically, and can thus remain submerged for 15 minutes or longer. In addition to the warning dive, beavers have a "quiet" dive which they use when undisturbed, and a "fright" dive, which is very abrupt and used when alarmed. On land, they have a slow gait, walking on the sole of the foot with the heel touching the ground.

Beavers feed on the bark, cambium, twigs, leaves, and roots of deciduous trees and shrubs such as willow, alder, birch, and aspen, and on various parts of aquatic plants, especially the young shoots of water lilies. These rodents anchor sticks and logs under water to feed on during winter. The plants (including trees of more than a half meter in diameter) are felled by a gnawing action of the lower teeth, the upper teeth acting as levers. The trees are cut into sections which can be handled readily and dragged down a slope to the water, or in more level areas, floated to the pond through a number of beaver-made canals.

The beaver is one of the few monogamous mammals; the female is thought to mate for life, although the male may breed with other females. Beavers do not breed until the second mating season following birth. Mating generally occurs in January and February, and the single litter is born in April and May (sometimes as late as July). The number of young ranges from one to eight, although the usual number is two to four. The young weigh 230 to 680 grams and have hairs and open eyes at birth, nurse for six weeks, and stay in the family until maturity is reached in two to three years. The life span of beavers is from 15 to 20 years and longer in captivity.

The enemies of beavers include bears, wolves, fishers, otters, lynxes, and wolverines.

Much of the exploration of the North American continent was stimulated by the quest for beaver pelts. Beaver fur, after the guard hairs are removed, is dense and soft. Extensive trapping soon exterminated beavers from much of their range and greatly depleted the stock where they still exist. Today, through the efforts of the government and other agencies, C. canadensis is on the increase throughout most of its former range. The flesh is frequently eaten and is tasty.

Beaver ponds, by helping to control runoff, aid in checking erosion and in maintaining a suitable water table. The accumulation of sediment in a beaver pond eventually forces the colony to leave; this results in the pond site becoming a meadow which provides excellent land for grazing and cultivation. On the other hand, beavers destroy trees and flood and damage woodlands and highways. They also dam and block the routes of migrating salmon.

The geological range of this family is the early Oligocene to the Recent in North America, the late Oligocene to the Recent in Europe, and the late Miocene to the Recent in Asia. Giant beavers are known to have inhabited both the New and Old Worlds during the Pleistocene. *Trogontherium* is a large extinct European genus from the Pleistocene, and *Castoroides*, extinct North American beavers from the Pleistocene, were almost as large as black bears.

The type species of the genus is *C. fiber*, Linnaeus.

Beaver dam and house, photo by C. Grohman.

SCALY-TAILED SQUIRRELS.

THIS FAMILY of four genera and nine species inhabits tropical and subtropical forests of western and central Africa. Although these attractive animals resemble squirrels in external appearance (particularly "flying" squirrels), it is believed that the structural characters revealed by the teeth, skull, and other parts of their internal anatomy indicate that these rodents are not closely related to squirrels, but that the outward similarity is the result of an adaptation to a similar environment or parallel development. Actually, the systematic position of this family is uncertain. No fossils are known.

These rodents, with the exception of one genus (*Zenkerella*), have a gliding membrane on the side of the body which extends between the fore and hind limbs, and between the hind legs and the tail. This membrane is supported in front by a rod of cartilage which emerges from the elbow joint rather than from the wrist as in the true "flying" squirrels. All genera have two rows of overlapping, keeled scales on the underside of the tail near the base. The scales act as "antiskid" devices when they land on a tree trunk from a glide and also are an aid in climbing up the rough bark of trees. The upper side of the tail is bushy, and the tip of the tail is often tufted. The fur is silky and usually brilliantly colored. The ears and eyes are large. The digits are well developed and have strong claws. Males have a baculum. The length of the head and body is 60 to 380 mm., and the length of the tail is 90 to 290 mm.

The dental formula is as follows: i 1/1, c 0/0, pm 1/1, m 3/3 x 2 = 20. The cheek teeth are rooted (not ever-growing), and have flat crowns bearing four or five crests. The molar teeth are longer than they are wide.

Scaly-tailed squirrels den in hollow trees up to 35 meters above the ground or sometimes spend the day clinging on the trunk of a tree. They often associate in pairs and occasionally in groups; two species of *Idiurus* were observed sheltering in large numbers in the same hollow tree. Most forms are nocturnal, leaving their retreats soon after sunset in gliding flight from a high level in one tree to a lower level in another tree. *Zenkerella* is the exception; this genus lacks the gliding membrane and seems to be active mainly in the daytime. All the scaly-tailed squirrels can run along branches like true squirrels. Twittering calls have been noted.

These rodents eat fruits, seeds, nuts, leaves, bark, and insects. *Anomalurops* is reported to feed also on the soft cambium layer under the bark of trees. Scaly-tailed squirrels obtain at least some of their water from the small pools that collect in the forks of trees.

Pregnant females have been noted in June and July, with one species, *Anomalurus pelii*, known to have two litters per year. There usually are one or two offspring.

Natives eat these animals after capturing them by smoking them out of hollow trees.

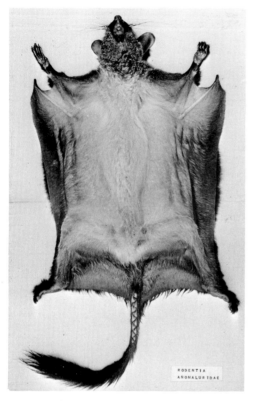

Ventral view of African Scaly-tailed "Flying" Squirrel (*Anomalurus* sp.) showing the scales, which are somewhat like the scales of pine cones, near the base of the tail, and the attachment of the cartilage extending the membrane at the elbow instead of at the wrist as in the gliding members of the family Sciuridae. Photo by Urs W. Rahm.

coloration varies. In some animals it is a finely mottled or grizzled gray; in others, gray with a slight to pronounced yellowish or brownish area the length of the back, and in some the color is dark brown or almost black. The under parts are usually the lightest —white, yellow, gray, or brown. White or light markings frequently occur on the throat and head. The fur is 25 mm. or more in length and is dense, fine, and silky.

The animals possess remarkable adaptations which consist of an extension of the body skin at the rear and on each side of the body which is spread by the arms, legs, and tail to form a broad area for gliding. This gliding membrane resembles that of the "flying" squirrels (*Glaucomys*, *Petaurista*, and *Pteromys*) and the Australian "flying" possum (*Petaurus*). However, the membrane is extended at the arm by a special cartilage attached at the elbow joint instead of at the wrist. In addition, the underside of the base of the tail is covered with two rows made up of about 15 fairly large-keeled scales having sharp points which project at a slight angle to the tail. These scales probably act as a brace when the animals "sit back" on a tree trunk. The stiff-pointed scales on the underside of the base of the tail are also useful in assisting the animal to climb a vertical tree trunk. The animal ascends by a series of leaps in which both fore legs go forward at the same time and then both hind limbs are brought up close to the fore feet. The tail with its spiny base acts as a brace to prevent the animal from falling backward. These rodents regularly travel by climbing to a high point in a tree, leaping into the air with the arms, legs, and tail extended, thus stretching the membrane so that the animal glides a surprising distance. They usually alight at a lower height on another tree, checking their speed by a slight turn upward in the last few feet of the glide. The claws of all feet are strongly curved and very sharp, like those of a house cat (*Felis*). The tails of some are well furred and bushy, others are only moderately furred.

Very little is known of their habits, except that their dens are in holes in trees at various heights. They are largely nocturnal but sometimes enjoy basking in the late afternoon sun. They live on berries, seeds, and fruits, and are fond of palm-oil nuts which they take to their nests to peel and eat. Their diet is probably supplemented with some green plant materials. It is likely that they are plentiful in some areas, but their nocturnal habits, the limited human population, and climatic conditions unfavorable to human activities impede the gathering of much data on *Anomalurus*.

Two or three, rarely four, young are said to compose the usual litter, and two litters a year are reported (one in September).

Natives are very fond of the flesh of these squirrel-like animals.

The fur is soft, dense, and attractive, but it does not wear well and the skin is very tender.

The genotype is *A. fraseri*, Waterhouse.

Scaly-tailed "Flying" Squirrel (*Anomalurus peli*), photo by George S. Cansdale. Inset: Jackson's "Flying" Squirrel (*A. jacksoni*), photo from New York Zoological Society.

SCALY-TAILED "FLYING" SQUIRRELS, FLYING "FOXES"; KUPUGUS, KIRENGA, ZEVU, SHAINTANI, MPEPE, LUCHIYU or LUKUYI (local vernaculars).

ABOUT FIVE SPECIES have a combined range from Sierra Leone to Uganda and Tanganyika, southward to northwest Angola and Northern Rhodesia. The principal habitat is heavy virgin rain forest, but they also inhabit second-growth forest areas.

The head and body length is from 216 to 432 mm., and the tails are from 140 to 456 mm. long. The

ANOMALUROPS

West African Scaly-tailed "Flying" Squirrel (*Anomalurops beecrofti*), adult and young, photo of mounted specimen from Ipswich Museum.

WEST AFRICAN SCALY-TAILED "FLYING" SQUIRRELS.

THE SINGLE SPECIES, *A. beecrofti*, lives in forested areas of Africa from Senegal and Sierra Leone to the Ituri forests in the Congo and on the island of Fernando Po.

The length of the head and body is 270 to 380 mm., and the tail length is 180 to 230 mm. The upper parts are grayish with a reddish, yellowish, or greenish cast, and the under parts are golden or reddish or have some bright orange patches. A loose fold of skin, covered with fur and extending along the sides of the body, is stretched between the arms and legs when gliding. As in the other members of this family, scales are present on the underside of the tail near the base. This genus differs externally from *Anomalurus* in its more bushy tail that is narrower at the end. The tail of *Anomalurops* is rather evenly furred on all sides and is not flattened or feather-shaped as in *Glaucomys*. The hairs on the sides of the tail of *Glaucomys* are much longer than those on the bottom and top. Internally, *Anomalurops* differs from *Anomalurus* in dental features.

Members of this genus use the gliding membrane to travel from higher to lower levels. The scales on the tail act as "antiskid" devices for landing on tree trunks and also they are an aid in clinging in a vertical position to the rough bark of trees.

So far as is known, their main diet consists of nuts, fruits, leaves, and bark. They may eat insects, including insect larvae, as do the American "flying" squirrels (*Glaucomys*).

One or two are probably the usual number of young per birth.

These gliding squirrels are active at night. During the day they rest in tree hollows and crevices.

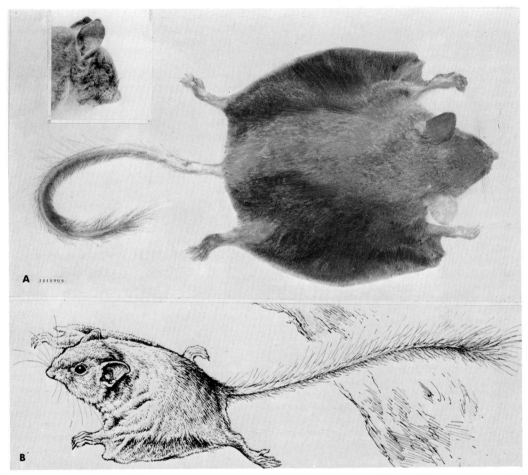

A. Small African "Flying" Squirrel (*Idiurus* sp.), photos from American Museum of Natural History. B. (*I. langi*), photo adapted from *Bull. Amer. Mus. Nat. Hist.*, J. A. Allen.

SMALL AFRICAN "FLYING" SQUIRRELS, PYGMY SCALY-TAILED SQUIRRELS, "FLYING" MOUSE SQUIRRELS.

THE COMBINED RANGE of the four species, *I. langi*, *I. macrotis*, *I. panga*, and *I. zenkeri*, extends from the Cameroons to Lake Kivu, central Africa.

The head and body length is 63 to 95 mm., and the tail length is 75 to 133 mm. The coloration above ranges from cinnamon-buff to sooty brown with lighter under parts. The gliding membrane, similar to that in *Anomalurus*, is an extension or fold of the skin attached to the sides and rear of the body; it joins the arms at the wrists and the legs at the ankles and extends onto the base of the tail. When these members are extended, the membrane is stretched to provide a considerable surface for gliding. The furry coat is fine, soft, and dense; some species have a sprinkling of hairs about twice as long as the average length interspersed through the fur. From 13 to 25 mm. of the underside of the tail is provided with a roughened, file-like surface, which serves the same purpose as the keeled, pointed scales in *Anomalurus*. The remainder of the long tail is somewhat scaly and scantily covered with long, loose, spreading hairs, longest near the tip, although some individuals have a covering of shorter hairs between the longer ones. There is also a tuft of hairs about the ankles and wrists and a line of hairs along the sides of the fore feet.

Information regarding their habits and life history is limited. Apparently they are mainly nocturnal, gregarious, and live in holes in tree trunks and limbs and in caves. These attractive little animals may be common, but they frequent a region so little explored that almost nothing is known of them.

The type species of the genus is *I. zenkeri*, Matschie.

FLIGHTLESS SCALY-TAILED SQUIRRELS.

THE SINGLE SPECIES, *Z. insignis*, inhabits the Cameroons in West Africa.

The head and body length is about 203 mm., and the tail is about 167 mm. long. The head, body, and base of the tail are ashy gray; the under parts are lighter, almost silvery, and the remainder of the tail is black. The fur is soft and dense, and the numerous whiskers are long and shiny black. On the underside of the tail near the base are 13 keeled scales with sharp tips that project away from the tail, similar to those in Anomalurus. *Zenkerella* is obviously related to *Idiurus* and *Anomalurus*, which it resembles, but it possesses no trace of a gliding membrane. The feet, particularly the claws, are not so strong as those of *Anomalurus*. The fore foot has four toes and the hind foot five. About the ankles of the hind feet are glandular swellings from which arise anklets of stiff, somewhat flattened, hollowed, and slightly curved hairs.

These animals also resemble African Dormice (*Graphiurus*) in general form.

They are either extremely rare or else their principal range has not been found, for few specimens have been taken. Nothing is known of their habits. Some authorities think that *Zenkerella* are diurnal because they lack a gliding membrane.

Two generic names were almost simultaneously applied: *Aethurus* and *Zenkerella*.

A paper by W. E. De Winton proposing the name *Aethurus* was received by the Zoological Society of London on May 11, 1898, and was published on May 20, 1898. Matschie described the animal under the name *Zenkerella* in a paper published May 17, 1898. The latter name, therefore, has three days priority in date of publication (*Aethurus* is considered a synonym).

The type specimen is in the Berlin Museum.

Flightless Scaly-tailed Squirrel (*Zenkerella insignis*), photo from *Proc. Zool. Soc. London.*

AFRICAN OR CAPE JUMPING HARES, SPRINGHARES;
SPRINGHAAS; NTOILE, TSHIPO; INZIPONDE; GOOB
(local vernaculars).

THIS FAMILY contains only a single Recent genus, *Pedetes*. The two species have the following distribution: *P. capensis* (*P. capensis* antedates *P. cafer*), east-central Africa (Kenya and Tanganyika) southward to the Cape; and *P. surdaster* (considered by some authors to be a subspecies of *P. capensis*), Kenya. Springhares inhabit dry, sandy soils in arid or semiarid country where vegetation is scanty or cultivated areas in arid regions. This family is of uncertain systematic position. It is known from the Miocene and the Pleistocene to Recent in Africa. The genotype is *P. capensis* (Pallas).

Except for the long, bushy tail, these rodents have a kangaroo-like appearance—the fore legs are short and the hind legs are long and powerful. The well-haired tail is as long as the head and body or longer and has a thick, dark-brown or black brush at the tip. The length of the head and body is 350 to 430 mm., and the length of the tail is 370 to 470 mm. Some animals weigh about 4 kg. The pelage is long, soft, and quite thin with no definite underfur. The upper parts are cinnamon-buff, tawny brown, reddish brown, or sandy, with a varying number of black or white hairs; the under parts are buffy white or white, with a line of similar color extending upward in front of the thighs and on the inside of the legs. The head is short and blunt, and the neck is thick and muscular. The eyes are large, and the ears are long and narrow, about 80 mm. long. The ears are thinly haired on the upper half and naked inside, with a tragus which folds backward and closes the opening to the ear, thus keeping out sand when the animal is digging. The front toes have five long, sharp, curved claws which are used for digging; the hind feet have four toes—the claws are wider than those of the fore feet and somewhat resemble small hoofs. The claw on the second toe from the inside is much larger than the others on the hind feet. In the lower trachea is a septum similar to that present in some birds, but this does not occur in other mammals. A female *Pedetes* has two pairs of mammae in the chest region.

Springhares have a dental formula as follows: i 1/1, c 0/0, pm 1/1, m 3/3 x 2 = 20. The cheek teeth are rounded in outline, or nearly so, and rootless, with a simplified pattern of enamel prisms. The skull is massive, with the nasals extending beyond the premaxillary bones.

These rodents dig both simple and complex burrows in firm, sandy soil for shelter. Loose soil encircles the openings. The tunnels may be blocked from the inside, but one exit is usually left open for escape purposes without excavated earth around it. Springhares are rapid diggers. A pair of springhares may have several burrows and may occupy them on successive days. Numerous burrows may be located in a given area, but community warrens are not formed (*P.*

Springhare (*Pedetes capensis*), photo by Howard E. Uible.

surdaster may be communal to some extent). The burrows are occupied by a single individual, or by one or sometimes several families. *Pedetes* is nocturnal but sometimes is active in the daytime. Springhares emerge from their shelters at dark, often by means of a great leap into the air which may render them less vulnerable to predators waiting by the burrow opening. During the rainy season, the animals seldom leave their burrows.

While sleeping, they sit on their haunches with the fore feet and head between the thighs and the tail curled about the head and body. They usually stand on the hind feet and brace themselves with the tail. While feeding or moving about undisturbed, they may travel on all fours like rabbits. When frightened, springhares usually jump on their hind legs like kangaroos (*Macropus*) toward the nearest burrow in erratic hops of 2 to 3 meters in length. The tail is carried horizontally or curled upward when the animal is jumping. It has been said that they can hop 6 to 9 meters. Springhares may travel several kilometers at night to feed; they have been reported to travel as far as 32 km. in one night to obtain water during a severe drought or when food was scarce. They seem to be bewildered in daylight and move slowly, but at night they are said to travel rapidly. Due apparently to their mode of locomotion, they avoid running down hill. They are alert and possess keen hearing, sight, and scent. They seek shelter at the least indication of danger, for kicking is their only method of defense. Springhares are rather silent; they occasionally emit a series of low grunts.

They eat vegetation such as bulbs or fleshy roots, although they may eat plant stems and grain at times. In cultivated areas they occasionally damage crops by feeding on maize (corn), ground nuts, wheat, barley, and oats. Perhaps locusts, beetles, and other insects are included in their diet.

One, or rarely two, offspring is born in a chamber of the unlined burrow during the South African summer. There is probably only one litter per year. There are two pectoral pairs of mammae. A single *P. capensis* born in captivity weighed 250 grams at birth and its eyes opened two days later. One springhare lived seven and one-half years in captivity.

Because members of the family Pedetidae sometimes damage cultivated crops, they are hunted by man. The light-colored flesh is firm but has little flavor. It is not often used as food by Caucasians but is prized by the Bushmen. *Pedetes* are also preyed upon by various carnivores. The skins are of little value for the fur trade. Despite their destruction by hunters and a rather low rate of reproduction, the number of springhares does not seem to be decreasing rapidly.

New World Rats and Mice, True Hamsters,
Mole Rats, Malagasy Rats, Maned Rats,
Voles and Lemmings, Gerbils.

This family of 100 genera is nearly world-wide in
distribution. Cricetid rodents are absent, however,
from certain islands, such as Ireland and Iceland, a
few Arctic islands, Antarctica, and the Austro-
Malayan area. They inhabit a wide variety of terrestrial regions. One genus (*Punomys*), for example, is
the only mammal restricted to an extremely high elevation (known only from elevations of 4,400 to 5,520
meters on the altiplano of Peru).

The size is variable, the total length ranging from
less than 100 mm. in *Baiomys* and some other genera
to more than 800 mm. in the muskrat (*Ondatra*).
Seven groups, based on structure and geographical
distribution, are recognized. The New World tribe of
the subfamily Cricetinae contains 53 genera of rats
and mice and is distributed from Alaska to Patagonia. Another tribe of the Cricetinae is that of the
true hamsters, six genera of mouse-like animals with
thickset bodies, short tails, and cheek pouches are
known from Eurasia and Africa. The single genus
Myospalax, the mole rat, a burrower from Asia resembling a pocket gopher in external appearance,
comprises the third tribe of the Cricetinae. The subfamily Nesomyinae consists of seven genera of rats
from Madagascar whose habits are not well known.
Another subfamily, the Lophiomyinae, contains the
single genus *Lophiomys* (maned rats), an arboreal
African form. The microtine rodents are a group of
19 genera forming the subfamily Microtinae; microtines live in the Northern Hemisphere and include
semifossorial, semiarboreal, and semiaquatic types.
They have a heavy-set body, a tail shorter than the
head and body (often shorter than half head and body
length), bluntly rounded muzzles, and short legs.
Thirteen genera of gerbils (subfamily Gerbillinae)
from Africa and Asia often externally resemble
jerboas or kangaroo rats and other genera having a
jumping mode of progression.

The skull differs greatly in form. The cheek teeth
are laminate, cuspidate, or prismatic; the cusps, when
present, are arranged in two longitudinal rows in
both the upper and lower molars. The members of
the subfamily Cricetinae generally have cuspidate
molars, whereas the microtines have prismatic, usually rootless (ever-growing) cheek teeth. The molars
vary from low crowned to high crowned. The dental
formula is as follows: i 1/1, c 0/0, pm 0/0, m 3/3 x 2 =
16.

The members of the family Cricetidae are primarily
terrestrial in habits, i.e., most forms scamper, jump,
or burrow, but a number of genera are semiarboreal
or semiaquatic. Actually, most of the scampering
forms are good climbers. The arboreal forms (the
New World genera *Nyctomys* and *Ochrotomys*) build
outside nests of plant material in shrubs and trees;
the nest of *Nyctomys* resembles that of the red squirrel
(*Tamiasciurus*). The scampering and jumping forms
generally shelter in nests of dry vegetation placed in
logs, crevices, or tunnels in the ground. Runways
may or may not be evident. Cricetid rodents are active
throughout the year, although a number of genera are
considerably less active during winter. Some members of this family are gregarious, even social, whereas
others tend to be solitary or associate only in pairs
and are very aggressive.

Remarkable fluctuations in numbers are observed
within this family, especially those of the microtines
(voles and lemmings) which are the most erratic
among terrestrial vertebrates. These fluctuations
must be considered in connection with the high reproductive capabilities these rodents have under opti-
mal conditions; in fact, they occasionally reproduce
so quickly that they exceed the abilities of their environment to support them. The increase of vole and
lemming populations is often followed by a sudden
crash. These fluctuations show a rather regular cyclic
periodicity of the short-term (3 to 4 years) type. We
are referring here to the mass, seasonal resettlements
of the population which occur each spring and autumn
and which are caused by the depletion of food supply
in an area, not the well-known migrations. Because
of the slow growth of arctic vegetation, the food
supply is quickly exhausted.

Most genera feed on plant material and invertebrates. Some forms also include carrion in their diet.
One genus, *Onychomys*, has become semicarnivorous;
most of its diet consists of invertebrates, but it also
preys on smaller rodents that can be overpowered.
The aquatic rats (such as *Ichthyomys*) presumably
gaff fish with their upper incisors; the remains of fish
with an average length of 150 mm. have been found
in the intestinal tract of members of this genus.
Some genera, particularly the hamsters, store food;
Cricetus, for example, may store as much as 90 kg. of
plant food in its burrow.

Cricetids seem to breed all year in the warmer parts
of their range if the temperature is not too high, but
the breeding season is restricted in the colder regions;
light seems to be the key factor in determining the
breeding season. The gestation period in most genera
is 20 to 33 days, and the number of young per litter is
1 to 18. The offspring generally weigh only a few
grams at birth but are full grown in several weeks or
months. The females of a number of genera begin to
breed when about six or seven weeks old or even
earlier in certain species of *Microtus*. Most individuals probably live less than two years and frequently less than a year in the wild, as they are the
victims of predators.

Several diseases, such as sylvatic plague, tularemia,
leptospirosis, and Rocky Mountain spotted fever, can
be transmitted from microtine rodents to man. Some
members of this family often eat seeds and seedlings
and are destructive to orchards, farms, and forests.
On the other hand, cricetid rodents supply much of
the food for fur-bearing mammals.

The geological range of this family is from the
Oligocene to the Recent in North America, Europe,
and Asia, the Pliocene (?) to the Recent in South
America, the Recent in Africa, and the Pleistocene to
the Recent in Madagascar. *Cricetinus* is a large, ham-
ster-like, Pleistocene genus known from China;
Allocricetus is a Pleistocene genus recorded from
Hungary, Austria, and Israel (about 65 known speci-

757

mens); the genus *Majoria* is known from skeletal material collected in the marshes of Sirabe in central Madagascar and aged as Pleistocene; *Mimomys* is a microtine genus known from the Pleistocene of Europe and Asia; *Tyrrhenicola* is a microtine genus from the Pleistocene of Sardinia, Corsica and Tavolara; *Pliolemmus* lived in the early Pleistocene of North America.

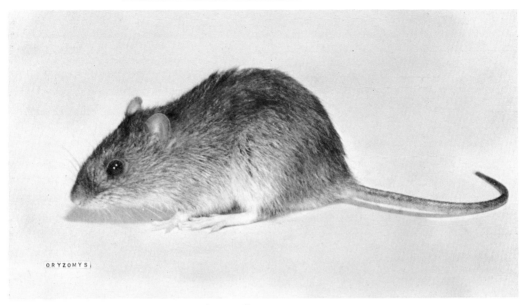

Rice Rat (*Oryzomys palustris*), photo by Ernest P. Walker.

RICE RATS; RATONES ARROCEROS; RATOS DAS TAQUARAS.

ABOUT 100 SPECIES have been named and described. This genus inhabits most of South America and extends northward through Central America and Mexico to eastern Kansas, southern Illinois, and New Jersey. Rice rats also are found on the Galapagos Islands. They live mainly in marshy areas along the coast, but some reside in brush in the mountains and in grassy areas in mesquite brush. The following groups are herein regarded as subgenera of *Oryzomys*: *Nesoryzomys*, Heller, 1904, *Oligoryzomys*, Bangs, 1900, *Microryzomys*, Thomas, 1920 (synonym: *Thallomyscus*), *Macruroryzomys*, Hershkovitz, 1948, *Micronectomys*, Hershkovitz, 1948, and *Oecomys*, Thomas, 1906.

The length of the head and body is 93 to 197 mm.; the length of the tail is 100 to 235 mm.; and weight is usually 40 to 80 grams. The upper parts are grayish brown to ochraceous tawny, mixed with black; the sides are paler, with less black; the under parts are white to pale buff, and the tail varies from brownish above and whitish below to uniformly dusky. The four longer hind toes in members of the subgenus *Oligoryzomys* bear tufts of silvery bristles that project beyond the ends of the claws. The form is mouse-like; the pelage is coarse but not bristly or spiny; the tail is usually long, with the annulations showing through the sparse hairs; and there are eight mammae. Rice

rats may be confused with cotton rats (*Sigmodon*), but the latter have longer grizzled fur and shorter, stouter tails.

Rice rats are somewhat gregarious and may be active at any hour of the day throughout the year. They swim and dive readily. They utter high-pitched squeaks. Their presence in an area can be confirmed by their feeding platforms, made by bending vegetation, and by their woven grassy nests (about 457 mm. in diameter). The nests are above the high-water level in clumps of vegetation, but in drier areas soil burrows are constructed without well-defined runways.

These rodents feed on the succulent parts of grasses and sedges, seeds, fruit, fish, and invertebrates. They are sometimes considered pests in rice fields.

Rice rats probably breed all year in the southern part of the range. On the Mississippi delta *O. palustris* breeds from February to November. This species has a gestation period of about 25 days and a litter size of 1 to 7, usually 3 or 4. The young weigh from 3 to 5 gm. at birth, are weaned and independent at 11 to 13 days, and are full grown in 4 months. Females of this species can breed when only 7 weeks old. Most *Oryzomys* probably live less than a year because they are prey to numerous animals. Population fluctuations are observed and the northern limit of the range of *O. palustris* changes due to variations in population density.

The type species of the genus is *O. palustris* (Harlan).

West Indies Giant Rice Rat (*Megalomys* sp.), photo by F. Petter.

WEST INDIES GIANT RICE RATS; PILORIE; "MUSK-RAT OF THE ANTILLES."

THREE SPECIES comprise this extinct (?) genus from the Lesser Antilles. They are: *M. desmarestii* from Martinique, *M. audreyae* from Barbuda, and *M. luciae* from Santa Lucia. These rodents apparently lived among the coconut trees. Only a few complete specimens of this genus are in existence. Two mounted specimens are in the Paris Museum.

The largest species had a head and body length of about 360 mm., and a tail length of about 330 mm. The fur was long and harsh but not spiny. The species *M. desmarestii* was glossy black in color, with a white chin, throat, under parts, and base of the tail. *M. audreyae* is known only from a portion of a mandibular ramus and an upper incisor. The Santa Lucia muskrat (*M. luciae*) was almost all brown. The well-developed ears were nearly naked.

These animals are said to have lived in burrows. When pursued, they would take to the water. They had glands which secreted a musky substance. The flesh was palatable and the natives hunted *Megalomys* for food. The hair was first burned off and the body was exposed overnight to the air; the carcass was then boiled. The strong musky odor was eliminated by throwing off the first water.

These animals destroyed crops on the plantations of the European settlers, who later exterminated them. They were also preyed upon by such animals as large snakes. Their natural habitats were probably destroyed, and they became extinct on many of the islands before 1900. In 1902 Mount Pelée erupted on Martinique and devastated the area from which *Megalomys* had been previously reported.

The type species of the genus is *M. desmarestii* (Fischer).

THIS GENUS OF eight species inhabits the Andean region of northwestern South America to northern Nicaragua. These animals range from sea level to at least 2,450 meters. They inhabit meadows and marshy areas, and they occur along watercourses in the higher elevations. Some species inhabit forests. Some authors regard *Melanomys* as a subgenus of *Oryzomys*. These rodents are robust in form, with a tail about three-fourths the length of the head and body. Head and body length ranges from 100 to 140 mm., and tail length, from 75 to 110 mm. The fur is thick and generally soft. Coloration is uniformly black; the undersides are not much lighter than the upper sides. Red or yellow hairs are often mixed with the black. The hind feet are broad and stout, and the digital bristles do not project beyond the ends of the claws.

Most of these rodents are nocturnal. They sometimes make runways along streams. The more aquatic species enter the water without fear and can swim and dive easily. They feed almost exclusively on green vegetation, although they occasionally eat seeds. The nest is made of plant fibers concealed in a shallow burrow or under matted vegetation. There is no definite breeding season except at the northern limits of the range. The litter size varies from three to seven, usually four or five. Like other small rodents, they are preyed upon by carnivorous mammals, owls, and snakes.

The type species of the genus is *M. phaeopus* (Thomas).

(*Melanomys caliginosus idoneus*), photos by P. F. Wright of specimen in U.S. National Museum.

Spiny Rice Rat (*Neacomys* sp.?), photo by Bruce J. Hayward. Skull: (*N.* sp.), photos from American Museum of Natural History.

BRISTLY MICE, SPINY RICE RATS.

THIS GENUS of four species occurs in Panama, Colombia, British Guiana, the northern Amazon region, southwestern Brazil, Ecuador, and Peru. The altitudinal range is from sea level to about 1,100 meters. These rodents have been taken under rocks and logs in dense humid forest and, in Panama, among grass and bushes along the rocky edge of a sugar-cane field.

The head and body length ranges from 64 mm. to 100 mm., and the tail is about the same length. A pregnant *N. spinosus* (three embryos) weighed 21 grams; the young were nearly ready to be born and altogether weighed 6 grams. The hairy coat is composed of a mixture of tubular bristles, interspersed with slender and fairly soft hairs. The spines are most abundant on the back, fewer on the sides, and almost none on the belly. The presence of spines is the most conspicuous difference between this genus and *Oryzomys*.

The coloration above ranges from dark rufous, dark fulvous, or orange-rufous to bright ochraceous, finely lined and darkened with the black tips of the spines. The coloration on the sides becomes lighter and clearer

as the numbers and extent of the dark tips on the spines are reduced. In some forms the sides are clear fulvous. In *N. pusillus* a clear deep orange-yellow band separates the dorsal and ventral surfaces and extends from the sides of the nose to the thighs. The under parts are white, creamy, or fulvous. The tail is scantily haired, brownish above and lighter beneath. Great differences exist among individuals.

It is possible that other forms will be found, as the four recorded species came from widely separated locations having considerable intervening areas from which no member of the genus is known.

Bristly mice resemble the spiny pocket mice (*Heteromys*), some of which inhabit areas in the same range as *Neacomys*. But unlike *Heteromys*, they have no external cheek pouches. The fifth hind toes are short and without nails, and digits 1 and 5 of the hind foot are much shorter than digits 2, 3, and 4.

Specific habits and biology are not recorded. Some females with embryos were taken in November and December. The number of young in a litter is two to four.

The type species of the genus is *N. spinosus* (Thomas).

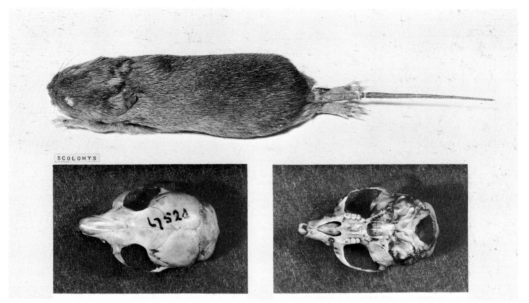

Spiny Mouse (*Scolomys melanops*), photos from American Museum of Natural History.

SPINY MICE.

THE ONLY information available is contained in the original description of the genus and single species, *Scolomys melanops*. Six specimens were taken at Mera in eastern Ecuador at an elevation of about 1,150 meters by G. H. H. Tate in 1924. These specimens are in the American Museum of Natural History and apparently no others have been collected since.

The length of the head and body is about 90 mm., and the length of the tail is about 70 mm. The pelage, except for a small patch on the throat, consists of flattened spines mixed with longer unmodified hairs. The six specimens show great differences in color, but all are some shade of brown above, and dull gray below. The upper parts give an impression of sooty black flecked with brown, the black is from the tips

of the spines and the brown from the tips of the hairs. The head is similar in color to the back. The color of the sides merges from the gray of the under parts to the black and brown of the upper parts. The hands and feet are gray; the digits are whitish, and the finely haired and annulated tail is the same color as the back above but somewhat lighter below.

The thumb has a broad, flat nail, and the proportions of the digits are the same as in *Neacomys*. Aside from the darker coloration, *Scolomys* closely resembles *Neacomys* in all external characteristics. In skull characters, however, these two genera are distinct. Among other features, the skull of *Scolomys* is short and broad, whereas that of *Neacomys* is long and slender. *Scolomys* has six mammae.

The natural history and habits of these rodents are not known.

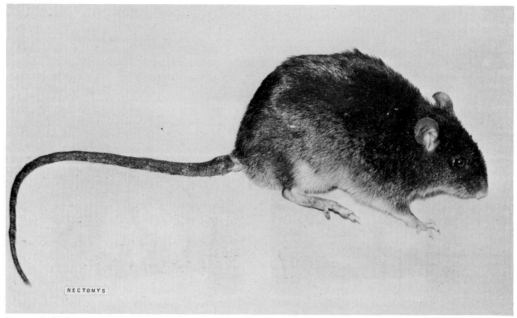

Neotropical Water Rat (*Nectomys squamipes amazonicus*), photo by Cory T. de Carvalho.

NEOTROPICAL WATER RATS; RATAS NADADORAS; QUIARAS; RATOS D'AGUA (local vernaculars).

TWO SPECIES of this genus have been recorded. *N. squamipes* inhabits Trinidad and northern and central South America to elevations of about 2,200 meters. It usually lives in forests. *N. alfari* is distributed from Nicaragua south to northwestern South America. *N. squamipes* has been found in buildings but is seen more often in woodland and cultivated areas near water; *N. alfari* has been noted in Panama in grassy clearings, old cane fields, and second-growth forest. The usual habitat of members of this genus, however, is near a swamp, lake, or stream. "*Nectomys*" *dimidiatus* is regarded as the type species of the subgenus *Micronectomys* of the genus *Oryzomys*, and the animal formerly known as "*Nectomys*" *hammondi* is now considered as the type species of the subgenus *Macruroryzomys* of the genus *Oryzomys*.

In *N. squamipes* the length of the head and body is 160 to 255 mm., and the length of the tail is 165 to 250 mm.; the body and hind foot of this species seem to grow in length after maturity and into old age. A series of 58 adults weighed from 160 to 420 gm. The length of the head and body in *N. alfari* is 115 to 152 mm., and the length of the tail is 150 to 190 mm. The upper parts in both species are buffy to tawny with mixtures of brown and the sides are paler. The under parts are not sharply defined; they are whitish or grayish, with a light to pronounced wash of reddish orange, at least on the chest and belly.

In addition to differences in size, the two species are distinguished from each other by the following characteristics: The pelage has long, glossy guard hairs in *N. squamipes*, whereas in *N. alfari* it has long, dense, woolly hairs; a swimming-fringe or keel of short stiff hairs lies on the underside of the tail in *N. squamipes* but is absent in *N. alfari*; the distinct fringe of the hind foot of *N. squamipes* is absent in *N. alfari*; and the webbing of the toes is well developed in *N. squamipes* and moderately developed in *N. alfari*. In both species, the hind foot is large and strongly built, it is longer than wide, and the three middle digits are longer than the outer toes. None of the characters of *Nectomys* is unique, but the genus has a singular combination of characters of the oryzomyine rodents.

In Venezuela this genus has been observed along rivers together with *Daptomys* and *Proechimys*. It is a good, fast swimmer. Apparently *Nectomys* is common in many parts of its range, but little has been recorded on its habits. Nests are built on the ground in woods and cultivated areas under old logs and brush heaps, but not necessarily near water. It is possible that this group of animals is in the process of evolving toward a more highly aquatic life.

The type species of the genus is *N. squamipes* (Brants).

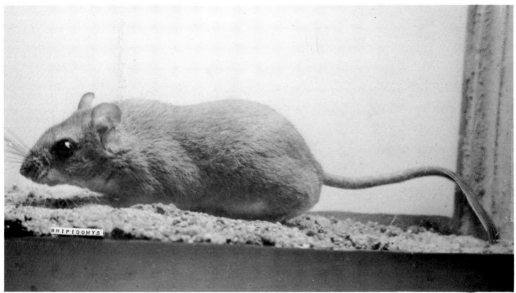

Climbing Mouse (*Rhipidomys venezuela nitela*), photo from Zoological Society of London.

CLIMBING MICE; RATAS ARBORICOLAS; RATO-DA-ARVORE.

TWENTY-SEVEN SPECIES are listed in J. R. Ellerman's *Families and Genera of Living Rodents*, Vol. II, but the author states that a study of the group may show that only one or two species actually exist. This genus is represented north of South America by only one specimen, *R. scandens*, which was collected in Panama. In South America, *Rhipidomys* is known in Colombia, Ecuador, Peru, Bolivia, northern Argentina, north and central eastern Brazil, British Guiana, Venezuela, and Trinidad. Forests are the usual habitats.

The length of the head and body is 80 to 210 mm. (usually more than 100 mm.). *R. rex* is more than 200 mm. in length. The tail is normally longer than the head and body and may be as much as 270 mm. in length. The coloration above ranges from pale grayish buffy, clay color, tawny ochraceous, and dull buffy through fulvous and brown to dark brown (almost black). The middle of the back is usually the darkest part of the body because the dark tips of the hairs present in this area are fewer or completely lacking over the rest of the body. The under parts are white, creamy, buffy, fulvous, or grayish. The line of demarcation between the color of the sides and the under parts is usually sharply defined. In many species a lateral line of buffy or yellow color separates the upper and lower surfaces. The fingers and toes are generally whitish, yellowish, or buffy, and the upper surfaces of the hands and feet are usually slightly darker than the feet. The tail is slightly darker than the back and is rarely bicolored.

In most species the fur is dense and soft, almost velvety. It varies from medium to long, although it may be short and dense. The tail is well haired and tufted terminally. The feet and hands are rather large and broad and are adapted to arboreal life. The fifth toe is quite long, and the claws of both hands and feet are large and efficiently curved for climbing. There are six mammae. Cranial and dental features distinguish *Rhipidomys* from similar genera.

Information regarding the habits of these animals is scarce. Field observers have noted them in trees and bushes, sometimes near streams, and also in houses. The only known specimen of *R. scandens* was shot in a tree 10.5 meters from the ground. This individual was active at dusk. Females with two or three young were observed in Terezopolis, near Rio de Janeiro, in October and December.

The type species of the genus is *R. leucodactylus* (Tschudi).

Thomas' Paramo Mouse (*Thomasomys cinereus*), photo from *Proc. Zool. Soc. London.*

THOMAS' PARAMO MICE; LAS RATAS Y RATONES
ARBORICOLAS; RATO-DO-MATO.

FORTY SPECIES are current in the literature. The
genus inhabits British Guiana, Venezuela, Colombia,
Ecuador, Peru, Bolivia, northern Argentina, and
southeastern Brazil. *Thomasomys* is common in the
forests on the eastern slopes of the Andes and ranges
up to about 4,200 meters in such areas as the moist
Urubamba Valley. It has not established itself on the
altiplano, however. The following names are herein
regarded as synonyms of *Thomasomys: Aepeomys*,
Thomas, 1898; *Erioryzomys*, Bangs, 1900; *Inomys*,
Thomas, 1917; and *Delomys*, Thomas, 1917.

The length of the head and body is about 90 to
185 mm., and the length of the tail is 85 to 230 mm.
The tail is normally longer than the head and body.
The fur is usually thick and soft. The coloration above
varies from olivaceous gray, dull olive fulvous,
yellowish rufous, orange-rufous, golden brown, reddish brown, and grayish brown, to dark brown or
almost black. The mid-dorsal region is usually slightly
darker than the rest of the body. The sides blend into
the under parts which are silvery grayish, soiled grayish, yellow, buffy, ochraceous buff, dark gray, or dark
brownish. The under parts are usually not much
lighter than the upper parts. The hands and feet are
similar in color to the under parts; often the central
part of the upper surface is darker and the fingers and
toes lighter, sometimes whitish. The coloration of the
tail varies from slightly lighter to slightly darker than
the back; the tail is normally moderately haired.

The hind foot is usually not modified for arboreal
life, but in several species it may be very similar to the
feet of *Rhipidomys*. It is difficult to differentiate this
genus from *Rhipidomys*. *Thomasomys* has six or eight
mammae.

Almost nothing has been recorded regarding the
habits of these rodents. Apparently some of the forms
are arboreal, while others are mainly terrestrial. The
species *T. lugens* is said to nest in trees, although it
has excessively small eyes. (Most animals with small
eyes are terrestrial or fossorial.) *T. collinus* and *T.
sublineatus* mate from August to at least January or
February. There are two litters a year with two to
four young in each litter. *T. rhoadsi* is reported to dig
burrows similar to those of North American microtine rodents, from 25 to 76 mm. below the surface of
the ground. *T. hylophilus* has been found with
Oryzomys meridensis in deep forests, living among the
natural galleries formed under moss-covered logs,
roots, and debris.

The type species is *T. cinereus* (Thomas).

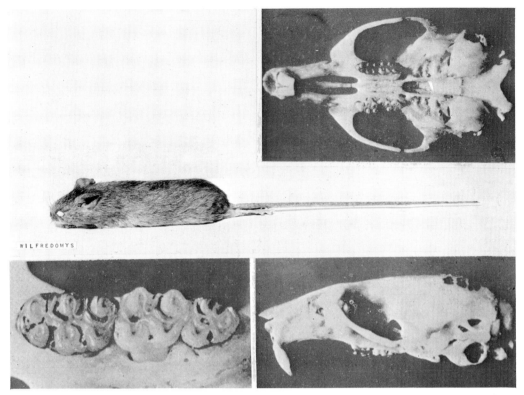

Red-nosed Mouse (*Wilfredomys oenax*), photo from the American Museum of Natural History. Skull, photos from *Arch. Soc. Biologia Montevideo.*

RED-NOSED MICE.

THIS GENUS is apparently known from only three specimens: (1) the type specimen, now in the British Museum, from San Lourenco in Rio Grande do Sul State, Brazil. It was named *Thomasomys oenax* by Oldfield Thomas in 1928. (2) An open skin with an incomplete skull, now in the Museu Nacional in Rio de Janeiro, which was collected at Curitiba in Paraná, Brazil, in 1944. (3) A specimen recently taken in Uruguay by Vaz-Ferreira. Critical comparison of the three specimens led Avila-Pires to separate the species *oenax* from *Thomasomys* to make a new genus, *Wilfredomys*. This same author considers *Thomasomys* to be restricted to the eastern slopes of the Andes.

The length of the head and body of one of the British Museum specimens was 110 mm. and the tail, 181 mm. The coloration of the upper parts is uniformly pale gray and the under parts are whitish, lightest on the throat. The belly is washed with buff; the bases of the belly hairs are dusky or slate gray. The nose and ears are bright ochraceous, and the long tail is covered evenly by short brown hairs and is almost unicolored.

No details of the life history of these rodents have been recorded beyond the fact that the specimen was captured at night.

The genus was named in honor of the late Wilfred Osgood, a mammalogist who worked for many years on South American mammals while at the Field Museum of Natural History.

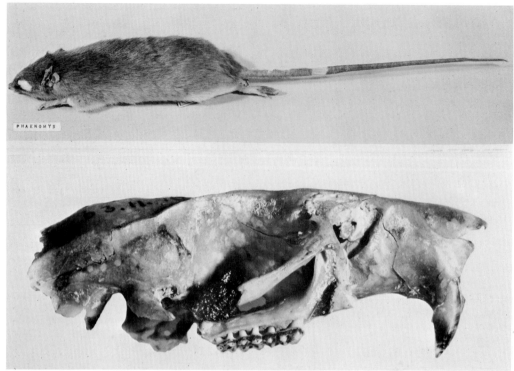

Rio de Janeiro Rice Rat (*Phaenomys ferrugineus*), photos from British Museum (Natural History).

RIO DE JANEIRO RICE RATS.

THE SINGLE SPECIES, *P. ferrugineus*, is known only from Rio de Janeiro in eastern Brazil. Specimens are in the British Museum (Natural History).

The length of the head and body is about 150 mm., and the length of the tail is about 190 mm. The upper parts are light red or brilliant rust. The dark tips on the hairs on top of the head and the center of the back give these areas a slightly darker appearance than the upper parts. The ears are small, well furred, and rust-colored, with a few whitish hairs just behind them. The under parts are white with a slight yellow-ish tinge. The hands and feet are pale reddish brown, and the fingers and toes are white in part. The fur is thick and straight.

This rodent was originally described as *Oryzomys ferrugineus*. The skull is slender. The incisor teeth are somewhat heavy. Although the claws are slender and not especially curved, the fifth hind toe is long and the hind foot seems to be slightly modified for arboreal life. The long tail is relatively well haired. There are eight mammae.

Natural history and habits have not been found in our search of the literature.

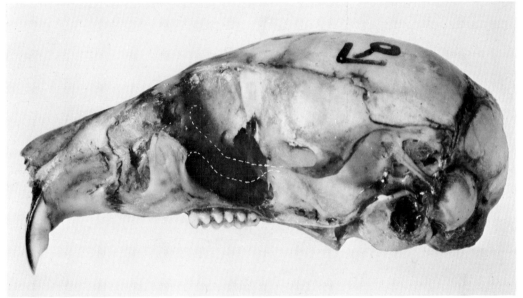

Colombian Forest Mouse (*Chilomys instans*), photos from British Museum (Natural History).

COLOMBIAN FOREST MICE.

THE SINGLE SPECIES, *C. instans*, occurs in Colombia at elevations of at least 3,200 meters. Specimens are in the British Museum (Natural History) and the Field Museum of Natural History.

The length of the head and body is 86 to 99 mm., and the length of the tail is 105 to 130 mm. The coloration above and below is slaty gray, although the face may be blackish from the nose to the eyes. The uniformly brown tail often has a white tip (10 or 20 mm.). The front and hind feet are brown, but sometimes the digits of all four limbs may be white. Some specimens have a white line from the throat to the middle of the belly, others have a bright buffy pectoral spot. The fur is soft and straight.

The body form is mouse-like, not particularly specialized. The skull is delicate, with a large rounded brain case and a small slender muzzle. The upper incisor teeth project forward, and the lower incisors are long and slender. The fifth toe reaches to the base of the second phalanx of the fourth digit. This genus is similar to *Oryzomys*, distinguished from it and other related genera mainly by skull and dental characters.

The Colombian forest mouse inhabits the dark and damp forests along with *Thomasomys hylophilus*. It is possible that members of *Chilomys* may be mistaken or overlooked for the more common *Oryzomys*. Members of the genus *Chilomys* are either rare or collectors have not found their preferred habitat. Natural history and habits are not known at the present time.

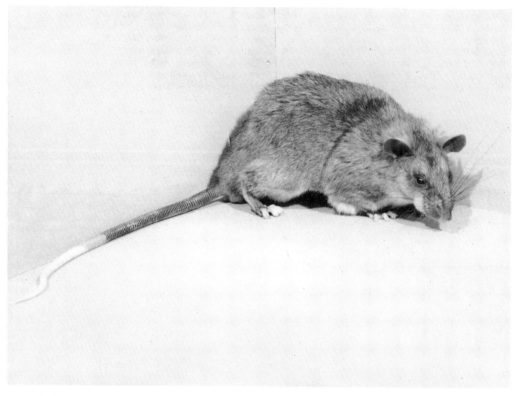

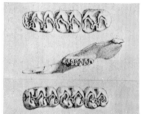
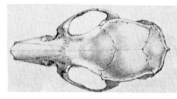
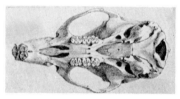

Climbing Rat (*Tylomys nudicaudatus*), photo by Robert Brown, through Rollin H. Baker, Michigan State Museum. Skull: (*T. nudicaudus*), photos from *Monatsberichte Königlich. Preuss. Akad. Wissenschaften Berlin.*

CLIMBING RATS; RATAS ARBORÍCOLAS.

SEVEN SPECIES currently stand in the literature. Their range extends from southern Mexico south through Central America to South America (only from Ecuador in South America). Heavily forested areas, often around rocky ledges, are preferred. The known elevational range is 175 to 1,375 meters.

The length of the head and body is 170 to 255 mm., and the length of the tail is usually 200 to 250 mm. A young adult male *T. nudicaudus* weighed 125 grams. The upper parts are usually some shade of gray or brown; one species is cinnamon-buff, with an admixture of brown, and in another the middle of the back is blackish. The under parts are white or fulvous. In the species *T. fulviventer*, a russet median line extends from the pectoral region to the base of the tail. The feet are brown or russet, and the toes are white or brown. The tail is dark brown to blackish, the proximal part being brown, glossy black, yellowish, or whitish. In some species the fur is close, thick, and glossy, and the whiskers are long, smooth, and black. The tail is slender and scantily haired. The ears are large and naked.

These rodents superficially resemble large specimens of *Rattus rattus*. The hind foot is suited to arboreal life, and all the feet are somewhat broad and short.

These animals have been taken among rocks, along logs, on the banks of streams, and at the base of palm trees in traps usually baited with banana. *Tylomys* have been shot as they climbed in palm fronds 9 meters above the ground. The natural history of this genus is not well known.

The type species of the genus is *T. nudicaudus*, Peters.

Big-eared Climbing Rat (*Ototylomys brevirostris* [?]), photo by Lloyd G. Ingles.

BIG-EARED CLIMBING RATS, LESSER CLIMBING RATS; RATAS ARBORÍCOLAS.

THIS GENUS of four species (*O. connectens, O. fumeus, O. guatemalae, O. phyllotis*) inhabits southern Mexico and Central America as far south as western Costa Rica. The range extends from about sea level to at least 1,810 meters in elevation.

The length of the head and body is 95 to 190 mm., and the length of the tail is 100 to 190 mm. Two individuals of the species *O. phyllotis* each weighed about 120 grams. The fur is moderately long, soft, and full. The upper parts are some shade of brown and gray, often intermingled with black hairs; the under parts are white or grayish. The fingers and toes are usually whitish. The inside of the hands and feet is whitish, but the central and outer parts are almost as dark as the outer side of the arms and legs. The color of the tail ranges from dark, dull, grayish brown to blackish above and slightly lighter below, but it may be dull yellowish in some species. The tail is naked except for a few scattered hairs.

These medium-sized rats with sparsely haired ears closely resemble *Tylomys*, but they are smaller, with somewhat shorter tails.

This is another genus of neotropical rodents whose natural history and habits are little known. Lesser climbing rats have been trapped on the forest floor among rocks and also from 3 to 4.5 meters above the ground on the lianas on tall trees. Other specimens, however, come from a dry *cenote*, a Mayan oven, and a house. *Ototylomys* is active at night.

A female collected in Chiapas, Mexico, in July was pregnant with two embryos, and two females collected in Yucatan in October were pregnant, each with two embryos.

The type species of the genus is *O. phyllotis*, Merriam.

Sumichrast's Vesper Rat (*Nyctomys sumichrasti*), photo from Zoological Society of Philadelphia.

VESPER RATS; RATÓNES TREPADORES.

THE SINGLE SPECIES, *N. sumichrasti*, ranges from central and southern Mexico south to Panama. This rodent lives in colonies and is local in distribution.

The length of the head and body is usually 110 to 130 mm., and the length of the tail is 85 to 155 mm. The fur is fine, short or long, and with little or no gloss. The short ears are scantily covered with fine hairs. Hairs on the tail hide the scales at all points; toward the tip, however, the hairs are slightly longer and heavier, giving the tail a brushy appearance. The upper parts are buffy, cinnamon, or tawny, with some dark hairs, especially along the middle of the back. The sides are usually paler, and the under parts are white or nearly so. The feet are usually white, but in some animals they may be dusky to brownish. The tail is usually brown. A dark ring around each eye or a dark area between the eye and the base of the whiskers are common.

The eyes are large, and the hind feet are modified for arboreal life. The hallux (big toe) is clawed as in *Rhipidomys*, and in both this genus and in *Rhipidomys* the pad representing the pollex (thumb) may be prominent. *Nyctomys* differs from *Rhipidomys* in coloration and a shorter, more fully haired tail. There are four mammae.

This brightly colored, arboreal mouse builds outside nests of twigs and fibers like those of the red squirrel (*Tamiasciurus*). Only occasionally does it descend to the ground. It seems to be mainly, if not entirely, nocturnal.

Fruits, such as wild figs and avocados, form a part of the diet. Vesper rats occasionally arrive in the United States in bunches of bananas.

A series of 15 *Nyctomys* were taken during the breeding season in Colima, western Mexico, during August and early September. Several females held two to four well-developed embryos (crown–rump length of app. 35 mm.).

Yucatan Vesper Rat (*Otonyctomys hatti*), photo by Robert T. Hatt.

YUCATAN VESPER RATS; RATÓNES TREPADORES YUCATECOS.

THE SINGLE SPECIES, *O. hatti*, is known only by three specimens taken near Chichén-Itazá, Yucatán. The genus and species were named and described in 1932 by Harold E. Anthony at the American Museum of Natural History. The species is named after Robert T. Hatt, the collector.

The length of the head and body is about 104 to 116 mm., and the tail on one specimen measures 127 mm. The upper parts are nearly uniformly russet to hazel, being darkest on the back; the sides are tawny to ochraceous-tawny; and the under parts are white with a creamy wash. The upper sides of the feet are whitish with a buffy wash or with tawny tones, and the tail is uniformly brownish and heavily haired. The external ear is similar to that of *Nyctomys*.

This rodent is much redder than *N. sumichrasti*; its pronounced russet coloration makes it the showiest among the neotropical climbing rats. It resembles *Nyctomys* in structural features, but the auditory bullae are much larger, the cheek teeth are smaller. and the tarsus is narrower. There are four mammae,

Hatt trapped two individuals in a thatched hut, on the shelf where the rafters meet the top of the wall. The habits of the Yucatán vesper rat are probably similar to those of *Nyctomys*, *Rhipidomys*, and *Oecomys*. It is possible that *Otonyctomys* is a fairly common rodent in Yucatán, but its comparative rarity may be due to its arboreal habits or to a specialized habitat.

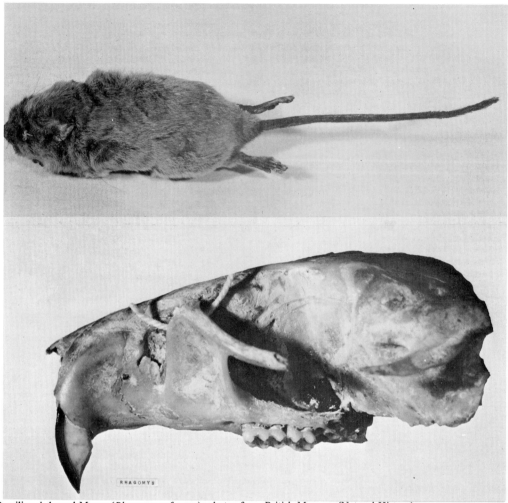

Brazilian Arboreal Mouse (*Rhagomys rufescens*), photos from British Museum (Natural History).

BRAZILIAN ARBOREAL MICE; RATO-DO-MATO LA-RANJA.

THE SINGLE SPECIES, *R. rufescens*, is listed from Rio de Janeiro, Brazil. Specimens are in the British Museum (Natural History). Information regarding this genus is meager.

The length of the head and body is about 94 mm., and the tail is about the same length. The general color is rich orange-rufous above and below; the hairs are slaty blue at their bases and rufous at their tips. The under parts are slightly lighter than the upper parts. The feet are yellow, the toes are whitish, and the tail is scantily covered with brown hairs that form an inconspicuous tuft at the tip. The ears are short, scarcely projecting beyond the fur, and are thickly covered with rufous-brown hairs.

This rodent is externally modified for an arboreal life. The fifth digit of the hind foot is long, and the hallux (great toe) in the type specimen appears to lack a claw. There are six mammae.

In regard to the status of *Rhagomys*, J. R. Ellerman (*The Families and Genera of Living Rodents* [London, 1941], p. 377) wrote: "This is a little-known genus, and the characters given must be accepted as provisional."

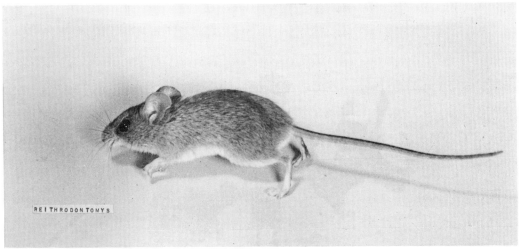

American Harvest Mouse (*Reithrodontomys fulvescens*), photo by Ernest P. Walker.

AMERICAN HARVEST MICE.

THIS GENUS of 16 species occurs from southwestern Canada southward into Mexico and through Central America to Colombia and Ecuador. It also occurs north to Ohio and Maryland in the eastern United States. The elevational range is from below sea level in places to above timber line on some Central American mountains. Habitats vary from salt marshes to tropical forests, but *Reithrodontomys* is usually associated with stands of short grass.

The length of the head and body is 50 to 145 mm., and the length of the tail is 65 to 95 mm. Adults usually weigh from 10 to 20 grams. The pelage is normal in most species, but in others it tends to be dense and somewhat woolly, and in still others it is thin and coarse. The coloration of the upper parts ranges from pale ochraceous-gray through ochraceous-buff and from pinkish cinnamon through browns to almost black. The sides are lighter and usually more ochraceous than the upper parts. The under parts are white, grayish, or one of these colors tinged with ochraceous-buff or pinkish cinnamon. The tail is dark above and light below or unicolor, and it is slender, scaly, and scantily haired. The juvenile pelage is more or less plumbeous, but the adult pelage is brighter. Adults apparently molt once a year.

American harvest mice resemble house mice (*Mus*) but have more hair on the tail and grooved upper incisors. The ears of harvest mice are conspicuous and sometimes large. There are six mammae.

The most noticeable evidence of *Reithrodontomys* is the presence of globular nests of grass about 150 to 175 mm. in diameter. The nests are usually constructed above ground in grasses, low shrubs, or small trees. Some winter nests are located in burrows and small crevices. These nocturnal mice are active throughout the year. They use the ground runways of other rodents and are nimble climbers. Their high-pitched bugling sound has been heard.

Food consists mainly of seeds and the green shoots of vegetation; the seeds are gleaned from the ground or cut from grass stems by bending the stem to the ground. Some insects are eaten. Harvest mice are of no economic importance as they do not thrive on cultivated land.

Harvest mice breed throughout the year except where the winters are severe. Studies indicate that breeding ceases during cold weather. Gestation periods of 21 to 24 days have been reported. The litter size is one to seven (the average is about four). The young are born in a woven grass nest and weigh about 1 gram at birth. In *R. megalotis* the young leave the nest after about three weeks and attain adult weight in about five weeks. Some females of this species breed when 17 weeks old.

The type species of the genus is *R. humulis* (Audubon and Bachman).

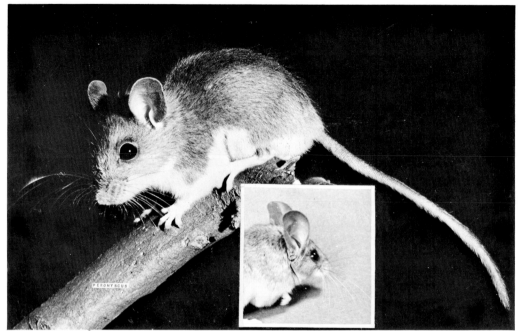

White-footed Mouse (*Peromyscus leucopus*), photo by Maslowski & Goodpaster through National Audubon Society. Inset: Big-eared Cliff Mouse (*P. truei*), photo by Ernest P. Walker.

WHITE-FOOTED MICE, DEER MICE.

AT THE PRESENT TIME 55 species of *Peromyscus* are recorded. The genus occurs from extreme northern Colombia, South America, northward to Alaska and Labrador; the only species in South America is *P. pirrensis*. Deer mice are found in almost every possible habitat within their range, where they are usually the most abundant of all mammals. These mice show a striking convergence to the Old World mice of the genus *Apodemus* (family Muridae) in shape, appearance, and habits.

The length of the head and body is 80 to 170 mm., and the length of the tail is 40 to 205 mm. Adults weigh from 15 to 50 grams. The pelage is usually soft and full. The coloration is quite variable, but the upper parts may be gray or sandy to golden or dark brown, and the under parts are white or whitish. Some species, however, are nearly white and others are nearly black. In general, deer mice inhabiting the cool woods are grayish, whereas those living in open or arid country are pale. Adults molt once a year.

The ears are large in relation to the rest of the body and are covered with fine hairs. The tail is at least one-third the total length of the animal; it is fairly well haired and often tufted. There are four or six mammae.

Thin squeaks and shrill buzzings are emitted. When excited, most species thump rapidly with the front feet producing a drumming noise. These mice are agile and active at night throughout the year. They rest during the day in nests of dry, unsoiled vegetation.

White-footed mice may live in true pairs, a relatively rare occurrence among small mammals. The nests are lined with down from plants or with shredded materials. Nests are placed in tunnels which the mice dig themselves and in burrows made by turtles (*Pseudemys floridanus*), or in logs, stumps, and crevices. *Peromyscus* seeks such soft materials as mattress stuffing when they enter camps or houses. A soiled nest is abandoned, so that several nests are made during the year. Home ranges are usually small, 0.1 to 0.6 acre, and inasmuch as individuals of the same species tolerate each other to some extent, the home ranges generally overlap.

The diet includes such diverse items as seeds, nuts, berries, fruits, insects and other small invertebrates, and carrion.

Such species as *P. leucopus* and *P. maniculatus* may begin breeding at seven weeks of age while in subadult pelage. Mating may continue all year, if the weather does not become too cold or too hot. The gestation period is usually 21 to 27 days, although it may be much longer. The litter size is one to nine (the average is four). Dispersal of the young takes place from three to six weeks after birth. Most individuals in the wild probably live less than two years; laboratory animals may live 5.5 years.

Deer mice are widely used in physiological and genetic studies because they are clean, live well in the laboratory, can be easily fed, and have a high reproductive rate.

The type species of the genus is *P. arboreus*, Gloger = *P. leucopus novaeboracensis* as currently arranged.

Golden Mouse (*Ochrotomys nuttalli*), photo by Ernest P. Walker.

GOLDEN MICE.

THE SINGLE SPECIES, *O. nuttalli*, occurs in the eastern and south-central United States. It inhabits brushy and wooded areas and is often found in thickets of honeysuckle (*Lonicera*) and greenbrier (*Smilax*). Dense underbrush is preferred throughout its range.

Head and body length is 80 to 95 mm.; tail length is 70 to 95 mm.; and weight is 15 to 30 grams. This mouse has a striking golden coloration and dense, soft pelage. The upper parts are rich golden brown or bright golden cinnamon, and the feet and belly are white, often washed with orange. The golden mouse differs from deer mice (*Peromyscus*) in external, skull, and dental characters, in the structure of the baculum, and in its habits.

Over most of its range, the golden mouse is mainly arboreal and builds nest-like structures in vines, bushes, and trees. At the western limits of its range, however, at least in eastern Texas, it is not arboreal. In Texas, and during the summer in other parts of its range, *Ochrotomys* seems to spend more time on the ground than in trees and presumably uses nests placed under logs and stumps. Golden mice have been trapped in a swamp in Florida in underground runways.

Typically, two kinds of nest-like structures are used. The nest proper, located from .4 to 4.5 meters above the ground and having the appearance of a solid mass, is a structure where one, two, or a whole family of mice may reside. The nest proper has an outer covering of leaves, grass, and bark, and an inner downy lining of milkweed fibers, feathers, or fur. The outer layer often envelops the abandoned nest of a bird, and the entire structure measures 100 to 200 mm. across. The same nest may be used for several generations, and suitable nesting sites may be used year after year. The other nest-like structure, similar in appearance but less bulky and in places 15 meters above the ground, serves as a retreat for feeding. These platforms are more numerous than the nests proper, and different individuals may use the same feeding platform. The diet consists mainly of plant seeds.

The golden mouse is an agile animal, using its tail as a balancing and prehensile organ when climbing. In eastern Texas, where the species seems to be mainly terrestrial, the home range is about 1.5 acres.

In the southern part of its range, *Ochrotomys* seems to breed during the cooler months, beginning in September; in other areas it may breed mainly from March through October. The golden mouse is known to mate almost throughout the year; the gestation period is about 30 days; litter size is usually 2 or 3; and the eyes of the young animals open from 11 to 15 days after birth.

Pygmy Mice (*Baiomys taylori*), photos by Ernest P. Walker.

PYGMY MICE.

THE THREE SPECIES are distributed as follows: *B. taylori*, Arizona and Texas south to central Mexico; *B. musculus*, from about 18° north latitude in Mexico south to Nicaragua; *B. hummelincki*, Aruba and Curacao Islands in the Netherlands West Indies. These small animals live in dense grass that furnishes protection.

The length of the head and body is 50 to 80 mm., and the length of the tail is 35 to 55 mm. The weight is about 7 or 8 grams. The color of the upper parts is blackish brown to light reddish brown, and the lower parts are dark gray to white or buffy.

This genus differs from *Peromyscus* in its smaller size, in having relatively smaller and more rounded ears, and in the shape of the coronoid process.

Pygmy mice are vocal, emitting a "high-pitched, barely audible squeal." They are probably mainly nocturnal, and they do not hibernate. Beneath the heavy canopy of matted grasses, these animals make a network of small narrow runways and also use the runways of other rodents. Tiny piles of green feces are found at the intersections. Although *Baiomys* may eat some seeds and insects, the bulk of their food consists of green vegetation. *B. taylori* has a home range of less than 30 meters in diameter, and the usual population seems to be six to eight adults per acre.

The breeding season probably extends throughout the year. The gestation period is 20 days or less. The number of young per litter varies from one to five, the usual number is three. A captive female had nine litters in 202 days. The young are born in a surface nest of dry grass located in a small depression in the ground or under a log. Pygmy mice weigh about 1 gram at birth. Both parents share in caring for the young, unlike most rodents in which only the female tends the young. The offspring seek their own food when about 18 to 22 days of age. Both sexes are capable of breeding when 10 weeks old.

These tiny animals are of little economic importance. Frequently the natives of an area are not aware that these mice exist. Pygmy mice are easily kept in captivity and live together peacefully.

The type species of the genus is *B. taylori* (Thomas).

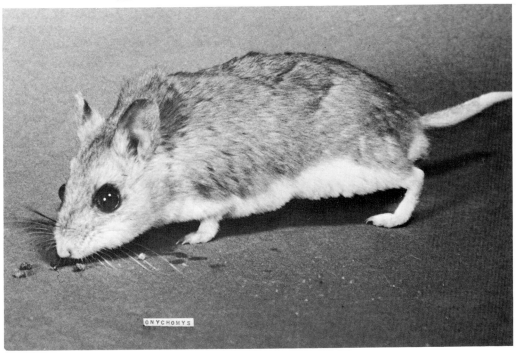

Grasshopper Mouse (*Onychomys leucogaster*), photo by Ernest P. Walker.

GRASSHOPPER MICE, SCORPION MICE.

THE TWO SPECIES are distributed in western North America; *O. leucogaster* ranges from southern Canada to extreme northern Mexico, and *O. torridus* inhabits the southern United States and northern Mexico. The genus does not occur in large areas of the higher Rockies or in the Pacific coast region. These rodents are usually found in arid to semiarid scrub desert. Where the ranges of the two species overlap, the southern species usually inhabits the lower regions.

The length of the head and body is 90 to 130 mm.; the length of the tail is usually 30 to 60 mm.; and the weight is usually 40 to 60 grams. The fur is fine and dense. The upper parts in *O. leucogaster* are brownish to pinkish cinnamon, or buffy, whereas the upper parts in *O. torridus* are grayish or pinkish cinnamon; in both species the tail is like the upper parts in the basal two-thirds, with a white tip and underside. The genus is distinguished by the stocky body and fairly short, club-like tail. In *O. leucogaster* the tail is usually less than half the length of the head and body, but in *O. torridus* it is usually longer than half the length of the combined head and body measurement. Grasshopper mice have six mammae.

These interesting mice are active at night and throughout the year. They have adopted carnivorous habits; most of the diet is animal matter, such as insects, larvae, and worms. *Onychomys* also feed on such small rodents as they can overpower. The prey is stalked and seized with a rush and then killed by a bite in the head. The animals close their eyes and lay back their ears while overpowering their prey. Even other grasshopper mice may be devoured. The common names for this genus refer to the two favorite insects in the diet. Seeds are sometimes eaten, particularly when animal food is scarce.

These rodents have the remarkable habit of calling in a high pitched "squeak" for about one second. When giving this call, they usually stand on their hind legs, point the nose to the sky, and open the mouth wide; although when giving less vigorous calls, they may not rise off their fore feet. This shrill call, which is often repeated several times and is audible for at least 15 meters, has been compared to a miniature wolf howl in its qualities of smoothness and prolongation, and in the posture of the animal when the call is given.

Grasshopper mice live in practically any shelter they can find at ground level. They are good climbers but apparently do not climb regularly. The nest is constructed in a burrow which may have been taken over from some other rodent. Breeding takes place all year, but especially in spring and summer. The gestation period is usually about 33 days, and the litter size is 2 to 6, usually 3 or 4. Female *O. leucogaster* breed when 3 months old.

These rodents make fascinating pets and generally become quite gentle in captivity. One captive had an interesting habit of chewing tobacco and then placing it on her fur. Perhaps the tobacco acted as an insecticide.

The type species of the genus is *O. leucogaster* (Wied-Neuwied).

South American Field Mouse (*Akodon olivaceus*), photo by Luis E. Pena.

SOUTH AMERICAN FIELD MICE, GRASS MICE.

THIS GENUS inhabits most of South America. J. R. Ellerman (*The Families and Genera of Living Rodents*, London, 1941) lists 63 named species. They occupy a habitat ranging from meadows to forest and from relatively arid regions to the humid forests of Tierra del Fuego, from 1,050 to 5,000 meters elevation.

This enormous assemblage of named forms has been divided into six subgenera by most mammalogists:

1. *Akodon*, Mayen, 1833, with type species *A. boliviensis*, Mayen.
2. *Abothrix*, Waterhouse, 1837, with type species *A. longipilis* (Waterhouse).
3. *Bolomys*, Thomas, 1916, with type species *A. amoenus*, Thomas.
4. *Chroeomys*, Thomas, 1916, with type species *A. pulcherrimus*, Thomas.
5. *Thalpomys*, Thomas, 1918, with type species *A. lasiotis* (Lund).
6. *Thaptomys*, Thomas, 1918, with type species *A. subterraneus* (Hensel).

The length of the head and body varies from 75 to 140 mm., and the tail length, from 50 to 100 mm. These animals have been described as heavy-bodied, short-limbed, short-tailed, vole-like mice. The pelage is soft and full, varying above from mouse gray to dark brown. Some species have a reddish hue to this fur. The underside is white to dark gray, tinged with fulvous. In one group there are white markings on the sides of the head. There are eight mammae.

Some of these mice are diurnal; others appear to be active both day and night. *A. arviculoides* is very common in the woods and cultivated areas in southeastern Brazil, where they live in galleries built under humus on the ground. Mating takes place between August and March, and the number of new born is usually three or four but sometimes as many as seven. There are probably two litters a year, born in November and March.

Frequently they leave their wild habitats and seek refuge in nearby houses.

CANE MICE; PISHUNA, PIXUNA, CAXEXO (local vernaculars).

ABOUT 17 SPECIES range from the southwestern corner of Costa Rica southward through Panama, including San Miguel Island, to Peru and eastern and central Brazil in South America. These animals live in open country and in areas of low bushes and thick ground cover, usually near water, from sea level to about 600 meters in elevation.

The head and body length is 95 to 155 mm., and the tail length from 35 to 130 mm. The tail is usually shorter than the head and body. In some species the coat is full, long, and soft, while in others it is short and harsh. The upper pelage is yellowish brown, reddish, or grayish; the sides are grayish to yellowish. The underside is grayish white to buffy gray. The tail and ears are brown. These mice resemble *Oryzomys* but may be distinguished by their proportionately shorter tail and shorter hind feet. Accurate generic distinction, however, is based chiefly on dental structures. Cane mice are medium-sized, ground-inhabiting rodents. The ears are small, and there are eight mammae.

These animals are similar to meadow voles (*Microtus*) in their habits. They make runways through the dense grass and are active during the night. The diet includes seeds, grasses (including corn and rice) and fruit. Nests are made of grass and the down of flowers. These are built at the ends of short burrows in banks or under tree roots. The gestation period is 28 days. From two to eight young are born (four is the usual number). The young leave the mother to forage for themselves at the age of 17 to 20 days and become sexually mature at 3 to 4 months of age.

These animals are used in the laboratory for research on yellow fever. They are easily kept in captivity and feed on a mixture of grains and fresh vegetables.

The type species of the genus is *Z. cherriei* (J. A. Allen).

Cane Mouse (*Zygodontomys c. ventriosus*), photos by P. F. Wright of specimen in U.S. National Museum.

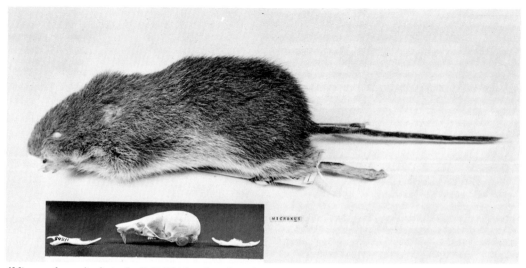

(*Microxus lanosus*), photos by P. F. Wright of specimen in U.S. National Museum.

THIS GENUS OF six species, *M. affinis*, *M. bogotensis*, *M. iheringi*, *M. lanosus*, *M. latebricola*, and *M. mimus*, inhabits Colombia, Peru, Ecuador, Rio Grande do Sul Province in Brazil, and Patagonia.

The length of head and body ranges from 80 to 105 mm., and the tail, from 70 to 100 mm. The fur is long, silky, and soft. The color above is yellowish brown to intense black. The lower parts are usually almost as dark. The ears are short, and the fore feet are normal with small claws. The eyes are very small.

The body form is unmodified, without special peculiarities. The species *M. iheringi* has six mammae.

In regard to this genus, J. R. Ellerman (*The Families and Genera of Living Rodents* [London, 1941], p. 419) comments: "The scattered distribution . . . suggests that it may not be a natural genus, but a series of parallel offshoots from *Akodon*, becoming transitionary towards *Oxymycterus*."

Habits and natural history are not recorded.

The type species of the genus is *M. mimus* (Thomas).

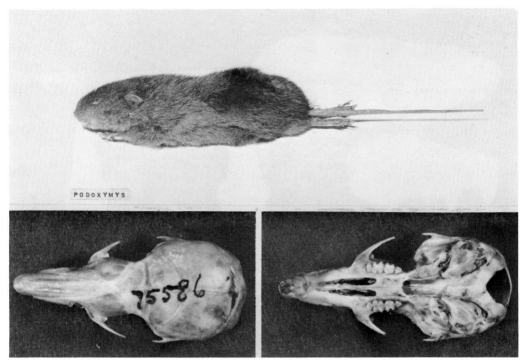

Mt. Roraima Mouse (*Podoxymys roraimae*), photos from American Museum of Natural History.

MT. RORAIMA MICE; HOCICUDOS DE RORAIMA.

THE ORIGINAL DESCRIPTION of the genus states that the type and four other specimens were taken on the summit of Mount Roraima, British Guiana, November 27, 1927, by G. H. H. Tate, of the American Museum of Natural History, New York City. Apparently J. R. Ellerman had no additional information regarding them. Only the one species, *P. roraimae*, is known and the limits of its range have not been ascertained.

The head and body length is 101 mm., tail, 95 mm., and hind foot, 23 mm. The original description reads: "Pelage long and lax, 10–11 mm. long on back, blackish slate at base and for most of the length of the hair, only the tip being colored. Above, finely mixed clay-color and blackish, the minute specks of color at the tip of the hairs being insufficient to dominate the black and general impression resulting in a rather dark pelage; there is a tendency (shown by two out of five specimens) for the color pattern to be darkest on the rump, but otherwise the upperparts are fairly uniform; sides of head and underparts slightly lighter in tone than back; hands and feet clove-brown above; tail about half of total length, very sparsely haired, hair brown above and below; ears of fair size but partially hidden in the long pelage; eye rather small; claws of forefeet long (third claw 3 mm. beyond pad), slender, strongly compressed laterally, slightly curved, those of hind feet a trifle shorter." (H. E. Anthony, "Two New Genera of Rodents from South America," *Amer. Mus. Novitates*, No. 383, Nov. 4, 1929, p. 1.)

In the original description, Anthony states it "appears to be somewhat intermediate in character between *Akodon* and *Oxymycterus*," and further writes "External appearance that of a dark-colored, long-tailed *Akodon*, with long slender claws (which suggest the generic name); skull with long, slender rostrum, narrow zygomatic plate and general appearance of *Oxymycterus*."

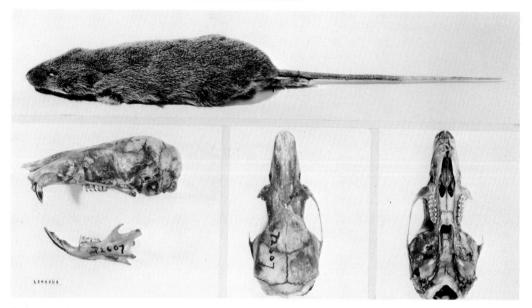

Andean Rat (*Lenoxus apicalis boliviae*), photos from American Museum of Natural History.

ANDEAN RATS, PERUVIAN RATS.

THE SINGLE SPECIES, *L. apicalis*, inhabits Peru and Bolivia. It lives in wooded areas between 1,850 and 2,450 meters in elevation. This animal was originally described as *Oxymycterus apicalis*.

The length of the head and body is 150 to 170 mm., and the length of the tail is 150 to 190 mm. Coloration is grayish black above, lighter on the sides, and grayish brown with a buffy wash or grayish white below. The tail is brown throughout except for the white terminal part. The large size, blackish color, and long, white-tipped tail are distinguishing external features. The body form is heavy and rat-like, the ear is large (about 20 mm.), and the claws are not enlarged.

This genus could be regarded as a non-fossorial member of *Oxymycterus*. Some individuals of *Lenoxus* have grooved upper incisors.

Habits and biology are not well known. Specimens are in the study collections of the American Museum of Natural History, the Field Museum of Natural History, and the British Museum (Natural History).

Burrowing Mouse (*Oxymycterus nasutus*), photo from *The Zoology of the Voyage of H.M.S. Beagle* . . . , Charles Darwin, *Mammalia*, G. R. Waterhouse.

BURROWING MICE; RATONES HOCICUDOS, RATOS PORCOS.

SEVENTEEN SPECIES have been named and described from central South America, from eastern Brazil, Uruguay, northern Argentina, Paraguay, Bolivia, and Peru. These rodents have been noted in swampy areas, brushy and wooded regions, or forests.

The length of the head and body is 115 to 170 mm., and the length of the tail is 70 to 145 mm. The fur is usually not thick. The upper parts are reddish, yellowish brown, dark brown, or blackish; the underparts are buffy, grayish brown, or grayish white. The tail, usually shorter than the head and body, is moderately or thinly haired; the snout is long and mobile; and the foreclaws are long and prominent. The outer digits of the hind feet are shorter than the central three digits. The dentition is weak in all species.

These animals are fossorial or, at least, semifossorial in habits, but specific traits and biology do not seem to be recorded. *O. quaestor* is abundant in cultivated areas, in both the crops and fields of the Serra do Mar, in the state of Rio de Janeiro, Brazil. The mating season is from August to March. There are at least two litters, one in October and the other in March, with two or three (usually three) young born. These mice live under fallen leaves and stones or in hollows of rotten tree stumps.

Specimens are in the British Museum (Natural History), the American Museum of Natural History, the Field Museum of Natural History, the Museum of Comparative Zoology at Harvard University, Museu Nacional in Rio de Janeiro, and Departamento de Zoología, São Paulo, Brazil.

The type species of the genus is *O. nasutus* (Waterhouse).

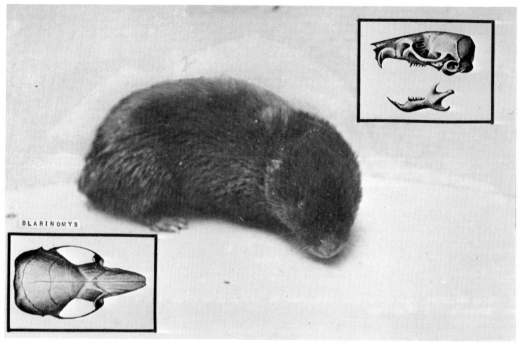

Brazilian Shrew-mouse (*Blarinomys breviceps*), photo by Joao Moojen. Insets: Photos from *Bol. Mus. Paraense.*

BRAZILIAN SHREW-MICE; RATONES HOCICUDOS.

THE SINGLE SPECIES, *B. breviceps*, is recorded from Lagoa Santa, eastern Brazil. Specimens have been taken in dense rain forests near the tops of hills at about 800 meters elevation or similar locations in less humid areas. Specimens are in the National Museum of Brazil and the British Museum (Natural History).

The length of the head and body is about 92 mm., and the length of the tail is about 45 mm. The fur is crisp and short. Coloration is a uniform dark slaty gray throughout, with brown tips on the hairs. The back is slightly iridescent with a ruby tinge, at least when the fur is wet. The hands and feet are brown above.

The body form is modified for fossorial life. The short and conical head has extremely reduced eyes and short ears that are hidden in the fur. The short tail is thinly haired. The hand has four functional digits, the fifth digit is strongly reduced, and the claws are well developed; the hind foot is broad, with prominent claws. No other South American mammal is known that closely resembles *Blarinomys*. This rodent resembles in external appearance the North American short-tailed shrews of the genus *Blarina*, from which *Blarinomys* is named.

Its burrow is made under the layer of litter on the forest floor. It is dug almost straight down for about 255 mm. and then goes into a sloping tunnel that continues downward, but not at such a steep gradient. An entire burrow has not been excavated.

One individual was captured on the surface of the ground in daylight, although *B. breviceps* undoubtedly lives underground. A pregnant female was captured in September in Terezopolis, near Rio de Janeiro. Mating was also observed in January. The animal can be handled and does not bite.

Long-clawed South American Mouse (*Notiomys valdivianus*), photo by Luis E. Pena.

LONG-CLAWED SOUTH AMERICAN MICE, MOLE MICE.

TEN SPECIES make up this genus which inhabits most of Argentina and Chile, including Patagonia. The natural abode of the various forms ranges from humid forest to dry grassland and extends into the Andes Mountains.

The length of the head and body varies from 75 to 140 mm., and the length of the tail, from 25 to 60 mm. The soft fur may be long or short and is mole-like in character. The upper parts are yellowish brown to reddish brown, and the lower parts are whitish gray. The tail, covered with short hairs, is pale fawn above and white below. The soles are naked. These stout-bodied, short-tailed mice are highly modified for a subterranean life. The claws are powerful, sharp, curved, and long, about 7 mm. in length. The tail is about half the length of the head and body. The ears are small. The genus *Notiomys* appears to be based chiefly on the foot structures, i.e., the presence of strongly developed foreclaws. *Notiomys* is more closely related to *Akodon* than to any other genus.

Notiomys burrows through the earth and spends most of its life underground; thus the name, mole mouse.

Its general appearance is frequently shrew-like, similar to the North American *Blarina* or the African shrew, *Crocidura*.

These animals apparently come to the surface only when the soil is saturated.

The type species of the genus is *N. edwardsi*, Thomas.

Water Rat (*Scapteromys tumidus*), photo from *The Zoology of the Voyage of H.M.S. Beagle* . . . , Charles Darwin, *Mammalia*, G. R. Waterhouse.

WATER RATS; RATAS ACUATICAS.

THE SINGLE SPECIES, *S. tumidus*, is distributed from the shores of the Rio de la Plata in Uruguay and Argentina to the coast of the Bahía de Samborombón, Buenos Aires Province, thence north along the Atlantic coastal swamps, lakes, and lagoons of Uruguay into Rio Grande do Sul, Brazil, on the east, and on the west into the flood plains of the Rio Uruguay and the Rio Paraná-Paraguay in Uruguay, Argentina, and, probably, extreme southwestern Paraguay.

The length of the head and body is from 150 to 200 mm., and the tail length varies from 120 to 170 mm. The pelage of the upper parts is grayish black and that of the under parts is grayish white. These animals are thickset and heavy, resembling the European black rat, but with a much longer tail. The feet are long and the middle toes of the hind feet are elongated. All the claws are long.

Scapteromys is partly aquatic in habits and is found in swamps and flood plains that are thickly covered with sedge. Rats of this genus are nocturnal and crepuscular, and swim well. They are omnivorous, but prefer earth worms and insect larvae. They apparently are not fossorial, but may dig small holes under vegetation for nesting sites. Water rats are reported to be good climbers, which permits them to live on flood plains where tall plants provide a haven from floods. The long claws and flexible tail are particularly useful in climbing.

Scapteromys has a highly developed sense of hearing and can perceive sounds of extremely high wave lengths. It is easily startled, and seeks safety by plunging into the nearest body of water.

Reproductive data are meager, but what are available indicate a breeding high in December, followed by a decline with a low in April and May. Two to four young comprise a litter; females have eight mammae.

South American Giant Rat (*Kunsia tomentosus*), photo from U.S. National Museum.

SOUTH AMERICAN GIANT RATS; COLORI; ARANTACÚ (local vernaculars).

THIS GENUS is comprised of two species, *K. tomentosus* and *K. fronto*. These are distributed in the mixed savanna-forest regions of the highlands of Brazil from Minas Gerais, west through Mato Grosso and possibly Rondonia, into the uplands of Beni, Bolivia, southward through the Río Paraguay-Uruguay-Paraná basin to northern Argentina; altitudinal range between sea level and 1,000 meters above. Both species were formerly included in the genus *Scapteromys*.

These are the largest of the living cricetines. Their external form is adapted for fossorial and palustrine life. The tail is short; fore and hind feet large, powerful, and provided with extremely long claws. Pelage is coarse, and thick on the upper parts, thinner underneath. Coloration on the upper parts is dark brown, mixed with grayish; under parts paler and more or less sharply defined from upper parts. The tail is uniformly colored dark brown or black.

This genus differs from *Scapteromys* in its larger size, much shorter tail, relatively shorter hind feet, and four rooted lower M1 (three rooted in *Scapteromys*). Adults have the following measurements: head and body length, 225 to 287 mm.; tail, 110 to 160 mm.

K. tomentosus is a burrowing animal. It may live almost entirely underground during the burrowing season but mostly above ground during periods of heavy rains or inundations. Perhaps because of the animal's large size and powerful body it has never been captured in ordinary snap traps. The few preserved specimens have either been seized by hand or captured by dogs.

Kunsia is one of the rarest of rodents in museum collections. Known preserved specimens are the type skin and shattered skull of *K. tomentosus* in the Berlin Museum; a fragmented skull and the remnant of a juvenile skull and some mandibles in the Copenhagen Zoological Museum; a specimen in the Naturhistoriska Riksmuseet, Stockholm; four specimens divided between the National Museum of Rio de Janeiro and the British Museum (Natural History); and finally, two specimens recently collected in Bolivia by the Middle American Research Unit, National Institutes of Health, one of which is in the Field Museum of Natural History, and the other in the U.S. National Museum.

RODENTIA; CRICETIDAE; **Genus: SCOTINOMYS, Thomas, 1913**

Brown Mouse (*Scotinomys teguina*), photo from *Biologia Centrali-Americana, Mammalia*, Edward Alston.

BROWN MICE.

THE FOUR SPECIES, *S. harrisi*, *S. longipilosus*, *S. teguina*, and *S. xerampelinus*, inhabit Central America from southern Mexico to western Panama. These mice seem to prefer rough, rocky terrain, but they also inhabit upland savannahs and clearings in forested areas. The altitudinal range is from 1,050 to 3,025 meters. *S. longipilosus* is known from a single specimen.

The length of the head and body is 80 to 85 mm., and the length of the tail is 48 to 70 mm; the sparsely-haired tail is usually about 70 per cent of the head and body length. The pelage of *S. teguina* is short and somewhat harsh, whereas that of the other three species is long and soft. Coloration of the upper parts is dark yellowish brown, reddish brown, or dull blackish brown; the under parts are reddish brown, buffy brown, or grayish. The ears, hands, feet, and tail are usually blackish. Until 1913 the members of this genus were included in *Akodon*; however, *Scotinomys* differs from *Akodon* in dentition.

The type species of the genus is *S. teguina* (Alston).

Vesper Mice (*Calomys bimaculatus*), photo from *The Zoology of the Voyage of H.M.S. Beagle* . . . , Charles Darwin, *Mammalia*, G. R. Waterhouse.

VESPER MICE; LAUCHAS.

THIS GENUS OF about ten species inhabits central and southern South America. *C. laucha* lives in forests and bushy thickets and along the open borders of forests. Two species, *C. lepidus* and *C. sorella*, occupy the grasslands on the altiplano, although they are not confined to this high plateau. Vesper mice often live in bunch grass or among stone walls and boulders. This genus has been extensively referred to in the literature as *Hesperomys*.

The length of the head and body is about 60 to 125 mm., the length of the tail is about 30 to 90 mm. and is usually shorter than the head and body (never much longer). A series of adult *C. laucha* from the Matto Grosso of Brazil weighed about 30 to 38 grams. The pelage is usually not very thick, but *C. lepidus* is a soft-furred form. Coloration of the upper parts is buff, tawny, dark brown, grayish buff, or grayish, whereas that of the under parts is usually grayish or whitish. Some species have a small white patch behind each ear. The tail is dark above and paler below in some forms and all white in others.

The body form is mouse-like. The ear is prominent, the hands and feet are narrow, and the tail is moderately haired. The number of mammae are apparently unknown in many species but have been given as 8, 10, or 14; the number may vary in individuals of the same species. The low-crowned cheek teeth distinguish *Calomys* from similar genera.

Lauchas find shelter in holes in the ground or in rotting tree stumps and among rocks. They are active mainly at night, also possibly in the evening and early morning.

The following information applies only to *C. laucha*, based upon observations in the Matto Grosso. This species travels along paths 3 to 5 cm. wide, and the animals do not detour around such obstacles as the high roots of the plank-root tree (*Urostigma*). An almost polished worn spot on the bark of these roots indicates the places used most often in ascending. A single animal seemed to have several paths that were not used by other vesper mice. The diet of this form consists mainly of plant material, insects comprise only a small part. Data on reproduction are not recorded for *Calomys*.

Injuries of the tail, in the form of a missing part or damaged skin, are fairly common in this genus and are probably caused by predators.

The type species of the genus is *C. bimaculatus* (Waterhouse). *Paralomys*, Thomas, 1926, is a subgenus often used to include the species *C. gerbillus* (Thomas).

Highland Desert Mouse (*Eligmodontia elegans*), photo from *The Zoology of the Voyage of H.M.S. Beagle* . . . , Charles Darwin, *Mammalia*, G. R. Waterhouse.

HIGHLAND DESERT MICE, GERBIL MICE; RA-TÓNES DEL ALTIPLANO.

THIS GENUS of about six species occurs in South America from southern Bolivia and northern Chile, east along the Andes Mountains, to southern Argentina. Members of this genus have been reported from dry, gravelly plains, from areas of thorn bushes or scattered grass clumps, and from bare, rocky hillsides up to about 4,575 meters in elevation.

The length of the head and body is 65 to 170 mm., and the length of the tail varies from 80 to 140 mm., usually being about the same length as that of the head and body. The coloration of the upper parts of these soft-pelaged, long-haired mice is pale brownish yellow. In some forms the entire under parts are pure white; in others the white is limited to the throat and upper breast. The tail is well-haired. The young are darker and grayer than the parents. The genus *Eligmodontia* is similar to the genus *Phyllotis* as members of both genera have slender bodies, long tails, and a silky pelage.

The ears are long and prominent; there are eight mammae. The recognition of *Eligmodontia* as a genus is based on the specialization of the hind feet. The hind feet are long, slender, and expanded toward the tips of the toes, and the soles are covered with short hairs. In addition, a hairy "cushion" is located on the ball of the feet.

These mice can jump and climb with amazing agility, their period of greatest activity being during the night. It is said that they do not dig their own burrows but inhabit the deserted dens of *Ctenomys*. They also live under old logs and bushes. Because they are not seen during the winter, it is assumed that they hibernate during this period. They begin foraging for food, believed to consist chiefly of insects, soon after dusk.

A female on July 31 and a female on August 1 were found to have considerable mammary tissue, but neither was pregnant.

Some species become so numerous at times that they invade homes and become pests by gnawing furniture and nibbling on unprotected food.

The type species of the genus is *E. typus*, Cuvier.

RED-NOSED MICE, CAATINGA MICE.

THE SINGLE SPECIES, *W. pyrrhorhinos*, has a large geographic distribution in Brazil. It has been found in the northeastern (Ceara, Pernambuco, Parailea), central (Minas Gerais, north of Matto Grosso), eastern (Bahía), and southeastern (Paraná, Rio Grande do Sul) regions of the country, and possibly in Paraguay. The habitat is scrub forests or caatingas. Specimens are in the American Museum of Natural History, the Chicago Natural History Museum, the British Museum (Natural History), and the Museu Nacional of Rio de Janeiro.

The length of the head and body is 100 to 120 mm., and the length of the tail is 160 to 205 mm. The coloration of the back is mixed buffy and brown, and the under parts are white; in contrast, the nose, eye ring, ears, the outer sides of all four limbs, and the rump are bright reddish orange. This rodent resembles *Wilfredomys oenax* in external appearance, and *Calomys* and *Eligmodontia* in cranial and dental characters. It is distinguished from other phyllotine rodents by the color pattern and by features of the skull and teeth.

The red-nosed mouse is an active climber. It utilizes the abandoned nests of birds for shelter and the rearing of young. Among such nests are those of the thorn bird (*Anabates rufifrons*). These nests are constructed of branches wound around liana vines and may be a few meters long. *Wiedomys* may also inhabit abandoned termite mud nests which were previously used by parrots. It also constructs its own nest of dry leaves and grass or cotton fibers in stone walls, hollow tree trunks, and shrub and palm thickets.

Red-nosed mice usually mate in August in northeastern Brazil. Litter size is from one to six, usually five. The red-nosed mouse apparently is gregarious, for 8 adults and 13 young of varying size were found in one termite nest.

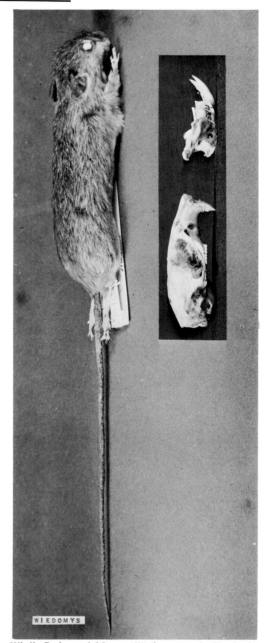

Wied's Red-nosed Mouse (*Wiedomys pyrrhorhinos*), the lower incisors are normally close together; but in this specimen the jaw was broken, so the incisors appear to be more separated than they are in life. Photos by P. F. Wright of specimen in U.S. National Museum.

RATO-DO-MATO.

THE GENUS *Pseudoryzomys* was proposed for the animal formerly known as *Oryzomys wavrini*. This rodent is apparently known from only three specimens: two from Paraguay and one from Argentina. The specimens are in the British Museum (Natural History) and the Field Museum of Natural History.

The length of the head and body is 100 to 125 mm., and the length of the tail is about 105 mm. The upper parts are buffy brown, and the under parts are dull whitish with a buffy tinge. The well-haired tail is brown above and white below. Distinctive features of this genus are the cranial and dental structures.

Pseudoryzomys is a swamp-rat and probably resembles *Oryzomys palustris* in habits.

Rato-do-Mato (*Pseudoryzomys wavrini*), photos from Field Museum of Natural History.

Leaf-eared Mice (*Phyllotis [Auliscomys] boliviensis flavidiar*), photo by O. P. Pearson.

LEAF-EARED MICE; PERICOTES.

ABOUT 15 SPECIES occur in South America from Ecuador south along the Andes and the Pacific coast to Argentina, the Straits of Magellan and the plains of Patagonia, and from sea level to about 5,000 meters. Typical habitat is on the bare ground, but near vegetation that will furnish food and some sort of shelter. Forests are rarely frequented. As herein treated, *Phyllotis* contains five subgenera, namely, *Phyllotis*, *Graomys*, Thomas, 1916, *Galenomys*, Thomas, 1916, *Auliscomys*, Osgood, 1915, and *Loxodontomys*, Osgood, 1947.

The length of the head and body is 70 to 150 mm., and the length of the tail is 45 to 165 mm. The ears are so large, usually 20 to 30 mm. long, that they give a leaf-like appearance. The upper parts are grayish, brownish, yellowish, orangish, buffy, or cinnamon, and the under parts are grayish, whitish, or buffy. In appearance, general habits, and ecology, *Phyllotis* appears to be the Andean equivalent of *Peromyscus*, the deer mice of North America.

Leaf-eared mice seek rocky places, stone walls, houses, or burrows constructed by other animals. They eat seeds, green plant material, and lichens. Some species are nocturnal, some are active occasionally during the day, and others are diurnal. As many as five species of *Phyllotis* may occur in the same area, but these rodents avoid competition and generally prefer separate habitats. These habits, together with their widely differing patterns of activity, have given rise to the distinctive characteristics of *Phyllotis*.

The diurnal species *P. boliviensis* is unusual in its association with the mountain viscacha (*Lagidium*). This pericote suns on rocks with the viscachas, scurries to shelter when *Lagidium* sounds an alarm whistle, and feeds with the larger rodents "like an elf among grownups." Another pericote, *P. sublimis*, confined to the altiplano, is apparently gregarious, for nine animals were dug from one burrow. There is some indication that this species estivates or, at least, remains below ground during summer (the wet season) in the Southern Hemisphere.

With the possible exception of *P. sublimis*, those species of *Phyllotis* that inhabit the altiplano usually breed and give birth toward the end and beginning of the year, i.e., during the fairly warm, wet season when plant growth is at its peak. Litter size is usually three to four.

The type species of the genus is *P. darwinii* (Waterhouse).

CHILEAN RATS.

THE SINGLE SPECIES, *I. tarsalis*, occurs from south-central Chile to Lake Nahuelhuapi in Argentina, and on the Guateca Islands and Chiloé Island. It lives in humid, temperate forests.

The length of the head and body is 125 to 140 mm., and the length of the tail is 160 to 190 mm. The upper parts are grayish reddish or grayish cinnamon, and the under parts are cinnamon with a buffy or pinkish wash. The ears are a contrasting black color. The fore feet and the hind feet are mainly whitish, and the tail is usually dark brown throughout. One structural feature, the grooving of the upper incisors, helps to distinguish this genus from other rodents.

Chilean rats are believed to be mainly arboreal in habits. They fluctuate considerably in numbers, perhaps in response to the fruiting of various plants such as bamboos. Specific habits and biology, however, have not been recorded.

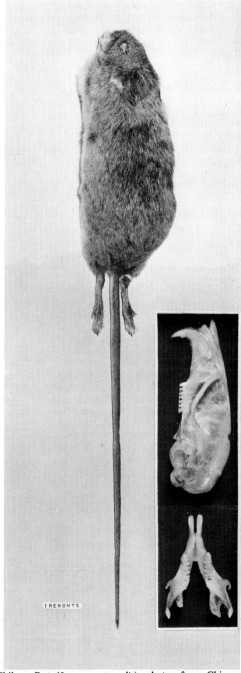

Chilean Rat (*Irenomys tarsalis*), photos from Chicago Natural History Museum.

795

Altiplano Chinchilla Mice (*Chinchillula sahamae*), photos by Hilda H. Heller.

ALTIPLANO CHINCHILLA MICE.

THE SINGLE SPECIES, *C. sahamae*, lives in the altiplano of northern Argentina, northern Chile, Peru, and Bolivia at elevations from 4,000 to 4,590 meters. Rocky places seem to be preferred.

The length of the head and body is 150 to 170 mm., and the length of the tail is 95 to 110 mm. The color pattern is distinctive: The upper parts are buffy or grayish with black lines, and the under parts are snow white, with the white hips and the white rump banded with black. The tail is fully haired. The fur is thick, soft, and silky, resembling the hair of chinchillas in texture and color. The ears are large and wide. The feet are broad, and the digits are normal.

In its high, relatively barren habitat, this animal is associated with such rodent genera as *Phyllotis*, *Akodon*, *Lagidium*, and *Punomys*. The chinchilla mouse is active at night, when it feeds on plants. It breeds in October and November at the end of the dry season, so that the young are born and raised when plant growth is at its peak.

Locally *Chinchillula* is trapped for its warm fur; the skins are used as trimmings or made into robes. A robe made from the pelage of chinchilla mice may contain more than 150 skins. In some areas extensive trapping may seriously reduce the numbers of this beautiful rodent.

PUNA MICE.

THE SINGLE SPECIES, *P. lemminus*, inhabits the altiplano of Peru at elevations of 4,450 to 5,200 meters. Several other mammals are found at such heights, but this is the only mammal that lives entirely at such an elevation. Puna mice usually dwell in barren, broken rock areas where *Senecio* plants abound.

The length of the head and body is 130 to 155 mm., and the length of the tail is usually 50 to 70 mm. The pelage is long, soft, and loose. The upper parts are dull buffy brown or grayish brown, and the belly is whitish or grayish, occasionally with a buffy wash. The hands and feet are usually dusky above and blackish below, and the tail is dusky above and white below or dusky throughout.

This genus is unique in its entire structure. The body form is stocky and vole-like, and the claws are uniformly small. The dentition is peculiar: The upper incisor teeth are fairly stout and heavy with smooth front surfaces, and the lower incisors are separated by a considerable space. The surface structure of the grinding teeth is unusually complex. The genus may be identified by its dull color and short tail and by the restricted range in which it lives. Samples of *Punomys* were not collected until 1939, perhaps because of the extraordinary area of its occurrence. The generic name refers to the puna or treeless zone in the higher parts of South America.

Puna mice are common within their range. They are active during the daytime, moving about from the shelter of one rock to another. Caged animals show no fear of people; in fact, puna mice in the wild sometimes allow themselves to be picked up after their rocky shelter has been removed and they are exposed.

The feeding habits of *Punomys* are interesting. These rodents exist mainly, if not entirely, on the two most offensive smelling plants in their range, *Senecio adenophylloides*, a fleshly leaved shrub, and *Werneria digitata*, an herb. Twigs, up to 510 mm. long, are cut from these plants to be stored under rocks in caches that may conceal 30 or more cuttings. These large twigs are manipulated with considerable dexterity as the puna mice consume them. The plants are not chewed thoroughly, so that the feces consist of large amounts of undigested material.

The young are apparently born during the warm, wet season, from November to April, when plant growth is at its peak. Two embryos were found in one female.

Puna Mouse (*Punomys lemminus*), photos from Field Museum of Natural History.

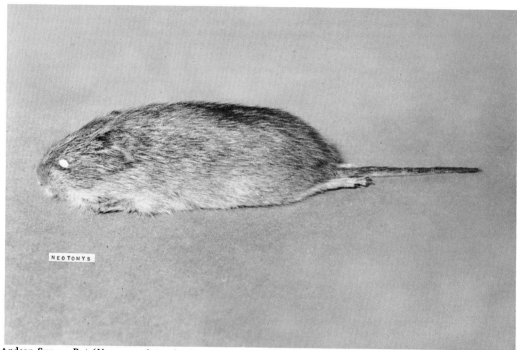

Andean Swamp Rat (*Neotomys ebriosus*), photo by B. Elizabeth Horner and Mary Taylor of specimen in Harvard Museum of Comparative Zoology.

ANDEAN SWAMP RATS, MARSH RATS, RED-NOSED MICE.

THE SINGLE SPECIES, *N. ebriosus*, inhabits the altiplano of Peru, Bolivia, and Argentina. Present evidence indicates that these mice prefer grassy areas having scattered shrubs that grow along the banks of streams and marshes between 3,400 and 4,525 meters elevation. *Neotomys* is not generally present in rocky or stony regions.

The length of the head and body is 176 to 225 mm., and the length of the tail is 70 to 88 mm. The pelage on the body and tail is thick. Coloration of the upper parts in *N. ebriosus* is grayish brown, the under parts are lighter, and the chest is dirty brownish, extending as a line along the median line of the belly for a short distance. The belly is whitish and the tail is gray to buffy below and brown above. The hands and feet are grayish to buffy, some with reddish brown on the ankles. *N. e. vulturnus* is slightly lighter than *N. e. ebriosus* both above and below, and the brown sternal band is reduced or lacking.

Neotomys is easily identified by a bright rufous nose, unusually long guard hairs, and broad incisors, the upper ones having a narrow groove at the outer corner. Although having the usual mouse body, they are quite stockily built. The females have eight mammae.

These alpine mice are active both night and day. The animals living at the higher elevations are possibly more active during the warmth of the day, whereas those inhabiting the somewhat lower elevations are nocturnal. Apparently, they are not abundant and their ranges are generally isolated from those of other rodents. They usually have their shelters under isolated rocks on level ground.

"Rabbit" Rat (*Reithrodon physodes*), photo from *The Zoology of the Voyage of H.M.S. Beagle* . . . , Charles Darwin, *Mammalia*, G. R. Waterhouse.

"RABBIT" RATS, CONEY RATS; RATAS CONEJOS.

THIS GENUS consists of two species: *R. physodes* lives on the plains and pampas of Chile, Argentina, and Uruguay, in open country, including cultivated fields; *R. typicus* has been found on stony hills, in corn fields, and along the sandy coasts of Uruguay, and probably also occurs in Brazil. This latter species is considered rare. The type species of the genus is *R. physodes*, Waterhouse.

The length of the head and body is 130 to 200 mm., and the length of the tail is 85 to 105 mm. One individual weighed 87 grams. The fur is thick and soft. The upper parts usually are buffy, often with a mixture of grayish or blackish hairs; the under parts are whitish or grayish, often with a buffy wash. In addition to the inguinal region and the inner side of the thighs, the hands, feet, and tail are often white. The outer hind toes are reduced, and there are webs between the middle hind toes; the soles are hairy from the back of the heel to the base of the outer digits. The ears are fairly large. Each upper incisor has a deep median groove.

This rodent is active day and night. It utilizes runways through brush and grass and feeds on plant material. The number of young produced by the "rabbit" rat fluctuates considerably. *Reithrodon* breeds throughout the year; females have eight mammae.

Patagonian Chinchilla-mouse (*Euneomys chinchilloides*), photo from *Mission Scientifique du Cap Horn*, 1882-83, A. Milne-Edwards.

PATAGONIAN CHINCHILLA-MICE; RATAS CONEJOS.

THIS GENUS of four species (?) occurs from central Argentina and Patagonia south to Cape Horn, and in Chile. *Euneomys* inhabits brushy and wooded areas.

The length of the head and body is 100 to 225 mm., and the length of the tail is 60 to 100 mm. The upper parts are cinnamon, reddish, reddish brown, or brownish, and the under parts are buffy or grayish. The hands and feet are usually white; the tail is usually brownish above and whitish below. A white stripe bordering the lips is present in some animals. The body form is stocky.

Habits and biology are little known. Individuals, not quite fully grown, have been seen in February in Patagonia. Breeding may take place near the end of the year. Females have eight mammae.

Specimens of *Euneomys* are in the following study collections: British Museum (Natural History), Paris Museum, American Museum of Natural History. Field Museum of Natural History, and the University of Chile.

The type species of the genus is *E. chinchilloides* (Waterhouse). *Chelemyscus*, Thomas, 1925, containing the single species *C. fossor* from northwestern Argentina, is considered by some mammalogists a subgenus of *Euneomys*; by others it is considered a valid genus. It is even more modified, externally, for a burrowing life, i.e., fur soft, ear conch greatly reduced, claws lengthened.

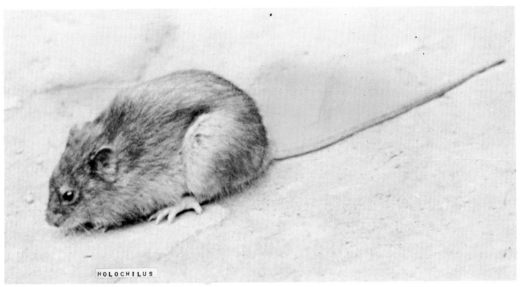

HOLOCHILUS

Web-footed or Marsh Rat (*Holochilus brasiliensis*), photo by Joao Moojen.

WEB-FOOTED OR MARSH RATS; RATAS ACUATICAS.

THIS GENUS OF two species, *H. brasiliensis* and *H. magnus*, lives in northeastern, central, and southern South America. Marshes, grassy stream banks, cane-brakes, and other moist, non-wooded areas from sea level to about 2,000 meters are inhabited.

The length of the head and body is 130 to 220 mm., and the length of the tail is 130 to 230 mm. *H. magnus* is larger than *H. brasiliensis*. The upper parts of *Holochilus* are buffy, orangish, or tawny, usually mixed with black; the sides are paler than above; and the under parts vary from white to orange, except for the white and gray throat and inguinal region. The tail is thinly haired and is uniformly brown or somewhat paler beneath. Some animals have a fringe of hairs on the underside of the tail that may serve as an aid in swimming. The toes are usually webbed. The body form is rat-like. *Holochilus* differs from the genus *Sigmodon* in having a conspicuous webbing of its toes and in the soft, not harsh, pelage. External, skull, and dental features distinguish marsh rats from other genera of swimming cricetines such as *Nectomys* and *Oryzomys*.

Web-footed rats are semiaquatic in habits. They construct nests on the ground or on reeds usually 20 to 40 cm. above the water. The nests are built of pieces of reed and cane firmly interlaced and woven together. The lower half of the nest is usually packed with plant material and the upper half contains the living quarters and the entrances. The floor has a bedding of soft plant substances. These nests may have a diameter of 40 cm. and a weight of 100 grams. When the animal is disturbed, it leaps from the nest into the water and swims away.

At certain times marsh rats increase to such proportions that they destroy cultivated crops in fields and warehouses. Some investigators have connected these outbreaks with the fruiting season of the bamboo (*Merostichis*). After depleting the bamboo seeds, these pests begin to feed on cultivated crops. However, high mortality rates of uncertain cause eventually bring about a decline in their numbers. Local destruction of bamboo has been suggested as a preventive measure against their increase.

Besides marsh plants, *Holochilus* also feeds on mollusks. Marsh rats are active mainly at night but also are abroad during the day.

The young are usually born in September. In specimens taken at Ceara, Brazil, in that month, four to six, usually five, embryos were found. In the region of Sao Francisco river, states of Bahai and Minas Gerais, Brazil, the period of pregnancy is from February to April with five to eight, or even ten, young. Another period of pregnancy is probably August to November.

The type species is *H. leucogaster*, Brandt = *H. brasiliensis leucogaster* as currently arranged.

Cotton Rat (*Sigmodon hispidus hispidus*), photo by Ernest P. Walker.

COTTON RATS.

ALL THE NAMED FORMS are probably derived from two or three species. This genus inhabits the southern United States and extends through Mexico and Central America into the tropical regions of northern South America. Grassy and shrubby areas, both moist and dry, are preferred. *Sigmomys*, Thomas, 1901, is regarded as a synonym of *Sigmodon* by some mammalogists, while others consider it a valid subgenus.

The length of the head and body is 125 to 200 mm.; the length of the tail is 75 to 125 mm.; and the weight is 70 to 200 grams. Coloration is grayish brown to blackish brown, mixed with buffy on the upper parts and grayish or buffy on the under parts. The tail is blackish above and lighter below. The fur is often harsh. The body form is stocky, the ears are small, and the three central digits of each hind foot are larger than the other two. The generic name refers to the S-shaped pattern of the molar cusps.

These animals are numerous wherever they occur, being the most abundant rodents in the southeastern United States as well as in Mexico and Central America. They are subject to population fluctuations, however. Their presence is indicated by surface trails and shallow burrows beneath small plants and by small piles of grasses and sedges that are cut and placed at irregular intervals in the runways.

Cotton rats are active day and night throughout the year. The home range probably has a radius of less than 30 meters. These omnivorous rats eat vegetation, small animals, and insects. In some areas they travel along ditches where they feed on crayfish and fiddler crabs. They destroy both the eggs and chicks of bobwhite quail and often become a menace by eating enormous quantities of sugar cane and sweet potatoes. Cotton rats, in turn, are preyed upon by a host of mammals, birds, and snakes.

The young are born in a nest placed in a runway or under a board or log. *Sigmodon* breeds practically all year. The gestation period is about 27 days, and the number of young is from 2 to 12, usually 5 or 6. The young leave the nest when about one week old and begin to breed when about six weeks old. Cotton rats are one of the most prolific mammals. Their maximum age in the wild is probably less than a year.

Cotton rats are used as laboratory animals in the study of bacteriology for medical uses.

The type species of the genus is *S. hispidus*, Say and Ord. If used subgenerically, *Sigmomys* has *S. alstoni* as type species.

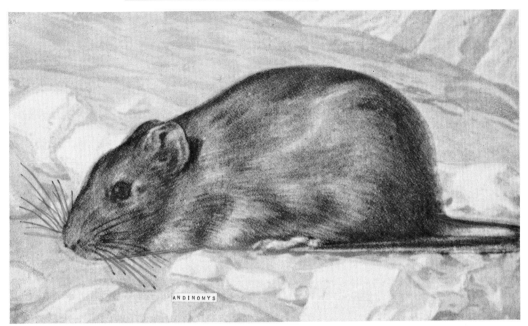

Andean Mouse (*Andinomys edax*), photo from *Mamiferos Sud-Americano*, Cabrera y Yepes.

ANDEAN MICE; RATAS ANDINAS; CHOZCHORITOS.

THE SINGLE SPECIES, *A. edax*, lives at elevations of 1,675 to 4,850 meters in the altiplano of southern Peru, Bolivia, and northwestern Argentina. They have been captured among rocks on the bank of a stream and in bushy thickets.

The length of the head and body is 135 to 165 mm., and the length of the tail is 110 to 150 mm. Coloration is dark buffy above and gray below. The body form is stocky. This rodent resembles *Punomys* but can be distinguished externally by its longer tail.

Andinomys is nocturnal. Collectors have remarked that it lives in the branches of trees, where it makes its nest, and in round holes carpeted with very fine straw. Its diet consists of green plants.

The Andean mouse breeds at the end of the dry season; the young are thus born and raised when plant growth is at its peak. A female pregnant with three embryos has been noted in December. *Andinomys* has eight mammae.

Mexican Volcano Mouse (*Neotomodon alstoni*), photo by William B. Davis.

MEXICAN VOLCANO MICE; RATA DE LACATON.

THE SINGLE SPECIES, *N. alstoni*, inhabits grassy slopes in forests on the volcanic mountains of central Mexico. The elevational range is 2,600 meters to near the timber line at 4,300 meters.

The length of the head and body is about 100 to 130 mm., and the length of the tail is about 80 to 105 mm. Adults usually weigh from 40 to 60 grams. The fur is soft and dense. The upper parts are grayish to grayish buff, occasionally, in season, becoming fulvous brown; the under parts are whitish, often faintly washed with buff on the chest. The tail is bi-colored, dusky above and white below; it is relatively well-haired. The ears are large and nearly naked. There are six mammae.

This genus was named and described by C. H. Merriam in 1898, who thought that the grinding teeth resembled those of *Neotoma*, hence the generic name. A recent study, however, indicates "that on the basis of general shape of skull, dental characters, and habits, *Neotomodon* is much closer to *Peromyscus* than to any other recent genus" (W. B. Davis and Lewis A. Follansbee, "The Mexican Volcano Mouse, *Neotomodon*", *Jour. Mam.*, Vol. 26, 1945, p. 405).

Volcano mice are nocturnal and are most active shortly after dark. Distinct runways are not usually made as the tall grass (*Zacaton*) on which these rodents live is readily available, making runways unnecessary. The burrows are of fairly simple design—short, shallow, and about 50 mm. in diameter. The openings are usually concealed by vegetation. Volcano mice may also use the abandoned burrows of small pocket gophers (*Thomomys*). *Neotomodon* lives in close association with the black-eared mouse, *Peromyscus melanotis*, and has habits similar to those of this burrowing, nocturnal species of deer mouse.

Volcano mice breed from early June to September. One female may have two or more litters per year, and some individuals may mature sexually and bear a litter during the same year in which they are born. Litter size ranges from two to five.

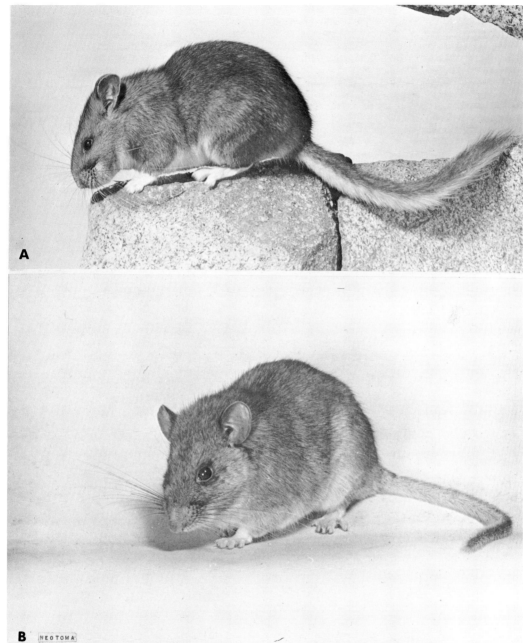

A. Bushy-tailed Wood Rat (*Neotoma cinerea occidentalis*), photo by John Wanderer. B. Allegheny Wood Rat (*N. magister*), photo by Ernest P. Walker.

WOOD RATS, PACK RATS, TRADE RATS, MOUNTAIN RATS, BRUSH RATS, CAVE RATS; RATU NAPALERA.

HALL AND KELSON recognize 22 species that inhabit western North America from northern British Columbia southward to Nicaragua and Guatemala and eastward to South Dakota, Missouri, and Alabama. *Neotoma* also occurs in the Allegheny region from about New York State to the extreme northern part of Alabama. Another isolated range of these rodents is in eastern Florida, eastern Georgia, and extreme southern South Carolina. Wood rats are found from low, hot, dry deserts or humid jungles to rocky slopes above timber line; usually rocky places are preferred. *Teanopus*, Merriam, 1903, *Hodomys*, Merriam, 1894, and *Teonoma*, Gray, 1843, are herein regarded as subgenera; however, some mammalogists who know the animals in the field think that *Hodomys* is a valid genus, as it has some habits quite different from *Neotoma*.

The head and body length is 150 to 230 mm.; the length of the tail 75 to 240 mm.; and the weight is 199 to 431 grams. The fur is soft to somewhat harsh. Its delicate coloration ranges from pale, buffy gray to darker gray and cinnamon-buff above, and the under parts are pure white, pale grayish, or buffy. Coloration is bright rufous in *Hodomys* and *N. chrysomelas*. In one group, the so-called round-tailed wood rats, the tail is very scantily haired which gives it the appearance of the common rat (*Rattus*). In the bushy-tailed wood rats, the tail is fairly well covered, so that it has somewhat the appearance of a short-haired squirrel tail.

Neotoma builds nests of whatever material is at hand, generally twigs or sections of cactus. Such houses sometimes will be nearly 2 meters in diameter. The nests rest on the ground or are placed against rocks or the base of a tree. Those species inhabiting regions where spiny cactus is available seek this material and build their home almost entirely over this plant. The nests are so placed that it is almost impossible for an enemy to encroach without being impaled and yet the wood rats dash in and out of their homes unharmed. To give an alarm signal, they drum on the ground with their feet. Several fairly well-defined trails lead to these nests, but the paths are often obstructed by cactus or other material. The nests are often built as high as 6 meters in the trees. Some of those that live near lakes and streams build their nests over water in mangrove trees often 46 to 69 meters from the shore. The animals are not aquatic and regularly forage on land. None of the group willingly enters the water.

Neotoma picks up material for its nests while foraging and carries it to the homesite. If these rodents find a more attractive substance, they will drop the material they are carrying and take the new piece. They often select pieces of silverware or other shining objects from camps and deposit the material they have been carrying. This trait has given them the name of "trade rat" or "pack rat."

Their food consists almost entirely of such plant tissues as roots, stems, and leaves, seeds, and some invertebrates. They do not drink much water, but during dry seasons they make heavy inroads on the fleshy stems of cacti and other plants that are well filled with water.

From 30 to 37 days after mating, one to four young are born in a lined nest in their "house" or in a rock cranny. In the north there appears to be a single litter in the spring, but in the south breeding apparently takes place throughout the year. Sexual maturity is reached before the end of the first year. Captives have lived three to four years.

In some sections of their range, these rodents live so close to farms that they are pests, but in general they live so far from cultivated areas that they are of little economic importance.

Neotoma is an expert climber but does not ordinarily go far up trees. Both *N. phenax* and *N. fuscipes*, however, regularly nest and move about in trees. They are particularly fond of cliffs and dwell in the crevices of rocks in many areas.

Wood rats are neat animals and make pleasing pets if their extreme timidity can be overcome.

The type species of the genus is *N. floridana* (Ord).

Nelson's Wood Rat (*Nelsonia neotomodon*), photo by Howard E. Uible of skin in U.S. National Museum.

NELSON'S WOOD RATS.

THE SINGLE SPECIES, *N. neotomodon*, inhabits the mountains of west-central Mexico. It frequents rocky areas in pine, Douglas fir, or true fir from 1,810 to 3,010 meters elevation.

The length of the head and body is 120 to 130 mm., and the length of the tail is 105 to 130 mm. The soft pelage of the upper parts is grayish brown, sometimes with a buffy wash; the sides are usually pale reddish; the under parts are whitish; and the feet are white to dusky. The tail is tufted terminally. Externally, this rodent looks like a large, hairy-tailed species of *Peromyscus*; internally, *Nelsonia* most resembles the genus *Neotoma* and could be regarded as a small wood rat, the flat-topped prismatic pattern of the teeth are a typical example of this likeness.

Crevices in cliffs and in rimrock are used for shelters, these places are apparently cool and moist. Nelson's wood-rat is mainly nocturnal; it seems to feed mostly on the needles of Douglas fir and juniper. Females collected in March were not pregnant.

Some 50 specimens are in the following study collections: American Museum of Natural History, British Museum (Natural History), Museum of Comparative Zoology at Harvard, University of Michigan Museum of Zoology, the U.S. National Museum, the Los Angeles County Museum, and Instituto de Biología, National University of Mexico.

MAGDALENA RATS.

THE SINGLE SPECIES, *X. nelsoni*, has been recorded from three localities in Mexico: Chamela Bay, Jalisco; Pueblo Juarez, Colima, the type locality; and Armeria, Colima. The specimens were collected from about sea level to approximately 450 meters elevation. There are four original specimens, three are in the U.S. National Museum and one is at the University of Michigan.

The length of the head and body is 157 to 165 mm., and the length of the tail is 143 to 170 mm. This attractive rodent has a white spot over each eye and a white spot below each ear; the upper lips and cheeks are white more than halfway to the eyes. The upper parts are deep tawny red or fulvous, and the under parts are creamy white. The tail is well haired and the fur is soft. The ears, about half as long as the head, are nearly naked. This rodent resembles the small wood-rat (*Neotoma*) in general external appearance and form, but the coloration is different. The skull and teeth resemble those of *Neotoma* more than any other genus. The auditory bullae of *Xenomys* are inflated, and the molar teeth are rooted.

The collector of the type series remarked that these animals dwell in hollow trees, and that one was caught in a low dense wood near a river.

Xenomys are nocturnal and arboreal. They live in thorn forest and tropical deciduous forest in a restricted area of coastal western Mexico. They are quite agile animals in the trees, moving about freely and without apparent hesitation. Pregnant females were taken in August.

Only 13 specimens are now known, as a series of 9 was taken recently (1958) at the type locality by W. J. Schaldach, Jr.; these specimens are in the Los Angeles County Museum.

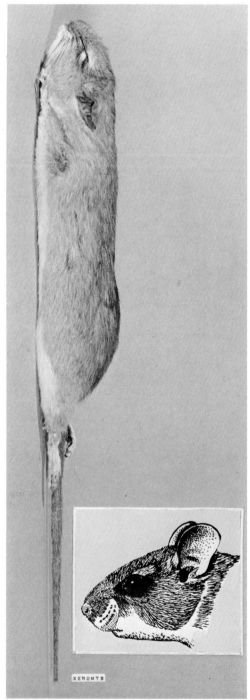

Magdalena Rat (*Xenomys nelsoni*), photo by Howard E. Uible of skin in U.S. National Museum. Inset: Drawing by Joseph A. Davis, Jr.

Fish-eating or Aquatic Rat (*Ichthyomys stolzmanni*), photo from *Proc. Zool. Soc. London.*

FISH-EATING OR AQUATIC RATS.

SEVEN SPECIES have been described from Peru, Ecuador, Colombia, and Venezuela. Streams and swampy areas from 600 to 2,800 meters in elevation are frequented. Much of their former range is now under cultivation, forcing the animals to seek homes elsewhere.

The length of the head and body is 145 to 210 mm., and the length of the tail is 145 to 190 mm. The pelage is thick and not so soft as that of allied genera. The upper parts are dark olive-brown, grayish, or blackish, often with a buffy wash, and the under parts are whitish. The tail is fully haired. These animals, about the size of common rats (*Rattus*), are modified in body form for an aquatic and predaceous life. The head is depressed; the skull is fairly smooth, lacking prominent ridging; the eyes and ears are small; the whiskers are long and stout; the fur is thick; the large hind feet are broad with swimming fringes; the hind toes are partly webbed; and the tail has a bristly undersurface. The outer corner of each upper incisor projects downward as a sharp point, and the cutting edges of the two upper incisors form an inverted V. There are six mammae.

Fish-eating rats are believed to feed mainly, if not entirely, on water animals. Remains of fish having an average length of 150 mm. have been found in the intestinal tract of *Ichthyomys*. Presumably these rodents spear fish with their simple, gaff-like upper incisors. The caecum is small and not well developed, but this organ is prominent and well developed in vegetarian cricetid rodents.

Söderström, who first made known the fish-eating rats, states that they usually live under rocks during the day.

The type species of the genus is *I. stolzmanni*, Thomas.

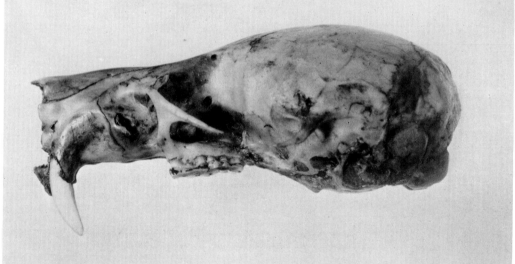

Fish-eating Rat (*Anotomys leander*), photos from British Museum (Natural History).

FISH-EATING OR AQUATIC RATS.

THE SINGLE SPECIES, *A. leander*, is known from only a few specimens in the British Museum (Natural History) and in the American Museum of Natural History which were taken at an altitude of 3,600 meters on the slopes of Mt. Pichinche, Ecuador, in a swift mountain stream. This genus is less highly specialized for catching and eating fish than are some of its close relatives such as *Ichthyomys* and *Daptomys*. However, it is more highly specialized for an aquatic existence, as is evidenced by the following characters: the external ear is lacking, and the slit-like ear opening can be closed by muscular contractions to keep out water; the fur is velvety, similar to the fur of *Hydromys*, *Neomys*, *Nectogale*, and other highly specialized aquatic mammals; and the feet are lined by coarse, stiffened hairs which increase the surface of the foot for swimming. The upper parts of the animal are dark slaty with paler sides; the under parts are whitish gray. The whiskers, or vibrissae, are dark on the upper part of the face and white on the lower part. A distinct round white patch lies around each ear opening.

The length of the head and body in a British Museum specimen was 128 mm., the tail, 125 mm., and the hind foot, 32 mm. Little is known of the habits of these water rats.

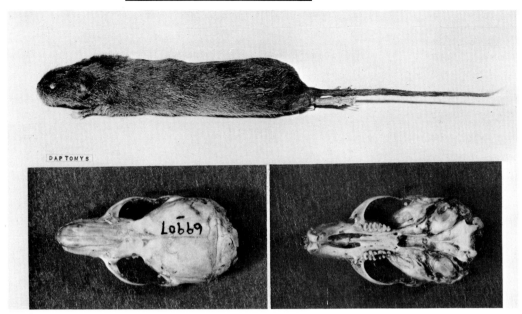

Fish-eating Rat (*Daptomys venezuelae*), photos from American Museum of Natural History.

FISH-EATING OR AQUATIC RATS, EL RATON
OBSCURO DE VENEZUELA.

THE TYPE and one other specimen on which
Anthony based the genus and the single species, *D.
venezuelae*, were taken at Naveri, about 25 km. west
of Cumanacoa in northern Venezuela, at an elevation
of about 750 meters. The specimens were collected
March 8, 1925, by G. H. H. Tate of the American
Museum of Natural History, New York City. Ellerman apparently had no more information regarding
the form than appeared in the original description.
The following information is based upon Anthony's
original study.

The length of the head and body is 131 mm., and
the length of the tail is 105 mm. The pelage is made
up of hard glistening guard hairs and a dense, close
underfur. The coloration of the upper parts is blackish brown, created by black tips of the guard hairs
and their gray bases. The sides of the head and body
are slightly lighter than the top, and the under parts
are grayish to slate. The tail is brownish black. The
toes of the fore feet are whitish, but the toes of the
hind feet are brownish.

Daptomys belongs to the fish-eating group which
is typified by *Ichthyomys*. However, members of
Daptomys are not so highly modified for aquatic life
as their hind feet are of normal proportions. The incisors are sharp, and the outer surfaces are slightly
inclined toward each other. *Daptomys* superficially
resembles *Neusticomys monticolis* of the Ecuadorean
Andes, similar in such features as the structure of the
hind foot, texture and color of pelage, etc., but
differing in some cranial structures.

These aquatic rats are apparently hard to trap or
their numbers are extremely few, for specimens are
rare.

Central American Water Mouse (*Rheomys thomasi*), photo from *Jour. Mam.*, R. A. Sirton.

CENTRAL AMERICAN WATER MICE, FISHING RATS.

THIS GENUS of six species, *R. raptor* of southern Mexico and El Salvador; *R. mexicanus* of Oaxoca, Mexico; *R. underwoodi*, *R. hartmanni*, and *R. thomasi* from Central America; and *R. trichotis*, native to Colombia, South America, inhabits small streams and creeks in the jungle.

Head and body length is 105 to 188 mm., and tail length is 95 to 150 mm. The short, glossy fur is colored dark brown or mixed black and cinnamon on the upper parts and grayish or whitish beneath. The tail may be tipped with white. The external features are similar to those in *Ichthyomys*. Ears are present, but they are small and almost hidden by the fur. The webs and toes of the feet are fringed with bristles. The upper incisors are sometimes grooved so that the edges become deeply notched with age.

Small piles of empty snail shells found along streams in a habitat of *Rheomys* suggest that these rodents include snails in their food supply. There is no evidence that they prey on fish, although they are suspected of doing so. Specific habits and biology of these animals are little known. *Rheomys* is usually caught by placing the trap in a narrow, shallow stream where the water is swift.

Hall and Kelson (*Mammals of North America* [New York, 1959], Vol. II, p. 708) note that there is some evidence which suggests that this group would be better treated as a subgenus of the South American fish-mice *Ichthyomys*, as the two are quite similar morphologically.

The type species of the genus is *R. underwoodi*, Thomas. *Neorheomys*, Goodwin, 1959, was recently proposed as a subgenus for the species *R. mexicanus*.

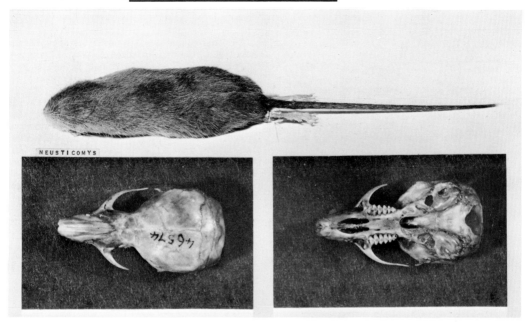

Aquatic Rat (*Neusticomys monticolus*), photos from American Museum of Natural History.

FISH-EATING OR AQUATIC RATS.

THE SINGLE SPECIES, *N. monticolus*, inhabits Ecuador. This genus and species were described in 1921, and the type material is in the American Museum of Natural History.

The head and body length is about 95 mm., and the tail length is about 110 mm. The soft fur is reddish brown above and grayish below; the tail is colored like the back, but with scattered whitish hairs. An external ear is evident, and the feet and toes are weakly fringed with hairs. This genus is similar to the other aquatic rats of the *Ichthyomys* group (*Ichthyomys, Anotomys, Daptomys, Rheomys*) but differs from them in the reduced hallux (first digit of the hind limb) and in dental characters. It appears to be one of the least specialized of the fish-eating rats.

Specific habits and biology, if known, are not recorded. It is assumed to feed, at least in part, on aquatic life. G. H. H. Tate ("Random Observations on Habits of South American Mammals," *Jour. Mam.*, August, 1931, Vol. 12, p. 251) observed that these animals were plentiful, saying that they could be taken along small "azequias" or irrigation brooks. He says that when trapping, the trap should be placed where the current is rapid and where the banks encroach. *Neusticomys* is frequently taken close to small waterfalls and in places exposed to spray from the water.

Mouse-like Hamster (*Calomyscus bailwardi*), photo from *Proc. Zool. Soc. London.*

MOUSE-LIKE HAMSTERS.

THE SINGLE SPECIES, *C. bailwardi*, is known from Iran, Baluchistan, Afghanistan, southern Transcaucasia, and South Russian Turkestan. It seems to prefer rocky, arid mountain regions up to about 2,750 meters elevation.

Head and body length is 70 to 85 mm., and tail length is 75 to 100 mm. The pelage is fine and soft in texture. The upper parts are pinkish buff, sandy brown, or grayish brown, and the under parts, hands, and feet are white. The tail is dark above and white below. It is thickly haired, tufted, and is longer than the head and body. The large ears are conspicuous. There are no cheek pouches. This animal, grouped with the Old World hamsters, is similar to the New World *Peromyscus*; one feature distinguishing the mouse-like hamster from *Peromyscus* is the number of roots of the molar teeth. The female has six mammae.

Calomyscus is active only at night during the summer, but it is also active by day in the autumn and winter. These rodents feed mainly on seeds and also consume flowers and leaves and readily eat animal food.

From three to five young are born from March through June; some females have two litters a year. The newly-born young are hairless; 13 days after birth, when their eyes open, they have a gray pelage. Adult coloration and size is attained in six to eight months.

W. H. Osgood ("Cricetine Rodents Allied to Phyllotis," *Jour. Mam.*, Vol. 28, No. 2, p. 166) states that they are very limited in distribution, and doubtless on the way to extinction. He states further that *Calomyscus* is so similar to the American *Peromyscus*, that it probably signifies a late Pleistocene invasion from North America.

Dwarf Hamster (*Phodopus sungorus*), photo by Bernhard Grzimek.

SMALL DESERT HAMSTERS, DWARF HAMSTERS;
ZUNGARIAN OR DJUNGARIAN HAMSTERS (native
names); MAI-TSANG-OR.

THE TWO SPECIES, *P. roborovskii* and *P. sungorus*,
have a combined range extending from Siberia
through Manchuria and northern China. It appears
that they inhabit somewhat arid regions in stiff grass
on plains and sand dunes.

The length of the head and body is from 53 to
102 mm., and the length of the tail is 7 to 11 mm. The
length of the tail is generally less than a fifth of the
head and body length. The upper parts are grayish
to pinkish buff, and the under parts are whitish; the
two colors meet to form four re-entrants into the dorsal mantle, one before and one behind each leg,
leaving a narrow tongue of the mantle extending down
on the upper part of each leg. The ears are blackish,
with white on the inside. The sides of the muzzle,
upper lips, lower cheeks, lower flanks, and limbs, as
well as the tail and ventral surfaces are pure white.
Sometimes there is a dark dorsal stripe.

These hamsters have a robust body, prominent
ears, and internal cheek pouches. The feet are short,
broad, and densely hairy throughout. There are eight
mammae.

Apparently little has been recorded about their
habits. They appear to be most active in the evening
and early morning, and, to some extent, throughout
the night. A. S. Loukashkin ("On the Pikas of North
Manchuria," *Jour. Mam.*, Nov. 1940, Vol. 21, p. 404)
said that he observed *P. sungorus* in association with
pikas (*Ochotona*) and that the hamsters made use
of their paths, tunnels, and burrows, especially in
winter. *Phodopus* are quite clean. Undoubtedly their
feeding habits are somewhat similar to their close
relatives, for they eat seeds and any available plant
material. Observers report that these animals will fill
their pouches, seemingly almost to the bursting point,
with millet or grain seeds, distorting the shape of the
body. Then, when teased, disturbed, or in depositing
the food in their burrows, they will push the pouches
with their forepaws, thus causing the grain to pour
out of their mouths.

These animals are easy to tame, do well in captivity,
and make good pets with their interesting habits and
amusing ways. They have a docile disposition and do
not attempt to bite or to run away.

The type species of the genus is *P. bedfordiae*
(Thomas) = *P. roborovskii bedfordiae* as currently arranged.

Korean Gray Hamster (*Cricetulus triton*), photo by Ernest P. Walker.

RAT-LIKE HAMSTERS, GRAY LONG-TAILED HAMSTERS; TSANG-ERH, PAN-TS'ANG.

THIS GENUS of seven species occupies a combined range extending from southeastern Europe through Asia Minor to northern Asia (as far as southern Siberia). These animals frequent open, dry country, fields, and borders of deserts.

The length of the head and body varies widely, ranging from 80 to 200 mm., and the tail length is from 25 to 106 mm. (*C. triton* is the largest of the species). The fur is quite long (about 15 mm. in length on the middle of the back) and is usually mouse-gray in color. However, coloration is sometimes reddish or buffy. The under parts are light gray or white. The feet and terminal end of the tail are white. In some species there are other white markings, and in *C. barabensis* there is a dark brown dorsal stripe. These hamsters have robust bodies, blunt muzzles, fairly short legs and tails, and huge internal cheek pouches. The female has eight mammae.

Cricetulus is reported to be an extremely savage rodent; it makes a vigorous defense by throwing itself on its back and opening its mouth, exposing formidable incisor teeth. In the spring and summer, these hamsters are active both day and night, but as winter approaches, they become more nocturnal. In winter they do not hibernate continuously but awaken from time to time to eat the stored food. As the weather becomes colder, they sleep more heavily, and the intervals between feeding are longer. Their homes are burrows in the ground which they dig themselves; some species, at least, burrow almost straight down as far as 1.2 meters. Some burrows have a single entrance, but others have two or three. These burrows contain chambers which serve as areas for food storage, nesting, living quarters, and other domestic uses.

The diet consists of young shoots and seeds, and apparently the most preferred delicacies are soybeans, peas, and millet seeds. The cheek pouches are so large that it does not take long to store a bushel of beans in the burrow. One author reports that he took 42 soybean seeds from the cheek pouches of an individual, and in this case the head was so large that it comprised one-third of the body.

During the first part of March these rodents (*C. triton*, at least) come from their winter burrows; the males begin to seek females, entering almost all the burrows that they can find. The males stay about ten days with the females and this, the breeding season, continues until the middle of May. At this time the testes of the male become so large that they attain one-fifth the size of the body. Four to six (usually six) blind, hairless, helpless young are born from May to June. Occasionally there are two litters per year.

The Siberian yellow mink (*Mustela lutreola novikovi*) and the yellow ermine (*Mustela sibirica*) are the main predators of *Cricetulus*. Many are also killed by dogs, cats, foxes, and birds of prey. The poorer Chinese peasants in some regions make a living by digging up the grain stores of these little rodents.

The type species of the genus is *C. griseus*, Milne-Edwards.

Black-bellied Hamsters (*Cricetus cricetus*), photo by Ernest P. Walker.

COMMON OR BLACK-BELLED HAMSTERS.

THE SINGLE SPECIES, *C. cricetus*, occurs in Europe and parts of Russia eastward into Siberia. It may also occur in Asia Minor. The northern limit of its range, which appears to be about 60 degrees latitude, is in the U.S.S.R. The common hamster lives on steppes, plowed land, cultivated fields, and along riverbanks. In the western part of its range, it is strictly limited to loessal districts.

Head and body length is usually more than 200 mm.; maximum length is 280 mm. or more; weight is 112 to 908 grams. The tail is vestigal. The thick fur is usually light brown above, mostly black below, and white on the sides. Cheek pouches are present, and the feet are broad, usually with well-developed claws.

This rodent lives in burrows. The summer burrows are usually shorter and shallower than the winter homes and have less storage space for food. Each burrow has several oblique and vertical entrance tunnels, compartment (or compartments) for storing food, a nest, and a section for excrement. *Cricetus* hibernates during the winter and eats from its cache of food when it occasionally wakes up. About one burrow per two hectares was noted in the Kaluga district, U.S.S.R. The female has eight mammae.

The hamster may store up to 90 kgs. of cereal seeds, peas, or potatoes in its burrow. Its diet consists of grains, beans, lentils, roots, and green parts of plants as well as insect larvae and frogs. In captivity this animal does well on dog biscuit, lettuce, and corn.

Cricetus occasionally swims, inflating its cheek pouches with air for greater buoyancy before taking to the water.

The breeding season extends from spring to August; the number of litters is uncertain, probably two litters per year. In captivity females may have litters each month throughout the year. Gestation period is 16 to 20 days, and the number of young is 4 to 18, usually 6 to 12. Females are receptive to males when 43 days old and may bear young when 59 days old. The life span is about two years.

Cricetus often destroys crops and is trapped for its skin in some areas. It has been described by Petsch (*Zool. Anz.*, 1951, 147: 237–46 and *Zool. Anz.*, 1953, 161 :134–38) and by Eibl-Eibesfeldt (*Z. Tierpsychol.*, 1953, 10: 204–54).

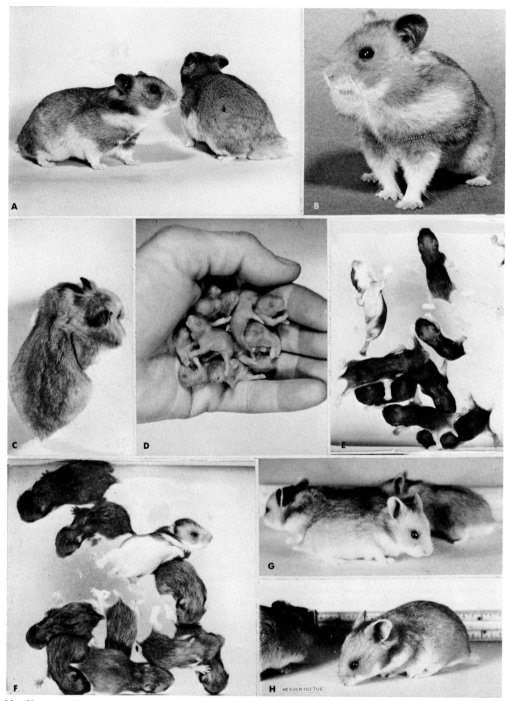

Golden Hamsters (*Mesocricetus auratus*), A. Adults; B. A hamster with its cheek pouches filled with food; C. Dorsal view showing distended cheek pouches; D. Two-day-old hamsters; E. Eight days old; F. Thirteen days old; G. Twenty-two days old; H. Twenty-nine days old; photos by Ernest P. Walker.

Golden Hamsters, Goudhamsters.

THE SINGLE SPECIES, *M. auratus*, occupies an area from Rumania and Bulgaria southeastward through Asia Minor, the Caucasus, Israel, and the northwestern section of Iran. In the wild these animals live on brushy slopes and steppes.

The length of the head and body is about 170 to 180 mm., and the length of the tail is about 12 mm.; a large male weighed 130 grams. Females are slightly larger than males. The general coloration above is light reddish brown, and beneath it is white or creamy; one form has a distinct ashy stripe across the breast. The skin of these animals is quite loose, and the enormous cheek pouches, which open inside the lips, extend well back of the shoulders. When filled they more than double the width of the animal's head and shoulders. There are 14 to 16 mammae. The greater number of nipples, the smaller size, and the short tail, together with some cranial characters, distinguish *Mesocricetus* from *Cricetus*, with which genus it is sometimes confused.

The golden hamster is essentially nocturnal in habit but may be active at times during the day. The animals generally live alone in extensive burrows of their own making and will fight others of their kind, although families often live together in harmony in close quarters. In captivity these animals soon become tame and, unlike most hamsters, can be handled easily. They have little or no body odor and are remarkably free from disease. In the wild they generally will defend themselves when frightened, but when assured that harm does not threaten, they become docile. They appear to be almost omnivorous, eating many kinds of green vegetation, seeds, fruit, and meat.

The usual number of offspring is 6 or 7 per litter, but litters of 4 to 15 individuals are not unusual. Litters have been born every month of the year, at least in captivity, with a marked decrease in fertility during the winter months. It is believed that copulation takes place during the night. Like most of their relatives, the young are born in a helpless state. They are weaned when about three weeks old, and they are capable of breeding when eight to ten weeks old. The life span appears to be two to three years.

Although originally described in 1839, little was known about them until 1930, when a female and 12 young were obtained in Syria and brought to Israel. It is from this stock that all the present domesticated strains have been developed. These hamsters were first brought to the United States in 1938. The progeny from the Syrian stock has thrived and their descendants are now widely scattered in laboratories, zoos, and homes throughout Europe and the United States.

White-tailed Rat (*Mystromys albicaudatus*), photo by H. J. Bohner, National Institutes of Health.

WHITE-TAILED RATS; WITSTERTROTTE.

THE SINGLE SPECIES, *M. albicaudatus*, inhabits the grassy flats and dry sandy regions of southern Africa from the Molop and Limpopo rivers southward.

The length of the head and body is 136 to 184 mm., and the length of the tail is 50 to 82 mm. Their soft, long, rather woolly pelage is buffy grayish to brownish above, suffused with numerous black-tipped hairs which become fewer on the sides, finally blending into the white under parts. The bases of the hairs on the upper surface are slate gray, whereas the hairs on the lower surface are all white. The sides of the face and the limbs are lighter than the back; the hands, feet, and tail are dull white; and the ears are dark brown. The tail is covered with short, stiff bristles. Members of this genus are thick-bodied, rat-like animals with large, broad ears and slender limbs, hands, and feet. The incisors are ungrooved and pale yellow. Short, slightly curved, and sharp-tipped claws are almost concealed by the long white hairs of the feet. Unlike some of their relatives, these animals do not possess cheek pouches. There are two pairs of inguinal mammae.

White-tailed rats live in holes in the ground. One author observed them using the burrows of the carnivore *Suricata*; they also shelter in cracks in the soil. They are nocturnal in habit and are said to be particularly active and bold during rainy weather. It is reported that if individual rats are evident in a given area, some can be caught at night by placing a lighted lantern on the ground which draws the animals to its light. It is believed that these rodents secrete some protective substance which repels carnivores since *Mystromys* do not appear to be preyed upon by carnivorous animals. At sunset these rodents emerge from seclusion to feed upon seeds and other vegetable matter.

They apparently breed throughout the year, the litters usually contain four or five individuals, and the gestation period is about 37 days.

It is reported that white-tailed rats breed well in captivity and are tame and playful.

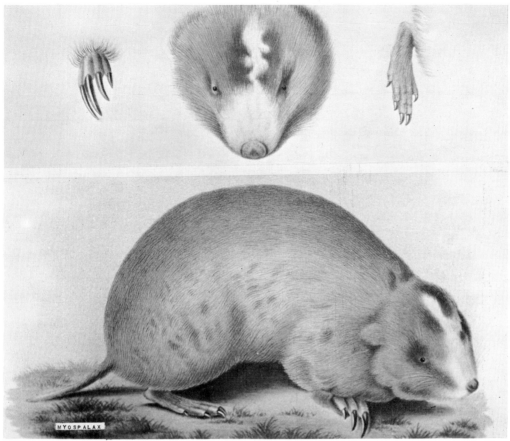

Mole-rat or Zokor (*Myospalax aspalax*), photos from *Recherches pour servir à l'Histoire Naturelle des Mammifères,* M. H. Milne-Edwards and M. Alphonse Milne-Edwards.

MOLE-RATS, RODENT-MOLES; ZOKORS; HA-WHEI; HA-LAO; HSIA-LAO, TI-PAI (local vernaculars).

FIVE SPECIES make up this genus. These species have a combined range extending from central Russia through northern China, Mongolia, Manchuria, and eastern Siberia. Wooded areas, especially valleys between mountains from 900 to 2,120 meters elevation, are frequented. Some authorities recognize a subgenus *Eospalax*, G. Allen, 1938, in this genus.

The length of the head and body is 155 to 270 mm., and the length of the tail is 29 to 69 mm. The pelage is composed of long, soft, silky hairs, lacking coarse guard hairs; there are a few short whiskers. The coloration of the upper parts varies with the species from gray, grayish brown, or light russet to pinkish buff. Usually the individual hairs are bicolored, the tips being lighter than the bases. The lower parts are generally lighter than those above. In some species the tail is grayish above and white below. *M. fontanierii* has an all white tail and a white patch on the upper lip and muzzle.

The mole-rat is a stout chunky animal with short, powerful limbs; the fore feet are armed with long heavy claws for digging. These front claws are doubled under when the animal is walking. The middle or third claw is the largest and heaviest; on the hind feet the claws are much shorter. There are no external ears, and the eyes are so small that they are nearly hidden in the fur. There are three pairs of mammae, two abdominal and one pectoral pair.

These subterranean rodents inhabit burrows, some of which are 40 meters in length, dug among the roots of trees and bushes. These animals can dig with amazing speed, kicking away the loose earth with the hind feet after every three or four scrapes with the powerful foreclaws. Every 3 to 6 meters along the tunnel a pile of earth is thrown out. These animals seldom venture above the ground, although they must seek food occasionally at night, for their remains have been found in owl pellets. When frightened or angered, mole-rats utter a peculiar little squeal. Even though their eyes are small, they are sensitive to light and, if brought to the surface, they always seek a darkened place. Their diet consists of roots and grain.

The Chinese peasants believe that they can forecast the weather by observing the opening of a burrow. When the burrow is left open, fair weather may be expected, but when the opening is closed, unpleasant weather is in store.

The type species of the genus is *M. myospalax* (Laxmann).

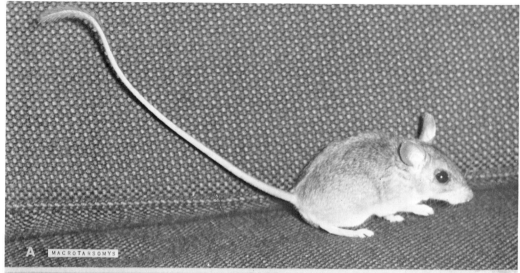

(*Macrotarsomys ingens*), A. Photo by F. Petter. B. Photo by Howard E. Uible.

Two species, *M. bastardi* and *M. ingens*, have been described from Madagascar. The former species inhabits forests, scrubby growth, and grassy plains.

The following account applies only to *M. bastardi*: Head and body length is 80 to 100 mm., and tail length is 100 to 145 mm. Thus this animal is the smallest of Madagascar mice. The only other species from Madagascar sometimes under 100 mm. in head and body length is *Eliurus minor*. The back of *M. bastardi* is brownish, and the belly is covered with white, woolly hair. The tail has a dark terminal tuft.

The body form of *Macrotarsomys* is like that of the Gerbillinae. The ear is large (20 to 25 mm. long in *M. bastardi*), the hind foot is long (22 to 28 mm. in *M. bastardi*), and the tail is elongated. The three central toes are longer than the first and fifth digits, and the fifth toe is longer than the reduced first toe. The first toe bears a claw that is located fairly low on the foot. The inflation of the bullae gives the skull a unique appearance among the genera of mice from Madagascar.

Field notes indicate the following information for *M. bastardi*: The burrow, which may be 1.5 meters or more in length, is often located under a rock or a small bush. One individual was found in an abandoned termite nest. At certain times of the year this species lives alone, but at other times four or more adults may occupy the same burrow. The plugging of the burrow holes may be related, at least in part, to the large number of snakes in the area, as the burrows seem to be filled more often in regions where snakes are plentiful than in places where reptiles are less common. The diet of this rodent consists of berries, fruits, seeds, roots, and plant stems.

The number of young in a litter is usually two or three. *M. bastardi* has breeding colonies.

The type species of the genus is *M. bastardi*, Milne-Edwards and Grandidier.

Nesomys rufus), photo by Constance P. Warner.

THE THREE SPECIES, *N. rufus*, *N. lambertoni*, and *N. audeberti*, are native to the forests of eastern and northeastern Madagascar.

The length of the head and body is 186 to 230 mm., and the length of the tail is 160 to 190 mm. The pelage is fairly long, soft, smooth, and shiny. The fine-textured black whiskers on the muzzle extend beyond the tips of the blackish brown ears. The coloration of the upper parts is dark rust-brown mixed with brownish yellow which gives the animal a fawn color. The basal part of the hairs are usually slate-colored. The sides of the head, body, and limbs are reddish, whereas the lips, throat, breast, middle of the belly, and underside of the tail are white. The upper part of the tail is rust-red. A white tuft occurs on the end of the tail in *N. audeberti*.

The general appearance of these animals is similar to that of *Mus*, but a split upper lip is the distinctive feature of *Nesomys*. The incisors are smooth and whitish toward the points; the upper teeth are brownish orange and the lower ones are yellowish. The long, well-developed feet help these animals to leap about freely. The three middle toes are elongated (particularly the center one), whereas the outer ones are much shorter. The claws of the fingers are slightly more than half as big as those of the toes, the latter being very strong. The almost straight, brownish-white claws are partially concealed by long rigid hairs growing from the root of the nails.

The habits' of *Nesomys* apparently have not been recorded in the literature.

The type species of the genus is *N. rufus*, Peters.

(*Brachytarsomys albicauda*), photo by F. Petter.

THE SINGLE SPECIES, *B. albicauda*, is native to the island of Madagascar.

The length of the head and body is from 210 to 250 mm., and the length of the tail is about 185 mm. The soft, dense, woolly pelage is grayish brown on the upper parts, rufous on the sides, and white on the under parts. The head is reddish brown and the nose and lips are blackish. The anterior half of the sparsely haired tail is black, but the posterior half is white.

The appearance of this genus is similar to that of *Nesomys*, but *Brachytarsomys* differs from *Nesomys* in having shorter legs and a different cranial structure. These animals have a short snout, small eyes and ears, five rows of moustache hairs, prominent claws, and the hind foot has a long fifth digit. The incisors are not grooved.

This animal does not burrow but usually seeks shelter in holes in the bases of trees.

FIVE SPECIES, *E. myoxinus, E. majori, E. tanala, E. penicillatus,* and *E. minor,* are native to Madagascar, apparently preferring the heavy forested areas to scrub forests or stream banks.

The length of the head and body is 95 to 160 mm., and the length of the tail is 125 to 189 mm. The species of *Eliurus* are known to weigh from 35 to 103 grams. These animals have a fairly soft pelage, the upper parts being uniformly brownish gray or yellowish gray; the latter effect is caused by gray bases and fawn tips of the individual hairs. The feet and lower surfaces are generally light gray. In *E. myoxinus,* the tail is so well clothed with long, moderately stiff, deep-brown hair that it looks almost bushy. In other species the basal third is almost naked, and the rest of the tail is slightly bushy or penciled. The pencil on the tail of *E. tanala* and *E. penicillatus* is white. *E. tanala* has a dark gray spot in the middle of the back and yellowish-white under parts. In *E. majori* there is an indistinct ring around the eyes. The ears are dark and almost naked, the palms are pink, the moustache is black with long whiskers, and the eyes are large and conspicuous. The female has two pairs of inguinal mammae. A female was observed nursing in early November.

Trappers report that *Eliurus* is generally arboreal, but in the eastern section of the island the animals make their burrows in the ground (except *E. minor*). A recent field observation showed that a species of *Eliurus* of the central plateau was found in runways in dense, matted grass and reeds in a large, moist meadow; the *Eliurus* were trapped in association with *Microgale, Brachyuromys,* and *Rattus.*

Although these animals are plentiful at some locations, the details of their ranges and life habits have not been published. One author casually compared *Eliurus* with the dormouse (*Muscardinus*) and another with *Platacanthomys* of India.

Two specimens recently taken were both from stream banks.

The type species of the genus is *E. myoxinus,* Milne-Edwards.

(*Eliurus minor*), photo by Howard E. Uible. Insets: (*E. majori*), photos by P. F. Wright of specimen in U.S. National Museum.

VOALAVOANALA (native name).

THE SINGLE SPECIES, *G. roberti*, inhabits the island of Madagascar.

The length of the head and body is 125 to 160 mm., and the length of the tail is 152 to 175 mm. The upper parts are blackish gray or slaty, and the under parts are white or yellowish white. Long whiskers (from 50 to 60 mm.) are present, and the bicolored, scaly tail is scantily haired. The body form is rat-like, and the white feet are quite broad with fairly long fifth digits. This genus is best characterized by the pattern of the cheek teeth, which are completely flat-crowned, laminate, and tightly compressed.

The habits and biology of this endemic Madagascan rodent are little known. Pregnant females have been collected in June and July, each bearing two embryos.

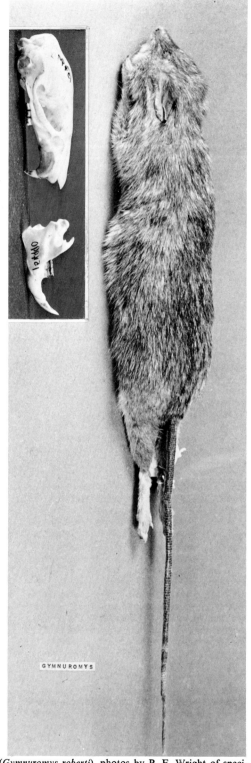

(*Gymnuromys roberti*), photos by P. F. Wright of specimen in U.S. National Museum.

Votsotsa (*Hypogeomys antimena*), photo by F. Petter.

VOALAVO VOUTSOUTSE, VOTSOTSA (native names).

THE SINGLE SPECIES, *H. antimena*, lives in the thickest virgin forests of Madagascar. Many forests have been cut and burned and are now mainly in second growth so that this rodent is quite local in distribution (and may have been greatly reduced).

The length of the head and body is 300 to 350 mm., and the length of the tail is 210 to 250 mm. The ears are large (50 to 60 mm.). The pelage is harsh. The upper parts are gray, grayish brown, or reddish, the head is darkest, and the limbs, hands, feet, and under parts are white. The dark tail is covered with stiff, short hairs. The hind foot is quite long with well-developed claws.

This large rodent builds long, deep burrows, much like those of the rabbits. It feeds mainly on fallen fruit. It appears that these animals are the ecological equivalents of rabbits in Madagascar. One offspring seems to be the usual number produced.

827

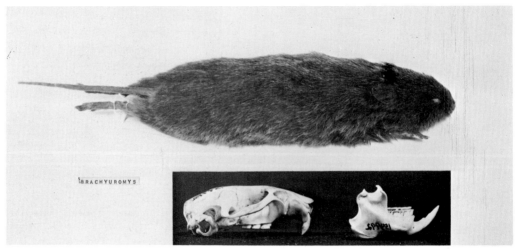

Ramirohitra (*Brachyuromys ramirohitra*), photos by P. F. Wright of skin and skull in U.S. National Museum.

VOLANE ANDRIVO (*B. betsileoensis*), VOALAVOA-NALA OR RAMIROHITRA (*B. ramirohitra*) (native names).

THE TWO SPECIES, *B. betsileoensis* and *B. ramiro-hitra*, inhabit the island of Madagascar. They are not rare in the central plateau. Head and body length is 145 to 180 mm.; tail length is 60 to 105 mm.; and weight is from 85 to 105 grams. The upper parts are brown mixed with red and black, and the under parts are reddish. The fur is thick and soft; the individual hairs have gray bases and brown apexes. The external form is somewhat vole-like. The tail is short, dark, and somewhat hairy. The skull is broad and massive, and the head is broad and rounded. The ears are well haired and the palms are dark. Females have three pairs of mammae.

Habits and biology of these endemic Madagascan rodents have apparently not been recorded in much detail. However, *Brachyuromys* has recently been trapped in a large, moist meadow on the central plateau. The mice were living in dense, matted grass and reeds, in association with *Microgale*, *Eliurus*, and *Rattus*. The grass and reed stems were so matted down and densely tangled that no sunlight reached the runways where the mice were traveling. They were active at all hours, during both the night and day.

The type species of the genus is *B. ramirohitra*, Forsyth-Major.

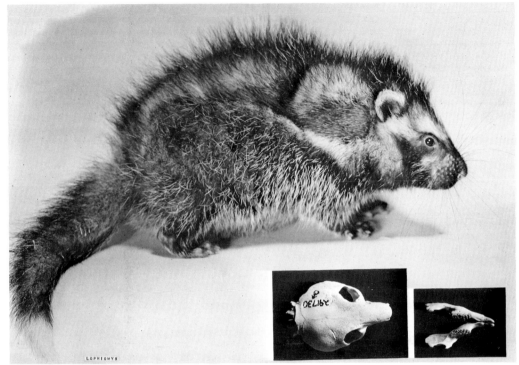

Maned or Crested Rat (*Lophiomys imhausi*), photo by Ernest P. Walker. Insets: Photos by P. F. Wright of specimen in U.S. National Museum.

MANED RATS, CRESTED RATS; YAIDADOS.

A SINGLE SPECIES, *L. imhausi*, inhabits eastern Africa from the Kassala district of the Sudan to Somalia, Kenya, and Ethiopia. *Lophiomys* frequents thick forests above 1,210 meters elevation.

The length of the head and body is 255 to 360 mm., and the length of the tail is 140 to 175 mm.; in most instances the female is the larger of the two. The coloration is usually either black and white or brown and white, in a fairly definite pattern of stripes and spots or blotches. The variation is caused mainly by the intensity or purity of the coloration and by the relative size of the differently colored areas; variation in color is also affected by the differing extent of the light and dark parts of those hairs that are banded or tipped with light or dark pigmentation.

The most common coloration gives an iron-gray effect, but the color ranges from a general overall grayish tone (occasioned by a preponderance of white, gray, or white hair on tips of the hairs) to almost dark brown or black (brought about by predominance of hairs largely or entirely black).

In all forms there is a prominent erectile mane from the top of the head, along the back, and along a quarter of the tail (the tip of the tail is white). On either side of the mane, along the back, the hair is shorter and lighter colored than the surrounding hair, giving the effect of a furrow in the fur and emphasizing the mane. In some animals the mane is scarcely apparent on the head and is reduced on the tail. The fur is generally dense, long, and fine to silky, except along the mane where it is coarse. The under parts are gray to black, and the hands and feet are jet black.

The tail is densely bushy. The great toe is partially opposable, and the hands have four well-developed digits and are specialized for arboreal life. The ear is small. The skull is unique among rodents in that the temporal fossae are completely roofed by bone. The surfaces of these and some of the other bones of the skull are granulated. The incisors are moderately broad.

These rodents do not resemble a rat, as the head is similar to that of a guinea pig, and the body (when viewed from a distance) looks like that of the small porcupine (*Erethizon*). When the animal becomes excited or frightened, its crest erects, and it exposes a glandular area along its flanks. This trait may be a protective measure to frighten its enemies into mistaking the maned rat for a porcupine. The voice of these rats is peculiar: one or two hisses or snorts, followed by a growl. These arboreal rats are quite adept in climbing, even descending headfirst, but they move slowly. These strictly nocturnal animals leave their burrows or holes among the rocks at dusk to search for food which consists of leaves and tender shoots. *Lophiomys*, when eating, grasps its food in its hands while sitting on its haunches.

Several of these animals have been successfully kept in captivity where they like meat, bread, and corn but prefer vegetables.

Collared Lemming (*Dicrostonyx hudsonius*); Inset: Left foreclaws, photos by Ernest P. Walker.

COLLARED LEMMINGS, ARCTIC LEMMINGS, VARY-
ING LEMMINGS, HOOFED LEMMINGS.

THE FIVE SPECIES in this genus have a combined
range covering most of the Arctic regions of Canada,
Russia, and Siberia. They are found from Alaska to
Labrador, including the northern coast of Greenland,
and from the east coast of the White Sea eastward to
the Anadyr region and Novaya Zemlya. Adjacent
islands are also included within their range. Dry,
sandy, and gravelly areas with some plant cover, but
above the timber line, are frequented.

The length of the head and body is 125 to 150 mm.,
and the length of the tail is 10 to 20 mm. In summer
the general coloration above varies from light grayish
tuft to dark gray, strongly tinged with buffy to reddish
brown. Some *Dicrostonyx* are colored a deep, rich
buff and others are merely grayish tinged with reddish
brown. The under parts are whitish, grayish, or
buffy. There are definite dark lines or stripings from
the top of the head along the middle of the back and
on the sides of the head. In winter all species are entirely white. They are the only true rodents that turn
white in winter. They are short, stockily built creatures whose third and fourth claws on the fore feet
are unusually large and well adapted to digging. In
summer the claws are about normal as to type, but
with the approach of winter, the claws develop a
peculiar double effect in a vertical plane which makes
them very strong and well suited for burrowing in the
frozen earth or in snow and ice. Both winter and
summer coats are thick and heavy. The ears are so

small that they are little more than rims, completely
hidden in the fur. These animals are closely related
to the true lemmings (*Lemmus*) and the meadow
mice (*Microtus*). *Dicrostonyx* makes extensive burrows through the soil, under and around stones,
and builds shallow runways on the surface, although
these paths are not so pronounced or well defined
as those of *Microtus*. Collared lemmings feed
mainly on plant materials, although it is possible
that they consume insects and meat when available.

Three to four young, born early in the summer in
underground nest chambers lined with grass and moss,
appear to constitute the usual litter. Adults have at
least two litters during the warm months. The gestation period is about 20 to 22 days. The collared
lemmings rarely make the large migrations for which
the common lemmings are noted in both the Old and
the New World. *Dicrostonyx* may become so plentiful at times, however, that these lemmings are forced
to make short migrations to new locations in search
for food. They swim readily and, when in migration,
cross streams and behave much like common lemmings. Their numbers are held in check because they
are preyed upon by hosts of creatures, die of disease,
or starve during the winter. The remarkable development of their third and fourth claws in winter distinguishes them from all other similar small rodents.

The beautiful white winter coats are used by the
Eskimo for garment trimming, and the Eskimo
children use the little skins to make doll clothes.

The type species of the genus is *D. hudsonius*
(Pallas).

Bog Lemmings (*Synaptomys cooperi*), A. Photo by Paul F. Connor. B. Photo by B. Elizabeth Horner and Mary Taylor of specimen in Harvard Museum of Comparative Zoology.

LEMMING MICE, BOG MICE, BOG LEMMINGS.

TWO SPECIES comprise this genus: *S. cooperi* inhabits eastern North America from New Brunswick southward to North Carolina and westward to Kansas; and *S. borealis* is native to an area from Newfoundland westward to the Pacific Ocean and north to the northern coast of Alaska. These animals seem to occupy small, local isolated areas; their spotty occurrence makes a general map of their ranges appear misleading. In the southern part of their range, they are strictly limited to the scattered cold bog and cold spring areas. Further north they have a more general distribution, living usually in moist areas, although in the humid Pacific Northwest, they have been found near rocky cliffs.

The length of the head and body is 100 to 130 mm.; the length of the tail is 16 to 27 mm.; and the weight is 21 to 50 grams. The general coloration above is a grizzled grayish cinnamon-brown, composed of a mixture of gray, yellowish brown, and black in varying degrees. The under parts are soiled whitish over the slate-colored bases of the hairs. The tail is brownish above and whitish below. The body form is thickset, with long, loose, and coarse pelage; the incisors are orange, the upper incisors having a shallow longi-tudinal groove at the outer edge; and the nail of the first finger is flat and strap-shaped. There are three or four pairs of mammae.

Lemming mice do not hibernate and are active at any hour of the day or night. They make surface runways and subsurface tunnels as do voles, although they occasionally occupy the tunnels and use the runways made by other small mammals. Their powerful jaws are probably an indication that they gnaw through tangles of roots, moss, and soil. It is believed that each sex makes its presence known by secretions from glands in the groin. The voice has been described as a sharp, short, squeak. Apparently lemming mice feed almost entirely on plant tissues, mainly green parts of low vegetation, and probably slugs, snails, and other invertebrates.

The breeding season extends from March to October, and from one to seven young apparently constitute a litter, although the average is three. They begin breeding before they are full grown.

Enemies of *Synaptomys* are snakes, hawks, owls, weasels, foxes, and other carnivorous creatures. Populations fluctuate greatly, from plentiful one year to almost non-existent another.

The type species of the genus is *S. cooperi*, Baird.

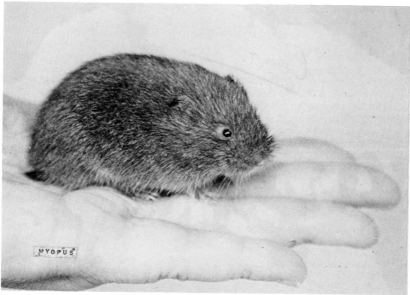

Wood Lemming (*Myopus schisticolor*), photo by Erna Mohr.

WOOD LEMMINGS, RED-BACKED LEMMINGS, GRAY LEMMINGS.

A SINGLE SPECIES, *M. schisticolor*, inhabits a range extending from Norway eastward through Sweden, across northern Russia and northern Mongolia, to Siberia. These animals live in mossy bogs and coniferous forests at 600 to 2,450 meters elevation.

The length of the head and body is 75 to 110 mm., and the length of the tail is 14 to 18 mm. The pelage is soft, dense, and slaty black above, with a definite reddish-brown area on the center of the back extending from the shoulders to within about 15 mm. of the base of the tail. The remainder of the coat is uniformly a dark slaty gray, slightly paler on the ventral surface; the upper surface has a peculiar metallic luster that is produced by silvery tips on the shorter hairs, with an indistinct showing of black guard hairs. The feet and tail are black, but the hairs on the undersurface of the tail have a silvery luster. The palms are naked; the tail is heavily furred. The hind feet are densely haired behind the pads but are naked in front of the pads, similar to the palms of the fore feet. The coloration beneath is similar but lacks the reddish-brown stripe along the back. These small, thick-set rodents have ears that are small but well developed, rounded and well haired, within and without, projecting little beyond the fur. The ear has a valve which can regulate the size of the ear opening. The thumb of the hand is small but bears a large, flattened nail with parallel sides and notch at the end, somewhat resembling the thumbnail of *Lemmus*, but smaller. There are eight mammae. There is no material difference in the coloration of the sexes, nor is there much seasonal variation in color. The winter coat is slightly longer than the summer pelage.

The animals are rare and practically nothing is known about them. They live in the dark recesses of the fir forests and are so scarce that they are usually taken only by accident or in years when the rodent population becomes unusually numerous. Its runways have been found in moss, under the roots of trees, and beneath fallen trunks; *Myopus* is known to eat certain mosses (*Dicranum*), stems of red wortleberry, and the bark of juniper.

Wood lemmings make migrations and their relative numbers fluctuate. Not less than two litters are reared each summer.

Point Barrow Brown Lemming (*Lemmus trimucronatus*), photo by Ernest P. Walker.

TRUE LEMMINGS.

THE FOUR SPECIES comprising this genus are distributed as follows: *L. trimucronatus* (brown lemming), Baffin Island westward across northern Canada to the west coast of Alaska; *L. nigripes* (black-footed lemming), St. George Island off the coast of Alaska; *L. sibiricus* (Siberian lemming), Arctic U.S.S.R. from the White Sea to Siberia, including islands in the Arctic Ocean; and *L. lemmus* (Norway lemming), Norway, Sweden, Finland, Kola Peninsula, and northwestern Russia. These animals inhabit tundra areas where the principal vegetation is sedges and grasses.

The length of the head and body is 100 to 135 mm.; the length of the tail is 18 to 26 mm.; and the weight is 40 to 112 grams. Throughout the year their coloration remains about the same. Above, it is grayish or brownish, with a heavy tinge of buffy and dark brown in some species. Beneath, the animals are light gray, buffy, or brownish. In *L. nigripes* the feet are black throughout the year. They are heavily furred, stockily built, and well adapted to the rigorous conditions of their environment. True lemmings have short tails and ears so small that they are almost concealed by fur. A claw on the thumb, which is most conspicuous in winter, is long and flat. They are active both night and day throughout the year, burrowing through the soil, where they make nests of grass, moss, and lichens.

The migrations of lemmings are one of the amazing wonders of the animal kingdom. The Norway lemming is the one whose journeys are best known, although other lemmings occasionally make similar migrations. When food is plentiful, their numbers increase enormously, but when the available supply is gone vast hordes of lemmings swarm from their native haunts to seek food in new territories. They travel through swamps, cities, lakes, rivers, and forests—stopping for no obstacle and proceeding in one direction. Many of the lemmings eventually reach the sea which, to them, is another obstacle to conquer. They plunge in and swim on until they are exhausted and finally drown. Populations preceding these remarkable migrations build up every three or four years. All lemmings feed on vegetable matter—sedges, grasses, bark, leaves, berries, lichens, and roots.

Breeding apparently begins before the animals are full grown; the period continues from spring to fall, for several litters are produced annually. After a 20 to 22-day gestation period, 3 to 9 young are born in a spherical nest of shredded plant fibers, moss, and lichens, located under a rock or in a burrow.

Lemmings compete for food with the caribou and reindeer. When these rodents are so numerous that they eat most of the food supply, the caribou and reindeer starve and their population decreases. This shortage of meat, in turn, endangers the lives of those in the North who depend upon the caribou and reindeer as their principal source of food.

Lemmings are the victims of carnivores and birds of prey.

The type species of the genus is *L. lemmus* (Linnaeus).

Korean Red-backed Mouse (*Clethrionomys rufocanus*), photo by Ernest P. Walker.

RED-BACKED MICE, BANK VOLES; CAMPAGNOLES; WÜHLMÄUSE; ROSSE WOELMUIZEN.

THE FIVE SPECIES of this genus are distributed as follows: *C. gapperi*, from Canada and the northern United States southward along the highlands of the Appalachian and Rocky Mountains; *C. occidentalis*, along the Pacific coast from British Columbia to northern California; *C. rutilus*, Alaska, Yukon, Mackenzie, and Keewatin in Canada, and also Japan and Siberia to Norway; *C. glareolus*, from Great Britain through Europe, Asia, Asia Minor, to Japan. *C. rufocanus* lives in the boreal part of this area. These widely distributed rodents inhabit cold, mossy, rocky forests and woodlands in both dry and moist areas. They also inhabit tundra and bogs.

The length of the head and body is 70 to 112 mm.; the length of the tail is 25 to 60 mm.; and the weight is about 15 to 40 grams. The fur is dense, long, and soft in winter but shorter and harsher in summer. The general coloration above is dark lead-gray with a pronounced reddish wash, becoming less prominent on the sides which are grayish. The under parts are dark slate-gray to almost white. The tail has a slight terminal pencil of hairs. The short thumb is provided with a flat nail; the ears are slightly more conspicuous through the fur in *Clethrionomys* than in *Microtus*, and the eyes are also more prominent. There are eight mammae.

These rodents are active night and day, summer and winter, scurrying and climbing about stumps, fallen logs, and rough-barked trees. Usually their individual range is small, but its extent is affected by the amount of available food. Populations run in cycles; approximately every fourth year the mice become extremely abundant. When disturbed, they may utter a chirp-like bark that can be heard from 1 to 2 meters, and they flee or freeze in position depending upon their location and preceding activity. They also gnash or chatter their teeth. One observer noted that red-backed mice do a minimum of burrowing, preferring to nest along decayed logs, stumps, rock ledges, and even occasionally in a crevice high in a tree. These mice appear to be much more social than *Microtus*. The food of these colorful little mice consists of tender vegetation, nuts, seeds, bark, lichens, fungus, and insects. Food is often stored in the nest for use when the supply is short.

These animals breed during the season in which they are born, although breeding usually begins in the late winter and continues until late fall. One to eight young, usually four to six (a litter of 11 was born to a female Swedish *C. rufocanus*) are born in a nest of shredded vegetation after a gestation period of 17 to 20 days.

Red-back mice occasionally damage trees by girdling them, especially in winter. Although they are consumed by carnivores and birds of prey, they seem to be abundant throughout most of their range. They destroy quantities of insect larvae and are also important as food for fur-bearing animals.

The type species of the genus is *C. rutilus* (Pallas). *Evotomys*, *Aschizomys*, and *Craseomys* are synonyms of *Clethrionomys*.

Père David's Vole (*Eothenomys melanogaster*), photo from *Recherches pour servir à l'Histoire Naturelle des Mammifères*, M. H. Milne-Edwards and M. Alphonse Milne-Edwards.

PÈRE DAVID'S VOLES, PRATT'S VOLES, DAWN MEADOW MICE.

THIS GENUS of about six species inhabits Japan, Taiwan (Formosa), China, northern Indo-China, northern Burma, and northern Assam. These animals frequent banks and slopes that can be easily tunneled, both in wooded growth and mountain meadows. Their elevational range is from about 1,800 to at least 4,400 meters.

The length of the head and body is 90 to 126 mm., and the length of the tail is 30 to 55 mm. Coloration above is usually dark reddish brown with a peculiar metallic reflection due to the burnished tips of a portion of the longer hairs. Some writers refer to this coloration as a brassy shine. The under parts are bluish gray. The young are blackish. The pelage is fairly short and smooth. The soles of the feet are hairy behind the pads, and the tail is covered with stiff hairs that form a short, thin terminal pencil. Females have four mammae. *Eothenomys* is perhaps intermediate between *Clethrionomys* and *Microtus*, as it possesses some characteristics common to both genera.

These voles tend to be active both day and night. Some forms seem to spend more time underground than others. Burrows open to the surface at frequent intervals, and numerous surface runways may be evident. They also use the surface runways of other animals, such as those of moles. Their habits are presumably similar to those of *Clethrionomys* and *Microtus*.

Apparently they breed throughout the year, or nearly so, as embryos have been found from the months of February to October, the number ranging from one to three.

The type species of the genus is *E. melanogaster* (Milne-Edwards). *Anteliomys*, Miller, 1906, is considered a separate genus by many mammalogists, for the species *A. chinensis* and *A. custos*. Others, however, place these forms as species of *Eothenomys*, with *Anteliomys* as a synonym.

High Mountain Vole (*Alticola* sp. ?), photo by Howard E. Uible of mounted specimen in U.S. National Museum.

HIGH MOUNTAIN VOLES.

THIS GENUS OF five presently recognized species, *A. roylei*, *A. macrotis*, *A. stoliczkanus*, *A. strelzowi*, and *A. bhatnagari*, inhabits mountainous and rocky areas of central and eastern Asia. High mountain voles occur in Afghanistan, Kashmir, Nepal, and India south to Kumaon, Tibet, Russian Turkestan, Chinese Turkestan, Mongolia, Siberia, and possibly Kansu, China for *A. stoliczkanus*. The elevational range is about 900 meters to at least 5,700 meters.

The length of the head and body is about 80 to 140 mm., and the length of the tail is less than half the length of the head and body (15 to 40 mm.) Ten specimens, with an average length of 108 mm., weighed from 35 to 49 grams. The coloration above is usually some shade of gray or brown; the gray is mixed with ash, silver, buff, or yellow, and the browns, when present, with grays or reds. The under parts are usually white or buffy white. The feet are generally white or grayish white, and the well-haired tail in most forms is white or buffy white throughout. The soles are usually haired posteriorly. The fur is thick, soft, and long; it is possible that the winter coat is longer and lighter in color than the summer coat.

The external form is not modified for burrowing. The eyes are moderately large, and the ears are of moderate size, although they are often concealed in the long fur. The flattened skull in *A. strelzowi* is probably an adaptation for living under rocks. High mountain voles have eight mammae.

Alticola seems to be the Asian equivalent of the snow vole, *Microtus nivalis*, of Europe, which has a white tail and lives at high elevations in the mountains. *A. strelzowi* usually lives in colonies. It is mainly diurnal, whereas *A. roylei*, an inhabitant of Mongolia, is partly diurnal but mainly nocturnal.

Most, if not all, forms store food for the winter. The stems and leaves of herbaceous plants and shrubs may be dried first in the sun and are then piled into heaps or stuffed into stone crevices. *A. roylei* deposits its banana-shaped droppings at the entrance to the burrow, a definite sign of its presence. This form is fearless, sometimes coming within 4 cm. of a person's hand.

There are apparently 2 to 3 litters a year, with 5 to 11 (usually 5 to 8) young in each litter.

The type species of the genus is *A. stoliczkanus*, Blanford.

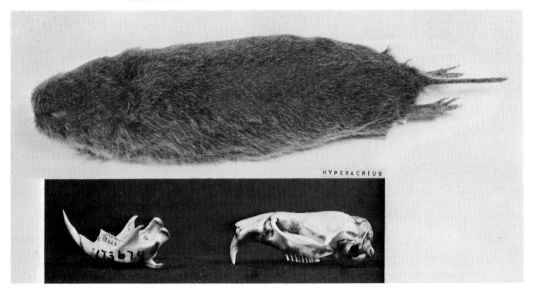

True's Vole (*Hyperacrius fertilis brachelix*), photos by P. F. Wright of specimen in U.S. National Museum.

KASHMIR AND PUNJAB VOLES.

THE COMBINED RANGE of *H. fertilis* (True's vole) and *H. wynnei* (Murree vole) is limited to the mountains of Kashmir and Punjab in northern India from 2,100 to 3,500 meters in elevation. These animals prefer grassy areas in pine forests, but often occur well above timber line.

The length of the head and body is 95 to 116 mm., and the length of the tail is 18 to 45 mm. The pelage is shorter and more dense than that of *Alticola*. Coloration of *H. fertilis* is deep reddish brown on the upper parts which gradually becomes dull ochraceous below. The feet are dusky; the tail is slightly bi-colored, sepia above and dirty white below. *H. waynnei* occurs in two distinct colorations, apparently color phases. In the light phase, the upper parts are yellowish brown, and the under parts are grayish tinged with wood-brown. The feet and hands are grayish brown on the upper surface. The tail is slightly bicolored, dark grayish brown above and paler gray below. In the dark phase, the upper parts vary from a lustrous seal-brown to a glossy blackish brown. The under parts are duller and somewhat paler than those above and are lightened by short whitish or yellowish-tipped hairs of the ventral surface. The hands and feet are dark gray above; the tail is dusky gray and only slightly bicolored. The whiskers are short, scarcely reaching to the ears, and the feet are well haired.

The general appearance of members of this genus is similar to that of *Pitymys* and *Alticola*, the principal means of differentiation are in cranial and dental structure. The well-developed claws on all four limbs are long and slender; the pollex is provided with a flattened, fairly large nail. Four inguinal mammae are present.

Kashmir and Punjab voles are definitely burrowing animals; Robert Traub informs us that he never trapped any on the surface of the ground. The dark phase of *H. waynnei* is unusual among animals of this type, and it is thought that it may be a natural result of retaining the darker coat of the immature form, owing to the fact that the animal has adopted a subterranean life away from light. One observer, Major H. H. Dunn, who has noted the animals in the wild, states that these voles are mole-like in their habits.

The type species of the genus is *H. fertilis* (True).

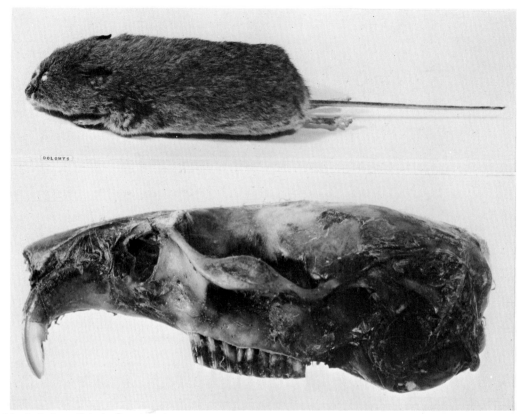

Martino's Snow Vole (*Dolomys bogdanovi marakovici*), photos from British Museum (Natural History).

MARTINO'S SNOW VOLES.

THE SINGLE LIVING SPECIES, *D. bogdanovi*, exists in Yugoslavia. The known elevational range is about 680 to 2,100 meters. Several fossil forms have been named and described from Europe. This genus is one of the few based upon fossils analyzed before living specimens had been studied by zoologists. *Dolomys* was described in 1898 on the basis of a fossil species of cricetid rodent from Hungary; it was not recognized as a living genus until 1925.

The length of the head and body is about 130 to 140 mm., and the length of the tail is about 50 to 90 mm. The tail is usually more than half the length of the head and body. The fur is dense, soft, and moderately long. The upper parts are grayish brown, buffy grayish, or bluish gray, and the under parts are usually paler, often grayish white. The feet are white, and the tail is usually dark brown above and white on the sides and below. The thinly-haired tail has a short, stiff, thin pencil line about 5 to 6 mm. in length. The palms and soles are naked except near the heels. The large ears are densely haired.

The small thumb bears a small, flattened nail. The other digits have short, sharp claws about equally long on the hands and feet. Noticeable skull characteristics are the broad and faintly-grooved upper incisors and the large, inflated bullae, although the mastoids are comparatively small.

These rodents are active at night throughout the year. They find shelter and build nests under rocks and isolated stones on Mt. Trebevic (south of Sarajevo). Thawing snows and spring rains force them to settle on drier ground.

Dolomys feeds on grasses and stores food for the winter.

Breeding usually occurs twice a year, in March and again in June, the time of the second breeding varies more than that of the first. The study on Mt. Trebevic showed that only one litter was born during the dry year of 1946. The gestation period is believed to be at least one month, and there are usually two or three good-sized young per litter. Young are reported to come out of the burrows in July.

Water Vole (*Arvicola terrestris*), photo from A. van Wyngaarden.

WATER VOLES; CAMPAGNOLS AMPHIBIES; WASSER-
RATTEN, WOELRATTEN.

THE SINGLE SPECIES, *A. terrestris*, inhabits most of
Europe, parts of Russia and Siberia, Asia Minor,
northern Syria, Israel, and Iran. These rodents live
on the banks of streams in areas where the water
level is constant. Sometimes they are found in orchards, market gardens, and melon fields.

This is the largest microtine rodent in the Old
World. The length of the head and body is usually
over 150 mm. and often over 200 mm., and the length
of the tail is about half that of the head and body.
The fur is thick. The general coloration ranges from
moderately light brown to dark brown above, and
from buffy to slate-gray below. Black individuals
sometimes occur locally. Slight aquatic modifications
are developed at times, such as the small, hairy
swimming fringe on the foot. The tail is well haired,
and the sole of the hind foot is generally haired. The
claws on all four limbs are well developed. Both sexes
possess flank glands, and females have eight mammae.
The animals of this genus seem to grow throughout
life. Bank voles have ever-growing cheek teeth.

Arvicola is active at night or during the day. In
areas where nocturnal animals predominate, water
voles are more active during the daytime. They do
not hibernate but burrow under the snow. Water
voles live in burrows, often in colonies. They are
generally good swimmers, although some forms are
more aquatic than others. The aquatic forms dive
freely. They swim on the surface or under water,
sometimes near the bottom of the pool or stream,
where they enter burrows that terminate beneath the
water. They generally keep their well-defined runways on the surface of the ground, although these
passages usually lead to the edge of the water.

Water voles feed principally on reeds and other
aquatic plants along the grassy banks of streams.
Food is usually stored for the winter.

The nests of grass and other plant tissues are built
in burrows in the ground, slightly above water level,
or placed under logs, driftwood, or dense vegetative
cover on the surface. At least two litters are born
each year. A gestation period of 42 days (?) has been
reported. The number of young is two to seven, usually five to six. Water voles born early in the year may
breed the same year. Few individuals survive a second
winter. Males fight one another in the spring and
summer; females fight each other, but not to the same
extent as the males.

In Russia this species is trapped for its fur. It
carries the virus for tularemia.

Muskrat (*Ondatra zibethicus*), photo by Ernest P. Walker.

MUSKRATS; MUSQUASHS; RATSMUSQUES; BISAM-RATTEN; MUSKUSRATTEN; L'ONDATRA; LE RAT MUSQUE.

THE TWO SPECIES are distributed as follows: *O. obscurus* is native to Newfoundland; and *O. zibethicus* has a range extending from Alaska to Labrador, southward to South Carolina, westward to Texas and Arizona, and to northern Baja California. They do not occur along the California, Georgia, or South Carolina coast, or in Florida. These animals inhabit fresh and salt water marshes, lakes, ponds, rivers, and streams. They have been extensively introduced into Europe, where they have become pests.

The length of the head and body is 229 to 325 mm.; the length of the tail is 180 to 295 mm.; and adults weigh from 681 to 1,816 grams. The pelage is composed of two elements: a short, soft, dense, fine under-fur, interspersed with a thick, protective coat of long, coarse, dark, shining guard hairs which produce the dominant color of the upper parts. The general coloration ranges from a medium silvery brown to dark brown or almost black in some of the dark forms. The lower surface is generally somewhat lighter than the upper parts. The hands, feet, and tail are dark brown to black.

Muskrats are adapted particularly to swimming: the hind foot is partially webbed and along its edge is a row of closely set, short, stiff hairs, commonly called the swimming fringe. The scaly, almost hairless tail is flattened laterally and is used as a rudder. There are six mammae.

Muskrats get their name from the pronounced musky odor that comes from the secretion of glands in the perineal area. This musk is similar to that used in perfumes.

Muskrats live in two types of locations: open swamps, in which their houses are constructed of cattails and other vegetation, piled into mounds from several centimeters to 1.2 meters high and 1.5 or 1.8 meters in diameter with the nest near the center; these homes connect with the outside world by one or more tunnels having underwater exits; and earth banks where the dens are well above high water mark and the tunnels lead into the water below the lowest depth to which the water freezes. Often elaborate tunnels are dug through the banks to connect different burrows. Muskrats also make fairly well-defined channels through the marginal vegetation and construct slides along the banks down which they travel and play. They are expert swimmers and can remain submerged up to 12 minutes which they do when danger threatens. When disturbed, they utter a whinish-growl. They feed mainly on many kinds of plant material, such as the roots of cattails and lilies, or on stems, and like material. Sometimes they forage in adjacent fields for corn or other crops. They also eat some animal tissue, such as mussels, crayfish, and occasionally fish.

In the north, breeding takes place from the beginning of spring to autumn, but in the south breeding is continuous. The majority of the young, however, are born from November to April. After a gestation period of 22 to 30 days, from 1 to 11 (usually 5 to 7) young are born. The female is bred again while she is still nursing so several litters are produced annually. The young are weaned in about one month.

In North America, trappers make more money from selling muskrat pelts than from any other source of fur trapping. It is said that muskrat pelts are 40 per cent more durable than other pelts. Their carcasses, termed "Marsh-rabbit," can be prepared into tasty meals. These animals sometimes become a nuisance by burrowing through dams, irrigation banks, channels, and other obstructions.

The type species of the genus is *O. zibethicus* (Linnaeus).

Round-tailed Muskrat (*Neofiber alleni*), photo by James N. Layne.

ROUND-TAILED MUSKRATS, FLORIDA WATER RATS, EVERGLADE WATER RATS.

A SINGLE SPECIES, *N. alleni*, inhabits most of Florida, including many adjacent islands and the Okefinokee Swamp region in southern Georgia. These animals inhabit fresh water bogs, swamps, lake margins, streambanks, and brackish waters of river deltas. They seem to choose bogs rather than the aquatic habitat preferred by the true muskrat (*Ondatra*). They apparently like heavily vegetated areas.

The length of the head and body is 185 to 215 mm.; the length of the tail is 100 to 170 mm.; and the weight is 190 to 325 grams. The fairly long fur is composed of glistening guard hairs and short, soft underfur. The general coloration of the upper parts is brown to blackish brown, whereas the under parts are whitish or tinged with buff. The feet are not modified for aquatic life to the pronounced degree of *Ondatra*, but they do have small swimming fringes. The scaly, scantily-haired tail is round; the ears are small and nearly concealed in the fur. The females have six mammae.

Although these animals are more terrestrial than true muskrats, they are nevertheless good swimmers. The round-tailed muskrats tend to be gregarious. Their presence is generally first noted by their nests which are mounds 305 to 457 mm. high and 305 to 610 mm. in diameter. The nest is on the ground and is composed of any available vegetation. The nest

chamber, which is not much larger than necessary to accommodate the animal, is placed in the middle of the mound. The mounds are almost invariably provided with two tunnels leading downward in opposite directions from the nest chamber. These passages are dug through the soft, moisture-soaked ground so that they actually become water-filled tunnels. A network of surface trails about 75 mm. wide entwines the vegetation near their homes and leads into the water. These nests and the floating platforms which they construct are favorite sunning sites for the cottonmouth moccasin. These reptiles will eat the rats, however.

The diet consists of rushes, sedges, sawgrass, sugar cane, mangrove bark, and other kinds of plant life. Food may be consumed where it is found or carried to the feeding platforms; it may be eaten in runways or carried back to the nest.

It is believed that round-tailed muskrats breed throughout the year and that several litters are born annually. The gestation period is from 30 to 47 days, and the number of young per litter is probably two.

Usually these animals are not sought for their pelts, but they are preyed upon by carnivorous animals, birds, snakes, alligators, and turtles. Although *Neofiber* is of little or no significance to man, these rodents occasionally harm crops. However, some of the damage attributed to them may be caused by the cotton rat (*Sigmodon*).

A. Tree Mouse (*Phenacomys silvicola*), photo by Alex Walker. B. Phenacomys Voles (*P. ungava*), young are ten days old, photo by J. B. Foster.

HEATHER VOLES, TREE MICE, SPRUCE MICE.

THERE ARE FIVE SPECIES comprising this genus: *P. intermedius*, native to most of Canada and western United States along the Rocky mountains southward to northern New Mexico; *P. longicaudus* and *P. albipes* of the coastal region of Oregon and northern California; *P. silvicola*, which occupies a small area along the coast of central Oregon; and *P. ungava*, which inhabits most of Canada. *P. intermedius* prefers grassy forest glades, mossy regions, heather, etc., from low elevations to near the snow line on the mountains. The remaining three species live on the ground and in trees, although they prefer forests of spruce, hemlock, and Douglas fir near water.

The length of the head and body is 104 to 106 mm.; the length of the tail is 26 to 87 mm.; and the weight varies from 27 to 56 grams. The fairly long, fine-textured pelage ranges from agouti gray to cinnamon-brown, with some of the hairs sparingly tipped with black. The lower parts are whitish, gray, or pinkish buff. In *P. intermedius* the face is sometimes yellowish. The general appearance of these animals so closely resembles voles (*Microtus*) and red-backed mice (*Clethrionomys*) that positive identification cannot be made until the skull and dentition are examined

closely. The tail of *P. intermedius* is of medium length, whereas the other species have long tails.

These animals are rare throughout their range, and little is known of their habits. The males of *P. longicaudus* live in burrows on the ground or in piles of debris, but the females live in trees. The males climb the trees to mate and to build small temporary nests. The females also build nests 228 to 305 mm. in diameter and 4.5 to 15 meters from the ground. The nests are made of accumulations of twigs and discarded spines of fir and spruce leaves; they are generally placed at a forked branch or over a nest that has been discarded by birds or squirrels. The tender terminal twigs of coniferous trees are cut for food. They are carried to the nest where the needles are eaten and the spines are used to enlarge the nest. These animals also eat willow bark and berries. Unlike most mice, the movements of *P. longicaudus* are slow and cautious, particularly along branches where care is taken to obtain a firm grasp on a new support before leaving a safe foothold. They can be picked up easily and rarely bite if not grasped too tightly. These rodents do not hibernate.

P. intermedius is born in a ground nest.

The type species of the genus is *P. intermedius*, Merriam.

Pine Mouse (*Pitymys pinetorum*), photo by Ernest P. Walker.

PINE MICE, PINE VOLES; CAMPAGNOLS; SONBER-RAINS; KURZOHRWÜHLMÄUSE; ONDERGRONDSE WOELMUIZEN.

ELEVEN SPECIES constitute this genus. *P. pinetorum* ranges from central Texas to Wisconsin and eastward to the Atlantic coast (except Florida); *P. parvulus* occurs in northern Florida; and *P. quasiater* is native to east-central Mexico. The other eight species have a combined range covering most of Europe and Asia Minor. Members of this genus live in many different habitats, from open fields to tamarack swamps. *Neodon*, Hodgson, 1849, and *Phaiomys*, Blyth, 1863, are herein regarded as subgenera. Some authors include *Pitymys* as a subgenus under *Microtus*.

The length of the head and body is 83 to 120 mm.; the length of the tail is 15 to 40 mm.; and the weight of adults is 25 to 39 grams. The color of the upper parts of the soft, dense pelage (short to fairly long) is tawny, russet brown to grayish brown, frequently with black-tipped hairs on the back and rump. The under parts are whitish to dusky; the tail is usually about the same color as the back. The *Pitymys* and *Phaiomys* groups have become modified for a semifossorial and subterranean existence through the reduction of the eyes, external ears, tail, and a close, velvety pelage. The foreclaws are somewhat enlarged for digging. The *Neodon* group, on the other hand, is terrestial and has normal-sized eyes, ears, and tails, and a full, shaggy fur.

With particular reference to *P. pinetorum*, this rodent dwells in thick leafmold and loose soil (usually in deciduous forests) and burrows aimlessly along the surface; normally it burrows no deeper than 100 mm. below ground. It also uses the burrows of moles, large shrews, and other mice. A high-pitched note is given when alarmed. The diet consists of succulent roots and tubers, seeds, leaves, nuts, and fruits. It is said to store food in its burrow.

A spherical nest is built under a rock or log or in its burrow. The nest is lined with shredded vegetation. Breeding usually takes place from March to November. About 21 days later from 2 to 5 helpless young are born, which are weaned in about 17 days.

During a severe winter, the feeding habits of *P. pinetorum* cause damage in some areas, particularly in orchards in the United States where these rodents eat the bark from the roots and lower trunks of trees. The losses are very heavy when the snow and fallen leaves are mounded around the base of the tree. These animals may consume insects, but conclusive evidence for this has not been found. Moles living within the range of pine mice are often unjustly accused of damage to bulbs, seeds, and other crops, but the pine mice cause the injury as they cross the burrows of the moles or eat these stores in their own burrows. *Pitymys* are frequently mistaken for moles.

The type species of the genus is *P. pinetorum* (Le Conte).

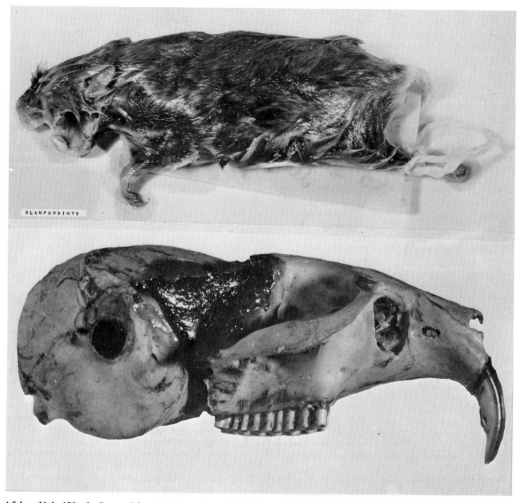

Afghan Vole (*Blanfordimys afghanus*), photos from British Museum (Natural History).

AFGHAN VOLES.

A SINGLE SPECIES, *B. afghanus*, inhabits the arid steppes of Afghanistan and adjoining Russian Pamir. Kuznetzov regards this species as a member of the genus *Microtus* (subgenus *Phaiomys*), but other mammalogists regard it as a distinct genus.

The length of the head and body of the type specimen, an adult female in the British Museum (Natural History), is 93 mm., and the length of the tail is 23 mm. The pelage is straight, fairly coarse, and not mole-like. The coloration of the upper parts is buffy to grayish brown, while the undersurface is washed with buffy white. The tail is bicolored, dark on top and lighter underneath. Afghan voles have short and rounded ears, fairly long claws on all limbs, a relatively short tail, and eight mammae. The bullae are enormous and distinguish the genus from all other microtines.

We have found no information regarding their habits and general biology.

Korean Meadow Vole (*Microtus montebelli*), photo by Ernest P. Walker.

MEADOW MICE, VOLES; CAMPAGNOLS DES CHAMPS; FELDMAUSE; WOELMUIZEN; METORITOS; KURO-HATANEZUMI, CHOSEN-KOMIMI-HATANEZUMI, YOSI-NEZUMI; VELDMUIZEN. (Included are vernaculars used in other countries.)

As HEREIN TREATED, this genus includes 44 species having a combined range covering most of North America southward to Guatemala and the northern two-thirds of the Eurasian continent. Most species prefer moderately moist meadowlands and semi-swampy areas; others are found in woodland clearings and wastelands; some forms live on desert terrain. The length of the head and body varies from about 85 to 175 mm.; the length of the tail, always less than half that of head and body, is from 15 to 95 mm. The short tail is an important distinguishing feature. The weight ranges up to about 115 grams. The pelage is usually quite long and loose. The general coloration of the upper parts is grayish brown, the darker forms approaching a sooty black and the lighter forms being reddish and yellowish; the lower parts range from grayish through pale brown to whitish. Meadow mice have short, rounded ears which are nearly concealed by the pelage. There are usually eight mammae.

Most species make clearly-defined surface runways under low vegetation, but when ground cover is scant, some species dig short ground burrows; other species of *Microtus* dwell among rock crannies. Although terrestrial, these animals swim and dive well. *Microtus* does not hibernate. When frightened, they may emit a high-pitched squeak, gnash their teeth, either flee or freeze, depending upon their location and previous activity. These animals are strictly vegetarians; within a 24-hour period, they consume nearly their own weight in seeds, roots, bark, and leaves. Some northern species store food. Meadow mice build spherical nests, usually of shredded plant fibers. Nests are located in their burrows under logs, stumps, or stones.

Breeding is promiscuous. Female meadow mice begin mating when about three weeks old and produce up to 13 litters per year and 4 to 8 young per litter. Males reach maturity in about 45 days. The gestation period is 21 days. In the south breeding

takes place throughout the year, but in the north it is limited to the summer months, the length of day apparently being the limiting factor. The young are weaned in two weeks, and the life span is thought to be just over a year. Populations seem to run in cycles, and in the western United States they may number up to 12,000 per acre. Similar periodic increases have occurred in the British Isles and Europe. The size of the average colony, however, is probably about 300. The intense intraspecific aggressiveness may be a major limiting factor, though much mystery concerning the dynamics of population cycles remains. They do appear less hardy than related genera, their physiological balance being easily disturbed. These rodents do not have migrations as do the lemmings (*Lemmus*). When compared to *Clethrionomys*, these animals appear very slow moving, are docile, and easily trapped and tamed.

When their numbers are normal, they do no serious harm to crops and are kept in control by predators, but if they become overabundant locally, serious damage occurs.

This genus has been split into many genera in the past, of which the following are considered valid subgenera today:

1. *Microtus*, Schrank, 1798, with type species *M. arvalis* (Pallas).
2. *Chilotus*, Baird, 1857, with type species *M. oregoni* (Bachman).
3. *Lasiopodomys*, Lataste, 1887, with type species *M. brandti* (Radde).
4. *Aulacomys*, Rhoads, 1897, with type species *M. arviculoides*, Rhoads = *M. richardsoni arviculoides.*
5. *Herpetomys*, Merriam, 1898, with type species *M. guatemalensis*, Merriam.
6. *Orthriomys*, Merriam, 1898, with type species *M. umbrosus*, Merriam.
7. *Stenocranius*, Kastschenko, 1901, with type species *M. slowzowi*, Poljak.
8. *Pedomys*, Baird, 1857, with type species. *M. ochrogaster* (Wagner).
9. *Proedromys*, Thomas, 1911, with type species *M. bedfordi*, Thomas.

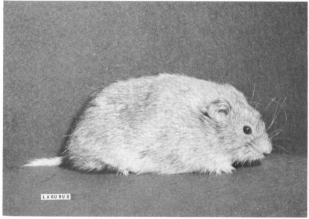 

Sagebrush Voles (*Lagurus curtatus*), photos by Murray L. Johnson.

SAGEBRUSH VOLES, STEPPE LEMMINGS.

THE THREE SPECIES are distributed as follows: *L. lagurus*, southern Russia, western Siberia, Kazakstan, and east to Zungeria; *L. luteus*, Chinese Turkestan, Tsaidam, and Mongolia; *L. curtatus*, the western United States and extreme southwestern Canada. In the Old World they inhabit steppes and semideserts and occasional pastures and cultivated fields; in the New World they occur in sagebrush areas where the grass is sparse and in open grassy ridges or high prairies.

The length of the head and body is 90 to 135 mm., and the length of the tail is 10 to 30 mm. Adults weigh from 15 to 25 grams. The pelage is longer and usually softer than the fur in species of *Microtus*. In the species *L. lagurus* the back is light gray or cinnamon-gray, with a black stripe along the spine; *L. luteus* has a sand-yellow back. In *L. curtatus* the upper parts are pale buffy gray to ashy gray; the sides are paler; and the under parts are silvery or soiled whitish to buffy. The body is somewhat stocky and lemming-like. The short tail is about the length of the hind foot. Some modifications for burrowing in sandy soil are evidenced in *Lagurus* in their small ears, short tail, stout claws, and haired palms and soles. Females have eight mammae.

Unlike most voles, the members of this genus live in arid regions. They are mainly nocturnal, but indi-viduals move about in the daytime. *Lagurus* is active the year round. These rodents generally live in colonies, but not on a permanent basis. Their burrows are usually short and are composed of numerous tunnels having a number of entrances and several nest chambers. Occasionally the tunnel systems of other rodents are used (such as those of *Thomomys* in the New World). Their runways are poorly formed, at least when their numbers are limited. Population fluctuations occur; *L. lagurus* is said to undergo mass increase and mass migration in years of overproduction.

The diet is mainly green foods rather than the seeds which most desert rodents enjoy. Winter food storage has been reported in *L. luteus*.

Nests of dry plant fibers are located in the tunnel chambers. The species *L. curtatus* seems to breed throughout the year, and *L. lagurus* has up to five litters during the summer. The former species has a gestation period of 24 to 26 days. The number of young per litter is usually four to seven. Females often live together while raising the young. Individuals of *L. curtatus* weigh about 1.5 grams at birth and gain about one-third gram daily until weaned at about three weeks. Females of this species are sexually mature at an average age of 60 days, and the males at 60 to 75 days.

The type species of the genus is *L. lagurus* (Pallas).

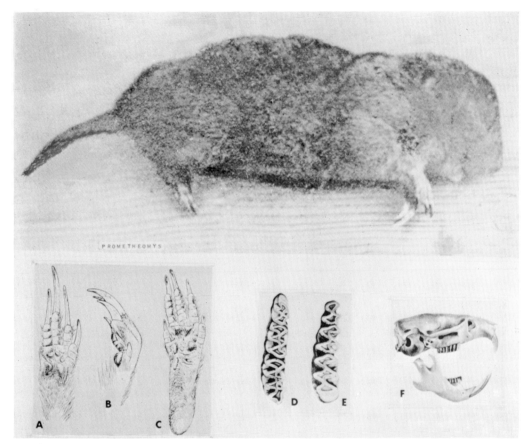

Long-clawed Mole-vole (*Prometheomys schaposchnikowi*), photo from *Jour. Mam.*, Ognev. A. Left fore foot; B. Lateral view of right fore foot; C. Left hind foot; D. Upper teeth; E. Lower teeth; F. Skull; photos from *Proc. Zool. Soc. London.*

LONG-CLAWED MOLE-VOLES, PROMETHEUS MICE, "TAGWY."

THE SINGLE SPECIES, *P. schaposchnikowi*, inhabits alpine and subalpine meadows and open spaces in the forests of the main range of the Caucasus Mountains from the Black Sea east to the Georgian Military Road.

Head and body length is 125 to 160 mm., and tail length is 45 to 65 mm. Coloration on the upper parts is dull grayish brown, suffused with cinnamon, while the under parts are light plumbeous-gray with a cinnamon tint. The fully-haired tail is unicolored brownish gray. This stocky rodent has a round head and large claws on the fore feet. The claw of the middle digit of the hand is the longest, over 5 mm. in length. The eyes and ears are reduced; the upper incisors are grooved; and the molars are rooted. There are eight mammae. The tail is swollen at the tip.

This burrowing rodent builds complex mounds and throws the excavated dirt on top of the ground in the form of heaps. The claws are used rather than the teeth in digging. A grass-lined nest appears to be the center of a burrow system as from here many burrows radiate, gradually coming nearer the surface. The animal comes to the surface only when its burrows have been destroyed, and at this time *Prometheomys* is quite easy to capture. It is active throughout the year. It feeds underground on the subterranean roots of herbaceous plants; it leaves the burrow for short intervals to feed above ground on the stems and leaves of herbs. The long-clawed mole-vole damages hayfields in some areas.

It appears to have only one litter per year (in June).

Mole-vole or Mole-lemming (*Ellobius fuscocapillus*); Inset: *E. talpinus*, photos by P. F. Wright of specimens in U.S. National Museum.

MOLE-VOLES OR MOLE-LEMMINGS; SLEPUSHONKA.

THE TWO SPECIES of *Ellobius* are distributed as follows: *E. talpinus*, southern Russia, Russian Turkestan, Chinese Turkestan, and Mongolia; and *E. fuscocapillus*, eastern Asia Minor, Transcaucasia, Iran, Baluchistan, Afghanistan, and southwestern Russian Turkestan. Habitats are grassy mountain slopes, arid steppes, clay deserts, and orchards and gardens.

The length of the head and body is 100 to 150 mm., and the length of the tail is 5 to 22 mm. The upper parts are dull or bright cinnamon, pinkish buff or buff, or brownish, and the under parts are grayish, brownish, or whitish. A dark face-patch may be present. The fur is velvety or plush-like, resembling the hair of other mammals that spend their lives underground. These small burrowing rodents have a round head and reduced eyes and ears. The claws are small. The incisors are large, those of the upper jaw protruding forward and downward; earth is loosened and roots are cut with the incisor teeth. This is probably the most specialized fossorial microtine rodent.

Two types of burrows are constructed: The passages near the surface are feeding tunnels, in which the animal searches for roots, bulbs, and rhizomes of herbaceous plants (earth is ejected from side passages of these surface tunnels); and the deep tunnels contain the living quarters and nests.

There seem to be two litters a year of one to seven young, usually three to five.

Mole-voles damage crops in some areas. They have some value in the fur trade.

The type species of the genus is *E. talpinus* (Pallas).

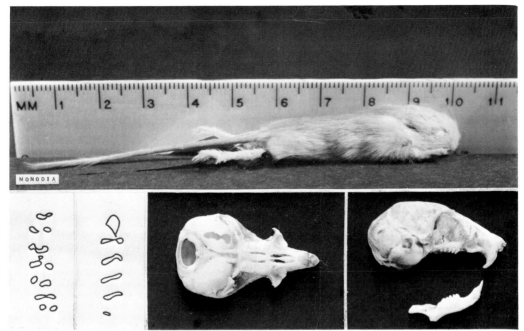

(*Monodia mauritaniae*), photos by P. F. Wright of specimen from Museum National d'Histoire Naturelle, Paris. Tooth pattern, photo from *Mammalia*, Paris.

ONE SPECIES, *M. mauritaniae*, occurs in the Sahara Desert, in the northwestern part of French West Africa.

The length of the head and body is about 55 mm., and the length of the tail about 75 mm. The coloration is similar to that of many other desert rodents. The upper parts are a sandy color, and the lower parts are white. The tail has short yellowish-gray hairs which become longer toward the tip.

Monodia is characterized by the structure of the third (last) molar tooth and the sole of the foot.

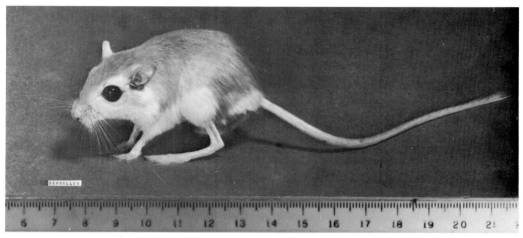

Gerbil (*Gerbillus gerbillus*), photo by Ernest P. Walker.

SAND RATS, GERBILS, PYGMY GERBILS; PAEBA GERBILLES; HAARSTAART MUIZEN; MBADYA; DWERG-SPRINGHAASMUIS, NEWANGO; SEI-EB; NANIA AND BERG DAMARA, HUI; GAU-BA; NDI; KITUI; KLEIN NAGMUIS (native names).

FIFTY-FOUR SPECIES are currently standing in the literature. The genus is native to open, dry, sandy, and sparsely vegetated areas extending from southern Africa northward to Morocco and Egypt, eastward through Sinai, Palestine, Syria, northern Arabia, Iraq to West Pakistan. *Dipodillus*, Lataste, 1881, and *Microdillus*, Thomas, 1910, are herein regarded as subgenera, although some taxonomists consider them as valid genera.

The length of the head and body is 80 to 130 mm., and the length of the tail is 75 to 120 mm. The coloration above ranges from pale yellowish gray, clay color, or sandy buff to sandy red, mouse-gray, dark fulvous or brilliant reddish brown. The median line of the back is usually slightly darker; the sides and flanks are paler, blending into the white, creamy, or pale gray of the under parts. The hands and feet are usually the same color as the under parts. In *G. dunni* and *G. brockmani* a white area extends from side to side across the shoulders. The tail is moderately to well furred, generally with a slight tuft near the tip. In many species there is a slight crest on the upper side of the distal half. The underside of the tail is usually light, the upper part near the body is darker, and the terminal portion darkest (dark brown or almost black in some). Most forms have a light-colored spot above the eye or behind the ear, or in both places.

Gerbils are characterized by a slender form, a long, somewhat bristly tail, and fairly long ears. The slender upper incisors are grooved, although sometimes indistinctly. The claws are fairly long. There are six to eight mammae. The hind legs are elongated and the soles of the hind feet are hairy.

These animals inhabit small, short, simple burrows of their own construction. The sand is so loose that the entrances are usually closed, thus it is difficult to locate the burrows. Many, if not all, of the species are gregarious, the individuals making their burrows so near to each other that definite colonies may result. The animals are most active during the night, although they tend to remain in their burrows on cool, windy nights. One author reports that these rodents are attracted to campfires and hop up and down in the outer fringes of the light. Their diet consists of roots, nuts, grass, and insects.

Most (probably all) of the species are polyestrous. The litter size ranges from one to seven, usually about four, and the gestation period is 20 to 21 days. A captive specimen of *G. gerbillus* lived in the London Zoo more than five years.

These animals appear to be plentiful throughout most of their range. Snakes apparently prey heavily upon them.

The type species of the genus is *G. gerbillus* (Olivier).

Large Naked-soled Gerbils (*Tatera schinzi shirensis*), photo by Ernest P. Walker.

LARGE NAKED-SOLED GERBILS; NAGMUISE; HAAR-STAART MUIZEN, INGOMBWE; ISAGAI; BUMBI GU-BARA; MPYNYA (native names).

THE SPECIES *T. indica* is known from Ceylon, India, West Pakistan, Turkey, the Punjab, Iran, Iraq, Syria, and Arabia. About ten other species have a combined range that includes most of Africa, except the equatorial forests. They inhabit plains, savannahs, and woodlands, and at times gardens and cultivated fields.

The length of the head and body is about 90 to 190 mm., and the length of the tail is 120 to 245 mm. The hind foot is 28 to 45 mm. in length. Adults usually weigh from 30 to 100 grams. The pelage is medium or soft. The coloration above ranges from pale sandy gray or pale buffy gray to dark buffy, blackish cinnamon, sandy brown, or dark gray; the under parts are white or whitish. The hands and feet are light-colored. In most forms the tail is slightly darker above and below than the back; the sides are light; and in most forms the terminal part is whitish or tufted with long dark hairs. There are usually light-colored or white spots above and behind the eyes, ears, and on the sides of the nose. This gerbillid genus may be characterized by the grooved upper incisors and naked soles. The body form is often heavy and rat-like. Females have six or eight mammae.

These rodents are nocturnal. They are gregarious, although single burrows are built occasionally. Short burrows, the so-called "bolt-holes," are excavated for sudden retreats, but deeper burrows are used as the living quarters. The animals burrow in sandy soil to a depth of one meter or more. Their tunnel systems are practically underground labyrinths in some areas, with numerous entrances and exits. *T. indica* often has the nest chamber located in the center of the tunnel system. The entrances to the burrows are usually blocked with loose earth.

Family groups often move from one warren to another, but true migrations are not undertaken. These animals usually walk on all four limbs, but when alarmed they flee by means of running bounds of up to 1.5 meters in height. *T. indica* is said to be able to jump 3.5 meters in one leap.

The diet consists of bulbs, roots, seeds, green plant material, and insects. The species *T. indica* seems to have carnivorous tendencies, as it sometimes feeds on smaller individuals of its own kind in the wild. This species also eats eggs and young birds.

In some species, such as *T. brantsii*, breeding takes place throughout the year, whereas in other species, such as *T. afra*, there are definite breeding seasons. The young, usually four to eight per litter, remain in the nest for three to four weeks. An average gestation period of 22.5 days has been reported for *T. afra*. Ecologically, gerbils of this genus are suitable hosts for the bubonic plague bacillus. Members of the Union of South Africa Health Department have had to destroy them on occasion to prevent the spread of the disease.

The type species of the genus is *T. indica* (Hardwicke).

Small Naked-soled Gerbil (*Taterillus nigeriae*), photo by Jane Burton.

SMALL NAKED-SOLED GERBILS.

THE RANGE of this genus is Africa, including Senegal, Nigeria, Lake Chad, Sudan, eastern Congo, Uganda, Kenya, and Abyssinia. Fifteen species have been described, but all the forms of this genus may be referable to one species. The usual habitat is a treeless plain or thorny scrub terrain.

The length of the head and body is 100 to 140 mm., the length of the tail is about 140 to 170 mm., and the length of the hind foot is 28 to 32 mm. The coloration above ranges from pale yellow through light buffy, clay color, light reddish brown, and tawny olive to dark tawny brown. The sides are paler, and the under parts, including the hands and feet, are white or almost white. Most forms have light areas or spots on the sides of the face, above the eyes, and back of the ears, and some forms have faint dark markings on the face. The tail is usually well tufted and darkest toward the tip. Externally, this genus is similar to *Tatera*, but it is usually smaller and the soles are sometimes partially haired, not completely naked. As in *Tatera*, the upper incisors are grooved.

Specific habits and biology are not recorded. Like other gerbils, these animals dig burrows, excavating the earth in the form of surface mounds. They live in these underground burrows.

The type species of the genus is *T. emini* (Thomas).

Cape Short-eared Gerbil (*Desmodillus auricularis*), photo from South African Union Health Department through D. H. S. Davis.

CAPE SHORT-EARED GERBILS, CAPE SHORT-TAILED GERBILS, NAMAQUALAND GERBILS; KORT STERT-NAGMUIS; NAMAKWALANDSE NAGMUIS.

THE SINGLE SPECIES, *D. auricularis*, occurs in southwestern Africa and southern Africa. It inhabits open sandy plains, dry tablelands, and cultivated areas.

The length of the head and body is 90 to 125 mm. The length of the tail is about four-fifths and the length of the hind foot about one-fifth that of the combined head and body length. The color above varies from uniform orangish to tawny brown, with a white spot behind the ears on the back of the neck. The under parts, including the hands and feet, are white. *Desmodillus* is characterized by short ears with a white spot behind them, enlarged auditory bullae, dental features, and a tail that is haired but not tufted. The hind feet are somewhat unspecialized for jumping.

This animal runs like an ordinary rat and is not noticeably saltatorial. Its burrows are recognizable by the small surface heaps of earth thrown up like those of other gerbils, but the mounds are not as complicated as those built by other Gerbillinae. The burrows usually do not penetrate more than 2 meters, and they have blind passages or perpendicular tunnels for refuge or escape. A nest of dried straw or sticks may be located in a chamber at the end of the tunnel. When the animal is within the burrow, a heap of prickly seeds of a terrestrial creeping plant lies in front of the entrance on the mound of earth. This gerbil lives singly, in pairs, or in family groups. In captivity, however, this rodent is reported to be quite pugnacious; the adults may kill smaller rodents confined with them, including their own kind. However, they are extremely docile when handled.

The short-eared gerbil is mainly nocturnal, and it feeds on seeds, grain, and insects such as locusts and grasshoppers. It usually takes the food to the entrance of the burrow where it sits down and eats, leaving husks and wings around the entrance. During droughts this rodent may migrate or, at least, disperse.

Litter size is two to six, and *Desmodillus* is probably polyestrous.

(*Desmodilliscus braueri*), adapted from *Proc. Zool. Soc. London*, St. Leger. Inset: Tooth pattern, photo from "Evolution du dessin de la surface d'usure des molaires des Gerbillidés," *Mammalia*, Paris, F. Petter.

THE SINGLE SPECIES, *D. braueri*, inhabits the Sudan and northern Nigeria.

The length of the head and body is 50 to 70 mm.; the length of the tail is about three-fourths of the combined head and body length; and the length of the hind foot is about 15 mm. The pelage is quite soft, sandy fawn on the upper parts, somewhat paler on the sides, and white on the undersurface. Postauricular white spots are evident. The tail is haired but not tufted. *Desmodilliscus* is similar to *Desmodillus* and *Pachyuromys* but is distinguished from both of them by the presence of large, conspicuous cheek pouches. The auditory bullae are enlarged. The presence of three cheek teeth above and two cheek teeth below (making a total of ten cheek teeth) is said to be unique in the rodent families Cricetidae and Muridae; the incisors are narrow and furrowed. The skull resembles that of a *Desmodillus* in miniature.

Relatively few specimens have been taken, and almost nothing is known of this species in the wild.

Fat-tailed Gerbil (*Pachyuromys duprasi*), photo by Ernest P. Walker.

FAT-TAILED MICE, FAT-TAILED GERBILS; "ABO-LEA."

THE SINGLE SPECIES, *P. duprasi*, inhabits the sandy, scantily-vegetated areas of northern Africa from the Algerian Sahara to southwestern Egypt.

The length of the head and body is 105 to 135 mm., and the length of the tail is 45 to 60 mm. The soft pelage of the upper parts ranges from light yellowish gray to buffy brown, with a white spot behind each ear. The under parts, hands, and feet are white. The well-furred tail is bicolored: coloration above is similar to that of the back, and below it is whitish. Some forms have pinkish buff along the sides and on the rump. The ears are short and buffy white, but the extreme edges are brown.

Pachyuromys is stockily built with well-developed claws on the fingers, slightly grooved upper incisors, and, as is the case with many desert mammals, the auditory bulla and mastoid are so inflated that they extend beyond the foramen magnum. Their common name is derived from the peculiar shape of the tail which is short, noticeably thickened, and club-shaped.

Three to six young constitute a litter, and the gestation period is 19 to 22 days.

Captive specimens are used for laboratory studies.

Ammodille (*Ammodillus imbellis*), adapted from *Proc. Zool. Soc. London*, St. Leger.

AMMODILLE, WALO.

THE SINGLE SPECIES, *A. imbellis*, is native to Somaliland. One collector reported that he took specimens in sandy soil near wells.

The length of the head and body is 106 to 110 mm., and the length of the tail is about 144 mm. The coloration of the upper parts is reddish fawn; the hairs of the back are tipped with black, as are the hairs of the sides, but to a lesser degree, thus being a clearer, lighter fawn. On the eyebrows, cheeks, and fronts of the arms, the hairs are tipped with fawn. Distinct white spots are visible at the bases of the ears and above the eyes. The hands and feet, chin, cheeks, and under parts are white. The tail is darker above than below, scantily haired on the basal portion, but tufted terminally with brownish hairs 8 to 10 mm. in length. The feet and hands are scantily covered. The hairless pads and soles are covered with conspicuous scale-like granulations.

Although these animals are noted for fighting among themselves, they have an extraordinary weakness in the lower jaw as the coronoid process of the mandible is absent. This structural feature led to the choosing of the specific name, *imbellis*, which means "feeble."

The life habits of this desert rodent are not recorded.

Jird (*Meriones unguiculatus*), photo by Ernest P. Walker.

JIRDS, TAMARISK GERBILS, SAND RATS.

THE 12 SPECIES of this genus have a combined range that includes northern Africa, central Asia, and Asia Minor. Its members live in clay and sandy deserts, bush country, arid steppes, low plains, cultivated fields, grasslands, and mountain valleys. Some taxonomists regard *Parameriones*, Heptner, 1937, *Cheliones*, Thomas, 1919, and *Pallasiomys*, Heptner, 1933, as subgenera; they are herein included as such.

The length of the head and body is 114 to 130 mm., and the length of the tail is 90 to 110 mm. An adult male weighed 62 grams. The dense pelage is fairly long and soft in most forms, although it is short and harsh in others. The covering on the tail is short near the base and progressively longer toward the tip, so that the tail is slightly bushy in most of the forms and has a slight crest in some of the others. Coloration of the upper parts varies from pale, clear yellowish to sandy through grayish and brownish. The sides of the body are generally lighter than the back due to the absence of black-tipped hairs. The under parts, including the hands and feet, are white, pale yellowish, buffy, or pale gray. Frequently there are light areas about the face.

Externally *Meriones* is quite rat-like; it has narrow well-developed ears, a tail length which approximates that of the head and body, upper incisors with a narrow groove on the anterior surface, and slightly elongated hind legs for leaping. The claws are strong.

These animals are reported to be active both day and night. They burrow into fairly soft soil to form their homes. These burrows, which are relatively simple in structure, frequently have several exits. Sand rats often live close together, thus forming colonies which are usually partially sheltered by shrubs or other vegetation. Their diet consists of seeds, leaves, bulbs, stems, and roots, which, in at least some cases, are stored in the burrow. They are reported to hibernate. *M. unguiculatus* of Mongolia and northern China has a high capacity for temperature regulation, in comparison with many desert rodents.

Meriones are said to be monogamous, and most litters are born between April and September. The gestation period is 25 to 29 days, although the average litter size is three or four, it varies from one to seven. The young mothers have the largest families; there are several litters per year. The young are able to look after themselves in about three weeks. The life span is about five and one-half years.

M. shawi, a common field rodent of Tunisia, is frequently used as an experimental laboratory animal.

The type species of the genus is *M. tamaricinus* (Pallas).

Bushy-tailed Jird (*Sekeetamys calurus*), photo by Ernest P. Walker.

BUSHY-TAILED JIRDS.

THE SINGLE SPECIES, *S. calurus*, occurs through Palestine, Sinai, and eastern Egypt. It inhabits deserts and rocky slopes that are characterized by broken ground and hard surfaces.

The length of the head and body is 100 to 125 mm.; the length of the tail is 110 to 160 mm.; and the length of the hind feet is 29 to 35 mm. Coloration above is yellowish or reddish, washed with black; the tail is brownish, and the fore and hind feet and the under parts are whitish. The tail is bushy and usually bears a white tuft on the tip; a central black terminal tuft may be present, with white tufts on either side. The soles of the hind feet are naked.

The bushy-tailed jird burrows under boulders and rock ledges; it shows considerable climbing ability in its rocky habitat.

The average number of young for 47 litters born in the Giza Zoological Gardens was 2.9, and the largest number of young in one litter was six; the animals were born throughout the year.

This rodent was originally described as *Gerbillus calurus* and later was regarded as *Meriones calurus*. In 1947 a new subgenus *Sekeetamys* was formed for its retention in *Meriones*. Chromosome studies, however, do not favor its inclusion in the genus *Meriones* or in the genus *Gerbillus*, and ecologically this animal also seems to be quite distinct. *Sekeetamys* has thus been raised to generic rank.

Przewalski's Gerbils (*Brachiones przewalskii*), A. Photo from *Mammalia of Central Asia*, E. Büchner. B. Photo by P. F. Wright of specimen in U.S. National Museum.

Przewalski's Gerbils.

The single species, *B. przewalskii*, inhabits the Central Asiatic deserts of Chinese Turkestan and Mongolia.

The length of the head and body is 80 to 95 mm.; the length of the tail is 70 to 80 mm.; and the length of the hind foot is 23 to 28 mm. Coloration is pale grayish yellow, pale yellowish buff, or light sandy gray; the hands, feet, and under parts are white, and the tail is buffy or whitish throughout. The slender, tapering tail is not tufted. The soles are densely haired, whereas the palms are naked. The skull is quite different from that of *Meriones*.

The thickset body, reduced ears, shortened tail, long foreclaws, and hairy soles indicate that this rodent has developed burrowing habits. Specific habits and biology do not seem to be recorded.

859

Diurnal Sand Rat (*Psammomys obesus*), photo by Robert E. Kuntz.

FAT SAND RATS, DIURNAL SAND RATS.

THE TWO SPECIES are distributed as follows: *P. obesus*, in Algeria, Tunisia, Libya, Egypt, the Sudan, Israel, and Saudi Arabia; *P. vexillaris*, in Libya and Algeria.

The length of the head and body is 130 to 185 mm.; the length of the tail is 110 to 150 mm.; and the length of the hind foot is 30 to 36 mm. Coloration in *P. obesus* is reddish, usually with a black wash, yellowish or yellowish sandy, or reddish brown; the tail has a black and tufted tip; and the hands, feet, and upper parts are buffy or yellowish. In *P. vexillaris* the upper parts are pale sandy buffy with an ochraceous or cinnamon-buff wash; the belly is whitish, and the tail yellowish white. The tail is fully haired, and the external form is stocky. This genus is distinguished from *Meriones* by its non-grooved incisors and short (10 to 15 mm.), thick, rounded ears.

Psammomys is mainly diurnal and lives in colonies in sandy regions of scant vegetation. In northern Sinai the flooding of salt marshes in winter forces the sand rat to seek refuge in nearby hilly areas.

The complicated burrows have several openings. Plants and parts of plants are stored in food chambers; nine species of plants were found in one burrow, and 500 heads of barley were found in another.

Fat sand rats sit up on their hind legs and tail but quickly retreat into their burrows when alarmed.

The litter size is three to five, and at least one litter is born in March or April. The nest is constructed of finely cut grass in a chamber in the burrow.

The type species of the genus is *P. obesus*, Cretzchmar.

Great Gerbil (*Rhombomys opimus opimus*), photo from *Mammalia of Central Asia*, E. Büchner.

GREAT GERBILS; LARGE PESCHANKA OR ZAMAN-CHIK.

THE SINGLE SPECIES, *R. opimus*, occurs in Iran, Afghanistan, Russian Turkestan, Chinese Turkestan, and Mongolia. It usually inhabits sandy deserts but also occurs in clay deserts and the foothills of the Central Asiatic mountains.

The length of the head and body is 150 to 200 mm.; the length of the tail is 130 to 160 mm.; and the length of the hind foot is 42 to 48 mm. The upper parts are sandy yellow, orangish buff, or dark grayish yellow, and the under parts are whitish. The fur is thick and soft, and the tail is hairy, almost bushy.

The external form is stocky, the claws are large, and the soles are hairy. Two longitudinal grooves are present on each upper incisor.

Great gerbils are mainly diurnal. They do not hibernate, although their activity in winter is greatly reduced in many areas. These rodents live in large colonies in complex and deep burrows, the distribution of the burrows apparently is influenced by the topography. Little contact is made between individual *Rhombomys* and those living in neighboring colonies, at least in winter when many areas are covered with snow. In a study conducted in winter in the northern Lake Aral region, the maximum length of a trail in the snow was 20 meters, and 83 per cent of the tracks examined were in the immediate vicinity of the burrow exit.

The winter activity of *Rhombomys* is in direct proportion to the air temperature and in inverse proportion to the depth of the snow. By midwinter, in those parts of the range with a snow cover, only a few of the burrow exits are open and air holes are predominant. In many colonies where the burrows are completely covered with snow for a long time, the animals come to the surface only rarely.

The diet consists of a variety of desert plants. In some areas the food is stored for winter use (up to 60 kg. or more per burrow), but in other regions the animals feed mostly on the surface. The food reserves for winter are located in compartments in the burrow, but in some places the plants are stored in heaps on the surface.

Two or more litters of two to eight young are produced each year (average is four or five to a litter). Some individuals may live for more than two years in the wild. Two-year-old animals comprised 3.3 per cent of the population in one study. A given population of *Rhombomys* was reduced greatly during the winter by predatory small carnivores.

These rodents are pests in the U.S.S.R., for they damage crops, railway embankments, and the sides of irrigation channels. In some areas *Rhombomys* are trapped for their skins.

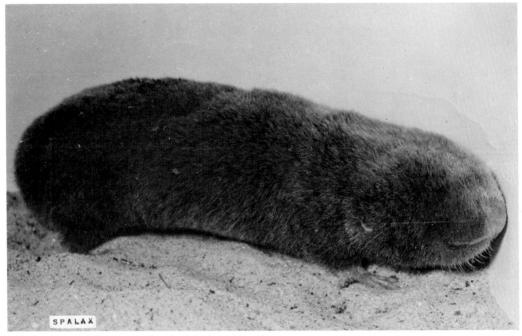

Palestine Mole-rat (*Spalax ehrenbergi*), photo by Eviatar Nevo.

MOLE-RATS; BLINDMAUSE; QUERA; KHILDE, KHLUNT, ABU AMMA (local vernaculars).

THIS FAMILY of a single genus, *Spalax*, occurs in the eastern Mediterranean, eastern Europe, Asia Minor, and southern Russia. The number of species is uncertain, but three are usually recognized. *S. leucodon* is the lesser mole-rat, *S. microphthalmus* is the Russian mole-rat, and *S. chrenbergi* is the Palestine mole-rat. Mole-rats seem to burrow in any area where the soil is suitable for digging, and they inhabit any type of soil that has more than 100 mm. of rainfall annually; they do not live in true desert. They are known from plains located below sea level to cultivated fields, hilly areas, upland steppes, and clearings in the mountains up to elevations of 2,600 meters.

These heavy-bodied, short-legged, powerful animals have projecting incisors and small claws. The external form is mole-like. The length of the head and body is generally 150 to 300 mm., and there is no external tail. Weight ranges from about 133 to 295 grams. The color varies from dark gray to yellowish gray, often with a yellowish or golden sheen. A white central stripe on the snout and one on each cheek may be present. The dense, soft fur is nearly reversible. A line of bristles, apparently serving as tactile aids, extends from each side of the flattened snout along a ridge to about the location of the eye. Members of the genus *Spalax* can be distinguished from all other rodents by the absence of external openings for the eyes, although small eyes are present beneath the skin. The external ears are reduced to low ridges. Mole-rats recognize objects by touching them with the nose. The fore feet and hind feet have five digits.

The incisors are broad and heavy, and the cheek teeth are rooted (not ever growing), with "Z" or "S" enamel patterns after they become worn. The dental formula is: i 1/1, c 0/0, pm 0/0, m 3/3 x 2 = 16.

Mole-rats are extensive burrowers. Most of the digging is done with the incisors, the whole head acting as a bulldozer blade. Specialized jaws and strong muscles aid the teeth in loosening the soil. Almost all of the orbit, for example, is occupied by muscles for working the teeth. Another aid in burrowing is the broad, padded, horny snout with which excavated ground is packed into the burrow walls. Although the feet are small and quite delicate, the fore feet aid to some extent in breaking the soil, and the hind feet help push the dirt out behind.

The annual cycle of mole-rats reflects that of the seasons in its habitat. In the Mediterranean region, during the wet winter season, *Spalax* builds "breeding" mounds which resemble those of pocket gophers (Geomyidae). They are quite elaborate and large, usually about 1,600 mm. long, 1,350 mm. wide, and 400 mm. above the surface of the ground. They may even reach the dimensions of 2,500 mm. in diameter and 1,000 mm. high. In the dry Mediterranean summer, mole-rats build "resting" mounds which are generally smaller and less complex, with deep tunnels. These are usually 1,000 mm. in diameter and 250 mm. above the surface of the ground but may be as large as 1,600 mm. long, 1,200 mm. wide, and 350 mm. high. At the higher elevations of their range, they may dig deeper tunnel systems in winter and become less active.

The construction of the breeding mound begins just after the first rains in the fall. The large breeding mound is surrounded by radial rows of smaller mounds which are believed to be occupied by the males during the breeding season. These smaller mounds are connected to the larger breeding mound by feeding tunnels sometimes 36 or more meters in length. Within the center of the big mound is a nest chamber, about 200 mm. in diameter, filled with dry grass and similar material. Beneath this chamber are smaller storage chambers and connections with the feeding tunnels. In the mound portion itself are additional storage chambers, galleries, and occasional rooms for their droppings. There were 28 bulbs in a single storage chamber. The mound itself is a solid dome of earth through which runs a labyrinth of permanent galleries with hard, smooth walls. The only loose, soft earth is the covering of the dome. From recent studies made on *Spalax* in Israel by Eviatar Nevo (1961), a ratio was found between the level of the water table and the height and complexity of the mounds. In very wet, poorly drained areas, the breeding mounds tend to be much bigger and more elaborate, protecting the mole-rats from floods.

In contrast to the breeding mound is the resting mound, the usual summer dwelling of mole-rats. They are found usually in groups of 15 to 20 with one large one surrounded by smaller mounds. It is composed of crumbly rather than packed soil, and has only a few simple tunnels and storage chambers. In the center is a nest chamber, as in the breeding mound, but this is used only for sleeping and resting, never for newborn young. Each mound is owned by a single individual, for these rodents are solitary except during the mating season. Activity goes on even during extremely hot periods or drought, though there is perhaps less digging, and burrows are made deeper.

Spalax feeds generally on roots, bulbs, tubers and various other subterranean parts of plants. Although true subterranean rodents, mole-rats are at times nocturnally active above ground. During such ventures, they eat grasses, seeds, superficial roots, and perhaps insects. Half-grown young sometimes wander about the surface quite extensively from March to May in search of a new home. Grunting noises have been noted which are quite unlike the usual rodent squeak. *Spalax* is sometimes preyed upon by the eagle-owl (*Bubo bubo*), the long-eared owl (*Osio otus*), or the barn owl (*Tyto alba*).

The mating season is from about November to January, and the gestation period lasts probably about a month. A single litter of two to four young is born from January to March in the Mediterranean region. The newborn young average almost 5 grams in weight and 50 mm. in length. They are naked, helpless, and pink. After about two weeks, they are covered with long gray fur which is quite different from the short hair of the adult. At this time they weigh about 23 grams and are about 80 mm. long. At four to six weeks of age, they leave the nest.

Spalax is referred to in the Bible as the mole (Isaiah ii: 20). Some interesting beliefs have arisen in regard to this animal. Henry W. Setzer (*A Review of Libyan Mammals*, 1957, p. 66) comments: "... We could not induce the local people [of Libya] to procure them because of a belief that when one touches or has contact with a mole-rat blindness will ensue." In Assyrian folklore these mammals are regarded "as a magical curative agent for diseases of the female breast." (D. L. Harrison, *Footsteps in the Sand*, 1959, p. 178). When plentiful in agricultural lands, they may be pests.

The geological range of this family is the upper Pliocene to the Recent in Europe, and the Recent over the remainder of its present range.

The type species of the genus is *S. microphthalmus*, Guldenstadt.

AFRICAN MOLE-RATS.

THIS FAMILY consists of three genera, distributed as follows: *Tachyoryctes*, 14 species currently recognized, eastern Africa (a hematological study indicates a position in the rodent family Muridae); *Rhizomys*, three species, southeastern Asia and Sumatra; and *Cannomys*, a single (?) species, southeastern Asia. The members of this family inhabit sandy flats, grassy areas (including mountain clearings), forests, and bamboo thickets.

These rodents have a compact body modified for a burrowing life. They resemble American pocket gophers (Geomyidae) in external appearance but lack the external cheek pouches of that family. The length of the head and body is 160 to 460 mm., and the length of the tail is 50 to 150 mm. The pelage is soft and dense. The ears are hidden in the hair or they are visible. The limbs and claws are short. There are eight or ten mammae in *Rhizomys* and *Cannomys*.

The incisors are stout, and the cheek teeth have a tendency to be ever growing (at least in *Tachyoryctes*). The dental formula is as follows: i 1/1, c 0/0, pm 0/0 or 1/1, m 3/3 or 2/2 x 2 = 16.

Tachyoryctes is a burrowing form that throws up mounds of earth similar to those of the Geomyidae. In this genus the limbs and the claws are the main tools in digging, the teeth are used mainly to cut inter-vening roots. The burrows of the African mole-rat may become so abundant in some areas that a horse will break into a runway at nearly every step. In *Rhizomys* the teeth and the claws are used in digging. This genus commonly cuts and eats bamboo underground, but it also leaves its burrows at times to feed on the surface. It is aggressive when disturbed. *Cannomys* also uses its teeth and limbs in digging. The members of this genus leave their burrows in the evening to feed on plant material above ground. *Rhizomys* and *Cannomys* are reported to come above ground occasionally during the day to cut bamboo and other grasses, much in the manner of woodchucks. The members of this family are preyed on by small carnivores and owls.

In *Tachyoryctes* one young constitutes a litter (?), whereas in *Rhizomys* the number of offspring is usually three to five, and the gestation period is at least 21 days.

The members of all three genera are regularly eaten by the natives who dig them out or trap them.

The geological range of this family is the Pleistocene to the Recent in Africa, the upper Oligocene in Europe, and the upper Miocene to the Recent in Asia. *Bramus* is a Pleistocene genus from northern Africa (Tunis). Remains of this genus have been found in phosphorite Quarternary beds.

African Mole-rats (*Tachyoryctes splendens ibeanus*), A. & B. Photos by C. A. Spinage. C. Photo from *Museum Senckenbergianum*.

AFRICAN MOLE-RATS.

FOURTEEN SPECIES are currently described in the literature. The genus inhabits eastern Africa, Ethiopia, Somaliland, Kenya, Uganda, the eastern Congo, and northern Tanganyika. These rodents range from sandy plains to bamboo forests and moorland at elevations up to 3,700 meters.

The length of the head and body is about 180 to 250 mm., and the length of the tail is about 50 to 80 mm. The short tail is about twice the length of the hind foot and is usually well haired. The fur is thick and soft. The coloration is quite variable; some animals are shining black throughout and others are black only when young, still others are brownish, reddish brown, pale gray, or cinnamon-buff. Most young are black. Albinos and partial albinos are as common as black adults. The under parts are usually slightly lighter than the upper parts and often have a silvery effect.

The body form is stocky and mole-like. The eyes are small but plainly visible and functional, and the ears are small. There are stiff hairs on the face of *Tachyoryctes* which are undoubtedly tactile. The thick, projecting incisors are not grooved and are deep orange in color. Although the claws are not particularly large, the hands and feet are well developed, and the short, powerful legs are suited to digging. The appearance of the African mole-rats is similar to that of the American pocket gophers (Geomyidae), except that external cheek pouches are lacking, the pelvis is peculiar, and the fur is somewhat longer and more fluffy on *Tachyoryctes*.

African mole-rats apparently are most active at night, sometimes even leaving their burrows. They are seemingly entirely fossorial, although sometimes their hind legs may be seen sticking above ground as they kick earth out. However, if caught, they are active in the light. They have a characteristic attitude of defense when cornered, holding the head erect with the mouth wide open, and can give a vicious bite.

They are quite common in some areas where their burrows may become so abundant that a horse will break into a runway at nearly every step. Their underground tunnels are evidenced by the heaps of earth thrown up at intervals. Nests of dried grass are located in side tunnels. The limbs and claws are the main tools in digging, and the teeth are used to remove obstructing roots. Individuals begin to dig with the forelimbs and have been observed to kick the dirt backward with the forelimbs and the hind limbs; when considerable earth has accumulated, they turn about and push it away with the chest.

The only information recorded on their breeding habits is that one young constitutes a litter (?).

These rodents are regularly eaten by the Wanderobos who pour water into their holes, thus making them surface and easy to catch. The Kikuyu tribe eliminate them from their cultivated fields with a special trap.

The type species of the genus is *T. splendens* (Rüppell).

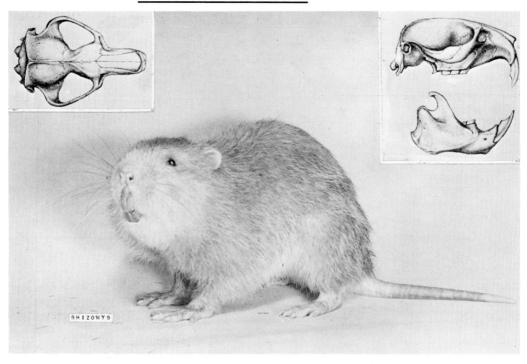

Sumatran Bamboo Rat (*Rhizomys sumatrensis*), photo by Ernest P. Walker. Insets: (*R. pruinosus*), photos from *Anatomical and Zoological Researches: Zoological Results of the Two Expeditions to Western Yunnan in 1868 and 1875*, John Anderson.

BAMBOO RATS; T'U LUN; DĚ KAN.

THIS GENUS is composed of three species which are distributed as follows: *R. sinensis*, southern China and northern Burma; *R. pruinosus*, Assam, Burma, Indo-China, Siam, Malay peninsula; and *R. sumatrensis*, same range as *R. pruinosus*, but also includes Sumatra. These animals are inhabitants of bamboo thickets from 4,000 to 13,000 feet elevation. *Nyctocleptes* Temminck, 1832, is herein included as a subgenus for the species *R. sumatrensis*.

The length of the head and body is 230 to 480 mm.; the length of the tail is 50 to 150 mm. *R. sumatrensis* is the largest of the three species. In the northern areas the pelage is soft, thick, and silky, but the fur becomes harsh and scanty in the tropical forms. The coloration of the upper parts ranges from slate through pinkish gray to brownish gray; the under parts are generally somewhat lighter. Some individual hairs may be tipped with white.

Bamboo rats resemble American pocket gophers with their thick, heavy bodies, short legs, and short scantily-haired tails. These animals are equipped with strong digging claws (the third digit has the longest nail); the pads of the feet are distinct and granulated, and the cheek pouches are absent. Members of this genus are distinguished from *Cannomys* in having nearly vertical upper incisors and also by their larger size. The stout incisors are orange and are prominent, since they are not covered by the lips. The eyes and ears are fairly small. There are eight mammae.

Bamboo rats spend much of their life underground among the roots of dense stands of bamboo. They live in burrows which they dig by using both their teeth and their claws. An individual bamboo rat usually has several burrows, only one or two of which may be in active use. They commonly cut and eat bamboo roots underground but also leave their burrows at times to feed above ground. Most of the food is eaten on the spot, but some is taken to the burrow. Other grasses, seeds, and fruits are also eaten, although the roots and shoots of bamboo seem to be preferred. Apparently they do not drink water.

Although powerfully built, these animals move slowly; their gait is a cumbersome waddle. If they sense that they are going to be overtaken or if they are cornered, bamboo rats become quite fierce, making short rushes at anything put in front of them, and biting savagely. At the same time a grunting noise is emitted, coupled with a peculiar grinding action of the teeth. Even captives are said to be vicious.

Blind young have been found in nests during the latter part of December, and young have been observed in June, July, and November. The offspring usually numbers three to five, and the gestation period is at least 21 days (based on a birth from a captive mother).

Natives dig them out or trap them for food.

The type species of the genus is *R. sinensis*, Gray.

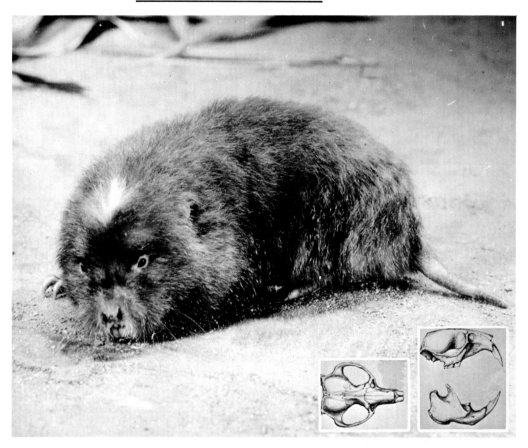

Lesser Bamboo Rat (*Cannomys badius*), photo by Constance P. Warner. Insets: (*C. badius*), photos from *Anatomical and Zoological Researches: Zoological Results of the Two Expeditions to Western Yunnan in 1868 and 1875*, John Anderson.

LESSER BAMBOO RATS.

THE SINGLE SPECIES, *C. badius*, inhabits Nepal, Assam, Burma, Tenasserim, and Thailand. It burrows in grassy areas, forests, and sometimes in gardens.

The length of the head and body is usually 165 to 255 mm., and the length of the tail is usually 60 to 70 mm. The fur is fairly thick on the head and body and very thin on the tail. The color ranges from reddish cinnamon and chestnut-brown to ashy gray and plumbeous. Individuals are almost uniformly colored throughout. There may be a longitudinal white band on the top of the head and a narrow white line from the chin to the throat.

Cannomys differs from *Rhizomys* in that it is usually smaller and the incisors are inclined forward rather than being vertical in position. The external form is much like that of the American pocket gophers (Geomyidae), except for the absence of external cheek pouches. *Cannomys* has eight mammae.

These animals construct their own burrows; they are rapid diggers, using their powerful teeth as well as their claws in the process. The tunnels are often very deep and located in hard, stony ground. Above ground lesser bamboo rats move slowly, although they are said to be fearless when surprised by an enemy. They leave their burrows in the evening to feed on various plant materials, including shrubs, the young shoots of grasses and cereals, and roots. "Bamboo rat" is somewhat of a misnomer, as all kinds of vegetation are consumed.

They are sometimes common in tea gardens and have been reported to damage tea plants, although the amount of damage they cause may be exaggerated.

This animal is eaten by many of the Burmese hill tribes.

Rodentia; Family: MURIDAE

OLD WORLD RATS AND MICE.

THE NATURAL RANGE of the members of this family of 100 genera is Africa, Europe, and Asia (except in the extreme north), England, Japan, the Malayan region, Australia, Tasmania, and Micronesia. The members of the family Muridae are most abundant in the tropics and subtropics in practically all habitats. At the present time the distribution of *Rattus* and *Mus* through introduction by man is nearly world-wide.

In total length, murid rodents range from about 111 mm. (*Micromys*) to 800 mm. (*Phloeomys*). They weigh from 5 to approximately 1,500 grams. The tail is usually naked, scaly, and semi-prehensile in a few climbing forms, but it is well furred in *Crateromys*. Some of the arboreal genera have opposable first digits on the hand or foot with nails on some of the digits instead of claws. The soles of the feet are naked. Only three genera (*Beamys*, *Saccostomus*, and *Cricetomys*) have cheek pouches. Some forms have a spiny pelage. Six subfamilies are recognized. The subfamily Murinae, 70 genera, is nearly world-wide in distribution. The subfamily Dendromurinae is a group of six genera that inhabits Africa. The three genera of the subfamily Otomyinae that inhabit Africa resemble microtine rodents in appearance, with rather large, high-crowned molars. The subfamily Phloeomyinae is a group of seven genera of large rats from the Australian-Oriental region; Rhynchomyinae contains a single genus *Rhynchomys* from Luzon; and Hydromyinae is a group of 13 genera, characterized by the reduction in the dentition, from part of the Australian-Oriental region.

The dental formula is i 1/1, c 0/0, pm 0/0, m 3/3 x 2 = 16, or i 1/1, c 0/0, pm 0/0, m 2/2 x 2 = 12, or (in the genus *Mayermys*, a member of the Hydromyinae from New Guinea) i 1/1, c 0/0, pm 0/0, m 1/1 x 2 = 8. The molars are rooted or rootless and are laminate or cuspidate. The laminae of the molars are not separated by wide folds or valleys, as in the Cricetidae, but are pressed tightly together. When cuspidate, the cusps are arranged in three longitudinal rows, but the inner row is vestigial in some members of the subfamily Dendromurinae. *Hapalomys* is the only genus with three rows of cusps on the lower molars. The cheek teeth are never prismatic, as in the microtines.

Little is known of the habits of members of many genera of this family. Some are terrestrial, others burrowing, climbing, arboreal, or semi-aquatic. Most of the running terrestrial forms are good climbers. There also are a few hopping and jumping forms (*Notomys* and *Lorentzimys*). Murid rodents shelter in tunnels, under suitable objects, in logs, crevices, buildings, in a nest above the ground, or in a hole in a tree trunk. Sometimes they live in abandoned birds' nests. Some forms dig their own burrows, and others occupy the abandoned tunnels of other animals. *Arvicanthis* sometimes lives in abandoned termite mounds which are also occupied by elephant shrews (*Elephantulus*). Members of the genus *Leporillus* often build large nests of sticks on the ground, and members of the subfamily *Otomyinae* frequently pile sticks and weeds together for shelter. *Mus musculus* (the house mouse) and several species of *Rattus* and *Acomys* often occupy shelters made by man. Murid rodents are diurnal or nocturnal. The arboreal forms are usually nocturnal. Some members are gregarious, dwelling in groups or colonies, others live alone and associate in pairs or small family groups.

Most genera feed on various plant material and invertebrates. Some forms include in their diet small lizards, snakes, and the eggs and nestlings of birds, and the aquatic forms in Hydromyinae feed extensively on mussels, crustaceans, snails, and fish. Those that live near human habitation eat practically any food that is available. Seeds and other plant material are sometimes stored for winter use, although there are no reported cases of hibernation in the family Muridae.

The gestation periods range from about 18 to 42 days, and the number in a litter ranges from 1 to 22. The common house mouse may begin to breed when 35 days old, but the majority of individuals of most genera do not conceive until several months after birth. In the warmer parts of their range, most forms breed throughout the year, often with several peaks of gestation. In the wild, most individuals live less than two years, and many less than one year. An *Arvicanthis niloticus* lived in captivity for six years, eight and one-half months. The population of some species, particularly certain Australian species, seems to have declined to a great degree.

The house mouse and the albino strain of the black rat (*Rattus rattus*) are used extensively in laboratory research. Some forms occasionally damage crops and young trees, and they often harbor various diseases. On a world-wide basis, the direct damage caused by black and norway rats reaches billions of dollars.

It is believed that the Muridae did not emerge until late in Miocene times. The geological range of this family is the Pliocene to the Recent in Europe and Asia, the Pleistocene to the Recent in Australia, the Recent in Africa, and throughout the world after introduction by man. Four genera, now extinct, are known from the Pleistocene of the Old World: *Rhagamys*, from Sardinia, Corsica, and Tavolarna; *Parapodemus*, from Italy; *Stephanomys*, from China; and *Coryphomys*, from the East Indies.

Asiatic Climbing Rat (*Hapalomys longicaudatus*), photos by Jane Burton. Skull, photo by P. F. Wright of specimen in U.S. National Museum.

ASIATIC CLIMBING RATS, MARMOSET MICE.

THE SINGLE SPECIES, *H. longicaudatus*, is known from the Malay Peninsula, Tenasserim, Thailand, Indo-China, and Hainan.

The length of the head and body is about 120 to 135 mm., and the length of the tail is about 140 to 170 mm. In some forms the tail is considerably longer than the head and body, in others it is slightly longer. The fur is thick and soft. The coloration above is buffy, dull reddish gray, or brownish gray; the sides are generally paler than above, and the under parts, including all four legs to below the knee, are white. The limbs are usually buffy gray, and the hands and feet are buffy gray or brownish white. The tail is thinly haired and sometimes pencilled terminally. The vibrissae are prominent and slightly longer than the head.

The hind feet are specialized for arboreal life in that they have enlarged toepads consisting of two flat plates with a groove between them; the toes are long and slender, the middle three are almost equal in length. The large toe is wide, without a claw, and opposable. An opposite large toe is rare in other orders of mammals. There are four fingers—numbers two through four each have a small claw nearly embedded in the pad. The first finger is said to be little more than a slight projection on the inner side of the hand without trace of a nail. The general body form is rat-like. Females have eight mammae (?).

The incisors are broadened and powerful. This is the only genus of the family Muridae with three rows of cusps on the lower cheek teeth. Some authorities consider that the presence of three rows of tubercles on the lower molar teeth indicates that this animal has retained the characteristics of its primitive ancestors to a greater degree than any other Muridae. This information suggests that the ancestors of *Hapalomys* were arboreal.

Specific habits and biology of this climbing murid rodent are not recorded.

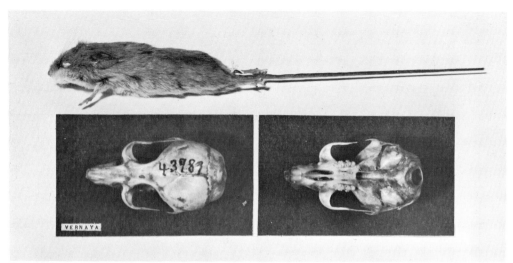

Vernay's Climbing Mouse (*Vernaya fulva*), photos from American Museum of Natural History.

VERNAY'S CLIMBING MICE.

THE SINGLE SPECIES, *V. fulva*, is native to tangled thickets of low shrubbery in rocky outcrops of mountain ridges and slopes at about 2,250 meters elevation in northern Burma, and in southwestern China. Although there are few specimens presently classified within this species, it is possible that other specimens of this genus may be in collections under the name of *Chiropodomys* or *Vandeleuria*, or possibly *Micromys*, as these genera are so similar in general appearance that they can only be distinguished by minute, and sometimes microscopic, examination.

The length of the head and body is about 90 mm., and the length of the tail is approximately 115 mm.

The nature of the pelage, the long, non-tufted tail, and the reddish color of the coat resemble characteristics typical of *Vandeleuria*. *Vernaya* differs from *Chiropodomys* and *Vandeleuria* in the development of the digits of the hands and feet. In *Vernaya* all digits except the pollex, which is vestigial and has an extremely small flat nail, have characteristic pointed claws. The incisor teeth are not grooved.

A search of the literature reveals that little has been recorded on the biology and life habits of this small, long-tailed mouse. Although *Vernaya* reportedly appears to be rare, this may not be true since they live in a restricted range and in a habitat that is difficult to penetrate. In addition, they are wary of man and evade his traps well.

LONG-TAILED CLIMBING MICE; PODI-GAS MIYA OR
KOSATTA-MIYA, SUND'-ELLI (native names).

THE SINGLE SPECIES, *V. oleracea*, inhabits Ceylon,
the southern peninsula of India, Kumaon, Nepal,
Assam, Burma, Indo-China, and Thailand and is said
to have been recorded from Yunnan, China.

The length of the head and body is about 55 to
85 mm., and the length of the tail is usually 90 to
130 mm. The upper parts vary from light buffy
through dull brown to dark reddish brown, and the
under parts are white or cream color. The fur is full,
soft, and almost silky. The tail is fairly well haired
but is not tufted at the tip as in *Chiropodomys*.

This genus of small tree-mice is distinguished by
the structure of the hands and feet and by features of
the teeth and skull. The first and fifth digits on both
the hand and the foot have a flat nail instead of a
claw; the claws on the remaining digits are small.
The limbs are adapted to grasping and climbing by
the opposition of the first digit on both the hand and
the foot, the shortness of the foot, and the development of the terminal pads of the fingers and toes.
This genus may be distinguished from *Chiropodomys*,
which has similar hands and feet, by its mouse-like
size and non-tufted tail. Females of *Vandeleuria* have
eight mammae.

These rodents are nocturnal and essentially arboreal. They usually spend the day in a nest above
the ground or in a hole in a tree trunk. They are quite
active as they run about among branches and twigs,
using the tail as a balancing organ as they run up or
down vertical shoots and out to the tips of slender
twigs. Sometimes the long, almost prehensile tail is
wound loosely around a twig to steady the animal.
Long-tailed climbing mice are much less active and
slower on the ground where they come only to collect
leaves and grasses for their nests.

Vandeleuria usually builds its nests in the branches
of a tree or shrub or occasionally on rooftops. The
nest is made of grass sometimes mixed with dried
leaves. The young are born and raised in such a
shelter. There are usually three or four to a litter,
although litters of six individuals have been seen.
Apparently, the older males live alone.

The diet in the wild is probably fruit and the buds
and shoots of trees and shrubs. An individual kept
in captivity thrived on bread, milk, and such fruits as
plantains and pawpaw. This captive specimen became fairly tame after a few weeks and spent most of
the day asleep with its tail curled around its body.

VANDELEURIA

Long-tailed Climbing Mouse (*Vandeleuria oleracea*),
photo by Howard E. Uible of skin in U.S. National
Museum.

Amami Spinous Rat (*Tokudaia osimensis*), photo by Hajeme Tezuka through Michi Nomura.

LIUKIU (RIU KIU) SPINY RATS, RYUKYU SPINY RATS.

THIS GENUS was erected by N. Kuroda for the animal formerly referred to as *Rattus jerdoni osimensis*. It is named after the Japanese zoologist, M. Tokuda. The single species, *T. osimensis*, is found on the Amami-Ōshima and Okinawa islands in the Liukiu (Riu Kiu) island chain.

The length of the head and body is 125 to 175 mm., and the length of the tail is 100 to 125 mm. The upper parts are mixed black and orange-tawny, and the under parts are grayish white with a faint orange wash. The tail is bicolored throughout. Externally, these animals look like large voles. The body is short and thick, and the pelage is dense. Two types of hairs are noted: fine hairs and coarse, grooved spines. The latter are present on all parts of the body except for the region around the mouth and the ears, feet, and tail. The dorsal spines are black throughout, and the ventral spines are usually white with rufous tips.

Females have four mammae.

Thirteen specimens in the U.S. National Museum were collected on northern Okinawa in a thick, shrubby forest, about 3 meters high, with an undergrowth of coarse grasses and brake ferns. A piece of spiny skin found on a trail was the first indication of the presence of this species on Okinawa Island.

Old World Harvest Mice (*Micromys minutus*), photo by Eric J. Hosking.

OLD WORLD HARVEST MICE; RATS DES MOISSONS, ZWERGMÄUSE, DWERGMUIZEN, MOU-TOU-SHOUS, CHÔSEN KAYANEZUMI (local vernaculars).

THE SINGLE SPECIES, *M. minutus*, inhabits Great Britain, most of Europe, and parts of Asia. These rodents live in tall vegetation such as hedgerows, weedbeds, tall grass, reeds, and bamboo thickets.

The length of the head and body is 55 to 75 mm.; the length of the tail is 50 to 75 mm.; and the weight is 5 to 7 grams. The pelage is brownish with a yellowish or russet tinge on the upper parts and white to buffy beneath. The tail is bicolored. The fur is somewhat longer in winter than in summer. These animals are among the smallest rodents.

Their small size is typical as are their short rounded heads, small rounded ears, fairly broad feet, and hairless condition of the upper portion of the tip of the tail. The foot structure facilitates scampering up stems, and the nakedness of the tail indicates that it is semi-prehensile.

Nests of members of this genus are more or less spherical, about 60 to 130 mm. in diameter, and are composed of blades of grass and other vegetation entangled and woven compactly. They are located 1 to 1.3 meters above the ground and have no regular opening. The animals push their way out of the sphere at any convenient spot. Except for the breeding season, these mice live in holes and under haystacks or straw. They do not hibernate. Harvest mice are diurnal rather than nocturnal in their habits as they climb about thick vegetation seeking seeds and insects in the daytime. It is said that insects form a large part of their diet during the summer. Occasionally, quantities of seeds are stored for use during the winter.

The litter size is generally 5 to 9, although as many as 12 young have been noted. The young are born in a nest in the trees after a gestation period of about 21 days. The life span is approximately 2½ years.

Although *Micromys* is widely distributed, in areas where modern farm machinery is used these little mice appear to be on the decrease. Their food and shelter may be destroyed by reaping machines which leave a much shorter stubble than does a manual scythe.

Old World Wood or Field Mice (*Apodemus agrarius*), photos by Ernest P. Walker.

OLD WORLD WOOD AND FIELD MICE; SOURIS LAYERS, BRANDMÄUSE, BOSMUIZEN, RATONES DEL CAMPO, CHOSEN SESUZI-NEZUMI, HANTO-AKANE-ZUMI, MULOTS (local vernaculars).

THIS GENUS of seven species (?) inhabits the temperate and subtropical regions of the Old World from Ireland to Japan and Formosa south to northern Burma and the Mediterranean region of Africa. Habitats include woodlands, grassy fields, and alpine meadows. *Apodemus* has recently been found in northern Formosa in grass and wild ginger growths adjacent to hillside rice paddies at an elevation of about 70 to 75 meters.

The length of the head and body is 60 to 125 mm., and the length of the tail is 70 to 125 mm. The tail may be shorter or longer than the head and body. Adults usually weigh from 15 to 25 grams. The fur is usually soft, although it may be bristly in *A. speciosus*, and the tail is moderately haired. The general coloration above is grayish buff, grayish brown, brown mixed with yellow or red, light brown, or pale sand-colored. The under parts are white or grayish, often suffused with yellow, and the hands and feet are usually white. Some forms have a reddish-yellow chest patch, and *A. agrarius* has a black mid-dorsal stripe. The tail is not prehensile like that of the Old World harvest mouse (*Micromys*), which it resembles in general appearance. The distinguishing features of *Apodemus* are in the skull and teeth. Females have six or eight mammae.

These mice are not such expert climbers as *Micromys* but are more active jumpers. They spend the day in a deep burrow, although *A. flavicollis* occasionally occupies hollow trees. The nest of shredded grass and leaves, usually located in a chamber at the end of the burrow, provides shelter for the adults and the young. Several adults, at least in *A. sylvaticus*, may live in the same nest. Members of this genus normally spend their lives within a diameter of 180 meters.

Apodemus feeds on many kinds of plant material, including grains, seeds, berries, and roots, and on insects. Food may be stored for the winter.

These rodents can mate when several months old, and adult females may have up to six litters in one year. The mating season is not always of the same duration every year. The gestation period is 21 to 29 days, and the number of recorded young is 2 to 9, usually 4 to 6. The females apparently do not permit the males to enter the nest when the young are present. The average life span is probably a year or less. *Apodemus* is usually numerous where the habitat is suitable. *A. sylvaticus* seems to undergo periodic fluctuations in population.

These rodents are sometimes destructive to young cereal crops and to saplings in forest and orchard plantations. *A. speciosus* from Japan is a carrier of scrub typhus, and *A. agrarius* is a possible carrier of hemorrhagic fever.

The type species of the genus is *A. agrarius* (Pallas).

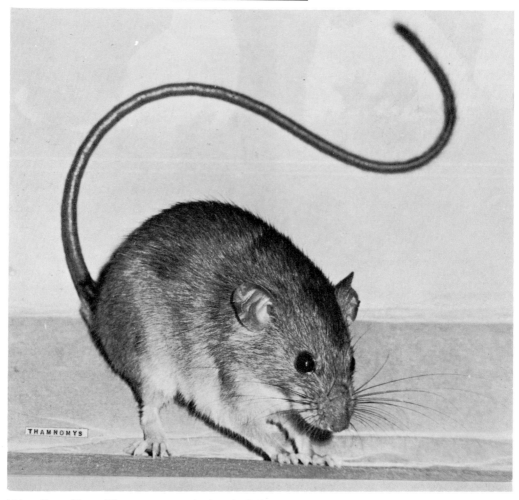

African Forest Mouse (*Thamnomys venustus*), photo by F. Petter.

FOREST MICE; DORINGBOOMROTTE, BOSMUISE, SERERI, NSUNTO, SAKASSE, NYALUTANDA, TENGELA (native names).

THIS GENUS of about four species is found in Africa, from Ghana eastward to the Ruwenzori Mountains in western Uganda. These animals live in forests and brush, among evergreens, and at elevations of more than 4,000 meters.

The length of the head and body is 100 to 145 mm., and the length of the tail is 140 to 200 mm. The pelage is fairly long and soft in some animals but crisp in others. At the higher elevations the fur on the back may be 20 mm. long. The coloration ranges from dark chestnut brown to light reddish brown or orange-rufous. The rump is generally more reddish than the back and the flanks are even lighter, becoming buffy or yellowish gray. The under parts are white. The tail is fairly well haired and slightly tufted at the tip. Members of this genus are characterized by

their long tails, short curved claws, and white under parts. They are small and slender. Some authors state that there are four mammae, but others say that there are six. The hind foot is short and broad, apparently an adaptation for arboreal life. The toes are short except for the great toe, which is somewhat longer.

These rodents are nocturnal and arboreal. They build formless homes of leaves, dried grass, and tangles of vegetation in hollow trees or in the forks of smaller trees. *Thamnomys* spends the daylight hours and rears its young in these nests. At least one observer has noted the parents and the young of two litters occupying the same nest.

Some authors refer *Grammomys* to the genus *Thamnomys* or at most give it subgeneric rank within *Thamnomys*. *Grammomys* is herein treated as a genus.

The type species of the genus is *T. venustus*, Thomas.

Forest Mouse (*Grammomys ruddi*), photo from the Nyasaland Museum through P. Hanney.

BUSH RATS, FOREST MICE, AFRICAN THICKET RATS; MBEWA, AJAKAYUYUIR, NSUMFO, KURU, BOSMUISE (native names).

AT THE PRESENT TIME eight species are recognized. These animals occur from the Sudan southward through Kenya, Uganda, Republic of Congo, Nyasaland, Angola, and southern Africa. They inhabit vegetated areas, usually in drier regions than those occupied by *Thamnomys*.

The length of the head and body measures from about 100 mm. to 160 mm., and the length of the tail, from 130 to 205 mm. The average length is about 110 to 120 mm. for head and body, and for the tail, 160 to 190 mm. The feet measure 22 to 25 mm.; the ear is 15 mm. The coloration on the back ranges from dark brown or reddish brown to brownish gray and clay color, with paler flanks and sides. The under parts are white, creamy white, buffy, or gray. A fairly clear line of demarcation usually is noted between the colors of the upper and under parts, and frequently there is a yellowish or buffy streak at this line extending to the nose. The cheeks are sometimes light-colored. Occasionally there is a dark stripe down the center of the metatarsals. The tail is finely scaled and scantily haired except for the terminal third which is somewhat brushy. The fur is generally soft and of medium length. Black or dark brown hairs are usually present, at least near the middle of the back where they produce a slightly darker or speckled effect.

The external characters are quite similar to *Thamnomys*, but the feet are less specialized for arboreal life; also there are some dental differences. Females usually have four inguinal mammae, sometimes they have two additional abdominal mammae.

In a description of *G. ruddi* from Tette, Portuguese East Africa, Oldfield Thomas and R. C. Wroughton (*Proc. Zool. Soc. Lond.*, 1908, p. 549) quote the field notes of the collector, C. H. B. Grant, as follows: "This species, although undoubtedly common, is difficult to secure owing to its arboreal habits. It inhabits the hollows of decayed and dead trees, in which it makes warm nests of leaves, etc., of no particular shape, nearly filling up the cavity with debris. Strictly nocturnal, one specimen was shot at night whilst climbing among the branches of a small tree when I was setting up for *Galago*." Other meager information regarding *Grammomys* is in close accord with the above statement, but one writer records seeing these rodents climbing in a thicket in the daytime. They are also said to occupy birds' nests.

The type species of the genus is *G. dolichurus* (Smuts).

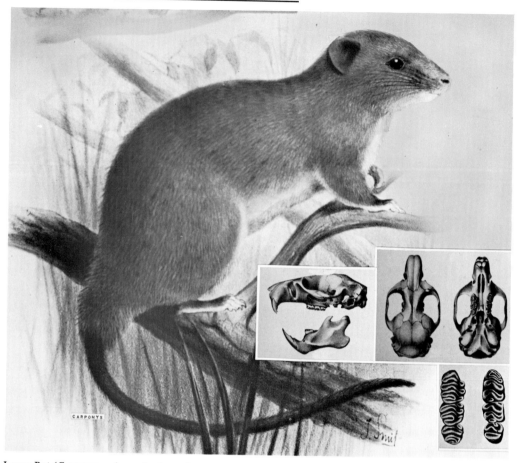

Luzon Rat (*Carpomys melanurus*), photos from *Trans. Zool. Soc. London.*

LUZON RATS.

TWO SPECIES inhabit the highlands of northern Luzon in the Philippines. *C. melanurus* is known from only four specimens, now in the British Museum (Natural History), which were collected on Mount Data. The other species, *C. phaeurus*, is known from three specimens also in the British Museum and collected on Mount Data, and by one specimen in the Chicago Museum of Natural History collected in 1946 in a mossy forest on Mount Kapilingan at 2,110 meters elevation. The Mount Data plateau is described by Whitehead, who collected the British Museum specimens in 1895, as a table-topped mountain from 2,110 to 2,400 meters in elevation, about 5 km. long by about 1/3 km. wide. "The vegetation consists chiefly of oaks and pines, all well clothed in lichen(s) and other . . . plants," and "the undergrowth of bamboo, fern, and raspberry is very thick."

The two species differ in the color of the tail, the amount of hair on the tail, and the size of the teeth. In *C. melanurus* the tail is a deep, shining black and is thickly furred for 25 to 50 mm. next to the body, and the incisors are quite large. In *C. phaeurus*, however, the tail is dark brown or blackish but never

shining black and is furred for only a short distance; it is more thinly haired on the remainder of its surface than in *C. melanurus*, and the incisors are much smaller. The length of the head and body is about 200 mm. in *C. melanurus* and from 175 to 195 mm. in *C. phaeurus*; the length of the tail in the former species is about 210 mm., and 160 to 180 mm. in the latter. The coloration of the two species is similar; the upper parts are deep fulvous, coarsely lined with black, and the under parts are yellowish white. The bases of the hairs are slate or buffy white in *C. melanurus*, but they are not slaty in *C. phaeurus*. The black-tailed form, *C. melanurus*, is quite similar in external appearance to *Batomys*, another rodent that inhabits the same area.

In both species the body form is somewhat heavy. The soft fur is fluffy and thick. The broad hind foot is arboreal in form, but the large toe is clawed and not opposable. The only digit with a nail instead of a claw is the thumb. There are four mammae.

The native Filipinos obtained the specimens of *C. phaeurus* (for Whitehead) by digging them out from among the roots of trees.

The type species of the genus is *C. melanurus*, Thomas.

Mindanao Rats.

THE SINGLE SPECIES, *M. salomonseni*, is known from Mindanao Island in the Philippines, and from three specimens in the Zoologisk Museum, Copenhagen. The type locality is Mt. Katanglad, 1,600 meters high, in Bukidnon Province. The animals were collected as recently as 1951 by Finn Salomonsen, and the genus and species were named and described in 1953 by C. C. Sanborn.

The type specimen, an adult male, measures as follows: length of head and body, 175 mm.; length of tail, 140 mm. The general color of the upper parts is dark brown; the sides are lighter and more buffy; the hairs on the under parts have gray bases and long buffy-yellow tips, and the tail is blackish brown above and below. With the exception of one of the hands, which is wholly white, the hands and feet of the type specimen have a dark line from the wrist and the ankle to the digits; the remainder of the hands, feet, and digits are white. The fur is soft and thick, and the tail is fairly well haired.

The external form does not have any unusual features. The teeth resemble those of *Carpomys*, differing in that they lack one plate in each upper molar tooth. The skull resembles that of *Batomys* in general shape but differs from it in having smaller bullae and shorter palatine foramina.

C. C. Sanborn comments: "Luzon Island has long been known for its great number of peculiar genera of rodents, some of which are found on other islands. This new genus, which resembles in part two of the Luzon genera, shows that on Mindanao also distinct forms developed." (*Vidensk. Medd. fra Dansk naturh. Foren*, 1953, bd. **115**:283–88.)

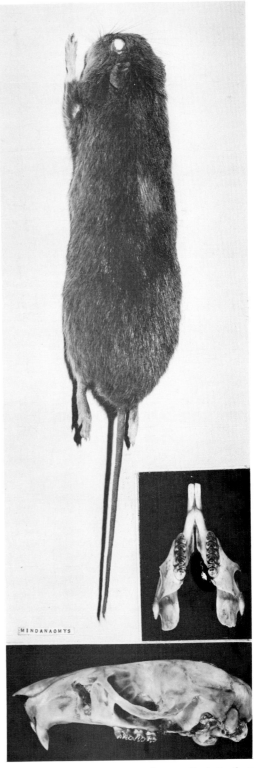

Mindanao Rat (*Mindanaomys salomonseni*), photos from Field Museum of Natural History.

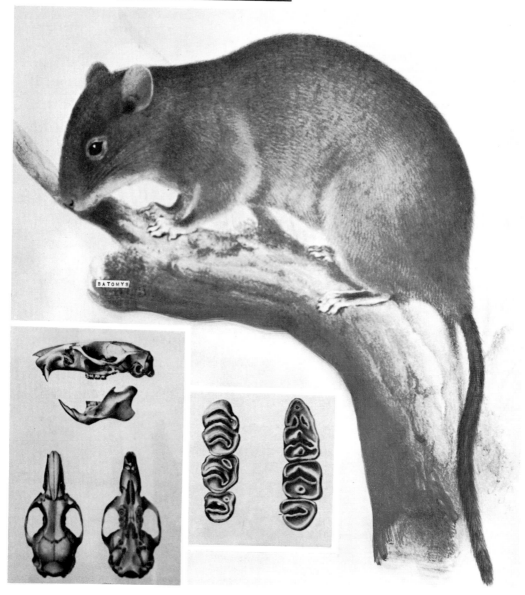

Luzon Forest Rat (*Batomys granti*), photos from *Trans. Zool. Soc. London.*

LUZON FOREST RATS.

TWO SPECIES inhabit the highlands of northern Luzon in the Philippines. *B. granti* is known from five specimens collected on Mount Data, three of which were collected in 1895 for the British Museum (Natural History) and the other two were taken in 1946 and are in the Field Museum of Natural History. The Mount Data plateau is described by Whitehead, the collector of the specimens in the British Museum (Natural History), as a table-topped mountain from 2,100 to 2,400 meters in elevation, about 5 km. long by 1.5 km. wide, with oak and pine growth and a thick undergrowth. The notes on the natural enviro-

ment of specimens deposited in the Field Museum read: "Thick bushes, mossy forest in gully." The other species, *B. dentatus*, is known only from the type specimen in the U.S. National Museum, collected in 1907 at Haight's Place, Benguet, at an elevation of 2,154 meters.

The measurements of the type of *B. granti*, an adult male, are: Head and body 204 mm., tail (probably not perfect) 121 mm. The type of *B. dentatus*, also an adult male, has a head and body length of 195 mm., and length of tail is 185 mm. The upper parts of *B. granti* are fulvous and black, becoming rufous towards the rump, and the under parts are slaty buff. The hands and feet are brown, with whitish digits. The tail is dark brown to black. In *B. dentatus* the upper parts are uniformly light brown, and the under parts are ochraceous buff. The hands and feet are dull buffy gray, and the tail is uniformly blackish brown basally and white toward the tip. The two forms differ in the following characteristics: The under parts in *B. dentatus* are more buffy than those in *B. granti*, the tail is thinly covered and the terminal half is white. The area around the eyes is furred normally, but in *B. granti* the eyes are surrounded by a seminaked or finely haired ring and the tail is covered with thick hair.

These rats resemble *Carpomys* in external characters. *Batomys* is more easily distinguished from *Carpomys* by dental features.

Nothing has been found regarding the biology and natural history of these rats. Native Filipinos, with the aid of their small terriers, captured the specimens of *B. granti* for Whitehead.

The type species of the genus is *B. granti*, Thomas.

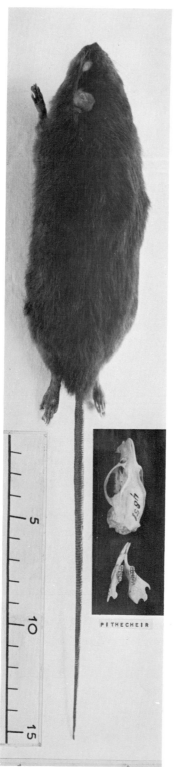

RED TREE RATS, RED BUSH RATS, MALAYAN TREE RATS.

ONLY A LIMITED NUMBER of specimens of the single species, *P. melanurus*, have been obtained. This rodent is native to the lower part of the Malayan Peninsula, Sumatra, and Java, from approximately 1,300 to 1,600 meters elevation. Heavy forest is the usual habitat.

The length of the head and body is 209 to 227 mm., and the length of the tail is 140 to 186 mm. The long, soft, and dense pelage is reddish to tawny on the upper parts but becomes buffy on the sides of the abdomen and rump and blends into pure white on the under parts. On the back, the bases of the individual hairs are mouse gray. The scantily haired tail, ears, hands, and feet are reddish (although in some animals the feet are white). The nails are horn brown, and the whiskers are long and numerous.

The hind foot is modified for arboreal life because the first toe on the hind foot is thumb-like and opposable; thus the origin of the scientific name which means "ape-hand." The pollex is very small and the hallux is large and suited for grasping. The tail is prehensile. The incisors are moderate. There are four mammae.

The movements of this rodent are quite slow and cautious. The tail is used for grasping as the animal climbs and scampers about limbs and branches. The diet may be mostly green plant material, although a captive lived on plantains and crickets.

Two globular nests, made of leaves, were found in Java. One was on the trunk of a tree fern and the other on the trunk of a tree. These nests, held in place by climbing plants, were about 150 mm. in diameter and about 2 and 3.5 meters above the ground. An animal was also noted during the daytime in a hollow tree in a nest made of moss. These nests are used for resting and as shelters in which to give birth and raise the young.

Single young have been noted from April to September in Java. The mother apparently carries her offspring with her when she feeds. The youngster seems to hold onto the teats of its mother with its sharply pointed, bifid incisors. In one instance, a rodent more than half grown was still being carried by its mother.

Malayan Tree Rat (*Pithecheir melanurus melanurus*), photos from Museum Zoologicum Bogoriense.

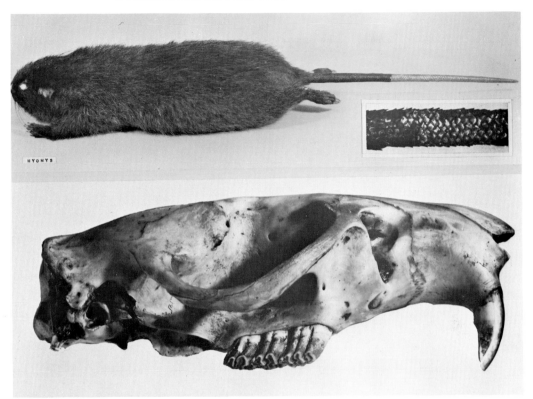

New Guinean Giant Rat (*Hyomys goliath*), photos from British Museum (Natural History). Inset of tail from *Zeitschr. Saugetierk.*

NEW GUINEA GIANT RATS.

THE SINGLE SPECIES, *H. goliath*, is known from New Guinea. Specimens are in British Museum (Natural History), the Paris and Berlin museums, and the American Museum of Natural History.

The length of the head and body is 295 to 390 mm., and the length of the tail is 255 to 380 mm. The fur is coarse and harsh. The color of the upper parts is usually mixed gray and fuscous or dark slaty gray; in some individuals the guard hairs are gray with white subterminal bands, and in others they are black with white tips or are white throughout. The under parts are grayish, buffy gray, or dull white. The tail in *Hyomys* is coarsely scaled and almost naked, and the scales appear even rougher and more naked than those in *Mallomys*.

H. goliath is a large rat with a somewhat bulky form. The large toe has a broad nail. Members of this species have small ears, well-developed claws, and tails with large, overlapping scales. The scales are subject to considerable wear. The skulls are extremely massive and heavy, and the molar teeth are large. The large size of some individuals is caused by a period of growth which apparently continues after maturity is reached. Females have four mammae. *Hyomys* seems to be an isolated genus in the sense that it has no close relatives.

Information on habits and natural history is not recorded. Oldfield Thomas has suggested that the large pointed scales serve a purpose analogous to that of the caudal climbing irons of *Anomalurus*. (Rodentia, Anomaluridae).

Rabbit Rats (*Conilurus albipes*), photo from *The Mammals of Australia*, John Gould.

RABBIT RATS; PELKE (native name for *C. penicillatus*).

THE TWO SPECIES are distributed as follows: *C. albipes*, southern Australia, and *C. penicillatus*, northern Australia and southern New Guinea. Members of this genus have many kinds of habitats: beaches along the salt water, in swamps, grassy plains, and well-timbered areas.

The length of the head and body is 165 to 200 mm., and the length of the tail is 180 to 215 mm. The pelage of *C. albipes* is close and soft, whereas in the other species the pelage is rigid and almost spiny. Coloration of the upper parts ranges from blackish brown to grayish and sandy, with tinges of buff. The under parts and the feet are white or buffy, and occasionally there is a rusty tinge on the nape and crown. The tail of *C. albipes* is distinctly bicolored, dark brown above and white below for its entire length, whereas the tail of *C. penicillatus* is wholly black or has a terminal black tip. The tail is usually uniformly haired through-

out and tufted at the tip. These animals have fairly large ears and a moderately long hind foot.

The beautiful and harmless *C. albipes* apparently has not been reported for about 50 years. It was probably exterminated as civilization advanced and by an increase in fox population.

C. penicillatus is nocturnal in habits, sleeping during the day in hollow trees and limbs, where it constructs a comfortable, well-lined nest of pieces of shrubs, foliage, and grass. In the evenings these animals run along the edge of the surf, apparently feeding on matter that is thrown upon the beach by the waves.

Observers note that the females have been seen scampering about with the young firmly attached to their nipples. This has also been noted in other genera. Also the young of *Conilurus* seem to be more fully developed than the offspring of most other Muridae.

The type species of the genus is *C. albipes* (Lichtenstein).

THICK-TAILED RATS.

THREE SPECIES, *Z. argurus*, *Z. woodwardi*, and *Z. pedunculatus*, are native to Northern Territory of Australia (*Z. argurus* has recently been discovered in Queensland); the first two species are known from the Kimberly district of Western Australia, and *Z. pedunculatus*, from the southern part of the Northern Territory. All three species live in rocky hills and cliffs. *Laomys* is usually regarded as a synonym of *Zyzomys*.

The length of the head and body is 85 to 177 mm., and the length of the tail is 95 to 135 mm. *Z. woodwardi* is the largest of the three species. The pelage is crisp, harsh, and almost spinous; it is brownish, grayish, buffy, to reddish sandy on the dorsal surface, and shades into white on the ventral surface. On some animals all ventral hairs are white, whereas on others the white-tipped hairs have grayish bases. The hands and feet are white. The tail of *Z. woodwardi* is bicolored, as is that of *Z. a. inductus*—brownish on top, white below, and brushed at the tip—the remaining forms have tails that are entirely white.

These delicately built animals have a characteristic thickening of the tail which is caused by a proliferation of the skin at this point; it is not primarily a reservoir of fat, as is the case in some mammals. The oldest individuals have the thickest tails, while the youngest specimens show only a slight enlargement. Many of the specimens have lost part of their tails which would indicate that the terminal section is brittle and breaks easily. This characteristic is noted particularly in *Z. woodwardi*. The feet are short and broad; the ears are fairly small and rounded; and there are four mammae. The skin is quite thin and easily torn.

Little has been recorded concerning the habits of *Zyzomys* except that it is caught most often during the night and thus is assumed to be nocturnal.

The type species of the genus is *Z. argurus* (Thomas).

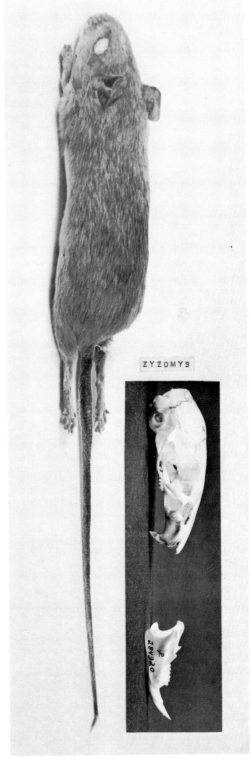

Thick-tailed Rat (*Zyzomys argurus indutus*), photos by P. F. Wright of specimen in U.S. National Museum.

Mantbul (*Mesembriomys gouldi*), photo from *The Mammals of Australia*, John Gould.

MANTBUL (aborigine name for *M. gouldi*); KAT-KOMBA (native name for *M. macrurus*).

THE TWO SPECIES are distributed in Australia as follows: *M. gouldi*, Melville Island, the northern part of the Northern Territory, and northern Queensland; *M. macrurus*, coastal regions of northern Western Australia and the northwestern part of the Northern Territory. They usually inhabit open forests of eucalyptus shrubs.

In *M. gouldi* the length of the head and body is 240 to 350 mm., and the length of the tail is 270 to 390 mm.; in *M. macrurus* the length of the head and body is 240 to 260 mm., and the length of the tail is 350 to 370 mm. The fur in both species is rather rough. The upper parts in *M. gouldi* are yellowish gray or yellowish brown, with black guard hairs, and the under parts are whitish, creamy, or slaty gray. The hands and feet are black, although the feet are irregularly blotched with cream and brown. The upper parts in *M. macrurus* are usually bright rufous or buffy brown; the sides are buffy gray, and the under parts are creamy white. The hands and feet are white. In both *M. gouldi* and *M. macrurus* the tip of the white

tail is tufted, but it is not so well haired near its base, where the scales can be traced.

The ears are moderate in size, and their outer surfaces are quite densely haired. The foreclaws are fairly large, and the hind foot is somewhat broad, with large claws. The skull is heavily built. Females have four mammae.

These rodents are arboreal and nocturnal. During the day they find shelter and rest in hollow trees; at times they live near wooden buildings and climb about the rafters at night. A nest, mainly of leaves and bark, may be located in a tree. One nest, covering part of the main cavity of the trunk, was found in a tree about 3.5 meters above the ground.

The species *M. gouldi* is said to feed chiefly on the fruits of the corkscrew palm (*Pandanus*). It is quick in its movements and capable of inflicting a painful bite. Because of its size and tasty flesh, some native Australians eat *Mesembriomys*.

There are records of one and two young. Individuals were still alive in the London Zoological Gardens almost four years after their arrival.

The type species of the genus is *M. gouldi* (Gray).

Rufous-nosed Rat (*Oenomys hypoxanthus*), photo by F. Petter.

RUFOUS-NOSED RATS; PUCHERANS; ICHIKELA-MANENGA, IKELA-MANENGA, KAMBUNDJA-MANEN-GA, TUMBUNDJA-MANENGA (native names).

THE SINGLE SPECIES, *O. hypoxanthus*, is found in Africa from Kenya and Uganda westward to Ghana and southward through the Congo to northern Angola. These rodents are plentiful in forest clearings from about 300 to 3,000 meters elevation.

The length of the head and body is 135 to 180 mm., and the length of the tail is 170 to 205 mm. The pelage consists of soft, woolly underfur, about 15 to 17 mm. in length, and long, fine, guard hairs, which on the back reach a length of 25 to 30 mm. The general coloration of the upper parts ranges from sepia, rufous, olive, to slate, occasionally brushed with black. The rump is generally somewhat reddish, and the flanks are somewhat lighter than the rump. The nose, or at least the sides of the face, is reddish; this coloration produces the common name, rufous-nosed rats. The under parts are white, often tinged with buff, and some forms have a definite buffy line

where the light color of the under parts joins the darker coloration of the sides. The feet and hands are white, brownish gray, or rufous.

The tail is practically naked so that the large scales are exposed (about 12 scales to the centimeter). The ears are fairly large, rounded, and hairy. The hind feet have naked soles and large plantar pads, and the fifth digit is slightly longer than the first. There are six mammae. The dentition and complex digestive organs indicate that members of this genus are vegetarian. It is reported that *Oenomys* raids the millet and rice crops or other grainfields of the native Africans. In Ghana this species lives in grassy patches in large forest clearings, making a series of tunnels just beneath the surface of the ground and nesting there. These rodents are usually found singly.

One author reports that the breeding season is from October through April; another cites that females, collected in September in Angola, appeared to have been lactating.

These animals are eaten by the African natives.

African Groove-toothed Rat (*Mylomys cuninghamei*), adapted from *Proc. Zool. Soc. London*, St. Leger.

AFRICAN GROOVE-TOOTHED RATS.

THE SINGLE SPECIES, *M. cuninghamei*, inhabits the following localities in Africa: the Sudan, Kenya, Uganda, the Congo, Cameroon, and Ghana. It has been seen in meadows, lowlands, and in orchard-bush country.

The length of the head and body is 135 to 190 mm., and the length of the tail is 100 to 180 mm. The upper parts have a grizzled appearance much like that of *Arvicanthis*, but the hairs are longer and glossier in *Mylomys*. The coloration above in *M. cuninghamei* is yellowish buffy lined with black, brown or dull buffy, or mixed black and buffy. The type specimen of one subspecies (*M. c. richardi* from the Congo) has a pronounced bluish green iridescence on the upper parts. The rump may be ochraceous or rufescent. The under parts are usually white (buff in the sub-species *M. c. richardi*). The upper surfaces of the hands and feet are pale buff, tawny, or black, and the moderately haired tail is dark above and lighter below.

The body form is stocky. Only three digits are well developed on the hands and feet. Each of the upper incisors has a single groove, and the lower incisors are not grooved. *Pelomys* is similar to *Mylomys* in external appearance, but the grooving of its incisors is much less pronounced and the surface structure of the molars is different.

Information on biology and habits is not available.

Shaggy-haired Rat (*Dasymys incomtus rufulus*), photo by Jane Burton.

SHAGGY-HAIRED RATS, MARSH OR WATER RATS; BARASUGBA, GARU, VLEI OR WATERROTTE (native names).

THE SINGLE SPECIES (?), *D. incomtus*, inhabits central and southern Africa. The northern limits of its range are Liberia, Ghana, Nigeria, the Congo, the Sudan, and Ethiopia. Although it has been reported from forests and savannahs in mountains in Nigeria, it is typically an inhabitant of stream banks, reed beds, and marshes.

The length of the head and body is 135 to 190 mm., and the length of the tail is 105 to 185 mm. The tail is usually somewhat shorter than the head and body. The texture of the fur varies widely. In some animals it is long, soft, straight, and silky; in others it is loose and coarse; in still others the hairs are shaggy. This variation produces a harsh coat if the hairs are coarse or a crisp coat if the hairs are fine and only moderately stiff. The hands and feet are usually only scantily haired, and the tail is almost naked. The upper parts are olive-brown, yellowish brown, brownish mixed with black, or slaty black. The under parts are grayish white, whitish, pale buff, or olive-buff. The hands and feet are usually light brownish, and the tail is dark brown above and below, or slightly lighter below.

Dasymys is a thickset, heavy rodent with five digits on the hands and feet. The toes are fairly short, and the claws are not suited to climbing. The small ears are rounded and evenly fringed with hair. The incisors are not grooved. Females have six mammae.

Shaggy-haired rats seem to be active both day and night. They are somewhat aquatic, for they take to the water and swim and dive readily when pursued by an enemy. They feed mainly on vegetation along the shore and on the green shoots of water-loving weeds. In certain areas they are associated with *Otomys* and *Pelomys* and are usually numerous in their habitat. They seem to find shelter in holes above the water level along the banks of streams but do not burrow. Grass nests are located in shallow tunnels among the matted vegetation.

The number of young is usually two to four. Many newborn young and pregnant females have been collected in the Okavage Swamp in southwestern Africa from June to October; a female collected in Angola in August was lactating.

Kusu Rat (*Arvicanthis niloticus*), photo by Ernest P. Walker.

GRASS MICE; KUSUS, ANYOR, GUA, MHONI, YENDAKADZUA, NDIDJIJI (native names).

THIS GENUS of four species (?) inhabits southern Arabia and most of Africa, particularly eastern Africa, south to the Congo and Northern Rhodesia. Grass mice have been reported from savannahs, scrubby thickets, and forests. The elevational range is from sea level to at least 2,000 meters. The striped mice herein treated under *Lemniscomys* have been discussed by some authors under the name *Arvicanthis*.

The length of the head and body is 120 to 190 mm., and the length of the tail is 90 to 160 mm. The tail is usually shorter than the head and body. The hairs are generally coarse and stiff so that the coat is slightly harsh and somewhat spiny. The tail is fairly well haired. The coloration above varies from tawny olive, grayish olive, and light gray to blackish chestnut; a definite buffy tinge is present in some animals, but others are quite light in color. Some forms have a slight dorsal stripe. The tips of the hairs are usually dark or black, but a subterminal band of gray on buffy hair produces a lighter tone in some grass mice. The light-colored forms resemble the American cotton rat (*Sigmodon*). The under parts of *Arvicanthis* are slightly lighter than the upper parts: buffy white or grayish in the light-colored forms and lead color or brownish dark gray in the darker forms. There is usually no sharp line of demarcation between the upper and under parts, but some individuals do have a sharp dividing line. The ears are usually reddish (occasionally brick red); the hands and feet are gray,

yellowish, or almost as dark as the body; and the tail is definitely bicolored. Some grass mice have a small light-colored area back of the ears.

The fifth finger is considerably reduced but is functional and bears a claw. The second, third, and fourth toes are rather long, although the first and fifth are short. The ears are fairly large and rounded. The incisors are not grooved.

Arvicanthis is plentiful over much of its range. Grass mice live in burrows, rubbish heaps, and in stables and barns. Sometimes they take cover in deserted termite mounds with elephant-shrews (*Elephantulus*). The grass nests are often located in their burrows, but nests have been reported on the surface. *Arvicanthis*, taken in Kenya in 1958, showed habits similar to those of *Microtus*. These mice had networks of runways in thick grass cover mixed with dead logs, piles of branches, and similar vegetation. The runways radiated from their nests. Grass mice are gregarious and often live in colonies. Apparently they are diurnal, at least in some areas where they are destroyed by hawks. The Asenga's name for these rodents means "he who walks in the sun."

The diet consists of such diverse items as sweet potatoes, cassava, the leaves and shoots of plants, and grass seeds. *Arvicanthus* digs about in stored grain in search of food.

An individual *A. niloticus* lived in the London Zoo for nearly seven years.

The type species of the genus is *A. niloticus* (Desmarest).

Manipur Bush Rat (*Hadromys humei*), photo from *Proc. Zool. Soc. London.*

MANIPUR BUSH RATS, HUME'S RATS.

THE SINGLE SPECIES, *H. humei*, inhabits Manipur and Assam (India). Seven specimens were collected for the Zoological Survey of India in connection with a scrub typhus outbreak in 1945. The British Museum (Natural History) also has specimens. The specimens collected in 1945 came mainly from an oak parkland habitat, described by M. L. Roonwal (*Trans. Nat. Inst. Sci. India*, 1949, **3**: 67–122) as follows: "Fairly thickly covered semi-scrub of moderately tall oak trees (up to 9–12 meters high)... on hill-sides at 1,200 meters and probably higher altitudes.... Soil loamy with rock beneath and with practically no humus. Usually not associated with streams.... Tree canopy very open. Very tall grass, over 3–4 meters high. Hardly any shrubs. Ground canopy also very open."

The length of the head and body is about 95 to 125 mm., and the length of the tail is about 105 to 140 mm. An adult male weighed 65.5 grams. The fur is thick and soft, and the tail is fairly well haired. The upper parts are blackish gray, the middle area of the back is sometimes darker than the head and shoulders. The rump has a reddish wash. The belly is yellow or orange, with a slaty tinge. The inner sides of the thighs are rufous, and the hands and feet are yellowish white. The tail is distinctly bicolored—black above and whitish below.

The body has a fairly stout form. The fifth finger and the fifth toe are short. The teeth are large and powerful; the incisors are not grooved; and the molars are broad and heavy. Females have eight mammae. The general external appearance of *Hadromys* is similar to that of *Golunda* except that the tail is slightly longer and the fur is not spiny (or somewhat less spiny). The upper incisors in *Golunda* are grooved.

Leaves of grass which had been cut and eaten were found in the stomach of an adult male.

A pregnant female was collected in September.

Indian Bush Rat (*Golunda ellioti gujerati*), photo by P. J. Deoras.

INDIAN BUSH RATS, BUSH-RATS, FIELD-RATS OR COFFEE-RATS; MIYA OR COPPIE-WATTE-MIYA, COPPIE' ELLI OR SARAK' ELLI (native names).

THE SINGLE SPECIES, *G. ellioti*, occurs in Ceylon, the Punjab (India), western Pakistan, Nepal, and Bhutan. It usually inhabits swamps, grasslands, the vegetation at the edges of cultivated areas, and jungles (at least in Ceylon).

The length of the head and body is usually 110 to 150 mm., and the length of the tail, 90 to 130 mm.; the tail is shorter than the head and body. The texture of the pelage varies considerably. In some animals the covering is fairly soft with only a few harsh hairs; in others it is coarse, and the longer hairs, some of which are spiny, are flattened and grooved. The coat is generally thin, but the hairs are rather long. The coloration above is grayish, yellowish brown, reddish brown, or fairly dark brown; the darker color is produced by a fine speckling of fulvous and black hairs. The coloration below is light gray, bluish gray, or whitish.

These rodents are thickset and heavy, rather vole-like in appearance. The head is short and rounded, and the ears are rounded and hairy. The tail, stout at the base, tapers toward the end and is covered with coarse, short hairs. The upper incisors are grooved, and the pattern of the molar teeth is somewhat unusual. Females have eight mammae.

These animals generally live alone or in family groups; they are most active in the early morning and evening. Some observers have stated that *Golunda* is slow in its movements; others consider it to be quick. These rodents are good climbers, but they usually move about on the ground in definite runways. Their food is almost exclusively plant material, normally the roots and stems of such plants as the "dub" or "nariyali grass" (*Cynodon*). When coffee was raised in Ceylon, bush rats became extremely abundant and did great damage to the crops by eating the buds and blossoms of the coffee plant. It has been suggested that they migrated to the plantations, but it is possible that they actually increased in numbers when the food supply was abundant. Coffee is no longer planted in Ceylon, and the number of bush rats has decreased significantly.

Golunda rarely burrows, locating its nest on the ground or just above the ground, usually in dense grass. The globular nest is made of plant fibers and is from 150 to 230 mm. in diameter. The usual number of young is three or four.

892

Groove-toothed Swamp Rat (*Pelomys campanae*), photo by F. Petter.

GROOVE-TOOTHED SWAMP RATS, CREEK RATS; NYABE, SINZA, MINDE KUBWA, MENDI, DIVUDI, MAVUDI, GROEFTANDROTTE (native names).

IN REGARD to *Pelomys*, J. R. Ellerman (*Families and Genera of Living Rodents* [London, 1941], p. 127) comments: "In this genus, I include all the *Arvicanthis*-like rats from Africa in which the incisors are grooved, except *Mylomys*." Three subgenera are recognized: *Pelomys* with four species, from Mozambique and southwestern Africa north to Uganda and the Congo; *Desmomys*, Thomas, 1910, with three species from Ethiopia; *Komemys*, De Beaux, 1924, with the species *P. isselli* from Kome Island in Lake Victoria; the species *P. minor* from Northern Rhodesia, Angola, and the Congo; and the species *P. hopkinsi* from Uganda and the Congo. Members of *Pelomys* usually inhabit wet, boggy areas, the banks of streams and lakes, and meadows near water. They sometimes live in grassy areas at the edges of a forest.

The length of the head and body is 125 to about 215 mm., and the length of the tail is usually 100 to 180 mm. The tail may be shorter, the same length, or longer than the head and body. The hairs are usually coarse, slightly stiff, and shiny, sometimes with a greenish brown or olive iridescence. The tail is moderately haired. The upper parts are tawny yellowish, yellow and black, dusky and tawny, or buffy clay, blending into the gray, buffy, or whitish of the under parts. Some forms have a single, dark, mid-dorsal stripe, which is often indistinctly defined from the upper parts. The tail is frequently dark above and light below. The nose may be more brightly colored than the face, and the ears are usually thinly covered with reddish hairs.

The short fifth finger is clawed in the subgenus *Komemys*, but it lacks a nail in the subgenus *Pelomys* and in two of the three species in the subgenus *Desmomys*. The outer toes are short. Females have eight mammae. *Pelomys* occurs with *Dasymys* and *Otomys* in certain areas; it may be distinguished from *Dasymys* by its grooved upper incisors, and from *Otomys* by its lower incisors which are not grooved.

These rodents, at least those of the subgenus *Pelomys*, seem to be diurnal. They have been observed sunning themselves and diving into the water during the day. They feed on swamp vegetation. Although in certain areas they are reported to burrow, they usually live above ground. At least one litter is reported to have been born in April in Angola (usually two or three young).

Certain natives of Angola seem to relish the flesh of *P. fallax*.

The type species of *Pelomys* is *P. fallax*, Peters; the type species of the subgenera are: *Komemys* = *P. isseli*, de Beaux and *Desmomys* = *P. harringtoni* (Thomas).

Striped Grass Mouse (*Lemniscomys striatus striatus*), photo from New York Zoological Society.

SINGLE STRIPED FIELD MICE, STRIPED GRASS MICE, ZEBRA RATS; NYANGDOR, SIKE, EENSTREEPMUIS, OHUAKUA AND ONGELA, MAKLANGANE, MATSUTSA, MHONI, NTUNU, CHIWANGARANGA, SHANCHEY, GESTREEPTE MUIZEN, USALAMSANYA, MPERA, MPONI, NANGWARI (native names).

THIS GENUS of six species is found throughout most of the African continent. These rodents live in a variety of habitats: grass near swamps, vleis, forests, river banks, reed beds, plains, and bush country. In Ghana *L. striatus* is most typical of the induced grass areas in forest clearings. The elevational range is up to about 2,100 meters.

The length of the head and body is 100 to 140 mm., and the length of the tail is 102 to 155 mm. These animals are covered by thin fur which is unusually rough and coarse.

Three distinct patterns of coloration are noted in striped grass mice. In one group a dark mid-dorsal stripe extends from between the eyes in some animals to the base of the tail. On either side of the body alternate light and dark stripes may extend from the shoulders onto the rump. There are usually five or six of the wide light stripes, but they are shorter than the mid-dorsal stripe. The intervening dark stripes are about the same width as the light stripes; they generally have a faint light stripe, or a row of light spots, extending along their middle line. The combination of dark colors ranges from a medium clay color through dull, dark browns to almost black, and the light stripes range from a light buffy to a dull, dark-clay color. The ground color of the sides and those areas of the upper parts that are not striped ranges from clear buffy through light clay to fairly

dark gray tinged with buffy. The under parts vary from white or buffy white to medium buffy gray. The tail above is almost as dark as the mid-dorsal stripe, and the sides and under portions of the tail are almost as light as the light stripings.

The second group of *Lemniscomys* has essentially the same pattern as the heavily striped group except it has rows of more or less confluent light spots instead of light stripes. In some animals the spots are definitely separated, and in others they tend to run together on their long axis.

The third group has only the mid-dorsal dark stripe, and the remaining color pattern is similar to the ground color of the striped forms.

There are eight mammae, two pairs are pectoral and two are inguinal.

Striped grass mice are diurnal and terrestrial, although *L. striatus* is sometimes trapped at night in Ghana. One author mentions that these mice, at the slightest sound, will jump straight into the air and then scamper hurriedly away. Under normal conditions they live in the grass nests which they have built, but during forest fires these mice seek refuge in the burrows of other animals. They feed upon all kinds of vegetable matter such as bananas, cassava, and potatoes, but they show a preference for soft seeds. In captivity they are omnivorous.

From 2 to 12 young have been reported, the usual number is 2 to 5. Some forms breed throughout the year, and others seem to have definite breeding seasons. This genus has bred in the Pretoria Zoo and in several British zoos.

The type species of the genus is *L. barbarus* (Linnaeus).

Striped Field Mouse (*Rhabdomys pumilio*), photo by Don Davis.

STRIPED FIELD MICE, FOUR-STRIPED GRASS MICE; STREEPROT, STREEPMUIS, SCHANCY (native names).

THE SINGLE SPECIES, *R. pumilio*, occurs from Tanganyika, Kenya, and Uganda southward to the extreme southern tip of the African continent. These rodents have been noted in dry river beds, tall grass, semi-dry vlei country, high velds, bush and scrub country, edges of forests, and at the base of hills; they are especially attracted to cultivated areas. Members of this genus are also found along stone walls and in outbuildings.

The length of the head and body is from 90 to 130 mm., and the length of the tail varies from 80 to 135 mm. The fur is quite coarse. The striping on the dorsal surface on most forms is constant, but the tones of the color vary considerably. The striping consists of a light mid-dorsal streak which extends from the back of the neck to the base of the tail. This streak is bordered by two dark lines on each side. One form has only two dark lines, others have the customary four. The dark stripes range from light golden brownish or clay color to dark chocolate-brown or almost black. The light stripes range from pale yellowish gray to buff. The remainder of the upper parts differ in color from yellowish gray or pale yellowish brown to light grayish brown. The under parts are lighter than above. The tail is scaly and thickly covered with short hairs.

These medium-sized mice have tails that are generally slightly shorter than the head and body. The females have four pairs of mammae. This genus is distinguished from *Lemniscomys* by its functional fifth digit. The skull is similar to that of *Arvicanthis*.

Striped field mice are rather common, diurnal, and enjoy basking in the sun on cool days. Some authors report that *Rhabdomys* lives in burrows with a single slanting entrance which is usually located near a shrub; others have noted these rodents in nests made from grass, leaves, fibers, and moss. The nests are built in a dense shrub, a bunch of grass, or among tree roots. Although these animals are not classed as arboreal, they have been seen climbing about low branches of shrubs. Their diet consists of grass, bark, roots, seeds, berries, and cultivated grains, as well as snails, insects, and eggs.

It is said that they breed from September through April. Reports indicate that they have 4 litters per year, with 4 to 12 individuals per litter. Puberty is attained at about 3 months of age. Family groups of 12 to 30 have been noted living in the same nest.

One-striped Mouse (*Hybomys* [*Typomys*] *trivirgatus pearcei*), photo by Jane Burton.

ONE-STRIPED MICE.

THE TWO SPECIES are distributed as follows: *H. trivirgatus*, Ghana and Nigeria, and *H. univittatus*, Liberia, Gaboon, Nigeria, and Uganda. These mice prefer a forest habitat.

The length of the head and body ranges from 108 to 130 mm., and the length of the tail is from 95 to 115 mm.; both species are about the same size. The fur is usually soft, although inclined to be coarse in some individuals; the tail is thinly haired. The coloration of the upper parts ranges from light yellowish brown to quite dark brown, almost black in some individuals. Generally, the coloration of *H. univittatus* is much darker than that of *H. trivirgatus*. The former species usually has a dark brown or black mid-dorsal stripe that extends from the nape to the base of the tail. The latter species usually has a dark mid-dorsal stripe with a lateral stripe close to it on either side. These lines are often faint or entirely lacking in some individuals. The under parts range from tawny, ochraceous, to grayish white. The upper surfaces of the hands and feet are usually the same color as the back; the tail is similarly colored and in some cases it is entirely black.

Although *Hybomys* externally resembles *Arvicanthis* in such features as its dorsal stripe, it differs from that genus by its more slender form and almost naked tail. The soles of the feet have five well-developed tubercles and a rudimentary sixth, whereas the palms have six tubercles that are well developed. The thumb is small with a blunt nail. The hind foot is narrow. There are two or three pairs of mammae.

Little has been published regarding the habits and general biology of members of this genus, although they seem to be fairly common throughout their range. In Ghana *H. trivirgatus* is quite uncommon and is found on the ground in high forest areas or more commonly in clearings or secondary forest. This species appears to be largely or entirely diurnal. They have been reported to live around water and swim well. They are known to feed on fruit and have been reported to be extremely destructive to cassava roots.

Pregnant females with one to three embryos have been noted. From Ghana there is a report that young have been born there in August.

The type species of the genus is *H. univittatus* (Peters).

Soft-furred Rats (*Millardia gleadowi*), photo from *Proc. Zool. Soc. London.*

SOFT-FURRED RATS.

THE THREE SPECIES of *Millardia* are distributed as follows: *M. meltada*, Ceylon and India north to the Punjab; *M. gleadowi*, West Pakistan; and *M. kathleenae*, Burma. The species *M. meltada* has been noted in tall swamp grass, in dried swamps, in broken rocky ground, and in cultivated fields.

The length of the head and body and the length of the tail in the three species are as follows: *M. meltada*, about 105 to 160 mm., and 95 to 140 mm.; *M. gleadowi*, 97 mm. or slightly less, and about 75 mm.; *M. kathleenae*, about 130 to 160 mm., and the same measurement for the tail. A specimen of *M. meltada* weighed 70 grams. The fur is soft. The upper parts in *M. meltada* are sandy gray, grayish brown, or whitish buff lined with brown, and the under parts are whitish or grayish. The tail is dark above and light below. In *M. gleadowi* the upper parts are light grayish brown or sometimes fawn-colored, and the undersides are white. The tail is light brown above and white below. *M. kathleenae* is a light-colored form with a white-tipped tail.

This genus resembles *Rattus* in appearance; *Millardia* has been characterized by the suppression (total or partial) of the pads of the soles of the feet. The fifth toe is short. The ears are rather large, and the tail is quite well haired. The number of mammae differs in the three species: *M. meltada* has eight; *M. gleadowi* has six; and *M. kathleenae* has four.

M. meltada is said to live in groups of from two to six individuals, at least in parts of India. It shelters in short burrows, in stone heaps, and in the abandoned burrows of other rodents. During the hot months it often seeks the cracks formed in the soil as it dries. Many individuals are trapped in these fissures with the coming of the rains. The diet consists of grain, seeds, and swamp vegetation. Litter size is usually six to eight. *M. meltada* may increase in number to plague proportions at times and cause considerable damage to crops.

In the Clifton Plain, Karachi, *M. gleadowi* is reported to shelter in burrows at the base of saltwort bushes. These rodents leave their burrows toward nightfall and become quite active.

The type species of the genus is *M. meltada* (Gray).

897

LARGE-TOOTHED GIANT RATS, MILLARD'S RATS.

THE SINGLE SPECIES, *D. millardi*, inhabits the Darjeeling area of Assam southeastward to the Laos region in Indo-China from about 1,000 to 1,800 meters in elevation.

The length of the head and body is 228 to 290 mm., and the length of the tail is 308 to 335 mm. The somewhat coarse pelage is short and thin, and the individual hairs on the back are 15 to 16 mm. in length. The general coloration of the upper parts is olive-brown to grayish or smoky brown, becoming lighter on the sides as it blends into cinnamon-drab or pale brownish of the under parts. The gular, inguinal, and axillary areas are creamy or white. The ears and hands are brown and the fingers are white. The finely ringed tail (about 10 scales to the centimeter) is scantily sprinkled with fine short hairs.

Dacnomys is a large, ordinary-looking rat, with no special external distinguishing characteristics. It derives one of its common names from the relatively large size of the molar teeth. The sole pads are large and rounded, and the fifth toe of the hind foot is without a claw. The number of mammae is eight.

Little is known about numbers of this genus at the present time, and few specimens are available for study. Information is limited concerning habits and general biology.

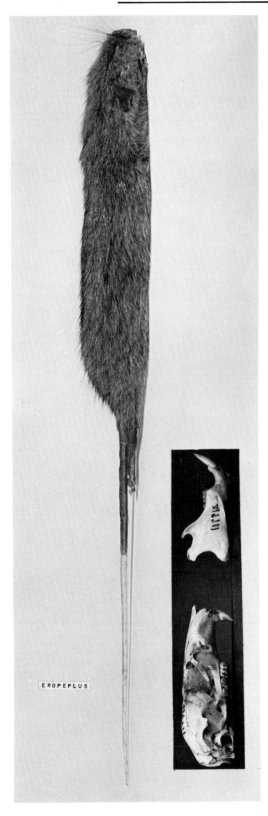

EROPEPLUS

CELEBES SOFT-FURRED RATS.

THE SINGLE SPECIES, *E. canus*, lives only on Celebes Island (Sulawesi). Several specimens have been collected at about 1,800 meters' elevation. The type specimen is at the U.S. National Museum and was collected in 1917 at Goenoeng Lehio in Middle Celebes. The British Museum (Natural History) also has specimens.

The length of the head and body is 195 to 230 mm., and the length of the tail is 265 to 290 mm. The soft pelage is made up of a coat of underfur, which is about 25 to 28 mm. in length, and of longer guard hairs, which are 35 to 45 mm. long on the back and flanks. The general coloration of the upper parts is brownish gray. Each hair has a pale slate base which terminates in a 3 to 5 mm. tip of pale buff color. The under parts are light gray, but there is no sharp line of demarcation. The feet are scantily covered with short black hairs; the whiskers are also black. The moderately haired tail is long, and the terminal third (or half) is white.

Eropeplus is similar to *Rattus* but is distinguished from that genus chiefly by its longer tooth row. The feet are normal.

Celebes Soft-furred Rat (*Eropeplus canus*), photo by Howard E. Uible of specimen in U.S. National Museum. Inset of skull: Photo by P. F. Wright of specimen in U.S. National Museum.

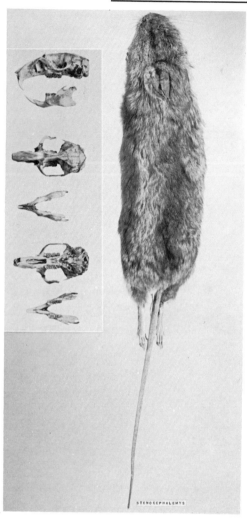

Ethiopian Narrow-headed Rat (*Stenocephalemys albo-caudata*), photo from Carnegie Museum. Inset: Photo from *Ann. Carnegie Mus.*

ETHIOPIAN NARROW-HEADED RATS.

THE SINGLE SPECIES, *S. albocaudata*, occurs only in the Chilalo Mountains in southern Ethiopia. Five specimens, collected in 1911 at about 3,000 meters elevation, are the only known examples of this genus for study. These specimens are in the Carnegie Museum at Pittsburgh and the U.S. National Museum (and the British Museum ?).

The length of the head and body is about 145 to 190 mm., and the length of the tail is about 145 to 165 mm. The thick fur is soft and long, and the tail is fairly well haired. The coloration of the back is mottled umber, the mottling due to intermixed black hairs. The sides are pinkish buff, and the under parts are gray. The outer parts of the upper arms and thighs are pinkish buff mixed with gray, and the inner parts are gray. The lower arms and legs, the hands and feet, and the tail are white.

Stenocephalemys is distinguished from *Rattus* by its extremely constricted frontal skull bones. *Dasymys* also has narrowed frontals but differs from *Stenocephalemys* in molar pattern and other distinctive skull features. The narrow-headed rat from Ethiopia has large ears and a small first digit on the hands which has a nail instead of a claw.

Habits and biology are not recorded in the literature.

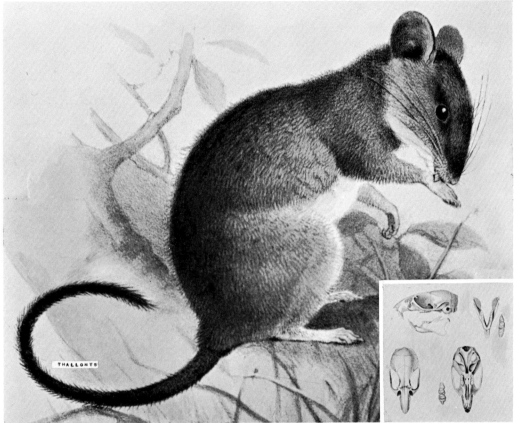

Acacia Rat (*Thallomys nigricauda*), photo from *Proc. Zool. Soc. London.* Inset: (*T. namaquensis arborarius*), photo from *Naturw. Reise nach Mossambique*, W. Peters.

ACACIA RATS, TREE RATS, BUSH RATS; BOOM-ROTTE.

THIS GENUS is composed of five species which have a combined range from Kenya to Angola southward through southern West Africa, Rhodesia, Bechuanaland, and the Transvaal to the southern tip of South Africa. These mice are generally found in the vicinity of acacia and camelthorn trees that are located near watercourses and old river beds.

The length of the head and body is about 120 to 158 mm., and the length of the tail is 130 to 210 mm. The fur is generally quite long. In some animals it is soft and fine, in others it is rather coarse. The coloration of the upper parts ranges from light buff through yellow-fawn to brownish gray. The dorsal surface is usually darker than the sides, and the sides of the face are generally grayish; the under parts are white. *T. nigricauda* has a black tail, but in other forms the tails are generally brown. The hands and feet are light grayish or white. The scantily haired ears have a reddish tinge.

Members of the genus *Thallomys* are characterized by their long tails and short feet. There are three pairs of mammae.

Acacia rats, as the name indicates, usually are found near acacia trees where they live in crevices in the trunk, under loose bark, in holes in the ground at the base of a tree, in hollow limbs, or in the branches of a tree where they build nests of twigs and other vegetable matter. The animals spend the daylight hours in these retreats and emerge after sunset to scamper about the limbs or search for food. A large tree occasionally harbors a small colony of *Thallomys*. This group probably consists of a family, since there are seldom more than two pairs of adults in the colony and the other mice are not yet mature. These animals are shy but quite active; they peer from their nests at the slightest strange noise and run to the dense foliage to escape danger. Occasionally, they will drop to the ground in an effort to escape. They are expert climbers. These rodents feed upon seeds of various kinds as well as berries and the gum of thorn trees; apparently they do not drink water.

Pregnant females with one to four embryos have been noted. In captivity they have mated quite regularly during the summer months, but not in winter.

The type species of the genus is *T. nigricauda* (Thomas).

TYPICAL RATS; RATTEN.

Rattus IS A difficult genus to define. It has more named forms than any other genus of mammals, about 570 in all. *Rattus* has the largest number of forms in tropical southeastern Asia and Africa, but it also lives in nearly all parts of the world and in practically all land habitats.

The length of the head and body is 80 to 300 mm. The tail may be shorter or longer than the head and body and is usually thinly haired. In some forms the pelage is soft and in others it is coarse, but in some species the hairs are enlarged and stiffened into bristles or spines. The upper parts are black, grayish, dark brown, or yellowish or reddish brown, and the under parts are usually grayish or whitish.

The external features differ greatly. The body form may be stocky or somewhat slender; certain digits are reduced in some forms but are long in others. In some members of the genus the feet are modified for terrestrial life, whereas in others the feet are adapted to an arboreal existence. The mammae number 4, 6, 8, 10, or 12, and in the subgenus *Mastomys* the females have at least 8 pairs of mammae and may have 12 pairs.

Rattus shelters in a variety of locations including burrows in the ground or under rocks, in logs, and in piles of rubbish. Those forms that are good climbers prefer to nest in trees and other elevated positions. Some, such as the Polynesian rat (*R. exulans*) from the Pacific Islands, are mainly diurnal, while others are active mostly at night. The diet consists of a wide variety of plant and animal foods, such as seeds, nuts, grains, vegetables, fruits, meat, fish, and invertebrates.

The gestation period in most forms is 21 to 30 days, and most species reproduce extensively. At times the population of this genus increases to plague proportions, although this great increase is often due in part to man's removal of natural enemies of *Rattus* by cultivation of its habitat. Several diseases are carried by these rodents. They may damage grains and other crops, but, with the exception of black and norway rats, most species cannot be termed serious pests. Some, in fact, are quite inoffensive and gentle and seldom go near man and his habitations.

Because of the tremendous economic importance of the black rat and the norway rat, they are herein discussed in some detail. The black rat (*R. rattus*) is native to Asia Minor and the Orient and the norway rat (*R. norvegicus*) is native to Japan and eastern Asia (?). The former species was brought to Europe at the time of the Crusades, although an incidence is said to have occurred in the ninth century in Ireland. The black rat is believed to have first arrived in North America on the ships of the early explorers. It is a better climber than the norway rat, which is mainly a burrowing species. The norway rat lived along streambanks in Asia and spread rapidly into the canals and ricefields, although in Malaya, it is strictly confined to sea ports. This species was not known in Europe until about 1553. These species live in different habitats and scarcely meet. Their abundance and distribution varies according to environment and their habits. The norway rat probably came into western Europe via ships, instead of overland caravans. It arrived in North America about 1775.

The black rat weighs about 115 to 350 grams, and the norway rat, about 200 to 485 grams. The black rat under tropical and subtropical conditions sometimes lives in areas removed from human habitation. The norway rat is more often associated with populated regions, but at temperatures above 11 degrees C. free living populations exist. Both species are extremely adaptable and inquisitive, but they tend to avoid new objects in a natural environment. This latter trait may account for much of their craftiness.

Black and norway rats eat practically anything they can cut, but a group of experimental animals, given a free choice of food over a five-year period, selected different foods in such proportions as to maintain good health. These rodents destroy far more than they eat; they also gnaw insulation from wires and occasionally cut through lead pipe and concrete dams. On a world basis, the direct damage caused each year by these two species amounts to billions of dollars.

R. rattus and *R. norvegicus* harbor and carry such diseases as bubonic (black) plague, typhus, *Salmonella* food poisoning, rabies, tularemia, and trichinosis. The plague, which is transmitted to human beings by rat fleas, reduced the population of Europe by one-fourth or more at various times. Zinsser, in his volume on *Rats, Lice and History*, states that rat-borne typhus has altered human destiny more than the influence of any person whose name appears in history. Rat-borne diseases are believed to have taken more human lives in the last ten centuries than all the wars and revolutions ever fought. On the other hand, the common laboratory rat, an albinistic strain of the black rat, is used in many phases of biological research, including the study of the diets, diseases, and genetics of man.

Due to the extensive variation found among these rats, which differ from small to large, slim to robust, spiny-furred to sleek-furred, etc., about 570 forms have been named in the genus. Mammalogists have strived for years to arrange this genus in more or less natural groups or assemblages of species under many generic names. Most of the following names, however, are today considered as subgenera. The true relationships of these various groups must await further research.

1. *Rattus*, Fischer, 1803, with type species *R. norvegicus* (Berkenhout).
2. *Aethomys*, Thomas, 1915, with type species *R. hindei* (Thomas).
3. *Lenothrix*, Miller, 1903, with type species *R. canus* (Miller).
4. *Stenomys*, Thomas, 1910, with type species *R. verecundus* (Thomas).
5. *Apomys*, Mearns, 1905, with type species *R. hylocaetes* (Mearns).
6. *Cremnomys*, Wroughton, 1912, with type species *R. cutchicus* (Wroughton).
7. *Maxomys*, Sody, 1936, with type species *R. bartelsi* (Jentink).
8. *Tarsomys*, Mearns, 1905, with type species *R. apoensis* (Mearns).

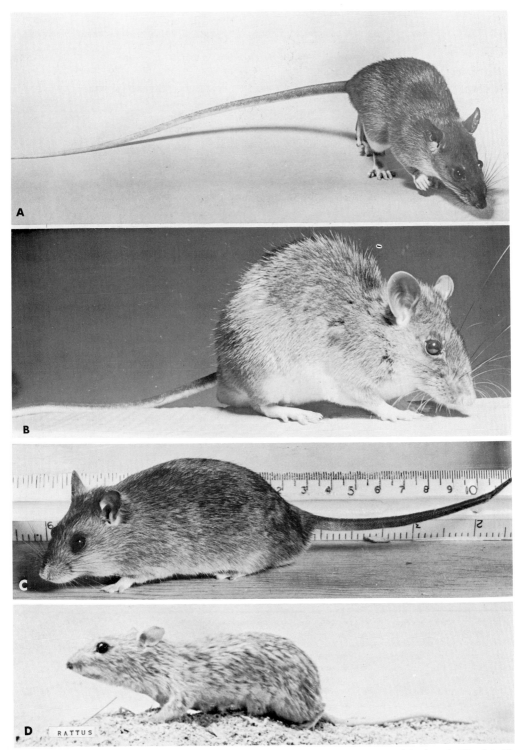

(1) A. Noisy Rat (*Rattus sabanus*), photo by Ernest P. Walker. B. Rajah Rat (*R. rajah surifer*), photo by Lim Boo Liat. C. Multimammate Rat (*R. natalensis*), photo by H. S. Davis. D. Woosnam's Pallid Rat (*R. woosnami*), photo by James A. Bateman.

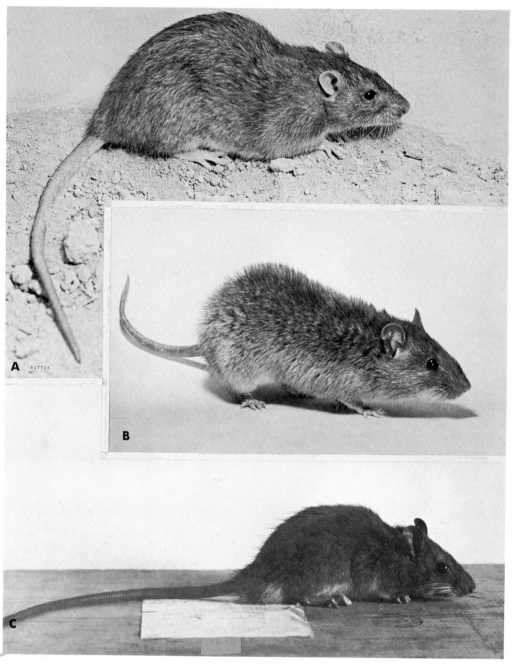

(2) A. Norway Rat (*Rattus norvegicus*), photo from U.S. Fish and Wildlife Service. B. Thai or Thailand Rat (*R. rattus thai*), photo by Ernest P. Walker. C. Roof Rat (*R. rattus*), photo from U.S. Fish and Wildlife Service.

9. *Leopoldamys*, Ellerman, 1947, with type species *R. sabanus*, Thomas.
10. *Berylmys*, Ellerman, 1947, with type species *R. manipulus*, Thomas.
11. *Micaëlomys*, Ellerman, 1941, with type species *R. granti* (Wroughton).
12. *Hylomyscus*, Thomas, 1926, with type species *R. aeta* (Thomas).
13. *Stochomys*, Thomas, 1926, with type species *R. longicaudatus* (Tullberg).
14. *Limnomys*, Mearns, 1905, with type species *R. sibuanus* (Mearns).
15. *Ochromys*, Thomas, 1920, with type species *R. woosnami* (Schwann).
16. *Dephomys*, Thomas, 1926, with type species *R. defua* (Miller).
17. *Paruromys*, Ellerman, 1954, with type species *R. dominator* (Thomas).
18. *Praomys*, Thomas, 1915, with type species *R. tullbergi* (Thomas).
19. *Mastomys*, Thomas, 1915, with type species *R. natalensis* (A. Smith).

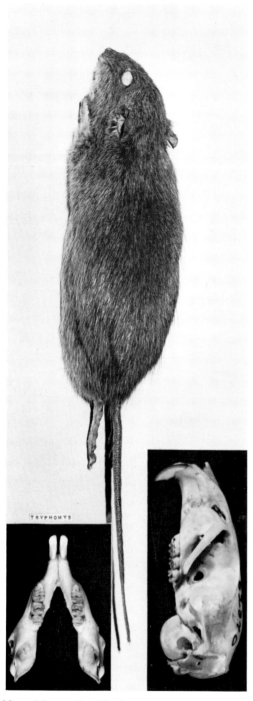

MEARNS' LUZON RATS.

THE SINGLE SPECIES, *T. adustus*, is known only from a few specimens. It was first collected by Edgar A. Mearns at Haight's Place, Benguet, on the island of Luzon in the Philippines, on July 26, 1907, at an elevation of about 2,460 meters.

The length of the head and body is 174 mm., and the length of the tail is 150 mm. The fur of the back is coarse and harsh, the tips of the shorter hairs tending to curve toward the head, giving the pelage a peculiarly scorched appearance. The back and sides are a coarse grizzle tending toward wood brown and black, with the brown predominant particularly on the sides; the median dorsal region is abruptly more grizzled than the sides. The bases of the individual hairs are slate gray, streaked by the lighter gray of the slender, grooved bristles. The color of the head and face is similar to that of the back, but with a grayish cast. The under parts and cheeks are buffy white, dulled by a slate gray undercolor. The feet are also the color of the upper parts, but they have a brownish tinge. The tail is uniformly dark brown.

This rat-like animal is of medium size with a robust form. The tail is coarsely and conspicuously scaled. The claws are well developed, those of the hind foot being larger. The nail of the thumb is small and appressed. The sole of the foot is naked with five well-developed tubercles. The teeth are similar to those of *Rattus*; the skull is large and heavily built; and there are five pairs of mammae.

The type specimen is in the U.S. National Museum, Washington, D.C.

Mearns' Luzon Rat (*Tryphomys adustus*), photos from Field Museum of Natural History.

Australian Field Mouse (*Gyomys albocinereus*), photo from *W. Australia Fisheries Dept., Fauna Bull.*, ". . . Bernier and Dorre Islands . . .," W. D. L. Ride *et al.*

AUSTRALIAN FIELD MICE; NOO-JEE, JUP-PERT (aborigine names).

THE COMBINED RANGE of the eight species which compose this genus includes all of continental Australia except part of the Northern Territory. They also inhabit small nearby islands. Members of this genus have been noted on sandy plains, stony ridges, timbered regions, and in areas of tall grasses. *G. fumeus* was taken in a shaded gully near a creek in a well-grown eucalyptus forest with a low ground cover of ferns, grasses, logs, and rocks. *Gyomys* was originally proposed as a subgenus of *Pseudomys*.

The length of the head and body is 68 to 132 mm., and the length of the tail is 61 to 137 mm. Two adult *G. apodemoides* weighed 16 and 18 grams, and a *G. fumeus* weighed 63 grams. In most species the hair is soft, but in *G. desertor* the coat is harsh. The coloration of the upper parts ranges from pale blue-gray, pale ashy gray, sandy brown, and clay to tawny olive. The under parts and generally the hands and feet are white, except in *G. pumilus* where the coloration is olive-buff. The head and ears are usually lighter than the remainder of the upper parts. The tail is moderately haired, dark above and white to buffy below, and slightly pencilled with white hairs in the species *G. albocinereus*.

These mice have large heads and moderate to small ears. *G. fumeus* has four abdominal mammae. *G. pumilus* is the smallest known mouse indigenous to Australia and the small adjacent islands.

Little has been recorded concerning the habits of *Gyomys*. *G. albocinereus* burrows in the sand about a meter below the surface. These burrows have several openings, at least one of which is used exclusively for throwing sand to the surface from the tunnel. Many of the entrances have surplus sand piled around the opening. Most of the occupied burrows are difficult to locate as the mice often close the entrances from the inside. One observer noted on Bernier Island that the mice surrounded the open "escape exits" by a delicate network of small twigs and shredded vegetation. It is believed that this barricade prevents loose sand from filling the openings. A recent expedition to this island found more of these barricades. Apparently the habit of closing the entrance from within is similar to that of pocket mice (*Perognathus*) and kangaroo rats (*Dipodomys*) of western North America. *G. novaehollandiae* has been observed under stones or slabs of bark left near the aborigines' camps, and they have been seen darting from fissures in the ground in tall grass.

The diet is believed to be omnivorous, consisting primarily of ground-dwelling insects, seeds, and other vegetable matter. In captivity they readily eat mealworms, sunflower seeds, and fruit.

A female *G. fumeus* taken in early November was carrying five fetuses, probably more than the usual number of young.

The type species of the genus is *G. novaehollandiae* (Waterhouse).

907

Australian Stick-nest Rat (*Leporillus conditor*), photo from the South Australian Museum.

AUSTRALIAN STICK-NEST RATS.

THREE SPECIES of *Leporillus* have been named: *L. conditor* and *L. apicalis* in south-central Australia, and *L. jonesi* on Franklyn Island off the coast of South Australia.

The length of the head and body is about 140 to 200 mm., and the tail is shorter (*L. conditor* and *L. jonesi*) or longer (*L. apicalis*) than the head and body. The length of the tail in *L. apicalis* may be as much as 250 mm. The tail is fairly well haired, with the somewhat longer hairs toward the tip. The pelage is thick and soft. The upper parts are light yellowish brown, light brown, dull brown, or pale grayish brown. The under parts in *L. conditor* and *L. jonesi* are usually grayish, whereas in *L. apicalis* they are white. When resting, these fluffy-haired animals with their blunt noses and large ears look like small rabbits with rat-like tails. Females have four mammae.

Two of the species, *L. conditor* and *L. jonesi*, build "houses" about 6 meters in diameter and 1.25 meters in height of sticks which may be 1 meter long and 25 mm. thick. The shelter is constructed with the utmost care and involves a great amount of work.

These nests of sticks, which provide protection against predators and strong winds, vary in size and construction due to local conditions. They are often built around a small bush or placed against a rock, but in areas where there is little woody growth, these rodents may live in loose heaps of sticks placed over rabbit warrens to provide instant escape. The latter type of home often has small stones placed on top and among the sticks to anchor the structure against strong winds. The shelters or "wurlies" contain numerous passage-ways with several grass nests; they are inhabited by pairs or colonies of *Leporillus*. The wurlies of *L. jonesi* are shared at times with bandicoots, penguins, and even snakes. Along the beaches the shelter of *L. jonesi* may consist of some debris or seaweed placed among the boulders. *L. apicalis* is a nocturnal and gregarious species which shelters in hollow trees and the abandoned wurlies of *L. conditor*.

A hawk's nest with three eggs was found on the top of a *L. conditor* nest; under such conditions, the rodents may prey on the eggs and even the young hawks, but *Leporillus* is mainly a vegetarian.

Leporillus is usually tame and gentle in captivity.

The type species of the genus is *L. apicalis* (Gould).

Australian False Mouse (*Pseudomys ferculinus*), photo by W. D. L. Ride.

AUSTRALIAN FALSE MICE.

ABOUT TEN SPECIES of *Pseudomys* inhabit south-western, central, and eastern Australia, and one species, *P. higginsi*, lives in the lowlands and hills of Tasmania. Species of *Thetomys*, Thomas, 1910, are herein regarded as referable to *Pseudomys*. Habitats vary with the species, extending from grassy plains to timbered sand ridges. Swampy brush country and areas near small, dry, salt-water lagoons are also included within the ecological distribution.

The length of the head and body is 75 to 160 mm., and the length of the tail is 70 to 180 mm. Weights in *P. higginsi* and *P. minnie*, species with a length of head and body of about 130 mm., are usually 70 to 80 grams. Coloration varies with the species. The upper parts display different shades of brown or yellow, and the under parts are buffy white, yellowish white, or grayish white. Some species have bicolored tails, i.e., dark above and white below. "The main constant character separating this genus from *Rattus* is the specialized condition of the anterior border of the zygomatic plate ... taken altogether, the skull and molars and external characters of the group seem to be distinct from *Rattus* and other genera." (J. R. Ellerman, *Families and Genera of Living Rodents* [London, 1941], p. 223). Female *Pseudomys* have four mammae.

These murids live in burrows and in sheltered depressions. The species *P. minnie* burrows in clay flats and river banks. On the flats its burrows are shallow, that is, not more than 150 to 200 mm. deep, usually have only one opening, and lack side passages. Some individuals of this species rest during the day in a shallow excavation under a disk of cattle dung. When driven out of their retreats in the daytime, these rodents move slowly and can easily be captured by natives on foot. Australian false mice are active at night and feed mostly on vegetable matter. Their fluctuations in reproductive activity often cannot be correlated with specific ecological conditions. The number of young is usually two to four.

These soft-furred, attractive animals have a relatively mild and gentle disposition.

The type species of the genus is *P. australis*, Gray.

RUMMLER'S MOSAIC-TAILED RATS.

FOUR SPECIES, *P. mayeri*, *P. bruijni*, *P. sevia*, and *P. ruemmleri*, inhabit New Guinea. The species *P. bruijni* is a lowland rain-forest animal, whereas the other species live at higher elevations.

The length of the head and body is 130 to 190 mm., and the length of the tail is about 140 to 210 mm. The dorsal pelage of *P. bruijni* is slightly crisp and that of *P. ruemmleri* is rather long. The upper parts are brownish, usually reddish brown or dark brown, and the under parts are whitish, grayish, or buffy. The hands and feet are yellowish brown to whitish. These rats have a prehensile tail, and the scales on the tail are six-sided with one, three, or many hairs per scale. The feet have large claws. There are four mammae. "*Pogonomelomys* must be regarded as a highly specialized offshoot of the stock from which *Melomys*, *Xenuromys* and *Uromys* have risen." (Tate and Archbold, *Results of the Archbold Expeditions*, No. 31 [New York, 1941], p. 5).

Because of their arboreal habits, these rats are difficult to study and collect.

The type species of the genus is *P. mayeri*. These rats are often included in the genus *Melomys*.

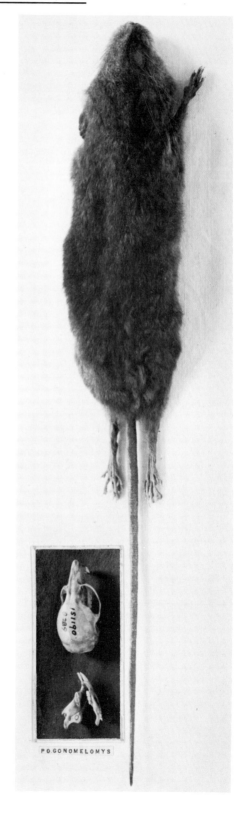

Rummler's Mosaic-tailed Rat (*Pogonomelomys ruemmleri*), photos from Museum Zoologicum Bogoriense.

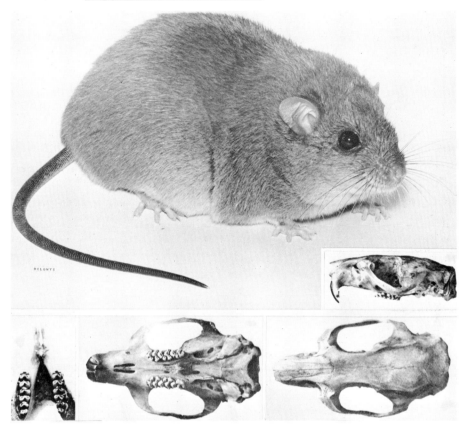

Mosaic-tailed Rat (*Melomys littoralis*), photo by Stanley Breeden. Anatomy: (*M. ponceleti*), photos from *Rec. Australian Mus.*

MOSAIC-TAILED RATS, BANANA RATS; ITUOKO (native name).

ABOUT A DOZEN species make up this genus. *Melomys* has a combined range which includes Ceram, New Guinea, Melville Island, the Northern Territory, Queensland, and New South Wales of Australia, the Bismarck Archipelago, and the Solomon Islands. They also inhabit smaller adjacent islands. Members of this genus show a preference for forested areas, grasslands, and sugar cane, usually near water. *Paramelomys*, Rümmler, 1936, is herein regarded as a subgenus.

The length of the head and body ranges from 90 to 175 mm. and that of the tail from 110 to 170 mm. *M. cervinipes* weighs about 25 grams. The pelage is usually soft, thick, woolly, and sometimes fairly long. The coloration of the upper parts ranges from tawny through several shades of brownish to russet; the under parts are white, creamy, or pale gray. These rodents are easily recognized by their almost naked, file-like tails. The appearance of the tail is due to the scales which form a somewhat mosaic pattern in opposition to the evenly ringed tails of the typical rats. These animals are distinguished externally from *Uromys* by their smaller size.

Members of this genus are chiefly arboreal.

Melomys are well adapted to this type of life for they have broad feet, well-developed pads, and a semiprehensile tail. Mosaic-tailed rats nest in plants and trees, and occasionally in burrows, which usually have a single entrance. The arboreal nests are made of grass or leaves, are spherical, and are usually from 125 to 200 mm. in diameter. They are found from .25 to 1 meter above the ground in cane or tall grass; they are also located among roots, in hollow timber, and under rock ledges.

These rodents are said to feed upon fruits and berries of various kinds.

Mating takes place during the rainy season, November to March. There are four mammae situated at the posterior end of the abdomen, and the young rats hold onto them almost continuously during the first two weeks of life. Thus the young are dragged about by the mother as she forages, and the erroneous impression has arisen, particularly among early writers, that *Melomys* is a marsupial. After about two weeks, the young become more independent but still hold onto their mother's mammae when disturbed. Captive mosaic-tailed rats usually produce their first litter at the age of seven months.

The type species of the genus is *M. rufescens* (Alston).

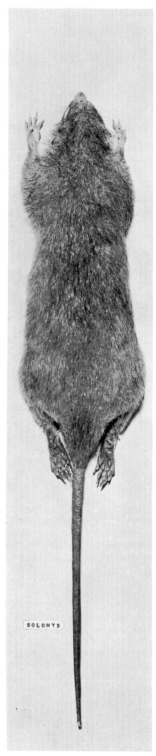

Naked-tailed Rat (*Solomys sale-brosus*), photo from the Australian Museum, Sydney.

NAKED-TAILED RATS; NAGARA (native name for *S. ponceleti*).

THIS GENUS of three species, *S. sapientis*, *S. sale-brosus*, and *S. ponceleti*, inhabits thick woods in the Solomon Islands. Some authors have considered *Solomys* as a subgenus of *Melomys*.

The species *S. sapientis* has a head and body length of about 250 mm. and a tail length of about 250 mm.; coloration is cinnamon-brown above and on the sides, and pinkish buff below. The species *S. salebrosus* has a head and body length of about 230 mm. and a tail length of about 215 mm.; coloration is yellowish brown above, cinnamon-buff on the sides, and pinkish buff below. *S. ponceleti* is the largest species: a young adult female measured 330 mm. in head and body length and 340 mm. in tail length. The color of this species is brownish black above and below. The hair in *S. ponceleti* is long and fine, without woolly underfur, whereas it is coarser in the other two species. The tail is prehensile and naked, that is, it lacks hairs for most of its length. The feet are well padded and supplied with mobile and strongly clawed digits.

The structure of the tail and feet and the following comment in Ellis Troughton (*Rec. Australian Mus.*, 1936, 19:347) would indicate that *Solomys* have arboreal habits: *S. sapientis* "cracks the Ngali (*Canarium*) nuts and gnaws coconuts, and is found in trees felled by the natives...." There are four mammae. The incisors are broad and stout. The natives of the Solomon Islands occasionally eat these rats.

The type species of the genus is *S. sapientis* (Thomas).

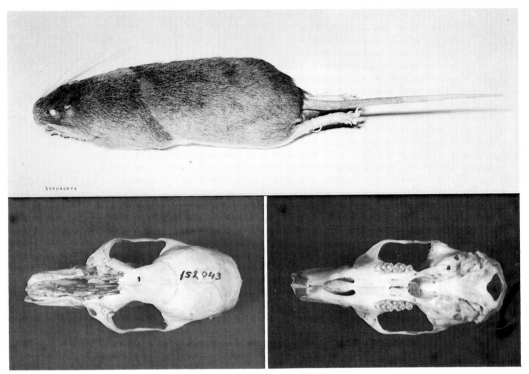

White-tailed New Guinean Rat (*Xenuromys barbatus*), photos from American Museum of Natural History.

WHITE-TAILED NEW GUINEA RATS.

THE SINGLE SPECIES, *X. barbatus*, is known from two male specimens. One specimen was collected about 1900 in British New Guinea and is in the Paris Natural History Museum. The other was collected in 1939 in a heavy forest at an elevation of 75 meters near the Idenburg River in Netherlands New Guinea. This specimen is in the American Museum of Natural History.

These two males measure 275 and 310 mm. in head and body length and 220 and 281 mm. in tail length. One male is reddish brown above and buffy below, whereas the larger animal is gray above and white below. The hands and feet are so scantily haired that they appear naked. The tail is white for at least half its length. These are "large rats having the general appearance of *Uromys* but with the normal overlapping tail scales of *Rattus*" (G. H. H. Tate, *Results of the Archbold Expeditions*, No. 65—"The Rodents of Australia and New Guinea" [New York, 1951], pp. 284–85). The tail is coarsely scaled, and the unkeeled scales are arranged annularly instead of spirally.

"Unique or unusual habits may be implied by its rarity, but its feet and tail show no structural feature to indicate whether it is particularly arboreal or fossorial, nor does the pelage suggest aquatic habits" (*Ibid.*, p. 285).

Giant Naked-tailed Rat (*Uromys caudimaculatus*), photo by Stanley Breeden.

GIANT NAKED-TAILED RATS.

THE FIVE SPECIES which comprise this genus can be divided into three categories on the basis of both structure and geography. *U. neobritannicus* is the largest of the species, has a well-developed squamosal crest (cranial structure), and ears which are quite large. It inhabits the highlands of New Britain. *U. caudimaculatus* and *U. anak*, the former the larger of the two species, lack the cranial structure present in *U. neobritannicus*; the ears are relatively long, and the general coloration of the back is brownish. These rodents have a combined range which includes New Guinea, Aru and Kei Islands, the Bismarck Archipelago and the Solomon Islands, and Queensland, Australia.

U. imperator and *U. rex*, the former the larger of the two species, lack the cranial structure of *U. neobritannicus*; the ears are short, and the general coloration of the back is grayish. These two species inhabit the Solomon Islands.

The length of the head and body ranges from 290 to 355 mm., the length of the tail varies from about 255 to 350 mm., and the weight of one species, *U. caudimaculatus*, is 425 to 850 grams. The pelage is fairly short, dense, and relatively coarse except in *U. caudimaculatus* in which it is somewhat scant. Although coloration is generally as described above, it has a variation which ranges from grayish through shades of brown to gray-black. Coloration of the under parts is from gray to white. In some species the tail is entirely black, but in others it is white or yellowish toward the tip. The hairs of the tail number only one per scale. The scales of the tail form a mosaic pattern, whereas in most other genera of this family the scales of the tail are flat and overlapping. The incisors are massive and powerful. There are two pairs of mammae.

Uromys are arboreal and are excellent climbers. The tail facilitates climbing as it curls over a limb and grips by means of its rasp-like scales. These animals have well-clawed, broad hands and feet. *U. caudimaculatus* in New Guinea feeds principally upon coconuts which are dislodged from the palm trees. It has been recorded as nesting in hollow trees.

The type species of the genus is *U. caudimaculatus* (Krefft).

Big-eared Swamp Rat (*Malacomys edwardsi*), photo from *Proc. Zool. Soc. London.*

BIG-EARED RATS, SWAMP RATS, LONG-TAILED FOREST MICE, LONG-LEGGED MARSH RATS.

THE TWO SPECIES which comprise this genus are distributed as follows: *M. edwardsi*, from Liberia to Nigeria; *M. longipes*, Angola and the Congo westward to Liberia. These animals usually inhabit areas of dense vegetation, preferably near water or swampy regions.

The length of the head and body ranges from 130 to 180 mm., and the tail is slightly longer. The pelage is thick, soft, and velvety, similar to that of certain shrews. The texture of the fur is so fine that it has been compared to the bloom of a peach. General coloration of the upper parts is dark brown with a sprinkling of grayish. The sides are ochraceous and the under parts are gray. In one form of *M. longipes*, there is often a pale spot, usually grayish white, on the forehead. *M. edwardsi* has an oval, sooty-colored patch around each eye. The hands and feet are plentifully sprinkled with fine-textured short hairs; the whiskers are fine, long, and dark; and the tail is so poorly haired that in some specimens it appears almost naked.

These medium-sized, slender-bodied rats have large ears, long and narrow skulls, long and slender hind feet, and long tails. Some zoologists believe that the structure of the feet permits the paws to spread more than those of most terrestrial rats as an adaptation in traveling over swampy ground. There are six mammae.

Little information has been published concerning the habits and biology of these animals. *Malacomys* seems to be mainly nocturnal. One author reported that *M. longipes* breeds from March to June in central Africa.

The type species of the genus is *M. longipes*, Milne-Edwards.

Pygmy Tree Mouse (*Haeromys margarettae*), photo from *Mammals of Borneo*, Charles Hose.

PYGMY TREE MICE, RANEE MICE (*H. margarettae*).

TWO SPECIES make up this genus. *H. margarettae* is known from the Penrisen Hills and Mt. Kina Balu in Borneo, and *H. minahassae* is from North Celebes.

Haeromys seems to be one of the smallest genera within Rodentia. The length of the head and body of the type specimen of *H. margarettae* is 76 mm., and the length of the tail is 144 mm. In *H. minahassae* the length of the head and body is 77 mm., and the length of the tail is about 110 mm. The pelage is long and soft. Coloration of *H. minahassae* is rufous on the upper parts, with dull back and bright sides. In *H. margarettae* the general coloration of the upper parts is deep chestnut-rufous with a grayish cast resulting from gray hair bases, but the coloration is clearer on the sides where it forms a rufous lateral band. In both forms the under parts are white and the whiskers are black. In *H. minahassae* the tail is brown, and in *H. margarettae* it is greenish gray. In both forms the tail is unicolored and covered with short hairs.

This genus resembles *Chiropodomys* in having a muzzle which is short and slender, and ears which are relatively small, oval, and sparsely haired. The hands and feet are of an arboreal type, with opposable great toe. The thumb has a large nail, whereas the other digits have short, sharp, curved claws. *H. margarettae* has six mammae.

Nothing has been recorded on the habits and general biology of *Haeromys*, other than a statement that they are tree mice.

The type species of the genus is *H. margarettae* (Thomas).

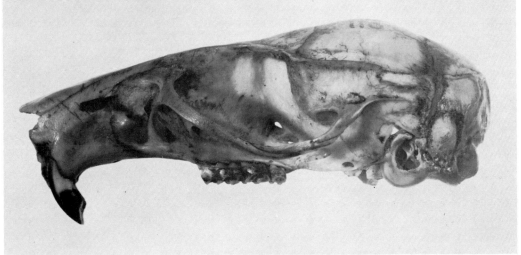

Asiatic Tree Mouse (*Chiromyscus chiropus*), photos from British Museum (Natural History).

ASIATIC TREE MICE.

THE SINGLE SPECIES, *C. chiropus*, inhabits Burma, Thailand (specimen in the U.S. National Museum), and parts of Indo-China. The species was first described by O. Thomas in 1891 as *Mus chiropus* from a specimen which was collected in the Karin Hills of Burma and preserved in alcohol. It did not again come to attention until 1924 when H. Stevens, on the Sladen-Godman Expedition to Tonkin, collected a specimen at Bao-Ha at an elevation of about 90 meters in the forest country of the Red River. This specimen became the type of the genus established by Thomas.

The length of the head and body is 127 to 160 mm., and the length of the tail is 203 to 240 mm. The pelage is rather bristly. Coloration of the upper parts is "warm lined buffy" suffused with black. The sides of the face are ochraceous, the color extending up behind the ears, and there is a dark area surrounding each eye. The rump is bright ochraceous, the throat is rusty, and the under parts are creamy. The flesh-colored ears are covered with short hairs. The long slender tail is also covered with fine, short, light-colored hairs, and is slightly pencilled.

Members of this genus are similar to *Rattus*. The hind foot of *Chiromyscus* is specialized for climbing; the great toe is opposable and large digital pads are present. The claws on all the digits are short. The female has eight mammae.

This rodent is represented by only a limited number of specimens. Because of the apparent scarcity of this genus, little has been recorded concerning its life habits and general biology other than the fact that *Chiromyscus* is probably arboreal.

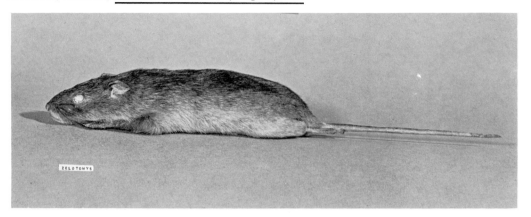

Broad-headed Mouse (*Zelotomys hildegardeae*), photo by Howard E. Uible of skin in U.S. National Museum.

BROAD-HEADED MICE.

ALTHOUGH THERE ARE SEVERAL named species at the present time, it seems likely that only a single species exists, named *Z. hildegardeae*. *Zelotomys* ranges from Kenya southward through the Congo to Northern Rhodesia and westward to Angola. One author reports that *Zelotomys* occurs near the native millet plantations in Angola.

The length of the head and body is 115 to 137 mm., and the length of the tail is 88 to 115 mm. The upper parts range in coloration from dark gray, slate-gray, and buffy brown to pinkish buff. The flanks are grayish to yellowish; the hands and feet are pinkish buff to white; and the under surface is light gray, pinkish buff, or whitish. The short, stiff hairs which form the sparse tail covering are white to grayish brown.

There are no outstanding external peculiarities except the slightly broadened head, a feature which is reflected in the common name. The generic name, meaning imitator, refers to the external resemblance of *Zelotomys* to the genus *Rattus*, subgenus *Mastomys*.

The incisors are rather slender and slightly protruding, whereas in most rodents the incisors curve back toward the mouth. The moderate-sized ears are rounded. The female has ten mammae.

Information concerning the habits and general biology is meager. It is said that these rodents seldom enter houses. A female *Z. hildegardeae*, taken in November on Mt. Sagalla in eastern Africa, was pregnant with seven embryos.

918

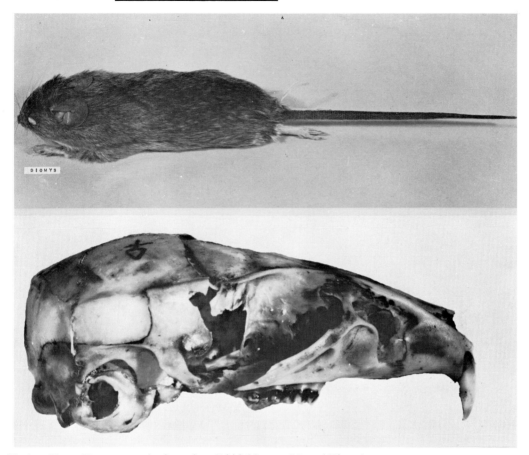

Manipur Mouse (*Diomys crumpi*), photos from British Museum (Natural History).

MANIPUR MICE, CRUMP'S MICE.

THE SINGLE SPECIES, *D. crumpi*, was long known from only one specimen, a skull collected at a 1,300-meter elevation on Mt. Paresnath, Bihar, India, among rocks. Oldfield Thomas in 1917 based the genus on this single broken skull, and it was not until 25 years later that a series of 30 specimens was secured from Bishenpur, Manipur, India. All the specimens of this genus are in the British Museum (Natural History).

The length of the head and body is 100 to 135 mm., and the length of the tail is 105 to 135 mm. The back is blackish gray; the rump is usually black, and the feet are white. The under parts are whitish gray, and the tail is black above and white below. The fur is thick and soft, and the tail is scantily haired. "The genus *Diomys* stands on the important character that the incisors are so proodont, that the condylobasal length normally is at least as long as the occipitonasal length, and often exceeds it (three exceptions in twenty measurable skulls). This is very rare in Asiatic Muridae; the only other murid genera from Asia with this character normally present are the very different Bandicoot Rats, *Nesokia* and *Bandicota*" (J. R. Ellerman, *Ann. and Mag. Nat. Hist.* [London, 1946], 13:205).

Stripe-backed Mouse (*Muriculus imberbis*), photo from Museum Senckenbergianum.

STRIPE-BACKED MICE.

THE SINGLE SPECIES, *M. imberbis*, is known only from Ethiopia. It inhabits open slopes in grassy or rocky regions up to the upper limit of forests, about 3,200 meters in elevation.

The length of the head and body is 70 to 95 mm., and the length of the tail is about 45 to 60 mm. The thick pelage is rather crisp, or it may be soft with no suggestion of spines. The hairs of the upper parts, at least in some individuals, have dark blue-gray bases and dark yellowish brown tips. A mid-dorsal stripe is usually present from about the middle of the back to the base of the tail, although it may extend forward as a faint line almost to the shoulders. The under parts are tawny-ochraceous, creamy, or almost white. Sometimes there is a tawny-ochraceous tuft of hairs at the front base of the ears. The closely and finely haired tail is usually dark brown above and yellowish gray below.

Muriculus resembles *Mus* in external appearance but is easily distinguished from that genus by the dark dorsal stripe. However, this stripe may be poorly defined in some individuals. The head is relatively short, and the ears are of medium size and rounded. The claws are short. The incisors are narrow with a smooth front surface and are so inclined forward that the tips of the upper incisors do not curve backward toward the body.

This rodent shelters in holes in the ground and is associated with *Arvicanthis abyssinicus*, at least in some areas. Specific habits and biology are not recorded.

A. House Mouse (*Mus musculus*), photo by Ernest P. Walker. B. (*M. minutoides pretoriae*), photo by K. B. Newman. C. Laboratory Mice (*M. musculus*), photo by Ernest P. Walker.

HOUSE MICE; HAUSMAUSE, HUISMUIZEN, SOURIS, LAUCHAS, HUISMUISE, TIKUS-PITI, RATONES CASE-ROS. (Included are vernaculars used in other countries.)

THIS GENUS INCLUDES the common house mouse, *M. musculus*, and some 15 other species. Through introduction by man, the common house mouse now frequents most of the world. There are both commensal and wild forms of the house mouse; the commensal forms often move out from buildings into surrounding fields in the spring and summer and return to the shelter of buildings in the fall. Some other species of *Mus* are also associated with man and his habitations, whereas others live in fields or wooded areas. *M. mayori* of Ceylon, for example, lives among rocks and low vegetation in damp woodlands. There are no native forms of *Mus* in the Western Hemisphere. *Coelomys*, Thomas, 1915, *Mycteromys*, Robinson and Kloss, 1918, and *Leggadilla*, Thomas, 1914, are regarded as subgenera of *Mus*. *Leggada*, *Tautatus*, *Nannomys*, *Pseudoconemys*, *Drymomys*, and *Hylenomys* are herein regarded as synonyms. The type species of the genus is *M. musculus*, Linnaeus.

Measurements and weights for the common house mouse are as follows: Length of head and body, usually less than 100 mm. but generally 65 to 95 mm.;

length of tail, about 60 to 105 mm.; and weight, usually 18 to 30 grams. Although the length of the head and body for the genus is usually less than 100 mm., it may be as long as 125 mm. The length of the tail also varies in the different species and among individuals of the common house mouse. Some forms of *Mus* from Africa and India are among the smallest living rodents. The heart beat is 620 to 780 beats per minute.

The fur may be soft, harsh, or spiny. The tail appears to be naked but has a covering of fine hairs. The coloration above ranges from pale buff or pale gray through dull grayish browns and grays to dark lead color or dull brownish gray. The sides may be slightly lighter and the under parts are usually lighter than the upper parts. The common house mouse is light brown to black above, and whitish below, often with a buffy wash, and the tail is lighter below than above. Commensal forms of *M. musculus* tend to have longer tails and to be darker than the wild forms. Domesticated strains have been developed of *M. musculus*, the most common being the albinos. Other developed strains have a black and white piebald pattern and some carry various shades of black or gray.

The genus is distinguished mainly by the formation of the teeth and jaw. It resembles *Rattus* in a number of features, although size will not distinguish some species of *Mus* from *Rattus*, as some of the larger species of *Mus* may be larger than some of the smaller forms of *Rattus*. The hind foot is usually narrow and the outer digits tend to be shortened. There are 10 or 12 mammae in most forms. The skull is light and usually rather flat, and the upper incisors are notched.

The commensal forms of *Mus* are active at any hour, but the wild forms seem to be active mainly at night. Most forms are good climbers, and the common house mouse also swims well. The daily range of movement of a common house mouse may be an area of only 15 square meters. Nests are made of soft, shredded material wherever suitable cover and food are present.

The commensal forms feed on any human food that is available, and also on paste, glue, soap, and other household articles. They damage much more than they eat and seem to survive on very little, hence the term "poor as a church mouse." In the wild they eat many kinds of vegetables, such as seeds, fleshy roots, leaves, and stems. Insects and some meat may be eaten when available. *Mus* may also store food at times.

Members of this genus breed throughout the year, at least in the warmer parts of the range, and may have five or more litters in a year. The gestation period is 18 to 21 days, and the litter size is 3 to 12 but usually 4 to 7. Young *M. musculus* are furred in 10 days, the eyes open at 14 days, and they are weaned in 3 weeks, at which time they disperse. The common house mouse may breed at 35 days of age. Captives have lived for six years. *Mus* is quite prolific and populations attain plague proportions at times. Population increases of *M. musculus* occured in 1926-27 and 1941-42 in the Central Valley of California. A population of more than 82,000 per acre was estimated in the first of these "ecological explosions," and the mice had worked the sparsely vegetated soil until it appeared to be recently cultivated. Millions of mice were swarming around the area until the population trend was reversed.

The "singing," "waltzing," and "shaker" mice are common house mice. Faint but audible twittering sounds, emitted by house mice when in their shelters, have been reported from various parts of the world. The other types are defective in their balancing apparatus and waltz or shake instead of moving about like normal mice.

Common house mice cause food spoilage, damage household articles, and transport the hosts of typhus, spotted fever, and possibly other human diseases. The albino strains of *M. musculus* are used extensively in laboratory work. In fact, the genetics of the house mouse has been more thoroughly studied than that of any other mammal.

Australian Delicate Mouse (*Leggadina delicatula*), photo by Basil Marlow. Inset: Pile of pebbles assembled by *Leggadina*, photo by Stephen Davis.

AUSTRALIAN NATIVE MICE.

SEVEN SPECIES inhabit northern and eastern Australia. They frequent such habitats as dry grassy plains, forested sand ridges, and coastal regions.

The length of the head and body is 50 to 97 mm., and the length of the tail is 50 to 90 mm. The species *L. hermannsburgensis* usually weighs from 12 to 16 grams. The pelage of this species is soft and sleek, whereas *L. forresti* has a crisp pelage with a considerable proportion of stout guard hairs. The upper parts are pale gray, yellowish brown, or pale brown, and the under parts are white or grayish white. These small, attractive mice are distinguished from related genera by differences in the skull and dental features. They have a broad head, a blunt muzzle, and short, broad ears.

These rodents usually live in burrows, but *L. waitei* may occupy shallow depressions at the base of *Triodia* tussocks. Another species has been found under seaweed on a beach. The burrows are usually simple in structure: Those of *L. delicatula* are located some 60 mm. below the surface and, after about 1.5 meters, they terminate in a circular space containing a nest of dried grass; those of *L. hermannsburgensis* are about 200 mm. in depth and 1 meter in length. Five is the highest number of the latter species taken from one tunnel. On several occasions the gecko, *Nephurus laevis*, was living in the burrows occupied by *L. hermannsburgensis*.

Australian native mice feed on such vegetable matter as seeds, grass roots, and tubers.

Most reproductive activity takes place after the heavy rains, but species of *Leggadina* breed throughout the year. The number of young is usually three or four.

One species of this genus, most likely *L. hermannsburgensis*, living in inland Western Australia, apparently builds low mounds of pebbles over its burrow systems. These pebbles are of a uniform size and cover a large area, often a meter in diameter. The pebbles are probably collected both by excavation and from the surface. Some local mammalogists believe these are used as dew-traps. Since the air around the pebbles warms more rapidly as the sun rises than the pebbles themselves, dew forms on the pebbles by condensation. As the areas in which these mounds are found are quite dry except after heavy rains, these dew-traps solve the problem of water shortage. Local farmers use these many pebble mounds for mixing concrete. It is believed that the ancients of the Mediterranean region used a dew-trap method similar to that of *Leggadina*.

The type species of the genus is *L. forresti* (Thomas).

COLOMYS

African Water Rat (*Colomys goslingi*), adapted from *Proc. Zool. Soc. London*, St. Leger.

AFRICAN WATER RATS; MONBONGOLO, TCHIZAM-BULA-PEMBA OU SANA-MEIA (native names).

THE SINGLE SPECIES, *C. goslingi*, inhabits Abyssinia, Angola, the Cameroons, the Congo, and Kenya in Africa. In Kenya, it has been taken at a 2,400 meter elevation. One report cites that *Colomys* lives in thick forests. Because of their long hind feet, it has been surmised that these rodents inhabit swampy areas, but this fact has not definitely been verified.

Nilopegamys plumbeus Osgood is regarded by Hayman (*Annals of the Royal Museum of Central Africa*, Series 8, Zool. Sci., 144, 1966, pp. 29–37) as being conspecific with *Colomys goslingi*.

The length of the head and body is about 123 to 140 mm., and the length of the tail is 145 to 180 mm. The pelage is thick, short, and soft, with a velvety texture. The upper parts range in coloration from cinnamon to wood-brown and dark brown, the darkest coloration being just behind the middle of the back. The under parts, including the hands, feet, forearms, and lower legs, are generally white. Occasionally the coloration of the under parts extends in a line onto the upper arms and sometimes appears as a ring about the ankles. The dark color of the upper parts and the light color of the under parts meet in a distinct line of demarcation. There is generally a white or light-colored spot just below the ear. The large grayish ears are practically naked. The tail varies from light brown to almost black on the upper part and slightly lighter beneath; the hairs on the lower part of the tail are white or at least light in color and slightly longer than those of the basal part. The tail is, however, scaly and poorly haired.

Colomys has a light and slender body form; the feet are definitely lengthened, and the four fingers are long. There are eight mammae in the female. The incisors are not grooved and are flat or slightly concave on the front surface.

Little has been recorded regarding their mode of life.

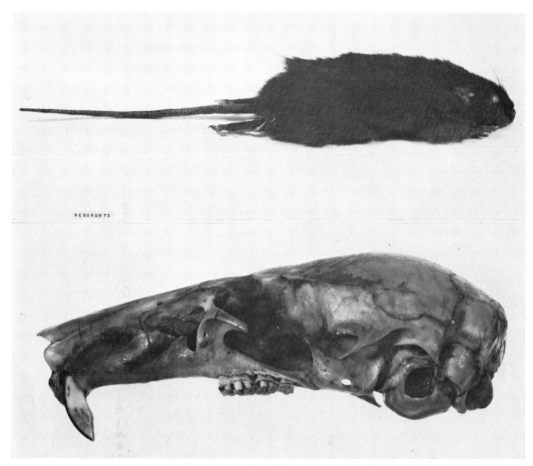

Ceram Island Rat (*Nesoromys ceramicus*), photos from British Museum (Natural History).

CERAM ISLAND RATS.

THE SINGLE SPECIES, *N. ceramicus*, has a range that is believed to be limited to the island of Ceram in the East Indies. The type specimen was trapped in heavy jungle on Mt. Manusela at about an 1,800 meter elevation.

The length of the head and body of the type is 135 mm., and the length of the tail is 140 mm. The pelage is fine, soft, and thick. The general coloration of the upper parts is a fine speckling of olive brown; the under parts are somewhat lighter due to the dull drab tips of the hairs. The short ears are almost black; the hands and feet are dark brown; and the tail, which is almost naked, is also dark brown.

This species was originally described as a member of the genus *Stenomys*, which is now considered a subgenus of *Rattus*. *Nesoromys* is distinguished from *Rattus* by its long narrow muzzle. The hind foot is narrow.

Probably because of its limited range and remoteness, little information has been published concerning members of this genus.

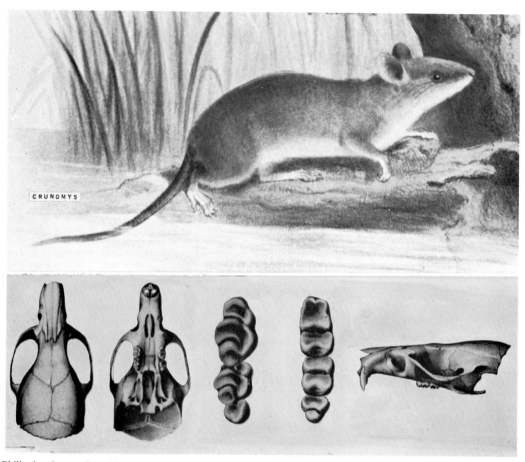

Philippine Swamp Rat (*Crunomys fallax*), photo from "Mammals from the Philippine Islands," Thomas, *Trans. Zool. Soc. London.*

PHILIPPINE SWAMP RATS.

THIS GENUS of two species is confined to the Philippine Islands: *C. fallax* is known from Luzon and *C. melanius* from Mindanao. At the present time there are apparently three specimens of this genus, all in study collections. *C. fallax* is known from the type collected by Whitehead in 1894 in Isabela Province, Luzon, at an elevation of approximately 307 meters, and *C. melanius* is known from the type collected by Anderson in 1906 on Mount Apo, Davao, Mindanao, at an elevation of about 924 meters. In 1923 Taylor obtained another specimen of *C. melanius* in the forest at sea level at Saub, Cotabato, Mindanao.

The type specimen of *C. fallax* has a head and body length of 105 mm., and the length of the tail is 79 mm. The pelage consists of close, short fur which is profusely mixed with flattened spines. The whiskers are long and the tail is uniformly covered with short hair. The general coloration of the upper parts is pale grayish, but rather yellowish on the back. The dorsal spines have white bases and black tips. The sides of the nose and the ears are brown; the hands and feet are grayish brown; and the digits are white. The under parts are grayish white, and the black tail shades somewhat lighter ventrally. Whitehead (*In*: Oldfield Thomas, *Trans. Zool. Soc. London*, 1898, XIV, p. 394) reported that he shot the animal beside a stream, where it was foraging for food among large stones.

C. melanius has a head and body length of 98 to 122 mm., and the length of the tail is 68 to 79 mm. The fur, which is close and fine, is intermingled with flattened spines. The general coloration of the upper parts is blackish brown; and the limbs, hands, and feet are similarly colored. The tail is uniformly blackish. The under parts are only slightly lighter than the upper parts. There are six mammae in this form.

There is an implication that these rodents may be aquatic. Thomas, who proposed the genus, seemed to think that they might be related to the Hydromyinae, a subfamily of Muridae.

The type species of the genus is *C. fallax*, Thomas.

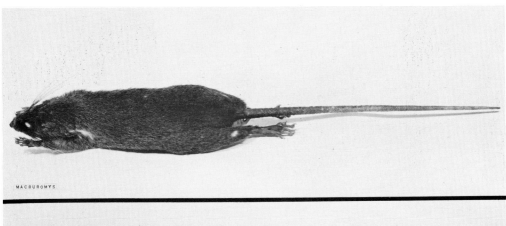

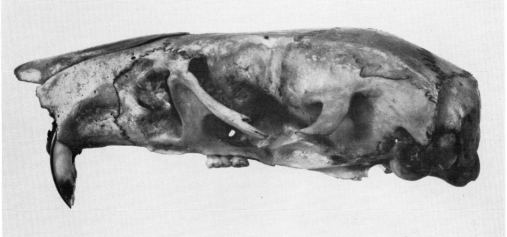

New Guinean Rat (*Macruromys major*), photos from British Museum (Natural History).

NEW GUINEAN RATS.

THE TWO SPECIES of *Macruromys* inhabit New Guinea. *M. elegans* is known from 1,400 to 1,800 meters elevation on Kunupi in the Weyland Mountains, western Netherlands New Guinea, and *M. major* is known from 1,200 to 1,500 meters elevation on the northern slopes of the central mountain range in Northeast New Guinea from the headwaters of the Mamberano River to the Kratke Mountains.

In *M. elegans* the length of the head and body is 150 to 160 mm., and the length of the tail is 205 to 220 mm. In *M. major* the length of the head and body is 225 to 250 mm., and the length of the tail is 315 to 340 mm. Coloration in *M. elegans* is grayish brown above and whitish below; the pelage is not so coarse as that of *M. major*. The latter species has mottled yellowish-black upper parts—the over all impression along the middle of the back is blackish brown—and grayish under parts. In *M. elegans* the tail is dark above and white below; in *M. major* the terminal two-thirds of the tail is white.

J. R. Ellerman (*The Families and Genera of Living Rodents* [London, 1941], Vol. II, p. 260) regards the small tooth row as the outstanding structural feature of *Macruromys*. G. H. H. Tate (*Results of the Archbold Expeditions*, No. 65, "The Rodents of Australia and New Guinea" [New York, 1951], p. 272) describes these rats as being ". . . externally like *Rattus* or *Uromys* but with the normal overlapping tail scales of *Rattus* and scale hairs in three's slightly longer than a scale."

Habits and biology have apparently not been recorded.

The type species of the genus is *M. elegans*, Stein.

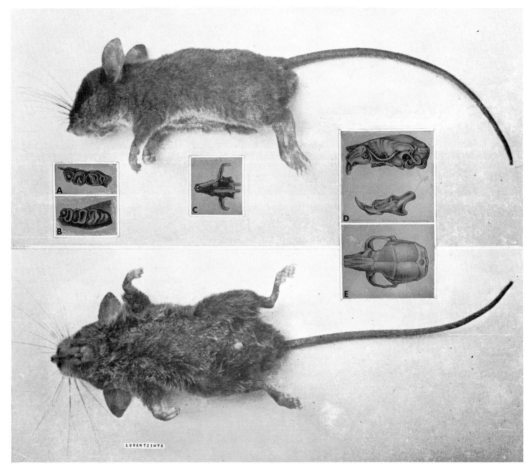

New Guinean Kangaroo Mouse (*Lorentzimys nouhuysii*), photos from Archbold Expeditions, American Museum of Natural History. Insets: A. Upper right teeth; B. Lower right teeth; C. Ventral view of skull; D. Lateral view of skull; E. Dorsal view of skull; photos from *Mammals Collected by the Dutch New Guinea Expedition*, F. A. Jentinck.

NEW GUINEAN KANGAROO MICE, NEW GUINEAN JUMPING MICE.

THIS GENUS is represented by a single species, *L. nouhuysii*. One form inhabits the lowland slopes of the central mountain range in Netherlands New Guinea from sea level to about 900 meters elevation. One animal was trapped in a hollow log which was lying on the ground in a dense rain forest. Another form inhabits high mountain slopes of Netherlands New Guinea, Papua, and northeastern New Guinea, between 600 and 3,000 meters elevation.

The length of the head and body ranges from 75 to 85 mm., and the length of the tail is from 103 to 110 mm. The pelage in one form is long and soft, whereas in the other form it is short and more crisp. Coloration of *Lorentzimys* on the upper parts is reddish brown, and the lower parts are buff or reddish brown tinged with white around the mouth. The feet are white. The head is slaty around the eyes and ears, and the under part of the neck is whitish. In one form the hairs of the tail are white, in the other they are black, but in both forms a pencil of hairs appears at the tip of the tail. The whiskers are numerous and fairly long.

Members of this genus are distinguished by the cranial structure. The upper incisors are inclined slightly forward. The feet are slender, and the ears are narrow and taper to a rounded point. There are six mammae. There are five fingers, four of which are armed with sharp, arched claws, but the fifth is so small that only a flat nail is visible.

Although *Lorentzimys* has been described as a jumping rodent, because of its long, slender hind feet, it may be mainly a scansorial form. Little has been published concerning its general biology and life habits.

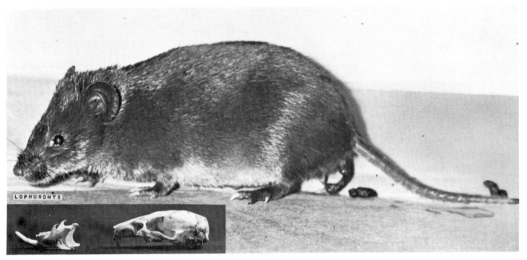

Harsh-furred Mouse (*Lophuromys sikapusi*), photo by F. Petter. Inset: (*L. aquilus*), photo by P. F. Wright of specimen in U.S. National Museum.

HARSH-FURRED MICE, RED-BELLIED MICE; TO-SIRE, KURSI, NDOGO, FUDI, MENDE, ETWA, NGU-SUKA, TOBORA (native names).

THIS GENUS of about ten species has a range which includes Ethiopia, Kenya, Uganda, Tanganyika, Northern Rhodesia, Angola, the Congo, Cameroons, the Gabon region, and Ghana. These mice live in a wide variety of habitats; they occur from grassy plains and swampy areas to elevations of about 3,750 meters (timber line). They also frequent forests, bushy country, and the edges of rice fields and weed beds.

The length of the head and body is 100 to 145 mm., and the length of the tail is 50 to 111 mm. The color pattern is of two types. One is rather uniformly dark brown or olive gray on the upper parts, lacking spots and streaks, and deep dull orange or cinnamon on the under parts. In the other pattern the coloration of the upper parts ranges from sandy buff through olive-gray and olive-brown to dark brown with fine streaking or various degrees of speckling from whitish to orangish. The under parts range from cream to wood-brown, orange, cinnamon, or clay color. In some forms the hairs of the body are orange at the base, which may be unique among African mammals. The upper surfaces of the hands and feet are usually somewhat lighter than the back. The tail is well furred in some forms, but in others it is scantily covered with fine, short hairs. The upper surface of the tail is almost as dark as the back, whereas the lower surface is usually light-colored. The pelage in most forms is fairly long, sleek, and thick, and is unique in structure. The hairs are slightly coarse and flattened and tapered at either end. In some forms the tail is distinctly bicolored.

These rat-like animals have five fingers and five toes, the former provided with rather large, stout claws and the latter with long, slender, slightly curved claws. The incisors are thin and are occasionally inclined forward. The skin is tender and easily torn, and it is not unusual for the tips of the tail to be missing.

Reports indicate that these animals are both diurnal and nocturnal. *L. aquilus* is said to be fearless. This form feeds on mahoga (a native ground root), worms, grubs, and sometimes toads. These rodents often shelter in grass or dead-leaf nests under logs or roots. Another source reports that harsh-furred mice are swift diggers, excavating long, straight burrows.

The number of young per litter is usually one to four.

The skin is very delicate and almost impossible to prepare. The live animal is very sensitive and hard to handle without causing injury or death. They will take insects in captivity.

The type species of the genus is *L. afer* (Peters). *Neanthomys*, Toschi, 1947, is a synonym of *L. flavopunctatus*, Thomas.

GROOVE-TOOTHED FOREST MICE.

AT THE PRESENT TIME this genus is represented by two specimens. These were collected at Bismarkburg, Togo, and Dahomey, West Africa, and were described in 1893 as *L. buttneri*. These specimens are in the Berlin Museum.

The original description states that the length of the head and body is 118 mm., and the length of the tail is 37 mm. The coloration of the upper parts is dark brown to grayish brown, resulting from the in-dividual hairs which are gray at the base, light brown in the middle, and black at the tip. The shoulders and flanks are light brown. The feet are covered by short, brown hairs. The small ear is well haired. The claws of the fore feet are fairly long but somewhat shorter than those of the hind feet. In this respect *Leimacomys* is similar to *Stenomys* (a subgenus of *Rattus*), but its tail is shorter than that of *Stenomys*. The upper incisors have a broad shallow groove.

Members of this genus are probably related to *Steatomys* and *Lophuromys*.

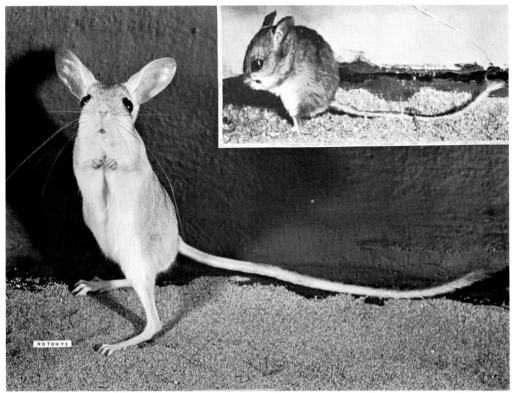

Australian Kangaroo Mouse (*Notomys filmeri*), photo from Queensland Museum. Inset: (*Notomys* sp.), photo by Shelley Barker.

JERBOA MICE, KANGAROO MICE, AUSTRALIAN HOPPING MICE; KAHL-PE-RE, GUNDING, ULA-BAIYA, TALAMBA, DARGAWARRA (native names).

THIS GENUS, made up of about ten species, has a range that embraces most of the Australian continent. *Notomys* inhabits lightly timbered areas, grasslands, sandy dunes, and plains.

The length of the head and body is 91 to 177 mm., and the length of the tail is 125 to 225 mm. The general coloration of the upper parts varies from pale sandy brown through yellowish brown to ashy brown or grayish; the under parts are white in all species except *N. mitchelli*, which is whitish gray below. The body covering is fine, close, and soft in most forms, the long hairs near the tip of the tail make a brush effect.

These rodents are characterized by their strong incisors, long tails, large ears, and their extremely lengthened and narrow hind feet, which have only four sole pads. In the species that were formerly included under *Ascopharynx*, a distinct glandular pocket occurs on the throat with a lip or fold at the rear edge. The remainder of the species *may* have traces of such a patch. The female has four mammae.

These rodents spend the daylight hours sleeping in the nest, but toward dusk they become quite active. Normally, they move about awkwardly on all fours, or make short hops, but if they are startled, they bound gracefully for several feet. *N. mitchelli* can even jump sideways. Hopping mice live in burrows which they dig themselves. Some are of simple construction, but others are rather complex. In sandy soil the burrow of *N. mitchelli* leads downward at an angle of about 40 degrees for 1.2 to 1.5 meters, then levels off and leads into a nest chamber, whence it leads almost straight upward to the exit. A mound of excavated soil around the openings is often lacking. The diet of *Notomys* consists of berries, leaves, seeds, and other available vegetation or vegetable fibers. This genus is commonly found in association with *Antechinomys*, its marsupial parallel, and sometimes both species inhabit the same tunnel system.

Two to five young constitute a litter. It is believed that their life span exceeds three years.

Hopping mice are easily kept in captivity and are gentle. They are eaten by natives in certain areas.

The type species of the genus is *N. mitchelli* (Ogilby).

Broad-toothed Rat (*Mastacomys fuscus*), photo by Ederic Slater.

BROAD-TOOTHED RATS.

THIS GENUS consists of two species, *M. fuscus* and *M. wombeyensis*. *M. fuscus* inhabits the island of Tasmania and southeastern Australia. The type material, a living specimen, was taken in Tasmania and is now in the British Museum (Natural History). Later fossil specimens were recorded from the Wellington Caves of New South Wales (now in the National Museum, Melbourne), and another modern specimen was taken from the Fish River Caves, Blue Mountains, New South Wales, which is now exhibited in the British Museum. *M. wombeyensis* is known only from the left maxillary tooth row, with zygomatic plate and maxillary portion of the zygomatic arch. The remains, originally in the Anatomical Museum, Edinburgh University, are now in the Australian Museum, Sydney. The type locality is Wombeyen Caves near Taralga, New South Wales. Most mammalogists now consider *M. mordicus*, formerly arranged as a distinct species, a subspecies of *M. fuscus*, representing the Pleistocene (?) form from South Australia.

This genus was founded on a single live specimen from Tasmania. Since then, both live and fossil specimens have been taken from southeastern Australia and the high swamp country in Tasmania. In these specimens the length of the head and body is 145 to 185 mm., and the length of the tail is 95 to 115 mm. An adult female weighed about 160 grams. The dense hair is long and silky, and the coloration throughout is sooty brown to grayish brown. The skin of the tail and feet is dark-colored. Typical of this genus are the broadened molar teeth and the narrowed palate. *M. wombeyensis* is distinguished from *M. fuscus* by the presence of a small additional cusp on the third upper molar. Broad-toothed rats are vole-like in appearance and habits. There are four mammae.

In Cradle Valley in northwestern Tasmania, these rats live at 900 meters elevation among matted "wire" grass in alpine heath vegetation. Tunnels and runways had been constructed through the grass. Swamp-rats (*Rattus lutreolus*) were also present at this locality, which in winter is often covered by snowdrifts several feet deep. *Mastacomys* has been found in Victoria in thick, very wet forest near a bracken-covered clearing.

The broadened and heavy molars may be adapted to the consumption of coarse vegetation, although fungus is believed to form a part of the diet.

The type species of the genus is *M. fuscus* (Thomas).

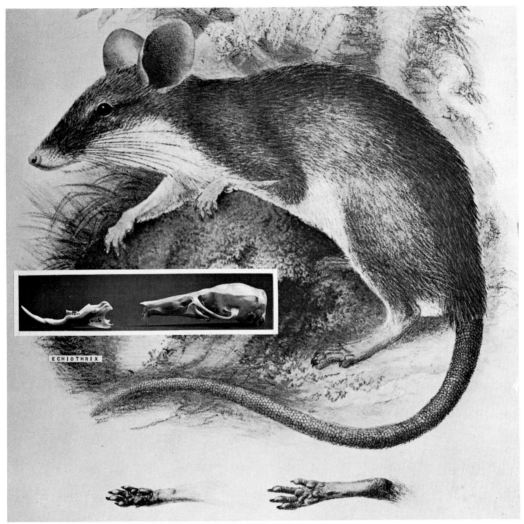

Celebes Spiny Rat or Shrew Rat (*Echiothrix leucura*), photo from *Abh. Zool. Anthrop.-ethn. Mus. Dresden*, "Säuge-tiere vom Celebes- und Philippinen- Archipel," Adolph B. Meyer. Skull, photo by P. F. Wright of specimen in U.S. National Museum.

CELEBES SPINY RATS OR SHREW RATS, WITBUIK-RAT.

THE SINGLE SPECIES, *E. leucura*, inhabits Celebes.

The length of the head and body is 200 to 250 mm., and the tail is always shorter. The upper parts are grayish or dark gray-brown, with black-tipped hairs on the back and sides; the undersides are whitish, yellowish, creamy buff, or reddish buff. The fur is of two types; soft hairs and bristles. The nearly naked, cylindrical tail has rings of square scales. The head and nose are elongated and give *Echiothrix* somewhat the appearance of a shrew.

The upper incisors are short, and each has two longitudinal grooves. The lower incisors are elongated, arched, widely divergent from each other, and ". . . it is difficult to see how they can function, as they close on either side of the premaxillae, more or less, and evidently do not touch the upper incisors at all" (J. R. Ellerman, *The Families and Genera of Living Rodents* [London, 1941], p. 269).

The habits of shrew rats are not known. Specimens are in the British Museum (Natural History) and the U.S. National Museum.

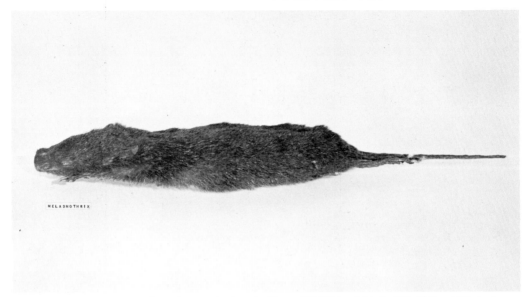

Celebes Long-clawed Mouse (*Melasmothrix naso*), photo by Howard E. Uible of skin in U.S. National Museum.

CELEBES LONG-CLAWED MICE, LESSER SHREW RAT.

AT THE PRESENT TIME this genus is known from the type specimen which was collected January 2, 1918, by H. C. Raven at Rano Rano, Middle Celebes. From this single specimen the genus and species, *M. naso*, was described. The animal was trapped under a rotten, moss-covered log. The skin and skull, which are in good condition, are in the U.S. National Museum.

The length of the head and body of the type specimen is 124 mm., and the length of the tail is 90 mm. The dense pelage has a velvety texture, and its general coloration is rich blackish bay on the upper parts. The hairs of the underfur have slate-colored bases and golden-brown tips, whereas the slightly longer hairs which are scattered throughout the pelage are glossy black for their entire length. The under parts are quite similar in coloration to the back and sides but may be somewhat lighter and glossier. The hands, feet, ears, and tail are brownish black.

Melasmothrix has an elongated snout and long claws on the fore feet. The thumb is reduced to a tubercle with a flattened nail. The ears are short. The rings of scales on the tail are practically concealed by dense, close hairs.

Although nothing is known concerning the mode of life of this rare mammal, the texture of its fur suggests that its habits are semiaquatic.

Egyptian Spiny Mice (*Acomys cahirinus*), light and dark subspecies, photos by Ernest P. Walker. Animal in lower picture has lost tip of tail.

SPINY MICE, PORCUPINE MICE; GOUP OR SHOE-SHABGOOP, HADENDOWAH, GWET OR GWEGWET, RATS EPINEUX, STACHELMÄUSE. (Included are vernaculars used in other countries.)

FOUR OR FIVE SPECIES can be found from Sind, Pakistan, through southern Iran, Israel, and Arabia, and throughout most parts of Africa. The usual habitat is a rocky area, but *Acomys* sometimes inhabits sandy valleys. They are common in the crevices of termite hills in areas of dense vegetation. And *A. cahirinus* is mainly found near human habitation in Egypt.

The length of the head and body is 70 to 125 mm., and the length of the tail is 60 to 125 mm. The average weight of a newborn *A. dimidiatus* is between 5 and 6 grams, and adult *Acomys* usually weigh between 50 and 90 grams. Coloration above is pale yellowish or reddish brown, reddish, or dark grayish; the under parts are white. The back and the tail are covered with coarse, inflexible spines. The brittle tail is easily broken. The tail appears to be practically naked, but the scales are conspicuous. It may be whitish above and below, bicolored, or uniformly dark. The ears are large and erect. There are four or six mammae.

Although their native habitat is in rocky country, spiny mice apparently use gerbil burrows quite extensively in the sandy areas, where they may compete with gerbils if the food is scarce. *Acomys* is active mainly in the early morning and late afternoon, although individuals have been seen among the rocks at all hours. Spiny mice are omnivorous but feed mainly on plant material, especially grain. Commensal forms are similar to *Mus*, feeding on nearly anything they can find, including fibrous mats.

Most births occur between February and September. The gestation period in *A. dimidiatus* is about 42 days, with a litter size of one to five (average is about three). In this species the eyes open on the third day and weaning occurs about two weeks after birth when the young weigh 9 to 16 grams. In other species of *Acomys* the young are born with the eyes open and with little of the helplessness of most newborn rodents. Male *Acomys* are capable of breeding when about seven weeks old.

The type species of the genus is *A. cahirinus* (Desmarest).

African Big-toothed Mouse (*Uranomys foxi*), photo by Jane Burton.

AFRICAN BIG-TOOTHED MICE, GIANT NAKED-TAILED RAT.

THIS GENUS is made up of about five species whose combined range includes Gambia, Ghana, Nigeria, Uganda, and Nyasaland in Africa.

The length of the head and body is 90 to 134 mm., and the length of the tail is 53 to 77 mm. The hairs on the back are fairly long, especially on the rump; they are slightly stiffened which gives the coat a crisp or brittle texture. In general, *U. ruddi* is uniformly grayish, but the usual coloration of the remaining species is a grizzled mixture of fawns, browns, and buffs. The under parts vary from grayish to white, with a tinge of buff in some individuals. The tail, which is scantily covered with short hairs, is dark above and slightly lighter below. The external appearance of *Uranomys* is similar to that of *Lophuromys* except that the backs of the hands and feet in the former genus are covered with fine white hairs, but they are brownish in *Lophuromys*. The incisors project forward. The skull resembles that of *Acomys*, the genus with which *Uranomys* is thought to be allied. The hind foot is broad, and the middle three digits are relatively long. There are 12 mammae.

Few specimens have been obtained, and the genus seems to be rare in all parts of its range.

The type species of the genus is *U. ruddi*, Dollman.

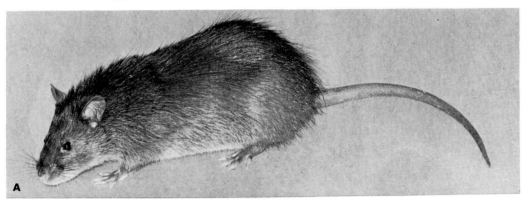

A. Taiwan Bandicoot Rat (*Bandicota indica nemorivaga*), photo by Robert E. Kuntz. B. Black Bandicoot Rat (*Bandicota bengalensis*), photo by Ernest P. Walker.

BANDICOOT RATS, MOLE-RATS; BORSTELRAT, WI-VOK, PADDY-FIELD RATS, WEL-MIYA, KURUMB-ELLI OR VIEL-ELLI, TIKUS-WIROK, TJANTUNG, TIKUS DJANTANG, KOK, REKYWEK, URU-MIYA, PERITCHE-'ELLI, BAMBOO RATS. (Included are vernaculars used in other countries.)

THIS GENUS of two species inhabits Ceylon, the peninsula of India, Nepal, Assam, Burma, southern China, Thailand, Indo-China, northern Malaya, Sumatra, Java, and Formosa, where it was introduced by the Dutch. *B. bengalensis* has been reported from evergreen jungles and oak scrub, and *B. indica* seems to be a commensal form with man, at least in some areas. *Gunomys* is regarded as a synonym of *Bandicota*.

The length of the head and body is quite variable, ranging from about 160 to possibly more than 360 mm.; and the length of the tail ranges from 140 to 258 mm. The weight ranges from 685 grams to 1,132 grams. The texture of the pelage varies from soft, fairly dense fur to thin, coarse fur, with wide differences in the length of the guard hairs. The general coloration of the upper parts ranges from light grayish to various shades of brownish or almost black. The lower parts are a dirty white. The tail is scantily haired. The front claws are large and the muzzle is short and broad. The mammae vary from 12 to 18. The incisors are yellow or orange in color.

Bandicoot rats are good diggers and construct elaborate burrows, throwing the earth from the burrows in numerous piles. Each burrow, apparently inhabited by a single animal, has one or more storage chambers, in which the heads of grain, tubers, fruit, and nuts are stored. Ordinarily these stout-bodied rodents leave their retreats only during the safety of darkness. They are said to be good swimmers. Bandicoot rats are characterized by their ferocious nature. When disturbed, they emit a harsh, nasal barking.

The species *B. indica* is said to have litters of 10 to 12. Breeding in Ceylon probably takes place throughout the year.

In cultivated areas, members of this genus seriously damage grains as well as root crops. They are pests on rubber plantations. These rats are sometimes eaten by the natives, and the storage chambers in the burrows of *Bandicota* are raided regularly by natives.

The type species of the genus is *B. indica* (Bechstein).

Pest Rat (*Nesokia indica suilla*), photo by Harry Hoogstraal.

PEST RATS, SHORT-TAILED MOLE RATS, SHORT-TAILED BANDICOOT RATS, ASIATIC BANDICOOT RATS; GIRDI, YENKRAI, KOK, GOLATTA KOKU, REKYWEH, MUGHI (native names).

THE SINGLE SPECIES, *N. indica*, inhabits Egypt, Israel, Syria, northern Arabia, Iran, Iraq, Afghanistan, West Pakistan, the northern half of India, Chinese Turkestan, and southern Russian Turkestan. Short-tailed mole rats usually live in moist areas in various habitats, from deserts to forests, gardens, grain fields, and along irrigation ditches from 26 meters below sea level to about 1,500 meters elevation.

The length of the head and body is from 140 to about 215 mm., the length of the tail is 88 to 127 mm. The adults weigh approximately 130 to 175 grams. The texture of the pelage differs widely, ranging from coarse, short, harsh, and semispinous coats to those which are long, fine, and silky. In some forms the coat is dense, in others it is thin. In all forms the tail is practically naked, and the hands and feet are scantily haired. The general coloration of the upper parts ranges from fawn or yellowish brown to grayish brown, mixed with red in places. The under parts are grayish to whitish. The color of the back gradually merges into that of the sides and flanks without a distinctive line of demarcation.

Members of *Nesokia* are characterized by a robust form; short, rounded head; short, broad muzzle; rounded ears; almost naked tail; and broad feet. All the claws, except the rudimentary thumb, are armed with strong, nearly straight nails. The incisors are stout and broad. The female has eight mammae.

These animals burrow extensively, usually from 150 to 600 mm. below the surface; the loose soil is thrown onto the surface of the ground about the entrances. In some regions at least, they make well-defined runways along the surface. *Nesokia* feeds on grass, roots, and grain. Sometimes this food is stored in the burrows; natives have found up to one pound of grain in the storage chambers.

In Iraq pregnant female *N. indica* were captured in March and April.

Pest rats do considerable damage by tunneling through irrigation walls and raiding grain fields. Natives eat these rodents as well as the grain stored in their burrows. They capture the animals by smoking the tunnels, or by pouring water into them, until the animal comes to the surface where it is captured, sometimes with the aid of a dog.

Long-tailed Pouched Rat (*Beamys major*), photo from Nyasaland Museum through P. Hanney.

LONG-TAILED POUCHED RATS; CHIDIUBAYA.

THE TWO SPECIES of *Beamys* are distributed as follows: *B. hindei*, Kenya, Africa, and *B. major*, Nyasaland, and the Nyika plateau of Northern Rhodesia (single specimen), Africa. *Beamys* is not known from the intervening region.

The species *B. major*, in which the length of the head and body is 145 to 160 mm., and the length of the tail about 130 to 145 mm., is larger than *B. hindei*, which has a head and body length of about 110 mm., and a tail length of about 105 mm. Coloration in both species is grayish or grayish brown above, and white below. *Beamys* is distinguished internally by dental and skull features and externally by the naked white-tipped tail of medium length. In the specimen from the Nyika plateau, the tail is dark on the upper proximal half, mottled the next quarter, and completely white the last quarter. The underside of the tail is dark on the proximal quarter and the rest of its length is whitish. The tail is flattened, with sharp edges, and the lower side is wider than the upper so that in cross section its shape resembles that of a truncated pyramid. Only the basal centimeter of the tail is hairy, and the tail is not noticeably scaly. Long-tailed pouched rats have cheek pouches.

In December, a female and her four, well-grown young were captured by a Chewa native. According to J. R. Ellerman (*The Families and Genera of Living Rodents* [London, 1941], Vol. II, p. 283), the hind foot is arboreal. Members of this genus are seldom collected, and little is recorded of their life habits and general biology. Specimens are in the British Museum (Natural History).

The type species of the genus is *B. hindei* (Thomas).

African Pouched Rats (*Saccostomus campestris*), photo by Ernest P. Walker.

AFRICAN POUCHED RATS; WANGSAKMUISE, PSUKU, SUGU, KATI, FUNDWE, CHATUTE, DUGU, SUKU (native names).

IT IS PROBABLE that a single species, *S. campestris*, constitutes this genus. These animals inhabit Africa from Kenya, Uganda, and Tanganika to the extreme southern tip of the continent. They frequent scrubby areas, grassy places in the open forest, cultivated fields, bare sandy locations, and refuse dumps.

The length of the head and body is 120 to 150 mm., and the length of the tail is 30 to 57 mm. The pelage is quite long, dense, and fine in texture. Coloration of the upper parts ranges through several shades of grayish, usually slightly darker on the nape and mid-dorsal region. Although the sides are only somewhat paler than the back, there is a sharp line between the sides and the under parts, for the latter are pure white or yellowish white. The front legs are generally white. The tail, lightly covered with short hairs, is usually bicolored (dark on top and light below).

African pouched rats have robust bodies; broad, thick heads; and short, strong legs and toes. The ears are short and rounded, the eyes are small, and there are 10 or 12 mammae. The tail is short and thick at the base. *Saccostomus* derives its common name from a cheek pouch which opens inside the lips at each side of the head and extends back to about the shoulders. The incisors are not grooved.

Members of this genus are nocturnal, slow moving, and appear to be rather solitary in their habits. They generally live near cultivated areas where food is plentiful and dig burrows that have a separate entrance and exit. They excavate chambers which serve as dwellings and storehouses. Pouched rats, at least in the southern portion of their range, accumulate seeds during the summer for use in the winter. This food is transported from the field to the storage chambers in the cheek pouches. Their diet is said to include grain and acacia nuts, and, occasionally, insects.

Embryos have been noted in December (South-West Africa), July (East Africa), and a nestling male was found in February (Nyasaland).

Pouched rats are eaten by natives. They make nice pets and never appear to bite when handled.

Giant Pouched Rats (*Cricetomys gambianus*); Inset: Animal with its cheek pouches well filled; photos from New York Zoological Society.

AFRICAN GIANT POUCHED RATS; REUSEROT, KU-RUBINI, SIGWENYE, BUKU (native names).

THE SINGLE SPECIES, *C. gambianus*, inhabits most of the African continent from Gambia eastward to the Sudan and Kenya, and southward to northern Transvaal. African giant rats are forest and thicket dwellers.

The length of the head and body is 240 to 450 mm., and the length of the tail is 365 to 460 mm. They weigh about 1 kg. The fur is short and thin; in some forms it is coarse and harsh, but in others it is relatively fine and sleek. The coloration of the mid-dorsal region ranges from dark grayish brown to medium grayish with a tinge of brown or clear reddish brown. The general coloration becomes lighter on the sides, sides of the face and flanks, ranging from soft gray with a brownish tinge to reddish brown, vinaceous, or buffy. The under parts are soiled white, white, or creamy. The fairly conspicuous ears are practically naked; the tail is almost naked, dark grayish for the dorsal two-thirds, and the remainder soiled white or soiled creamy. Many individuals are mottled with gray or almost spotted, mainly on the anterior half of the upper parts. This mottling may be inconspicuous or form irregular small spots òr large blotches, or it may cover almost all of the upper parts. In some forms there is a fairly definite, almost white, stripe across the back just behind the shoulders.

These large rats have a rather long, narrow head, ungrooved incisors, cheek pouches, and a scaly tail. There are eight mammae, both inguinal and pectoral pairs.

Cricetomys is nocturnal, although these rodents have been seen foraging during the day, when they behave as if they are almost blind, sitting on their haunches and sniffing in all directions. They generally live singly in burrows of their own excavation. These burrows have two to six openings and are frequently located at the base of a tree or among dense vegetation; the holes are often closed from the inside with leaves. Some authors also have seen these rodents in old termite mounds. They are thought to swim well. They use their long tails as balancing organs and climb shrubs and small trees in search of fruit and seeds.

African giant rats mate at various seasons. The gestation period is about 42 days, and probably two to three young are produced at a birth. The life span is about four and one-half years.

These animals are timid but soon become tame in captivity and make delightful pets. A peculiar parasite, a species of wingless earwig (*Hemimerus talpoides*), is found only on this mammal. The earwig probably feeds upon scurf and fungus spores on the skin. These rats are in great demand as food for native tribes. In some West African towns, *Cricetomys* has become a sewer rat and is killed along with *Rattus* by the rat catchers.

Powerful-toothed Rat (*Anisomys imitator*), photos from Museum Zoologicum Bogoriense.

POWERFUL-TOOTHED RATS.

THE SINGLE SPECIES, *A. imitator*, inhabits the New Guinea rain forests from about 900 meters to 2,700 meters elevation.

The length of the head and body is 244 to 300 mm., and the length of the tail is 285 to 330 mm. The coat is composed of short, coarse hairs. The upper parts are blackish fawn, and the under parts are dull buffy white. The head is nearly blackish. The arms and legs are grayish and the hands and feet are brown, becoming white on the digits. Hexagonal scales show through the scantily haired tail. They have small ears, strong scansorial feet, and a long tail. The great toe has a broad nail. There are six mammae.

In external appearance these animals resemble *Uromys*, but internally they are peculiar in that they have disproportionally narrow and deep lower incisors. The molars, however, are quite small. The dental characters of this genus are considered by some authorities as almost sufficient reason for placing *A. imitator* in a separate subfamily.

It would be interesting to learn the kind of food that accounts for the peculiarities of dentition in *Anisomys*. One author believes that it may feed on coconuts or other hard-shelled nuts. Such a diet, he cites, might demand such powerful cutting incisors and the small and delicate molars would be sufficient to grind the soft contents of the nuts.

Although this animal is fairly well represented in study collections, little information has been published concerning its life habits and general biology.

African Climbing Mouse (*Dendromus mesomelas*), photo from Nyasaland Museum through P. Hanney.

AFRICAN CLIMBING MICE, TREE MICE; BOOM-MUIS, NZELE, SOHNO, MSUNTWA, KLIMMUISE (native names).

FOUR SPECIES, *D. mesomelas*, *D. mystacalis*, *D. lovati*, and *D. melanotis*, have a combined range which includes most of Africa from the Sahara southward to the extreme southern tip of the continent. Members of this genus favor damp, grassy country, reed-beds, and areas of bushes and tangled shrubs, from sea level to more than 4,300 meters elevation. They invariably live near water.

The length of the head and body is 60 to 100 mm., and the length of the tail is 70 to 117 mm. The pelage is soft and woolly. The upper parts are grayish or brownish with a black dorsal stripe, and the under parts are whitish or yellowish. The finely scaled and scantily haired tail is either entirely dull brownish or slightly bicolored, in which case the underside is lighter. Like many nocturnal tree mammals, *Dendromus* usually has well-defined dusky "spectacles" encircling the eyes. African climbing mice are remarkable for their long, semiprehensile tails. They are usually distinguished by their fore feet, which have only three, well-developed digits; the hind feet are

normal. The upper incisors are grooved. There are eight mammae.

These animals are quite active and, although not strictly arboreal, they seldom wander far from trees, bushes, vines, and tall grasses upon which they climb with great agility. When alarmed, however, they generally descend to the ground to seek safety. The members of this genus are nocturnal, spending the daylight hours in globular nests of shredded plant fiber located in tangled undergrowth, high sedges, or in burrows in the ground. They have also been known to reline and occupy the nests built by weaverbirds.

The diet is composed of berries, seeds, insects, small lizards, and the eggs and nestlings of small birds.

A female *Dendromus* with five embryos was taken in July and another with three embryos was taken in January, both in East Africa. Another source states that unstriped, immature specimens have been noted from March to September.

Collectors report that these rodents do not bite and can be caught by hand, at night, after they have been dazed by shining a light in their eyes.

The type species of the genus is *D. mesomelas* (Brants).

Long-eared or Gerbil Mouse (*Malacothrix typicus*), photo by James A. Bateman of mounted specimen.

GERBIL MICE, LONG-EARED MICE; LANGOOR-MUISE, GROOTOORMUISE (native names).

THE SINGLE SPECIES, *M. typicus*, inhabits the southern tip of the African continent from southern Angola through South-West Africa, Bechuanaland, and Transvaal to the Cape Province. Gerbil mice are associated with sandy plains and inland grassy velds.

The length of the head and body is 65 to 95 mm., and the length of the tail is 28 to 42 mm. The coat is made up of long, dense, silky fur. The coloration of the upper parts ranges from pale brownish or buffish to reddish brown, with a more or less distinct dark dorsal stripe and a dark crown spot; there is a sprinkling of black or brown hairs on the back and sides. The under parts, feet, and tail are white, the latter scantily haired. Members of this genus are distinguished by their hind feet, which have only four toes each, and their hairy soles and slender limbs. The ears are large. The teeth are similar to those of *Dendromus* and *Steatomys*. There are eight mammae.

Gerbil mice are nocturnal creatures. They may travel about 4 km. from their burrows. They generally follow cattle tracks, foot paths, or sandy roads, and their presence is frequently noted by their tiny footprints along these routes. Before dawn they return to their burrows. The burrows are constructed by digging a passageway which slants downward to a depth of 0.6 to 1.2 meter, where a chamber is excavated and the soil used to fill up the passage. A nest is made of grass and often of feathers, in which the young are reared. From the nest chamber a new tunnel is made to the surface. The soil from this tunnel is also transported to the original passageway beyond the chamber, so that a mound of dirt is not formed near the tunnel exit. The deceiving pile of freshly excavated soil is some distance away.

M. typicus is fond of seeds of various kinds and seems to like the food discarded by the native people.

Mating takes place three times per year, with three to seven young comprising the normal litter. The young begin mating when about three months old.

Like *Dendromus*, gerbil mice are attracted to light and are easily caught at night with the aid of a lantern. They are not aggressive, tame easily, and make interesting pets.

RODENTIA; MURIDAE; **Genus DENDROPRIONOMYS, F. Petter, 1966**

THE SINGLE SPECIES, *D. rousseloti*, is known from only three specimens collected on the grounds of the Jardin Zoologique de Brazzaville, in Brazzaville, the Congo. All three specimens are preserved as skins and skulls in the Paris Museum.

The pelage is velvety and mole-like as in *Prionomys*; the dorsal coloration is brownish, like that of *Dendromus*, lighter on the flanks, the line of demarcation between the dorsal and ventral surfaces being tawny. The venter is entirely white, but the base of the hairs are gray for half their length. A black area underlines the eyes.

No external measurements are available for the three known specimens, but the ears appear to be relatively well-developed and pigmented gray. The tail is scaled and longer than the head and body. The fore feet are provided with four well-developed toes as in *Prionomys*. As in both *Prionomys* and *Dendromus*, the hind feet have five digits.

The dentition is such as to imply a diet that is at least partially insectivorous. The upper incisors are furrowed longitudinally.

Dendroprionomys, as implied by its generic name, exhibits certain characters of *Dendromus* and others of *Prionomys*, and appears to be an intermediate genus between the two.

Nothing is known of the habits of *Dendroprionomys*.

PRIONOMYS

Dollman's Tree Mouse (*Prionomys batesi*), adapted from *Proc. Zool. Soc. London*, St. Leger.

DOLLMAN'S TREE MICE.

THE SINGLE SPECIES, *P. batesi*, is native to the Cameroons in Africa. The type specimen was taken at Bitye, Ja River, by G. L. Bates in 1910 at an elevation of about 600 meters.

The length of the head and body is about 60 mm., and the length of the tail is about 100 mm. The short, velvety fur resembles that of shrews. The coloration of the upper parts is pinkish chocolate; it is lighter on the sides and blends almost imperceptibly into the grayish-pinkish-buff under parts. The face is slightly lighter than the remainder of the upper parts; the sides of the face below the eyes are washed with pinkish buff and the eyes are encircled with narrow blackish rings. The scantily haired, finely scaled tail is dark brown, almost black. There appears to be no hair on the dorsal tip of the tail which suggests that it may be prehensile.

The size of *Prionomys* is comparable to that of a large *Dendromus*. The ears are rather small and rounded. The fore feet have four well-developed fingers, although the thumb is absent. The second and fourth fingers are moderately elongated and have short claws; the outer finger is only half the length of the two middle fingers and bears a small nail. The hind foot has five toes, all of which are armed with claws. The inner toe is about half as long as the middle digit, and its claw is smaller and more blunt than those of the other toes. The upper incisors are short, slender, ungrooved, and project forward; the slender lower incisors are sharply pointed.

Apparently nothing has been published concerning the life habits and general biology of these animals.

Rock Mouse (*Petromyscus collinus*), photo by James A. Bateman of mounted specimen.

ROCK MICE, KOPJE MICE; KLEINKLIPMUIS, KLIP-MUIS.

THE TWO SPECIES of this genus, *P. collinus* and *P. monticularis*, have a range extending from south-western Angola through South-West Africa to the Cape Province. Rock mice inhabit dry barren mountains; they prefer areas where large quantities of loose boulders and rocky outcrops predominate.

The length of the head and body is about 70 to 90 mm., and the length of the tail is 80 to 100 mm. These animals are covered by a fine, straight, soft, silky, and rather thin pelage, without guard hairs. The coloration of the upper parts ranges from various shades of buffy to brownish or drab gray. The individual hairs of the under parts have slaty bases with white tips, which gives them a grayish appearance. The hands, feet, and tail are uniformly white to buffy in all forms except one, in which the bi-colored tail is drab gray above and white below. The tail is moderately well haired, but the hairs are too scanty to hide the coarse scales. These long-tailed rodents have rather long ears (particularly *P. collinus*) and short legs. In *P. collinus* the length of the tail is longer than the head and body, but in *P. monticularis* the tail length is shorter than the combined head and body measurement. The short, broad feet have the normal number of digits. The upper incisors are not grooved. There are six mammae, but occasionally only four in some specimens.

Members of the genus *Petromyscus* are nocturnal; they hide by day under rocks or in crevices and stealthily creep between the boulders at night, unlike *Aethomys* which is much more active. Reports indicate that rock mice are omnivorous in diet.

A female *P. collinus* collected in September had two embryos.

Although *P. collinus* is relatively plentiful, *P. monticularis* is known from only two specimens.

The type species of the genus is *P. collinus* (Thomas and Hinton).

946

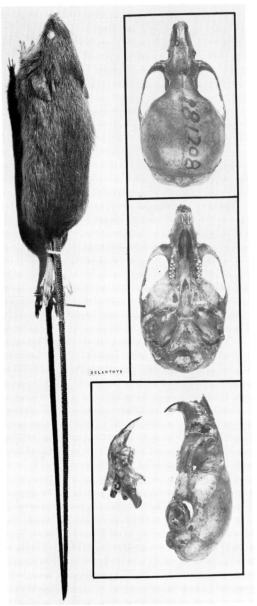

Delany's Swamp Mouse (*Delanymys brooksi*), photos from American Museum of Natural History.

DELANY'S SWAMP MICE.

THE SINGLE SPECIES, *D. brooksi*, is known from Echuya (or Muchuya) Swamp, near Kanaba, Kigezi, in southwestern Uganda, and from Kivu, Tshibati, in the Congo at an elevation of about 2,000 meters. The type was collected by M. J. Delany, for whom the genus is named.

These rodents are very small mice which inhabit, as far as is known, swampy areas covered by tall sedges among which they live without making any definite runway system. The sedges occur in clumps, in water of up to 25 mm. in depth. The type specimen was caught at the base of a sedge clump.

The type, an adult male with somewhat enlarged testes, had a head and body length of 57 mm. and a tail length of 100 mm. It weighed 5 grams. A female specimen (American Museum of Natural History No. 181208) had a head and body length of 59 mm. and a tail length of 102 mm. There were three early embryos found in the uterus. The coloration of the upper parts is a warm russet. The chin is whitish and the remaining under parts are a warm buff. The bases of the hairs, both dorsally and ventrally, are grayish.

The animal is considered by Hayman to be a member of the subfamily Dendromyinae, with its nearest relative apparently *Petromyscus*. The resemblance is marked in a number of cranial and dental features, but in other respects they are widely different.

There are three specimens of this newly discovered genus at the American Museum of Natural History.

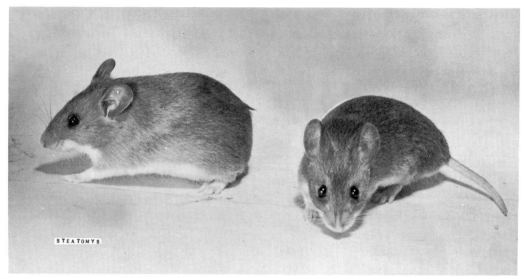

Fat Mice (*Steatomys pratensis*), photo by Ernest P. Walker.

FAT MICE; VETMUISE, SHANA, NSANA, NGAMBWA (native names).

ALTHOUGH A NUMBER of forms have been named and described, it seems likely that only two species, *S. pratensis* and *S. bocagei*, are valid. *Steatomys* inhabits most of Africa from the Sudan to Cape Province and is usually found in dry areas. Some forms prefer open sandy plains and rocky regions, others live in forest and brush country.

The length of the head and body ranges from 70 to about 120 mm., and the length of the tail is 40 to about 50 mm. The pelage is thick, short, soft, and silky. The general coloration of the upper parts ranges through various shades of brown and buff, frequently mixed with blackish. The under parts are white. The dorsal surface of the scantily bristled tail is generally colored like that of the back, and the ventral surface is white, but in at least one form the tail is all white.

These animals have a thick form, rather large and rounded ears, and a thick tail which tapers to a point. The four fingers have slightly curved claws that are suited to burrowing, and there are five toes. The upper incisors are grooved.

These rodents are nocturnal and live singly or in pairs; numerous burrows of individual animals usually are present in a given area. The excavated ground is deposited in mounds on the surface. Fat mice burrow to a depth of 0.9 to 1.2 meters and a distance of 1.5 to 1.7 meters. The entrance is generally closed with loose sand. A nest, constructed of shredded vegetation, is concealed in a large chamber at the bottom of the tunnel. If pursued while in their burrows, fat mice will rapidly dig a new tunnel, carefully filling up the passage behind with the excavated loose sand.

During the autumn these animals become enormously fat and store up nourishment for winter within themselves. The dormant period extends approximately from April to October. The diet is composed of seeds, grass bulbs, and insects.

An average litter is said to contain four to six young.

Steatomys is regarded by the natives as a special delicacy due to its high fat content.

The type species of the genus is *S. pratensis*, Peters.

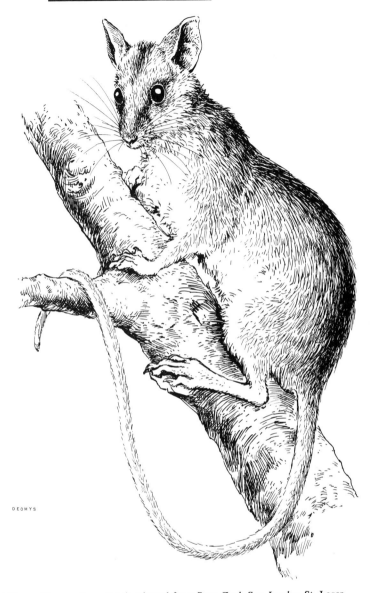

Congo Forest Mouse (*Deomys ferrugineus*), adapted from *Proc. Zool. Soc. London*, St. Leger.

CONGO FOREST MICE.

THE SINGLE SPECIES, *D. ferrugineus*, inhabits forests in the Congo Basin of central Africa.

The length of the head and body is 125 mm. to 160 mm., and the length of the tail is 172 to 205 mm. The long fur is quite stiff but not spiny. The coloration of the upper parts is pale red or reddish fawn, mixed with black along the middle of the back. The individual hairs on the upper parts have white bases, slate-colored middle portions, and reddish tips; along the back some of the hairs are completely black. The face and sides of the head are lighter and more dull in color than the back, except for a poorly defined blackish ring around each eye. The under parts, the insides of the arms and legs, and the hands are white. The slender, coarsely-haired tail is distinctly bicolored in one form, slate gray above and white below, but in another form the terminal 25 to 76 mm. of the tail is entirely white.

Deomys has large, rounded ears; long, narrow hind feet; and orange upper incisors each with two minute grooves, and smooth yellow lower incisors. There are four mammae. Their tails may be prehensile.

These rodents are said to be nocturnal and to travel in great bounds, their hind legs acting as springs. Apparently they eat fruit which has fallen from trees in the forest.

Little has been published on the habits and biology of *Deomys*.

Swamp Rat (*Otomys irroratus*), photo from South African Union Health Department through D. H. S. Davis.

SWAMP RATS; VLEI OTOMYS, VLEIROT, VLEI-MUISE, MBURUGI, IBUSI (native names).

ABOUT 24 SPECIES have been named, which have a range including most of Africa from the Sudan southward to the tip of the continent. *Otomys* usually lives in damp grassy areas and reedbeds near streams and marshes, but some forms inhabit forested mountain slopes, and others are found in dry regions. *Anchotomys*, Thomas, 1918, and *Lamotomys*, Thomas, 1918, are herein included as subgenera.

The length of the head and body is about 130 to 200 mm., and the length of the tail is 55 to 170 mm. The pelage varies in density, texture, and length. The general coloration of the upper parts ranges from light buffy through shades of brownish to dark brown or bright rusty. The under parts are white, creamy, buffy, brownish, or dull dark grayish, generally lighter than the upper parts. The short tail is fairly well haired, but it is not penciled and is usually darker above than below.

Swamp rats are characterized by having at least one conspicuous groove on all four incisors. The upper incisors are strongly curved backward into the mouth. The head of *Otomys* is rounded and rather vole-like, and the ears are relatively small. In Africa the mammal *Dasymys* most closely resembles *Otomys* in external appearance, but that genus lacks the grooved incisors and has a longer tail. Swamp rats have quite plump bodies.

Most forms generally shelter above ground, although some have been reported to live in burrows or crabholes. Above ground, their nests are constructed of shredded plant material and twigs, usually at the base of a small shrub, but swamp rats that occupy burrows make a nest of fine grass at the end of the tunnel. These rodents are active both day and night (mainly in the daytime) and make conspicuous trenches or runways through the grass and swamp vegetation. Although they are not strong swimmers, they enter water freely to swim from one reed patch to another, and they can dive and stay under water for a short time to escape their enemies. Their food consists of a variety of seeds, berries, tender shoots, grasses, roots, reeds, and bark. Apparently they do not harm cultivated crops.

Breeding appears to take place throughout the year; two to four, usually three, young constitute a litter.

Collectors report that swamp rats do not take bait readily from traps left in the open, but that specimens can be obtained by concealing a baited trap in their runways.

The type species of the genus is *O. irroratus* (Brants).

Bush Otomys (*Myotomys unisulcatus unisulcatus*), photo from *The Mammals of South Africa*, Austin Roberts, through John Voelcker and the Transvaal Museum.

BUSH OTOMYS RATS, BUSH KARROO RATS; BOS-KARAROT, BOSKAROMUISE (local vernaculars).

THE SINGLE SPECIES, *M. unisulcatus*, is known from Cape Province, South Africa. Some mammalogists refer this species to the genus *Otomys*. It frequents sandy areas in shrub growth and piles of rock.

The length of the head and body is 130 to 180 mm., and the length of the tail is 80 to 120 mm. The upper parts are grayish, grayish yellow, or buffy yellow, and the under parts are buffy whitish or whitish. The fur is thick and soft, and the body form is stocky.

Bush Otomys rats are common in their native habitat; they are active mainly during the day. Their shelters are usually constructed above ground in shrubs and less commonly in trees or around matted clumps of grass. *Myotomys* sometimes constructs extensive burrow systems in sandy areas, often under sandstone rocks. In such locations they may not build above-ground homes. The tunneled shelters are made of sticks or of weeds and grasses, the burrows extending below the ground. The female makes a soft nest of dry grass and twigs in a subterranean burrow, and a pair of animals usually occupy a single shelter. Surface paths or runs connect one refuge with another, and when the animals are disturbed, they use these paths to reach another shelter.

This rodent can be observed running about and even sitting upright during the daytime. *Myotomys* feeds on green plant material.

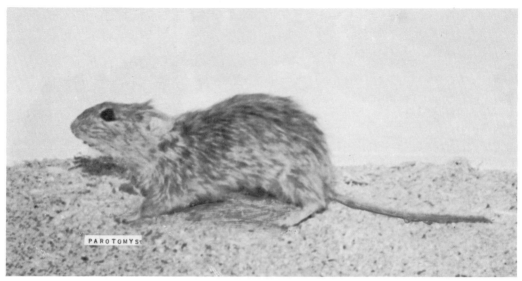

Littledale's Karroo Rat (*Parotomys littledalei*), photo by James A. Bateman of mounted specimen.

KARROO RATS; KARO-ROTS, BOESMANLANDSE KA-ROROT, SAND RATS, KARO-ROTTE (local vernaculars).

THE TWO SPECIES are distributed as follows: *P. brantsi*, the Cape Province of Africa, and *P. littledalei*, South Africa and South-West Africa. They are native to sandy velds and high and low flats, generally near karree or saltbushes. *Liotomys*, Thomas, 1918, is herein regarded as a subgenus for the species *P. littledalei*.

The length of the head and body is 135 to 170 mm., and the length of the tail is 75 to 120 mm. In *P. brantsi* the general coloration of the upper parts is rusty yellowish, variegated with blackish or brownish to form delicate streaks. The sides of the head, neck, and body, as well as the under parts, are grayish white. In one form the basal half of the tail is reddish orange and the terminal half is brownish red, but in another form the tail is black except for a tawny-buffish base. In *P. littledalei* the upper parts vary from tawny to cinnamon buff, the sides and under parts are buff to whitish buff. The upper portion of the tail is similar in color to that of the back and the underside is lighter.

These animals have small ears, but the auditory bullae are considerably enlarged and spherical. *P. brantsi* has definite grooves on the upper incisors, but the incisors of *P. littledalei* lack grooves. The female has four mammae.

Members of the genus *Parotomys* are diurnal and gregarious. They live in burrows which they dig in sandy velds. Both species, but particularly *P. littledalei*, build conspicuous nests of interwoven sticks and grass up to about 0.6 meter in height among the tangled roots and branches of shrubs above the burrows. Karroo rats seldom venture far from their shelters. They are quite wary and at the slightest indication of an intruder quickly seek the safety of their homes. Their diet is said to consist principally of the leaves of saltbush and the annual succulent, mesembryanthemum.

It is said that they breed as often as four times per year and that the young become sexually mature when three months old. A litter consists of two to four young.

They do not harm the crops of the natives and apparently are of little economic importance.

The type species of the genus is *P. brantsi* (Smith).

Celebes Rat (*Lenomys meyeri*), photo from *Abh. Zool. Anthrop.-ethn. Mus. Dresden*, "Säugetiere vom Celebes- und Philippinen- Archipel," Adolf B. Meyer.

CELEBES RATS, TREFOIL-TOOTHED GIANT RATS; POENGALADEN, TANGKARA, PANGOESAIO, MEA (native names for *L. longicaudus, Celebes*).

THIS GENUS is represented by two species, *L. meyeri* and *L. longicaudus*, both of which inhabit the island of Celebes.

The length of the head and body ranges from 235 to 290 mm., and the length of the tail is 210 to 285 mm. The pelage is thick, soft, and rather woolly, with elongated guard hairs. The general coloration of the upper parts is fuscous to drab olive-black, with a sprinkling of whitish; a dorsal line is present that is somewhat darker than the sides. The head is the same color as the body. The under parts are buffy white, blending gradually into the color of the sides, and leaving no conspicuous line of demarcation. The individual hairs of the under parts have gray bases and white tips. The feet and hands are brownish gray. The terminal section (one-half to three-fifths) of the tail is flesh-colored; the tail is quite scantily haired.

Information concerning the life habits and general biology of *Lenomys* is limited at the present time.

The type species of the genus is *L. meyeri* (Jentinck).

PREHENSILE-TAILED RATS.

THIS GENUS is comprised of about nine species that have a range including New Guinea and small adjacent islands, Japen Island, New Britain, Ferguson Island, and Goodenough Island and extending from sea level to about 2,700 meters elevation. *Chiruromys* Thomas, 1888, is herein included as a subgenus, for the species *forbesi*, *lamia*, and *vates*.

The length of the head and body ranges from 115 to 170 mm., and the length of the tail is 165 to 250 mm. The pelage is dense, woolly, and quite soft with few guard hairs. The numerous whiskers are long, dark, and conspicuous. The general coloration of the upper parts ranges from grayish through rufous and reddish brown to dark brown or almost black. The lighter-colored forms have a sprinkling of silver hairs on the upper parts. The under parts are white, buffy, yellowish, or reddish. The long, scantily-haired tail is coarsely scaled and brownish in color, except the upper terminal part which is flesh-colored, naked, and smooth.

These moderately large to rather small rats are similar in external appearance to *Mus*. Members of the genus *Pogonomys* have a slightly opposable hallux with a fully developed claw. The hands and feet are short, broad, and modified for climbing. The female has six mammae.

Although there is little published material concerning the life habits and general biology of *Pogonomys*, it is known that these rodents are highly arboreal. That they are adapted to climbing is evidenced by the prehensile tail, which curls backward or up at the tip and is influenced by a hairless tactile area on the terminal 10 to 20 mm. of the upper surface. This characteristic is unusual for it is unlike that of most prehensile-tailed mammals wherein the tip of the tail curls downward.

The type species of the genus is *P. macrourus*, Milne-Edwards.

Prehensile-tailed Rat (*Pogonomys* sp.), photo by Carlton J. Phillips, Univ. Maryland Medical Team. Insets: **A.** Left upper teeth; **B.** Left lower teeth; **C.** Dorsal view of middle of tail and tip of tail; photos from *Proc. Zool. Soc. London.*

Malayan Pencil-tailed Tree Mouse (*Chiropodomys penicillatus*), photo by Ernest P. Walker.

PENCIL-TAILED TREE MICE, COMPLEX-TOOTHED
TREE MICE.

SEVEN OF THE EIGHT SPECIES that make up this genus
are native to Assam, the Malay Peninsula, Sumatra,
Java, Borneo, and smaller adjacent islands; the other
species, *C. calamianensis*, inhabits Calamianes Island
in the Philippines. These animals appear to be confined to forested areas. The species *C. fulvus*, known
from Yunnan in southern China, has been separated
from *Chiropodomys* and made the type of the new
genus *Vernaya* on the basis of its having a claw on
the hallux which *Chiropodomys* lacks.

The length of the head and body is about 76 to
133 mm., and the length of the tail is 80 to 155 mm.
The pelage is soft, dense, and uniform in length,
without conspicuous guard hairs or spines. The
general coloration of the upper parts is dull grayish
brown or buffy brown, and that of the under parts is
white to pale creamy. The tail is dark grayish throughout, and rather thinly covered with short hairs near
the base, becoming more or less penciled terminally.
The whiskers are numerous and long.

These rodents have short, broad feet and long tails.
The first digit of both the hands and the feet is short
and stumpy with a flat nail; the other digits have
short, slightly curved claws. The digit pads are large
and the sole of the hind foot is naked. The ears are
moderately large, thin, and nearly naked. Some forms
have four mammae while others are reported to have
eight.

Pencil-tailed tree mice are arboreal in their habits.
One author cites that these animals are most active
during the night, although if disturbed during the day
they become quite active and agile. They are said to
be aggressive little rodents that try hard to bite an
adversary. Members of the genus *Chiropodomys* are
quite clean and dainty in their habits. One specimen,
which was captured in the top of a tall tree and kept
in captivity, remained healthy on a diet of fruit, including bananas.

The type specimen of *C. niadis*, an adult female,
contained three small embryos. It was collected in
March on Sumatra.

The type species of the genus is *C. penicillatus*,
Peters.

Giant Tree Rat (*Mallomys rothschildi*), photo by Howard E. Uible of skin in U.S. National Museum. Insets: Section of tail from *Zeitschr. Saugetierk*. Lower jaw from *Mammals Collected by the Dutch New Guinea Expedition*, F. A. Jentinck.

GIANT TREE RATS.

THE SINGLE SPECIES, *M. rothschildi*, inhabits most of New Guinea between 1,350 and 2,750 meters elevation. One source indicates that these rodents live among rocks in the mountains.

The length of the head and body ranges from 345 to 440 mm., and the length of the tail is 365 to 420 mm. There appears to be considerable variation in both texture and color of the pelage. The fur is quite long, thick, and has a tendency to be somewhat woolly in most specimens. The general coloration of the upper parts is dark brown to fuscous brown or grayish, with the guard hairs being all black or black with white tips. The shades of coloration are dependent upon the abundance and color of the guard hairs. In at least one form the crown is light brown. The under parts are creamy or dull white, and the individual hairs are unicolored. In a few of the specimens a white band is present which extends across the middle of the under parts and well up on the sides. The hands, feet, and whiskers are black. The scantily-haired tail is coarsely scaled; the basal part is brownish, and approximately the terminal half is white.

Giant tree rats have the usual murid body form and large, broad, heavy feet; the pollex has a short nail, and the remainder of the digits have considerably enlarged and slightly curved claws. The moderately broad incisors are ungrooved and project slightly forward. The muzzle is short and the skull is heavy and thick.

Little has been published concerning the life habits and general biology of *Mallomys*. These animals are arboreal and are known to feed on such plant material as fern shoots.

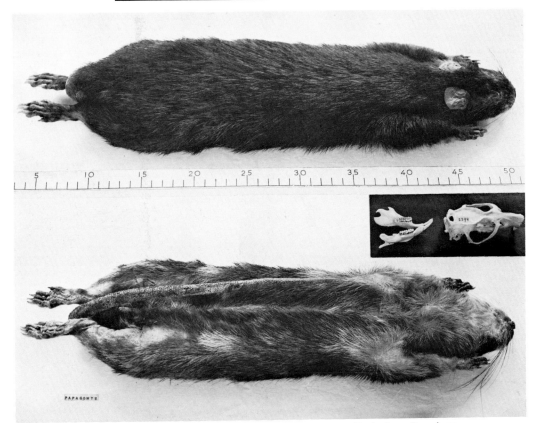

Flores Island Giant Tree Rat (*Papagomys armandvillei*), photos from Museum Zoologicum Bogoriense.

FLORES ISLAND GIANT TREE RATS.

THE SINGLE SPECIES, *P. armandvillei*, is known only from Flores Island in the East Indies. It was originally described in 1892 by F. A. Jentinck as *Mus armandvillei*.

The length of the head and body is 410 to 450 mm., and the length of the tail is 330 to 370 mm. The hairs comprising the underfur of the upper parts have reddish brown tips, and the hairs and bristles of the under parts are tipped with white. Spines are also present in the pelage. The hands and feet are covered with short dark hairs extending to the tips of the fingers and toes. The naked tail is covered with thick, long scales, each having three short, stiff hairs. The tail of *Papagomys* is yellow in color for part of its length. This animal resembles *Mallomys*, differing from it in skull and dental features.

Specimens of this uncommon and relatively unknown animal are in the following study collections: Leiden Museum, Netherlands; Berlin Museum; and the Zoological Museum and Laboratory, Buitenzorg, Java, N.I.

Slender-tailed Cloud Rat (*Phloeomys cumingi*), photo by Ernest P. Walker.

SLENDER-TAILED CLOUD RATS, PHILIPPINE VARI-COLORED RATS; YUT-YUT, EUT-EUT (native names).

TWO SPECIES, *P. cumingi* and *P. pallidus*, which inhabit the Philippine Islands, comprise this genus. Their elevational range extends from sea level to the high mountains of northwestern Luzon.

Members of this genus are the largest animals within the family Muridae. The length of the head and body of *P. cumingi* is 480 to 485 mm., and the length of the tail is 200 to 320 mm. In *P. pallidus* the length of the head and body is 375 to 400 mm., and the length of the tail is 315 to 350 mm. The former species has a pelage which is rather rough, suberect, and intermixed with long hairs. In *P. cumingi* the general coloration of the upper parts is blackish brown washed with dirty yellowish or reddish yellow, and there may be an irregular reddish-brown blotch on the dorsal surface. The under parts are paler than those above. The pelage of *P. pallidus* is long, dense, and soft in comparison with that of *P. cumingi*. The general coloration of the upper parts of *P. pallidus*

results from the longer individual hairs that have brown or reddish-brown bases and white tips; the shorter fur is uniformly brownish. The hairs on the anterior part of the body have gray to gray-brown bases and black tips. The ears are black, the cheeks are gray, and the tail is black to brownish black. In both species the well-haired tail is not bushy.

Phloeomys has broad incisors, a blunt muzzle, and small ears. The feet are large and wide, adapted to arboreal life; the foreclaws are large. The female has four mammae.

One collector reports that he shot two of these large rodents early in the morning as they were climbing trees. Another reference indicates that members of this genus live in old tree trunks.

These animals are apparently relatively scarce throughout their range, and there is limited published information regarding their life habits and general biology. One collector obtained only four specimens within a six month period, all of which were captured by native Igorotes with the aid of their dogs.

The type species of the genus is *P. cumingi*, Waterhouse.

Bushy-tailed Cloud Rats (*Crateromys schadenbergi*), photo by Ernest P. Walker. Insets: A. Upper molars; B. Lower molars; photos from *Trans. Zool. Soc. London*, "Mammals from the Philippines," Oldfield Thomas.

BUSHY-TAILED CLOUD RATS, SCHADENBERG'S GREAT RATS; BU-UT.

THE SINGLE SPECIES, *C. schadenbergi*, appears to be quite common among the high mountains and plateaus of northern Luzon in the Philippine Islands. Members of this genus prefer a forest habitat.

The length of the head and body ranges from 325 to 360 mm., and the length of the tail is 355 to 407 mm. The pelage is quite dense, consisting of woolly underfur and long, straight, or wavy guard hairs. The general coloration of *Crateromys* is highly variable, but it is usually dark brown to black on the upper parts, dark grayish on the sides, and iron gray on the under parts. Some individual rodents, however, are whitish or brownish on the anterior part of their body and, occasionally, the under parts are irregularly whitish. The long tail is exceptionally heavily haired and is thickly bushy, a unique characteristic among the family Muridae.

These large rodents have an elongated body, slender muzzle, and small eyes and ears. The hands and feet each have five digits, the thumb has a well-developed flattened nail, and the remainder of the fingers and toes have powerful, slender claws. Strong tufts of hair occur at the base of each claw. The hind foot is broad.

Bushy-tailed cloud rats are arboreal and are most active after sunset. During the day they sleep in cavities in the trees or in holes among roots of trees. These animals have a strange cry, so shrill that it is similar to that of some insects. They are said to feed upon the buds and bark of young pine-tree sprouts and on fruit; the latter is eaten while on the tree rather than after it has fallen to the ground.

Igorote natives from Mount Data trap these animals and sell their pelts in the market at Baguio. The wool-like pelt is attractive and serviceable. There are several instances in which *Crateromys* were kept as pets, but no notes were made on their temperament.

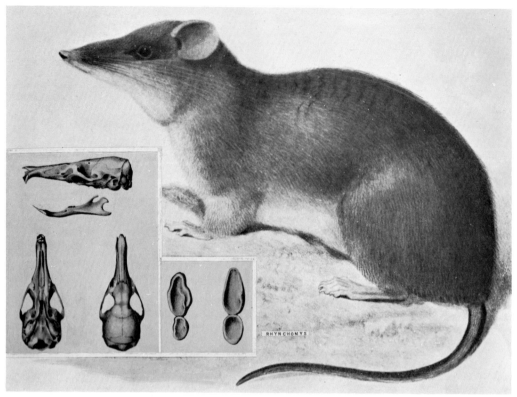

Shrew-like Rat (*Rhynchomys soricoides*), photo from *Trans. Zool. Soc. London*, "Mammals from the Philippines," Oldfield Thomas. Insets: Skull; left teeth, upper row; right teeth, lower row; photos from *Proc. Zool. Soc. London*.

SHREW-LIKE RATS.

THE SINGLE SPECIES, *R. soricoides*, is known from seven specimens. Five of these were collected by Whitehead in 1895 on Mount Data, Luzon, Philippine Islands. These animals were captured at an elevation of about 2,460 meters. In 1946 two specimens were collected on Mount Data at about 2,286 meters; they were trapped in thick bushes and mossy forests in a gully.

The length of the head and body is 188 to 215 mm., and the length of the tail is 142 to 146 mm. The fur is said to be thick, close, and velvety. The coloration of the upper parts is uniformly dark olivaceous gray, without markings; the under parts are dirty gray and are not sharply defined from the back. A whitish patch is sometimes present on the throat. The tail is fairly well covered, not tufted and is blackish above and slightly paler below. These animals have an elongated muzzle, like shrews; the feet are similar to those of rats (*Rattus*), and the teeth are extraordinarily reduced. The upper incisors are white and the lower ones are pale yellow. The skull is greatly elongated in front, resulting from a long, slender, straight lower jaw. The great toe has a broad nail and the eyes are small.

Due to their apparent scarcity and limited range, practically nothing has been recorded about the life habits and general biology of *Rhynchomys*. Because of the small cheek teeth, it has been suggested that their diet consists of soft food, mainly insects and worms, rather than plant material.

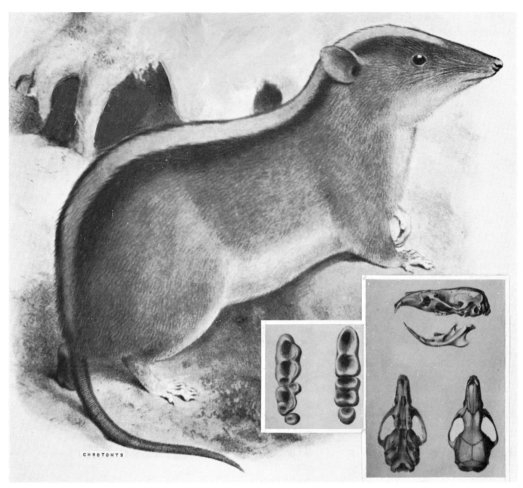

Luzon Striped Rat (*Chrotomys whiteheadi*), photo from *Trans. Zool. Soc. London,* "Mammals from the Philippines," Oldfield Thomas. Insets: Left teeth, upper row; right teeth, lower row; skull; photos from *Trans. Zool. Soc. London.*

LUZON STRIPED RAT.

THE SINGLE KNOWN SPECIES, *C. whiteheadi*, is recorded from Mount Data, the type locality, at an elevation of about 2,460 meters; Ivisan, Benguet; and Lepanto Province, all in the mountainous region of northern Luzon, Philippine Islands.

The head and body length is about 196 mm., the tail is 111 mm., and the hind foot is 35 mm. The general coloration above is grayish brown, some individuals have a rufous tinge. A well-defined bright buff or orange line, bordered on either side by broad shining black bands, extends from the middle of the face along the middle of the back almost to the tail. The ground color of the back gradually shades lighter on the sides to slaty gray on the under parts. The fingers and toes are white, and the remainder of the hands and feet are shiny gray. The tail is thinly haired, blackish above and paler beneath, with the tip sometimes white. The short fur is soft and straight. The pollex has a rounded nail, whereas the other fingers and toes have well-developed, slightly curved claws. The incisors are pale yellow and project forward somewhat. The eyes are quite small, and the ears are fairly large and covered with short, fine hairs.

It is said that the genus *Chrotomys* eats sweet potatoes and grass and lives near plantations. No other information was noted on the habits and biology of these rodents.

It is similar to *Celaenomys silaceus* of the same locality.

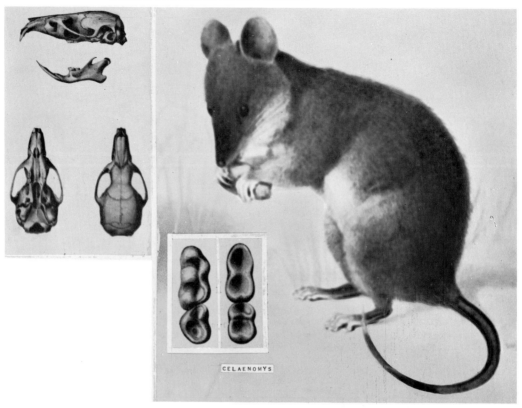

Luzon Shrew-like Rat (*Celaenomys silaceus*), photos from *Trans. Zool. Soc. London,* "Mammals from the Philippines," Oldfield Thomas.

SHREW-LIKE RATS.

THIS GENUS, represented by a single species, *C. silaceus*, is known from six specimens. Whitehead in 1895 collected two specimens; Hollister reported a single specimen taken by Mearns, and the Philippine Zoological Expedition of the Chicago Natural History Museum in 1946–47 obtained three specimens. Mearns collected his specimen at Haights-in-the-Oaks, Benguet, Luzon; the other examples were taken on the table-topped summit of Mount Data, between 2,100 to 2,400 meters elevation. Sanborn writes that the specimens obtained by the Philippine Expedition were trapped in densely vegetated gullies and mossy forests.

The length of the head and body of the type specimen is 195 mm., and the length of the tail is 110 mm. These animals are covered by a soft, close, velvety pelage which is a uniform gray on the upper parts. The under parts are paler than the back, but the line of demarcation is not sharply defined. Most of the individual hairs are slaty gray on the basal part and washed with buffy white on the tip. The sides of the muzzle are almost black; the ears are grayish; the feet are dark gray as far as the digits, but the digits are whitish or flesh colored. The thinly-haired tail is white except for the upper basal part which is brownish.

Members of *Celaenomys* have a shrew-like body form, and at a glance these animals could be mistaken for *Rhynchomys* but they are distinguished from that genus by their larger teeth and shorter muzzle. The incisors project forward similarly to those of the genus *Rhynchomys*, but they are larger and more powerful. The eyes are small and the ears are short. The sharply pointed muzzle is produced by a wedge-shaped skull. It is believed that this genus is related to *Chrotomys*.

Nothing has been published regarding the general biology and life habits of these rodents.

Earless Water Rat (*Crossomys moncktoni*), photo from Basil Marlow, Australian Museum, Sydney.

WATER RATS, EARLESS WATER RATS; CON-DO-MIN (native name).

THE SINGLE SPECIES, *C. moncktoni*, inhabits New Guinea. These animals occur at 600 to 3,000 meters elevation, and their habitat appears to be limited to areas along rivers and streams.

The length of the head and body is about 205 mm., and the length of the tail is about 220 mm. The dorsal pelage is long and soft, and the underfur is dense, soft, woolly, and rather glossy. The general coloration of the upper parts is mottled brownish gray with a pale yellowish-olivaceous wash. The few scattered guard hairs have black tips and subterminal brownish rings. The soft, cottony hairs of the under parts are pure white to the base. The well-defined line, where the two colors meet, occurs quite high on the sides. The tail is light gray above and white below, with two rows of long white hairs which begin at either side of the body and gradually converge into a single row. This stripe continues along the underside of the tail to the tip.

Members of this genus have waterproof fur, greatly reduced ears, fairly well-webbed hind feet, and the above-mentioned unusual tail structure; these adaptations make *Crossomys* even more specialized for aquatic life than *Hydromys*. In addition, their hands are quite small, their wrists slender, and the claws are small, delicate, and strongly curved. The coat and feet are similar to those of *Ondatra*, whereas the swimming fringe on the tail is similar to that of the European water shrew (*Neomys*). The incisors are narrow and beveled on the sides. There are four mammae.

Nothing seems to be recorded on its habits other than that *Crossomys* is amphibian. Apparently the diet consists of fresh-water mussels, mollusks, and other aquatic organisms.

963

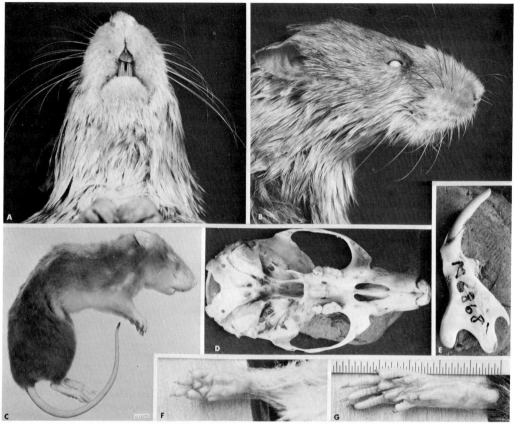

False Water Rat (*Xeromys myoides*), F. Left fore foot; G. Right hind foot; A, B, D-G. Photos from American Museum of Natural History. C. Photo from Australian Museum, Sydney.

FALSE WATER RATS; SCHWIMMRATTEN.

THE SINGLE SPECIES, *X. myoides*, is native to Queensland, Australia, and generally lives near water. One specimen was trapped in a swamp that was thickly overgrown with tall grass, shrubs, and pandanus.

The length of the head and body is 110 to 114 mm., and the length of the tail is about 88 mm. The general coloration of the upper parts is dark slaty gray, gradually blending into the lighter under parts, with no distinctive line of demarcation. The limbs are similar in color to the back, and the hands, feet, and tail are scantily covered with fine white hairs. Fine scales are conspicuous on the tail.

Members of this genus are quite small and have an outward appearance similar to that of rats (*Rattus*) or large house mice (*Mus musculus*). *Xeromys* is distinguished, however, by short, broad ears and a white-haired, finely-scaled tail. The eyes are small. The pelage and feet are not modified for an aquatic life. There are four mammae. The ungrooved incisors project slightly outward; the upper incisors are yellow or orange and the lower ones white.

Ellis Troughton (*Furred Animals of Australia* [New York, 1947]) is of the opinion that the dental structure of false water rats suggests an intermediate ancestral type from which the truly aquatic *Hydromys* evolved, thus indicating the ancient Australian origin of the latter species.

These animals have been described as aquatic-feeding land rats. Their diet consists of hard-shelled mussels, and undoubtedly a variety of other mollusks and aquatic animals and vegetation. At the present time, little information has been published regarding the life habits and general biology of *Xeromys*.

Australian Water Rat (*Hydromys chrysogaster*), photo by Stanley Breeden.

AUSTRALIAN WATER RATS, BEAVER RATS; SCHWIMMRATTEN.

THIS GENUS is made up of three species: *H. habbema* from the mountains of central New Guinea, *H. neobrittanicus* from New Britain, and *H. chrysogaster*, which is native to Tasmania, Australia, Melville Island, New Guinea, Aru Islands, Kei Island, Waigeu Island, Bruni Island, and D'Entrecasteaux strait. Some authors recognize only a single species, *H. chrysogaster*. Beaver rats occur wherever there are streams, swamps, marshes, backwaters, or estuaries which provide suitable aquatic environments.

The length of the head and body is 205 to 350 mm., and the length of the tail is 200 to 350 mm. Adults weigh from 400 to approximately 1,300 grams. The pelage is composed of shiny guard hairs, and dense, soft underfur. Coloration of the upper parts ranges from dark brown, almost black, to golden brown or dark gray, and the under parts range from brownish to yellowish white or bright orange. The well-haired tail is dark except for a white tip.

These large water rats have a sleek, streamlined appearance. Aquatic adaptations are as follows: the long, flattened head; forward-thrust nostrils; high-set eyes; small ears; seal-like fur; and partially webbed, broad feet.

In Victoria these animals breed in late winter and spring; the litter size is one to seven (usually four or five). The offspring are sexually mature when a body weight of 400 to 600 grams is attained and fully developed in less than a year.

Members of the genus *Hydromys* spend the day sleeping in a hollow log, an old swan's nest, under a pile of debris, or in a burrow in a bank. At dusk they leave their nest of shredded weeds to hunt for food. Their diet consists chiefly of mussels, crustaceans, and snails and also includes fish, frogs, water birds and their eggs, and vegetation. *Hydromys* will generally take food to a stone or a log before eating it.

These rodents were trapped extensively for their pelts beginning about 1937. At that time there was a shortage of muskrat pelts and a single *Hydromys* skin would bring up to 65 cents. Measures for their protection have now been taken, at least in some areas.

The type species of the genus is *H. chrysogaster*, É. Geoffroy.

MOUNTAIN "WATER" RATS.

THE SINGLE SPECIES, *P. asper*, apparently inhabits only mountain slopes, preferably rocky places, in the forests of New Guinea at an elevation of 600 to 2,700 meters.

The length of the head and body is about 240 mm., and the length of the tail is about 260 mm. The pelage is firm to bristly, short, and not so dense or sleek as the pelage of *Hydromys*. The general coloration of the upper parts is brownish gray; the ends of the longest hairs are black and those of the shorter ones are dull creamy whitish. The under parts are dull white with a buffy wash and without a sharp demarcation from the color of the sides. The numerous whiskers are stiff, the upper ones black, the lower ones white. The finely-haired ears are grayish brown; the upper surfaces of the hands and feet are pale brownish; and the well-haired tail is basally brownish black, with a distinctive white, brushed tip.

Some authors discuss the enlarged upper lip in these rodents which may be connected with the highly developed vibrissal armament and used for the detection of food. The first and last toes have practically no webbing. The soles are smooth and slightly granulated, and the pads are distinct. The ears are well developed but small. There are four mammae. The incisors grow with their roots wide apart and their tips converging.

These animals are about the size of a small *Hydromys*, and it has been assumed (in some instances) that their habits were similar to those of *Hydromys*. However, *Parahydromys* is not associated with streams, swamps, or other aquatic habitats, in spite of some structural modifications for aquatic life.

Mountain "Water" Rat (*Parahydromys asper*), photos from Museum Zoologicum Bogoriense.

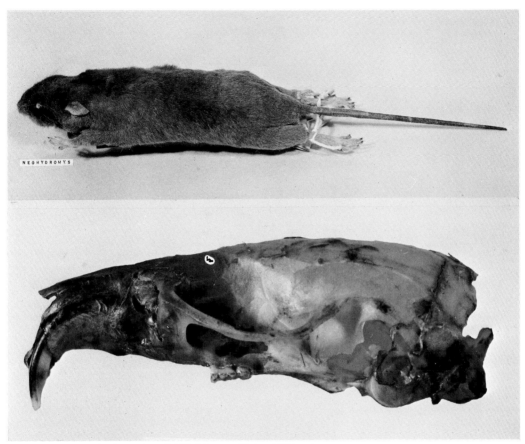

(*Neohydromys fuscus*), photos from British Museum (Natural History).

THE SINGLE SPECIES, *N. fuscus*, inhabits the rainforest mountain slopes of New Guinea from 2,400 to 3,000 meters.

The length of the head and body of the type specimen, an adult female, is 92 mm., and the length of the tail is 78 mm. The upper parts of this rodent are smoky gray, and the under parts are slightly lighter. The tail is brownish above and below, except for a whitish terminal area of some 15 mm. This small, mouse-like hydromyine murid is not modified for aquatic life. *Neohydromys* is distinguished from the other Hydromyinae by its small molar teeth, fairly long muzzle, and other dental and skeletal features.

The type specimen was collected by Shaw Mayer on June 19, 1949; the animal was named and described by Eleanor M. O. Laurie in 1952. It is in the British Museum (Natural History). Its habits and biology are not known.

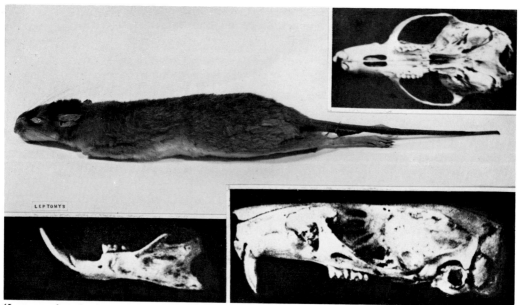

(*Leptomys elegans*), photo of skin from British Museum (Natural History). Insets: Skull (*L. elegans*), photos from *Das Aquarium*.

THE TWO SPECIES, *L. elegans* and *L. ernstmayeri*, are native to New Guinea, having been reported from eastern Papua, Northeast New Guinea, Arfak Mountains, and northwestern Netherlands New Guinea, from sea level to about 3,000 meters elevation.

The length of the head and body is 144 to 162 mm., and the length of the tail is 150 to 160 mm. The fur is close, soft, and velvety. The general coloration of the upper parts is rufous-fawn to brownish. The shoulders, flanks, and hips are bright rufous, and the black on the upper side of the muzzle extends backward to form an indistinct ring around the eyes. The cheeks, inner sides of the arms, and the under parts from the chin to the arms are creamy white, the hairs evenly colored to the bases. One form, however, has a grayish-brown abdomen resulting from the individual hairs having gray bases, and then the light brown changes into an almost imperceptible white tip. The upper surfaces of the thinly-clothed hands and feet are white.

The finely-scaled tail is brown on the basal dorsal surface with a white tip and white undersurface.

These murine-like animals have rather small, naked ears, small eyes, normal fore feet, and elongated hind feet. The three center toes of the hind foot are considerably longer than the others, and there are five sole pads on the front feet and six on the hind feet. The incisors are broad, flattened in front, and pale yellow with white tips. The female has four mammae.

Apparently nothing has been recorded concerning the habits of *Leptomys*, although one author states that the elongated metatarsal bones of the hind limbs of *L. elegans* suggest that the animals may have leaping habits.

Specimens of *Leptomys* are in the Berlin Museum, the British Museum (Natural History), the Leiden Museum, and the American Museum of Natural History.

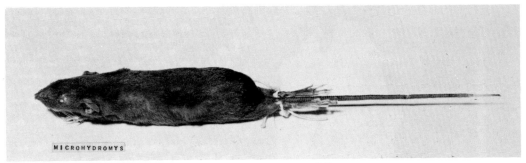

(*Microhydromys richardsoni*), photo from American Museum of Natural History.

THE SINGLE SPECIES, *M. richardsoni*, is apparently known from one specimen, collected by W. B. Richardson in 1939 near the Bernhard Camp, Idenburg River, Netherlands New Guinea, at an elevation of 850 meters. "A genus seemingly of the lower mid-montane areas but . . . known only from the mountain slopes bounding the Idenburg River on the south. It can be expected to extend to west and east for considerable distances at the level of 600 to 900 meters." (G. H. H. Tate, "The Rodents of Australia and New Guinea," *Results of the Archbold Expeditions*, No. 65, *Bull. Amer. Mus. Nat. Hist.* [New York, 1951], p. 225). The type specimen, an adult male, is in the American Museum of Natural History. This animal was named and described by Tate and Archbold in 1941.

The type specimen has the following measurements and coloration: Length of the head and body, 80 mm.; length of the tail, 92 mm.; grayish-black upper parts, with slightly lighter under parts, and terminal 10 mm. of the tail white. This rodent is distinguished from the other Hydromyinae by its small size, short muzzle, and grooved upper incisors.

Aquatic habits are not indicated by the structure of the feet. The specific habits and biology of *Micro-hydromys* are not known.

THE TWO SPECIES of *Paraleptomys* are distributed as follows: *P. wilhemina* inhabits the central mountain range in central Netherlands New Guinea from 1,800 to 2,700 meters elevation; and *P. rufilatus* apparently is known from only two specimens from Mount Dafonsero, Cyclops Mountains, northeastern Netherlands New Guinea, at 1,450 meters elevation. Some 80 specimens of *P. wilhelmina* are in the American Museum of Natural History, and the specimens of *P. rufilatus* are in the Chicago Natural History Museum.

The length of the head and body is 120 to 140 mm., and the length of the tail is 130 to 140 mm. *P. wilhelmina* is grayish brown above and dusky white below. The tail is gray above and white below, with a white tip. *P. rufilatus* is distinguished from *P. wilhelmina* by its white throat, broad reddish-brown lateral line, and more reddish head and hind legs. *Paraleptomys* is similar to *Leptomys* but differs from that genus by the non-elongated foot and in the absence of the third upper and lower molars.

The species, *P. wilhelmina*, is common in the highlands of central New Guinea from 1,800 to 2,700 meters elevation, but little is known of the specific habits and biology of members of this genus.

The type species of the genus is *P. wilhelmina*, Tate and Archbold.

(*Paraleptomys wilhelmina*), photos from Museum Zoologicum Bogoriense.

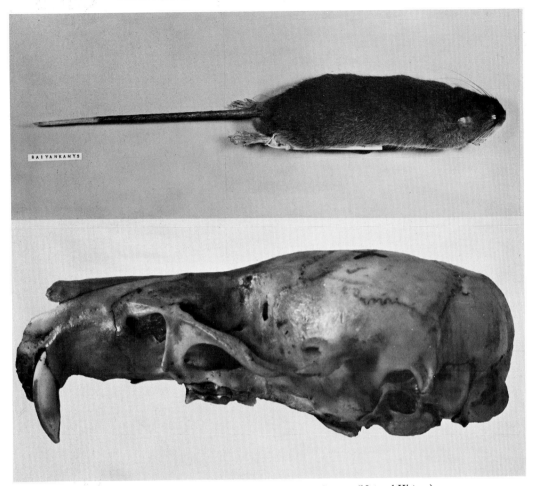

Baiyanka Water Rat (*Baiyankamys shawmayeri*), photos from British Museum (Natural History).

BAIYANKA WATER RATS.

THE SINGLE SPECIES, *B. shawmayeri*, inhabits the mountain slopes of northeastern New Guinea. Apparently the statement by G. H. H. Tate ("Rodents of Australia and New Guinea," Results of the Archbold Expeditions, No. 65, *Bull. Amer. Mus. Nat. Hist.* [New York, 1951], p. 226) still applies: ". . . as yet known only from the top of the main cordillera of New Guinea at longitudes 147° to 148° E." The generic name refers to Baiyanka, the type locality, and the species name commemorates F. Shaw Mayer, the collector of the type specimen for the British Museum (Natural History).

In the type specimen (a male), the length of the head and body is 146 mm., and the length of the tail is 176 mm. The Baiyanka water rat is dark gray above and paler gray below. The fur is thick, and the well-haired tail is white for its terminal fourth. This murid rodent differs from the other Hydromyinae in dental and skull features. It has two upper cheek teeth, three lower cheek teeth, and a proportionately shorter palate than in related genera. "The dental formula appears to be unique in the whole family Muridae." (M. A. C. Hinton, *Ann. and Mag. Nat. Hist.*, Vol. 10 [London, 1943], p. 552)

Baiyankamys is an aquatic rodent. The small hands are apparently not webbed, but the middle digits of the large feet are slightly webbed. The type specimen was collected in June, 1940, by a stream in the open grass country.

971

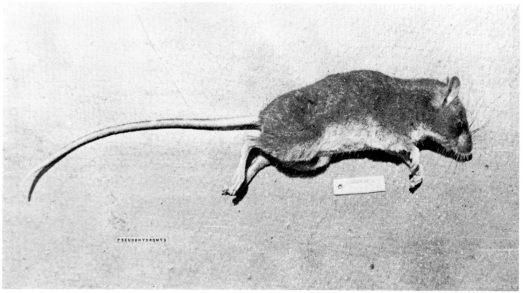

False Water Rat (*Pseudohydromys* sp.), photo from Archbold Expeditions, American Museum of Natural History.

FALSE WATER RATS, NEW GUINEA WATER RATS.

THE TWO SPECIES are distributed as follows: *P. murinus* from the mountain slopes of Northeast New Guinea, at 2,100 to 2,700 meters elevation; *P. occidentalis* from the region around Lake Habbema, north of Mount Wilhelmina, Netherlands New Guinea, at 3,200 to 3,600 meters elevation. The former species is apparently known from only four specimens; the type is deposited in the Museum of Comparative Zoology at Harvard University and three specimens are in the British Museum (Natural History). *P. occidentalis* is apparently known from only five specimens which are now in the American Museum of Natural History.

The length of the head and body of *P. murinus* is 85 to 105 mm.; the length of the tail is 90 to 95 mm.; and the body coloration is dark gray above and somewhat lighter below. One of the four specimens has a white tip to the brown tail. In *P. occidentalis* the length of the head and body is 100 to 115 mm., the length of the tail is 90 to 95 mm., and it is dark brownish gray above and somewhat lighter below. *Pseudohydromys* is a genus of small, shrew-like hydromyines.

These animals appear to be non-aquatic, the feet have pads and soles of a terrestrial type. Specific habits and biology have not been recorded.

The type species of the genus is *P. murinus*, Rümmler.

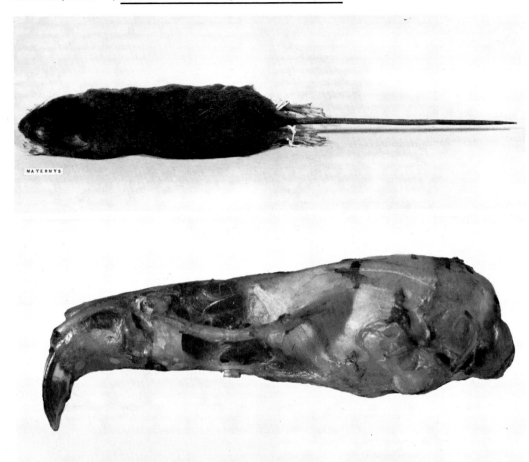

Shaw-Mayer's Mouse (*Mayermys ellermani*), photos from British Museum (Natural History).

SHAW-MAYER'S MICE.

THE SINGLE SPECIES, *M. ellermani*, inhabits forested mountain slopes of New Guinea, from 1,800 to 2,700 meters elevation. The genus is named after the collector, F. Shaw Mayer, and the species is named after J. R. Ellerman. Apparently only four specimens are known which are in the British Museum (Natural History).

The length of the head and body is 90 to 105 mm., and the length of the tail is 100 to 110 mm. Coloration above is smoky gray with one or two white flecks; below, the color is somewhat lighter, and two speci- mens have a small white spot in the middle of the chest. The tail is brownish, with short, white hairs and a whitish tip. *Mayermys* is distinguished from other rodents, in fact from all other mammals, by having only one molar tooth on each side of the upper and lower jaws. The incisors are well developed, not grooved, and the uppers are slightly curved forward.

The feet of *M. ellermani* are described as being of the terrestrial type, but with a slight membrane between the fingers and toes. Specific information on the habits and biology of this rodent are not published.

Dormice and Hazel Mice.

This family consists of seven genera and ten (?) species. One genus, *Graphiurus*, inhabits Africa south of the Sahara, and the other six genera inhabit the Palearctic region, i.e., England, Europe from southern Scandinavia to the Mediterranean, northern Africa, Asia Minor, Russian Asia, and Japan (*Glirulus*).

Dormice live in trees and bushes (wooded areas, hedgerows, and gardens), rock walls, and crevices in the rocks.

Dormice look like squirrels but are smaller, with one genus (*Glirulus*) resembling chipmunks. The length of the head and body is 60 to 190 mm., and the length of the tail is 40 to 165 mm. The pelage is soft, and the tail is bushy (except in *Myomimus*). The eyes are well developed, and the ears are rounded. The legs and toes are short, and the short, curved claws are adapted to climbing. The fore feet have four digits and the hind feet have five, the underside of the feet and digits are naked. Female dormice have 8 to 12 mammae.

The dental formula is as follows: i 1/1, c 0/0, pm 1/1, m 3/3 x 2 = 20. The outer part of the tips of the incisors is quite pointed, and the low-crowned cheek teeth have a series of parallel ridges of enamel across the crown.

Typical dormice are active at night. They are climbing animals, although some forms frequent the ground and one genus (*Myomimus*) is said to be terrestrial. They are squirrel-like in some of their habits. These rodents shelter in hollow trees, on the branches of trees or shrubs, among rocks, in the deserted burrows of other animals, and in the attics of buildings, generally in a nest of plant material. During the late summer and early autumn they generally become quite fat, and from October to April, they are dormant in a curled-up, circular position. Dormice, at least the members of the genus *Muscardinus*, remain active at environmental temperatures above 16 degrees C. All of the dormant forms awake from time to time to eat the food which they have stored.

The members of the family Gliridae eat fruits, nuts, insects, and the nestlings and eggs of birds. Some genera (*Eliomys*, *Graphiurus*) include small rodents in their diet. A *Dryomys* in captivity lapped water like a dog.

Spitting and snarling sounds and a cry like a marmoset have been noted in *Dryomys*, and loud, shrill cries have been reported for *Graphiurus*.

Dormice have one litter (occasionally two) per year of two to nine offspring. Gestation periods of 21 to 28 days have been reported. The young are born in a nest, often lined with moss, in a tree hollow, on a tree branch, or sometimes in a ground shelter. The eyes of one species (*Eliomys quercinus*) open after about 21 days. Dormice live from two to approximately five and a half years in the wild.

These rodents may be destructive in orchards by eating only a part of the ripening fruit. They may deprive birds of their nesting sites and prey on their eggs and young, thus reducing the bird population in some areas.

The geological range of the family Gliridae is the Eocene (?), Oligocene (?), and Miocene to the Recent in Europe, and the Recent in Asia and Africa. Two extinct genera are known from the Pleistocene of the Old World. They are *Leithia*, from Malta, a large dormouse with squared upper molars and skull constricted in the orbital region; and *Hypnomys*, from the Balearic Islands, with a more robust skull, lower jaw, and limb bones than those of the genera of the Recent.

Common Dormouse (*Glis glis*), photo by R. Pucholt.

COMMON DORMICE, EDIBLE DORMICE, FAT DOR-
MICE; LOIRS, SIEBENSCHLÄFER, RELMUIZEN. (Included are vernaculars used in other countries.)

THE SINGLE SPECIES, *G. glis*, inhabits most of Europe
and Asia Minor, from northern Spain and France
eastward to western and south-central European
Russia. These rodents occur also on some of the
Mediterranean islands and have been introduced to
Great Britain. Members of this genus frequent woods,
particularly deciduous growth.

The length of the head and body is 150 to 190 mm.;
the length of the tail is 130 to 165 mm.; and the weight
of adults is about 170 grams. The short, soft, thick
pelage is silvery gray to brownish gray on the upper
parts, lighter on the flanks, and white or yellowish on
the under parts. These squirrel-like animals have
large round ears, small eyes, and long, densely bushy
tails. The hands and feet with their rough pads are
adapted to climbing.

Glis shelters in hollow trees, deserted rabbit burrows, gardens, attics, and outhouses. Their nests are
constructed from plant fibers and moss. These animals spend most of the evening and night climbing
about in low trees and bushes. Their diet includes the
following: nuts, acorns, seeds, berries, soft fruits, and
occasionally insects and small birds. During the
winter dormice are dormant for long periods (September to April in some areas), but occasionally wake to
feed on stored food.

One source reports that mating occurs in June, but
another states that the young are born in June or
July. A litter is recorded which was born in September. There is only one litter per year, and the number
of young is two to six.

In February, 1902, Lord Rothschild released several *Glis* in Tring Park at Hertfordshire, England.
They rapidly increased in numbers and caused so
much damage to crops that a campaign for their
extermination was initiated. Their numbers were
greatly reduced, but today they are common in parts
of England.

During the time of the Roman Empire, colonies of
dormice were kept in specially planted enclosures of
oak and beech. Prior to a feast, individual animals
would be confined to earthen urns and fattened on
acorns and chestnuts, for the Romans considered
their flesh to be of the highest quality.

Hazel Mouse (*Muscardinus avellanarius*), photo from Zoological Society of London.

DORMICE, HAZEL MICE; HASELMAÜSE, MUSCAR-DINES, HAZEL MUIZEN. (Included are vernaculars used in other countries.)

THE SINGLE SPECIES, *M. avellanarius*, inhabits a vast range extending from England through most parts of Europe to Asia Minor and western Russia. Dormice usually are found in thickets and in forests where there is an abundance of undergrowth.

The length of the head and body is about 75 to 90 mm., and the length of the tail is 70 to 75 mm. The general coloration of the upper parts is a rich yellow-ish brown or yellowish red with creamy white on the throat and chest. The toes are also white. The tail is well haired. These medium-sized mice have blunt snouts, large eyes, and rather small ears.

Dormice are arboreal and scramble about with great agility but limit their climbing to the lower branches. During the daylight, they sleep in a globular nest constructed of shredded bark, leaves, grass, and moss. An investigation carried on in the Alps indi-cated that most nests were located in the lower branches of young pine trees, in red beech, and in blackberry bushes, each animal having its own nest. The female also builds a larger nest above the ground, which is carefully lined and well constructed, in which she gives birth to her young. The winter is spent in dormancy in still another nest, which is located on the ground, usually beneath debris, roots, or in a stump. This nest is constructed of plant material and is bound together by a sticky secretion from the salivary glands. In England, dormancy lasts from late October to early April. Dormice remain active at environmental temperatures of more than 16 degrees C. During their deepest dormancy, the temperature of the blood falls to 0.5 degrees or 0.25 degrees C., whereas the nor-mal temperature of the blood is 34 degrees to 36 degrees C. Like other animals which become dor-mant, these rodents awake from time to time to eat the food which they have stored. According to one writer, dormice are just as incapable as other mice of opening hard hazel nuts. Nevertheless they are able to gnaw a hole in fresh nuts, thus getting the seeds out in little pieces. They recognize empty shells as such and do not try to open them. In addition they eat berries, seeds, buds, leaves, and insects, and they have also been said to eat the eggs and nestlings of birds.

Mating probably takes place throughout the sum-mer; about 21 to 28 days later 2 to 9 young are born.

Owls are the principal natural enemies of *Muscar-dinus*.

A. Southwest Asian Garden Dormouse (*Eliomys mela-nurus*), photo by Eviatar Nevo. B. Garden Dormouse (*E. quercinus*), with extra fatty tissue in preparation for hibernation, photo from Archives of Zoological Garden Berlin-West.

GARDEN DORMICE, ORCHARD DORMICE; GARTEN-SCHLÄFER, EIKELMUIZEN, LEROTS. (Included are vernaculars used in other countries.)

THE TWO SPECIES which comprise this genus, *E. quercinus* and *E. melanurus*, have a combined range which includes most of continental Europe, areas of Russia, Asia Minor, and the northern part of Africa. Members of this genus live in a variety of habitats, including cultivated and rocky areas, forests, and swamplands.

The length of the head and body ranges from 110 to 175 mm., and the length of the tail is 100 to 135 mm. The pelage is short except at the tip of the tail, where it is long and forms a tuft. The general coloration of the upper parts includes several shades of grayish or brownish; the under parts are creamy or white. As a rule some black markings occur on the face, and the tail is usually black with a white tip. Garden dormice have four well-marked digits on the fore feet. The female has eight mammae.

These rodents shelter in diverse places, such as hollow trees, branches of shrubs, and among rocks, also often near buildings. Nests built by birds and squirrels are sometimes used as a foundation for their shelters, but when garden dormice construct a nest it is made of leaves and grass, globular in shape, compact, and usually 0.8 to 3 meters above the ground. These animals are more arboreal in some areas than in others. During the coldest part of the winter *Eliomys* may become dormant in some regions.

The diet consists of acorns, nuts, fruit, insects, small rodents, and young birds.

Eliomys is believed to be polyestrous from May to October, at least in Europe. A litter of two to seven young are born after a gestation period of about 22 to 28 days. The eyes of *E. quercinus* open after about 21 days, and the life span for the genus is about five and a half years.

In some sections of their range they cause damage to orchards. By depriving birds of their nest-sites and consuming their nestlings, *Eliomys* may considerably reduce bird populations in some areas.

The type species of the genus is *E. melanurus*, Wagner.

Tree Dormouse (*Dryomys nitedula*), photo by R. Pucholt.

TREE DORMICE, FOREST DORMICE; BAUMSCHLÄFER, SIEBENSCHLÄFER, LEROTINS. (Included are vernaculars used in other countries.)

THE SINGLE SPECIES, *D. nitedula*, inhabits most of Europe and parts of Asia Minor. It is found in deciduous forests, mixed woods, orchards, and bushy areas.

The length of the head and body is 80 to 100 mm., and the length of the tail is 80 to 90 mm. The general coloration of the upper parts is grayish brown to yellowish brown, and that of the under parts is buffy to white.

Members of this genus are similar to dormice of the genus *Eliomys* but are smaller in size, have a more uniform tail which is flattened and moderately bushy, and flattened cranial features. Female *Dryomys* have eight mammae.

Tree dormice are skillful climbers, scrambling about the branches of bushes and trees during most of the night. They also descend to the ground. During the night they emit spitting and snarling sounds and often cry like marmosets. The cry sounds like "oo-eess-tee-tee." The nest is usually situated in the open but may be located in the hollow or crevice of a tree.

Tree dormice become dormant from about mid-October to April. During dormancy they curl up like a ball while sitting on the hind legs, the tail is wrapped around the body, and the hands are pressed onto the cheeks. Tree dormice emerge occasionally from their winter sleep to eat and drink.

A captive adult consumed various seeds and kernels, tree buds, nuts, carrots, fruit of all kinds, mealworms, caterpillars, insects, two-day old white mice, and sparrow eggs. It refused snails, earthworms, wood lice, spiders, millipedes, centipedes, and moths. While drinking, this individual lapped water like a dog. Locally they cause much damage in coniferous forests by gnawing the bark of trees.

There is one or possibly two litters per year, with three to six being the usual number of young per litter.

Tree dormice are quite aggressive and never really become tame in captivity. They may be brought to a point where they will allow themselves to be petted, but they usually bite with their sharp incisors when an attempt is made to hold them. If disturbed while resting, they often lie on their backs or sides and scratch with their legs; if disturbed further, they may suddenly leap high into the air and spit and hiss.

Japanese Dormouse (*Glirulus japonicus*), photo by Michi Nomura.

JAPANESE DORMICE; YAMANE.

THE SINGLE SPECIES, *G. japonicus*, is found in Japan on the islands of Honshu, Shikoku, and Kyushu. It inhabits mountain forests from about 400 to 1,800 meters in elevation; apparently an individual captured in a cottage at 2,900 meters established the highest recorded elevation at which these rodents have been taken.

The length of the head and body is 65 to 80 mm., and the length of the tail is 40 to 55 mm. The coloration is pale olive-brown with a dark-brown to black dorsal stripe. This stripe varies in width and sometimes the coloration is very obscure. The fur is soft and thick. A tuft of long hairs lies in front of the ear, and the tail is flattened from top to bottom.

This arboreal, nocturnal animal rests during the day in a hollow in a tree. It sometimes builds a nest among branches. The round nest is covered on the outside with lichens and on the inside with bark.

Glirulus becomes dormant in hollow trees, cottages, or bird houses, and has been used in the study of dormancy. A case of apparent dormancy in July has been reported; a semidormant individual was captured in a snow depression in a ravine of the Japanese Alps, but after several minutes it awakened and escaped from the container.

The Japanese dormouse gives birth to a litter of three or four young (rarely up to seven) in June or July. The occasional births in October probably represent a second litter. The young are sometimes raised in bird cages. Miss Michi Nomura of Japan, who is raising *Glirulus*, has found that the number of young at birth ranges from three to five (the average litter produces four). She found the gestation period to be about a month.

The diet is fruits, seeds, insects, and bird's eggs. This rodent does well in captivity on rice, peanuts, sweet potatoes, fruits, and insects.

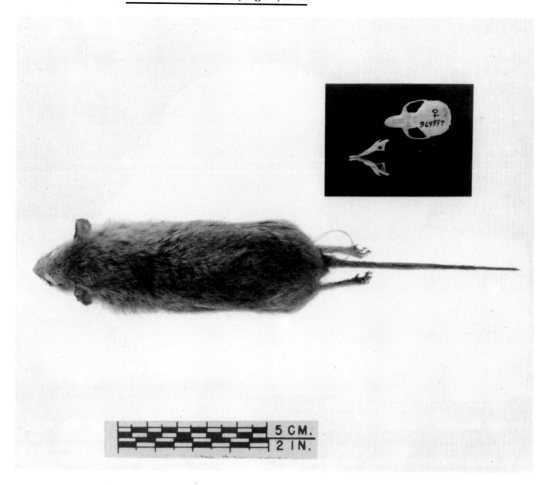

Asiatic Dormouse (*Myomimus personatus*), photo from U.S. National Museum.

MOUSE-LIKE DORMICE; ASIATIC DORMICE.

THE SINGLE SPECIES, *M. personatus*, appears to be known from only the type specimen which was collected in Transcaspia, near the border between Iran and Russia, and four specimens in the U.S. National Museum collection taken in northern Iran.

The length of the head and body of the type is 60.9 mm., and the length of the tail is 58.7 mm. The general coloration of the upper parts is a closely mixed combination of ochraceous and gray. The under parts, insides of the legs, and the feet are white, with a sharply defined line of demarcation. Unlike other dormice, which have rather bushy tails, members of this genus have thinly-haired, mouse-like tails covered with short, white hairs.

The general biology and life habits of *Myomimus* do not seem to be recorded. It is said to be a terrestrial animal.

African Dormouse (*Graphiurus murinus*), photo by Ernest P. Walker.

AFRICAN DORMICE; BOS-STAART MUISEN, ZEVEN-SLAPER, GEMSBOKMUIS, WAAIERSTERTMUIS, SINDI-WARA, MDERI, ULENGERA (native names); BLACK AND WHITE DORMICE.

AT THE PRESENT TIME there are about 20 species recorded in the literature, although it is possible that only about three species are valid. These dormice inhabit most of the African continent from the Sahara and the Sudan southward to Cape Province. They frequent forests and, in South and East Africa, rocky areas in the dry tablelands, generally along waterways. *Claviglis*, Jentink, 1888, and *Gliriscus*, Thomas and Hinton, 1925, are included herein as subgenera.

The length of the head and body is 80 to 165 mm., and the length of the tail is 80 to 135 mm. The fur differs in texture; it is rather soft and dense in most forms, quite soft in a few, and slightly coarse in others. The general coloration of the upper parts ranges from pale ashy gray to dark slaty gray or from buffy to reddish brown, tinged with grayish. The under parts are white to grayish, often tinged with buffy or reddish brown. Occasionally the fur on the throat and chest may be stained by plant or fruit juices. There are black and white markings on the face, variously arranged. The top of the tail is usually black or dark brown and the bottom is whitish. In most forms the tail is well furred. As is the case with many crevice-dwelling animals, the skull is flattened. There are eight mammae.

African dormice are principally nocturnal, but in dense, dark forests they are occasionally active by day. Many animals of this genus shelter in trees and shrubs, making their nests in cavities and among the branches. Others shelter in rock crevices about cliffs and stone fences, and some live in thatched roofs. They are sometimes found in boxes of rubble or upholstery of old furniture in houses and storerooms. The call of *Graphiurus* is described as shrill and loud. Seeds, nuts, fruits, insects, and the eggs and young of snakes, lizards, and birds are the principal items of diet. By the end of autumn, in at least parts of their range, these animals have become quite fat and retire to a retreat in which they can become dormant through the winter.

The young appear to be born from October through December, at least in certain areas. Litter size is usually two to five.

Occasionally they become a nuisance by raiding poultry yards of the native inhabitants. In captivity they take meat scraps but seem very lethargic.

The type species of the genus is *G. ocularis* (Smith).

Spiny Dormice and Chinese Pygmy Dormice.

In this family are two genera, each with one species, namely *Platacanthomys* (the spiny dormice) from southern India, apparently most common in rocky, forested vales and ravines, and the genus *Typhlomys* (the Chinese pygmy dormice) from southeastern China and northern Indo-China, an inhabitant of rugged, forested mountains. No known fossils of this family exist.

These rodents are much like dormice in form. The length of the head and body is 70 to 212 mm., and the tail ranges from 75 to 135 mm. in length. The tail is shorter than the head and body in *Platacanthomys* (the larger genus), but it is longer than the head and body in *Typhlomys* (the smaller genus). In both genera the basal half of the tail is sparsely haired and scaly, and the terminal part bears long hairs which form a brush. In *Platacanthomys* the fur on the back is mixed with flat, stiff spines, whereas in *Typhlomys* the soft fur is spineless. The ears are nearly naked. The thumb is short or represented by a pad, and the slender hind feet are elongated, the first toe barely reaching the base of the second toe. The claws of the digits are slender and compressed.

The family Platacanthomyidae is distinguished mainly by the unique features of the skull and teeth. These rodents have one less cheek tooth than the true dormice (*Gliridae*). The dental formula is as follows: i 1/1, c 0/0, pm 0/0, m 3/3 x 2 = 16. The cheek teeth tend to be high crowned and generally have parallel oblique cross ridges of enamel on the crown. These ridges are broadened, and the depressions tend to become isolated on the surface of the crown.

Practically nothing has been recorded on the natural history of *Typhlomys*, although the native people seem to understand their habits and trap them quite readily. The natives claim that cats will not eat the Chinese pygmy dormouse. The spiny dormouse shelters in hollow trees and clefts in rocks, often building nests out of the epiphytes growing in the tops of old hollow trees. The genus *Platacanthomys* eats fruits, seeds, grain, and roots. Information on the reproductive biology of these two genera is not recorded.

Spiny Dormouse (*Platacanthomys lasiurus*), photo from *Proc. Zool. Soc. London*, 1865.

SPINY DORMICE, LONG-TAILED SPINY MICE, PEP-PER RATS, MULLILLI.

THE SINGLE SPECIES, *P. lasiurus*, inhabits rocky hills and ranges between 600 and 900 meters elevation in southern India.

The length of the head and body is about 130 to 212 mm., and the length of the tail is 75 to 100 mm. The weight of one specimen, an adult female, was 75 grams. The upper parts are densely covered with sharp, flat spines, intermixed with thin, delicate under-fur, but the under parts have fewer, smaller, and finer spines. The general coloration of the upper parts is light rufescent brown, the forehead and crown are more reddish; the under parts are dull whitish. The tail is somewhat darker than the general body color, becoming lighter at the thick bushy tip. The feet are whitish.

Spiny dormice have a pointed muzzle, small eyes, thin, naked ears, and broad hind feet. The thumb on the fore foot, although short, is well developed. The incisors are smooth and compressed.

Members of the genus *Platacanthomys* live mainly in trees, making their homes in cavities of trunks and branches, and in clefts among rocks. Their nests are constructed principally of leaves and moss. The long, tufted tail is undoubtedly helpful as a balancing organ as the animals move about and leap in trees. A captive specimen was sluggish during the day and, although it allowed itself to be handled without fear or attempting to escape, it would inquisitively bite at a finger. The diet consists of fruit, seeds, grain, and roots.

Natives call these rodents "pepper-rats" because they destroy large quantities of ripe peppers. It is also reported that they frequently get into "toddy-pots," containers in which palm juice is collected.

In some areas they are so plentiful that they have become pests.

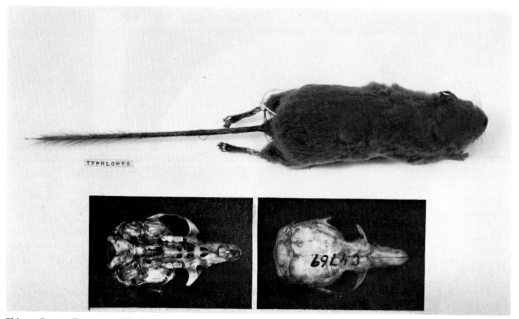

Chinese Pygmy Dormouse (*Typhlomys cinereus*), Skin: Photo by P. F. Wright of specimen in U.S. National Museum. Skull: Photos from American Museum of Natural History.

CHINESE PYGMY DORMICE, "BLIND" DORMICE; CHU-WEI-HAO-TZE.

THE SINGLE SPECIES, *T. cinereus*, inhabits forested mountain slopes of southeastern China and northern Indo-China at elevations between 1,200 and 2,100 meters.

The length of the head and body is 70 to 98 mm., and the length of the tail is 95 to 135 mm. The short, dense, close pelage is uniformly deep mouse-gray on the upper parts. The under parts and inside of the limbs are light grayish, and the bases of the individual hairs are gray with white tips. The hands are whitish and the feet are dusky. The long, gray tail is sparsely haired, scaly on the basal half, and becomes more heavily covered toward the tip with longer hairs which form a distinct terminal brush. The tip is usually white.

Typhlomys is quite mouse-like in external appearance. These animals have prominent, scantily-haired ears, small eyes, and long, slender hind feet. The claws of all the digits are slender and compressed.

These rodents dwell in mountains that are abundantly covered with dwarfed, moss-laden deciduous trees with an undergrowth of small bamboos. Little is known of their life habits and general biology.

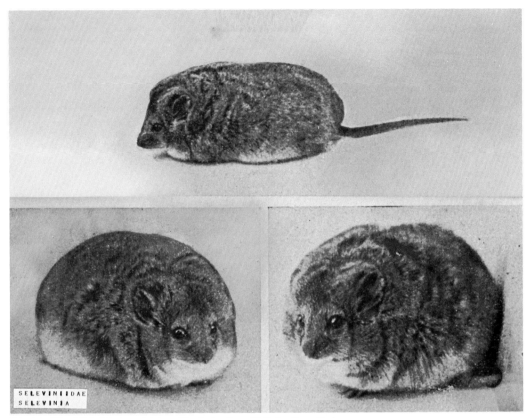

Selevin's Mice (*Selevinia betpakdalaensis*), photos from *Zeitschr. Saugetierk.*

DESERT DORMICE, SELEVIN'S MICE.

THIS FAMILY contains a single genus, *Selevinia*, and the single species *S. betpakdalaenis* is known from clay and sandy deserts in central Kazakhstan, U.S.S.R. It has been reported from the Bet-Pak-Dala desert, the eastern Pribalkhasha, and the Alakul'sk Basin. The distribution is sporadic. Desert dormice occur among thickets of spirianthus, growths of wormwood and kokpek, and among boyalych (*Salsola laricifolia*). The generic name refers to W. A. Selevin, the collector of the type material, and the specific name refers to the Bet-Pak-Dala desert. Fossils referable to this family have not been found.

It has been suggested that *Selevinia* is a highly modified and aberrant dormouse. These round-bodied rodents have a long tail and are somewhat larger than the common house mouse (*Mus musculus*). The length of the head and body is approximately 70 to 85 mm. and that of the tail is about 72 to 96 mm. A pregnant female *Selevinia* weighed 24 grams; another pregnant female weighed 21.4 grams, and a small male weighed 18 grams. The molt method is unusual; the epidermis becomes detached in layers along with the hairs growing on it, rather than a sloughing off of the individual hairs. Dense young hairs are already growing in an area where patches of skin and the old hairs have fallen off. Molting begins

at the back of the neck (between the ears) and then proceeds along the back and sides; the entire process takes about a month. The new hairs grow in quickly, growing up to 1 mm. in a 24-hour period; in winter, the individual hairs attain lengths of 10 mm. The external ears extend beyond the fur. The tail is covered with short hairs, but the scales are not visible. Desert dormice are grayish above, and whitish below. The hand has four digits and the foot has five; the palms and soles are naked.

Selevinia has four teeth (one fairly blunt incisor and three extremely small molars) on each side of the upper and lower jaws, making a total of 16 teeth (dental formula: i 1/1, c 0/0, pm 0/0, m 3/3 x 2 = 16). The larger upper incisors have a deep groove on their front surface, and the single-rooted cheek teeth have a rather simple enamel pattern. Enormous and hollow tympanic bullae are present.

Selevin's mice possibly live in burrows under bushes, but a captive animal dug a burrow (28 cm. long) only when the temperature was low; on other occasions this individual sheltered under a leaf or a small stone. Signs of their presence are not extensive in a given area, and it has been suggested that these rodents lead a migratory life in summer. Some observers report that *Selevinia* is active during the daytime, but most of them come out at twilight and work throughout the night. Thus they avoid the high temperatures. The captive mentioned above, when brought out into the sunlight for five minutes during midday in March, had its ear muscles burned so badly that it almost died. Desert dormice, when undisturbed, travel at a leisurely ambling gait, but when alarmed they progress by small leaps. They do not jump higher than about 200 mm. These rodents are good climbers. They are quite active at moderate temperatures and venture far from their shelters, but at temperatures of approximately 5 degrees C. or below, they go into a state of dormancy, during which time the rate of breathing may decrease from 108 to 25 breaths per minute. Although this behavior has been observed only in animals in captivity, it is reasonable to assume that it takes place in nature. The lethargy might explain the apparent scarcity of these animals during the colder parts of the year.

The diet seems to consist solely of invertebrates, such as insects and spiders. The intestinal tracts of insects, at least of mealworms, are not eaten. Selevin's mice eat up to three-fourths of their weight in a 24-hour period. About one-fourth of the insect food eaten by a captive *Selevinia* was discharged as feces, mostly in the form of indigestible chitinous material. These rodents readily drink water in captivity. Peculiar chirping sounds are emitted when they are feeding or disturbed.

Mating takes place in May and possibly again in July. Pregnant females of *Selevinia* that gave birth to six or eight embryos have been reported.

Desert dormice are quite gentle in captivity. They do not attempt to bite when caught and held in the hand.

BIRCH MICE AND JUMPING MICE.

THIS FAMILY of four genera and approximately 11 species occurs in northern and eastern Europe and middle and eastern Asia (for *Sicista* and *Eozapus*); and in North America from Arctic Canada southward to about latitude 35 degrees N. (for *Zapus* and *Napaeozapus*). Its members inhabit forested areas, thickets, meadows, swamps, bogs, and sagebrush flats.

These are small, mouse-like animals, modified for jumping, with longer hind limbs and feet in the subfamily Zapodinae (genera *Eozapus*, *Zapus*, and *Napaeozapus*). In the subfamily Sicistinae (genus *Sicista*) the hind quarters are only slightly modified for jumping. The length of the head and body is 50 to 100 mm., and that of the tail is 65 to 160 mm. In the subfamily Zapodinae the length of the hind foot is 25 to 34 mm., but in the genus *Sicista* it is only 14 to 18 mm. Zapodid rodents weigh from 6 to about 28 grams; they are heaviest just before they go into dormancy. Internal cheek pouches are present. The tail in *Sicista* is semiprehensile. Female birch mice have four pairs of mammae.

In the Zapodidae the neck vertebrae are not fused nor are the three central bones of the hind feet united as in most jerboas (Dipodidae). The upper incisors are grooved in the Zapodinae, but they are smooth in the Sicistinae of the Recent. The cheek teeth are low-crowned in *Sicista* but have a tendency to be high-crowned and cuspidate in the subfamily Zapodinae. The dental formula is as follows: i 1/1, c 0/0, pm 1-0/0, m 3/3 x 2 = 18 or 16. The auditory bullae of the skull are not enlarged but are relatively small.

These are scampering and jumping rodents. *Sicista* is not so good a jumper as are members of the subfamily Zapodinae. When startled, members of the genera *Eozapus*, *Zapus*, and *Napaeozapus* can jump as far as 2 meters. The long tail is a balancing organ when leaping. Runways are generally not made by the Zapodinae. *Sicista* and *Napaeozapus* sometimes climb small plants and *Zapus* is a good swimmer. The members of this family are active mainly at night. They usually live alone or associate in pairs. They shelter in ground burrows, either dug by themselves or those of other animals, or under rotting logs and fallen trees. Their rather inconspicuous burrows are not marked by a mound of earth. Zapodids gain weight in the fall and then become dormant for six to eight months in burrows lined with plant material and occasionally with hair and paper.

The diet consists of berries, seeds, and small invertebrates (mainly insects). Their food is not stored, and these rodents drink free water.

One or two litters of one to eight young are born each year. The gestation period in *Sicista betulina* has been estimated as four to five weeks, and gestation periods of 18 to 23 days have been reported for the American Zapodinae. The offspring are independent in about four weeks and sexually mature in several months. *S. betulina* is estimated to live about 40 months in the wild.

The geological range for this family is the Oligocene to the Recent in Europe, the lower Pliocene to the Recent in Asia, and the early Miocene to the Recent in North America.

BIRCH MICE, BUSH MICE; BIRKENMÄUSE, SICISTES (local vernaculars).

THIS GENUS of six species, *S. betulina, S. caucasica, S. caudata, S. concolor, S. napaea,* and *S. subtilis,* is found in northern and eastern Europe and middle and eastern Asia from Norway, Sweden, and Germany to Siberia and China. Birch mice usually inhabit deciduous woods, thickets, and scrubby ravines, as well as moors, subalpine meadows, and steppes.

The length of the head and body is 50 to 90 mm.; the length of the tail is 65 to 110 mm.; and the length of the hind foot is 14 to 18 mm. Individuals of the species *S. betulina* weigh about 12 grams in the fall and may weigh only about 6 grams in the spring after dormancy. The upper parts are light or dark brown to brownish yellow, and the under parts are paler, usually a lighter brown. *S. betulina* and *S. subtilis* differ from the other species in having a sharply defined black stripe down the middle of the back. Birch mice are small, mouse-like rodents with a fairly long, semiprehensile tail, but without special elongation of the legs or feet.

They travel on the ground like the jumping mice, that is, by leaping. They readily climb bushes and shrubs; the outer toes hold onto twigs and the tail curls around other branches for further support. Oval-shaped nests are constructed underground of dry grass stalks and cut-up plant stems. Birch mice, at least *S. subtilis* and *S. betulina,* live in shallow burrows which they dig themselves. The members of the genus *Sicista* become dormant for six to eight months in holes in the ground. It has been suggested that *S. betulina* spends the summer in wet meadows and migrates to forests in the winter.

Birch mice are generally active at night when they feed on berries, seeds, and insects. They can survive for long periods without food—longer than other mice—and can eat extremely large quantities of food at one time.

A study of *S. betulina* in the Bialowieza National Park in Poland indicated that one litter is born per

Birch Mouse or Birkenmaus (*Sicista betulina*), photo by Liselotte Dorfmüller.

year and that a given female gives birth only twice during her lifetime. Females were found to be in estrus from May to about the end of June. The gestation period for this species was estimated at four to five weeks, and the duration of parental care of the young ends in four weeks. Animals born in the spring were sexually mature, or nearly so, the following spring, after emerging from their first dormant period. In the wild normal mating may occur in the second year of life in this species, the longevity of *S. betulina* is estimated as 40 months.

Birch mice are quite hardy in captivity.

The type species of the genus is *S. subtilis* (Pallas).

North American Meadow Jumping Mouse (*Zapus hudsonius*), photo by Ernest P. Walker.

JUMPING MOUSE; LA GERBILLE DU CANADA, KWA-KWASH'-KAN-AH'-BE-GAB-NOT'-SEE, KWASH-KWASH-KWUT-TAH'-BE-GAH-NOT'-SEE. (Included are vernaculars used in other countries.)

THREE SPECIES inhabit most of forested North America as far south as North Carolina, Missouri, New Mexico, and California.

The head and body length is from 76 to 110 mm., and the tail 150 to 165 mm. The coloration is grayish brown on the back; the sides are yellowish brown, and the under parts are white. The shades vary somewhat in the different species. The posterior part of the body is much heavier than the fore part, and the hind limbs are much larger and more powerful than the forelimbs. There are internal cheek pouches, and the upper incisors are narrow and grooved in front.

The general appearance of jumping mice is somewhat like that of the kangaroo rat (*Dipodomys*), but members of the genus *Zapus* do not inhabit arid regions. They prefer moist areas; some choose forests close to streams, and others frequent grassy places. When alarmed, they make leaps of 2 to 2.5 meters and sometimes as far as 4 meters. The long tail aids in balancing when jumping. Some forms are excellent swimmers.

Five to eight young are born from May to September, usually early in the season. The late litters may be second families. These rodents eat seeds, acorns, fruits, and certain fungi; insect material, especially lepidopterous larvae and Coleoptera, are very important in their diet.

In the summer one or two adults may occupy a compact, globular nest made of grasses woven together, with an entrance on the side. The summer nest is usually placed on the ground or in vegetation near the surface. During the remainder of the year they occupy snug nests of moss, grass, and plant fibers in holes (from several mm. to 1.9 meters deep) in the ground, or under logs or other shelters. They become quite fat with the approach of fall and go into dormancy before freezing weather. When dormant, they almost invariably curl into a ball, with the nose and feet on the abdomen and the tail curled around the body. During warm spells they arouse and become active but become dormant again if cold weather returns. A captive jumping mouse (*Z. trinotatus*) from Humboldt County, California, became cold and inactive on foggy and cloudy days, but not necessarily cold days. The outward appearance of the animal was that of a torpid animal. It was not aroused by handling.

The natural enemies of jumping mice are hawks, owls, weasels, skunks, and coyotes.

Preble (N. A. F. 15) revised the group in 1899.

The type species of the genus is *Z. hudsonius* (Zimmermann).

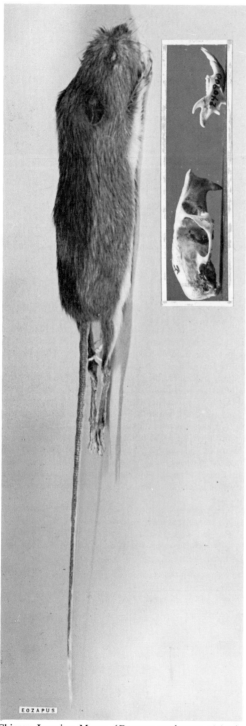

EOZAPUS

Chinese Jumping Mouse (*Eozapus setchuanus vicinus*), photos by Howard E. Uible (skin) and P. F. Wright (skull) of specimens in U.S. National Museum.

CHINESE JUMPING MICE.

THE SINGLE SPECIES, *E. setchuanus*, is known from the Chinese provinces of Szechwan and Kansu. Specimens come from high mountain elevations, and there is some indication that the preferred habitat is beside streams in cool forests.

The length of the head and body is 80 to 100 mm.; the length of the tail is 100 to 150 mm.; and the length of the hind foot is 25 to 33 mm. The upper parts are tawny orangish; the under parts are white with or without a median tawny or buffy stripe. The tail is dark above and white below. As in *Zapus* and *Napaeozapus*, the hind legs, hind feet, and tail of *Eozapus* are proportionately much longer than in *Sicista*. *Eozapus* is distinguished structurally from the American jumping mice by the pattern of the molar teeth. Externally, it can be distinguished from *Zapus* only by the dark streak down the middle of the breast and belly, and because about an inch of the tip of the tail is white.

Specific habits and biology are not known, and apparently only 10 or 12 specimens have been collected. These are in the Paris Natural History Museum, the Museum of the Academy of Sciences at Leningrad, the British Museum of Natural History, the U.S. National Museum, the American Museum of Natural History, and the Academy of Natural Sciences in Philadelphia.

Woodland Jumping Mouse (*Napaeozapus insignis*), photo by Ernest P. Walker.

WOODLAND JUMPING MICE.

THE SINGLE SPECIES, *N. insignis*, lives in eastern Canada and the north-central and northeastern United States. The usual habitat is near water (usually a stream) in a wooded area or the edge of a glade which has sufficient open space to allow for leaps and jumps.

The length of the head and body is 80 to 100 mm.; the length of the tail is 125 to 160 mm.; and hind foot length is 28 to 34 mm. Individual animals usually weigh about 20 grams in May and June, and from 25 to 28 grams before dormancy. At birth *Napaeozapus* weighs about 1 gram. The upper parts are yellowish brown; the sides are yellow gold, reddish yellow, or tawny; the under parts are white; and the tail, usually tipped with white, is dark brown above and white below. This rodent is one of the most attractive small mammals of eastern North America, but its colors quickly fade after death. It is distinguished externally from *Zapus* by its brighter coloration and white-tipped tail. These animals have internal cheek pouches and grooved upper incisors.

Napaeozapus is nocturnal. It occasionally utters soft squeaks but is usually silent. Woodland jumping mice dig their own shallow burrows and also use the passages excavated by moles, the larger shrews, and other rodents. Sometimes they shelter under rotting logs and fallen trees. Their nests are constructed of available material, usually grass. The young are born in a grass-lined nest of dried leaves, which is usually placed in the underground chamber of a tunnel. While the nest is being built and while it shelters the young, the entrance to the tunnel is closed during the day.

The gestation period is 21 to 23 days, and from 1 to 6, usually 4, young form a litter. The young are born naked, blind, and without the facial vibrissae present in most young rodents. Some females have two litters in one season, one in June or July and another in September. Immature *Napaeozapus* probably enter dormancy later in the fall than the adult animals, and the males of this group are believed to emerge first in the spring. Woodland jumping mice are dormant from about November to late April or early May.

Napaeozapus may climb vines and bushes but usually forages on the ground for seeds, fruits, fungi, and small invertebrates. Food is not stored. The home range is one to two acres, and fall populations are about three per acre.

These animals are said to be difficult to keep in captivity.

JERBOAS.

THIS FAMILY of 10 genera and 25 species inhabits northern Africa and southwestern Asia, through central Asia to northern China and southern Manchuria. It is probably Asiatic in origin. Jerboas live in deserts, semidesert areas, and steppes; patches of bare ground are an essential environmental condition.

Dipodidae are characterized by their remarkable adaptations for jumping and their burrowing habits in arid regions. The hind legs are at least four times longer than the front legs. They are more protracted in relation to the front limbs than are the hind legs in any other group of jumping rodents. The length of the hind foot is 20 to 70 mm. With the exception of two genera (*Cardiocranius* and *Salpingotus*), the three central foot bones are fused to form a single cannon bone which gives great support and strength. There is often a reduction in the number of hind toes to three; when five hind digits are present, the first and fifth (the lateral digits) are so small that the three central digits support the foot. The only jerboa with four hind digits is *Allactaga tetradactylus*. Jerboas living in sandy soils have tufts of bristly hairs under the digits and soles of the hind feet. These tufts act as friction pads and tend to support the animal on loose sand; they also aid in kicking the soil backward, after it has been accumulated by the fore limbs in burrowing. Another adaptation of jerboas that live in sandy areas is the tuft of bristly hairs around the opening of the external ear, which guards against the entrance of wind-blown sand. These ear and foot

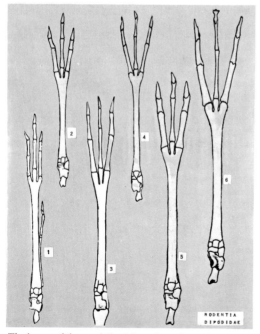

The bones of the specialized feet of members of the Dipodidae: 1. *Allactaga tetradactylus*; 2. *Stylodipus telum*; 3. *Dipus sagitta*; 4. *Jaculus lichtensteini*; 5. *J. orientalis*; 6. *Paradipus ctenodactylus*; photos from *Faune de l'URSS, Mammifères*, B. S. Vinogradov.

tufts are lacking or are not so well developed in jerboas living in loamy soils.

The coloration is usually sandy or buffy, resembling the color of the ground in which jerboas burrow. The hair is generally satiny or velvety. The length of the head and body is 40 to 150 mm., and the length of the tail is 70 to 250 mm. The long tail, which is longer than the head and body and often has a white tuft at the tip, is used as a prop when the animal is sitting upright or as a balancing organ when the jerboa is jumping. At least in *Jaculus*, a thickened fold of skin over the nose can be drawn forward to protect the nostrils when the animal is pushing earth with its snout. A bony mechanism in front of the orbital cavity on the skull of some jerboas protect the eye when the head is used in digging. The jerboas, in common with most nocturnal mammals, have large eyes. Certain desert mammals have enlarged tympanic (auditory) bullae (among the jerboas, mainly those species with small external ears). "The cavities of these bullae are said to contain air of very high humidity, which may check dehydration of the middle ear and the fluid it contains, but this suggestion has still to be investigated experimentally. The occurrence of enlarged bullae in some marine Cetacea does not accord well with this idea, and in some cases at least the bullae could act as resonators, facilitating the perception of vibrations in soil or water." (Bourliere, *Natural History of Mammals*, 1954, p. 260).

The dental formula is: i 1/1, c 0/0, pm 1-0/0, m 3/3 x 2 = 16 or 18. The cheek teeth are rooted, high-crowned, and cuspidate.

Jumping is probably an adaptation for escape from predators in open country. When proceeding slowly, however, jerboas may hop, rabbit-like, on all four legs with one foot preceding the other, but usually only the hind limbs are used in locomotion. In a slow gait the animal usually walks bipedally with alternate movements of the hind legs. The front feet can then be used to search for food. In moving rapidly, jerboas leap and spring with the hind legs; these bounds, covering 1.5 to 3 meters, are their main defense against predators.

In the late spring and summer, jerboas plug their burrows during the day and sometimes when leaving the burrow at night. Thus they keep the heat out and the moisture in and maintain a suitable microclimate within the burrow during the hottest parts of the year. This is characteristic of many burrowing mammals and is an essential survival mechanism in arid regions. The permanent burrows may have emergency exits, that is, side tunnels ending at or near the surface through which the jerboa "bursts" when threatened by a predator. Except for females with dependent offspring, a single burrow is generally inhabited by one animal. Jerboas often lie on their sides when sleeping so as to better accommodate their long legs. Most species are dormant during the winter, but food is not stored in the winter burrows.

Rodents of the family Dipodidae feed on the succulent parts of plants and plant seeds which grow above ground and subterraneously. In certain areas, some species (particularly *Allactaga*) destroy watermelons, muskmelons, and rubber plants. Insects are also eaten. In Transbaikalia *Allactaga saltator* lives mainly on insects (mostly beetles and their larvae) and *Dipus* feeds on the insect grubs in gallnuts. Jerboas apparently do not require free water in nature, although they drink readily in captivity.

When handled or disturbed, these animals sometimes emit grunting noises or shrill shrieks, but they are usually voiceless. Tapping sounds, made within the burrow by the hind legs, have been reported for some species.

Some females of most, possibly all, species breed more than once a year. *Allactaga elater* of central Asia probably reproduces more than twice in one year. The gestation period of *Dipus* is 25 to 30 days, and that of *Jaculus orientalis* is 42 days. The litter size is two to six young (average about three). An individual of the species *J. orientalis* was kept in captivity for five and a half years.

The geological range of this family is the upper Miocene to the Recent in Asia, the Pleistocene to the Recent in Europe, and the Recent in Africa.

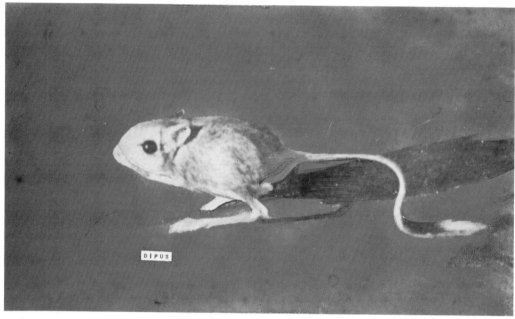

Feather-footed Jerboa (*Dipus sagitta*), photo from *Zeitschr. Saugetierk.*

HAIRY-FOOTED JERBOAS, ROUGH-LEGGED JERBOAS, FEATHER-FOOTED JERBOAS, NORTHERN THREE-TOED JERBOAS; "T'IAO-ERH".

THE SINGLE SPECIES, *D. sagitta*, is known from the Caucasus and Russian Turkestan north to the Altai Steppe, and Chinese Turkestan, Mongolia, southern Manchuria, and northern China. It inhabits sandy regions, living among dunes, shrubby areas, and pine (*Pinus*) forests.

The length of the head and body is 105 to 130 mm.; the length of the tail is 150 to 190 mm.; and the length of the hind foot is 60 to 70 mm. Males weigh from 70 to 85 grams during the spring and summer and about 100 grams just before dormancy; females weigh about 75 grams in spring and from 90 to 110 grams in the fall. *Dipus* apparently has two pelages, a bright one (orangish mixed with black hairs) and a pale one (sandy buff). The paler coat seems to be the summer pelage. The hip stripe and undersides are white. Characteristic features are the three toes on each hind foot, with a stiff brush of hairs on each toe, and the grooved and yellow upper incisors.

The burrows are usually located in the larger sand hillocks. At least in the Volga-Ural sandy areas, *Dipus* constructs three kinds of shelters: permanent summer burrows, in which the young are born and reared; temporary summer burrows, usually short, unbranched tunnels, utilized during the nocturnal excursions; and winter burrows for dormancy. *Dipus*

is dormant for about four and a half months, from November to March, and begins to mate and dig the permanent summer burrows shortly after awakening. The reproductive period continues for about four months; a female may have two litters in one season, and females born in April may breed a few months later. The gestation period is 25 to 30 days, and the number of young is 2 to 5, usually 3. The young reside in the family burrows until attaining a weight of about 50 grams. The highest population figure obtained in the Volga-Ural sands was 11 inhabited burrows and 21 animals from one hectare.

The entire population in a given area tends to emerge from the burrows at about the same time each evening. Traveling to the feeding areas which may be several hundred meters away, they make long leaps, covering 2 to 3 meters when pressed. *Dipus* relishes plants with milky juices; it uses its sense of smell in digging for subsurface sprouts and the insect grubs in gallnuts on the underground parts of certain plants. It returns to its burrow about dawn on warm evenings, but on colder nights *Dipus* may be active for less than an hour. The winter burrows are constructed in October; the nest chamber at the end of the burrow, usually from 800 mm. to 2 meters in depth, is placed at a greater depth than that of the summer burrow. The young born later in the year continue to be active in November and probably perish during the winter.

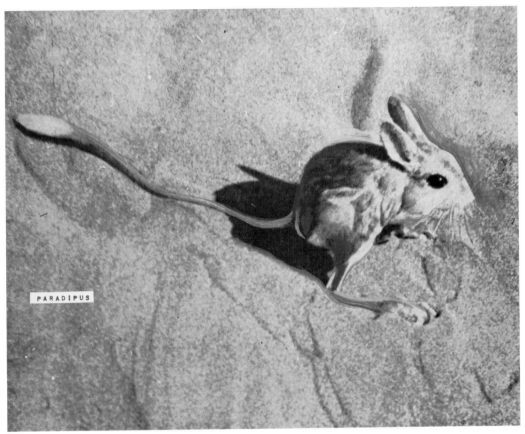

Comb-toed Jerboa (*Paradipus ctenodactylus*), photo from *Zeitschr. Saugetierk.*

COMB-TOED JERBOAS.

THE SINGLE SPECIES, *P. ctenodactylus*, is known only from southwestern Russian Turkestan; it was originally described as *Scirtopoda ctenodactyla*. It usually inhabits barren, desert sand dunes, but its burrows and tracks have also been noted in an extensive sandy plain. *Paradipus* feeds in areas where a fairly thick vegetative cover has stabilized the sand.

Comb-toed jerboas are externally large; the length of the hind foot is about 78 mm. The back is hazel to pinkish cinnamon, and the belly is white. The cheeks have rusty-yellow spots extending to the throat where they form a rusty-yellow area. The hind foot has three digits of unequal length; the middle toe is the longest. The lateral toes are padded with a comb of bristly hairs, whereas the bristles of the middle toe consist of two rows that diverge distally. The claw on the middle toe is about 1 mm. long; the claws on the lateral toes are about 7.5 mm. in length. Other structural features are the non-grooved, white upper incisors, and the ears which are larger (about 30 mm.) than those in other three-toed jerboas.

In sand dunes, the burrow entrance is usually on the lee side of a dune near its base: occasionally the entrance is on the border of an indentation not far from the base of a dune. The burrow is usually left open and leads obliquely downward, somewhat at a right angle to the slope of the dune. Vinogradov and Argyropulo (*Zeitschrift für Säugetierkunde* [Berlin, 1931], 6 (4): 165) excavated 30-odd burrows, and nest chambers were not found in any of them. Side branches were noted in only one burrow. One of these had a length of 1.5 meters and the other, 2 meters. Both side branches ended in loose sand. None of the burrows had emergency exits; the animal apparently leaves its shelter by the main tunnel. It is not certain if *Paradipus* lives in permanent burrows or digs new ones each night, for numerous freshly-dug burrows are visible in the morning.

A tapping sound of two quick beats with a long pause between has been described for this species. It takes place while the animal is in the burrow. The characteristic track made by this rodent is larger in size than that made by *Dipus*; it has a constriction in the middle and prominent lines on the side. Furthermore, the tracks of *Dipus* occur usually in pairs, whereas those of *Paradipus* are usually one in front of the other in a diagonal line. The comb-toed jerboa leaps and plays in the sand like *Dipus*, but further observations on its habits and life history are clouded by its secretive and cautious traits. The number of burrows and tracks indicates that *Paradipus* is numerous over its range.

Desert Jerboa (*Jaculus jaculus*), photo by Ernest P. Walker.

DESERT JERBOAS, HAIRY-FOOTED JERBOAS; JAR-
BOUA, GAURTI, SIEBOD (local vernaculars).

THE FOUR SPECIES are distributed as follows: *J. jaculus*, northern Africa and southwestern Asia; *J. orientalis*, northern Africa; *J. blanfordi*, Iran; and *J. lichtensteini*, Russian Turkestan. Desert jerboas burrow in a variety of habitats, such as sandy deserts, both rolling and relatively flat, saline deserts, rocky valleys, and meadows. Their burrows have been seen in barren areas and where there is scattered vegetation. *Eremodipus*, Vinogradov, 1930, is herein included as a subgenus for the species *J. lichtensteini*.

J. jaculus is the smallest species, and *J. orientalis* is the largest. The length of the head and body is 100 to 150 mm.; the length of the tail is 150 to 250 mm., and the length of the hind foot is 55 to 75 mm. *J. jaculus* usually weighs from 50 to 70 grams. The color is pale to dark sandy or buffy above, with a whitish stripe on the hips, and the under parts are whitish. There are three toes on each hind foot, with a cushion or fringe of hairs under the toes. The eyes and ears are fairly large, and the upper incisors are grooved.

Only scattered notes are available on the biology of desert jerboas. The burrows have one main tunnel and one or several emergency exits. *J. orientalis* places the nest chamber at a depth of up to 1,250 mm., whereas the length of the tunnel exceeds 2,500 mm.; its nests, when found, are usually made of rags and wool fibers taken from Arab tents and of shredded grass. Often two to three jerboas are found sleeping together in a single nest. Desert jerboas are quite sociable animals, often forming loosely defined colonies. Wet weather reduces their activity, but one observer found (in Iraq) that even the coldest weather did not force them into dormancy. In long, hot, dry spells, however, they apparently retire to their burrows and estivate. Five captive animals kept in a cage were quite gentle and slept together in a huddled mass. They ate grass, seed tops of grasses, clover, wheat, barley, cabbage, and dates. These captives could make vertical leaps of almost a meter from a standing position. The long tail is held curved and the tuft touches the ground, thus providing three point support while standing. Desert jerboas are nocturnal and quite shy; they progress along the ground with leaps that measure several meters. They are said to feed upon grasses, bulbs, and roots. They probably derive sufficient metabolic water from vegetation and seeds, as captive animals have refused to drink water for long periods, although the water was placed in their cages daily.

The following data were reported on reproduction in *J. jaculus*: A female with three young was taken in the eastern desert of Egypt in November; a female with four, recently born young, in Iraq in December; and a pregnant female with four embryos, in southeastern Egypt in February. The gestation period in *J. orientalis* is about 40 days. Certain individuals of *J. jaculus* become dormant over the winter months in Iraq, as reported by Robert T. Hatt (*Misc. Publ.*, Mus. Zool., Univ. Mich., No. 106, 1959, p. 82). *J. jaculus* has a lifespan of five and a half to six and a half years.

J. jaculus has been found to be susceptible to scrub typhus infection.

The type species of the genus is *J. orientalis*, Erxleben.

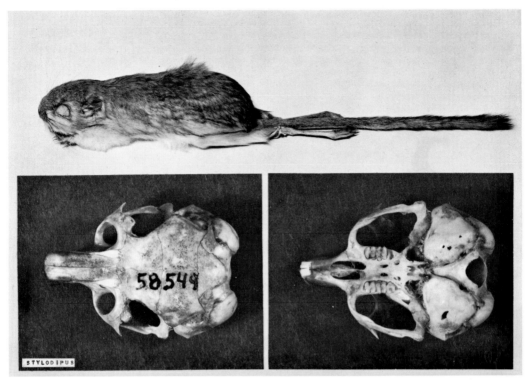

Thick-tailed Three-toed Jerboa (*Stylodipus telum*), photos from American Museum of Natural History.

THICK-TAILED THREE-TOED JERBOAS, FEATHER-TAILED THREE-TOED JERBOAS; EMURANCHIK.

THE SINGLE SPECIES, *S. telum*, inhabits eastern Europe and western Asia; it is not known outside the U.S.S.R. Deserts of clay and gravel are the usual habitat, but *Stylodipus* also has been noted in sandy areas, saline places, and in melon fields.

The length of the head and body is 110 to 130 mm.; the length of the tail is 140 to 150 mm.; and the length of the hind foot is 45 to 60 mm. The sandy or buffy upper parts are darkened somewhat by black-tipped and completely black hairs. The hairs along the sides of the body have white bases and bright, buffy tips. The stripe on the hip, the under parts, and the backs of the feet are white. The tail is similar in color to the back, except for its base, which is encircled in white.

Stylodipus can be distinguished externally by its tail and three toes on each hind foot. The tail lacks a distinct tuft of black hairs and a white tip; the middle hind toe is the longest, and each digit of the hind feet has a stout claw concealed by stiff hairs. The soles of the hind feet are also haired.

This jerboa seems to be common locally. G. M. Allen (*The Mammals of China and Mongolia*, Part 2 [New York, 1940], p. 1094) mentions an individual caught in a trap set in the hole of a ground squirrel. Deep burrows with one entrance and several emergency exits and shallow temporary burrows are constructed. The openings are "plugged" by the animals when entering the burrow, thus making their presence less obvious. They emerge from their burrows soon after dusk and return shortly before dawn. *Stylodipus* becomes dormant in winter. Cereal grains, juicy parts of plants, grass bulbs, and various roots and rhizomes constitute their diet. One or possibly two litters of three to five young are produced each year.

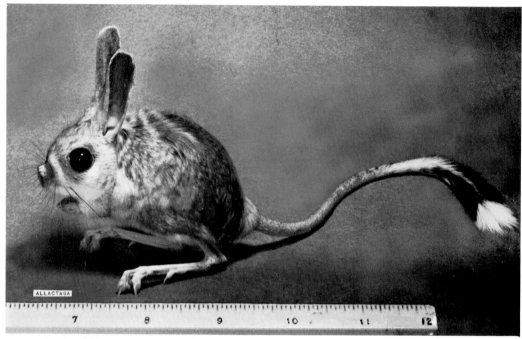

Four-toed Jerboa (*Allactaga tetradactyla*), photo by Ernest P. Walker.

FOUR- AND FIVE-TOED JERBOAS, EARTH HARES; TIAO-TU-TZE.

THERE ARE NINE SPECIES of five-toed jerboas and one species of four-toed jerboa.

The nine species with five toes on each hind foot inhabit southwestern Asia eastward and northward through central Asia into Mongolia, northern China, and Korea. The single species with four hind toes, *A. tetradactyla*, is known only from Egypt. *Allactaga* burrows in steppes, deserts, and semideserts. *Scarturus*, Gloger, 1841, type species *A. tetradactyla*, and *Allactodipus*, Kolesnikov, 1937, type species *A. bobrinskii*, are included as subgenera. The type of the genus is *A. major* (Kerr).

The length of the head and body is 90 to 150 mm.; the length of the tail is 160 to 220 mm.; and the length of the hind foot is 60 to 75 mm. The coloration is mixed russet and black to sandy and grayish buff on the upper parts and whitish on the under parts, with a white stripe on the hip. All species of *Allactaga* have five toes on each hind foot except *A. tetradactyla*, which has only one small outer toe instead of two. The three central digits on each hind foot are larger than the side toes and support the foot. The sole of the hind foot has a tuft of stiff hairs. The species *A. bobrinskii* differs from the other species in Russia because the hind digits are covered beneath by a brush of hairs. The ears are long and slender, about as long as the head.

These animals are nocturnal. The four-toed *A. tetradactyla* burrows in flat areas and in dry salt marshes among hills. The main tunnel rarely branches and is less than a meter in length; the nest chamber is located at a depth of 400 to 600 mm. The smallest species of the genus, *A. elater*, burrows in hard and solid ground; its heaps of excavated dirt are not much larger than those left by certain ground beetles. It often digs in depressions in the ground, such as in wagon tracks, and in such places the excavated material may fill the depression so that it is very difficult to find the small burrow. *A. elater* constructs escape tunnels which end near the surface. The species *A. severtzovi* constructs a main tunnel with two or more chambers and usually shelters in the deepest chamber; escape tunnels (emergency exits) may also be constructed. Some species dig temporary summer burrows which are short and usually unbranched tunnels like those built by *Dipus*.

Most individuals of the genus *Allactaga* are dormant from four to seven months each winter.

One or two litters are born each year, but I. I. Kolesnikov (*Rodents Injuring the Rubber-plant Tan-saguyr*, Middle Asia Publ. House [Moscow-Tashkant, 1934], pp. 1–96) has suggested that *A. elater* of Middle Asia reproduces more than twice in one year.

An individual of *A. elater*, fed in captivity, ate green wheat, rice, lucerne or maize, raw potatoes, grain, and hay biscuit. Some individuals wander into pastures where they damage cultivated crops. A possible connection between *A. sibirica* and plague has been suggested.

The ten species of *Allactaga* are: *A. sibirica, A. elater, A. euphractica, A. williamsi, A. hotsoni, A. bullata, A. bobrinskii, A. severtzovi, A. major*, and *A. tetradactyla*.

Lesser Five-toed Jerboa (*Alactagulus pumilio*), photo by F. Petter.

LESSER FIVE-TOED JERBOAS, LITTLE EARTH HARES.

THE SINGLE SPECIES, *A. pumilio*, inhabits most of Russia, from the northern Caucasus to Inner Mongolia. It lives in clay and saline deserts and steppes. In Russian Turkestan, for example, it burrows in wide, relatively flat, saline plains which are almost completely barren of plant growth.

The length of the head and body is 88 to 125 mm.; the length of the tail is 107 to 133 mm.; and the length of the hind foot is 34 to 52 mm. The long, narrow ears are about as long as the head. The coloration is dull buffy mixed with black on the head, body, limbs, and proximal section of the tail. There is a white stripe on the hips, and the under parts are white. There are five toes on each hind foot; the first and fifth digits are short, but the three central digits are long and support the foot. The soles of the hind feet are naked but fringed at the sides. *Alactagulus* is similar to *Allactaga* but differs structurally from that genus in its dentition and the enamel pattern of the teeth.

The burrows of the little earth hares have a characteristic appearance. The excavated ground is deposited in the form of a flat "hill" around the burrow; this hill may be 0.75 meters in cross section and usually has an irregular outline. The initial tunnel is horizontal and is plugged for 50 to 100 mm. Beyond the plug, the tunnel is usually closed for 2 to 4 meters and thus is difficult to trace. This tunnel usually splits into two branches beyond the plugged and closed sections: one branch leads downward and terminates in a chamber, and the other leads to the side, then upward, and ends either at the surface or 10 to 20 mm. below the ground. In some areas, the burrows have an airhole or vent, i.e., a special passage which leads to the surface as a narrow half-closed column. These rodents are nocturnal in their habits. They are said to feed upon the juicy parts of plants, grass bulbs, and a variety of roots and rhizomes.

Some females of *A. pumilio* give birth more than once during a season. Two pregnant females, each with three embryos, and a female in a burrow with five half-grown young were noted in the same month in the same area. The little earth hares are dormant during the winter.

Fat-tailed Jerboa (*Pygeretmus platyurus*), photo from *Traite de Zoologie* . . . , Pierre-P. Grasse. Inset: Head (*P. shitkovi*), photo from *Faune de l'URSS, Mammifères*, B. S. Vinogradov.

FAT-TAILED JERBOAS.

THERE ARE TWO SPECIES: *P. platyurus* which inhabits northwestern Russian Turkestan, and *P. shitkovi* of northeastern Russian Turkestan. Fat-tailed jerboas inhabit clay and saline deserts.

The measurements of *P. platyurus* are: length of the head and body, 75 to 95 mm.; length of the tail, 78 to 90 mm.; and length of the hind foot, 32 to 35 mm. The measurements of *P. shitkovi* are: length of the head and body, 97 to 122 mm.; length of the tail, 94 to 128 mm.; and length of the hind foot, 40 to 45 mm. The ears are about as long as the head. Coloration is sandy brown above and white below.

There are five digits on each hind foot. The thickness of the tail is due to fat deposited under the skin; the tail is not tufted.

The biology and habits of these jerboas are not well known. However, some details are given in S. I. Ognev's *Mammals of the U.S.S.R.*, 1935.

The type species of the genus is *P. platyurus* (Lichtenstein).

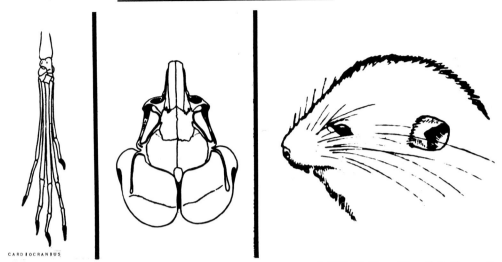

Five-toed Dwarf Jerboa (*Cardiocranius paradoxus*), photos from *Faune de l'URSS, Mammifères*, B. S. Vinogradov.

FIVE-TOED DWARF JERBOAS; KHONI-ALAGDAGA.

THE SINGLE SPECIES, *C. paradoxus*, inhabits northern Kansu, China, and Mongolia.

The length of the head and body is 60 to 75 mm.; the length of the tail is 70 to 75 mm.; and the length of the hind foot is 25 to 30 mm. The upper parts are grayish buff; the hairs on the dorsum have slaty-gray bases and dark-brown tips. The tail is light brown above and white below, and the chest and belly are white. The scantily-haired tail is constricted at the base where it suddenly expands and then tapers toward the end. The tip has a small tuft of hairs. In addition to the unique tail, *Cardiocranius* differs from other jerboas by its small size, short ears, and five-toed hind foot. The outermost toe (digit 5) is about 4 mm. shorter than the fourth digit, and the innermost or smallest toe (digit 1) extends beyond the base of the second digit by about 8 mm. The soles of the hind feet have a tuft of bristly hairs. The upper incisors each have a deep groove on the front surface. When viewed from above, the skull has a heart-shaped appearance, thus the origin of the generic name.

Practically nothing is known of this rodent. Two specimens taken in the northern Gobi Desert "were dug out of the burrows which were found among sand-hills covered with *Nitraria schoberi*. Both these specimens lived some time in captivity; they refused whatever vegetable food was offered to them. When they were put together into a box they fought very fiercely, this made it necessary to separate them" (G. M. Allen, *The Mammals of China and Mongolia*, Part 2, [New York, 1940]).

At the present time this genus is known from only five specimens. The type specimen is in the Zoological Museum of the Academy of Sciences, Leningrad, Russia.

Three-toed Dwarf Jerboa (*Salpingotus michaelis*), photo by J. FitzGibbon.

THREE-TOED DWARF JERBOAS.

THE FOUR KNOWN SPECIES of *Salpingotus* are distributed as follows: *S. crassicauda*, the basin of the Tchernii Irtish River, U.S.S.R. and northern Mongolia (the Gobi-Altai); *S. kozlovi*, Mongolia (the Gobi Desert) and Siberia (Irtish River); *S. thomasi* (the locality is not definitely known, but probably from Afghanistan); and *S. michaelis*, desert plateau of Nushki, northwestern Baluchistan. These rodents inhabit sandy deserts and may be typical animals of the great central desert area of central Asia.

In *S. crassicauda* the length of the head and body is 41 mm.; the length of the tail is 93 mm.; and the length of the hind foot is 20.5 mm. The corresponding measurements in *S. kozlovi* are 51 mm., 126 mm., and 25 mm.; and in *S. thomasi*, 57 mm., 105 mm., and 23 mm. The latter species is known only from the type specimen. The coloration is sandy or buffy above with whitish or pale yellowish under parts. In *S. crassicauda* and *S. thomasi* the proximal third or half of the tail is swollen from fat accumulation under the skin, but the tail in *S. kozlovi* is not expanded, and only two out of fifteen specimens of *S. michaelis* had fat accumulation. The ears are short, and the hind feet are three-toed, with tufts of hairs beneath the toes. The small size, short ears, three hind toes, and non-tufted tail distinguish these jerboa from others of their kind. In all three species the upper incisors are ungrooved. The female has eight mammae.

The natural history of this genus is not known. An individual of the species *S. crassicauda* was kept in captivity for ten days and ate only invertebrates.

Specimens are in the Zoological Museum of the Academy of Sciences, Leningrad, Russia.

The type species of the genus is *S. kozlovi*, Vinogradov.

Long-eared Jerboa (*Euchoreutes naso*), photo from *Proc. Zool. Soc. London*.

LONG-EARED JERBOAS.

THE SINGLE SPECIES, *E. naso*, is known from Chinese Turkestan and Inner Mongolia and may be characteristic of the central Asiatic desert. The known specimens come from sandy areas.

The length of the head and body is 70 to 90 mm.; the length of the tail is about 150 mm.; and the length of the hind foot is 40 to 45 mm. The upper parts are reddish yellow to pale russet in color in contrast to the sandy or buffy upper parts of most jerboas. The short-haired tail is tufted at the tip and is encircled in white just short of the tuft and at the tip and is black between. The under parts are white and there is a partial white stripe. The outstanding feature of *E. naso* is the large ear, about a third again as long as the head. There are five toes on each hind foot, namely, three long central digits and two lateral digits. The toes are tufted beneath with bristly hairs. The incisors are quite narrow and white. The female has eight mammae.

The habits and biology of *Euchoreutes* are not known, and there are only a few specimens in study collections. They have been collected in sandy valleys covered with low bushes of *Haloxylon ammodendron*, and sometimes in the huts of nomads. One long-eared jerboa was kept alive in captivity for four days; it had a strong tendency to bite.

OLD WORLD PORCUPINES.

THIS FAMILY of 4 genera, *Thecurus*, *Hystrix*, *Atherurus* and *Trichys*, and approximately 20 species occurs in Africa and also eastward from Italy to southern China, Indonesia, and the Philippines. Old World porcupines inhabit deserts, savannahs, and forests. Their presence is largely dependent on the food supply and available sites for their dens.

These large, heavy-set rodents have a spiny cover on the body and tail. The spines, stiffened, sharpened, and thickened hairs, are as much as 350 mm. in length in the genus *Hystrix*. Some forms of *Hystrix* have a crest of long, flexible bristles. The end of the tail has a set of short, stout spines, attached to the skin by a slender stalk; these spines rattle when the tail is shaken. The length of the tail is less than the combined length of the head and body, the body measures from 380 to 710 mm. Adult *Hystrix* weigh as much as 27 kg. The coloration is brownish or blackish, often with white bands on the hairs and spines. The limbs are short. There are five digits on the fore foot, the thumb is reduced, and there are five digits on the hind foot. The soles of the feet are smooth. Female porcupines have two or three pairs of mammae, located on the sides of the body. The intestinal tract is approximately 7,900 mm. in length (not including the stomach or the caecum).

The dental formula is as follows: i 1/1, c 0/0, pm 1/1, m 3/3 x 2 = 20. The four cheek teeth are flat, with a wavy enamel pattern. They are incompletely rooted and moderately to strongly high crowned. The facial part of the skull is inflated by pneumatic cavities.

Of the four genera, *Hystrix* is the best known, and most of the following information is based on the habits of this genus. Old World porcupines are mainly terrestrial, walking ponderously on the sole of the foot with the heel touching the ground. They run with a shuffling gait or gallop clumsily when pursued. While moving about, they rattle their spines, especially when disturbed, and may also stamp their feet when alarmed. An Old World porcupine may rush an attacker with its spines erected. The temperament of these animals, at least in captivity, differs with the species and also among individuals, ranging from shy and nervous to docile. Piping calls and a pig-like grunt have been reported for *Hystrix*. These nocturnal rodents are sometimes seen in pairs. They are common in some areas.

Members of the family Hystricidae shelter in natural or self-excavated dens in caves, crevices, and aard-vark (*Orycteropus*) holes in Africa. One burrow, 18 meters in length, terminated in a chamber 1.5 meters below the surface of the ground and had three "escape holes." Sometimes these animals rest in scrub or tall grass while feeding in cultivated areas. Gnawed bones and loosened quills scattered around the burrow entrance and along paths leading outward from the den often reveal the homesites. As many as ten individuals were found in a single burrow, and these animals may occupy a common warren of burrows. Nests of plant material are located within the main chamber within the tunnel. Old World porcupines may become inactive during cold weather. Occasionally they may travel 10 miles from their den to the feeding area, often along well-marked paths.

Old World porcupines eat carrion and plant material such as bulbs, tubers, roots, fruit, the bark of trees, and also melons, pumpkins, corn, and other cultivated crops. They leave their typical elongate droppings.

Breeding occurs in the spring in Europe and there are two litters per year (at least in captivity). The gestation period of *Hystrix* has been reported as 6 to 8 weeks and also approximately 112 days (16 weeks). The 1 to 4, usually 2, offspring are born with their eyes open and with soft, short quills. When the quills have hardened, after a week or so, the young may leave the nest with the mother. The life span in the wild is probably 12 to 15 years, whereas in captivity Old World porcupines may live 20 years. They are preyed upon by the larger members of the cat family (Felidae). They are also killed by the natives to protect the crops and for their tender flesh, as well as for their spines, which are used as ornaments and hatpins.

The geological range of this family is from the Oligocene to the Recent in Europe, the middle Pliocene to the Recent in Asia, and the Pleistocene and Recent in Africa.

Sumatran Porcupine (*Thecurus sumatrae*), photo by Ernest P. Walker.

INDONESIAN PORCUPINES, LANDAK.

THE THREE SPECIES are distributed as follows: *T. sumatrae*, Sumatra; *T. crassispinis*, Borneo; and *T. pumilis*, the Palawan, Balobac, and Calamian Islands in the Philippine group.

The length of the head and body of *T. sumatrae* is about 540 mm., and the length of the tail is about 100 mm. Corresponding measurements for *I. crassispinis* are 570 and 160 mm.; and for *I. pumilis*, 450 to 500 mm., and 40 to 100 mm. The body of these animals is densely covered with flattened spines, each of which is deeply grooved longitudinally and somewhat flexible, becoming more rigid toward the rump. The spines are smaller along the tail. "Rattling-quills" are present on the tail.

These quills are slender for most of their length and are of much greater diameter for about the terminal fifth of the quill. The expanded portion is hollow and thin-walled, so that several quills vibrating together produce a hissing-like rattle. Long, stiff bristles are thinly scattered along the back and sides. Short, fine hairs appear between the spines. The under parts are also covered with grooved spines, but these quills are much more flexible than those of the upper parts. Coarse, bristle-like hairs cover the feet. Of these three species, the spines are most prominent in *T. crassispinis*.

The general coloration of the anterior part of the back is a dark, drab brown, whereas that of the posterior part is darker, in fact almost black. The individual spines have light-colored bases and light tips. The sides are lighter than the back and have a flecked appearance caused by variations in the number of white tips present. The under parts are buffy white. The face, limbs, hands, and feet are brownish.

Members of the genus *Thecurus* resemble those in Malaya of the subgenus *Acanthion* of the genus *Hystrix*.

Information concerning the life habits and biology of these animals in the wild has not been found.

The type species of the genus is *T. sumatrae*, Lyon.

A. African Porcupines (*Hystrix galeata*), mother and young 51 days old, photo by Ernest P. Walker. B. Malayan Porcupine (*H. brachyurum*), photo by Lim Boo Liat.

OLD WORLD PORCUPINES; PORCS-EPIE, YSTER-
VARKE, STACHELSCHWEINE, NIS, CHIEN CHU AND
HSIANG LING CHU, CRESTED PORCUPINES, SENDJI-
A-MIS. (Included are vernaculars used in other
countries.)

THE GENUS *Hystrix* includes about a dozen species
whose combined ranges extend over southern Europe,
most of Africa, India, and southeastern Asia, Sumatra,
Borneo, Java, and adjacent smaller islands. These
animals inhabit forested areas, rocky hills, ravines,
and valleys in which there is sufficient shelter to provide homes and refuge. *Acanthion*, Cuvier, 1822, is
herein regarded as a subgenus.

Members of this genus are the only porcupines
native to Europe and they are the largest African
rodents. The length of the head and body is about
600 to 800 mm.; the length of the tail is about 125 to
150 mm.; and adults weigh 17 to 27 kg. The upper
parts are covered by stout, cylindrical black, dark-
brown and white, or yellowish-banded quills, among
which may be mixed longer, more slender, and more
flexible quills which are usually all white. The species
in the subgenus *Hystrix* have long quills along the
nape and back which, when raised, give a crested
appearance, usually black in color. The under parts
are scantily covered with short, rather coarse, straight,
usually black hairs. The broad fore feet have four
well-developed digits, each armed with a thick claw;
the hind foot has five digits. There are six mammae.
When born, the young have well-formed spines which
are soft but soon harden.

These porcupines are almost entirely nocturnal;
they spend the day in a burrow which they make in a
natural cavity or crevice. They rarely climb trees. If
alarmed they generally try to escape by means of a
clumsy gallop, but if closely approached, they face
away from the enemy, stamp their feet, raise their
quills, and vibrate them so that the long, large,
almost hollow quills rattle together and produce a
sound somewhat like that of a rattlesnake's rattle.
If the enemy continues to threaten, the African crested
porcupines run backward rapidly and spear the enemy
with their long sharp quills. Men on foot chasing
them in the so-called sport of "pig sticking" with a
spear have had the porcupines reverse the game and
drive their quills through a leg.

During the night these porcupines shuffle along,
usually singly, in search of fruit, bark, roots, tubers,
and other succulent vegetation. They have been reported to eat carrion; they gnaw on bones and re-
putedly on ivory. Bones are frequently found in
porcupine burrows.

In Europe breeding takes place in the spring. One
to four well-developed young are born after a gestation period of about 112 days. Two litters per year
are common. The life span is up to about 20 years.

These animals injure crops of sweet potatoes,
cassava, and maize. The flesh of *Hystrix* is considered
to be excellent.

The type species of the genus is *H. cristata*,
Linnaeus.

A. West African Brush-tailed Porcupine (*Atherurus africanus*), photos by Ernest P. Walker. B. Asiatic Brush-tailed Porcupine (*A. macrourus*), photo by Lim Boo Liat.

BRUSH-TAILED PORCUPINES; CHOOK-CHOOK, KA-HEGENYA, TSETANG, LANDAK BATU, BABI-LANDAK AND BOELOEBABI (native names).

THIS GENUS of four species inhabits southern China, Assam, southeastern Asia, and Sumatra, and central Africa from Kenya westward through the Congo to Sierra Leone. These animals live in forests, especially those near waterways.

The length of the head and body is 400 to 550 mm., and the length of the tail is 150 to 250 mm. The pelage is almost entirely spiny; the spines of the mid-dorsal region are the longest. Most of the spines are flattened with a groove on their dorsal surface. Interspersed among the flattened grooved spines on the lower back are a few rounded, stiff bristles. A few thick, circular quills are present among the spines of the back in the African forms but apparently are absent in the Asiatic forms. The basal part of the tail is covered with spines similar to those of the lower back; the mid-portion is scaly, and a thick tuft of bristles is present at the tip. The head, legs, and under parts are covered with softer spines. The general coloration of the upper parts is grayish brown to blackish brown, with whitish tips on the individual

hairs. One Malayan species is striped. The sides are lighter than the upper parts and the under parts are white. The tuft of bristles at the tip of the tail is whitish to creamy buff in color.

Atherurus has a relatively long body, short, stout limbs, and short, rounded ears. The feet are partially webbed and are armed with blunt, straight claws. The tail breaks easily and is often lost.

These animals are strictly nocturnal in their habits, sheltering during the day in burrows among roots of forest trees, or among rocks, under termite mounds, or under stream banks. Six to eight individuals have been observed living in a single shelter. These porcupines are able to swim quite well; they run swiftly and climb trees fairly well. The Sumatran species, however, cannot climb trees. During cold weather they are said to be dormant. Several individuals generally roam together in search of food, which consists principally of green plants, bark, roots, tubers, and insects.

The natives of Wattreki enjoy their flesh and pursue these porcupines with dogs and spears.

The type species of the genus is *A. macrourus* (Linnaeus).

Bornean Long-tailed Porcupine (*Trichys lipura*), photos by Ernest P. Walker.

LONG-TAILED PORCUPINES; ANKIS, BURA (native names).

THERE ARE TWO SPECIES. *T. lipura* inhabits Borneo, and *T. macrotis* inhabits the southern Malay Peninsula and Sumatra. They probably prefer a forest habitat.

The length of the head and body ranges from 380 to 460 mm., and the length of the tail, from 175 to 230 mm. Quills and modified tail bristles are absent. These animals are covered with flattened, flexible, grooved spines of moderate length. Interspersed among these spines are a few longer, cylindrical, spine-like hairs. The head and under parts are hairy and the underfur is rather woolly. The base of the tail is clothed like the back; the middle of the tail is scaly, and there is a cluster of straight unmodified bristles at the tip. The general coloration of the upper parts is brownish—the individual hairs have white bases and brown tips. The coloration gradually becomes lighter on the sides and finally blends into the white under parts.

Except for a long tail, these animals are similar in form to *Atherurus*. A substantial number of *Trichys* specimens are lacking any appreciable tail, which would indicate that the long tail must break quite easily from the body. The broad fore feet have four well-developed digits, each armed with a thick claw.

Members of the genus *Trichys* cannot produce the bristling and rattling effect of other porcupines. They are reported to destroy pineapples in some areas. The tail seems to be of some value to the natives and is therefore severed from the hide. Some natives, however, claim that there are two species, one with and one without a tail. Published material on general biology and habits is not extensive.

The type species of the genus is *T. lipura*, Günther.

NEW WORLD PORCUPINES.

THIS FAMILY consists of 4 genera (*Erethizon, Coendou, Echinoprocta* and *Chaetomys*) and about 23 species. The range is North America from the Arctic Ocean southward to Sonora, Mexico, the upper Mississippi Valley, and the Appalachians for the genus *Erethizon*; and southern Mexico, Central America, and South America on the eastern side of the Andes for the other three genera. *Erethizon* inhabits wooded areas, preferably those of conifers and poplars, but west of the Rocky Mountains, it regularly moves along streams and rivers in prairies or deserts, especially in the sagebrush-juniper regions; the other genera occupy tropical forests.

Like the Old World porcupines (Hystricidae) the members of the family Erethizontidae are heavy-set, rather large rodents. A noticeable difference between these two families, however, is that the New World porcupines have a foot that is modified for an arboreal life, i.e., the sole is widened and the first digit on the hind foot (in the more advanced forms) is replaced by a broad, movable pad. Each limb has only four functional digits, with strong, curved claws. In one genus (*Coendou*) the tail is prehensile. The limbs are fairly short. Some of the hairs on the body and tail are modified into short, sharp spines with overlapping barbs; the spines vary in distribution on the body. Long, wavy bristles are present on the back. The pelage is marked with blackish to brownish, yellowish, or whitish bands. The length of the head and body is 300 to 860 mm., and the tail measures from 75 to 450 mm. The weight of adults averages about 7 kg., with some individuals of the genus *Erethizon* weighing as much as 18 kg. Female porcupines have two pairs of mammae, and the males have a baculum. The body temperature is recorded as 38 degrees C. The length of the intestinal tract is approximately 3,330 mm.

The following dental formula is evident: i 1/1, c 0/0, pm 1/1, m 3/3 x 2 = 20. The cheek teeth have enamel re-entrant folds and are rooted. The genus *Chaetomys* is unique among Rodentia because the orbit is almost ringed by bone.

Of the four genera, *Erethizon* is the best known and most of the following information is based on the habits of this genus. These porcupines are arboreal or terrestrial and appear rather clumsy on both the ground and in trees. They climb surely, although slowly, and have excellent balance. They do not jump in climbing or descending. Porcupines can swim, the hollow quills furnishing considerable buoyancy. Any opening that provides protection may be used as a den (beneath a boulder, a log, or under crusted snow). More than one den is used, and temporary shelters often supplement the main habitations. There is usually only one porcupine in a single den. Porcupines are mainly nocturnal, but some forage during day. They are inactive during cold weather. Seasonal migrations occur in some areas (*Erethizon* in some parts of Arizona). These migrations are influenced by the amount of food available for their summer or winter needs.

Porcupines may wear a distinct path from the den to the feeding area, which may be 90 meters distant. They eat leaves, needles, bark, the cambium layer of wood, buds, and twigs, and are fond of salt. The preference for certain species of tree or shrub may vary with the season. Porcupines may climb 18 meters above ground for their food, which they handle with their hands. They sometimes consume 450 grams of food in a day and excrete about a fifth of this weight in the form of brown, crescent-shaped droppings.

The members of the genus *Erethizon* have poor vision. They have good hearing and sense of smell and sniff the air almost continuously. Various sounds are emitted vocally and by chattering the teeth.

Mating, in *Erethizon*, generally takes place in November or December. The male *Erethizon* usually showers the female with urine before the reproductive act, and the female repels the male after mating. One to four offspring are born in the spring, about seven months later. At birth, the young are well covered with long, black hair and short, soft quills. The eyes are open and they walk unsteadily. They also exhibit the typical defense reaction of turning the tail. Young *Erethizon* chatter their teeth when five days old and gain about 450 gm. per month. At least in some cases, the males are capable of mating when 16 months old. A captive female *Erethizon* lived more than ten years.

These animals protect themselves by climbing or fleeing. Some stand their ground and strike at the attacker with the tail. Often porcupines hunch the back if approached closely. Their quills are formidable weapons and can cause death if they penetrate vital organs. The penetration rate is up to 1 mm., or more, per hour. Despite these defense mechanisms, porcupines are preyed upon by many carnivores and the great horned owl. The fisher (*Martes pennanti*) is being introduced into parts of Oregon to control the population of porcupines.

The damage porcupines do to timber is probably overestimated, although quantitative studies are few. One such study estimated the timber loss due to porcupines at only 0.7 percent.

The geological range of this family is from the Oligocene to the Recent in South America, and from the upper Pliocene to Recent in North America.

NORTH AMERICAN PORCUPINES.

THE SINGLE SPECIES, *E. dorsatum*, inhabits most of the timbered areas of Alaska, Canada, and the United States (except the southeastern quarter) south to extreme northern Mexico. Wooded areas of conifers, junipers, and poplars are the preferred habitat.

The length of the head and body varies from 645 to 860 mm.; the length of the tail is 145 to 300 mm.; and the weight is usually 3.5 to 7 kg., but large males may weigh 18 kg. The upper parts of the body are covered with thick, sharp, barbed quills which are distributed among longer, stiff guard hairs; the underfur is woolly. The under parts lack the sharp quills. The general coloration of the upper parts is usually dark brown or blackish; the individual quills have yellowish-white bases.

Porcupines have a robust body, small head, short legs, and a stout tail. Their feet are modified for arboreal life.

These animals are principally nocturnal, spending the day in crevices, caves, hollow logs, burrows, or crude nests in trees. Although they tend to be solitary, several animals may occasionally shelter in a favorite den, especially in winter. Porcupines do not become dormant, but they hole up during bad weather. These slow moving, clumsy creatures are said never to attack. If cornered they erect their quills, turn their rump toward the source of danger, and rapidly swing their barbed tail at the adversary. Porcupines do not throw or shoot their quills; the spines are so lightly attached that when they enter the skin of the enemy they become detached from the porcupine. The animals emit various moans, whines, grunts, and coughs.

Porcupines climb and swim well. In the winter they feed upon the cambium and bark of trees and evergreen needles, but in the spring they consume buds, tender twigs, and leaves.

Mating occurs in the fall or early winter, at which time the male wanders in search of a female. An elaborate courtship precedes mating. Generally a single young is born after a gestation period of 210 to 217 days. The well-developed young weigh about 1.5 kg. at birth, climb trees in two days, and become sexually mature in their second year. A captive female lived more than ten years.

Although they often damage the bark of trees and may kill valuable timber and ornamental trees, this type of destruction is generally insignificant. The young red fir (*Abies magnifica*) of the Sierra Nevada in California are occasionally destroyed by porcupines. When the snow is deep, an animal lives in the same tree for some time until all the bark is stripped above the snow line. The denuded upper part of such trees dies the following spring. They are pests near camps as they will gnaw anything that contains salt, such as canoe paddles, ax handles, saddles, or other objects affected by salt from perspiration. Indians used the quills for decorations.

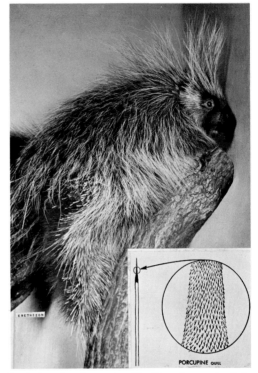

North American Porcupine (*Erethizon dorsatum*), photo by Ernest P. Walker. Inset from *The Mammal Guide*, Ralph S. Palmer.

North American Porcupine (*Erethizon dorsatum*), baby only a few days old, photo by Arthur Ellis, Washington Post Newspaper.

Prehensile-tailed Porcupines (*Coendou prehensilis*), photo by Ernest P. Walker.

PREHENSILE-TAILED PORCUPINES, CENTRAL AND
SOUTH AMERICAN PORCUPINES; JINJA-MAKA,
PUERCOS ESPINOSOS, HUISTLACUACHES, COANDÚ,
OURIÇOS CACHEIROS (local vernaculars).

THIS GENUS is made up of about 20 named species
whose combined ranges extend from Mexico through
Central America to Panama, Colombia, Venezuela,
Brazil, Bolivia, Peru, and Ecuador in South America.
Members of this genus live in forests. *Sphiggurus*,
Cuvier, 1825, is included as a subgenus. The type
species of the genus is *C. prehensilis* (Linnaeus).

The length of the head and body is about 300 to
600 mm.; the length of the tail is 330 to 450 mm.; and
the weight of adults is 900 to 4,310 grams. In the subgenus *Coendou*, the body is clothed with short, thick
spines, but in *Sphiggurus* the spiny covering of the
back is mixed with or covered by long, thick fur, and
the covering of the chest and under parts is considerably softer than in *Coendou*. In some forms there is a
woolly underfur. The general coloration of the upper
parts varies considerably from light yellowish through
shades of brown to almost black, and some forms are
speckled; the under parts are usually grayish.

The long tail is prehensile and lacks spines, in contrast to the short, spine-clad tail of the North American porcupines (*Erethizon*). The upper surface of the
terminal part of the tail in *Coendou* is naked and
modified for direct contact in coiling about branches.
The tip coils upward and has a callus pad on the
hairless upper side near the tip. The hands and feet
are highly specialized for climbing; there are four

digits on each limb, each of which is armed with a
long, curved claw.

Prehensile-tailed porcupines are principally nocturnal and arboreal in their habits; they are lazy and
slow in their movements but are sure-footed climbers.
They prefer to sleep in tangled vegetation among treetops, but they also shelter in hollow limbs, tree trunks,
and shallow burrows. These animals are inoffensive
and show no fear soon after their capture. Their diet
consists of leaves, tender stems, and such fruits as
bananas. Corn was found in the stomach of one
specimen. Their cry is plaintive, similar to that of an
infant. They have a strong odor. They frequently
sit on their haunches and shake their spines by moving the skin. These porcupines are pugnacious; they
bite and try to hit an adversary with their spines.

A single young is usually born. Births have been
noted in February, March, and May; pregnant females with well-developed fetuses have been taken in
March, May, August, and September. At birth the
young of *C. prehensilis* are large, weighing between
280 and 426 grams. They are covered with long,
reddish hair. From the top of the head to the base of
the tail they have short spines, almost always in
groups of three, which are flexible at birth but harden
soon afterward. In the species *C. prehensilis* the ratio
of size between newborn and mother is 1:3; in *C.
paraguayonsis* it is 2:3.

A captive *Coendou* which became quite tame lived
about three years, but the life span is probably much
longer.

Upper Amazonian Porcupine (*Echinoprocta rufescens*), photo from U.S. National Zoological Park.

UPPER AMAZONIAN PORCUPINES; EL PUERCO ESPÎN PEQUEÑO ANDINO.

THE SINGLE SPECIES, *E. rufescens*, is known from Colombia.

The length of this animal from the tip of its snout to the end of its tail is about 500 mm. The tail is short, about as long as the hind foot. Coloration on the back and sides is pale brown to blackish. The chin, throat, and underside are pale brown, and the feet and tail are dark gray to black. The head is whitish, speckled with brown and black. There is a short, white streak in the center of the nose, and a slight crest on the nape, formed by a few white spines.

The spines gradually become thicker, stronger, and shorter from the head to the rump; on the posterior part of the back, above the tail, the spines are well developed, short, and thick. The tail is hairy and not prehensile. The whiskers are black, and the incisors are slender and yellow.

The habits and biology of this porcupine are not well known. It is arboreal and appears to be fairly common around Bogota at elevations of 800 to 1,200 meters, but specific data on its life history have not been recorded. Specimens are in the Paris Natural History Museum, the British Museum (Natural History), the American Museum of Natural History, and the La Salle Institute in Bogota.

Thin-spined Porcupine (*Chaetomys subspinosus*), photo by Joao Moojen.

THIN-SPINED PORCUPINES; OURIÇO-PRETO.

THE SINGLE SPECIES, *C. subspinosus*, inhabits bushes and tangled vegetation around open savannahs in eastern and northern Brazil.

The length of the head and body ranges from about 430 to 457 mm., and the length of the tail is 255 to 280 mm. The general coloration of the upper parts is dull brownish or sometimes grayish white, and the under parts are slightly rufous-brown. The tail and feet are brownish black. The hands and feet each have four digits, armed with long, curved claws. The incisors are narrow. The covering on the back is peculiar—the hairs are more like bristles than spines. The pelage on the head, neck, and forelimbs is less flexible than that on other parts of the body, as the hairs are almost spine-like. All the large, coarse hairs are cylindrical and wavy. The fairly long tail is scaly throughout and only moderately enlarged in the basal part; the underside of the tail is covered with short, stiff hairs. Although the tip of the tail is naked and resembles that of *Coendou*, most authorities agree that it is not prehensile in *Chaetomys*.

Although thin-spined porcupines have been known to taxonomists for over a century, information about their life habits and general biology is extremely limited. They are known to live in woods, cultivated areas, and regions occupied by cocoa trees, the nut of which they eat. They are lazy and move slowly but are quick jumpers and climbers. They utter hoarse sounds. These porcupines are docile in captivity.

GUINEA PIGS OR CAVIES, MOCOS, AND PATAGONIAN "HARES" OR MARAS.

THIS FAMILY of 3 genera and approximately 23 species is confined to South America (geological range is from the middle Miocene to the Recent). The habitats of guinea pigs include rocky areas, savannahs, the edges of forests, and swamps; maras live in arid areas in coarse grass and scattered scrubs.

In guinea pigs and mocos the body form is quite robust, the head is large, the ears and limbs are short, the tail is vestigial, and the size is small (length of head and body from 225 to 355 mm.). In the patagonian "hares" the proportions are rabbit-like, the ears are long, the limbs are long and thin, the tail is short, and the size is large (length of head and body from about 450 to 750 mm.). The nails are short and sharp in *Cavia*, blunt but well developed in *Kerodon*, and hoof-like on the foot and claw-like on the hand in *Dolichotis*. All members of the family Caviidae have four digits on the fore foot and three digits on the hind foot. The soles are naked in *Cavia* and *Kerodon*, but haired for the most part in *Dolichotis*. The pelage in the wild forms is fairly coarse or crisp. Female *Cavia* have one pair of mammae.

The dental formula is as follows: i 1/1, c 0/0, pm 1/1, m 3/3 x 2 = 20. The incisors are short. The tooth rows tend to converge anteriorly, and the cheek teeth are rootless (ever-growing) with a rather simple pattern of two prisms having sharp folds and angular projections.

Kerodon is a little-known genus, but *Cavia* and *Dolichotis* are fairly common. These animals walk on all four limbs, and *Dolichotis* runs and leaps like a rabbit although it is not an especially fast runner. The members of this family are active during the night or in the evening (*Cavia* and apparently *Kerodon*) or during the day (*Dolichotis*). They do not hibernate. Guinea pigs live in pairs or in groups of up to 10 individuals, and maras often assemble in groups of up to 40 individuals. These rodents dig burrows in the soil or among rocks and sometimes use the burrows of other animals. *Cavia* is known to utilize the burrows of tucu-tucos (*Ctenomys*), and Patagonian cavies occasionally inhabit viscacha (*Lagostomus*) burrows. The diet consists of different kinds of plant material.

In *Dolichotis* the litter size is two to five, and the young are born in a nest in the burrow. Guinea pigs give birth to 1 to 4 offspring after a gestation period of about 60 to 70 days. *Cavia* generally breeds twice a year in the wild (more often in captivity). The offspring of guinea pigs are fairly large at birth, attaining sexual maturity in 55 to 70 days. Female guinea pigs have estrous cycles of 16 days and come into "heat" after giving birth (common to many rodents). The male guinea pig or mara may sprinkle the female with urine before the reproductive act as does the porcupine (*Erethizon*). Guinea pigs live nearly eight years in captivity.

All species of the family Caviidae are used as food by man, although the flesh of *Dolichotis* is said to be rather dry and flavorless. *Cavia porcellus* was domesticated by the Incas of Peru for food before the conquistadors arrived. Guinea pigs have an unpleasant odor, and when captured emit a scream rendered as "cui." Members of the genus *Cavia* are widely used in laboratory research, although they do not adjust well to sudden changes in temperature.

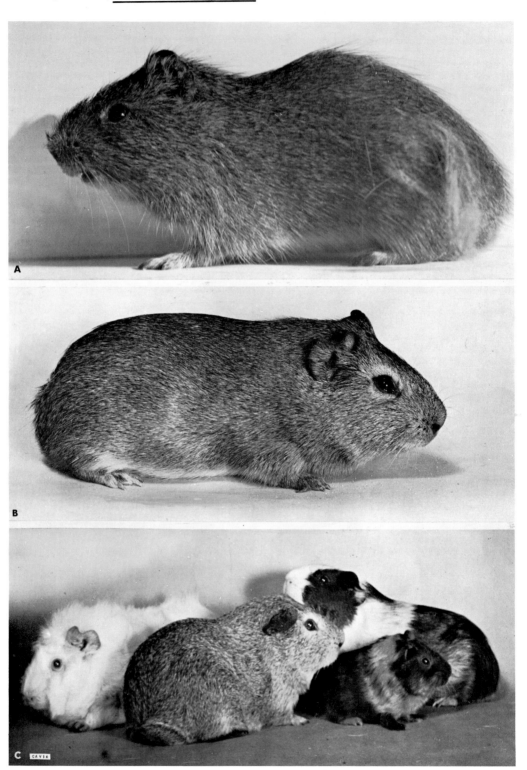

A. Wild Cavy (*Cavia tschudi*), photo by Hilda Heller. B. & C. Guinea Pigs, domestic strain (*C. porcellus*), photos by Ernest P. Walker.

GUINEA PIGS, CAVIES; HOKE, PORQUINHOS DA INDIA, PREÁS, MOKO, COBÁIA, APEREA, AGUTÍS, CONEJOS DE LAS INDIAS, GUINESE BIGGETJES, SCURI SABANERO, MEERSCHWEINCHEN, SANDHASE. (Included are vernaculars used in other countries.)

THIS GENUS of about 20 species occurs in South America from Colombia and Venezuela southward to Brazil and northern Argentina. Guinea pigs inhabit a wide variety of habitats such as rocky regions, savannahs, the edge of forests, and swamps. *Microcavia*, Gervais and Ameghino, 1880; *Galea*, Meyen, 1833; and *Monticavia*, Thomas, 1916, are regarded as subgenera.

The length of the head and body is 225 to 355 mm., and the weight of adults is 450 to 700 grams. An external tail is lacking. In the wild forms the pelage is fairly coarse and long, but in domesticated guinea pigs it varies from smooth and short, smooth and long, to coarse and short. In some forms the hairs radiate in rosettes. Although domesticated guinea pigs exhibit an extremely wide range of colors, the wild forms are generally grayish or brownish. Members of the genus *Cavia* have stocky bodies, fairly short hind legs, and short ears. The hind feet are long with three digits, and the fore feet have four digits, all of which are armed with sharp claws.

Guinea pigs live in burrows which they excavate themselves or in abandoned burrows of other animals. They generally associate in small groups, usually five to ten individuals, and are always prepared to flee at the slightest indication of danger. At nightfall they leave their burrows and follow paths to feeding places, where they eat many kinds of vegetation.

These animals mate throughout the year. One to four young constitute a normal litter in wild forms, but in domestic animals the litters are somewhat larger. The gestation period of about 60 to 70 days, at least in domestic forms, is rather long for an animal so small. The young are able to run within a few hours, nurse for about 3 weeks, and become sexually mature between 55 and 70 days of age. Their life span may last 8 years.

In spite of their unpleasant odor, guinea pigs make ideal pets as they are gentle, do not bite, and do well in captivity if kept warm and given a reasonable amount of care. They are used extensively in laboratory studies of disease, nutrition, and heredity, and in the development of serums. The Incas raised them (probably *C. porcellus*) for food, as their flesh is of excellent quality. *C. porcellus* is the wild form of domestic guinea pigs.

The type species of the genus is *C. porcellus* (Linnaeus).

Moco (*Kerodon rupestris*), photo from Chicago Natural History Museum. Inset: Left hand and foot, photo from *Proc. Zool. Soc. London.*

Mocos, Rock Cavies.

THE SINGLE SPECIES, *K. rupestris*, is known only from Brazil. Mocos inhabit arid and pebbly areas near stony mountains or hills, particularly in northeastern Brazil.

This rodent is about the same size as the guinea pig (*Cavia*) or somewhat larger; the tail is absent or only a vestigial projection. Adults weigh about 900 to 1,000 grams. The general color is grayish with white and black mottling on the upper parts; the throat is whitish, and the under parts are yellowish brown. This genus differs structurally from that of the guinea pigs due to its blunt but well-developed nails on the digits, and in skull features and other anatomical characteristics.

Mocos seek shelter under rocks or in the fissures between stones, sometimes making burrows under the stones. They leave their shelters late in the afternoon or evening and run on the ground or climb trees looking for food, mainly tender leaves. They descend by leaps or by a single jump at the slightest sign of danger. The feces are small, greenish, and capsule-shaped. The voice sounds like a shrill whistle; this is imitated by hunters trying to attract them. The natives are very fond of the flesh and prepare it for food or medicine.

Mating has been noted in March near Ceará. There are probably two litters a year, with one or two young in each litter. These rodents are easily domesticated and are suitable for pets. One individual was reported to have lived in captivity for 11 years.

Maras (*Dolichotis* sp.?), photo by B. Grzimek. Inset: A. Right hind foot; B. Side view of right hind foot; C. Right fore foot; D. Side view of right fore foot; photos from *Proc. Zool. Soc. London.*

PATAGONIAN CAVIES OR "HARES"; MARAS, LIE-BRES PATAGONICUS.

THIS GENUS of two species, *D. patagona* and *D. salinicola*, occurs in Argentina and Patagonia. Maras inhabit arid areas of coarse grass or scattered shrubs. *Pediolagus*, Marelli, 1927, is regarded as a subgenus of *Dolichotis* for the species *D. salinicola.*

The length of the head and body in *D. patagona* is 690 to 750 mm.; in *D. salinicola* the length of the head and body is considerably less, about 450 mm. In both species the tail is fairly short—the maximum length is about 45 mm. Large individuals of *D. patagona* weigh from 9 to 16 kg. The general coloration of the upper parts is grayish and that of the under parts is whitish. There is some yellowish brown on the limbs and feet. The pelage is dense; the individual hairs stand at nearly right angles to the skin. Although the hairs are fine, they have a crisp texture.

These rodents have a body form similar to that of long-legged rabbits and hares (Leporidae). The hind limbs are long, the hind foot has three digits, and each digit has a hoof-like claw. The fore foot has four digits, each bearing sharp claws. *Dolichotis* is modified for a cursorial life.

The members of this genus shelter in burrows of their own construction or in abandoned burrows of other animals. They are active during the day. Groups of three or four Patagonian cavies are often seen traveling together in single file, but occasionally a group of as many as 40 maras may be observed. Although *Dolichotis* hops like a rabbit or hare, it is not an especially fast runner and is always on the alert for danger. Patagonian cavies spend considerable time basking in the sun. They usually stand on straight legs, sit on the haunches with the fore part of the body resting on the fully extended front legs, and recline like a cat, with the front limbs turned under the chest—an unusual position for a rodent.

The diet consists of any available vegetation.

The two to five young are born in a nest within the burrow. The mother usually sits on her haunches nursing and the young must also sit erect to suckle.

The light-colored flesh is said to be quite dry and flavorless.

The type species of the genus is *D. patagona.*

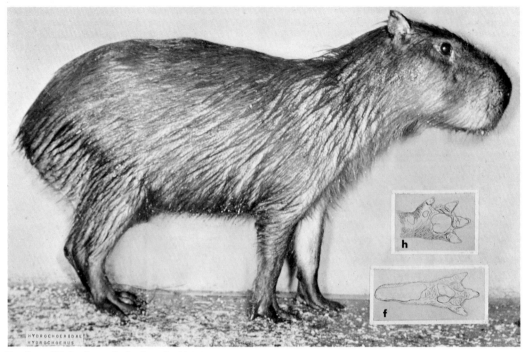

Capybara (*Hydrochoerus hydrochaeris*) which has just come out of water, photo by Ernest P. Walker. Insets: Bottoms of hand and foot, photos from *Proc. Zool. Soc. London.*

CAPYBARAS, CARPINCHOS, WATER HOGS; CAPU-GUA, PIROPIRO, CHIGUIRES, CARPINCHO, CAPI-VARAS (South American names).

THIS FAMILY contains a single Recent genus, *Hydrochoerus*. The two species are distributed as follows: *H. isthmius* in Panama, east of the canal; and *H. hydrochaeris* in South America, east of the Andes southward to the mouth of the Rio Parana. Capybaras inhabit woods with dense vegetation around ponds, lakes, rivers, streams, marshes, and swamps. These rodents resemble the Caviidae in a number of distinctive features and are regarded by some workers as a subfamily of Caviidae.

Capybaras look like guinea pigs but are gigantic in size and have a proportionately shorter body. These animals are robust, with a large head and a massive body. They are the largest living rodents, as the length of the head and body is 1 to 1.3 meters. The tail is very short. Capybaras may be 500 mm. high. The species *H. hydrochaeris* weighs 50 kg. or more, but the smaller species *H. isthmius* averages about 27 kg. in weight. The long, coarse pelage is so sparse that the skin is visible.

In the mature male, a bare, raised area on the top of the snout consists of greatly enlarged sebaceous glands. The coloration is generally reddish brown to grayish on the upper parts and yellowish brown on the under parts; occasionally there is some black on the face, the outer surface of the limbs, and the rump.

These rodents are distinguished by their large size, broad head, short and rounded ears, small eyes placed dorsally and relatively far back on the head, and

short limbs. The muzzle is heavy and truncate, and the upper lip is enlarged. The fore foot has four digits and the hind foot has three; all the digits are partially webbed and armed with short, strong claws. The fingers and toes are arranged in a radial pattern.

The dental formula is as follows: i 1/1, c 0/0, pm 1/1, m 3/3 x 2 = 20. The tooth rows tend to converge anteriorly. The white incisors are shallowly grooved, and the cheek teeth are rootless or ever-growing, with a similar but more complex surface pattern than that in the Caviidae. The cheek teeth of capybaras are noticeable due to the large amount of cement present.

Capybaras live in family groups or in bands of up to 20 individuals. In areas where they are not disturbed, these rodents are active in the morning and evening, resting during the heat of the day in a shallow bed in the ground. Capybaras do not construct dens. Like some other mammals, they have become nocturnal in regions where they have been molested. When alarmed on land, they run like horses, but when closely pursued they enter water, where they swim and dive with ease. While swimming, only the nostrils, eyes, and ears project above the water. They also swim underwater, often for considerable distances, or they may hide in floating vegetation with only their nostrils exposed. Capybaras are normally peaceful and quiet, spending much time seated on their haunches or wallowing in muddy pools. J. R. Ellerman (*The Families and Genera of Living Rodents* [London, 1941], Vol. 1, p. 253) reports that these rodents seem to possess considerable intelligence. When contented they may emit low, clicking sounds;

sharp and prolonged whistles and abrupt grunts have also been noted.

These semiaquatic rodents often stand belly deep in water, feeding on various aquatic plants. Grasses are also consumed. So far as is known, capybaras eat only plant matter. They sometimes graze with cattle and occasionally consume grains, melons, and squashes. Characteristic mounds of elongate fecal pellets are deposited.

A single litter of 2 to 8 offspring is born once a year, after a gestation period of 15 to 18 weeks. The young are rather well developed at birth; they weigh from 900 to 1,350 grams after five days and remain with the mother for a considerable time. The life span in the wild seems to be about eight to ten years.

Capybaras rarely fight among themselves or in defense against their enemies. They must be alert to survive, as they are hunted by jaguars on land, by alligators in the water, and by man both on land and in water. Man destroys these rodents because they are sometimes a pest in cultivated fields. Their flesh is eaten, although it is considered to be of poor quality; their thick, fatty skin provides a grease used in the pharmaceutical trade; and their incisors are often used as ornaments by the native people.

The geological range of this family is the Pliocene to the Recent in South America, the Pleistocene in North America (the southeastern United States), and the Recent in Central America.

The type species of the genus is *H. hydrochaeris* (Linnaeus).

False Paca or Pacarana (*Dinomys branickii*), photo from New York Zoological Society.

PACARANAS, FALSE PACAS, BRANICK RATS.

A SINGLE GENUS, *Dinomys*, constitutes this family. No extinct genera are known, since the family is recorded only from the Recent in South America. The single species, *D. branickii*, occurs in valleys and the lower slopes of the Andes in Colombia, Ecuador, Peru, Brazil, and Bolivia. Pacaranas inhabit forests or shelter in rocky cliffs and holes in the ground. This rare animal may be on the verge of extinction.

The common name "pacarana" means "false paca" in the native language, the latter name referring to the similarity in size and color pattern between *Dinomys* and the paca, *Cuniculus*, in the family Dasyproctidae. The pacarana differs markedly from the paca, however. It is thickset and has a stout tail which is approximately one-fourth the length of the head and body. The overall appearance of *Dinomys* reminds one of an immense guinea pig, almost as big as a bear. Pacaranas have a broad head, short, rounded ears, and short limbs with broad feet bearing four digits. All the digits are armed with a long, powerful claw. Adult pacaranas weigh from 10 to 15 kg. The length of the head and body is 730 to 790 mm., and the length of the tail is about 200 mm. The whiskers are quite long, about as long as the head. Cranial characteristics distinguish *Dinomys* from members of the families Caviidae and Dasyproctidae. The individual hairs are rather coarse, scant, and of varied length. The tail is fully haired. The coloration is black or brown, with two more-or-less continuous, broad white stripes on each side of the mid-line and two shorter rows of white spots on the sides. In older individuals the stripes seem to be broader and more conspicuously white. The under parts are paler than above and unmarked.

The following dental formula is recorded: i 1/1, c 0/0, pm 1/1, m 3/3 x 2 = 20. The incisors are broad and heavy; the cheek teeth are probably ever-growing (rootless) and are extremely high-crowned, each tooth consisting of a series of transverse plates.

Although the generic name means "terrible mouse," these rodents only fight as a last resort. In confinement, pacaranas are good natured and peaceful and do not attempt to bite or escape. They allow themselves to be petted and scratched, occasionally indicating displeasure by a low, guttural growl. Observations of captive specimens reveal that they move slowly and have placid temperaments. Pacaranas are terrestrial and normally progress by means of a waddling gait. When threatened by agile predators, such as ocelots and coatis, these rodents back up against cliffs and into holes to protect themselves and their vulnerable hind parts. The claws appear to be of the fossorial type, but captive animals have not used them for digging. When eating, pacaranas sit upon their haunches and, in a dexterous manner, carefully examine their food before consuming it. Their diet seems to consist mainly of fruit, leaves, and tender stems of plants. Pacaranas are probably nocturnal in the wild, although captives have been active at all hours.

Two appears to be the normal number of offspring per litter in the family Dinomyidae. Pregnant females with two fetuses each were taken in February and May.

The slow and inoffensive traits of this animal render it an easy victim for various predators. The native people seek it for food because of its large size. Although pacaranas tame readily and make interesting pets, they apparently do not thrive well in captivity.

RODENTIA; Family: HEPTAXODONTIDAE

THIS FAMILY of medium-sized rodents, all now extinct, consists of four genera of the Recent, known only from skeletal remains and teeth found in caves and kitchen middens on the islands of Hispaniola and Puerto Rico in the Greater Antilles, and Anguilla and St. Martin in the Lesser Antilles. All four genera are believed to be of Recent or sub-Recent age. The abundance of bones found with refuse and artifacts from human habitations indicates that some of these animals, at least, were utilized as food by the natives. Extermination of some of the genera appears to have occurred fairly recently, that is, at about the time that Columbus reached the islands. This assumption does not necessarily mean that extinction was caused by the European voyagers and early settlers. The closest living relatives of these rodents seem to be the pacaranas of the family Dinomyidae, and some zoologists regard the Heptaxodontidae as a subfamily of the Dinomyidae.

These rodents had massive skulls and stout bodies. All the forms were probably terrestrial. The family is characterized by the structure of the cheek teeth, each of which has four to seven laminae with nearly parallel crests arranged obliquely to the long axis of the skull.

Studies indicate that three other genera, *Clidomys*, *Speoxenus*, and *Spirodontomys*, also included in this family, existed before the Recent. They are, therefore, not treated herein. Accounts of the four Recent genera follow.

HEPTAXODON, Anthony, 1917

THE SINGLE SPECIES, *H. bidens*, was first described from cave deposits collected near Utuado, Puerto Rico, and other skeletal remains which were discovered later near Ciales and Morovis. Present evidence indicates that this genus was well distributed throughout the forested parts of the island at a fairly recent time. They apparently survived until about the time the island was discovered by the Spaniards.

Heptaxodon has only two cheek teeth in each molariform series. Judging from the skeleton, this animal was about the size of a woodchuck (*Marmota*). The palate is sharply constricted anteriorly by the convergence of the two upper tooth rows; it is quite short, with a deep and wide posterior notch which reaches nearly to the line of the front teeth.

Ray (*Bull. Mus. Comp. Zool.*, 131: 109–27, 1964) believes that *Heptaxodon* is only the young of *Elasmodontomys*.

ELASMODONTOMYS, Anthony, 1916

THE SINGLE SPECIES, *E. obliquus*, was originally described from Utuado, Puerto Rico, but additional skeletal fragments have since been excavated near Ciales and Morovis on the same island.

The skull resembles that of the nutria (*Myocastor*); it is flat-topped with rather large, laterally-compressed bullae. The total length of the skull is about 125 mm. This genus was about the size of a paca (*Cuniculus*) and appears to have had a heavy body. Its short digit bones indicate that *Elasmodontomys* had terrestrial rather than arboreal habits. These are the largest extinct rodents known from Puerto Rico.

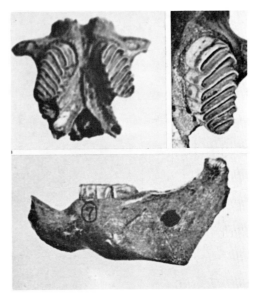

(*Heptaxodon bidens*), photos from *Bull. Amer. Mus. Nat. Hist.*, H. E. Anthony.

(*Elasmodontomys obliquus*), photos from American Museum of Natural History.

(*Amblyrhiza inundata*), the last two teeth of upper molar series, photo from *Bull. Amer. Mus. Nat. Hist.*, "New Fossil Rodents from Porto Rico," H. E. Anthony.

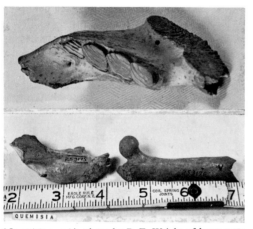

(*Quemisia gravis*), photo by P. F. Wright of bone material in U.S. National Museum.

AMBLYRHIZA, Cope, 1868

THE SINGLE SPECIES, *A. inundata*, is known from fragmentary skeletal material found in caves on the islands of Anguilla and St. Martin, at the extreme northeastern part of the Antillean chain.

This genus seems to be closely allied to *Quemisia*. *Amblyrhiza* was nearly the size of an American black bear (*Euarctos*); the length of its skull is approximately 400 mm. It is uncertain when this genus of large rodents became extinct.

QUEMISIA, Miller, 1929

THE SINGLE SPECIES, *Q. gravis*, is identified from cranial and dental fragments obtained in caves of St. Michel, Haiti, and Samana Bay, Dominican Republic.

The members of the genus *Quemisia* are the largest extinct Hispaniolan rodents. They appear to have been about the size of a paca (*Cuniculus*). The cranial peculiarities include a long union of the lower jaws, short lower incisors, and an unusual twisting of the enamel pattern of the cheek teeth.

G. S. Miller, in his description of this genus, suggests that this is the same animal referred to as "quemi" (hence Miller's usage of *Quemisia* for the generic name) by Oviedo in his account of the animals of Hispaniola, published approximately 25 years after the Spanish discovery of this island. Oviedo's brief description states that the "quemi" is similar in coloration to the "hutia" (*Isolobodon*) but slightly larger in size, and that it was used by the natives as a source of food. Kitchen middens have yielded skeletal remains of *Quemisia*. The extinction of this genus probably occurred soon after the arrival of the Spaniards or during the first half of the sixteenth century.

PACAS AND AGOUTIS.

THIS FAMILY of 3 genera (*Cuniculus*, *Myoprocta*, and *Dasyprocta*) and approximately 30 species occurs in a variety of habitats in tropical America, from central Mexico to southern Brazil, including the Lesser Antilles. Some authors refer one of these genera, *Cuniculus*, to a separate family, *Cuniculidae*. These rodents are known only from the Recent of tropical America.

Members of the family Dasyproctidae have a small, pig-like body with a rabbit-like head. The external form is modified for running, in that the limbs, especially the hind legs, are lengthened and the lateral toes on these members are reduced in size. The thumb is vestigial. In pacas (*Cuniculus*) the fore foot has four functional digits and the hind foot has five, whereas in the agoutis the fore foot has four functional digits and the hind foot has three. The claws are thick or hoof-like. The pelage is coarse and thick. Pacas display a spotted color pattern on a brownish or blackish ground color, but agoutis are usually uniformly colored above and pale below. The length of the head and body is 320 to 795 mm., and the length of the tail is 10 to 70 mm. Adults range in weight from approximately 1 to 10 kg. Pacas have two pairs of mammae and agoutis have four pairs. The anal glands of these rodents produce a distinctive odor.

In all species there are four cheek teeth and one incisor on each side of each jaw, making a total of 20 teeth. The incisors are fairly thin, and the high-crowned cheek teeth are semirooted. Part of the zygomatic arch of the skull in *Cuniculus paca* is greatly enlarged and contains a large sinus, a condition not present in any other mammal.

Pacas are active at night; agoutis seem to be nor-mally diurnal but become nocturnal in regions where they have been disturbed. The members of this family dig their own burrows, often in banks or under roots. Normally there is only one animal in a burrow, but *Myoprocta exilis* has been noted sheltering in holes in the bank of a river and apparently living in colonies. Pacas, when alarmed, take to water; agoutis are more terrestrial. Agoutis walk, trot, or gallop on their digits, and are agile and fast. When approached, they may "freeze" and then suddenly run away while emitting shrill screams. Agoutis often sit with the body erect and the ankles flat on the ground, a position from which they can dart off at full speed; or they pause, motionless, with one fore foot raised. Some-times when they are frightened, agoutis erect the long hair on the rump.

In addition to shrill screams, agoutis emit a squeak or short bark and a grumbling sound. Pacas produce an unusual rumbling sound and a low growl when angered.

These rodents eat leaves, stems, fruits, and vegetables (pacas also dig for roots). Agoutis may bury food.

Some forms, at least, seem to mate twice a year. Pacas usually have a single offspring (rarely twins), and agoutis have from two to six young. The gestation period in *Dasyprocta* has been reported as 64 to 104 days; the latter figure probably approximates more closely the actual gestation period. The youngsters of this genus are quite well developed at birth. They weigh up to 210 grams, are covered with hair, have their eyes open, will "freeze" when the mother does, and may attempt to nibble on green vegetation within an hour after birth. The life span for agoutis and pacas in captivity is 15 to 20 years.

All the members of the family Dasyproctidae are hunted for their excellent flesh.

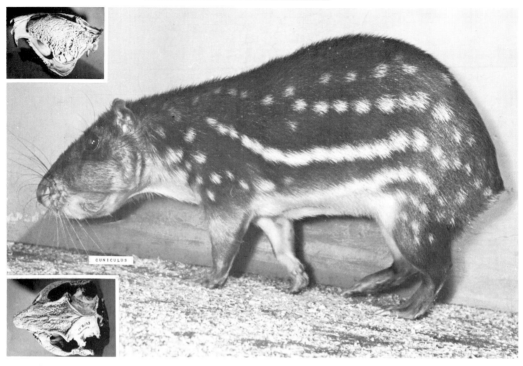

Paca (*Cuniculus paca virgata*), photo by Ernest P. Walker. Insets: Photos by Howard E. Uible.

PACAS; CONEJOS PINTADOS, LAPA, HEI, TEPEIZ-CUINTE (native names).

THIS GENUS of two species, *C. paca* and *C. tacza-nowskii*, inhabits tropical America from central Mexico southward to southern Brazil. Pacas live in a variety of habitats but usually seek forested areas near water. *Stictomys* is a synonym of *Cuniculus*.

The length of the head and body is 600 to 795 mm.; the length of the tail is 20 to 30 mm.; and the weight of adults is about 6.3 to 10 kg. The pelage is composed of rather coarse hair without fine underfur. *C. tacza-nowskii* has a somewhat thicker and softer pelage than *C. paca*, for it lives on the "paramos" in the Andes of Venezuela, Colombia, and Ecuador. There are usually four longitudinal rows of white spots on each side of the brownish to blackish body. The under parts are whitish or buffy.

Members of the genus *Cuniculus* have a robust body, with medium-sized ears, and four fingers and five toes. The female has four mammae. Part of the zygomatic arch of the skull in *C. paca* is specialized as a resonating chamber, a feature that is not found in any other mammal. This species utters a low growl when angered.

Pacas are nocturnal, spending the day in burrows of their own construction. These are located in banks, on slopes, among tree roots, or under rocks, and are usually provided with several escape exits that are often plugged with leaves. It has not been determined whether the paca places the leaves here or if they accumulate in the opening when a particular exit is not used for a long time. After dusk, pacas emerge to follow paths that lead to feeding grounds and water. They usually travel alone. Although pacas are ter-restrial, they enter water freely, swim well, and gener-ally attempt to make their escape in water if alarmed. Their diet consists of a variety of leaves, stems, roots, and fallen fruit; their favorite food appears to be avocados and mangos.

There are probably two litters a year; in Rio de Janeiro, one was noted in February, another in July. Usually a single young is born, rarely twins. A captive in the National Zoological Park lived slightly more than 16 years.

Occasionally pacas destroy yam, cassava, vegetable, and sugar cane crops. The flesh of these rodents is highly prized by the native people, who hunt them with dogs. The carcasses bring a high price in the market—up to 80 cents per kg. is paid for undressed animals.

The type species of the genus is *C. paca* (Linnaeus).

Agouti (*Dasyprocta* sp.), photo from San Diego Zoological Garden. Inset: Right forepaw and hind foot, photo from *Proc. Zool. Soc. London.*

AGOUTIS; AGUTÍS, NEQUIS, CUTIAS, COTIAS, KONKONI, COTUZAS, PICURE (South American names).

THE GENUS *Dasyprocta* is composed of about two dozen named species, having a combined range extending from southern Mexico through Central America to southern Brazil including the Lesser Antilles. Agoutis are found in cool, damp, lowland forests, grassy streambanks, thick brush, high, dry hillsides, savannahs, and cultivated areas.

The length of the head and body is 415 to 620 mm.; the length of the tail is 10 to 35 mm.; and the weight of adults is 1,325 to 4,000 grams. The pelage is usually quite coarse and glossy with the longest and thickest hairs on the posterior part of the back. In most forms the general coloration of the upper parts ranges from pale orange through several shades of brown to almost black; but under parts are generally whitish, yellowish, or buffy. In some forms slight stripes may be present, and in others the rump is of a contrasting color to the remainder of the back.

Members of this genus have a slender body form, short ears, and three toes bearing hoof-like claws on the hind foot. These animals are adapted to a cursorial life. The female has eight mammae.

Agoutis are diurnal, but in regions where they have been molested they do not leave their burrows until dusk. The burrows that they construct are dug among limestone boulders, along riverbanks, or under the roots of trees. Agoutis are shy and somewhat sequestered and it appears that each burrow is occupied by only a single animal. Well-defined paths radiate from their shelters. If danger threatens they usually "freeze" in an attempt to pass unnoticed, but when discovered they can travel with remarkable speed and agility in another direction or in dodging obstacles. They usually sit erect to eat, holding the food in their hands. The diet consists of fruit, vegetables, and various succulent plants. Corn, cassava root, and plantain have been found in the stomachs of various specimens.

Some forms seem to mate twice a year. The two to four young, usually two, are born in the burrow in a nest of leaves, roots, and hair after a gestation period which lasts about three months. The life span in captivity is 13 to 20 years.

Agoutis are hunted for their excellent flesh, owing to scarcity of fresh meat throughout much of their ranges. Occasionally they damage sugar cane. They tame easily and make affectionate pets; some refuse to return to the wild.

The type species of the genus is *D. aguti* (Linnaeus).

Acushi (*Myoprocta acouchy*), green color phase, photo by Constance P. Warner.

ACUSHI (also spelled ACUCHI, ACUSHY), AGOUTIS; CUTIAS DE RABO, CUTIAIAS, COTIARA (South American names).

THIS GENUS of about five species is known from Colombia, the Guianas, Ecuador, Peru, and Brazil.

The length of the head and body is 320 to 380 mm., and the length of the tail is 45 to 70 mm. On the basis of pelage color, the genus may be divided into two groups or sections: those that are reddish to blackish above and those that are dull green above. This unusual olive-green color effect is produced by pale yellow rings on black hairs. Species of *Myoprocta* often have the muzzle and sides of the head brightly colored with yellow, orange, or red. The undersides of long-tailed agoutis are orangish, yellowish, brownish, or whitish. This genus resembles *Dasyprocta*, but the teeth are smaller and the tail is longer in *Myoprocta*. The tail is haired and appears more whitish on the distal than on the basal part.

Specific habits and biology are little known. These rodents may be more common than records indicate as they resemble agoutis (*Dasyprocta*) so closely that laymen may consider this rodent an agouti.

M. exilis has been found in wet forests, apparently living in colonies. This form was noted in the morning, and it took refuge in holes in the bank of a river.

Specimens are in the Royal Natural History Museum in Stockholm, the British Museum (Natural History), the U.S. National Museum, the American Museum of Natural History, and the Chicago Natural History Museum.

The type species of the genus is *M. acouchy* (Erxleben).

VISCACHAS AND CHINCHILLAS.

THIS FAMILY of three genera and seven species is known only from South America (the geological range is from the early Miocene to the Recent). The species *Lagostomus crassus*, based on a single skeleton, is probably extinct. *L. maximus*, the living species of plains viscacha, inhabits the lowlands of Argentina. The four species of mountain viscachas (*Lagidium*) and the single species of chinchilla (*Chinchilla laniger*) occur on rocky slopes at elevations of 800 to 6,100 meters in Peru, Bolivia, Chile, and Argentina to about latitude 52 degrees S.

They are slightly slender, have a flattened, relatively large head, a broad snout, large eyes, rounded ears, and fine, long, dense pelage on the body. The pelage is coarser on the tail in all three genera, and shorter and coarser on the body in *Lagostomus* than in the highland genera *Lagidium* and *Chinchilla*. The forelimbs are short; the hands are small and have four functional, flexible fingers. The hind limbs are long and muscular; the elongated foot on *Lagostomus* has three toes, but *Lagidium* and *Chinchilla* have four toes. The foot is adapted to jumping, but it serves in a type of quadrupedal locomotion which differs from that of hares and rabbits. The palms and soles of chinchillid rodents are not haired. The claws of the digits are heavy and sharp in the plains viscachas, whereas they are weak and blunt in the mountain viscachas and chinchillas. The length of the head and body is 225 to 660 mm., and the length of the tail is 75 to 320 mm. Adults weigh 0.5 to 7 kg. In the true chinchilla (*Chinchilla*) the female is larger than the male. Females have a single pair of mammae located on the sides of the body in the chest region.

The dental formula is: i 1/1, c 0/0, pm 1/1, m 3/3 x 2 = 20. The incisors are fairly narrow, and the cheek teeth grow throughout life.

Chinchillids are active throughout the year. *Lagidium* is diurnal, and *Chinchilla* and *Lagostomus* are nocturnal. They live in groups, sheltering in rock crevices or burrows; from four to as many as 100 individuals inhabit a single colony. Family groups of two to five animals often occupy the same burrow. Chinchillids seldom fight with one another. Other vertebrates, including predators, are sometimes in a burrow with the chinchillids. These rodents run, leap, or creep on all four limbs.

New colonies of the plains viscacha (*Lagostomus*) are begun by solitary males; these warrens may be occupied continuously for many years. These animals, like prairie dogs, prefer open spaces, and in the past a person could ride 800 km. without losing sight of viscachas. Mountain viscachas shelter only near rocks, although they venture as far as 68 meters from their burrows to feed. They tire easily but are active and agile around their burrows. The members of the genus *Lagidium* are not strong diggers, although they gradually enlarge their burrows.

The diet of chinchillids consists of plant material.

These animals give birth to well-developed young. The gestation period is approximately three and a half months in *Chinchilla*, three months in *Lagidium*, and slightly less than five months in *Lagostomus*. The viscachas usually give birth to one or two offspring, whereas the litter size in *Chinchilla* is one to six. One or two litters are reared each year. In captivity *Chinchilla* has a 24-day estrous cycle, with two days of estrous.

The pelage in the family Chinchillidae attains its maximum beauty and value in the true chinchillas. Chinchillas are raised in captivity for their fur and for sale as breeding stock. The hair of mountain viscachas is woven with wool into cloth. All the species in this family are used as food by man. Although chinchillids have been reduced in numbers, their population seems to be increasing as a result of better protection.

Viscacha (*Lagostomus maximus*), photo by Ernest P. Walker. Under surfaces of right front and hind feet, photos from *Proc. Zool. Soc. London.*

PLAINS VISCACHAS; VIZCACHONES, VIZCACHAS.

A SINGLE SPECIES, *L. maximus*, inhabits Argentina. It lives in pampas and scrublands. Another form, *L. crassus*, is probably extinct; identification is based on a single skeleton found in Peru, and no subsequent specimens have been discovered. This skeleton was not fossilized, which indicates that these animals lived in Peru at a recent date.

The length of the head and body of *L. maximus* is 470 to 660 mm.; the length of the tail is 150 to 200 mm.; and the weight is about 7 kg. Judging from the skeleton, *L. crassus* appears to be larger and stouter than *L. maximus*. The coarse hair of these rodents is dark grayish on the upper parts and white on the under parts; there are black and white stripes on the face. The tail is fully haired. Plains viscachas have large blunt heads, four well-developed fingers on each hand, and three toes armed with stout, sharp claws on each hind foot.

These rodents live in colonies. Each colony occupies an extensive network of subterranean tunnels that have multiple entrances. These warrens are known as vizcacheras. Some vizcacheras have been in continual use for centuries. A colony usually consists of 15 to 30 individuals and is governed by a single adult male. These clean animals carry all refuse from the burrows and deposit it about the entrance. Here they also deposit all the hard objects they can carry. In the collections are bones, stones, plant stems, dry dung, and clods of earth. In addition, any object dropped by a man near a vizcachera is invariably salvaged and added to the miscellany. An accumulation of a bushel or two of objects appears to serve no useful purpose except perhaps to adorn their warrens. Plains viscachas appear to be extremely tolerant of other animals, for they share their warrens with burrowing owls, lizards, and snakes. In the evening they come out to feed upon grass, roots, and stems.

Parturition generally takes place in September after a gestation period of slightly less than five months. Two young are usually produced in the single litter per year.

Chiefly because of their heavy consumption of grass and their extensive burrowing, the viscachas have been regarded as a serious pest. Since 1907, intensive efforts have been made to exterminate them.

Mountain Viscachas (*Lagidium viscaccia*), photo by Ernest P. Walker. Insets: Hand and foot, photos from *Proc. Zool. Soc. London.*

MOUNTAIN VISCACHAS, PERUVIAN HARES, LAGID-
IUMS; BISCACHAS, CHINCHILLONES (South American names).

THIS GENUS of four species inhabits Peru, Bolivia, Chile, Argentina, and Patagonia to about latitude 52 degrees S. These rodents frequent dry, rocky, rugged, mountainous country where the vegetation is very sparse. Almost invariably they live near streams, at an elevation of 900 to 5,000 meters.

The length of the head and body is 318 to about 400 mm.; the length of the tail is 230 to 320 mm.; and the weight of adults is from 900 to 1,600 grams. The pelage is thick and soft except on the upper part of the tail where it is coarse. The coloration is variable; the upper parts range from creamy buff to dark gray, and the under parts are usually whitish, yellowish, or light gray. There may be inguinal patches of white and some forms have a black mid-dorsal stripe. The tip of the tail is black to reddish brown.

Mountain viscachas look like long-tailed rabbits. They have large ears, narrow hind feet, and four digits armed with blunt, weak claws on each hand and foot. There are two mammae.

These animals are diurnal and gregarious. They emerge from their retreats at sunrise to perch on a boulder or cliff where they spend most of the day dressing their fur and sunning themselves. Depending upon the food supply, colonies range in size from a few individuals to about 80; there are no records of single individuals being found. Members of the genus *Lagidium* shelter in deep rocky crevices, narrow stony tunnels, or burrows among boulders. They are poor diggers and no other animals in the same habitat leave burrows suitable for use by mountain viscachas. They run and leap among the rocks with confidence and agility. In the evening they forage until after sunset but return to their shelters before dark. Viscachas feed upon any plant growing near their colonies such as grasses, moss, and lichens.

Mating occurs in October and November. After a gestation period of about three months, usually a single young is born. There may be two or three litters per year. Males become sexually mature in seven months.

The hair of viscachas is mixed with wool and spun into yarn by natives, although the pelts do not wear well. The animals are hunted for food. They are easily killed and could soon become extinct in spite of their remote habitat.

The type species of the genus is *L. pervanum*, Meyen.

Chinchilla (*Chinchilla laniger*), the well-formed feces are clearly shown, photo by Ernest P. Walker. Undersurfaces of right front and right hind foot, photos from *Proc. Zool. Soc. London.*

THE SINGLE SPECIES, *C. laniger*, lives in rocky, relatively barren areas in the Andes Mountains of Chile and Bolivia from 3,000 to 6,000 meters elevation.

The length of the head and body is 225 to 380 mm., the length of the tail is 75 to 150 mm.; and the weight of adults is 500 grams to 1 kg. The silky pelage is exceedingly dense and soft. The general coloration of the upper parts is bluish, pearl, or brownish gray, with faint dusky or blackish markings; the under parts are yellowish white. The coarse, well-haired tail is heavily marked with black or brownish. The white or black mustache whiskers are quite long and bristly.

These animals have large, black eyes, large ears, and a wide head. The short fore feet have four main digits, and the long narrow hind feet have three main digits. The claws are weak. There are vestigial cheek pouches.

Chinchillas live in colonies and seek shelter in crevices and holes among the rocks. Before they were depleted, as many as 100 individuals were frequently observed together. While feeding, they sit on their haunches and hold the food in their hands. Chinchillas feed on almost any vegetation that is available at such barren, rocky heights. Although there is little water in these arid lands, they get sufficient moisture from small herbs that store dew.

Members of this genus are monogamous, that is, they mate for life. One to three litters consisting of one to six young are born after a gestation period of about 112 days. During courtship, the female is the aggressor. The young run about within a few hours, eat solid food within a few days, and become sexually mature in five to eight months. The life span is probably about 10 years; captive animals, however, have lived nearly 20 years.

The present distribution of chinchillas may be due to heavy destruction by the predatory South American Canidae at the lower elevations. In the high elevations of the Andes, chinchillas grew their warm fur coat, which, in turn, led to further slaughter, this time by man who sought the valuable skins. Chinchilla pelts were once in such demand that in a single year Chile exported over 200,000 skins. Coats made of wild chinchillas have sold for as much as $100,000. This animal was nearly exterminated as a result, but it is now increasing in numbers as a result of protection by the Chilean government.

The development of fur farms throughout the world has also tended to lower the price of chinchilla pelts, although they remain the most valuable, considering their size and weight.

Hutias and Coypus or Nutrias.

Eight genera are included in this family. Several of these genera contain both recently exterminated and living species. Three genera (*Hexolobodon, Isolobodon,* and *Aphaetreus*) are extinct. *Procapromys,* Chapman, 1901, for the species *P. geayi* from Venezuela, is herein not considered to be a valid genus, for this name is based on a single specimen and most likely represents a young *Capromys pilorides.* Although all the other genera of hutias are known only from the West Indies, they were originally transported by man to the islands. The single genus of coypus, *Myocastor,* is native to central and southern South America, but as a result of liberations and escapes from fur farms it now occurs in the wild in parts of the United States and Europe. Hutias live in forests and plantations, whereas the aquatic coypus inhabit marshes, lakes, and sluggish streams. In the Chonos Archipelago of Chile coypus occur in brackish and salt water. Some authors refer *Myocastor* to a separate family, Myocastoridae, and others consider this genus to be the sole representative of a subfamily of *Echimyinae.* The living genera are: *Capromys, Geocapromys, Plagiodontia,* and *Myocastor.*

Hutias and coypus have a robust body form and range in size from that of a guinea pig to that of a small dog. The length of the head and body is 200 to 635 mm., and the length of the tail is 35 to 425 mm. Adults weigh up to 9 kg. In *Myocastor* the body form is modified for an aquatic life, whereas in the hutias it is adapted to terrestrial habits. The head is somewhat triangular shaped in the coypus but is broad in the hutias. The eyes and ears are small in all the genera. The tail of a coypu is scaly, round, thinly haired and 255 to 425 mm. long; in a hutia it is more fully haired basally and shorter. The tail of *C. pilorides* is as long as that of the coypu (*Myocastor*) and slightly shorter than that of *C. prehensilis.* The limbs in all the genera are short. The foot of a coypu, which is much larger than its hand, has four webbed toes connected by skin, but the fifth toe is free and is possibly used in combing the fur. The first digit of the hand is reduced in all the genera. Hutias and coypus have prominent claws. The pelage is harsh in hutias but is soft and thick in coypus, which are called nutrias in the fur trade. Female *Myocastor* have six pairs of mammae situated well up on the side so that the young can nurse even when the mothers are in the water. Female hutias have two pairs of mammae.

The dental formula is as follows: i 1/1, c 0/0, pm 1/1, m 3/3 x 2 = 20. The incisors are narrow in hutias, and broad and strong in coypus. In *Myocastor* the cheek teeth decrease in size as they converge anteriorly. The extremely high-crowned upper molars are not rootless in coypus, whereas in the hutias they grow continuously and are not so high crowned.

The members of the genus *Capromys* seem to be diurnal, but hutias of the genus *Geocapromys* are chiefly nocturnal. The diet of hutias consists of different kinds of plant material and small animals such as lizards (*Anolis*), but coypus feed mainly on aquatic vegetation and shellfish. The members of the genus *Myocastor* make paths through the grass and wander about within a radius of approximately 180 meters.

Hutias of the genus *Capromys* generally give birth to litters of 1 to 3 offspring after a gestation period of 17 to 18 weeks. The young are well developed at birth, their eyes are open, they are fully haired and are capable of a variety of movements. Coypus can have litters of 9 young; the gestation period in this genus is 120 to 150 days. One to 3, generally 2, litters are born each year. Nutrias have a 24 to 29 day estrous cycle and are in estrous for 2 to 4 days. Their youngsters are weaned in 7 to 8 weeks and are mature in 3 to 8 months.

Nutrias have become pests in some of the areas where they have escaped from fur farms or where they have been released deliberately as a potential furbearer in the wild or to clear aquatic vegetation.

The decline in hutias seems to be due to trapping by man, predation by the introduced mongoose (*Herpestes*), and the shrinkage of their forest habitat as man has encroached on their homesites or removed the trees.

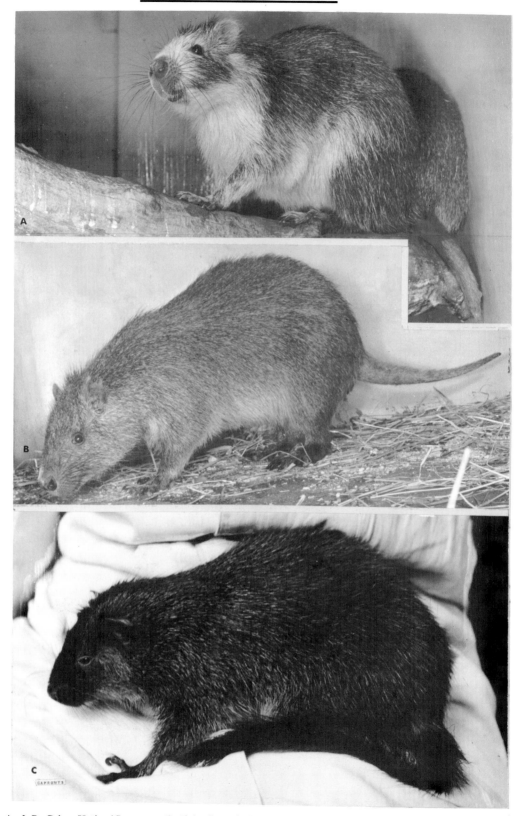

A. & B. Cuban Hutias (*Capromys pilorides*), photos by Ernest P. Walker. C. (*C. [Mysateles] melanurus*), photo by Erna Mohr.

CUBAN HUTIAS; HUTIAS, JUTIAS.

Capromys is made up of four species. *C. nana*, *C. melanurus*, and *C. prehensilis* inhabit Cuba; the latter species also occurs on the Isle of Pines (Isla de Pinos) along with *C. pilorides*. *C. nana* was described in 1917 from bones found in a cave; since that time, however, live specimens have been captured. Members of this genus live in forested areas.

The length of the head and body is about 300 to 500 mm.; the length of the tail is 150 to 300 mm.; and the weight of adults is 4 to 7 kg. The furry pelage consists of long, coarse guard hairs and moderately dense, softer underfur. Coloration is quite variable. The upper parts range from pale buffy, grayish, brownish or reddish to almost black. The under parts are usually lighter. The unicolored tail is buffy to dark reddish brown.

These animals look like large rats. The tail is prehensile, at least in *C. prehensilis*. Cuban hutias have broad feet with prominent claws. The stomach has two constrictions that divide it into three compartments, one of the most complex stomachs in rodents.

These animals live together in pairs until the male is driven off by a stronger male. Members of this genus are diurnal. They sun themselves during the morning on leafy boughs of tall trees, curling up in such a way that from the ground they appear as clumps of foliage. One source indicates that they seek refuge in holes in the ground. Cuban hutias feed on fruit, leaves, bark lizards, and small animals. The sounds they make are a chattering of the teeth and a shrill whistling, scolding, or alarmed note.

Apparently one to three young constitute a usual litter, and the gestation period is 17 to 18 weeks. The youngsters are active at birth and have a reddish pelage which soon becomes light grayish. They begin to take solid food in about 10 days. The female cycle is about 28 days.

The flesh of *Capromys* is relished by Cubans. The natives usually hunt with the aid of a dog, which scents the hutias and holds them at bay in the top of a tree. Hutias have been kept satisfactorily as pets.

The type species of the genus is *C. pilorides* (Say).

Bahama Island Hutia (*Geocapromys ingrahami*), photo by Garrett C. Clough.

BAHAMAN AND JAMAICAN HUTIAS.

THIS GENUS comprises three living species, *G. brownii*, which inhabits Jamaica; *G. thoracatus* from Swan Island in the Gulf of Honduras; and *G. ingrahami* from Plana Cays, Bahama Islands. *G. columbianus* is identified from subfossil fragments from Cuba. The range of *G. brownii* has been so reduced that at the present time these animals survive only in the most inaccessible areas in rugged and rocky regions. In Jamaica they are the only survivors of the indigenous mammals, with the exception of bats.

Jamaican hutias are about the size of a cottontail rabbit but are more stoutly built and have short legs and a short tail. The length of the head and body of *G. brownii* is 330 to 455 mm., and the length of the tail is 35 to 57 mm. The short, dense pelage is yellowish gray, dark brown, or blackish on the upper parts and buffy gray or dusky brown on the under parts. These animals are similar to *Capromys* but are distinguished externally from that genus by their shorter tails and less prominent claws. The short, rounded ears are covered with minute hairs.

Garrett C. Clough studied *G. ingrahami* on East Plana Cay, Bahama Islands, for four days in the spring of 1966. He tells us that these hutias are almost entirely nocturnal. Their food consists of leaves, bark, and complete small twigs of wood shrubs. They are extremely facile climbers and can maneuver well on trunks and larger branches, descending in a head-first fashion. Their homes are apparently under rocks or in the thick base of a bush. Clough estimates their population on East Plana Cay to be between eighteen and twenty-eight individuals.

Doubtlessly quite common at one time, *G. brownii* was an important food for the aborigines, for its bones were often found in the ashes of their camp sites. Because of their extreme scarcity today, however, little has been recorded concerning their life habits and general biology. It is said that the natives hunt these hutias with small dogs that wiggle into the animal's hole, grab it, and hold it until pulled out backward, still clutching the hutia. Hutias probably are also preyed upon by the Burmese mongoose, which was introduced on Jamaica in 1872. Since 1922 hutias have had full legal protection. The flesh of *G. brownii* is eaten by island inhabitants.

Haitian Hutia (*Plagiodontia hylaeum*), photo from New York Zoological Society.

HISPANIOLAN HUTIAS; JUTIAS.

THIS GENUS was first known from subfossil bone fragments; the type material of the genus is in the Paris Natural History Museum. Two living species and two extinct species have been described. The living forms, *P. aedium* and *P. hylaeum*, inhabit the Dominican Republic and Haiti. Numerous skeletal remains of *P. ipnaeum* have been found in kitchen-midden deposits in the Dominican Republic and Haiti, and *P. spelaeum* is described from fragmentary material found in a cave near St. Michel. Anderson (*Proc. Biol. Soc. Washington*, 78: 95–98, 1965) considers the living forms, *P. aedium* and *P. hylaeum*, to be only subspecifically distinct.

The length of the head and body of *P. aedium* is about 312 mm., and the length of the tail is about 153 mm. In *P. hylaeum* the length of the head and body is 348 to 405 mm., and the length of the tail is 125 to 145 mm. Judging from the skeletal remains, *P. spelaeum* appears to be the smallest species and *P. ipnaeum* the largest species in the genus. The short, dense pelage is brownish or grayish on the upper parts and buffy on the under parts. The tail is prac-

tically naked and scaly. There are five claws on each hand and foot, although that of the thumb is a short, blunt nail.

It appears that these hutias are active at night and hide during the day. They probably eat roots and fruits. Very little has been published on this genus. W. L. Abbott, (in G. S. Miller, "The Rodents of the Genus *Plagiodontia*," *Proc. U.S. Natl. Mus.*, Vol. 72, Art. 16) reports that ". . . an old man, stimulated by an offer of $5 apiece, brought me 11. He caught them with dogs in hollow trees down near a lagoon near the sea shore. Females all pregnant, one fetus at a time. . . . Another brought me two Hutias last night from about three miles west of Jovero. The Hutias must still be abundant in some districts. The Dominicans don't seem to eat them but some dogs hunt them. They can climb to some extent. They are doomed with the coming of the mongoose. Their slow breeding will probably help their extinction."

Another source indicates that the flesh of *Plagiodontia* was eaten by the early Haitians as indicated by the abundance of bones found in kitchen middens.

The type species of the genus is *P. aedium*, Cuvier.

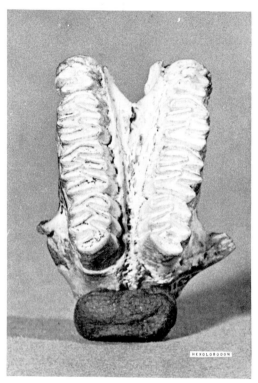

(*Hexolobodon phenax*), upper molar, photo by Howard E. Uible of specimen in U.S. National Museum.

Genus: HEXOLOBODON, Miller, 1929

EXTINCT HISPANIOLAN HUTIAS.

THE SINGLE SPECIES, *H. phenax*, is known from one palate, six mandibles, and four separate cheek teeth collected in 1925 in caves near l'Atalaye and St. Michel in central Haiti.

This extinct rodent resembles *Geocapromys* in dental features and is therefore placed in the family Capromyidae. "The less specialized condition of the roots of the cheek teeth and the extension of the lower incisor root to the outer side of the mandibular tooth row are characters which, like the enamel pattern of the upper teeth, sharply differentiate this genus from its Antillean relatives. . . ." (G. S. Miller, "A Second Collection of Mammals from Caves near St. Michel, Haiti," *Smithsonian Misc. Coll.*, Vol. 81(9), 1929, pp. 19–22). The size of this animal is comparable to *Capromys pilorides*, but with perhaps a shorter rostrum. It apparently was contemporary with the other extinct genera of hutias *Isolobodon* and *Aphaetreus*, and with the still living *Plagiodontia*. Some of the skeletal material is at the U.S. National Museum in Washington, D.C. *Hexolobodon* is believed to have been exterminated soon after white occupation.

Hexolobodon is usually placed by taxonomists between *Capromys* and *Geocapromys*, which it resembles most closely, but it is herein placed after *Plagiodontia* so as to be with the other extinct genera of the family Capromyidae.

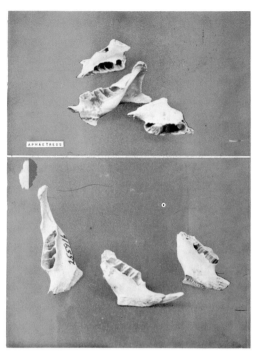

(*Aphaetreus montanus*), photos by P. F. Wright of specimens in U.S. National Museum.

Genus: APHAETREUS, Miller, 1922

MONTANE HUTIAS.

THE SINGLE SPECIES, *A. montanus*, is known only from skeletal remains from the mountains of Haiti, the Dominican Republic, and San Gabriel Island. The type material is at the U.S. National Museum.

The mandible and teeth are similar to those of *Isolobodon* and *Plagiodontia*, and *Aphaetreus* was probably about the size of *Isolobodon*. Since the original description which was based on two jaws, numerous remains of this animal have been found in caves, supposedly brought there by the now extinct giant barn owl (*Tyto ostolaga*). There is no evidence that these hutias were used as food by the aborigines, for no remains have been found in kitchen middens.

Montane hutias were apparently unknown to the early Spanish explorers; it is not known when these animals became extinct.

EXTINCT HUTIAS.

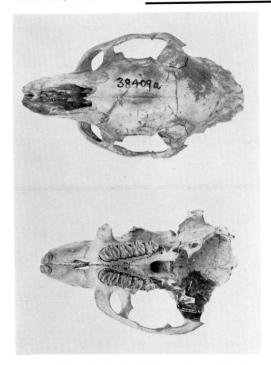

THIS GENUS of extinct hutias is made up of two species, *I. portoricensis*, of Puerto Rico, the Dominican Republic, and the Virgin Islands, and *I. levir*, which inhabited Haiti and the Dominican Republic. Perhaps natives transported *Isolobodon* to some of these islands as a source of food. These animals were about the size of *Plagiodontia*.

Isolobodon apparently became extinct shortly before America was discovered, probably due to excessive hunting by the natives to whom they were an important source of food, as their bones are abundant in kitchen middens and caves. The extinct giant barn owls (*Tyto ostolaga*) also preyed on these animals. They may have been semidomesticated and were perhaps bred in captivity as a source of food for the aborigines.

The remains can be distinguished from those of *Plagiodontia* by differences in the teeth and other characters.

The type material of *I. portoricensis* is in the American Museum of Natural History and that of *I. levir* is in the U.S. National Museum. The type species of the genus is *I. portoricensis*, Allen.

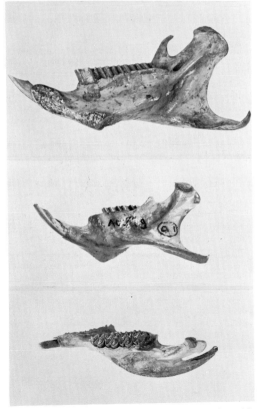

(*Isolobodon portoricensis*), photos from American Museum of Natural History.

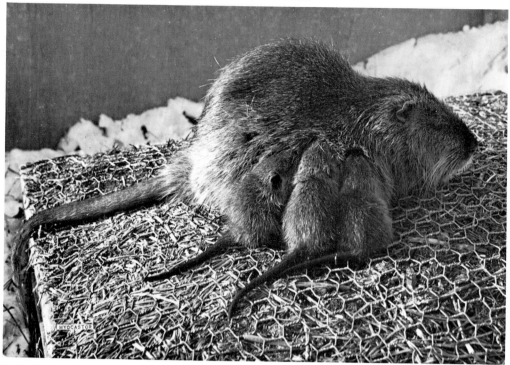

Nutria (*Myocastor coypu*) with nursing young, photo by H. L. Dozier from U.S. Fish and Wildlife Service.

NUTRIAS, COYPUS, SWAMP BEAVERS; QUOULYAS, RATÃO DO BANHADO, COIPUS (local vernaculars).

THE SINGLE LIVING SPECIES, *M. coypu*, is native to central and southern South America. As a result of escapes and liberations from fur farms, nutrias now inhabit many countries of Europe and various locations in the United States. They live in lakes, streams, swamps, and tidal waters. There are four extinct species, all of which are known from fossilized cranial fragments.

The length of the head and body is 430 to 635 mm.; the length of the tail is 255 to 425 mm.; and the weight of adults is 7 to 9 kg. The pelage consists of long, coarse guard hairs which nearly conceal the soft velvety underfur. The general coloration of the upper parts is dark yellowish brown or reddish brown, masking the dark slate underfur. The tip of the muzzle and chin are white.

These animals have the appearance of a large muskrat (*Ondatra*), except that their scaly, scantily haired tail is cylindrical, not laterally compressed. The hind feet are webbed, the incisors are large, and the female has six pairs of mammae. The nipples of the female are located so high on the sides of her body that the young are able to nurse while they ride on her back or while she is lying on her stomach.

Nutrias usually live in burrows in banks along the shore. If suitable locations are not available for burrowing, they may build nests of vegetation on the shore or in shallow water. They are excellent swimmers and spend much of their time in the water. It is said that the young often ride on the back of the mother as she swims. Although primarily vegetarians, nutrias frequently eat mollusks.

One source indicates that mating occurs in September and October, but another report indicates 2 or 3 litters per year. Up to 9 young are born after a gestation period of 120 to 150 days. The young are weaned in 7 to 8 weeks. During the mating season nutrias utter a peculiar moaning cry.

At the beginning of the nineteenth century, the velvety, plush-like underfur of coypus attracted the notice of Europeans; from that time until 1931 the animals steadily decreased in numbers. The Argentine government then began to take measures to prevent their extermination. Nutrias are also hunted for their palatable flesh. These animals thrive well in captivity. In many areas *Myocastor* has now become a pest; its population has increased so greatly that the food supply for other animals has been depleted. It burrows through irrigation ditches and dams and drives other furbearers from their range.

OCTODONT RODENTS.

THIS FAMILY of five genera and eight (?) species occurs in Peru, Bolivia, Argentina, and Chile. Octodonts inhabit coastal regions, foothills, and the Andes to elevations of 3,500 meters or more. These rodents live in both cultivated areas and barren, rocky slopes. The geological range of this family is the middle Oligocene to the Recent in South America, and the Pleistocene in the West Indies.

These stocky or somewhat stout rodents resemble a rat in general form and size. The length of the head and body is 125 to 195 mm., and the length of the tail is 40 to 180 mm. In three genera (*Octodon*, *Octodontomys*, and *Octomys*) the tail is about as long as the head and body; in the other two genera (*Aconaemys* and *Spalacopus*) the tail is much shorter than the combined length of the head and body. The coarse hair of the tail is short at the base, becoming longer toward the tip where it forms a tuft. The fur on the body is usually long, thick, and silky. The head is quite large and the nose is pointed. The moderate-sized ears are rounded and covered with short hair. The whiskers are long. The stiff, bristly hairs on the toes of the hind feet extend beyond the curved, sharp claws. The thumb is reduced. Female octodonts have four pairs of mammae.

The following dental formula applies: i 1/1, c 0/0, pm 1/1, m 3/3 x 2 = 20. The grinding surfaces of the cheek teeth are shaped like a figure eight or sometimes like a kidney.

These rodents are good diggers, especially *Aconaemys* and *Spalacopus*. They dwell in burrow systems of their own construction, in tunnels made by chinchillas, in crevices, or beneath rock piles, fences, and hedgerows. The fairly shallow tunnels of *Aconaemys* are connected by surface runways. Octodonts build nests of plant material in burrows or beneath bushes. *Octodon degus* is reported to be diurnal, but the other members of the family Octodontidae appear to be active mainly at night. These agile rodents carry their tails erect while running and sometimes climb shrubs or trees. They often sit on their haunches.

The diet consists of plant matter, such as bulbs, tubers, bark, and cactus. Occasionally these rodents eat growing cornstalks. *Spalacopus* is reported to hoard bulbs and tubers in its tunnels for winter use, and these stores are often raided by the native people for food.

Female octodonts generally give birth to two litters a year. The offspring are nursed for two months.

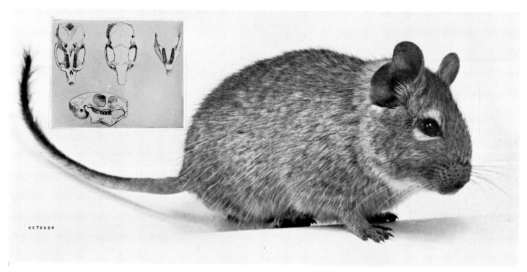

Degu (*Octodon degus*), photo by Luis E. Pena. Inset: Skull of *O. d. cumingii*, photo from *Trans. Zool. Soc. London*.

DEGUS (*O. degus*); CHOZCHORIS.

THE THREE SPECIES are distributed as follows: *O. degus*, in the coastal regions and into the mountains to about 1,200 meters elevation in Peru and Chile; *O. lunatus*, in the coastal hills in Chile west of the central valley; and *O. bridgesi*, at the base of the Andes in Chile, east of the central valley.

The length of the head and body is 125 to 195 mm., and the length of the tail is 105 to 165 mm. Coloration above is grayish to brownish, often with an orange cast, and the under parts are creamy yellow (at least in *O. bridgesi*). The species *O. degus* has a tufted, black-tipped tail; *O. lunatus* and *O. bridgesi* have only slightly tufted tails. In comparison with the other Octodontidae, *Octodon* is not modified in body form for fossorial life, for the tail is about as long as the head and body, the re-entrant folds of the upper molars do not meet in the middle of the teeth, and the cheek teeth are roughly kidney-shaped in the adult. In comparison with *Octodontomys*, *Octodon* has a less bushy tail and the bullae are somewhat smaller.

Osgood (*Mammals of Chile*, 1943, p. 108) refers to *O. degus* as "a diurnal rodent." Small rodent associates of *Octodon* are *Abrocoma, Phyllotis, Akodon,* and *Oryzomys*.

If the animal is caught by the tail and struggles to escape, the skin covering the portion of the tail that is grasped slips off and the animal may escape. After a degu becomes familiar with the person who handles it in captivity, it can be lifted by the tail and the rupture does not occur, perhaps because the animal does not struggle so violently. Only a small amount of blood is lost when the skin slips off. Later the animal cuts the exposed tendons and connective tissue with its incisors and the wound heals; this is facilitated by the thinness of the skin and the direction of certain elements of the connective tissue. The lost section is not replaced.

The type species of the genus is *O. cumingii*, Bennet = *O. degus cumingii* as currently arranged.

Chozchoris (*Octodontomys gliroides*), photo from *Proc. Zool. Soc. London.*

RATAS COLAS DE PINCEL, CHOZCHORIS, ACHACOS, BORIS (South American names).

THE SINGLE SPECIES, *O. gliroides*, is known from the altiplano of Bolivia and the mountains of northern Chile. It has been referred to as a highland representative of *Octodon*. The "rata cola de pincel" has been noted among rocks and cactus, in caves, and in old Indian tombs.

The length of the head and body is about 180 mm., and the length of the tail is about 150 mm. The coloration of the upper parts is drab gray, mixed with black; the under parts are snowy white. The outer sides of the limbs are similar in color to the back, but the inner sides are white. The upper surfaces of the hands and feet are white. With the exception of *Octodon*, the genus *Octodontomys* is structurally distinguishable from the other octodonts in that its external form is not modified for fossorial life, its tail is about as long as the head and body, and the re-entrant folds of the upper molars do not meet in the middle of the teeth. In comparison with *Octodon*, *O. gliroides* has a bushier tail and the bullae are somewhat larger.

This rodent seems to be active mainly at night; its specific habits and biology are not well known.

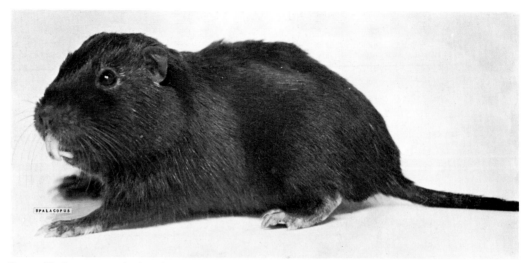

Cururo (*Spalacopus cyanus*), photo by Luis E. Pena.

CORUROS (also spelled CURUROS), CURUCHOS, CUYEITAS (South American names).

THERE ARE TWO SPECIES; *S. cyanus* inhabits the coastal region of Chile and the inland hills and mountains to elevations of about 3,000 meters, and *S. tabanus* inhabits southern Chile.

The length of the head and body is 140 to 160 mm., and the length of the tail is 40 to 50 mm. *S. tabanus* is generally larger than *S. cyanus*. The pelage is soft and glossy. The coloration is brownish black or black throughout, although one specimen was taken which had large, irregular, white pectoral and pelvic patches. The feet are dark gray. Coruros are stocky animals. The tail is cylindrical, scaly, almost hairless, and about as long as the hind foot. The claws are not greatly enlarged, and the ears are small. The reentrant folds of the upper molars do not meet in the middle of the teeth, and the upper incisors are strongly curved forward. "The broad abnormally lengthened upper incisors differentiate this genus clearly from all allies . . ." (J. R. Ellerman, *The Families and Genera of Living Rodents*, [London, 1941], p. 161).

Other than information on its burrowing habits, little data are recorded on this small animal. Bridges (G. R. Waterhouse, *A Natural History of the Mammalia*, Vol. 2 [Paris, 1848] p. 271) stated that *Spalacopus* "generally selects slopes of hills and mountains, where bulbs are found, especially in the interior parts of the country."

It is said that their burrows consist of horizontal tunnels of great length. In these shelters, the coruros deposit bulbs and tubers for use during the winter.

One source indicates that they have two litters per year consisting of numerous young.

The type species of the genus is *S. poeppigi*, Wagler = *S. cyanus* (Molina) as currently arranged.

Rock Rat (*Aconaemys fuscus*), photo from *Natural History of the Mammals*, G. Waterhouse.

ROCK RATS; RATAS RUPRESTES.

THE TWO SPECIES (?) are distributed as follows: *A. fuscus*, on the high slopes of the Andes of south central Chile and the coastal range of Nahuelbuta and the eastern slope of the Andes in Argentina (Valle de las Cuervas near the Chile-Argentina border); and *A. porteri*, known only from one specimen, probably collected in the mountains east of Osorno, Chile.

The length of the head and body is 150 to 185 mm., and the length of the tail is 55 to 75 mm. The coloration in *A. fuscus* is dark brown throughout; *A. porteri* differs from *A. fuscus* by its more woolly pelage and the bicolored tail which is black above and white below. These stocky rodents are modified for fossorial living. The tail is much shorter than the head and body (about as long as the hind foot). The genus *Aconaemys* differs from *Spalacopus* in that the reentrant folds of the upper molars meet in the middle of the teeth, and the upper incisors do not curve forward so markedly.

More than a hundred years ago, Bridges reported that *A. fuscus* was "very common on the eastern side of the Andes, where it completely undermines the face of the country, especially in dry places, making it very disagreeable for the rider, as the horses are continually plunging into the burrows." *A. fuscus* continues to honeycomb the ground with its burrows in certain areas, but: "*Aconaemys* appears to be an ancient type now reduced to a few small colonies and obviously on its way out, like the great trees (*Araucarias*) under which it makes its burrows" (Wilfred H. Osgood, *Mammals of Chile* [Chicago, 1943], p. 113).

Most of the burrows open flush with the ground and have a system of branching tunnels below the surface. The tunnels are fairly shallow. The burrows are also connected by surface runways, which are open or partly concealed by vegetation, located on well-drained ground or near ledges and boulders. Rock rats are active beneath the snow in winter. These rodents are mainly nocturnal, although they are active occasionally during the day.

Newborn young and a pregnant female with two embryos were noted in November.

The type species of the genus is *A. fuscus* (Waterhouse).

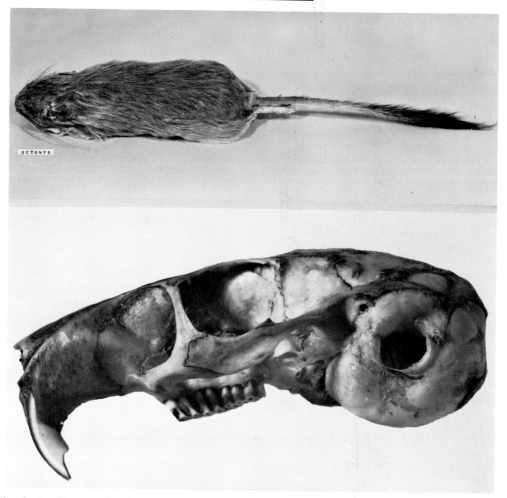

Viscacha Rat (*Octomys mimax*), photos from British Museum (Natural History).

LA RATA VIZCACHA DE LOS ANDES MERIDIONA-LES, VISCACHA RATS.

THE SINGLE SPECIES, *O. mimax*, is known from rocky areas at elevations of about 1,000 to 1,200 meters in Argentina. It appears to be rare and there is no evidence that its scarcity is caused by mankind, but rather that it is naturally uncommon. Specimens are in the British Museum (Natural History).

The length of the head and body is 160 to 170 mm., and the length of the tail is 170 to 180 mm. The upper parts are colored pale buff, and the under parts, including the hands and feet, are white. Externally,

this genus resembles *Octodontomys*, but the re-entrant folds of the upper molars in *Octomys* meet in the middle of the teeth. In *Octomys* the body form is not modified for fossorial life and the bushy tail is about as long as the head and body.

Viscacha rats spend the day sleeping in their burrows. This animal is described as rare and difficult to trap. It appears to be unknown to the native Argentines. The female produces several litters a year. At the present time there is no published material concerning the general biology and life habits of these rodents, other than the articles by Oldfield Thomas in *Annals and Magazine of Natural History*.

Tucu-tuco (*Ctenomys* sp.), photos by Ernest P. Walker.

TUCU-TUCOS, OCULTUCOS, TULDUCOS, ANGUD-YAS, CURUROS, TOCOROS, TOJOS (South American names).

THIS FAMILY contains a single genus of Recent time, *Ctenomys*. Approximately 50 species have been described, but many of these "species" are merely local variants. *Ctenomys* lives between 15 and 55 degrees south latitude, from the Atlantic to the Pacific coasts of South America, i.e., from the altiplano of southern Peru to Tierra del Fuego. Tropical to subarctic regions are inhabited; the favored areas include coastal regions, prairies and steppes, plains, forests, and the altiplano. The main requirement for the presence of *Ctenomys* seems to be a sandy, somewhat dry soil, although cultivated areas are usually avoided. This family of burrowing rodents contains one species (*C. lewisi*) that tunnels in stream banks and may be semiaquatic. Ctenomyid rodents are believed to be fossorial descendants of the octodont rodents (Octodontidae). The geological range of Ctenomyidae is from the Pliocene to the Recent in South America.

In outward appearance, these South American burrowing rodents strongly resemble the North American pocket gophers (Geomyidae) and their habits are similar; the most noticeable difference is the absence of external cheek pouches in the Ctenomyidae. Pocket gophers have better developed fringes of hair on the fore feet than do tucu-tucos; *Ctenomys* has larger fringes on the hind feet than do the pocket gophers. Also, pocket gophers lack the bristles arising near the bases of the claws of the hind feet in tucu-tucos; the presence of these combs (used to remove dirt from the fur) is reflected in the generic name *Ctenomys*. Otherwise, these two families of burrowing rodents (Ctenomydiae and Geomyidae) are very similar in external appearance, both groups, in turn, resembling other fossorial mammals in general body form. Tucu-tucos have a robust cylindrical body with a large head, flattened snout, short muscular neck and limbs, and a short, rounded tail. The eyes are small and the external ears are reduced. The

forelimbs are somewhat shorter than the hind limbs, and all the digits have strong claws for digging. The skin on the body is loose, and the pelage ranges from short to long and from dense to soft. The length of the head and body is 170 to 250 mm., and the length of the tail is 60 to 110 mm. Adult *Ctenomys* weigh from 200 to 700 grams. The coloration is dark brown, pale brown, grayish buff, or creamy buff. Female tucu-tucos, at least in *C. opimus* and *C. peruanus*, have three pairs of mammae.

The following dental formula holds: i 1/1, c 0/0, pm 1/1, m 3/3 x 2 = 20. The upper incisors are strongly developed. The crown pattern of the molars is kidney-shaped, and the last molar is reduced.

The common name "tucu-tuco" is an attempt to express in words the calls that some species emit when sighting an enemy or when a potential predator walks over its burrow system. These calls, which actually sound more like "tloc-tloc-tloc" than "tucu-tucu-tucu," seem to come bubbling up out of the ground, a single vocalization generally lasting from 10 to 20 seconds.

Tucu-tucos seem to be most active early in the morning and late in the afternoon and evening. Although pocket gophers remove most of the earth excavated from their tunnels by pushing with their head, chest, and fore feet, tucu-tucos sweep out the loosened dirt with their hind feet. The different digging techniques of these two groups are based, at least in part, on the difference in fringing of the hands and feet. It is not known if *Ctenomys* uses its incisors in digging, as do the Geomyidae. The entrances to the burrows of tucu-tucos are marked by heaps of excavated soil, and the openings to the burrows may be plugged or left open. The main tunnel, which follows a sinuous course, may have several short, blind tunnels branching away from it, but long secondary tunnels apparently are not common. The tunnels are fairly shallow, that is, they are located about .3 meter below the surface, with the grass-lined nest chamber being situated some distance below the bottom of the tunnel. The burrow systems also include chambers for food storage, but special side chambers do not seem to be constructed for sealing off excrement.

Tucu-tucos seldom venture more than a meter from the burrow entrance, and these short forays usually take place on sunny days. The position of the eyes—almost level with the top of the head—enables a tucu-tuco to look out of its shelter without appreciably exposing itself. Tucu-tucos probably have better vision than do pocket gophers; two species of *Ctenomys*, *C. peruanus* and *C. opimus*, can distinguish a moving human being at a distance of about 50 meters.

Population densities as high as 17 animals per acre have been recorded, but a single tucu-tuco per acre is more common in favorable habitat. Both sexes are usually the sole occupants of their burrow systems, although in at least one species (*C. peruanus*) several adult females will live in the same warren. Other animals, such as guinea pigs (*Cavia*) and lizards and possibly mice, share occupied tucu-tuco burrows.

Tucu-tucos feed on roots, tubers, and stems; they store food in their burrows. Not all of the stored food is utilized, however, but the unused plant materials decay and enrich the soil. *Ctenomys* apparently does not require free water. In parts of southern Peru the species *C. opimus* denudes the hillsides of the spiny grass (*Festuca orthophylla*). When tucu-tucos leave the area, other grasses grow and mice and lizards frequent the vacated burrows. Vicuñas (*Vicugna*) sometimes use the stripped areas for dusting themselves.

There is usually one litter a year of one to five off-spring. The gestation period in *Ctenomys torquatus* is 103 to 107 days. In Uruguay the mating season in this species extends from July to October (the wet or winter season in the Southern Hemisphere). Tucu-tucos, in southern Peru, mate at the end of the dry season and give birth shortly before and during the wet season, when plant growth is most abundant. The offspring are well developed at birth. In *C. peruanus* they are able to give the adult call, leave the nest, and feed on green vegetation almost immediately. Tucu-tucos are capable of breeding before they are a year old. The average life span in the wild seems to be less than three years. Their natural enemies include *Dusicyon culpaeus*, *Felis pajeros*, *Conepatus rex*, and hawks (*Buteo*).

Tucu-tucos are now greatly reduced in numbers or absent from some areas where they were formerly abundant, for example, in most of southern Patagonia east of the Andes, an area which is now largely fenced and devoted to sheep raising. Horseback riding in country frequented by tucu-tucos is sometimes dangerous, as the burrows cave in and cause the horses to break their legs.

These rodents can be maintained in captivity in sand cages placed in a sunny room with temperatures of 18 to 25 degrees C. A piece of wood, on which these animals can gnaw, should be provided. It is possible to maintain tucu-tucos for some time, but their mortality rate is often high, presumably from skin infections. *Ctenomys torquatus* is regarded as a suitable animal for physiological research.

The type species of the genus is *C. brasiliensis*, Blainville.

Chinchilla Rat (*Abrocoma bennetti*), photo by Ernest P. Walker.

CHINCHILLA RATS, CHINCHILLONES.

THIS FAMILY contains a single Recent genus, *Abrocoma*, with two living species. *A. cinerea* is known only from the altiplano of southern Peru, southwestern Bolivia, northeastern Chile, and northwestern Argentina at elevations of 3,700 to 5,000 meters; and *A. bennetti* is known from the Andes and coastal hills of Chile to elevations of approximately 1,200 meters. *A. cinerea* generally occurs in rocky areas, and *A. bennetti* has been taken in thickets. An extinct species of this genus, *A. oblativa*, has been recovered from burial sites in Peru. The geological range of this family in South America is from the upper Miocene to the Recent.

These rodents have long, soft, dense underfur, and fine, long guard hairs, resembling the pelage of *Chinchilla* but not so woolly. Their head and ears are proportionately longer than those in chinchillas, giving *Abrocoma* the appearance of rats and their common name, "chinchilla rats." The head and eyes are large, the nose is pointed, and the ears are large and rounded (disk-like in life). The cylindrical tail is shorter than the head and body and is covered with fine, short hairs. The limbs are short. The fore foot has four digits and the hind foot has five digits; the soles of the feet are naked and covered with small tubercles. The small, weak claws are hollow on the underside. Stiff hairs project over the claws of the three middle toes of the hind foot (as in the families Chinchillidae, Octodontidae, and Ctenomyidae), forming combs which are probably used to remove parasites and groom the pelage, or perhaps to aid in removing dirt loosened by digging. In *A. cinerea* the length of the head and body is 150 to 201 mm.; the length of the tail is 59 to 144 mm.; and the length of the hind foot is usually somewhat less than 31 mm. In this species the upper parts are silver-gray and the under parts are whitish or yellowish. *A. bennetti* is somewhat larger; the length of the head and body is 195 to 250 mm., the tail, 130 to 180 mm., and the length of

the hind foot, 31 to 38 mm. This species has brownish gray upper parts and brownish under parts. Chinchilla rats may have a whitish or yellowish area on the chest, marking a glandular region.

Female *Abrocoma* have four mammae. *A. bennetti* has more ribs than any other rodent, 17 pairs. The intestinal tract of chinchilla rats is long; the small intestine measures 1.5 meters and the large intestine, 1 meter. The voluminous caecum is 205 mm. in length.

The dental formula in the family Abrocomidae is as follows: i 1/1, c 0/0, pm 1/1, m 3/3 x 2 = 20. The incisors are narrow, and the cheek teeth continue to grow throughout life, the lowers having a different pattern of enamel folding than the uppers. The rostrum is long and narrow, and the braincap is rounded.

Chinchillones live in tunnels in the ground and among the crevices of rocks; the entrances to their tunnels usually are located at the base of a bush or under rocks. *Abrocoma* seems to be colonial; about half a dozen *A. cinerea* were noted living within 18 meters of each other. Chinchilla rats are said to be shy and rare, although the supposed rarity may be because their habitat is quite inaccessible. *A. bennetti* is reported to climb bushes and trees. A female of the species *A. cinerea*, caught in a trap by a fore leg, emitted a faint bubbling sound similar to that made by tucu-tucos (*Ctenomys*). Chinchilla rats eat many kinds of plant material.

The following records are for *A. cinerea*: A pregnant female, bearing two embryos, was taken in December in Peru, and a mother *Abrocoma*, accompanied by two youngsters about a week old, was obtained in April in northern Chile.

In some areas the natives sell the pelts of these animals to gullible travelers as chinchilla. In parts of Chile the skins are taken to the local fur markets, but they do not bring high prices.

The type species of the genus is *A. bennetti*, Waterhouse.

SPINY RATS.

IN THE FAMILY Echimyidae, 19 genera and about 75 species are recorded from the Recent. Four of the genera are extinct and are known from Cuba, the Isle of Pines, Hispaniola, and Puerto Rico. The living genera occur in Central America from Nicaragua southward; in South America south to Peru, Bolivia, Paraguay, and southeastern Brazil; and from Trinidad. The species Echimys armatus lives on the island of Martinique in the Lesser Antilles, apparently brought there by man. Spiny rats inhabit forests or clearings, often near water. The geological range of this family is the late Oligocene to the Miocene, and the Pleistocene to the Recent in South America, and from the Pleistocene to the Recent in Central America and the West Indies.

Echimyid rodents are rat-like in general appearance, with pointed or somewhat truncated noses and moderately sized eyes and ears. The ears are rounded or bluntly pointed and extend beyond the pelage. All the living genera, with five exceptions (Cercomys, Dactylomys, Lachnomys, Kannabateomys, and Thrinacodus), have a spiny or bristly pelage, consisting of flattened, stiff, sharp-pointed hairs attached to the flesh by narrow basal stalks. The length of the head and body is 80 to 480 mm., and that of the tail is 45 to 430 mm. The tail ranges from less than one-third to more than the combined length of the head and body, and it varies from well haired to scantily haired. The first digit of the fore foot is vestigial, and the other digits are short or elongate and somewhat united. Female Echimys have three pairs of mammae.

The dental formula is as follows: i 1/1, c 0/0, pm 1/1, m 3/3 x 2 = 20. The flat-crowned cheek teeth are rooted.

The members of the family Echimyidae are often common and are the most abundant mammals in areas of the range, but most of the genera are little known. Spiny rats may dig their own burrows or seek shelter beneath stumps, logs, or rocks. Several genera live in the hollows of trees, and members of the genus Proëchimys sometimes occupy the homes of natives. Sometimes these rodents live in small groups. One genus (Cercomys) has been noted in captivity leaping on its hind limbs, but another genus (Euryzygomatomys) apparently is fossorial. The other genera are climbing or scampering terrestrial forms. Echimyid rodents are reported to be good swimmers. They are usually active in the evening and during the night; one genus (Diplomys) is diurnal, at least in some areas. Most spiny rats die when exposed to heat and dryness. Various scolding sounds have been noted, but these animals are generally peaceful, at least in captivity. If handled carefully they do not attempt to bite, and when a number of Echimys are kept in one cage, they usually do not fight among themselves. The herbivorous diet includes grass, sugar cane, bananas, fruit, and nuts. Echimyids consume large amounts of water.

These rodents often lose their tails because these appendages fracture easily. This may help the animal to escape from a predator when seized by the tail.

Gestation periods have not been recorded. A female Echimys usually gives birth to two litters a year, the litter size ranging from one to six (usually one to three). The offspring are well furred at birth, and their eyelids are formed. Within a few hours they are active and nimble and can emit soft whistling sounds. The young begin to eat solid food in about 11 days and leave the mother in about two months. Proëchimys has lived for 38 months in captivity.

The native people relish the flesh of a number of genera; it is considered a delicacy.

HETEROPSOMYS, Anthony, 1916

THIS GENUS consists of a single extinct species, *H. insulans*, known only from the fragments of two skulls and a single mandible, all of which were found near Utuado, Puerto Rico.

The skull is somewhat smaller than *Dasyprocta*, having a total length of about 70 mm. The long upper incisors are weak. The upper cheek teeth have a single conspicuous internal fold with three separate, transverse, enamel-surrounded lakes.

The type material is in the American Museum of Natural History.

It is possible, however, that the species *antillensis*, placed in the genus *Homopsomys*, should be in *Heteropsomys* instead. The fragments available are not adequate to form a conclusive decision.

HOMOPSOMYS, Anthony, 1917

THIS GENUS of extinct mammals is represented by a single species, *H. antillensis*, which is known only from cranial and dental fragments found in a cave near Utuado, Puerto Rico. These few fragments indi-cate that the skull has a broad, flattened frontal area and bluntly pointed postorbital projections. There are four molars of nearly equal size in each jaw. *Homopsomys* is closely related to *Heteropsomys* but has heavier incisors and a longer palate.

Anthony, who described both genera, suggested in 1918 that better material might conclusively show that *Homopsomys* is merely a slightly larger animal than *Heteropsomys*; thus it is possible that the species *H. antillensis* belongs in the latter genus. Both of the species appear to have survived until relatively recent times.

The type material is in the American Museum of Natural History.

BROTOMYS, Miller, 1916

HISPANIOLAN SPINY RATS, MOHUYS.

THIS GENUS of extinct mammals is composed of two species that inhabited the island of Haiti. *B. voratus* is known from numerous skulls and mandibles

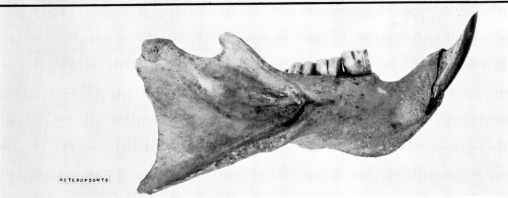

(*Heteropsomys insulans*), photos from American Museum of Natural History.

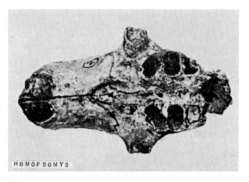

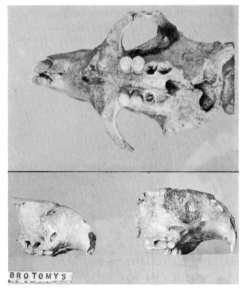

(*Homopsomys antillensis*), photo from *Bull. Amer. Mus. Nat. Hist.*, "New Fossil Rodents from Porto Rico," H. E. Anthony.

(*Brotomys voratus*, above, and *B. contractus*, below), photos from American Museum of Natural History.

(*Boromys offella*), photo from American Museum of Natural History.

found in caves and aborigine kitchen middens; and *B. contractus* is known from only a single palate found in a small cave near St. Michel, Haiti.

Brotomys was about the size of *Proechimys*, but had a heavier and less elongated head. The teeth were weak. Due to the frequency with which G. S. Miller found *B. voratus* bones in Indian deposits, it appears that this animal was abundant and widely distributed throughout the island in pre-Columbian time and was probably used for food by the natives. The animals were probably exterminated shortly after the island became inhabited by Europeans. Extermination, however, was possibly the result of other factors, such as the introduction of predatory animals and diseases.

The type material is in the U.S. National Museum. The type species of the genus is *B. voratus*, Miller.

BOROMYS, Miller, 1916

EXTINCT CUBAN SPINY RATS.

THIS GENUS of extinct mammals is represented by two species, *B. offella* and *B. torrei*. *B. offella* is the larger of the two species, and the bones were first discovered in excavations of an old native village site at Maisi, Baracoa, Cuba; thus this animal was probably used for food by the natives. *B. torrei* is abundantly represented in cave deposits in Cuba and the Isle of Pines. Since *B. torrei* has not been found in kitchen middens, it apparently was considered too small for a food animal.

The members of this genus closely resemble those of *Brotomys* but differ from that genus in having a swelling on the bone over the end of the root of the upper incisors, and there is a channel for the passage of the fifth nerve on the floor of the antorbital foramen. There are four cheek teeth in each tooth row. The incisors are orange-yellow.

The type material of *B. offella* is in the U.S. National Museum, and that of *B. torrei* is in the Museum of Comparative Zoology, Cambridge, Massachusetts. The type species of the genus is *B. offella*, Miller.

1052

Spiny Rat (*Proechimys setosus*), photo by Joao Moojen.

SPINY RATS; MACANGUES, SOIAS, CURAREQUE, CASIRAGUA, TUPÓNKA (Central and South American names).

ABOUT 20 SPECIES of *Proechimys* inhabit Central America, northern and central South America, and the island of Trinidad, from about latitude 12 degrees N. to latitude 22 degrees S. *Proechimys* frequents coastal areas and lives near water in the forested foothills. *P. trinitatis* extends its range to 1,200 meters altitude along coffee plantations but does not occur in the primary forests at the same elevation.

The length of the head and body is 160 to 300 mm., and the length of the tail is 120 to 320 mm. Adult *P. trinitatis* weigh from 300 to 380 grams in Venezuela. The tail is usually shorter than the head and body. The fur is spiny, but not to the same extent as in some other genera of Echimyidae. The general coloration of the upper parts is orangish brown, reddish brown, or light tawny mixed with black; the under parts are usually whitish. The thinly-haired tail is brown above and white below.

Spiny rats, like the common rats, occasionally live in the homes of the natives, but their typical habitats are holes in the ground, beneath tree roots, and among rocks. One or two adults generally occupy a shelter. Spiny rats are nocturnal. Members of the genus *Proechimys* eat many kinds of plant material; in captivity they accept bananas, fresh sweet corn, coconuts, cereals, and other grain mixtures.

The female usually has two litters per year. In parts of South America at least, one litter is born in the early spring and another in late summer. An average litter consists of two or three individuals, but litters have been noted to consist of one to six young. A mature animal lived in captivity for 38 months.

An unusual but quite common feature of the genus *Proechimys* and of other Echimyidae is its tailless condition. The tail of spiny rats fractures readily across the centrum of the fifth tail vertebra. This may have some value in allowing the rodent to escape from a predator when seized by the tail. The animal will survive but remains tailless throughout its life.

It is said that the meat of spiny rats is tasty. The susceptibility of *Proechimys* to influenza virus has been demonstrated (John M. Weir, *Jour. Infect. Dis.*, 1944, 74: 121–30).

The type species of the genus is *P. trinitatis* (Allen and Chapman)

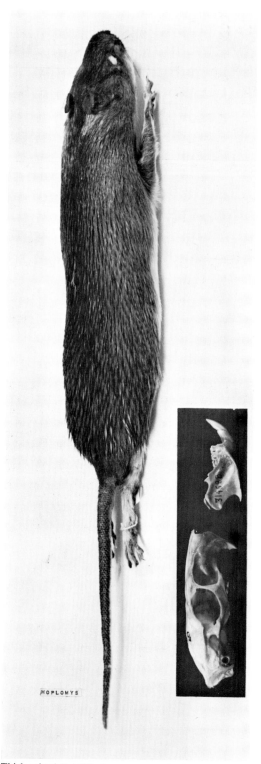

THICK-SPINED RATS, ARMORED RATS.

THE SINGLE SPECIES, *H. gymnurus*, occurs in Central America and South America from Nicaragua south through Costa Rica and Panama to Colombia and Ecuador. Its distribution in South America seems to be limited by the Western Andes. Thick-spined rats have been noted in fairly open rain forests, thickets, and grassy clearings, usually near large decaying logs.

The length of the head and body is 220 to 320 mm., and the length of the tail is about 150 to 250 mm. This genus is characterized externally by the abundance of spines, their development being more extensive than in any other genus of the family Echimyidae. The spines, best developed on the upper mid-back, are up to 33 mm. in greatest length and up to 2 mm. in greatest diameter. They are white basally and colored toward the tip. The spines on the upper parts are tipped with black; those on the sides are usually tipped with orange or banded with orange and black. Beneath the spines are soft hairs, usually orange- or yellow-colored. In one form these soft hairs are blackened to form a distinct stripe along the middle of the back from the snout to the base of the tail. The under parts are whitish; the scantily-haired, scaly tail is usually brownish above and whitish below. The sparsely-haired ears are dark brown to black.

Thick-spined rats are similar to *Proechimys* in body form. The hind feet are long and narrow, and the tail is shorter than the head and body.

Little information has been published on the habits and general biology of this genus. *Hoplomys*, like *Proechimys*, seems to be terrestrial. All the known specimens have been trapped on the ground under fallen trees, sometimes in rocky areas, and along river banks. As in most members of this family, the tail breaks easily.

Thick-spined Rat (*Hoplomys gymnurus*), photos by P. F. Wright of specimen in U.S. National Museum.

Guira (*Euryzygomatomys spinosus*), photo by Ernest P. Walker.

GUIRAS OR GUIARAS.

TWO SPECIES (?) are distributed as follows: *E. spinosus* in Brazil and Paraguay, and *E. guiara* in Brazil. "The range of the genus probably is throughout the pampa country of Paraguay, northern Corrientes, Parana, Santa Catharina, and Rio Grande do Sul, possibly in sandy areas" (G. H. H. Tate, *Bull. Amer. Mus. Nat. Hist.*, 1935:405). In Brazil it is known from the states of Minas Gerais, Espirito Santo, Rio de Janeiro, Guanabara, São Paulo, Santa Catharina, and probably Rio Grande do Sul. Guiras live in areas covered with grass, raspberry, and bushes.

The length of the head and body is 170 to 270 mm., and the length of the tail is about 50 to 55 mm. The male may be somewhat larger than the female. The coloration is a drab brown above and whitish below. The hands and feet are brown. As in the other Echimyidae, spines are present on the back.

The well-developed claws and short tail indicate fossorial habits, but specific information on its biology and life history is not known. *E. guiara* prefers grasslands near water. In Coxias, Rio de Janeiro, a female with three embryos was taken in November. In Minas Gerais two pregnant females with one embryo each were taken. Specimens of *Euryzygomatomys* are in the University of São Paulo, Brazil, the American Museum of Natural History, and the British Museum (Natural History).

The type species of the genus is *E. spinosus* (Desmarest).

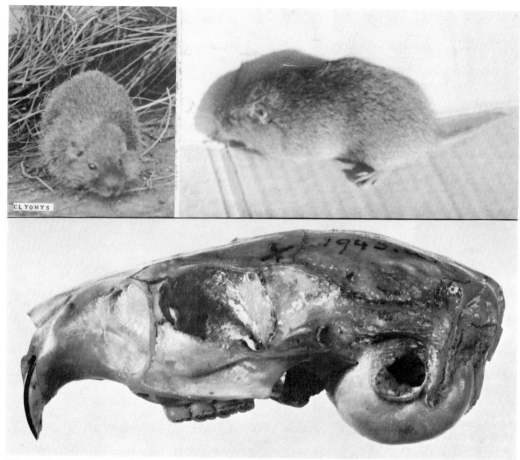

(*Clyomys laticeps*), photos by Joao Moojen. Skull photo from British Museum (Natural History).

THE SINGLE SPECIES, *C. laticeps*, is known from Lagoa Santa, Minas Gerais, Brazil, and from Paraguay. It may inhabit the entire savannah region of the South American central plateau. Two specimens were recently taken by Joao Moojen in Brasilia.

Head and body length is 105 to 200 mm., and tail length is 55 to 80 mm. The coloration above is grayish brown and black, mixed with rufous; the under parts are whitish or buffy. Grayish patches may be present in the throat region and in the middle of the chest and belly. The fur is bristly. *Clyomys* is distinguished from the other spiny rats of the family Echimyidae by the well-developed fossorial claws on the fore feet and the enlarged bullae of the skull.

The burrows of *Clyomys* have been noted in a natural clearing. This spiny rat appears to live in colonies. Moojen describes the nest where he caught his specimens: "The traps that caught both specimens alive were set at the mouth of the most elaborate rodent nest I ever saw. A very regular three-spiral helix wound around a large vertical root. The sloping passageway was 80 mm. wide and 90 mm. high and went down 850 mm. vertically to the main nest that was 250 mm. in diameter. Another nest was midway in the spiral and was only 170 mm. in diameter. The lower nest was covered with scant grassy materials, quite worn and old; the midway nest was clean with a few bits of a meaty sweet root (I tasted it) which I was not able to identify."

The few known specimens are in the study collections at the Rio de Janeiro Museum, the U.S. National Museum, and the British Museum (Natural History).

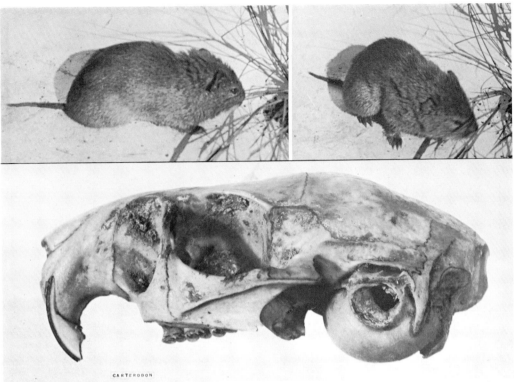

Owls' Rat (*Carterodon sulcidens*), photos by Joao Moojen. Skull photo from British Museum (Natural History).

OWLS' RATS.

THE SINGLE SPECIES, *C. sulcidens*, was described in 1841 from fossil remains collected in Lagoa Santa, Brazil. In 1851 living animals were found on the open pampas in Lagoa Santa. Another specimen, collected by Miranda Ribeiro in Campos Novos, Matto Grosso, is now in the Museu Nacional, Rio de Janeiro, Brazil. Two specimens were recently taken by Joao Moojen in Brasilia. They were a young male with only two upper molariform teeth and a female in puberty, about adult size, with three molariform teeth, the third molar just starting out. These were found in a nest about 200 mm. in diameter filled with dry grass and chewed roots at the end of a tube 800 mm. in length and 70 mm. in diameter. Owls' rats inhabit the large mesa, savannah-like *cerrado* region, about 400 meters above sea level, where there are two definite seasons: one from October to March when it rains about 2,030 mm. each year, and the other when the rain completely stops for about seven months. The vegetation is grass with scattered trees.

The length of the head and body is about 155 to 200 mm., and the length of the tail is about 68 to 80 mm. The upper parts are yellow-brown, shaded with black; the sides are grayish; the lower parts of the neck and throat are reddish; the sides of the belly are yellowish red; and the middle of the belly is white. The well-haired tail is black above and whitish yellow below. The back of *Carterodon* is supplied with bristles and spines; the relatively soft spines end in a hair-like point and are long and flexible. The upper incisors are grooved.

A few notes on habits were submitted more than a century ago by John Reinhardt, who states, "It inhabits the open *Campos*, overgrown with shrubs and trees, where it digs its residence, consisting of a rather long tube 3 to 4 inches [76 to 102 mm.] in diameter, and leading in a slanting direction into a chamber, scarcely beyond a foot [300 mm.] from the surface of the ground, which the animal lines with grass and leaves. The stomach of the two specimens which I examined was entirely filled with a yellow pasty substance, evidently of vegetable origin" ("Description of *Carterodon sulcidens*, Lund," *Ann. and Mag. Nat. Hist.*, 1852, (2)X: 420). The specimens analyzed by Reinhardt, apparently taken in the Southern Hemisphere in late fall or early winter, were an immature male and a pregnant female bearing a 25- to 37-mm. embryo.

Moojen cites Burmeister, who noted that *Carterodon* remains in its underground galleries during the day but emerges in the late afternoon or night, when it is easily captured by owls (*Tyto alba*). For this reason, the species was first known from balls vomited by this owl, particularly inside the caves of the Lagoa Santa area in Minas Gerais, Brazil.

(*Cercomys cunicularius*), photo by Joao Moojen.

Punarés, Rabudos (South American names).

Two species, *C. cunicularius* and *C. inermis*, inhabit eastern and central Brazil and Paraguay. *Cercomys* is common in central Brazil, even in the swampy areas. The usual habitats, however, are rocky and thickly vegetated areas.

The length of the head and body is 200 mm. to 290 mm., and the length of the tail is 180 mm. to 220 mm. The upper parts are dull brown and the under parts are grayish to whitish. This soft-furred, hairy-tailed echimyid rodent shows no signs of developing bristles.

Punarés live in rock crevices and under such vegetation as cactus plants. Their straw-lined nests are built in hollow trees or logs, in stone fences, or under stones. These rodents eat cotton seeds or cotton fruit and during the dry season feed on the tender parts of some cacti or the coconuts of some *Palmaceae*. In captivity, Punarés have been seen to leap only on the hind legs.

Mating may take place in August and September. Pregnant females have been taken in February and July. The number of young ranges from one to four, usually two.

Several specimens are at the National Museum at Rio de Janeiro, Brazil. The type species of the genus is *C. cunicularius*, Cuvier.

(*Mesomys ferrugineus*), photo from *Proc. Zool. Soc. London.*

SIX SPECIES inhabit most of Brazil, except the southern portion, and the Amazonian region from the Tocantins to eastern Peru and Ecuador. The six species are: *M. hispidus, M. ferrugineus, M. leniceps, M. stimulax, M. didelphoides,* and *M. obscurus. Mesomys* has been found at elevations of 90 to 1,950 meters.

The length of the head and body is 150 to 200 mm., and the length of the tail is 120 to 220 mm. The upper parts are various shades of brown; dark-brown and pale buffy bands on the spines of some species produce a speckled effect. The under parts of *Mesomys* are orangish, pale buffy, or whitish. The tail is usually brown throughout and tufted at the tip. The heavily spined fur resembles the pelage of *Hoplomys.* The short, rather broad feet suggest that these rodents are arboreal, but the natural history of *Mesomys* is not well known.

A female *M. hispidus* with a single embryo was taken in March near Rio Madeira, Amazonas, Brazil.

The type species of the genus is *M. ecaudatus,* Wagner = *M. hispidus* (Desmarest) as currently arranged.

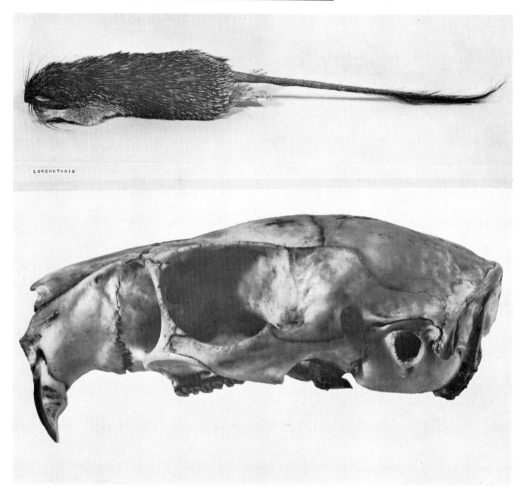

(*Lonchothrix emiliae*), photos from British Museum (Natural History).

RATOS DE ESPINHOS.

THE SINGLE SPECIES, *L. emiliae*, is known from the lower part of the Rio Tapajoz (Villa Braga) and from the Rio Madeira, Brazil; these rodents probably inhabit forests. Specimens are in the British Museum (Natural History), the American Museum of Natural History, and the Departamento de Biología, São Paulo, Brazil.

The length of the head and body is about 200 mm., and the length of the tail is about 190 mm. The colora-tion is dark brown above with buffy spots on the shoulder region. The sides are tawny, and the under parts are light tawny. The furless tail is scaly above and covered with short spines but is tufted at the end with hairs which may be 70 mm. long. The spines on the body are well developed, and and even the belly is somewhat spiny. The broadened hind feet suggest that *Lonchothrix* is arboreal in its habits, but the natural history of this animal has not been found in the literature.

A. Toro (*Isothrix villosus*), photo from "Animaux Nouveaux ou rares recueillis pendant l'Expédition dans les Parties Centrales de l'Amerique du Sud," *Mammifères*, Paul Gervais. B. Toro (*I. pictus*), photo from *Natural History of the Mammalia*, G. R. Waterhouse.

TOROS, CONOCONO PEQUEÑO (South American names).

FIVE SPECIES inhabit parts of Venezuela, Peru, and the western part of Amazonia, Brazil.

The length of the head and body is 220 to 290 mm., and the length of the tail is about 250 mm. The species *I. pictus* has a black or dark-brown and white color pattern; but *I. bistriatus, I. pachyura, I. pagurus,* and *I. villosus* are dull brown, sometimes suffused with an orange hue. The soft fur lacks spines and bristles, and the long bushy tail is almost squirrel-like. The hind feet are of the arboreal type.

Isothrix is said to live in holes about 10 mm. from the bases of large trees along river banks, and, during the afternoon, to sit in the entrance to the hole with only its head exposed. Specimens can be shot at dusk as they come out and sit before the entrance.

A female *I. bistriatus* carrying a single embryo was taken in May near the Cunucunuma River, Amazonia, Brazil.

The type species of the genus is *I. bistriatus,* Wagner.

Arboreal Soft-furred Spiny Rat (*Diplomys caniceps*), photo from *Proc. Zool. Soc. London.*

RATON MARENERO (*D. labilis* of San Miguel Island), ARBOREAL SOFT-FURRED SPINY RATS.

FOUR SPECIES, *D. caniceps*, *D. labilis*, *D. darlingi*, and *D. rufoforsalis*, are known from Panama, San Miguel Island, and from Colombia north and west of the Andes.

The length of the head and body is 250 to 480 mm., and the length of the tail is 200 to 280 mm. The coloration above is rusty brown, reddish, or orangish buffy mixed with black; below, the pelage is buffy, reddish, or reddish white. The harsh fur lacks spines.

The tail is thinly haired, brownish, and slightly tufted with black or white. The feet are of the arboreal type, short and broad with strongly curved claws. In *D. darlingi* the ears are short and conspicuously tufted.

These rodents have been noted climbing on tree trunks and branches and resting in the hollows of trees. *Diplomys* appears to be active during the day, at least in certain areas. Three young male specimens were collected on San Miguel Island in April and May.

The type species of the genus is *D. caniceps* (Günther).

A. Arboreal Spiny Rat (*Echimys lamarum*), photo by Joao Moojen. B. Arboreal White-faced Spiny Rat (*E. chrysurus*), photographer unknown.

SPINY RATS; SAVIÁS, TORÓS, CORÓS, CASIRAGUA (South American names).

SOME 20 SPECIES inhabit northern and central South America. *E. armatus* also occurs on the island of Martinique, apparently introduced there by man.

The length of the head and body is 170 to 350 mm., and the length of the tail is 150 to 300 mm. The upper parts are usually colored some shade of brown or red, such as pale yellowish brown, mixed with black, light brown, dark chestnut brown, buffy brown, golden brown, and rufous and black. The under parts are usually whitish or buffy. The species *E. saturnus* is dark above; the middle of the back is black and is whitish and coppery brown below. Some species have hairy tails, but in others the tails are scaly. In all species the tail is not tufted or bushy. The fur is bristly or spiny. The broad feet with prominent claws are adapted to an arboreal or scansorial life.

Echimys is arboreal and lives in trees on river banks or in flooded areas. The nests are built of dry leaves in hollow tree trunks or holes in trees, where small groups live. Spiny rats remain in their upper holes (usually they have two) during the day and come out on the branches at night. At night they give calls in a loud voice similar to "cró, cró" or "tró, tró," hence their vernacular names.

A female *E. armatus* with one embryo was taken in November. The number of young appears to be usually one, sometimes two.

The type species of the genus is *E. chrysurus* (Zimmermann).

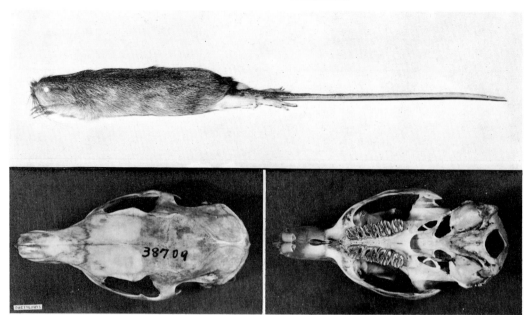

Coro-coro (*Dactylomys* sp.), photos from American Museum of Natural History.

CORO-CORO.

TWO SPECIES, *D. boliviensis* and *D. dactylinus*, are known from Ecuador, Peru, Bolivia, and the Amazonian region.

The length of the head and body is about 300 mm., and the length of the tail is 400 to 430 mm. The upper parts are olivaceous gray or grayish, often with a rusty suffusion, and the under parts are whitish. The soft fur lacks spines or bristles, and the tail is naked except for the well-haired basal part. The third and fourth digits of all four feet are elongated and broadened. It was noted, on internal examination, that the main lobes of the upper cheek teeth are not united by enamel bridges and the palate is constricted anteriorly.

These climbing rodents grasp branches and twigs between their third and fourth digits. They have been found near water living in bamboo bushes. They are active at night and can run swiftly. As is the case with most of the Echimyidae, little is known about habits and natural history.

The type species of the genus is *D. dactylinus* (Desmarest).

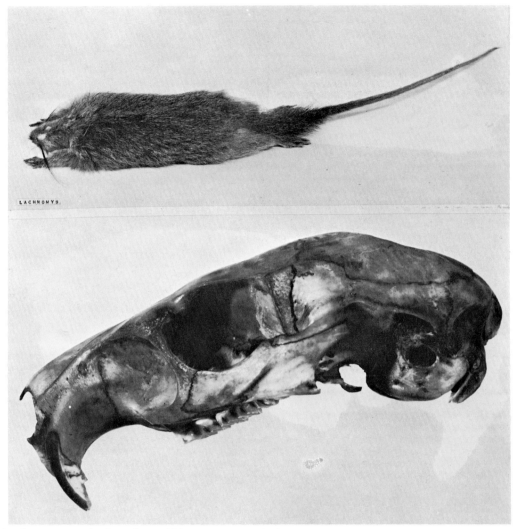

(*Lachnomys peruanus*), photos from British Museum (Natural History).

THE SINGLE SPECIES, *L. peruanus*, inhabits Peru. Some mammalogists include this species in the genus *Dactylomys*. The type specimen came from Juliaca, at an elevation of 1,800 meters, an area described by the collector as "very broken, with deep narrow canyons, and covered with a dense undergrowth of shrubs and vines, with here or there a palmetto or a cedar rising above the surrounding vegetation" (Oldfield Thomas, *Ann. and Mag. Nat. Hist.*, 1916, (8)18: 299).

The length of the head and body is about 250 mm., and the length of the tail is about 320 mm. The following coloration prevails: almost uniformly yellowish brown above, lighter yellowish brown on the sides, and white below. Most of the head and the basal part of the tail are gray. The soft fur lacks spines or bristles. *Lachnomys* resembles *Dactylomys* but differs from that genus in having a thicker pelage and a hairy tail. The tail is bushy on the basal half and more or less tufted at the end. Digits 3 and 4 of all four feet are elongated and broadened; the palate is constricted anteriorly; and the main lobes of the upper cheek teeth are not united by enamel bridges.

This rodent grasps branches between the third and fourth digits and is assumed to be a climbing animal. It has been noted running along a creek, and the stomach of the type specimen was "filled with the inside of a palmetto nut, or some white tender root." Specimens are in the American Museum of Natural History and the British Museum (Natural History).

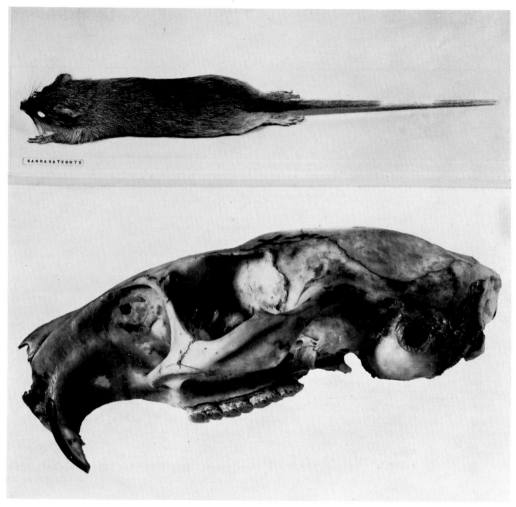

Rato de Taquara (*Kannabateomys amblyonyx pallidior*), photos from British Museum (Natural History).

RATOS DE TAQUARA.

THE SINGLE SPECIES, *K. amblyonyx*, inhabits southeastern Brazil, Paraguay, and Argentina.

The length of the head and body is about 250 mm., and the length of the tail is about 320 mm. The coloration on the upper parts is dull buffy yellowish, sometimes with an orangish cast, and is paler (buffy or whitish) on the under parts. The thick, soft fur lacks spines or bristles, and the tail is haired. The third and fourth digits on all four limbs are elongated and broadened. *Kannabateomys* differs structurally from *Dactylomys* and *Lachnomys* in that the palate is not appreciably constricted, and the main lobes of the upper cheek teeth are united by narrow enamel bridges.

In Brazil this rodent usually lives in bamboo thickets along stream banks. By grasping the bamboo shoots and stalks between its third and fourth digits, it climbs the plants and eats the succulent parts of the bamboo during the night. A pregnant *Kannabateomys* has been noted in November, and the usual number of young per birth appears to be one.

There are specimens in the British Museum (Natural History) and the Departamento de Biologia, São Paulo, Brazil.

(*Thrinacodus albicauda*), photo from *Proc. Zool. Soc. London.*

THREE SPECIES, *T. albicauda*, *T. apolinari*, and *T. edax* inhabit Colombia and Venezuela. Specimens have been collected at 2,000 and 2,800 meters elevation. In the mountains of Colombia, these rats live in thickets of one species of bamboo (*Chusquea*). They emit a whistling cry.

The length of the head and body is 80 to 240 mm., and the length of the tail is 250 to 350 mm. The upper parts are colored reddish brown or yellowish brown, and the under parts are yellowish white or white. A yellow line may occur along the sides. The fur is thick and soft without spines or bristles, and the tail is haired. Digits 3 and 4 of the limbs are elongated and broadened, but not to a marked degree. In *T. edax* the tail is completely white below and on the terminal half of the upper part. In *T. apolinari* there is no white on the upper part of the tail.

Specimens of this little-known rodent are in the American Museum of Natural History and the British Museum (Natural History).

The type species of the genus is *T. albicauda*, Günther.

Cane Rat (*Thryonomys swinderianus*), photo by Ernest P. Walker.

CANE RATS, AFRICAN SPINY RATS, GROUND HOGS;
REITROTTE, REITMUISE, KOKHALI (native names).

THIS FAMILY CONTAINS a single genus, *Thryonomys*,
of the Recent. This genus of six species is widely
distributed in Africa south of the Sahara, southward
to the Cape Province. Cane rats generally inhabit
reedbeds, marshes, swamps, and the borders of lakes
and streams, but occasionally they live among bushes
and rocks on higher ground. *Choeromys* is a synonym
of *Thryonomys*.

These heavy set, rather large rodents have a bristly
pelage. The length of the head and body is about 350
to 610 mm., and the length of the tail is 70 to 250 mm.
Adult cane rats generally weigh from 4 to 7 kg., with
individual animals occasionally attaining weights of
9 kg. The coarse, bristle-like hairs are flattened and
grooved longitudinally along their upper surfaces;
they usually grow in groups of five or six. Underfur
is lacking. The tail is scantily covered by short,
bristly hairs, with scales between the hairs. The
general coloration of the upper parts is speckled yellowish brown or grayish brown, that of the under parts
is grayish or whitish, and the tail is brownish above
and buffy white below.

Cane rats have short, rounded ears that barely extend above the spiny pelage. The palms and soles are
naked. The fore foot has three well-developed central
digits, but the thumb (first digit) is reduced and the
fifth finger is small and nearly functionless; the digits
on the hind foot are somewhat larger, although the
first digit is absent. The claws are thick and heavy.
A female *Thryonomys* has three pairs of mammae
which are located rather high on the sides of the body
so that she can suckle her offspring while lying on
her stomach.

The orange-colored incisors are broad and powerful; the upper incisors are three-grooved. The cheek
teeth are rooted and moderately high-crowned. The
dental formula is as follows: i 1/1, c 0/0, pm 1/1,
m 3/3 x 2 = 20. The massive skull is strongly ridged.

Cane rats are not strictly gregarious, although
several may live together in a favorable environment.
They are generally solitary; however, they become
active at night and follow well-defined paths of their
own making through dense reeds and grass. These
paths usually lead to water, as cane rats swim and
dive with ease. Their shelters are often located in
matted vegetation, but where the ground cover is
scanty they will excavate shallow burrows. In areas
where they are heavily preyed upon, cane rats may
hide in rock crevices or abandoned tunnels of the ant
bear (*Orycteropus*) or the porcupine (*Hystrix*). Generally, the dense vegetation of their habitat affords
sufficient cover for shelter. If startled in their above-
ground shelters, cane rats will bolt through the
matted vegetation with sudden and amazing speed,
often toward water.

These vegetarian rodents feed on the softer parts
of coarse grasses and shrubs as well as nuts and bark.
Trees are often stripped of their bark to a height
within the reach of cane rats. It has been recorded
that stored ivory has been gnawed by *Thryonomys*.

T. swinderianus, in southern Africa, give birth from
June to August, the litter size being two to four, usually three. The young are born and raised in a nest
of shredded vegetation, located in a burrow or in a
shallow depression in the ground. The offspring are
covered with hair and have their eyes open at birth;
they remain in the nest until they are able to run.
The life span for most members of the family Thry-
onomyidae probably does not exceed three years in
the wild.

Cane rats may do considerable damage in sugar-
cane fields, and as a means of reducing their numbers
in sugar plantations, the python is often protected.
Other predators of cane rats are mongooses, leopards,
various rapacious birds, and man. The flesh of
Thryonomys is delicate and an important source of
protein for many native people. Cane rats are hunted
with spears and dogs in organized drives. Sometimes
the natives set fire to the reeds to force the animals

from cover. The Zulus of southern Africa find these rodents make tasty food. However, like many other primitive people, they are reluctant to eat a rat. This aversion is circumvented by cutting the ratlike tail near its base when the animal is captured. After the hunt an examination of the mutilated cane rat reveals the "absence" of a tail and the animal can thus be eaten and everyone's self respect is maintained. It is said that the best way to prepare African spiny rats is to pluck them like fowls.

The geological range of this family is from the upper Miocene to the Recent in Africa, and the Pliocene of Europe and Asia.

The type species of the genus is *T. semipalmatus* (Heuglin).

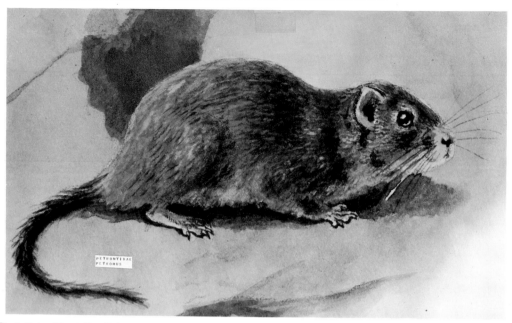

Rock Rat or Dassie Rat (*Petromus typicus typicus*), photo from *The Mammals of South Africa*, Austin Roberts, through John Voelcker and the Transvaal Museum.

ROCK MICE OR ROCK RATS, DASSIE RATS; NOKI, KLIPMUISE, DASSIEMUISE, DASSIEROT (local vernaculars).

THIS FAMILY CONTAINS a single genus, *Petromus*. There are no extinct genera, and the family is known only from the Recent in Africa. The single species, *P. typicus*, is associated with rocky areas on hills and mountains of southwestern Africa.

This rodent is somewhat squirrel-like in external appearance, but the tail, although not bushy, is covered with scattered long hairs. The length of the head and body is 140 to 200 mm., and the length of the tail is 130 to 180 mm. The limp body can be greatly compressed, so that with its flat skull, this rodent can squeeze into narrow crevices. The ribs are so flexible that *Petromus* can be pressed almost flat without injury to the body. The ears are short. The feet are narrow; the fore feet have four digits and the hind feet five. The claws are short, and some stiff, bristle-like hairs are associated with the claws of the hind feet. The pelage is soft and silky, but the underfur is absent so that the hairs stand out separately and have a wiry appearance on the living animal. The hairs grow in clusters of three to five, and the facial whiskers are long and black. The tail is haired. When these rodents lie flattened out on a rock, their only distinguishing mark is the yellowish nose, as the coloration of *Petromus* blends with that of the rocks on which it lives. Above, the fore parts are dark gray, light gray, yellowish, or pale buffy; the lower back is tawny, orangish tawny, or yellowish; the under parts are grayish or yellowish. Occasionally the upper parts are grayish throughout.

The mammae are lateral, placed high up on a level with the shoulder blades, enabling the young to suckle from the side when hiding in narrow rock crevices. Usually there are three pairs of mammae, but sometimes only two pairs are present. The male *Petromus* has a short baculum.

The following dental formula prevails: i 1/1, c 0/0, pm 1/1, m 3/3 x 2 = 20. The incisors are fairly narrow, and the high-crowned cheek teeth are rooted.

Dassie rats emerge from their rock shelters during the day, particularly in the early morning and late afternoon, to sun themselves and feed. Occasionally, they forage after sunset. They usually move about singly or in pairs as they seek food on the ground or in bushes on the rocky slopes. These vegetarian rodents eat a variety of green plant material, seeds, and berries. When resting or sunning themselves, they generally select a spot under a projecting rock that protects them from attack by birds of prey. Dassie rats, when undisturbed, are playful, often whisking about and playing with plant stems, but when alarmed they dart quickly to shelter, often uttering a warning note (a whistling call) upon reaching safety. They run on the rocks rather than jump, but they do spring from one rock to another on occasion. When jumping, they spread their flattened bodies somewhat like the flight of gliding squirrels.

Petromus mates during the early summer months in the Southern Hemisphere, i.e., from November through December; they give birth near the end of the year. The usual litter size is one or two. The young are born in an advanced stage, being quite large and covered with short hair.

The skin of the rodent family Petromyidae is very soft and tears easily when an individual is being skinned. The tail, which is supplied with soft joints, breaks readily, generally at the base.

AFRICAN MOLE RATS, BLESMOLS.

THIS FAMILY CONSISTS of five genera of the Recent and approximately 56 (?) species. About 50 species of *Cryptomys* have been described, but many of these are probably local variants. Blesmols are widely distributed in Africa, south of the Sahara; the usual habitat is an area of loose, sandy soil where bulbs and roots are plentiful. African mole rats occur in plains and deserts up to elevations of at least 1,800 meters.

The body form of these rodents is modified for a fossorial life. The general appearance is similar to that of other burrowing mammals: the body is stocky, the tail and limbs are short, and the eyes and ears are minute. Blesmols apparently see indistinctly for a very short distance and generally close the eyelids when the head is touched; external ears are represented by a small circle of bare skin around the ear opening. The hands and feet are large, and the palms and soles are naked. The five fingers and five toes have either long or short claws, depending on the genus. The hind claws are usually hollow on the underside and shorter than the foreclaws. The length of the head and body is 80 to 330 mm., and the tail is 10 to 70 mm. One genus (*Heterocephalus*) is practically hairless, but the other genera have thick, soft, and woolly or velvety pelage. The coloration differs, some forms having a whitish spot on the head. The female *Cryptomys* has three or four pairs of mammae.

The skull is stoutly built. The incisors are large, the upper incisors are grooved in some forms, and the high-crowned molars are rooted. The dental formula in all the genera except *Heliophobius* is as follows: i 1/1, c 0/0, pm 2-3/2-3, m 0-3/0-3 x 2 = 12 to 28. In *Heliophobius* the cheek teeth number 6/6, although not every tooth is in place at one time. This addition of teeth to the usual maximum rodent dentition may be due to a specialized condition of the milk teeth.

Cryptomys and *Heterocephalus* are reported to include invertebrates in their diet. All species of blesmols feed primarily on subterranean bulbs and roots that are found by tunneling from 10 to 300 mm. below the surface; the depth of the tunnel apparently is directly related to the looseness of the soil. The burrow systems of African mole rats include large chambers for storing food and sleeping; the excavated soil is thrown on the surface at intervals in the form of mounds. In some areas these rodents may so honeycomb the ground that a person sinks deep into the sand at almost every step when attempting to walk across the burrow systems. It is sometimes difficult to distinguish between the mounds of the different genera when more than one genus lives in a particular area. *Cryptomys*, *Georychus*, and *Bathyergus* are reported to occur together in parts of the Cape Province. This close association is unusual, as generally only one genus of a particular family of strictly burrowing mammals occupies a single habitat. Presumably, the different sizes of the tunnels eliminate actual contact between these blesmols. These rodents are well oriented, for when their burrows are destroyed, they dig new tunnels directly to their exits or special chambers. They seldom emerge above ground except when flooded out or when seeking new quarters. There is some indication that *Heliophobius* wanders above ground more than the other genera.

An individual of the genus *Bathyergus* in captivity made a chattering noise while burrowing and would turn and bite if interrupted. In this genus and in *Heliophobius*, the foreclaws are the principal tools for digging, whereas in *Georychus* and *Cryptomys* the lower incisors are used to a greater extent in burrowing than are the claws. These differences in digging mechanism are related to the anatomy of these genera: in *Bathyergus* and *Heliophobius* the foreclaws are well developed and the union of the lower jaws is such that the incisors cannot separate while digging; whereas in *Georychus* and *Cryptomys* the foreclaws are short and the lower incisors can be extended considerably. Blesmols use their hind limbs and the flattened rows of bristles on each side of the tail to remove the soil excavated by their foreclaws or incisors.

There may be a fixed breeding season, at least in some forms. The litter size is one to five. Newborn blesmols can inflict severe bites.

These rodents are reported to make interesting pets, but some species bite unexpectedly. Blesmols often destroy the tuber crops of natives, but, like all burrowing animals, they help to furrow and aerate soil. *Heliophobius* is occasionally eaten by the native Africans.

The geological range of the family Bathyergidae is upper Miocene (?), and the Pleistocene to the Recent in Africa, and the Oligocene in Mongolia. *Gypsorhychus* is an extinct giant sand mole, allied with the Recent genus *Georychus*. It is represented by skull and dental remains from Taungs, in Mongolia, and from South-West Africa.

Cape Mole-Rat (*Georychus capensis*), photo by G. B. Rabb, Chicago Zoological Park, Brookfield, Illinois.

CAPE MOLE-RATS; KAAPSE BLESMOLS, NOTA, KAKOKO (local vernaculars).

THE SINGLE SPECIES, *G. capensis*, inhabits southern Africa, namely, Natal and Namaqualand to the extreme southern tip of the Cape Province. Cape mole-rats prefer a habitat of loose sandy soil.

The length of the head and body is 150 to 205 mm., and the length of the tail is 15 to 40 mm. The soft pelage is so thick, fluffy, and long that it practically conceals the tail in many individuals. The tail has a flattened appearance because it is haired mainly on the sides. The general coloration of the upper parts is buffy to buffy orange, frequently with a brownish tinge; the under parts are somewhat lighter than above. The head has various black or dark-brown markings with white spots. The hands, feet, and tail are white. Partial albinism is not uncommon.

The general form of *Georychus* is similar to that of North American pocket gophers (Geomyidae), but cape mole-rats lack cheek pouches and are smaller. The external ears of cape mole-rats are represented by round openings, surrounded with thickened skin around the edges. The claws are only moderately developed and relatively weak. The incisors are white, ungrooved, and project forward to an unusual degree. Normally, there are three pairs of mammae, but it is not unusual for a female to have four pairs.

Members of the genus *Georychus* are strictly burrowers, and almost their entire lives are spent underground. It appears that the incisors are used more than the claws in digging, especially in hard soil. The earth from the tunnels is thrown out at intervals, which plainly marks the line of excavation. The burrows are occasionally near the surface and branch into blind tunnels. The main burrow eventually leads into a smooth-walled, somewhat globular chamber in which the mole-rat stores tubers, roots, and bulbs. It is said that the buds ("eyes") of bulbs and tubers are bitten off to prevent them from sprouting.

Cape mole-rats are notoriously destructive of the tuber crops of natives. They make interesting pets, but have the habit of biting unexpectedly. Information on the reproductive process apparently has not been published.

Cape Dune Mole-rat (*Bathyergus suillus suillus*), photo from *The Mammals of South Africa*, Austin Roberts, through John Voelcker and the Transvaal Museum.

MOLE-RATS, CAPE SAND-MOLES; MOLLEES, KEAPSE DUINMOL (local vernaculars).

THE SINGLE SPECIES, *B. suillus*, inhabits Namaqualand and the Cape Province at the southern tip of the African continent. The habitat of these mole-rats appears to be restricted to sand dunes and sandy flats from about 1,200 to 1,500 meters elevation, especially along the coast. On the basis of structural features, some authors think that this genus should be classified in a family by itself.

The length of the head and body is 175 to 330 mm., and the length of the tail is 40 to 70 mm. The thick, rather woolly pelage is cinnamon, drab gray, or silvery buff on the upper parts; in most forms the under parts are similarly colored, but in one form the ventral surface is black. Some forms have a dark median band on the upper parts. The pale-brown tail is fringed with whitish-slate hairs. White and piebald varieties of *Bathyergus* are common.

Mole-rats have short legs and five well-developed foreclaws, the second finger has the longest claw, and the third toe of the hind foot has a long claw. The tail has a flat, feather-like appearance resulting from long hairs growing outward from each side. The incisors are white; the upper ones are heavily grooved, and the lower ones are not grooved. Both sets of incisors project forward to an unusual degree. The eyes are quite small and there is no external ear. The female has six mammae.

Members of the genus *Bathyergus* spend their lives in burrows of their own excavation. Mole-rats push soil in front of them in the burrows as they excavate and throw it out through short side tunnels leading to the surface.

The food consists principally of bulbs and fleshy roots. When these rodents inhabit agricultural areas, they not only eat and damage the crops but they also collect a great surplus of food which they store away within the burrows.

The burrows of *B. suillus* are so extensive that they are a serious menace to horseback riders, weakening the ground to such an extent that it collapses under the weight of a horse. In addition, mole-rats also undermine railroad ties, causing the rails to drop under the weight of a passing train. They particularly damage potato crops.

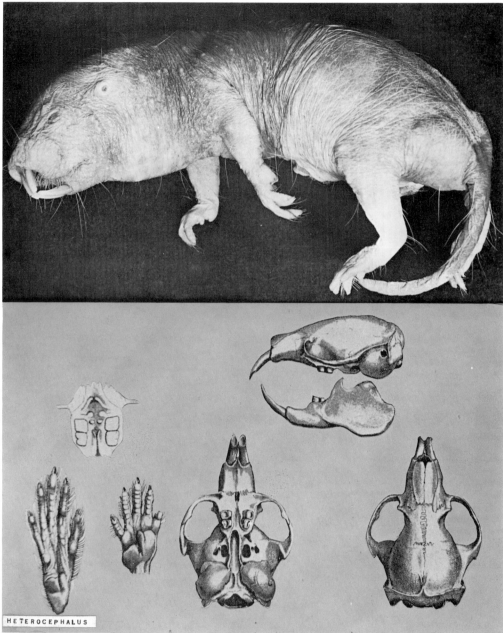

Naked Sand–Rat (*Heterocephalus glaber*), photo by Dietrich Starck. Anatomy (*H. g. phillipsi*), photo from *Proc. Zool. Soc. London.*

NAKED MOLE-RATS, SAND-RATS; FARUMS, FA-RUMFERS, FARANFAN (native names).

THE SINGLE SPECIES, *H. glaber*, inhabits eastern Ethiopia, all of Somaliland, and northern Kenya. These animals live in different kinds of soils, but they apparently prefer a light sandy soil in arid regions. The elevational range is 600 to 1,800 meters.

The length of the head and body is 80 to 90 mm.,

the length of the tail is 35 to 40 mm., and adults weigh 40 to 80 grams. This rodent appears to be naked and entirely lacking in hairs, but on closer inspection an extremely fine scattering of light-colored hairs is noticeable. Prominent vibrissae are present about the lips. The skin over the entire body is wrinkled and light reddish or yellowish in color.

Naked mole-rats have a short chunky head, minute eyes, no external ears, and protruding incisors. The front feet are large, with five broad, flattened fingers, each of which has a small conical claw. A typical characteristic of *Heterocephalus* is a fringe of fine hairs around the edge of the feet. These cilia, an unusual structure in a rodent, increase the spread of the foot without increasing its weight and help the animal to burrow more efficiently.

H. glaber spends practically its entire life underground where it constructs intricate burrows. The tunnels vary in depth from several centimeters to about a meter. At intervals the animal removes excess soil from the newly excavated tunnels by burrowing to the surface, pushing the loose sand upward with its head toward the exit and then forcefully kicking out the earth with its hind feet. This process, resembling a miniature crater in eruption, produces mounds 230 to 305 mm. in height. Although naked mole-rats have been observed to be active at all times, their period of greatest activity is in the morning and evening. They are said to live in colonies comprising 100 individuals. When frightened, they utter a squeaking note. The principal diet is composed of roots, bulbs, and tubers; insects and seeds have also been noted in stomach analyses.

Data on reproduction have apparently not been recorded. These animals, like other burrowing rodents, aid in the deep percolation of water and soil aeration but are a nuisance in cultivated gardens.

GUNDIS AND SPEKE'S PECTINATORS.

THIS FAMILY of four genera and six living species occurs in northern Africa from Morocco to Somaliland. These rodents inhabit arid and semiarid regions where there are caves or rocky ledges.

The members of this family have thickset and compact bodies, resembling guinea pigs in external appearance. There are four digits on each foot; the two inner digits of the hind foot have comb-like brushes of bristles for cleaning the fur. The claws are not enlarged. The length of the head and body is 160 to 240 mm., and the tail is 10 to 50 mm. The tail is fully haired, and the fur is soft.

The flattened skull is broad posteriorly. The upper incisors are slightly grooved (*Felovia*) or not grooved, and the cheek teeth are rootless (ever-growing). The following dental formula is recorded: i 1/1, c 0/0, pm 1-2/1-2, m 3/3 x 2 = 20 or 24.

With the exception of one genus (*Ctenodactylus*), little is known biologically about these rodents. The gundi (*Ctenodactylus*) is one of several mammals that "plays possum" when threatened, although its main protection against predators is running from danger. Gundis are quite shy; they squeak and jerk the tail and sit up like hamsters. They can withstand considerable fluctuations in temperature, but if their hair becomes wet they begin to shiver. The pelage does not protect the body against rain because the hairs stick together in small bunches when they become moist and thus expose the skin in a number of places. However, during storms these rodents normally shelter under overhanging rocks and large logs in relatively dry places. Gundis feed at twilight, and Speke's pectinators forage shortly after sunset and about dawn. The members of the family Ctenodactylidae apparently are more herbivorous than graminivorous.

The offspring of *Ctenodactylus* have their eyes open at birth and are haired and capable of running.

The geological range of this family is the Miocene in India, the Oligocene in Europe and Asia, and the Pliocene to the Recent in Africa.

Gundis (*Ctenodactylus gundi*), A. Photo by Schomber-Kock. B. & C. Right hind and front foot, photos by P. F. Wright of specimen in U.S. National Museum. D. Photo from the Archives of the Zoological Garden Berlin-West.

GUNDIS.

THE SINGLE SPECIES, *C. gundi*, is known from Libya, Tunisia, Algeria, and westward to Atlas, the mountains in Moroccan northern Africa. The habitat is a rocky slope on a hill or mountain.

The length of the head and body is about 160 to 200 mm., and the length of the tail is about 10 to 20 mm. The upper parts are buffy in color, occasionally a pinkish buff, and the under parts are lighter, usually whitish or slaty.

The generic name refers to the comb-like bristles on the toes of the hind feet. *Ctenodactylus* looks like *Pectinator* externally, but differs in its tail that is shorter than the hind foot.

The normal movement on a level surface is a quick run, with the belly almost touching the ground. On sloping surfaces, however, *C. gundi* presses its body against the wall and uses the slightest irregularities in the obstruction to ascend almost perpendicularly. Flat stones or logs are preferred for sunning and resting. The comb-like bristles on the hind feet are used to care for the fur on the flanks and belly; perhaps the loose, almost silky quality of the fur is the result of frequent combing.

This rodent is one of several that "play possum" when threatened. *C. gundi* will not bite when seized but "freezes" and remains completely motionless. When released, it continues to play dead for a few seconds and, if it has been badly scared, this rigidity may continue for a while; breathing may even cease completely for a minute. A captive *Ctenodactylus* had a "fear paralysis" that lasted for nearly 12 hours after being placed in a strange cage. Such behavior probably protects the gundi against predatory animals that hunt mainly by sight, but since many of its enemies also have a good sense of smell, the gundi apparently must depend upon speed as its best means of preservation.

These animals feed usually at twilight. This time of day, in the common speech of the Arabs, who snare *Ctenodactylus* for food, is called "the hour when the gundi comes out." These rodents seem to feed solely on plant material; once captive gundis become accustomed to other foods, they accept strange food with great difficulty. They apparently do not drink but obtain most of their water from plants they eat.

A female *Ctenodactylus* with three embryos was noted in April. The young are described as being born with hair and open eyes; they are able to run.

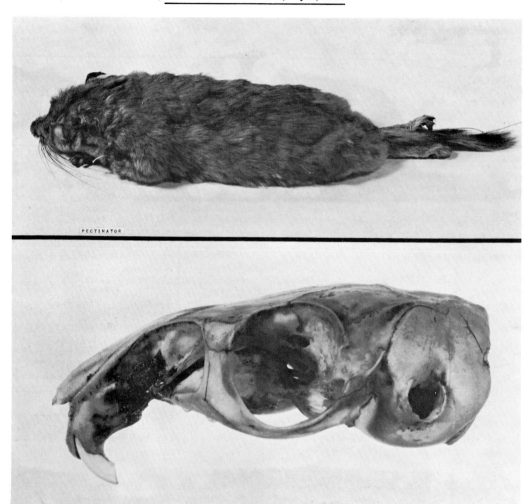

Speke's Pectinator (*Pectinator spekei*), photos from British Museum (Natural History).

SPEKE'S PECTINATORS, BUSHY-TAILED RATS.

THE SINGLE LIVING SPECIES, *P. spekei*, is known from former Eritrea, Ethiopia, and Somaliland, Africa. It usually inhabits rocky country. An extinct species, *P. sivalensis*, has been described from part of a left mandibular ramus which was discovered near Punjab, India. This specimen is of interest because all living forms are confined to the African continent.

The length of the head and body is about 170 mm., and the length of the tail is 40 to 50 mm. The pelage is quite soft. The upper parts are ashy gray, suffused with black or brown, and the sides are grayish; the hands, feet, and under parts are grayish white. Indi-vidual members of the genus *Pectinator*, taken from near the coast and from an elevation of 1,800 meters, seem to differ only slightly in color and thickness of fur. The whiskers are fairly long and the tail is bushy. The skin is said to be extremely thin and easily torn. The digits of the hind feet have brushes of comb-like bristles. The mandible and cheek teeth of *P. sivalensis* are essentially the same as in *P. spekei*.

Pectinator and *Procavia* (Hyracoidae, Procaviidae) often occur together. Speke's pectinator feeds on plants about dawn and shortly after sundown but often basks in the sun during the day. It shelters in rock crevices and cavities.

(*Massoutiera mzabi*), photo by Jean-Marie Baufle through F. Petter.

THREE SPECIES, *M. harterti*, *M. mzabi*, and *M. rothschildi*, inhabit the western and central Sahara of Africa.

The length of the head and body is 170 to 240 mm., and the length of the tail is about 35 mm. The coloration consists of different shades of yellow and brown. The inflation of the bullae and the mastoids is at a maximum for the family. There is a fringe of hairs around the inner margin of the ear, similar to that in jerboas and other desert rodents, which protects that organ from wind-blown sand. Differentiation among the three species is chiefly noticeable by the size of the bullae.

Specific habits and biology do not seem to have been recorded. These rodents are mainly diurnal; they live in natural rock crevices and feed on plant material.

There are specimens in the British Museum (Natural History).

The type species of the genus is *M. mzabi*, Lataste.

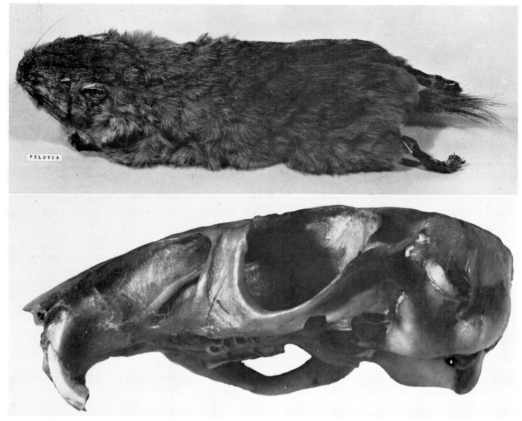

(*Felovia vae*), photos from British Museum (Natural History).

THE SINGLE SPECIES, *F. vae*, is known from Senegal in northwestern Africa. Practically nothing has been recorded regarding them, but H. W. Setzer tells us that a live specimen he collected was unusually docile, and sat calmly in the palm of his hand within one hour of its capture. The animal made little attempt to bite, and displayed no tendency toward playing "possum" as observed in members of the genus *Ctenodactylus*.

This rodent is of moderate size, with a head and body length of about 170 to 230 mm. The bushy tail is about as long as the hind foot. The upper parts are dark yellowish red, and the under parts are reddish. *Felovia* differs from *Massoutiera* in dental and skull features, but externally the two genera are quite similar. The upper incisors are slightly grooved.

There are specimens in the British Museum (Natural History), and the U.S. National Museum.

Order: CETACEA

BELUGAS, NARWHALS, WHALES, DOLPHINS, AND PORPOISES, COWFISH; SUSU, SISUMARA, SONS, SISHUK, SISHUMAR, SPITS DOLFYNEN, TSUCHIMBO AND TSUSHI-KUJIRA, BUTSKOPPEN, CACHALOTS, CACHALOTES, POTTWALE, POTVIS, BRUINVICS, BRAUNFISCH, MARSOUINS, HAI-CHU, BHULGA, KILLELAUAK, WEISSWALE, NARWHAL, GNAVEL-DOLFYNEN, TUCUXI, MADANA-IRUKA, BALLENAS AZULES, RORCUALES, FINWALE, NAGAS-KU-ZINA, VINVIS, RORQUALS BLEUS, BOW-HEAD WHALES, BALLENAS, GROENLANDSE WALVIS. (Included are vernaculars used in other countries.)

THIS ORDER of wholly aquatic mammals consists of three groups (suborders): Archaeoceti, the extinct forms with teeth differentiated into incisors, canines, and molars, and symmetrical skulls; Odontoceti, living forms with teeth of one type, and telescoped, non-symmetrical skulls; and Mysticeti, living forms with plates of baleen (modified mucous membrane) in the mouth, and symmetrical skulls. Living cetaceans comprise 38 genera and 90 species, arranged in 8 families; they occur in all seas of the world and in certain rivers and lakes. The extinct genus *Phocoenopsis* (family Delphinidae), known from certain New Zealand fossil beds, possibly may have been contemporary with man. The geological range of this order is the middle Eocene to the Recent.

A recent publication by Hershkovitz (*Smithsonian Inst. Bull.* 246) presents a number of changes from the cetacean nomenclature utilized herein. He employs the name *Pontoparia* for *Stenodelphis;* *Susu* for *Platanista; Neophoecaena* for *Neomaris;* and includes *Sousa* with *Sotalia*, and *Sibbaldus* with *Balaenoptera*. In addition, numerous specific names are changed, and many nominal species reduced to subspecific rank. Pending more widespread circulation and acceptance of Hershkovitz's views, however, we are adhering to the older nomenclature of the group.

The length of the head and body is taken in a straight line from the tip of the nose to the notch between the tail flukes. The length of the head and body varies from 1.25 to approximately 30 meters, and weights range from about 23 kg. to 136 metric tons. A cetacean may be distinguished immediately from a fish by the following characteristics: the tail flukes are set in a horizontal plane in cetaceans, whereas in fish the tail fin is in a vertical position. Other external features conspicuous in cetaceans are the torpedo-shaped body; front limbs which are modified into flippers and ensheathed in a covering; the absence of hind limbs but the usual presence of a dorsal fin; and scattered bristles of hair on the head. Cetaceans lack sweat glands and sebaceous glands. They have a fibrous layer filled with fat and oil, the blubber just beneath the skin, which assists in heat regulation. There are no external ears or ear muscles, and no scales or gills.

The nostrils open externally through a single blowhole in the toothed whales or a double blowhole in the baleen whales, usually located on the highest point of the head. The asymmetry of the skull of the toothed whales is in correlation with the reduction of one of the nasal passages, thus leaving the other as a single tube. There is a direct connection between the blowhole and the lungs so that milk in a suckling calf cannot enter the lungs. The blowhole is closed by valves when the animal is submerged. A greasy secretion of the tear glands protects the eyes against the irritation of salt water.

The bones are spongy in texture and the cavities are filled with oil. The vertebrae are fused in the neck of some forms, but all lack the complex articulation of vertebrae in land mammals and present a graded series from head to tail. There are no bony supports for the dorsal fin and the tail flukes. The pelvic girdle, represented by two small bones embedded in the body wall and free from the backbone, serves only as the attachment for the muscles of the external reproductive organs. Hind limbs are not necessary inasmuch as the tail supplies the driving force for swimming.

Propulsion is obtained by means of up and down movements of the tail, in such a way that the flukes present an inclined surface to the water at all times. The force generated at right angles to the surface of the flukes is resolvable into two components, one raising and lowering the body and the other driving the animal forward. The fins serve as balancing and steering organs.

Cetaceans do not blow liquid water out of the lungs. The visible spout when the animal exhales is from the condensation of water vapor entering the air from the lungs, and possibly from the discharge of the mucus-oil foam which fills the air sinuses.

Certain questions remain unanswered regarding the physiological adaptations of cetaceans in diving and temperature tolerance, but some of the general mechanisms are known. Before diving, a cetacean expels the air from its lungs. Some of the adaptations that make long dives possible are the following: (1) The oxygen combined with the hemoglobin of the blood and with the myoglobin of the muscles accounts for 80 to 90 per cent of the oxygen supply utilized during prolonged diving; (2) arterial networks seem to act as shunts, maintaining the normal blood supply to the brain but effecting a reduced supply to the muscles and an oxygen-debt which the animal can repay by breathing sufficiently when it again surfaces; (3) a decreased heartbeat further economizes the available oxygen; and (4) the respiratory center in the brain is relatively insensitive to an accumulation of carbon dioxide in the blood and tissues. The hydrostatic pressures encountered at great depths are alleviated by not breathing air under pressure and by the permeation of the body tissues with non-compressible fluids. The only substances in the body of a cetacean that can be compressed appreciably by the pressure of great depths are the free gases, found mainly in the lungs. The collapse of these gases drives them into the more rigid, thick-walled parts of the respiratory system. The body temperature is regulated by the insulation of the blubber, which retains body heat when the animals are in cold water, and the thin-walled veins associated with arteries in the fins and flukes.

The senses of hearing and touch are more acute than that of vision, and there is no sense of smell. Studies made with the use of the hydrophone in recent years have shown that cetaceans produce numerous underwater sounds and probably depend to a large extent on **echolocation for orientation and the**

#1 Humpback Whale (*Megaptera novaeangliae*)

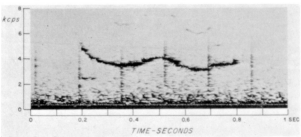

#2 *Globicephala macrorhyncha*

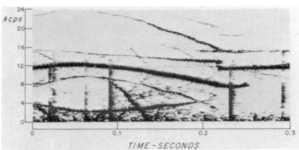

#3 White-sided Porpoise (*Lagenorhynchus acutus*)

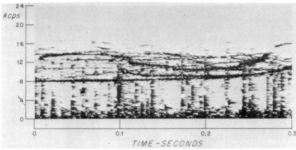

#4 *Stenella styx*

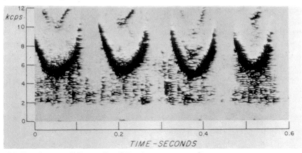

#5 Bottle-nosed Porpoise (*Tursiops truncatus*)

The five sound spectrograms shown above of Cetacean voices are copied from the publication, "Whale and Porpoise Voices," a phonograph record by William E. Schevill and William A. Watkins, Woods Hole Oceanographic Institution, Woods Hole, Massachusetts, 1962.

The back of a humpback whale (*Megaptera novaeangliae*), which has surfaced to breathe. The two openings on top of the head are the "blow holes," which the whale closes before submerging. These are comparable to the nostrils of other mammals. Photo by Vincent Serventy.

Cetacean Sounds

Recordings have been made of a considerable variety of vocal sounds made by Cetaceans under water. These have been converted into sound spectrograms for ease of study. The investigators have generally been careful not to ascribe meanings to the sounds and pictures thereof, but it appears that the sound pictures of Cetaceans show use of the voice to convey definite meanings, just as was found with regard to the Douroucouli (*Aotus*) voice. Many other sounds were recorded and pictures made of them, most with a knowledge of the circumstances under which they were uttered and the consequent possibility of interpretation.

securing of food. These sounds may also be used for communication between individuals.

The only toothed cetacean that regularly feeds on animals other than fish and cephalopods (nautili, squids, and octopi) is the killer whale, *Orcinus*. The conical teeth of the toothed cetaceans seize and hold slippery prey but are not adapted for chewing. Baleen whales feed on many different kinds of very small animals, collectively called plankton.

The gestation period in most cetacean forms is 11 to 16 months. The number of offspring is one, and the newborn young is usually one-fourth to one-third the length of the mother. Immediately after being born in the water, baby cetaceans must reach the surface of the water for a supply of air. The female *Tursiops* has been seen to push her baby to the surface; and undoubtedly most, if not all, cetacean mothers aid their young in this manner. The mother floats on her side when suckling the youngster so that the calf can breathe; later it can nurse under water. The teats of the mammary glands lie within paired slits on either side of the reproductive opening. The mammary glands have large reservoirs in which the milk collects and the contraction of the body muscles forces the milk by way of the teats into the mouth of the young. The rapid growth rate of most cetaceans is at least partly related to the high calcium and phosphorous content of the milk. Because cetaceans live in an aquatic environment and need not support their own weight, they can attain great size.

Approximately 800,000 cetaceans have been killed since 1900 for oil, spermaceti, meat, blubber, baleen, and bone. Significant milestones in the whaling industry have been the development by Svend Foyn in 1864 of the harpoon gun with a delayed explosive head; inflating the whale carcass with air so that it will not sink; the first Antarctic land station, started by C. A. Larson in 1904; the development of pelagic whaling with floating factories independent of ports between 1925 and 1930; and the protective and regulative international agreements in effect since 1937.

Bottle-nosed Dolphin (*Tursiops truncatus*), a baby being born tail first; photo from Miami Seaquarium.

FRESH WATER OR RIVER DOLPHINS, GANGES DOL-
PHINS; SUSU, SISUMARA, SONS, SISHUK, SISHUMAR
(local vernaculars).

THIS FAMILY, as herein recognized, consists of four
Recent genera, each with a single species. *Platanista*
(from India), *Inia* (from South America), and *Lipotes*
(from China) are apparently confined to fresh water,
whereas *Stenodelphis* (from South America) inhabits
estuaries and may migrate along the coast of South
America during the winter. The fossil record lends
support to a contrary arrangement of these genera:
the family Platanistidae would thus include only
Platanista; another family, Iniidae, would include the
genera *Inia* and *Lipotes*; and the genus *Stenodelphis*
would be placed in the family Delphinidae. The geological range of the family Platanistidae, as herein
recognized, is the lower Miocene to the Recent in
South America, the middle Miocene and the lower
Pliocene in North America, and the Recent in Asia.
Among the living genera only *Stenodelphis* is represented by fossils.

These are rather small, long-beaked cetaceans.
The members of this family are approximately 1.9
to 3 meters in length and do not exceed 225 kg. in
weight. The beak is long and narrow, and the lower
jaws are fused or at least closely appressed for most
of their length. The forehead is usually blunt, and a
distinct external neck occurs in the genera *Platanista*
and *Inia*. The flippers are short and broad; the upper
arm bone is longer than the lower arm bones. The
dorsal fin is small in *Platanista* and *Inia* but well developed in *Lipotes* and *Stenodelphis*. Vision is poorly

developed; in the genus *Platanista*, the eye lacks a lens.

The skull is nearly symmetrical. The members of
this family have 41 to 45 vertebrae, the neck vertebrae
being free. In *Stenodelphis* the total number of teeth
is 200 to 222; in the other genera they range from 100
to 130.

These curious and inoffensive dolphins often swim
around fishing boats. They generally travel singly or
in groups of 2 to 12 individuals; they are not so active
as the members of the family Delphinidae. Their
dives seldom last more than a few minutes. All members of this family make local migrations. Some
individuals of *Inia*, for example, swim into flooded
forests and into small streams and lakes during
periods of high water. They return to the larger
rivers, however, before the water level of the lakes
and streams becomes too low for egress during the
dry season. The diet consists mainly of aquatic
bottom dwellers, such as mud-frequenting fishes and
fresh-water crustaceans. Much of the food is obtained
by probing in the mud with the sensitive snout. *Inia*
apparently locates underwater obstacles and some of
its prey by means of echolocation.

The gestation period is not known, but is thought
to be eight to nine months in *Platanista*.

The flesh and blubber are sometimes eaten, medicinal value is attributed to the oil and blubber by certain
peoples, and the oils are occasionally used as illumi-
nants. Certain South American natives are reported
to believe that blindness will result if the oil of *Inia* is
used in lamps, but it is not known if this belief still
exists.

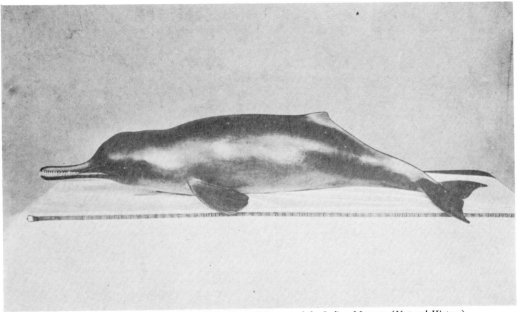

Ganges Dolphin (*Platanista gangetica*), photo from *Annual Report of the Indian Museum* (*Natural History*).

GANGES DOLPHIN; SUSU, SISUMÁRA, SONS, SISHUK, SISHUMÁR (local vernaculars).

THE SINGLE SPECIES, *P. gangetica*, inhabits the rivers of northern India. This mammal travels upstream as far as the water depth and rocky barriers allow. It apparently remains in fresh water throughout its life.

Head and body length is variable, but adults are usually 2 to 3 meters long. There is a record of a 4-meter female, however. The breadth or expanse of the flukes is about 460 mm. The back is dark lead-gray to lead-black, and the belly is somewhat lighter.

As regards distinguishing features: "[It has a] long, slender compressed beak with a formidable array of teeth; wedge-shaped forehead; small, degenerate, lensless eyes; longitudinal slitlike blowhole; distinctly constricted neck; low, ridgelike dorsal fin; and broad flippers cut off squarely at their ends" (Remington Kellogg, *Nat. Geog. Mag.*, January, 1940, p. 83). There are 28 or 29 teeth in each side of each jaw, and the snout and lower jaws are beak-like, 180 to 205 mm. long. The forehead rises rather steeply behind the beak to the upper surface of the head. A unique fea-ture is the presence of two plates of bone, one on each side of the skull, which project outward and nearly meet in front of the blowhole.

In rising to breathe, *Platanista* usually plunges out of the water upward or forward; occasionally it rises merely to expose the blowhole on the top of the head. The Ganges dolphin breathes every one-half to two minutes. It may undergo local migrations, is curious and inoffensive, and travels and feeds in schools of three to ten or more individuals. Being blind, *Platanista* probes with its sensitive snout for fish, shrimp, and other fresh-water organisms in the bottom mud.

After a gestation period of eight to nine months, a single young is born from April through July. The young are about 450 mm. long and weigh about 7 kg. at birth.

The flesh and blubber of *Platanista* are sometimes eaten. The oil is used as an illuminant and is also regarded "as of great value as an embrocation in rheumatism and for giving much strength when rubbed on the back and loins" (J. R. Norman and F. C. Fraser, *Giant Fishes, Whales and Dolphins* [New York, 1938], p. 341.

Amazon Dolphins (*Inia geoffrensis*), A. Photo from Fort Worth Zoological Park through Lawrence Curtis. B. Photo by James N. Layne. C. Photo from d'Orbigny and Gervais, "Voyage dans l'Amerique meridional."

AMAZON DOLPHINS; BOUTOS, BOUTU, BUFEOS, BOTO VERMELHO (South American names).

THE SINGLE SPECIES, *I. geoffrensis*, inhabits the interconnecting Amazonian and Orinocoan river systems of South America. It is restricted to fresh water.

Head and body length is 2 to 3 meters, and the expanse of the tail flukes is about 510 mm. One specimen weighed 125 kg. The variable coloration of this species is probably related to age: young individuals usually have grayish or black upper parts which shade into lighter gray under parts, whereas older, larger individuals become pale, pinkish, and even flesh-colored. However, these color changes can be reversible: a captive *Inia* kept in clear, shallow water becomes noticeably darker during a six-month period. It has also been noted that the darkest coloration in wild, adult Amazon dolphins is in the vicinity of the blowhole, an area that is frequently exposed to sunlight because the animal must surface in order to breathe. Perhaps the skin responds to such frequent exposure in clear waters and in surfacing by concentrating pigments, thus preventing sunburn.

A long, slender, slightly down-curved beak is characteristic. The teeth number about 33 to 34 on each side of each jaw, making a total of 132 to 136 teeth; the back eight or nine teeth have a distinct keel. The rounded head bears the blowhole on its summit, and the dorsal fin is long and ridge-like. The wide snout is covered with short, stiff bristles.

The action of breathing varies: sometimes only the blowhole and the top of the head are exposed, but frequently the dorsal fin and the ridge of the back are also exposed. When swimming rapidly and apparently when feeding, *Inia* rolls to breathe. Amazon dolphins breathe about every half minute, on the average. *Inia* seems to be less active than the delphinids but will occasionally leap out of the water to heights of 1.25 meters. Although it appears to scan its surroundings above water at times, the senses of hearing and touch are probably more acute than that of vision. *Inia* apparently utilizes echolocation to locate underwater obstacles and prey, and it also probes for food on the bottoms. This dolphin feeds on fish, including those that are habitually found on river bottoms. The prey is usually less than 305 mm. in length. Cory Carvalho has found remains of fish, gastropods, lamellibranchs, feathers of shore birds, and plant roots in the stomach of *Inia*. He believes that such contents come from the stomachs of fish eaten by the porpoise.

Inia usually travels singly or in pairs, but loose groups of up to six individuals are fairly common.

The single young is assumed to accompany the mother until it is almost as large as the parent. A lactating female has been collected in December; two immature individuals, weighing 36 kg., have been collected in February.

The following information is abstracted from a report by Dr. Lawrence Curtis, Director of the Fort Worth Zoological Park, Fort Worth, Texas.

In May, 1962, a female *Inia* was brought from Leticia, Colombia to Florida and then to the Fort Worth (Texas) Zoo. The animal was 1.7 meters in length. It was transported in a plastic-lined box only about 25 mm. longer than the animal. The box was kept as full of water as possible. While facilities were constructed for it at the zoo, it was in a covered pool. August 19, 1962, the female and a male, about 1.95

meters long, were placed in the newly constructed indoor pool. Both animals were carefully studied. It was observed that they can move the head more than some other small cetaceans. In captivity each animal ate about 8 pounds daily in two equal feedings of American smelt, *Osmerus mordax*, supplemented with multivitamin capsules, a brewers yeast tablet, and cod-liver oil and wheat germ oil perles. Occasionally the male would refuse the smelt and other fish but would accept fresh water catfish, *Ictalurus*. They were active both day and night, sleeping intermittently. They came to the surface to breathe about every 45 seconds.

The two specimens appeared to adapt themselves to captivity readily and they were inquisitive, alert, and intelligent. Their vision appeared to be good, although their eyes are relatively small. Their calls that were audible to the human ear were less frequent than those of *Tursiops* that had been observed by some of the persons who studied the animals.

White Flag Dolphin (*Lipotes vexillifer*), photo from National Geographic Society of painting by Else Bostelmann.

CHINESE DOLPHIN, WHITE FLAG DOLPHIN; PEH CH'I.

THE SINGLE SPECIES, *L. vexillifer*, is known only from Tungting Hu [lake], some 960 km. from the mouth of the Yangtze River, China, and from some adjacent parts of the river.

Head and body length is 2 to 2.5 meters, and coloration is pale blue-gray above and whitish below. One specimen weighed 160 kg. The long, beak-like snout is curved upward, and there are from 33 to 36 teeth in each side of the upper and lower jaws. The eye is small and degenerate. The low dorsal fin is said to resemble a flag when seen above water.

An individual, when shot, "gave a cry like that of a water-buffalo calf" (Charles M. Hoy, in G. S. Miller, "A New River-dolphin from China," *Smithsonian Misc. Coll.*, pub. 2486, vol. 68, no. 9, 1918, p. 1). Chinese dolphins have been noted in groups of 3 to 12 individuals. They feed on fish; two quarts of catfish were found in the stomach of the type specimen. The long beak is used to probe on the bottom for food. When lakes are rising in the late spring, Chinese dolphins are said to travel up small, clear rivers to breed. Medicinal value is attributed to their blubber by the Chinese.

The type specimen is represented by the skull and neck vertebrae in the U.S. National Museum. Two skulls are reported to be in the Shanghai Museum, and the Smithsonian Institution has a life-sized model of a white flag dolphin in the Natural History Building, Washington, D.C.

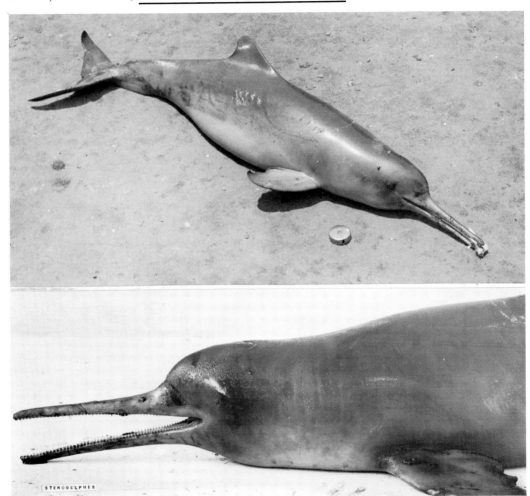

La Plata River Dolphin (*Stenodelphis blainvillii*), photos by Cory T. de Carvalho.

LA PLATA RIVER DOLPHINS; DELFINOS DEL PLATA, FRANCISCANAS, TONINHA (South American names).

THE SINGLE SPECIES, *S. blainvillii*, is found in the estuary of the Rio de la Plata and in the Atlantic coastal waters of South America.

Head and body length is 1.5 to 1.75 meter, and weight is 29 to 61 kg. Color is grayish above and paler beneath; the young are usually brownish. Conspicuous features are the long, slender beak; the 50 to 60 or more finely pointed, slender teeth in each side of each jaw, making a total of 210 to 242 teeth; and the triangular dorsal fin.

The overall distribution appears to be related to local movements and migrations: "They rarely are seen in the Plata estuary during the winter. Perhaps at this season most of the schools migrate northward along the Brazilian coast or frequent the high seas in approximately the same latitude" (Remington Kellogg, *Nat. Geog. Mag.*, January, 1940, p. 81). La Plata dolphins are curious and inoffensive, and often appear around fishing boats.

It is assumed that *Stenodelphis* locates its prey by echolocation and by probing in the bottoms with its long snout. The teeth are "marvelously adapted for catching and holding soft-bodied prey" (Ibid.). Fish, mainly the silvery mullet and some croaker-like forms, are eaten by this animal.

BEAKED WHALES, COW FISH; SPITS DOLFYNEN, BALEINES DE SOWERBY, SOWERBYS WALE, TSU- CHIMBO AND TSUSHI - KUJIRA, BOTTLE - NOSED WHALE, BUTSKOPPEN. (Included are vernaculars used in other countries.)

THIS FAMILY of 5 genera and approximately 14 species inhabits the oceans of the World, with at least one genus (*Hyperoodon*) migrating between cold and warm waters. Beaked whales are little known as a result of their oceanic distribution and the apparent natural rarity of some forms.

These medium-sized cetaceans have a distinct beak which is not marked off from the forehead as in the family Delphinidae. The length of the head and body is 4.5 to 13 meters, and the weight usually ranges from 1 to 4.5 metric tons. The flippers are rather small and ovate, and the sickle-shaped dorsal fin is located on the back half of the animal. One genus (*Ziphius*) has a low median keel from the dorsal fin to the tail. The tailflukes are not notched in the center as in other cetaceans. From two to six short throat furrows converge anteriorly to form a V pattern at the chin. The stomachs of beaked whales are divided into as many as 9 to 14 compartments.

Only one or two pairs of large functional teeth are present, depending on the genus; these are on the lower jaws. These teeth push through the gums sooner in males than in females; in some females they may never erupt. Series of small non-functional teeth are frequently present in the upper and lower jaws of *Mesoplodon*, *Ziphius*, *Berardius*, and *Hyperoodon*. The only genus with small functional teeth is *Tasmacetus*, which, in addition to having one pair of large functional teeth in the lower jaw, possesses small functional teeth in the upper and lower jaws. The bones of the skull are asymmetrical, except in the genus *Berardius*. Certain bones of the skull are crested or elevated and form large ridges in *Hyperoodon* and lesser ridges in some of the other genera. Several genera produce spermaceti, a waxy substance, in the forehead. The vertebrae number from 43 to 49, with those of the neck tending to fuse with one another.

Some beaked whales appear to be solitary, some travel in groups of 2 to 12 individuals, and others associate in schools of 40 or more, particularly *Ziphius*. Beaked whales generally swim and dive in unison and are noted for their rapid, deep dives to secure cephalopods and fish. Submergence usually lasts from 10 to 20 minutes, but harpooned *Hyperoodon* may stay under water for two hours.

The scratches on the hides of many beaked whales are mainly battle scars, for the males attack other males, and occasionally even females and young, during the breeding season. The gestation period lasts about a year, and the calves are born from late winter to early summer. The offspring are about one-third the length of the mother. In *Hyperoodon*, for example, the calf is approximately 3 meters long at birth, and in *Mesoplodon* the baby is from 2.5 to 2.9 meters in length. Calves of the genus *Mesoplodon* suckle for about one year and grow .9 to 1.2 meters during the period of nursing.

Berardius and *Ziphius* are hunted to some extent in Japanese waters, and *Hyperoodon* is sought for its oil and spermaceti.

The geological range of this family is the lower Miocene to the Recent; there are fossil records from the Americas and Europe. The only Recent genus with a fossil record is *Mesoplodon*.

True's Beaked Whale (*Mesoplodon mirus*), photo from National Geographic Society of painting by Else Bostelmann. Inset: (*Mesoplodon* sp.), photo from American Museum of Natural History.

BEAKED WHALES, COW FISH; SPITS DOLFYNEN, BALEINES DE SOWERBY, SOWERBYS WALE. (Included are vernaculars used in other countries.)

TEN SPECIES are found in the oceans of the Western and Eastern Hemispheres.

Head and body length is 3 to 7 meters, the pectoral fin length is 200 mm. to 500 mm., the dorsal fin height is about 150 mm., and the width of the flukes is about one meter. Color is variable but is usually slaty black to bluish black above and lighter below. Only two teeth become well developed, one in each side of the lower jaw. These are much larger in the male than in the female. Other small teeth may be present in the lower and upper jaws. A row of small vestigial teeth in each upper jaw seems to be a species character of *M. grayi*. The teeth may be lost in old age. The species of this genus are distinguished by features of the skull, lower jaw, and teeth. The bones of the rostrum are quite dense and heavy. In the species *M. densirostris* a measure of the specific gravity of the rostral bones indicated that they were 34 per cent heavier than elephant ivory.

Distribution and movements are not well known. These cetaceans have occasionally become stranded on coasts. In most cases these have been single individuals, but there is a record of about 25 individuals of the genus *Mesoplodon* that were stranded on the Chatham Islands. Thus they may travel in schools, in smaller groups, and singly. It appears to be a pelagic genus, spending most of its life far out from shore, and consequently is rarely stranded or encountered by man. Some species have yet to be observed in life, known only from stranded specimens. In the case of a few of the species, known specimens number less than 50.

Animals of the genus *Mesoplodon* feed on squids, other cephalopods, and fish. Breeding usually takes place in late winter and spring, with a gestation period of about one year. The calf is 1.5 to 2.5 meters long at birth, suckles for about one year, and grows 1.00 to 1.25 meters during the period of nursing. A 2-meter embryo, nearly ready to be born, has been found in a 5-meter female. The estimated weight of this embryo was 85 to 90 kg.

A Sowerby's whale, *M. bidens*, has been kept alive out of water for two days: "It emitted a low, cavernous sound like the lowing of a cow" (F. E. Beddard, *A Book of Whales*, 1900).

The type species of the genus is *M. bidens* (Sowerby).

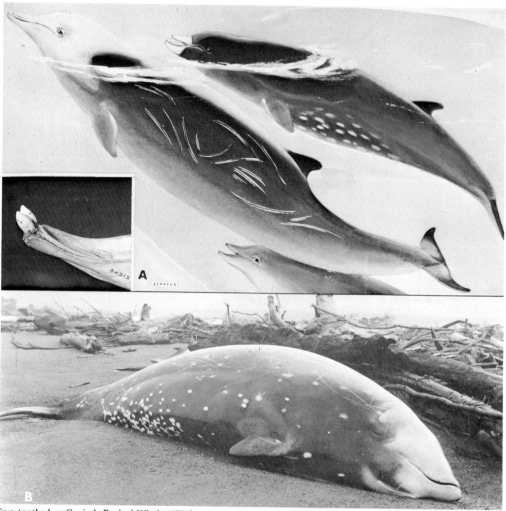

Two-toothed or Cuvier's Beaked Whales (*Ziphius cavirostris*), A. Photo from National Geographic Society of painting by Else Bostelmann. Inset: Lower jaw showing the two teeth, photo by P. F. Wright of specimen in U.S. National Museum. B. Photo by Warren J. Houck.

CUVIER'S BEAKED WHALE, GOOSE-BEAKED WHALE; CUVIER-DOLFYNEN, BALEINES DE CUVIER; CUVIER'S WHALE.

THE SINGLE SPECIES, *Z. cavirostris*, inhabits the oceans of both hemispheres.

Head and body length is 5.5 to 8.5 meters; the pectoral fin length is about 0.5 meters; the height of the dorsal fin is about 305 mm.; and the width of the flukes is about 1.5 meters. Estimated weights are usually around 1,600 kg., but a female, 6.6 meters in length, weighed 2,952.5 kg. The sectioned teeth of this female revealed 24 to 28 growth layers, each layer presumably representing one year of life. The flukes do not usually have a median notch, but two specimens have been found with a definite median notch.

Coloration is variable, but two frequently observed color schemes are as follows: face and upper back are cream-colored, the remainder of the body is black; the entire body is grayish fawn with some small blotches of slightly darker gray below.

This cetacean is distinguished from other genera of beaked whales in the family *Ziphiidae* mainly by features of the skull. The males have two functional teeth, one at the tip of each lower jaw; these are usually not visible in females. Rows of small rudimentary teeth are usually present in both jaws.

Groups of 30 to 40 often travel, dive, and feed together in fairly close association, often remaining underwater for periods exceeding 30 minutes. Different kinds of cephalopods seem to be the preferred food. Upon examination, the female with a length of 6.6 meters was found to have the remains of 1,304 squids in her stomach. Males seem to attain sexual maturity at a body length of approximately 5 meters, whereas most pregnant females are at least 6 meters in length. The young are born after a gestation period of about one year. Newly-born *Ziphius* individuals are about one-third the length of the mother.

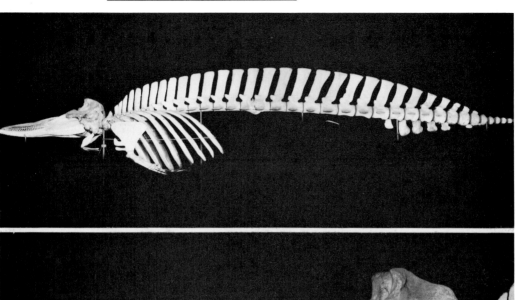

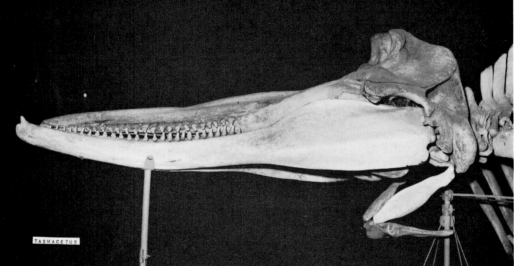

Tasmanian Beaked Whale (*Tasmacetus shepherdi*), photos by Eldon V. Burkett through Wanganui Public Museum.

TASMANIAN BEAKED WHALES, SHEPHERD'S BEAKED WHALES.

THE SINGLE SPECIES, *T. shepherdi*, was named and described in 1937 from a specimen cast up on the Ohawe beach of New Zealand. The skeleton of this animal is preserved in the Wanganui Museum, New Zealand. A lower jaw from another individual of the same species is in the Dominion Museum of Wellington, New Zealand. (The place of its discovery is not known.) The generic name comes from Tasman—the Tasman Sea, and from the Greek word *ketos*—whale; the trivial name refers to Mr. Shepherd, who obtained the skeleton of the type specimen.

The head and body length of the type was about 5 meters. Coloration was not given in the original description, since the animal had decomposed and been cut up by natives before the skeleton was secured. The beak is presumed to be about 460 mm. long. *Tasmacetus* may be distinguished from the other living genera of beaked whales by the following characters: the palatine bones are not exposed on the palate, and there are about 90 teeth in the lower and upper jaws. These teeth are assumed to be functional, since they show signs of wear. Two large terminal teeth are present in the lower jaw which have bulbous bases and conical crowns.

Baird's Beaked Whales (*Berardius bairdi*), A. & B. Photos from the Fisheries Research Board of Canada through I. B. MacAskie. C. Head showing teeth in lower jaw, photo from Tokyo Whales Research Institute through Hideo Omura. D. & E. Photos by Warren J. Houck.

GIANT BOTTLE-NOSED WHALES, PACIFIC BEAKED WHALES, BAIRD'S BEAKED WHALES (*B. bairdi*); TSUCHIMBO AND TSUCHI-KUJIRA.

THE TWO SPECIES are distributed as follows: *B. bairdi* in the North Pacific from Japan and California north to the Bering Sea; *B. arnouxi* in the Antarctic Ocean and adjacent waters. Their ranges do not appear to overlap.

Head and body length is usually 9 to 12 meters; the pectoral fin length is about one meter; the height of the dorsal fin is about 305 mm.; and the width of the flukes is 2.5 to 3 meters. These whales are uniformly brownish black, sometimes with white blotches on the under parts. These are among the largest of the beaked whales. The lower jaw extends slightly beyond the tip of the upper jaw, the snout is tapered, the forehead is well defined, and the skull is more nearly symmetrical than in the other beaked whales. Two

pairs of teeth are usually present in the lower jaw.

Animals of the genus *Berardius* often travel in tightly-packed schools of about 20 individuals. They raise their flukes in the air when diving. These whales are said to be alert and hard to capture: one harpooned individual dived straight down at an amazing speed, taking some 900 meters of line with it. They are known to feed on squid, octopus, rockfish, and herring.

The average body length at which sexual maturity is attained in *B. bairdi* is 9.8 to 10.5 meters. Calves have been noted in August off the coast of British Columbia. The gestation period is apparently about ten months, and the length of the young at birth is about one-third the length of the mother.

The commercial catch in Japanese waters in the years 1949 and 1950 was about 300.

The type species of the genus is *B. arnouxi*, Duvernoy.

Bottle-nosed Whale (*Hyperoodon ampullatus*), photo from *Endeavour*.

BOTTLE-NOSED WHALES; BUTSKOPPEN, SNAVEL POTVISCH, BUTYLKONOS, NABBVÄL, HOCICO DE BOTELLA. (Included are vernaculars used in other countries.)

THE TWO SPECIES are *H. ampullatus* and *H. planifrons*. The former species frequents the North Atlantic in the summer; it travels south, sometimes to the Mediterranean, in the winter. *H. planifrons* wanders from South Atlantic waters to the south and west coasts of Australia.

Full-grown males are about 9 meters long, and adult females about 7.5 meters. One female, 6 meters in length, weighed 2.5 metric tons.

Animals of the genus *Hyperoodon* become lighter in color with age: Calves are grayish to black, immature individuals are often spotted yellowish and white, and old individuals may be completely yellowish white. The head rises abruptly from the beak, imparting somewhat of a "bottle-nosed" appearance. Due to the enlargement of bone crests, the forehead becomes bulbous and notched with age in the males. Two teeth are usually present in the lower jaw of young males; older males, however, usually have only a single functional tooth in the lower jaw. These teeth are smaller in females. Rows of vestigial teeth are often present in the lower and upper jaws.

These whales can leap clear of the water and are dangerous to hunt because of the suddenness and great speed of their dives. They usually remain submerged from 10 to 20 minutes when feeding, but they may stay underwater several hours when harpooned. Schools of 4 to 12 travel together and will not desert a wounded member. Animals of the genus *Hyperoodon* probably feed at great depths. Squid and cuttlefish are the main food: 10,000 cuttlefish beaks have been found in the stomach of one *Hyperoodon* individual. It has been suggested that the migrations of these whales are in response to the movements of their prey.

The gestation period is about one year, and the young at birth are about 3 meters long. Young have been noted in May and June in Arctic waters.

A full-grown male 9 meters in length and 6 meters in circumference may yield two tons of oil and 100 kg. of spermaceti. The oil is similar to that of the sperm whale. In males, the cavity in front of the head bones contains fat, whereas this cavity in females contains an oil having twice the density of the blubber oil. *H. ampullatus* was harvested commercially in the western north Atlantic prior to 1900.

The type species of the genus is *H. ampullatus* (Forster).

SPERM WHALES, PYGMY SPERM WHALES, POT WHALES; CACHALOTS, POTVISSAN CACHALOTES, POTTWALE, POTVISCH, KASHALOT, KASKELOT, SPERMACETIVAL, POTTVAL, SPERMHVAL. (Included are vernaculars used in other countries.)

THIS FAMILY consists of two Recent genera: *Physeter*, for the single species *P. catodon*, the sperm whale, and *Kogia*, for the single (?) species *K. breviceps*, the pygmy sperm whale. Both genera inhabit all oceans. Some zoologists place *Kogia* in a separate family, the Kogiidae.

The two genera differ markedly in size and body form. In *Physeter* the males measure from 15 to 18 (rarely 20) meters and usually weigh from 38 to 55 metric tons, with the females measuring 10 to 12 meters. In *Kogia* the length is 2.8 to 4 meters and the weight is usually estimated at between 180 to 320 kg., with the males generally larger and heavier than the females. The outstanding feature in the sperm whale is the tremendous barrel-shaped head, whereas the pygmy sperm whale resembles a porpoise in body form, except for the underslung lower jaw which imparts a shark-like appearance. The greatest circumference in *Kogia* occurs in the region between the flippers and dorsal fin. The "S"-shaped blowhole is on the left side of the head and is located near the tip of the snout in *Physeter* and on the forehead in *Kogia*. The sperm whale is the only cetacean with a gullet large enough to swallow a man. Irregular longitudinal furrows occur on the throat. The flippers are broad and rounded. The dorsal fin is high and sickle-shaped in *Kogia*, low and rounded in *Physeter*. The blubber in the sperm whale is up to 355 mm. thick. A 13-meter adult male sperm whale, weighing 20 metric tons, had a heart which weighed 116 kg. when removed.

The skull of *Physeter* is more distorted from the usual symmetrical pattern than in any other mammal. As in the beaked whales (Ziphiidae), the skull in *Physeter* and *Kogia* is crested. The facial part of the skull is long in the sperm whale but among the shortest of any cetacean in the pygmy sperm whale. The strong, conical, functional teeth, 18 to 60 in number, are confined to the lower jaw and fit into sockets in the palate when the mouth is closed. Smaller nonfunctional teeth are embedded in the gums of the upper jaw. The vertebrae number 50 to 51, and most or all of the neck vertebrae are fused.

The habits of *Physeter* are fairly well known, but little information has been published on *Kogia*. The former genus emits a number of different sounds, which have been described as "a muffled, smashing noise"; "a grating sort of groan, very low in pitch," like "a rusty hinge creaking"; and most commonly, a "series of sharp clicks." The sperm whale sometimes lifts its head out of water to look and listen. It usually travels at a speed of 4 knots but can be pressed to 12 knots. The members of this genus usually travel in groups of 15 to 20 individuals, that is, an old male, the females of his harem, and their youngsters. *Physeter* travels back and forth between tropical and temperate waters, the schools often number in the hundreds. The apparent restriction of the range of the females within 40 degrees north latitude and 40 degrees south latitude is probably related to the effects of water temperature on reproduction. There is some indication that *Kogia* occurs in schools that migrate toward the polar regions in summer, returning to warmer waters in the fall and spring to give birth.

In *Physeter* the gestation period is approximately 16 months and in *Kogia* it seems to be about 9 months. Sperm whales attain sexual maturity at an age of 4 or 5 years.

The sperm whale feeds mainly on squid and cuttlefish, with fish, sharks, and skates as secondary items. Cephalopods, crabs, and prawns are included in the diet of the pygmy sperm whale.

Pygmy sperm whales have no economic value, but numerous commercial products are obtained from sperm whales. Sperm oil, which is associated with the

Sperm Whale (*Physeter catodon*), photo from American Museum of Natural History.

spermaceti in the cavities of the head and the blubber of the sperm whale, is used as an industrial lubricant. Spermaceti, which is also present in the pygmy sperm whale and other cetaceans, is used in making candles and ointments. It solidifies into a white wax upon exposure to air, but sperm oil remains fluid after exposure to air and cooling. Up to 30 barrels of sperm oil and 1 ton of spermaceti have been obtained from the heads of individual sperm whales. Ambergris, a substance unique to *Physeter*, is probably formed from solid wastes coalescing around a matrix of indigestible material, rather than being a solidification of bile or a substance formed in response to intestinal irritation. Apparently the heaviest authenticated mass of ambergris from a single animal weighed 450 kg. Ambergris is a fixative and has the property of retaining the fragrance of perfumes; current prices for it, based largely on color, range from $10 to $50 per pound. By international agreement, the meat of sperm whales may be discarded and most of it is thrown overboard in pelagic whaling. At the Pacific coastal whaling stations, however, the meat is frozen and sold as food for fur-bearing animals or treated to yield oil and meat meal.

The geological range of this family is the lower Miocene to the Recent; of the two Recent genera, only *Physeter* has a fossil record.

Teeth of Sperm Whale (*Physeter catodon*), photo by P. F. Wright of specimen in U.S. National Museum.

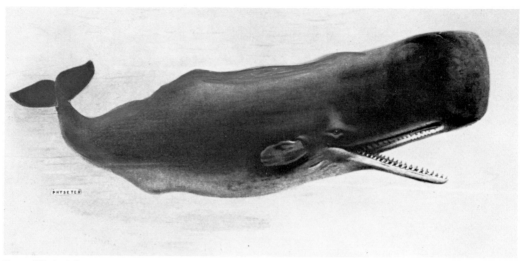

Sperm Whale (*Physeter catodon*), photo from *British Mammals*, Archibald Thorburn.

SPERM WHALES, POT WHALES; CACHALOTS, POT-VISSAN, CACHALOTES, POTTWALE, POTVISCH, KA-SHALOT, KASKELOT, SPERMACETIVAL, POTTVAL, SPERMHVAL. (Included are vernaculars used in other countries.)

THE SINGLE SPECIES, *P. catodon*, is found in the oceans of both hemispheres.

The males are nearly twice as large as the females: the head and body length of the males is 15 to 18 meters (rarely 20 meters), whereas that of the females is usually 10 to 11 meters (with a maximum of about 12 meters). The flippers are about 2 meters long, and the tail flukes are usually 4 to 4.5 meters wide. Males usually weigh from 35 to 50 tons. Color is gray to dark bluish gray and black. With increasing age, males may become paler and sometimes piebald. The enormous squarish head is the most striking feature, for the skull is more distorted in relation to the normal symmetrical pattern than is the case in any other mammal. The blowhole is located toward the tip of the snout, and the slender lower jaw is armed with 16 to 30 conical teeth on each side. These functional teeth may be more than 202 mm. in length. Smaller non-functional teeth are present in the upper jaw. Behind the rounded dorsal fin, a number of low humps are present.

The spout is characteristic in that it is directed obliquely forward. In diving, animals of the genus *Physeter* lift the tail flukes high in the air and descend almost vertically. Sperm whales feed at great depths, commonly at 360 meters or so. The diet is mainly squid and cuttlefish, with other fishes (barracuda, albacore, angler) and shark as secondary items. Sperm whales often bear the scars of combats with giant squids. Sperm whales have been known to descend to a depth of 1 kilometer but usually make a number of shallow dives after a prolonged submergence of 20 to 75 minutes. The descent to great depths may be facilitated by a buoying or stabilizing effect of the oil reservoirs in the head and in the humps on the back.

Sperm whales are gregarious and polygamous, usually traveling in schools of 15 to 20 individuals and often migrating in the hundreds. They are present in tropical waters in the winter and migrate in spring toward temperate regions. The adult males that wander farther north and south and possibly winter in polar and subpolar waters are probably those bulls that have failed to secure a harem.

Mating probably occurs after the departure to temperate waters. The gestation period is from 12 to 16 months. The single calf—rarely are there two—is about 5 meters long at birth, is suckled for at least six months, and is weaned when about 6 meters in length. Maximum age is not known, but marking records show that males can live 32 years and females at least 22 years.

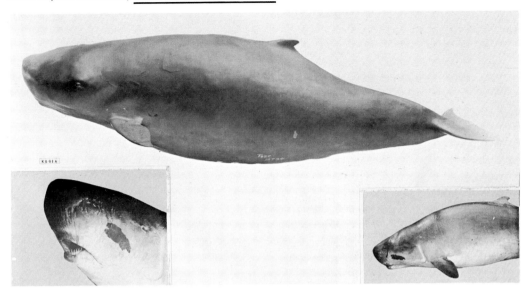

Pygmy Sperm Whale (*Kogia breviceps*), photo from U.S. National Museum. Insets: Photos from "Eastern Pacific Records and General Distribution of the Pygmy Sperm Whale," Carl Hubbs, *Jour. Mam.*

PYGMY SPERM WHALES, LESSER SPERM WHALES, SHORT-HEADED SPERM WHALES; DWERGPOTVISSEN, ZWERGPOTTWÄLE, CACHALOTS PYRENEES, DWERGPOTVIS. (Included are vernaculars used in other countries.)

THIS GENUS is found in the Atlantic, Pacific, and Indian oceans, and is comprised of two species, *K. breviceps* and *K. simus.*

Head and body length is 2.75 to 4 meters, the length of the flippers is about 405 to 610 mm., and the width of the flukes is about 610 mm. Estimated weights are usually from 180 to 320 kg. Males are usually larger and heavier than females. The skull is about .5 meters long and .4 meters wide; when viewed from above or below it forms a fairly straight-sided triangle. Coloration is black above and gray to grayish white below. *Kogia* individuals resemble *Physeter* individuals in the presence of a spermaceti reservoir in the head, in that the functional teeth are confined to the lower jaw, in characters of the skeleton, and in having the blowhole on the left side of the head. The blowhole in *Kogia* is located on the forehead. The head of the pygmy sperm whale is only about one-sixth of the total length. *Kogia* individuals resemble porpoises in the external outline of the head, but the blunted and pointed snout projects beyond the lower jaw. Nine to 15 sharp, curved teeth are present on each side of the lower jaw. Smaller non-functional teeth may be present in the upper jaw. The high dorsal fin is hooked or curved like a sickle and is located near the middle of the back.

The habits of these animals are not well known. There is some indication that they travel in schools, and that they migrate toward the poles in summer and return to warmer waters in the fall and winter to give birth.

Mating probably occurs over a considerable length of time, as pregnant females with fetuses less than 305 mm. in length have been noted from December to April. (There is also one record of a November birth: A 3-meter female, while stranded, gave birth to a 1.75-meter, 80-kg. calf.) The gestation period seems to be about nine months, and females mate every year. The calf appears to follow the mother for about one year.

Remains of squid, cuttlefish, crabs (including shore crabs), and prawns have been found in the stomachs of stranded individuals.

WHITE WHALES OR BELUGAS AND NARWHALES.

THIS FAMILY of two genera (the white whales or belugas, *Delphinapterus*, and narwhales, *Monodon*), each having only one species, exists in Arctic seas. Both species sometimes ascend rivers.

In the white whale the length of the head and body is usually 2.8 to 4.4 meters, the largest is about 5.5 meters. The length of narwhales is usually 3.7 to 4.9 meters, with a maximum length of approximately 6.2 meters. This length is exclusive of the tusk or "horn" which is really a tooth that projects beyond the end of the lower jaw. The members of this family attain weights of 223 to 907 kg. The body form resembles that of the members of the family Delphinidae. The snout is blunt; there is no beak. The blowhole is located well back from the tip of the snout. External grooves are not present on the throat. The flipper is short and rounded and the dorsal fin is not present, but *Monodon* has a low dorsal ridge. The tail is only slightly forked in the narwhale, but it is strongly forked (and asymmetrical) in the beluga.

The white whale has 32 to 40 teeth, and the narwhale has only two teeth, which are confined to the upper jaw. In the male narwhale the left tooth generally develops into a long spiral tusk, as much as 2.7 meters long, but in females little development of the tusk occurs or none at all. The teeth of female narwhales are usually embedded in bone. The tusk in the male sometimes develops on the right rather than on the left side, but it always spirals from left to right. It grows continuously and may be a structure specialized beyond usefulness. The skull in both genera lacks crests. The vertebrae number is 50 or 51, and the first two neck vertebrae are united.

A white whale 4.3 meters long had a heart which weighed 2,722 grams. An electrocardiogram, taken while the whale was engaged in exciting and strenuous activity, indicated a heart rate of 12 to 24 beats per minute. The general characteristics of the white whale's electrocardiogram were similar to those of other mammals.

These cetaceans usually live in schools, sometimes consisting of more than 100. Their migrations are largely in response to the shifting pack ice and hard winters. Individuals that become trapped in ice fields break through the ice by ramming it from the underside. The cushion on top of the head lessens the shock to the animal. Belugas can swim for hours at a speed of 9 kilometers per hour and can remain under water for periods of 15 minutes. Narwhales are rapid swimmers and are known to dive to depths of 60 meters. The small spout is not well defined. Both genera emit various sounds; it has been suggested that the sounds of the beluga are produced by the emission of a stream of bubbles rather than by the voicebox. These cetaceans are sensitive to sounds in the water but apparently disregard noises originating on land.

White whales and narwhales seem to eat mainly on the bottom and include cephalopods, crustaceans, and fish in their generalized diet.

The gestation period is not known for the narwhale; it is about 14 months in the white whale. The calf is approximately 1.5 meters long at birth and remains with the mother for some time.

Both genera are hunted by Eskimos and other natives of the Arctic. Economically important fisheries for the beluga are located in both the New World and the Old World. "Porpoise leather," formerly an important commercial item, is the tanned hide of a white whale.

The geological range for this family is the Pleistocene in North America and Europe, and the Recent in the Arctic. There are no extinct genera.

Beluga Whales (*Delphinapterus leucas*), photos from New York Zoological Society.

WHITE WHALES, BELUGAS, DELPHINAPTÉRES BLANCS, KĬLLĒLŪÄK, WEISSWÄLE. (Included are vernaculars used in other countries.)

THE SINGLE SPECIES, *D. leucas*, is found in the arctic regions of North America and Eurasia. It prefers shallow coastal waters and bays, but also ascends large rivers, such as the Yukon, Churchill, St. Lawrence, Amur, Anadyr, and Ob. White whales travel south in severe winters and have been recorded from Japan, Ireland, Scotland, and the Baltic Sea.

Head and body length is usually 3.75 to 4.25 meters; the average length of males is about 300 mm. more than that of females. The pectoral fin length is about 305 to 455 mm. The white-colored individuals weigh from 225 to 675 kg. Coloration becomes lighter with age: from dark gray, black, or bluish to yellowish, and finally white. Some populations pass through a mottled-brown color phase. The lightening of color is due to a reduction in the melanin in the skin, and the animals become white at four to five years of age. There are usually ten teeth in the upper jaw, and eight on each side of the lower jaw. Some semblance of a neck is present, and a dorsal fin is absent.

The sound of *Delphinapterus* individuals, "a low, liquid trill, like the cry of curlews in the spring," is reflected in their common name, "sea canary." Many animals produce underwater sounds, but few such sounds can be heard so readily above water as those of the beluga. White whales travel in schools, these sometimes number in the hundreds, but the number of individuals in actual association is usually less than ten. The beluga, a very supple animal, can scull with its tail and thus swim backward.

The generalized diet consists of fish, such as capelin, flounder, halibut, Arctic char, squids, and crustaceans. The white whale is largely a bottom feeder and is itself preyed upon by killer whales (*Orcinus*). The distribution of the beluga is largely dependent on the shifting pack ice rather than on the movements of its prey.

Females attain sexual maturity in their third summer, and at about 2.75 meters in length. The gestation period is about 14 months. Most births take place from March through May. A female appears to give birth every two or three years. The calf is about 1.5 meters long at birth and remains for some time with its mother. The growth rate is about one meter per year for the first two years, and then becomes much slower.

Commercial uses of the white whale are as follows: oil is secured from the blubber, leather for boots and laces is obtained from the hide, the flesh and blubber are eaten by men and sled dogs in the Arctic, and the flesh is processed for mink food. The protective blubber forms a layer 100 to 250 mm. thick which when rendered produces 100 to 200 liters of oil with large individuals producing as much as 300 liters.

The use of the name "beluga" for the white whale has been a source of considerable confusion since it is also applied to the great white sturgeon which is one of the principal sources of caviar.

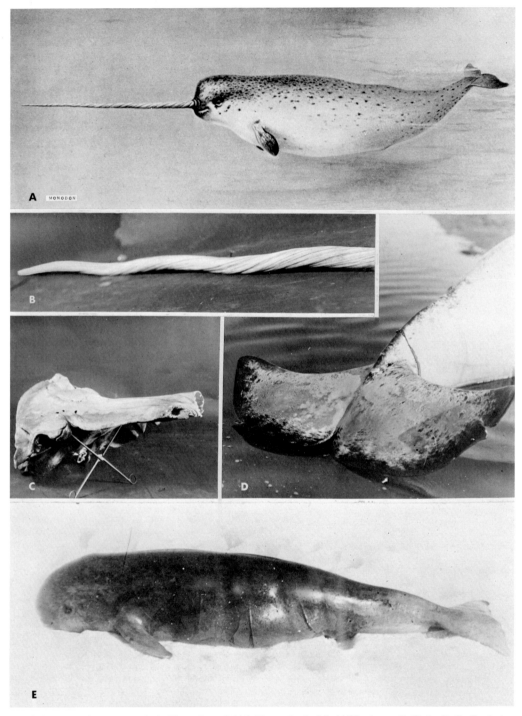

Narwhales (*Monodon monoceros*), A. Photo from *British Mammals*, Archibald Thorburn. B. Tusk; C. Skull; photos by P. F. Wright of specimen in U.S. National Museum. D. Tail; E. New-born baby; photos by Alwin Pedersen.

NARWHALES (NARWALS, NARWHALS); ADLUNG-
WÄK, NARWALLE.

THE SINGLE SPECIES, *M. monoceros*, inhabits the
Arctic seas. It is found along coasts, and sometimes
it ascends rivers. It has been recorded from as far
south as 71 degrees north latitude off the northern
coast of Alaska and from the White Sea.

Head and body length, exclusive of the tusk, is
3.6 to 5 meters. The pectoral fins are about 305 mm.
in length; a dorsal fin is absent, and the tail flukes are
1 to 1.2 meters in width. The adults have brownish
upper parts and whitish under parts, with a mottled
pattern of "leopard spotting" throughout. Coloration becomes lighter with age.

Secondary sexual characters exist in tooth structure:
of the two teeth, which are confined to the upper jaw,
usually only the left develops (commonly in the males
only). The spirally twisted tusk that develops from
this tooth protrudes through the upper lip and may be
2.8 meters in length. The tusk develops only slightly
or not at all in the females. The cavity of an uninjured
tusk is filled with a spongy core that is rich in blood.
Broken tusks are common; occasionally they are
filled with a smaller tusk of unknown origin. The
suggestion that the tusks are used to break the ice or
or that they are used in combat and feeding seems to
be invalid; it appears more probable that they represent structures specialized beyond usefulness. The
tusks were regarded as the horns of the unicorn in
medieval times and highly prized for reputable medicinal properties. They first appeared in Europe as
Norsemen trade articles from Greenland and Iceland.
Today the tusks are used in making various imple-
ments and in trade.

Members of *Monodon* emit a shrill whistle when
exhaling after a dive, and the female, when calling her
young, makes a deep roaring sound. Narwhales often
lie motionless for several minutes at the surface after
breathing. They are often noted in small groups of
six to ten individuals, often of the same sex. They
migrate in large numbers ahead of the ice in the fall
and return with the open water in the spring.

They feed on cuttlefish, crustaceans, and fish.
Killer whales (*Orcinus*) attack narwhales, and there is
one record of a walrus (*Odobenus*) attacking a narwhale and eating some of its blubber.

Narwhale calves are about 1.5 meters long at birth
and remain with the mother for some time.

In addition to the commercial value of their tusks,
narwhales also yield oil from the blubber and food for
Eskimos and dogs.

DOLPHINS AND PORPOISES, KILLELUAK, WEISS-
WALE, GNAVEL-DOLFYNEN, TUCUXI, MADARA-
IRUKA, COMMON PORPOISE, BRUINVISS, BRAUN-
FISCH, MARSOUINS, HAI-CHU. (Included are ver-
naculars used in other countries.)

THIS FAMILY of 18 genera and approximately 62
species inhabits all the oceans and the estuaries of
many large rivers; some forms occasionally ascend
rivers. Individuals of certain species of *Sotalia* and
some individuals of the genera *Orcaella* and *Neomeris*,
the "true porpoises," seem to prefer warm coastal
waters and do not live in polar waters.

The common name "dolphin" is generally applied
to small cetaceans having a beak-like snout and a
slender and streamlined body form, whereas the name
"porpoise" refers to those small cetaceans having a
blunt snout and a stout, rather stocky body form.
The length in most genera is 1.2 to 4.2 meters, and
the weight is 23 to 225 kg. *Orcinus* attains a length of
9.3 meters, the weight of a 4.1-meter female was
estimated at 830 kg. *Pseudorca* attains a length of
5.5 meters and a weight of 1.3 metric tons, and *Globicephala* attains lengths of 8.6 meters; the weight of a
4.4-meter male was estimated at 680 kg. The blowhole is located well back from the tip of the beak or
the front of the head. The flippers and dorsal fin are
sickle-shaped, triangular, or broadly rounded, with

Pacific Striped Dolphins (*Lagenorhynchus obliquidens*), which have been trained to leap unusually high. Many of the
smaller cetaceans regularly leap out of the water but rarely go more than a foot or two above the surface and re-enter
the water at a distance of only a few feet. Photo from Marineland of the Pacific.

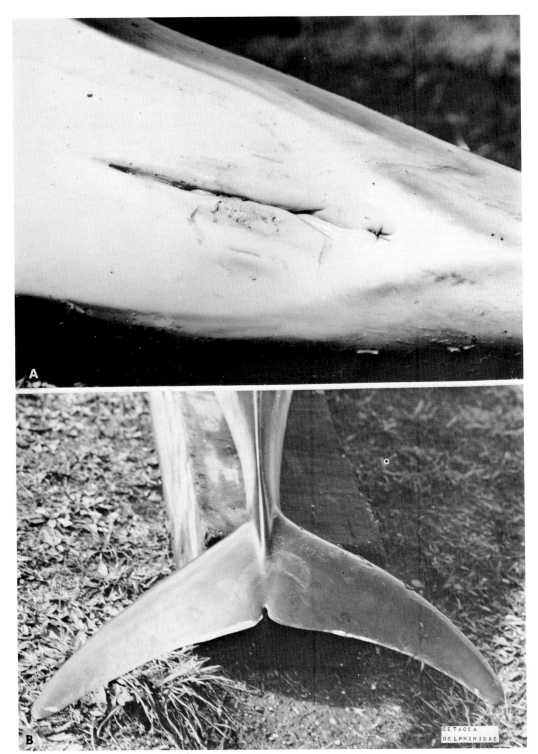

Pacific Striped Dolphin (*Lagenorhynchus obliquidens*), A. Uro-genital region of a young female. Note the mammary slits on each side of the uro-genital opening. The anus is to the right. B. Dorsal view of caudal flukes showing the deep tail notch typical of the Delphinidae and the prominent ridge on the top of the tail. Photos by Warren J. Houck.

the dorsal fin near the middle of the back. The genera *Lissodelphis* and *Neomeris* lack a dorsal fin.

Functional teeth are usually numerous in both the upper and lower jaws, numbering up to 260. In one genus (*Grampus*) there are only 6 to 14 teeth which are confined to the lower jaw. The three genera of "true porpoises" have spade-shaped teeth, and "gum-teeth" are present in *Phocoenoides dalli*. The skull lacks crests. The vertebrae number from 50 to 98, and the first two neck vertebrae are fused. Some features distinguishing Delphinidae from Platanistidae are as follows. The fusion of the lower jaws in delphinids does not exceed one-third their length, whereas this fusion is more than half the length in the Platanistidae. At least some of the neck vertebrae are fused in the dolphins and porpoises, but they are all free in the platanistids. Delphinids have a lesser number of double-headed ribs than do the platanistids.

Included in the family Delphinidae are the most agile and speedy of all the cetaceans; they have remarkable group precision and regularity of movement. They frequently leap clear of the water and are capable of speeds of up to approximately 25 knots (*Delphinus*). Many forms follow ships and frolic about the bow. Dolphins and porpoises usually associate in schools of five to several hundred individuals, although single individuals and pairs are sometimes seen. *Globicephala* and some species of *Lagenorhynchus* are conspicuous for their large gatherings. Migration is known to take place in some species, and local movements because of food supply occur in others. The members of this family will school when frightened and will attack any disturber. They sometimes kill large sharks by ramming them. They utter under water a wide variety of calls and noises including a danger whistle and a mating yelp. Co-operative behavior has often been observed when one or more cetaceans will come to the aid of another in an emergency, in injury, sickness, or birth, pushing it to the surface so that it can breathe.

The perception of objects by means of reflected sound was demonstrated in *Tursiops* in 1958 for the first time in marine animals. The sense of vision is not so well developed as is that of hearing, but *Tursiops* can see moving objects in the air about 15 meters away. Observations on the behavior of captive dolphins indicate that these animals are very intelligent. Adult delphinids will engage in complex play with various objects and small fish and can be trained to perform tricks.

The spout of dolphins and porpoises is usually not well defined, but that of *Globicephala* is about 1.5 meters. Breathing is often accompanied by a low hissing or puffing noise. The respiration rate of the bottle-nosed dolphin (*Tursiops truncatus*), taken in an aquarium where these cetaceans could swim freely, was 1.5 to 4 respirations per minute. This species has a heart rate of 81 to 137 beats per minute (the average is 100 per minute). *Tursiops* has been observed sleeping in calm water about 30 cm. below the surface; slight movements of its tail brought its head above water so that it could breathe.

The killer whales (*Orcinus*) feed on almost any type of animal food; the other members of this family feed mainly on cephalopods and fish.

The gestation period is 9 to 12 months in most forms. In *Tursiops truncatus* the calf is born with its eyes open, but the teeth do not appear until about six weeks later. The young of this species are usually born underwater and typically swim unaided to the surface to breathe, although they may be nudged by the mother. An offspring of the bottle-nosed dolphin that is born dead is generally pushed to the surface by the mother, often with the assistance of other adult females, apparently with the intention of giving it air. The maximum age in the wild seems to be from 25 to 35 years.

Globicephala is presently the major cetacean of the Newfoundland whaling industry. The genera occuring in Japanese waters are hunted commercially, and a few delphinids are taken off the Scandinavian coasts.

Thirty-two extinct genera are known in this family. The geological range is the lower Miocene to the Recent of Europe and North America, the upper Pliocene of Japan, and the Pleistocene of New Zealand. The extinct *Phocoenopsis*, from certain New Zealand fossil beds, possibly may have been contemporary with man.

Rough-toothed Dolphins (*Steno bredanensis*) stranded on a beach in Senegal, photos by G. Labitte, Institut Français d'Afrique Noire.

ROUGH-TOOTHED DOLPHINS; GNAVEL-DOLFYNEN, LANGSCHNAUTZ DELPHINE.

THE SINGLE SPECIES, *S. bredanensis*, has been noted in warmer waters of the Atlantic, Pacific, and Indian oceans, the Bay of Bengal, and the Red, Mediterranean, and Caribbean seas.

Head and body length is 1.75 to 2.5 meters; the length of the pectoral fin is about 305 mm.; and the height of the dorsal fin is about 150 mm. The upper parts are slate-colored or purplish black, with scattered spots and markings; and the belly is pinkish white or rose-colored, with slaty spots. The beak is white, and the flippers, dorsal fin, and tail flukes are dark.

This genus is characterized by dental features. The surfaces of the teeth are roughened and furrowed by vertical ridges and wrinkles. There are 20 to 27 teeth on each side of the upper and lower jaws. The beak is slender and compressed from side to side.

Habits are not known.

(*Sousa teuszii*), photo by J. Cadenat.

WHITE DOLPHINS, CHINESE WHITE DOLPHINS, PLUMBEOUS DOLPHINS, SPECKLED DOLPHINS, FRECKLED DOLPHINS.

ABOUT FIVE SPECIES are found in both salt and fresh warm waters of the Old World: *S. lentiginosa* from the south Indian coast and Ceylon; *S. plumbea* from the Indian Ocean east to the Straits of Malacca; *S. borneensis* from Borneo; *S. sinensis* from the coast of southern China; and *S. teuszii* from the Cameroons and Senegal, West Africa. These Old World dolphins inhabit river mouths, estuaries, and seas. *Sousa* has often been considered congeneric with *Sotalia*, but there are indications that the differences in the bullae warrant their generic separation. More information and revision are urgently needed for this genus.

Sousa resembles the bottle-nosed dolphins (*Tursiops*) and the rough-toothed dolphin (*Steno*) but is distinguished from them by 10 to 15 fewer vertebrae in the backbone and by the presence of more teeth. *S. plumbeus* is the longest and narrowest form with the most teeth. The beak is longer and more compressed, and the brain case is narrower in *S. plumbeus* than in *S. lentiginosa*.

The beak of *Sousa* is long and distinct, and the flippers are distinctly broad at the base. The dorsal fin is usually triangular in shape. Head and body length is 1.2 to 2.5 meters; the flipper length is 305 mm. or less; the height of the dorsal fin is about 150 mm.; and the width of the flukes is about 455 mm. An individual that was one meter in length was found to weigh about 37 kg., and one *S. teuszii* 2.3 meters long weighed 139 kg. Coloration is variable; most species are brown, gray, or black above and lighter beneath,

but the species *S. borneensis* and *S. sinensis* are white. *S. borneensis* is speckled with gray, while *S. sinensis* has pinkish fins and black eyes. *S. lentiginosa* is freckled with brown spots. The skull of *Sousa* differs from that of the other dolphins in the rather long symphysis of the jaws, and in the widely separated pterygoid bones which do not close together behind the palate. The number of teeth on each side of the upper and lower jaws is 23 to 37. The rostrum of *Tursiops* is always broader than in *Sousa*.

Sousa rolls to breathe. These dolphins sometimes leap out of water to a height of 1.2 meters. However, they seem to be slower moving than most dolphins. *Sousa* usually travels singly or in groups of two to five, but larger groups are occasionally encountered. The smaller groups usually swim close together.

When feeding, the dolphins appear to roll faster than when breathing. The diet consists of fish. The original specimen of *S. teuszii* from the Cameroon River was reported to have leaves, grass, and mangrove fruits in its stomach, which in the opinion of Cory Carvalho must have come from the stomachs of fish eaten by the porpoise. Several specimens of this species were obtained in 1958 and 1959 from the mouth of rivers in Senegal. They had only fish in their stomachs, among which the species *Ethmalosa dorsalis* and *Mugil* could be identified. Rather than being very rare as was formerly thought, *S. teuszii* were observed almost daily by zoologists in 1958 and 1959, especially during low tide, in the rivers and estuaries in Senegal from January to early April.

The number of young is one.

The type species of the genus is *S. lentiginosa*, Gray.

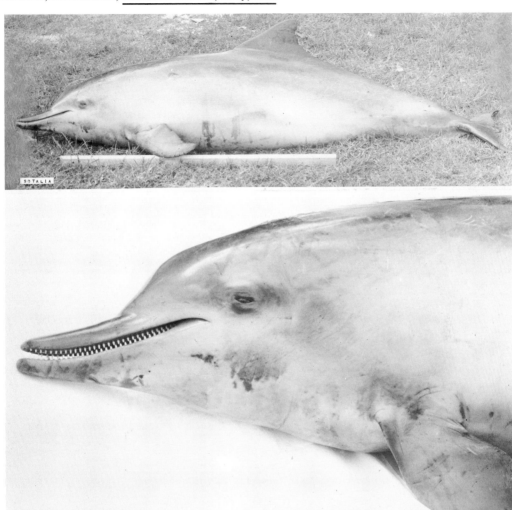

(*Sotalia* sp.), photos by Cory T. de Carvalho.

RIVER DOLPHINS; TUCUXI, PIRAYAGUARA, BOTO OR BOUTO (South American names).

FIVE SPECIES have been named in this genus: *S. brasiliensis* from the bay of Rio de Janeiro; *S. guianensis*, found along the coast of the Guianas; and *S. pallida*, *S. fluviatilis*, and *S. tucuxi*, all of which are found in the Amazon River and its great tributaries as well as in the Tocantins River where it often occurs with *Inia*. The first two species inhabit bays and estuaries, while the other three are found in the fresh waters of rivers and, occasionally during high water, in lakes. Cabrera and Yepes (1940) group these last three species into one, *S. pallida*, while Carvalho uses the name *S. fluviatilis* for river dolphins. Recent studies of river dolphins (James N. Layne, "Observations on Freshwater Dolphins in the Upper Amazon," *Jour. Mam.*, Vol. 39, No. 1, Feb., 1958, p. 12) made in

the upper Amazon region conclude: "A review of the descriptive material available for the three species of Amazon river dolphins strongly suggests that the principal characteristics employed to separate them may with equal justification be interpreted as being merely age differences of but a single species." It is not clear to us which of the specific names should be used for the river dolphins. Cory Carvalho doubts whether *S. guianensis* can be separated from the river porpoise.

The length of the head and body ranges between 915 and 1,650 mm.; the height of the dorsal fin is 110 to 127 mm.; the greatest girth is 700 to 980 mm.; and an adult male, 1,600 mm. long, weighed 47.36 kg. There are 26 to 35 teeth on each side. *Sotalia* is distinguished from *Inia* in the wild by the former's prominent dorsal fin. The beak is more slender than in *Sousa*. Its beak is shorter than that of *Inia*, and the bulge of the forehead is not so prominent, giving its head a more streamlined contour. The chief characteristics which distinguish *Sotalia* from *Steno* and *Tursiops* are the separation of the pterygoids, the fewer caudal vertebrae, and the greater numbers of teeth.

S. brasiliensis ranges from pale bluish gray to blackish above, and white below. The color of the back extends to a circle around the eye, onto the pectoral fins, in an oblique band on the flanks, and to the sides of the tail. The dorsal fin is the same color as the back except for an area of bright yellow on each side near the top; the sides of the dolphin are a yellowish orange. *S. guianensis* ranges from blackish, dull lead gray, or brown above, and from pinkish, violet gray to white along the lateral margins and on the ventral side. The pectoral fins are the same color as the back. Fresh water *Sotalia* are bluish or pearl gray above; the color is darker on the anterior part of the body. The pectoral fins, both below and above, are the same color as the back. The under parts are pinkish white to white. A prominent band of the ventral coloration extends upward on the sides of the body to slightly above the level of the eye; the dorsal color, however, extends down to a distinct line from the corner of the mouth to the base of the pectoral fin and includes the eye. The tip of the beak and the apex of the dorsal fin are conspicuously white. The larger dolphins are noticeably paler above.

S. brasiliensis often travels in bands of five, six, or eight individuals. They swim rather slowly in regularly and perfectly executed movement and rarely leap clear out of the water. On the other hand, the fresh water *Sotalia* of the Amazon were observed to be more active than *Inia*. They swim at a faster pace. These dolphins always roll out of the water when breathing. The head and trunk usually appear in smooth sequence; a short puff was the only sound heard when they breathed. The interval between breaths varied from 5 to 85 seconds, with a mean of 33 seconds. They were seen on several occasions to leap as far as 1.2 meters out of the water. *Sotalia* seems less inquisitive than *Inia*, although both apparently can see above water. No social action was ever observed between the two genera, although they were often in close proximity. The dolphins are most active in the early morning and late afternoon.

Sotalia have rather regular movements within the home range. These dolphins are apparently quite gregarious, and groups often swim and roll in tight formation and in nearly perfect synchrony, almost touching sides when they appear above the water. Their food appears to be entirely fish, but they eat some shrimp.

Natives regard *Sotalia* as a sacred animal, considering it as a good friend and protector of man which will bring the bodies of drowned persons to shore. This belief makes the obtaining of specimens rather difficult.

Nothing is known of its breeding habits.

The type species of the genus is *S. guianensis*, Van Beneden.

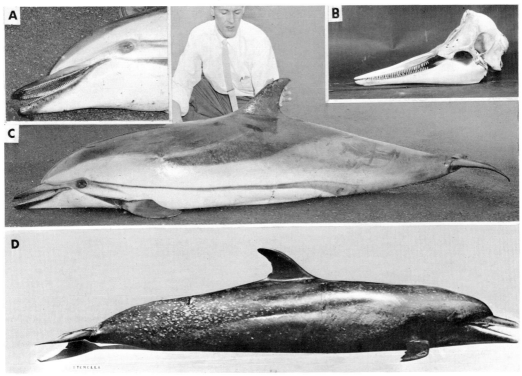

A. & C. Spotted Dolphins (*Stenella caeruleoalbus*), photos by Dick Bolding through Washington State Game Department. B. (*S. styx*), photo by P. F. Wright of specimen in U.S. National Museum. D. (*S. graffmani*), photo from Allan Hancock Foundation.

SPOTTED DOLPHINS, MADARA-IRUKA, GEVLEKTE DOLFYNEN (local vernaculars).

SOME TEN nominal species are found in the warmer waters of the world: *S. caeruleoalbus*, *S. attenuata*, *S. frontalis*, *S. graffmani*, *S. longirostris*, *S. microps*, *S. plagiodon*, *S. styx*, *S. malayana*, and *S. alope*. They seem to prefer the deeper and clearer offshore waters.

Head and body length is 1.2 to 3 meters; the flippers are 150 to 200 mm. in length; the height of the dorsal fin is about 180 to 305 mm., and the flukes are about 500 mm. broad. Adults of the larger species weigh about 165 kg. The adults are usually brown, gray, or black above, and paler below. Some species are spotted with white, and some species have longi-tudinal white, tan, or blue stripes on the sides of the head, shoulders, and back.

This genus is distinguished from the other genera of dolphins by internal features. The palate is not grooved on the inner side of the tooth row, and the union of the two branches of the lower jaw is short. The teeth number 37 to 52 on each side of each jaw.

The spotted and striped patterns can be seen when the animals roll at the surface or jump clear of the water. They often frolic about ships and can swim at a speed of 12 to 15 knots. The diet is fish. The gestation period is not known. The calf swims alongside its mother, rising and sinking in unison with her.

The type species of the genus is *S. attenuata* (Gray).

Common Dolphin (*Delphinus delphis*), photo by J. Cadenat.

COMMON DOLPHIN (*D. delphis*), BAIRD DOLPHIN, RED-BELLIED DOLPHIN (*D. roseiventris*), CAPE DOLPHIN (*D. capensis*); DELFINES, TONINAS.

THE THREE SPECIES are distributed as follows: *D. delphis* is worldwide in temperate and warm seas and occasionally occurs in cold northern waters; *D. roseiventris* occurs in the Banda Sea and Torres Strait; and *D. capensis* is known from South Africa and Japan.

The head and body length is 1.5 to 2.5 meters (rarely to 2.6 meters); the flipper (pectoral fin) length is about 0.3 meters; the height of the dorsal fin is about 0.6 meters; and the width of the flukes is about 0.5 meters. The weight is up to 75 kg. Over most of its range, the color of *D. delphis* is brown or black on the back and white on the belly, with bands and stripes of gray, yellow, and white on the sides. There is a dark stripe from the eye ring to the snout. However, *D. roseiventris* from the Molucca Sea and Torres Strait usually has pale rose-colored under parts, whereas the common dolphin in the Indian Ocean and certain Malayan waters is dark gray above and light gray below and has no stripes. The species *D. delphis* is gray to black above and white below and has two white stripes in the head and shoulder region; the species *D. capensis* is black above and light below.

The well-defined beak is narrow and sharply set off from the forehead by a deep V-shaped groove. The teeth number 40 to 50 on both sides of each jaw.

The species *D. delphis* occasionally enters fresh water. There is some indication that the species of this genus undergo a seasonal shift in range. These dolphins are among the swiftest of all cetaceans; although they usually travel at a speed of four to six knots, they are capable of swimming at 25 knots. They often frolic and leap about ships. *Delphinus* usually travels in groups of 20 to several hundred individuals and feeds on fish and cephalopods, mostly those found in shoals and near the surface. Flying fish are included in the diet; ear stones representing the remains of nearly 8,000 small fish have been found in the stomach of a single individual. *Delphinus* often feeds in company with *Lagenorhynchus*. In captivity, *Delphinus* is timid and notably less aggressive in its feeding habits than *Lagenorhynchus* or *Tursiops*.

The young are born from mid-winter to summer after a gestation period of about nine months.

The type species of the genus is *D. delphis*, Linnaeus.

Grampus (*Grampus griseus*), photo by Warren J. Houck.

RISSO'S DOLPHIN, GRAY GRAMPUS; ZWAARDRIS-
SEN, DAUPHINS GRISES.

THE SINGLE SPECIES, *G. griseus*, has been recorded from the west and east coasts of the United States, the North Atlantic, South Africa, the Mediterranean, the Red Sea, Japan, China, Australia, and New Zealand.

The adult *Grampus* is about 4 meters long; the pectoral fin is about 0.6 meters; the height of the dorsal fin is about 0.5 meters; and the width of the flukes is about 762 mm. The color varies with age, but adult dolphins are usually slaty or black above, tinged with blue or purple, and lighter beneath. The fins and tail are black. The whitish streaks on the body are probably healed scars from attacks by other *Grampus* and by squid.

G. griseus is distinguished from other dolphins by having only three to seven pairs of teeth in the front end of the lower jaws. One or two vestigial teeth are occasionally present in the upper jaw. A beak is lacking, and the front of the head rises almost vertically from the tip of the upper jaw. Field marks are the blunt snout and the pale gleam of the back in front of the high, pointed, and recurved dorsal fin.

Grampus is probably most common in the higher latitudes during the summer months. It is usually noted in groups of less than a dozen, but several such groups may associate in one area. *Grampus* is frolicsome, sometimes leaping clear of the water; Risso's dolphin sometimes falls back into the water head up, occasionally waving the back third of its body in the air. The diet includes cephalopods and fish.

A pregnant female dolphin, with an embryo nearly ready to be born, was noted in December.

The famous dolphin, "Pelorus Jack," believed to have been a gray grampus, received lifelong protection from an Order in Council (New Zealand) because of its habit of playing about ships and guiding them into Pelorus Sound. Some idea of the maximum age attained by dolphins is given by this mammal—Pelorus Jack carried on its activities from about 1896 to 1916.

Atlantic Bottle-nosed Dolphin (*Tursiops truncatus*), photo from Marineland of the Pacific. Skull of Red Sea Bottle-nosed Dolphin (*T. truncatus aduncus*), photo from *Mus. Senckenbergianum Säug. Zool. Samm.*, "Beschreibung mehrerer Neuer Säugethiere in der Zoologischen Sammlung der Senckenbergischen Naturforschenden Gesellschaft Befindlich," Eduard Rüppell.

BOTTLE-NOSED DOLPHINS; TUIMELAARS, SOU-FLEURS.

THE RANGE of this genus is worldwide. Two species are recognized: *T. truncatus* and *T. gilli*. The species *T. truncatus* is the only one about which much is known.

The head and body length is 1.75 to 3.6 meters; the length of the pectoral fin is 0.3 to 0.5 meters; the height of the dorsal fin is about 2.3 meters; and the width of the flukes is about 0.6 meters. Adults usually weigh from 150 to 200 kg. Most of the individuals are black, slaty blue, or gray above, with dark flippers and flukes, and lighter below. This genus is distinguished by the short, well-defined snout or beak, about 75 mm. long, and by the 20 to 26 teeth on each side of each jaw, each tooth being about 1 cm. in diameter. The common name is derived from the supposed resemblance of the beak to the top of an old-fashioned gin bottle.

On rare occasions, *Tursiops* ascends rivers. It is usually noted in bays and inshore waters, often in water shallower than 18 meters. *T. truncatus* is the most common dolphin off the eastern coast of North America and is usually associated in groups of five and more. This species appears to be migratory in coastal waters around England, the Netherlands, and North Carolina, but not in water along the Texas shoreline. It is said to be capable of speeds up to 20 knots, but a frightened and hard-pressed individual was timed at only 10 knots. In captivity these dolphins react with symptoms of fear to unfamiliar objects, but play with, and can be taught to fetch and carry, familiar objects. *Tursiops* feeds on a variety of fish, usually the most abundant species, and on sharks, shrimp, rays, and squid. Bottled-nosed dolphins are often found in association with pilot whales (*Globicephala scammoni*).

Most births seem to occur from March through May, after a gestation period of 11 to 12 months. At birth, the calves are about 1 meter long and weigh 12 kg. There is considerable variation in the time required for the transition from milk feeding to independent sustenance. One young animal began to eat squids when six months old, but another fed on milk until 18 months old. There is some indication that the females do not attain sexual maturity and rear young until about six years of age.

T. truncatus was formerly caught commercially with nets off the North Carolina coast, and the oil obtained from these mammals was used in chronometers. About 6,000 animals were caught in the period from 1907 to 1914.

The type species of the genus is *T. truncatus* (Montagu).

Pacific Striped Dolphin (*Lagenorhynchus obliquidens*), note the poorly defined beak. The ear opening is posterior to and slightly below the eye. Photos by Warren J. Houck.

STRIPED, WHITE-SIDED, AND WHITE-BEAKED DOL-
PHINS; WHITSNUIT DOLFIJNEN.

FIVE SPECIES inhabit the oceans of both hemispheres.

The head and body length is 1.5 to 3 meters; the
length of the pectoral fin is about 0.3 meters; the
height of the dorsal fin is 0.1 to 0.5 meters; and the
width of the flukes is 0.3 to 0.6 meters. A 1.9-meter
female weighed 75 kg.

Most of the species of *Lagenorhynchus* can be distinguished by their external color and pattern. They
are usually black or gray above and lighter below,
with various bands and stripes. In *L. albirostris* the
beak is white, and conspicuous yellowish brown and
grayish streaks are present on the side of the body in
L. obliquidens. The genus is also distinguished by its
internal features: the many vertebrae, 80 to 90, and
characteristics of the vertebrae and skull. Externally,
the short beak, pointed dorsal fin, and pointed flippers
are distinctive. The beak is short, about 50 mm. long,

and there are from 22 to 45 teeth in each side of each
jaw.

Lagenorhynchus occurs in groups of varying size;
some species usually live in schools of less than a
dozen individuals, whereas *L. acutus* and *L. albirostris* are often seen in groups of 1,000 to 1,500 members. These large schools usually become more
compact when the animals are not feeding. The
white-sided dolphin, *L. acutus*, is occasionally found
in association with the pilot whale, *Globicephala
melaena*. Some species appear to migrate, and *L.
obliquidens* seems to frequent offshore waters in
summer and fall and to move inshore during winter
and spring. These movements are probably related
to the availability of the food supply. *L. acutus*
feeding inshore in Newfoundland waters has been
driven ashore by whalers. *Lagenorhynchus* often
feeds with *Delphinus*; it eats fish, such as herring,
mackerel, capelin, and anchovies, crustaceans, squids,
and whelks. This genus is not like some dolphins
which are readily diverted from feeding and induced

to play around the bow of a ship. *Lagenorhynchus* plays with floating objects in captivity, but not to the same extent as *Tursiops*.

Mating usually takes place in the fall, and most of the young appear to be born in late spring and summer after a gestation period of about ten months. There is one record of a pregnant female bearing two embryos, each about 65 cm. long. The young at birth are about 1 meter in length.

Members of this genus are hunted commercially off Japan and occasionally in the North Atlantic.

The type species of the genus is *L. albirostris*, Gray.

(*Feresa attenuata*), A. Photo by Kenneth S. Norris. B. Photo by M. Nishiwaki through Tokyo Whales Research Institute.

THERE SEEMS TO BE a single recorded species, *F. attenuata*, although the Japanese who have been capturing and studying them recently in the Whales Research Institute in Tokyo recognize two species, *F. attenuata* and *F. occulta*. *Feresa* is known from the North and South Pacific, and from the African coast (Senegal). The probable distribution of this rare genus thus seems to be worldwide. Only four specimens are on record: Two skulls in the British Museum (Natural History), a skull in the Institut Francais d' Afrique Noire, and a skeleton in the University of Okayama,

Japan. The U.S. National Museum has a cast of one of the skulls.

The following measurements (in meters) are those of the female specimen taken in Japan: Head and body length, 2.35; length of flippers, 0.44; height of the dorsal fin, 0.24; breadth of the flukes, both sides, 0.18; and the length of each fluke, about one-third of a meter. The color of this specimen was dark gray throughout, with narrow white bands around the lips, and another white area around the vent or anus. There are 10 to 13 teeth in each side of each jaw.

Commerson's Dolphin (*Cephalorhynchus commersonnii*), photo from *Mamiferos Sud-Americanos*, Cabrera and Yepes.

COMMERSON'S DOLPHINS; TONINAS OVERAS.

FOUR SPECIES have been identified and described from the waters of the southern oceans.

The head and body length is 1.2 to 1.8 meters, the length of the pectoral fin is 0.15 to 0.4 meters, the height of the dorsal fin is about 0.1 meter, and the width of the flukes is about 0.3 meters. With its contrasting pattern of black and white, the Commerson's dolphin or piebald porpoise, *C. commersonii*, is probably the most conspicuously marked small ceta-cean of the Southern Ocean. The other forms also have a color pattern of black above and white below. A beak or snout is lacking, and teeth number from 25 to 32 on each side of each jaw.

These dolphins are mostly cold-water inhabitants and are known to feed on cuttlefish and shrimp. Hundreds have been noted around a vessel off southern South America; however, the specific habits and behavior of *Cephalorhynchus* are not known.

The type species of the genus is *C. heavisidii* (Gray).

Killer Whale (*Orcinus orca*), copy from color photo in *Natural History* by Morton Beebe.

KILLER WHALES; ORCAS, SAKAMATA KUZIRA, ORQUES EPULARDES, SCHWERT WALE. (Included are vernaculars used in other countries.)

THE SINGLE SPECIES *O. orca* is most common in Arctic and Antarctic waters but also occurs in all other oceans. The worldwide distribution of this genus may be related to its omnivorous diet and remarkable temperature tolerance.

A recent study in Japanese waters indicated an average length of approximately 6 meters for male and female *Orcinus*, whereas previous measurements have indicated a marked disparity in size between the adult males and females (males up to 9 meters and females from 4.5 to 6 meters). Furthermore, the flippers, dorsal fins, and tail flukes exhibit a disproportionately great increase in size in the older males. The weight of a 4-meter female was estimated at 850 kg. Externally, *O. orca* is distinguished by the bluntly rounded snout, the white patch just above and behind the eye, and the contrast of the black upper parts with the white under parts. The characteristic feature of the killer whale when swimming is "its erect black dorsal fin, rising like a pole every time the back comes up." (Remington Kellogg, *Nat. Geog. Mag.*, January, 1940, p. 71). There are from 10 to 14 large and powerful teeth on each side of each jaw.

Killer whales do not appear to migrate. Their usual speed is 10 to 13 km. per hour; in their extraordinary jumps they often cover 12 to 13.6 meters and clear the water by about 1.5 meters. They hunt in packs (usually 3 to 50 individuals), travel in close association, and attack larger prey simultaneously. The mouth and throat are large enough to swallow seals, young walrus, and the smaller cetaceans. When they see a bird, seal, or other food, near the edge of the ice, they will dive deeply and rush to the surface breaking ice that is 1 meter thick and dislodging their prey into the water. The stomach of one killer contained 24 seals and that of a 6-meter individual held 13 porpoises and 14 seals. *O. orca* also preys on the relatively defenseless baleen whales, literally tearing them to pieces; the sea otter, aquatic birds, fish, and cephalopods are also included in the diet. The approach of a pack of killer whales usually panics other marine vertebrates.

Although they may breed near the end of the year in some areas, killer whales appear to breed in spring and summer off the coast of the state of Washington (U.S.A.). The gestation period is about one year, and the young at birth are about 2 meters long.

Killer Whale (*Orcinus orca*), photo by Scanlan. Inset: Photo by P. F. Wright of skull in U.S. National Museum.

Right Whale Dolphins.

The two species of *Lissodelphis* are distributed as follows: *L. borealis* in the North Pacific Ocean from Japan to California; and *L. peronii* in the southern seas, probably worldwide in the Southern Hemisphere but only rarely penetrating into the Antarctic Ocean.

The species *L. borealis* has a head and body length of about 2.5 meters, whereas the head and body measurement in *L. peronii* is about 1.8 meters. The two species differ in color: *L. borealis* has black upper parts, flippers, and flukes, and white under parts; in *L. peronii*, the top of the head and the back are black or bluish black, and the beak, flippers, tail, sides, and under parts are white. The dark pigmentation is thus more extensive in the larger mammal, *L. borealis*. There is a short, distinct beak, and from 43 to 47 small, sharp pointed teeth on each side of each jaw. The vernacular name refers to the absence of a dorsal fin which is also lacking in the bowhead whales of the genus *Balaena*.

These largely oceanic animals usually appear in small schools away from the shore. They are quick and active in their movements and frequently leap out of water. *Lissodelphis* feeds on cephalopods and fish. Their habits and behavior are not well known.

The species *L. borealis* is hunted commercially off the coast of Japan.

The type species of the genus is *L. peronii* (Lacépède).

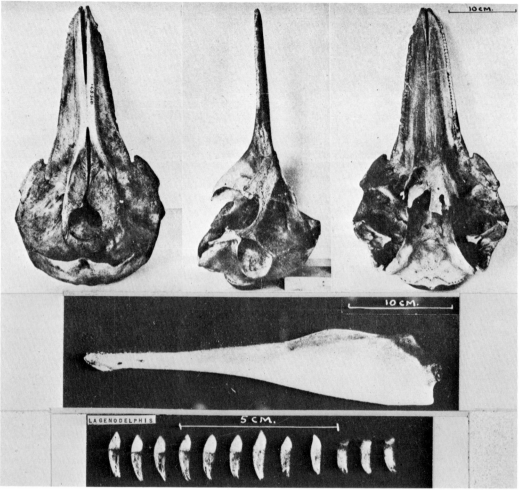

Bornean Dolphin (*Lagenodelphis hosei*), photos from *Sarawak Museum Journal*, F. C. Fraser.

BORNEAN DOLPHINS.

THE SINGLE SPECIES, *L. hosei*, is known only from a skull and skeleton in the British Museum of Natural History. The specimen was collected at the mouth of the Lutong River, Baram, Borneo. The generic name correlates the similarities in this animal to like characteristics in *Lagenorhynchus* and *Delphinus*, and the species name is after Charles Hose, a former resident of the Baram district, Sarawak, Borneo. This genus and species was named and described by F. C. Fraser in the December, 1956, *Sarawak Museum Journal*.

The head and body length of the type and only specimen is about 2.5 meters. From 40 to 44 teeth are present on each side of each jaw. The general structure of the skull is similar to that of *Lagenorhynchus*, but the facial part has a pair of deep palatal grooves and the premaxillary bones are fused dorsally in the midline. This fusion resembles that in *Delphinus* but is not so extensive.

Harbor Porpoise (*Phocaena phocoena*), photo from painting by Else Bostelmann. © National Geographic Society.

COMMON PORPOISES, HARBOR PORPOISES; BRUIN-
VISS, BRAUNFISCH, MARSOUINS. (Included are
vernaculars used in other countries.)

THE FOUR SPECIES of *Phocaena* are distributed as
follows: *P. phocoena*, European and African waters
from the North Sea and Arctic Ocean to west Africa,
the western Atlantic, and the Pacific Ocean from
Alaska to southern California; *P. sinus*, known only
from the Gulf of California, but probably also occurring along the west coast of Mexico; *P. spinipinnis*,
from the La Plata River around Cape Horn to Peru;
and *P. dioptrica*, from the La Plata River of South
America to South Georgia (British Antarctica).

The head and body length is 1.2 to 1.8 meters, the
length of the pectoral fin is 0.15 to 0.3 meters, the
height of the dorsal fin is about 0.15 meters, and the
width of the flukes is 0.3 to 0.65 meters. Adult porpoises usually weigh from 50 to 75 kg. The coloration
is black above and white below, or entirely black.
The conical head is not beaked, and the dorsal fin is
usually triangular in shape and located just behind
the middle of the back. From 16 to 27 teeth grow on
each side of each jaw; the spade-shaped teeth are
entirely crowned or bear two or three-lobed crowns.

Phocaena usually frequents coasts and the mouths
of large rivers; they sometimes ascend the rivers.

These porpoises travel in pairs and in schools of
nearly a hundred individuals. *Phocaena* seems to be
less playful than most dolphins and porpoises; it
seldom jumps out of water, and usually ignores a
passing boat. The species, *P. phocoena*, usually swims
just below the surface and rises to breathe about four
times per minute, but individuals have become trapped
in fishnets at depths of 75 meters. Unarmed fish
less than 30 cm. in length, including those that are
commonly found in schools near the bottom, probably
constitute the food preferred by these mammals.
Cephalopods and crustaceans are also eaten. Enemies
of *Phocaena* include sharks, killer whales, and man.

Mating usually takes place in the late spring and
summer; the gestation period is about 11 months and
the calves at birth are about half the length of the
mother.

A porpoise fishery formerly existed along the Nor-
mandy Coast; the meat was sold in markets and the
oil was used in lamps. The flesh of *P. phocoena* apparently formed a royal dish at the time of Henry VIII,
and the flesh of this species is still eaten occasionally
by certain North or South American Indians living
along the coast.

The type species of the genus is *P. phocoena*
(Linnaeus).

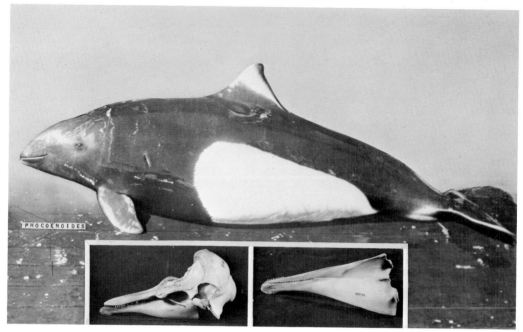

Dall Porpoise (*Phocoenoides dalli*), photo by Warren J. Houck. Inset: Photos by P. F. Wright of skull in U.S. National Museum.

DALL AND TRUE PORPOISES, PACIFIC PORPOISES.

THE TWO SPECIES of *Phocoenoides* are distributed as follows: *P. dalli*, in the cold waters of eastern Siberia, the Aleutian Islands, Alaska to California, and Japan; and *P. truei*, in Japanese waters. The ranges overlap for about 320 km. in the Japanese areas. Some mammalogists think that *P. dalli* and *P. truei* are referable to a single species, *P. dalli*.

The head and body length is as much as 2.36 meters; pectoral fin length is 200 to 250 mm.; the height of the dorsal fin is 130 to 160 mm.; and the width of the flukes is 400 to 460 mm. Mature individuals of *Phocoenoides* usually weigh from 80 to 125 kg. The two forms have black upper parts, but in *P. dalli* the white area on the sides does not extend far beyond the anterior margin of the dorsal fin, whereas in *P. truei* the white area extends laterally to the flippers. *P. dalli* also lacks a white throat patch often observed in *P. truei*.

Phocoenoides is distinguished structurally from *Phocaena* by its smaller teeth and greater number of vertebrae, and by its distinctive color. The senior author noted plates between the teeth on the lower jaw of one specimen which is illustrated. Behavioral differences are also evident between the two genera.

Phocoenoides, unlike *Phocaena*, often plays about ships and leaps out of water and also appears farther above the water when rolling. The head of *Phocoenoides* is sloping, and the lower jaw projects slightly beyond the upper. The dorsal fin is low and triangular. The spade-shaped teeth number 19 to 27 on each side of each jaw. An unusual feature in *P. dalli* is the presence of horny protuberances of the gums between the teeth. These "gum teeth" function as gripping organs and probably wear down with use to expose the teeth. The teeth thus seem to be functional mainly in older animals.

Dall and True porpoises are usually noted in groups of 2 to 20 individuals. Both forms appear to migrate twice yearly off the coast of Japan, and *P. dalli*, off the California coast, may move inshore in winter and northward and to the outer Aleutian Islands in summer. The diet is fish, mainly the small unarmed type, and squid. The calves are born in the spring and summer.

Phocoenoides forms part of the commercial porpoise and dolphin fishery in Japanese waters. Attempts to keep *Phocoenoides* in captivity have for the most part been unsuccessful.

The type species of the genus is *P. truei*, Andrews.

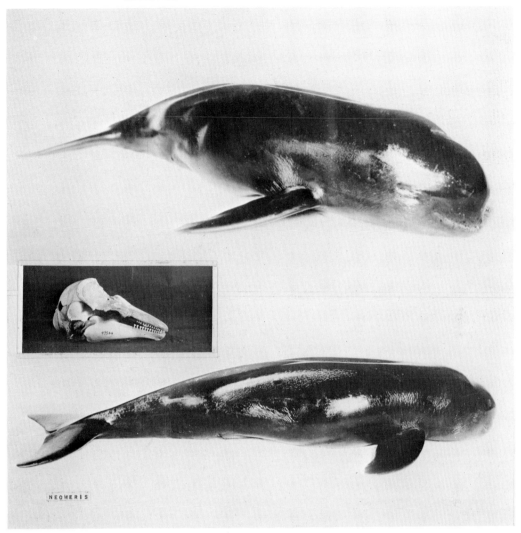

Asiatic Black Finless Porpoise (*Neomeris phocoenoides*), photos by Arthur Sowerby. Inset: Photo by P. F. Wright.

SOUTHEAST ASIATIC PORPOISES, BLACK FINLESS PORPOISES; HAI-CHU, BHULGA.

THE SINGLE SPECIES, *N. phocoenoides*, frequents the coasts, estuaries, rivers, and lakes of India, Pakistan, Java, Sumatra, Borneo, China, and Japan. It has been noted nearly 1,600 km. from the mouth of the Yangtze River.

The head and body length is about 1.5 meters; pectoral fin length is about 28 cm.; and the width of the flukes is about 55 cm. A 1.3-meter pregnant female weighed 27 kg. The color is dark slate gray to black, occasionally with pale-gray and purplish-red patches on the throat and lips. Distinctive features are the small size, the abruptly rising forehead, and the absence of a dorsal fin. The teeth are spade-shaped and number from 15 to 21 on each side of each jaw.

Neomeris is usually seen singly or in pairs, either a female and her calf or a male and a female. They are seldom seen in groups of more than four or five.

They are sluggish and slow moving and roll when rising to breathe. *Neomeris* may be the ecological counterpart of *Phocoena* in the Far East. The diet includes shrimps, fish, and small squid. The calves are said to be born in October.

Specimens are in the following study collections: Paris, Museum of Natural History; Leyden; London, British Museum (Natural History); Calcutta, Museum of the Asiatic Society; Karachi, Pakistan, Karachi Museum; Travancore, India, Trivandrum Museum; Washington, D. C., U.S. National Museum; and Cambridge, Massachusetts, Museum of Comparative Zoology.

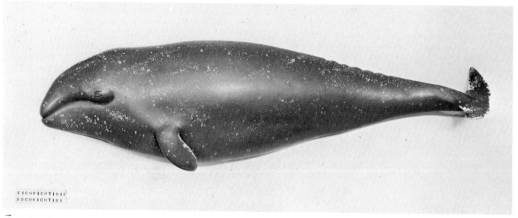

Gray Whale (*Eschrichtius glaucus*), photo from Field Museum of Natural History.

GRAY WHALES, GRAY BACK WHALES, CALIFORNIA GRAY WHALES, PACIFIC GRAY WHALES, DEVIL FISH, HARD HEADS, MUSSEL DIGGERS, RIP SACKS; KO-KUZIRA, BALEINES GRISES, GRAUWALE, GRŸZE WALVISSEN, SERYÏ KIT, BALLENAS GRIS, GRÅHVAL, GRÅVAL. (Included are vernaculars used in other countries.)

THIS FAMILY contains only a single genus, *Eschrichtius*, for the single living species, *E. glaucus*, of the North Pacific. Subfossil remains of this genus have been discovered in the northeastern Atlantic.

This is one of three families of baleen whales in the suborder Mysticeti. In these cetaceans the teeth in the embryos are replaced by baleen or whalebone as the mammals mature. Baleen, which is equivalent to modified mucous membrane, appears as a series of thin plates, one behind the other, suspended from each side of the palate and extending into the mouth cavity in two rows, one on each side. The plates hang at right angles to the longitudinal axis of the head. The outer borders of the baleen are smooth, whereas the inner borders are frayed into brush-like fibers. These baleen plates act as sieves or strainers. Water containing floating or weak-swimming forms of small crustaceans and mollusks is taken into the mouth and is then ejected by the piston action of the huge tongue, leaving the aquatic food entangled in the plates. The baleen in gray whales is yellowish white in color, with 130 to 180 plates constituting a series on each side of the mouth. The largest plates are from 34 to 45 cm. long. The two rows of baleen plates in gray whales do not meet in the front as they do in the family Balaenopteridae.

The length of the head and body is 10 to 15 meters; the length of the pectoral fin is approximately 2 meters; and the width of the flukes is approximately 3 meters. As in the other baleen whales, the females average about 0.5 meter longer than the males. Adults weigh from 24 to 37 metric tons. The coloration is black or slaty with many white spots and blotches, some of which are discolored patches of skin and others are areas of white barnacles. Gray whales are often infested with amphipod whale lice. The snout is high and rigid, and the throat has two or three (rarely four) short, shallow, curved furrows. Instead of a dorsal fin, a series of 8 to 10 low humps occur along the mid-line of the lower back.

Gray whales have 56 vertebrae, and the neck vertebrae are separate.

At the present time there are two isolated areas inhabited by gray whales. The California population spends the summer (June through September) in the northwestern Bering Sea and the Chukchi Sea, and migrates 9,600 km. in the fall and winter to calving and breeding lagoons and estuaries off the coasts of Baja California and to a limited extent those of the mainland of Mexico. The Korean population summers in the Okhotsk Sea and spends the winter in the waters off South Korea and possibly in the Yellow Sea, where calving and breeding apparently take place. These whales do not wander from the direct route when migrating, and there is some evidence that they eat little or nothing during migration.

The migration of the California gray whale to its wintering grounds is concentrated in time and space. Most of the migrants pass San Diego, for example, during a six week period (from the end of December to the beginning of February) and an estimated 95 per cent of the whale population travels from 3 to 5 km. offshore. These and the humpbacks are the only baleen whales that migrate close to shore, occasionally passing through beds of kelp. During the northern migration, which begins in March, the animals are more scattered, but they still remain fairly close to the shore line. A few gray whales remain all summer off the coasts of northern California and southern Oregon.

During migration these cetaceans usually travel singly or in groups of two or three at speeds of approximately 4 to 5 knots, but they can reach a speed of 7 to 8 knots under pressure. Gray whales submerge for 4 to 5 minutes at a time when traveling; the tail flukes usually appear above the surface just before deep dives but not before surface dives. The back is not arched before diving as in the humpback whale *Megaptera*. The spout rises to about 3 meters. Visual stimuli appear to be involved in the gray whale's orientation during migration. The appearance of killer whales usually elicits one of two reactions:

the gray whale will head for the safety of shore and shallow water, or it will float, belly up, apparently paralyzed with fear. Gray whales often play in heavy surf and shallow water along the shore, sometimes throwing themselves clear of the surface. They are occasionally stranded in less than 1 meter of water and will refloat on the next tide without injury. Gray whales have been observed to aid one another in an emergency such as injury, sickness, or birth, by pushing the one in need of help to the surface so that he can breathe. There is at least some indication that these whales feed more in deep water than they do in shallow places. The diet during the summer consists mainly of large plankton, especially euphausid shrimp, certain mollusks, and small fish.

This is the only baleen whale that enters shallow water to calve and breed. Most of the reproductive activity takes place in January, at least in the California population. The gestation period is 11 to 12 months. A female after giving birth ordinarily does not receive a male but devotes her time to her calf, which is weaned at six to eight months in the summer feeding grounds. Upon returning to the wintering grounds, these females breed again and others are giving birth so that a single female typically calves every other year. The young at birth are 4 to 5 meters long and weigh about 1.5 metric tons; they are about 7.5 meters long when weaned and grow approximately 5 meters during their first year of life. Calves born in one winter return alone to the warmer waters the following winter.

Gray whales were severely depleted in numbers in the 1830's but are now increasing in numbers as a result of international protection since 1938. About 6,000 gray whales are estimated now to winter in Mexican waters; and whale-watching has become a popular (and profitable) pastime in the San Diego area.

RORQUALS OR FINBACK WHALES, FIN WHALES, FINNERS, HERRING WHALES, RAZORBACKS, SEI WHALES, POLLACK WHALES, COALFISH WHALES, RUDOLPHI'S RORQUALS, BRYDE'S WHALES, LESSER RORQUALS, LITTLE PIKED WHALES, PIKE-HEADED WHALES, BLUE OR SULPHUR-BOTTOM WHALES, SIBBALD'S RORQUAL, GREAT NORTHERN RORQUAL, HUMPBACK WHALES, HUNCHBACKED WHALES, HUMP WHALES; RORCUALES, JOROBADAS, BALLENAS BRYDEAS, BALLENAS PEQUEÑAS, BALLENAS AZULES, BALLENAS DE ALETA, BALLENA BOBAS, GUBARTES, FINWALE, BUCKELWALE, BLAUWALE, GEWONE VINVISCH, NOORDSCHE, BRYDE VINVISCH, DWEG VINVISCH, BULTRUG, BLAUWE VINVISCH, RORQUALS COMMUNS, RORQUALS DE RUDOLF, BALEINES DE BRYDE, PETITS RORQUALS, MÉGAPTÈRE JUBARTE, RORQUALS BLEUS, BALEINES BLEUES, SELDIANOÏ KIT, FINVAL, MALYĬ POLOSATIK, KIT ZALIVOV, GORBATYĬ KIT, GORBACH, SINIĬ KIT, BLUVAL, FINHVAL, SEIVAL, RÖRHVAL, BRYDEHVAL, MINKE, VÅGEHVAL, VIKVAL, SILLVAL, SEJVAL, KNÖLVAL, PUCKELVAL, KNÖLHVAL, BUKKELHVAL, BLÅHVAL, BLÅVAL, NAGAS-KUZIRA, ZAKO-KUZIRA, SIRONAGASU-KUZIRA. (Included are vernaculars used in other countries.)

THIS FAMILY is composed of three genera and six species and occurs in all oceans.

Balaenopteridae is the second family of baleen whales, the cetaceans in which the embryonic teeth are replaced by baleen in the adult animals. In the members of this family, the color of the baleen plates is white, yellowish, or black, and the plates range in length from .2 to 1.01 meters. Each row of baleen on either side of the mouth may consist of more than 300 plates.

The length of the head and body is 9 to 30 meters, with the female whales averaging 0.5 meter longer than the males. The largest animal ever to have lived on earth, the blue whale, often weighs as much as 113 metric tons. The flipper is long and tapering, and the dorsal fin is triangular in shape and located near the tail. Longitudinal furrows, usually 10 to 100 in number and 2.5 to 5 cm. deep, are present on the

throat and chest. The name rorqual is said to mean "the whale having folds or pleats." These furrows increase the capacity of the mouth when opened. The Balaenopteridae can be distinguished from the right whales of the family Balaenidae by the more elongated and streamlined body form, a much smaller head in relation to its total length, the presence of throat and chest furrows, the shape of the flipper, the position of the dorsal fin, and shorter and less flexible baleen. The presence of a dorsal fin will immediately distinguish the Balaenopteridae from the gray whales of the family Eschrichtidae.

The vertebrae number 42 to 65; the neck vertebrae are generally free, but sometimes two or three are partly fused.

The members of this family are the fastest swimmers among the baleen whales. The common rorqual or fin whale (*Balaenoptera physalus*) can attain speeds of up to 48 kilometers an hour when pressed. Each species has a typical spout. These whales travel singly, in pairs, or in larger groups; several hundred may congregate where food is abundant.

Most of the six species feed mainly in the morning and evening. The diet, although it varies with the species and the locality, consists largely of shrimp of the family Euphausiidae (mainly species of the genera *Euphausia*, *Thysanoessa*, and *Meganyctiphanes*) and copepods (of the genera *Calanus* and *Metridia*), which comprise part of the floating and weak-swimming forms of animal life near the surface of the oceans, known collectively as zoöplankton. Other zoöplankton may be utilized as food by some species of this family; the amphipod, *Parathemisto gandichaudi*, for example, is a food of Sei whales (*Balaenoptera borealis*) in the Antarctic. Some members of this family consume fish and squid, and Bryde's whale (*Balaenoptera edeni*) has been reported to feed on sharks up to .6 meters in length and on penguins.

In colder waters there are fewer kinds of plankton, but the numbers of each kind are greater. Shoals of these organisms are concentrated in the upper layers of cold ocean waters in summer; it is this feature of polar waters that attracts the baleen whales. In the fall, baleen whales migrate to warmer waters. In the Antarctic the large baleen whales feed heavily on the shrimp *Euphausia superba*, whereas in the Atlantic the major food item for some species is another form of shrimp (*Meganyctiphanes norvegica*). The common rorqual feeds mainly on euphausiid shrimp in Antarctic waters, but in the Atlantic it also includes copepods and swarming fish in its diet; the Sei whale seems to prefer copepods; blue whales (*Sibbaldus*) live almost entirely on euphausiids; and humpback whales (*Megaptera*) largely consume euphausiids but also feed upon swarming fish.

Two methods of taking food are employed: gulping and swallowing, or skimming, and one species (the Sei whale) uses both methods. In the swallowing method, used by the common rorqual, the Minke whale (*Balaenoptera acutorostrata*), Byrde's whale, the blue whale, and the humpback whale, the animal turns over while feeding and often has part of its head above water when it swallows. When swarms of zoöplankton are scarce, these whales cannot feed as efficiently as those species which utilize the skimming method, i.e., the Sei whale on occasion, and the right whales of the family Balaenidae. In the skimming

Baleen from a whale (*Balaenoptera* sp.), photo by P. F. Wright of specimen in U.S. National Museum.

method the whale swims through the swarm of zoöplankton with its mouth open and its head above water to just behind the nostrils. When a mouthful of organisms has been filtered from the water by the baleen plates, the whale dives, closes its mouth, and swallows the food. The feeding habits and preferences for certain foods of the baleen whales are related to the formation of the baleen plates and characteristics of the head, mouth, and tongue.

All baleen whales give birth and breed in the warmer waters within their range. The larger species of the Balaenopteridae generally bear a single calf every other year, but the smaller forms breed more often. In the Minke whale, for example, most of the mature females (at least in Japanese waters) give birth once a year (in some animals the interval between births lasts 18 months). In this species (in Japanese waters) the females are apparently sexually mature when they attain a length of 7 meters and the males at a length of 6.5 to 7 meters, the age of sexual maturity is about two years in both sexes. The Sei whale attains sexual maturity at a length of approximately 12 meters. In the common rorqual, it occurs at an age of four to six years when the animal is about 18.2 meters long. Whales of this species are physically mature at an average age of 24 years; their maximum life span has been estimated as about 50 years. Females of the blue whale are sexually mature when 22.5 to 23.5 meters long. The humpback matures at 11.9 to 12.5 meters. The gestation period in this family is 10 to 12 months; the calves (depending on the species) are approximately 7 meters long at birth.

All baleen whales that are hunted commercially at the present time belong to this family.

The geological range of the Balaenopteridae is the upper Miocene and Recent in North America, and the Pliocene in Europe.

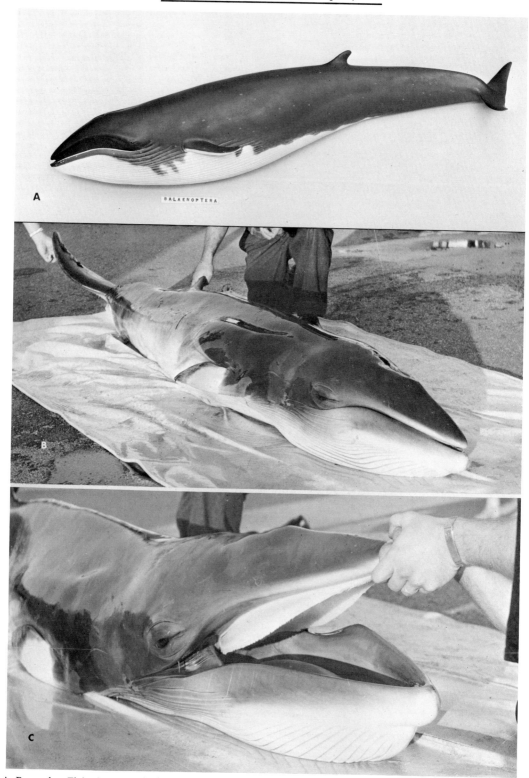

A. Rorqual or Finback Whale (*Balaenoptera physalus*), photo from Field Museum of Natural History. B. & C. Little Piked Whale (*B. acutorostrata*), photos from Marineland of the Pacific.

RORQUALS OR FINBACK WHALES, FIN WHALES, FINNERS, HERRING WHALES, RAZORBACKS, SEI WHALES, POLLACK WHALES, COALFISH WHALES, RUDOLPHI'S RORQUALS, BRYDE'S WHALES, LESSER RORQUALS, LITTLE PIKED WHALES, PIKE-HEADED WHALES; RORCUALES, BALLENAS DE ALETA, BALLENAS BOBAS, BALLENAS BRYDEAS, BALLENAS PEQUEÑAS, NAGAS-KUZIRA, FINWALE, GEWONE VINVISCH, NOORDSCHE, BRYDE VINVISCH, DWERG VINVISCH, RORQUALS COMMUNS, RORQUALS DE RUDOLF, BALEINES DE BRYDE, PETITS RORQUALS, SELDIANOÏ KIT, FINVAL, SEIVAL, MALYĬ POLESATIK, KIT ZALIVOV, FINHVAL, SEIVAL, VÅGEHVAL, RÖRHVAL, BRYDEHVAL, MINKE, SILLVAL, SEJVAL, VIKVAL. (Included are vernaculars used in other countries.)

THE FOUR SPECIES are *B. physalus*, the fin whale; *B. borealis*, the Sei whale; *B. acutorostrata*, the lesser rorqual or Minke whale; and *B. edeni*, Bryde's whale. Bryde's whale is known from South African seas and the West Indies; the other species are cosmopolitan.

The head and body lengths are as follows: *B. physalus*, an average of 18 to 20.5 meters but up to 24 meters; *B. borealis*, to 18 meters; *B. acutorostrata*, to 9 meters; and *B. edeni*, average length about 13 meters. The pectoral fin length is usually one-ninth to one-twelfth of the head and body length, and the height of the dorsal fin is usually 0.5 to 1 meter. Common rorquals killed in the Antarctic today average about 18 meters in length and 50 tons in weight. A 14.5-meter *B. borealis* weighed about 48 tons. The coloration varies among the species. The back is light gray, bluish gray, or bluish black, and the undersides differ in the extent of depigmentation. A series of longitudinal grooves or furrows, usually 30 to 60 in number, is present on the throat and chest region.

The tail stalk is strongly compressed with dorsal and ventral ridges and joins the flukes abruptly.

Rorquals are usually seen in groups of a few to several hundred individuals; the larger groups may be scattered over several square miles. The common rorqual may be capable of speeds up to 48 km. per hour when pursued. The species of this genus migrate or, at least, disperse to warm waters in the winter, although Bryde's whale may remain in warm waters throughout the year. West and east movements are also made by *B. physalus*. Experiments in which this aquatic mammal is marked indicate that the maximum movement to other longitudes in the Antarctic is 50 degrees in either direction. It is possible that only the younger whales wander to other longitudes before their habits become fixed.

Minute sea life, plankton, crustaceans and small fish are eaten; the diet seems to vary with the species and the season.

Mating takes place chiefly during the winter months. The species, *B. physalus*, usually bears one young every other year. Twin embryos have been found in about one out of one-hundred pregnant *B. physalus*, and there is one record of twin calves in *B. borealis*. The gestation period is 10 to 12 months. *B. physalus* almost doubles its length in the first six months of life. Calves are 6 to 6.5 meters long at birth. They are weaned in six months when they are about 12 meters long. Sexual maturity is attained in three and a half to four years.

From a commercial standpoint, the species *B. physalus*, *B. borealis*, *B. edeni*, and *B. acutorostrata* are, respectively, the second, fourth, fifth, and sixth most important baleen whales.

The type species of the genus is *B. acutorostrata*, Lacépède.

Hump-backed Whale (*Megaptera novaeangliae*), photo from Field Museum of Natural History.

HUNCHBACKED WHALES, HUMP WHALES, HUMP-BACK WHALES; GUBARTES, JOROBADA, ZAKO-KUZIRA, BUCKELWALE, MÉGAPTÊRE JUBARTE, KNÖLVAL, PUCKELVAL, KNÖLHVAL, BUKKELHVAL, BULTRUG, GORBATYÏ KIT, GORBACH. (Included are vernaculars used in other countries.)

THE SINGLE SPECIES, *M. novaeangliae*, inhabits warm waters during the winter and migrates north and south to polar waters in the spring. Humpback whales often frequent coastal areas and inlets.

The head and body length is 11.5 to 15 meters, the average is about 12.5 meters; the length of the pectoral fin is about one-third the length of the head and body; and the height of the dorsal fin ranges from 15 cm. to 60 cm. The average total weight for 270 humpbacks (averaging 12.6 meters in length) was about 29 tons. Coloration is black above, with white throat and breast. The outstanding feature of this animal is its long flipper. From 10 to 25 throat and chest grooves are present, and the body is stocky. Irregular knobs and protuberances occur on the head and flippers. Humpback whales are frequently heavily parasitized externally by amphipod whale lice and barnacles.

The sexes often mix in small groups consisting of a milking female and her calf. *Megaptera* usually lifts its tail flukes above the water just before taking a sounding dive and emits a short and broad spout, which distinguishes it from the higher, thinner blow of the common rorqual whale. In the Southern Hemisphere humpback whales tend to be concentrated in several separate communities, between which there is little interchange of animals. In the winter these communities migrate as far as the equator; it is not known if the southern and northern stocks mingle at this point. Migrations from the Arctic seem to be similar to those in the south to warm waters during the severe weather.

Crustaceans are probably the most important food item; small fish are also consumed.

While mating, the male and female lie side by side and administer alternate blows with their flippers, some individuals occasionally leap clear of the water. The gestation period is about 12 months. There is a record of a female in advanced pregnancy bearing two embryos. Caudal presentation at birth of a 4-meter calf weighing about 1,350 kg. has been noted in a 12.5-meter female. The age of weaning is about 11 months. Female humpbacks are sexually mature when 11.5 to 12.25 meters long.

The oil yield from a 12.2-meter humpback is usually 40 to 45 barrels, or about 8 tons. An animal of this size will also produce about 0.5 ton of meal and 1 to 2 tons of frozen meat.

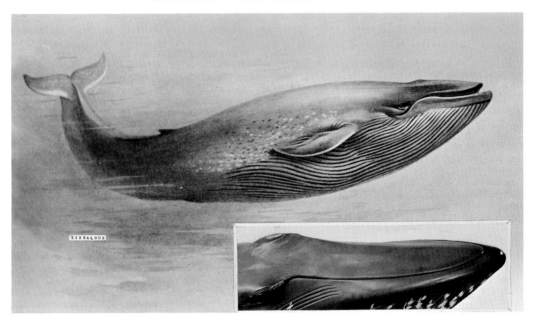

Blue or Sulphur-bottom Whale (*Sibbaldus musculus*), photo from *British Mammals*, Archibald Thorburn. Inset: Detail of part of head (*S. musculus*), photo from Smithsonian Institution of model in U.S. National Museum.

BLUE OR SULPHUR-BOTTOM WHALES, SIBBALD'S RORQUAL, GREAT NORTHERN RORQUAL; RORENDES, BALLENAS AZULES, SIRONAGASU-KUZIRA, RORQUALS BLEUS, BALEINES BLEUES, BLAUWALE, BLAUWE VINVISCH, SINÏĬ KIT, BLUVAL, BLÅHVAL, BLÅVAL. (Included are vernaculars used in other countries.)

THE SINGLE SPECIES, *S. musculus*, lives near the Arctic and Antarctic polar pack ice in the summer and is probably distributed between the edge of the ice and subtropical latitudes in winter. It usually avoids tropical waters.

This is the largest mammal that ever lived; the head and body length of the adults is 21 to 30 meters. The length of the flipper is about one-seventh of the head and body length, and the height of the dorsal fin is usually 15 to 45 cm. The blue whale weighs about 1 ton for each 0.3 meters in length, and the largest specimens weigh about 112,500 kg. The color is dark slate-blue throughout except for the tip and undersides of the flippers. The name, "sulphur-bottom" whale, refers to a yellowish film of diatoms (microscopic algae) that occasionally forms on the undersurface of *Sibbaldus*. There are usually 80 to 100 ventral grooves on the throat and belly.

The blue whale is usually observed singly or in pairs, seldom in large schools. It usually makes a number of shallow dives, lasting 12 to 15 seconds each, after a deep 10 to 20 minute dive. The tail flukes are lifted clear of the water in a deep dive. Blue whales usually travel at speeds of 10 to 12 knots, but can be pressed to swim at 15 knots or more. External parasites are uncommon.

Sibbaldus is more evenly distributed in the Antarctic than *Megaptera*; it may tend to concentrate in the same areas as the latter genus, but, unlike the humpback, the blue whale moves from one area to another. Crustacean krill is consumed almost exclusively. The stomach of a 26-meter individual was estimated to contain five million krill, weighing about 2 tons.

The blue whale breeds in waters warmer than those of the polar regions; at least two years intervene between successive pregnancies, i.e., the female does not breed when suckling her young. The period of gestation is about 10 or 11 months. Twins are rare, and single births are a common occurrence. The calves are 7 to 7.8 meters long at birth; their length doubles during the six- to seven-month period of suckling. Females mature sexually at about five years of age or when they measure 22.5 to 23.25 meters in length.

Sibbaldus was formerly the leading commercial baleen whale. Even allowing for size, its oil yield is greater than that of the common rorqual: the average oil yield of a blue whale is 70 to 80 barrels.

RIGHT WHALES, BOW-HEAD WHALES; BALLENAS, GROENLANDSE WALVISCH.

THIS FAMILY OF three genera and five species (the three forms of *Eubalaena*, *E. glacialis*, *E. sieboldii*, and *E. australis*, probably represent a single species) lives in all the oceans, although extensive whaling has greatly reduced the numbers of Bow-head or Greenland right whales (*Balaena*) and black right whales (*Eubalaena*). These two genera are now protected by an international agreement and seem to be gaining in numbers. Pygmy right whales (*Caperea*) are thought to be rare and have no commercial importance.

Balaenidae is the third family of baleen whales, all distinguished by the unique character of the baleen plates. In the genera *Balaena* and *Eubalaena* the baleen plates are grayish black or black in color, whereas in *Caperea* they are ivory-colored with dark margins. The baleen plates are 3 to 4 meters long in *Balaena*, 180 to 220 cm. long in *Eubalaena*, and up to approximately 70 cm. long in *Caperea*. More than 350 plates may comprise a series on each side of the upper jaw. The plates fold on the floor of the closed mouth and straighten when the mouth opens.

The enormous head, accounting for one-fourth to one-third of the total length of the animal, is its outstanding external feature. The length of the head and body in the pygmy right whales (*Caperea*) is approximately 6 meters, whereas in sexually mature individuals of *Balaena* and *Eubalaena* it is 13.5 to 18 meters, with the females averaging about 0.5 meters longer than the males. An 11-meter female of *Eubalaena sieboldii* weighed approximately 23 metric tons, and a 12.9-meter male weighed about 22 metric tons. The cleft of the mouth is curved, and the large and fleshy lip appears on the lower jaw which is bowed outwardly. Throat and chest furrows are not present. The flippers are short, broad, and rounded, and the only genus with a dorsal fin is *Caperea*. This family may be distinguished from the other families of baleen whales by its stocky body and huge head, the absence of furrows, the shape of the flippers, and the characteristic features of the baleen plates. The vertebrae number 54 in *Balaena*, 57 in *Eubalaena*, and 43 in *Caperea*; the 7 neck vertebrae are fused into a single unit.

Right whales are slow swimmers; their usual speed is about 8 kilometers per hour, although they make 15 kilometers per hour when pursued. The spout, at least of *Eubalaena*, is double, V-shaped, and projected forward. These cetaceans travel singly, in pairs, or in groups of several individuals. The migrations of *Balaena* seem to be determined by the seasonal movements of the edge of the ice; at the present time, this genus appears to be confined to the waters of Arctic Alaska, Siberia, and the western Canadian Arctic during the summer, and the Bering Sea and Kurile Islands during the winter. The migrations of *Eubalaena* are somewhat limited, for these whales seem to move between cold temperate and subtropical waters in both hemispheres. Black right whales (*Eubalaena sieboldii*) of the northern Pacific appear in the waters east of Honshu and south of Hokkaido, Japan, in April, remaining in this area until May when they leave for the Bering Sea to spend the summer. Pygmy right whales apparently do not undergo long-range migrations but remain in Australian and New Zealand waters all year, moving into shallow coastal waters in spring and early summer.

Right whales, at least *Balaena* and *Eubalaena*, feed on planktonic animal life, mainly crustaceans (various copepods and shrimp) and mollusks (pteropods). The floating and weak-swimming crustaceans of the oceans are sometimes referred to as krill. Bow-head and black right whales employ the skimming method of feeding, in which they swim through swarms of krill and mollusks with open mouths and their heads above water to just behind the nostrils. When a sufficient mouthful of organisms has been filtered

Dr. Roy Chapman Andrews, who was 6 ft. 1 in. in height, standing beside the skull of an Atlantic Right Whale (*Eubalaena* sp.). The plates of baleen are smooth on the outside, but on the inside they are fringed to form an effective strainer, photo from American Museum of Natural History.

from the water by the baleen plates, these whales dive, close their mouths, and swallow the food. Little is known about the habits of pygmy right whales, although they are suspected of feeding on the bottom of the sea.

Breeding in *Balaena* and *Eubalaena* seems to take place in late summer. The length of the gestation period is probably about 12 months, and the calves, which in *Balaena* are 3.5 to 4.5 meters long at birth, are nursed for about a year.

Balaena and *Eubalaena* were considered the "right" whales for commercial purposes. They are less active and slower than most baleen whales; their great buoyancy (hence a reduced tendency for the carcass to sink) was an important consideration before the development of techniques for inflating the body; and the products derived from these whales brought high prices. The baleen was used in many articles where a combination of strength and elasticity was desired (such as corset springs), and the oil was used as an illuminant, in soft soap, paints, and as a lubricant.

The geological range of the family Balaenidae is the lower Miocene and Pliocene in South America and the Pliocene and Recent in Europe.

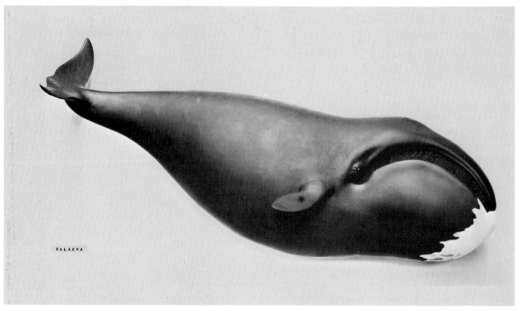

Bow-head or Greenland Right Whale (*Balaena mysticetus*), photo from Field Museum of Natural History.

BOW-HEAD OR GREENLAND RIGHT WHALES, GREAT POLAR WHALES, RIGHT WHALES, ARCTIC WHALES; BALLENAS, CABEZAS ARQUEANDAS, GROENLANDSE WALVISCH, BALEINES FRANCHES, BALEINES DU GREENLAND, GREENLANDSKIĬ KIT, GRÖNLANDSHVAL, SLETBAK, NORDHVAL, GRÖNLANDSVAL, AVIK. (Included are vernaculars used in other countries.)

THE SINGLE SPECIES, *B. mysticetus*, formerly occurred in the Arctic regions of Eurasia and North America but is now greatly reduced in numbers. The few remaining specimens appear to be confined to the western Canadian Arctic and Bering Strait in the summer and the Bering Sea in winter, with a few remaining in the eastern Arctic, some of which enter northern Hudson Bay. *Balaena* formerly entered Hudson Bay and moved as far south as Churchill. It also ranged south along the Labrador coast as far as the Gulf of St. Lawrence and southern Newfoundland. Almost exterminated by the early 1900's, the bow-head whale has not been commercially whaled since then and may now be increasing in numbers.

The head and body length is usually 15 to 18 meters; the flippers are about 2 meters long by 1.5 meters wide; and the tail flukes are 5.5 to 8 meters wide and 1.6 to 1.8 meters long. The adult *Balaena* is black, with cream-colored chin and throat and occasionally white under parts. This animal is about one-third mouth; the lower jaws are U-shaped in front and raised high on each side. The greatest circumference of the body is just behind the flippers; from here the body tapers conically toward the tail. A dorsal fin is absent.

The migrations of this mammal seem to be determined by the seasonal movements of the ice edge. From evidence suggested by recovered harpoons it would seem that this species is capable of "a transpolar passage between the Pacific and Arctic Oceans" (Robert Clarke, *Norwegian Whaling Gazette*, 1957, p. 618). Bow-head whales usually remain submerged from 10 to 30 minutes and, if not disturbed, often remain at the surface for 10 to 30 minutes between dives. The jaws form an efficient scoop for krill and small fish.

Breeding usually takes place in late summer; the gestation period is not known but is probably about one year. Births are usually single, but two calves have been noted with a single adult. After calving, the females seem to separate for some time from the adult males. The calves are 3.5 to 5.5 meters long at birth and are nursed for about a year.

The bow-head whale once supported a fishery "which at one time used to send two to three hundred ships a year northwards from British ports alone" (Fraser, in Norman and Fraser. *Giant Whales, Fishes and Dolphins*, 1938, p. 211). Overfishing nearly exterminated these whales, but the species is now protected by international agreement. The average yield of a bow-head was 70 to 90 barrels of oil and 680 to 760 kg. of baleen; in the heyday of the baleen whaling industry these products sold for about 8 thousand dollars or 2,200 pounds sterling, per single whale.

Right Whale (*Eubalaena glacialis*), A. Shows the baleen in place and the very large tongue; B. Shows the tongue and the rough surface of the top of the front portion of the head (the baleen has been removed); Inset: A smaller piece of baleen of lighter color; photos by G. C. Pike through I. B. MacAskie.

BLACK RIGHT WHALES, BISCAYAN RIGHT WHALES, NORTH ATLANTIC RIGHT WHALES, NORDCAPERS, NORTH CAPE WHALES, SCRAG WHALES, BLACK WHALES, SOUTHERN RIGHT WHALES; NOORD-KAPER, BALEINES DE BISCAYE, BALLENAS FRANCAS, NASTOIASCHIĬ KIT, SEVERO-ATLANTICHESKIĬ NA-STOIASCHIĬ KIT, RETHVAL, BISCAYERHVAL, NORD-KAPER, NORDKAPARE, BISCAYAVAL. (Included are vernaculars used in other countries.)

THREE SPECIES OF *Eubalaena* are usually recognized: one from the North Atlantic (*E. glacialis*); one from the North Pacific (*E. sieboldii*); and one from the Southern Hemisphere (*E. australis*). Many authors, however, consider the three forms as a single species. They apparently avoid tropical waters from about 30 degrees N. latitude to 30 degrees S. latitude. These whales seem "to make limited North–South migrations between cold temperate and subtropical seas in each hemisphere" (Robert Clarke, *Norwegian Whaling Gazette*, 1957, p. 618); they are now rare throughout their former range.

The head and body length is usually 13.6 to 16.6 meters and the pectoral fins are 1.8 to 2.1 meters long. The coloration is usually black throughout, but the belly is occasionally white. This genus resembles

Balaena in external features, differing from the bowhead whale in that the mouth is only about one-fourth the length of the head and body, the upper jaw is not so strongly arched, the outline of the lower jaw is different, the coloration differs on the under parts, and there are "bonnets" on the right whales. Bonnets are horny protuberances representing an accumulation of cornified layers of skin which are commonly infested with parasitic crustaceans and worms. The most conspicuous of these callosities is located on the tip of the upper jaw. As in the bow-head, a dorsal fin is absent on the black right whale.

These whales usually dive deeply for about 20 minutes after a series of five or six shallow dives and often remain near the surface for some time. They are more active than bow-heads and have been observed leaping nearly clear of the water, rolling on their sides and whacking the water with their flippers, swimming with the head and tail above the surface, and diving with the tail flukes above the water.

Small crustaceans called krill form the diet.

Mating probably occurs in late summer; the gestation period is assumed to be about a year, and the length of the young at birth is about one-fourth that of the mother. Calves are suckled for about a year.

Unrestricted hunting from about the twelfth into the nineteenth centuries nearly exterminated these whales as the females and calves that frequented inshore waters formed a major part of the kills. Formerly the north Atlantic form ranged from Greenland in summer as far south as the Carolina coast in winter, although it soon disappeared in the more temperate latitudes with the early whaling. By 1800 it became too scarce for commercial operations to continue. By 1850 it began to recover in numbers, but renewed whaling operations soon decimated it again. *Eubalaena* is now protected from exploitation by international agreement.

The type species of the genus is *E. australis* (Desmoulins).

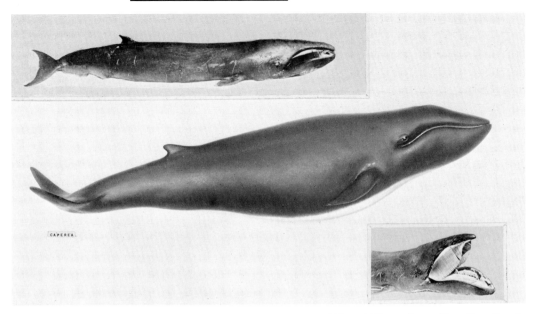

Pygmy Right Whale (*Caperea marginata*), photo from Field Museum of Natural History. Insets: Photo from *Rec. S. Australian Mus.*, H. Hale.

PYGMY RIGHT WHALES; BALEINES FRANCHES NAINES, DWERG WALVISCH, ENANAS. (Included are vernaculars used in other countries.)

THE SINGLE SPECIES, *C. marginata*, is an inhabitant of southern waters. It is known from only about 35 specimens taken in the vicinity of Australia, New Zealand, South America, and southern Africa. It seems to inhabit only the southern circumpolar area, with the majority of the population in the seas just south of Australia and New Zealand.

The length from tip of nose to notch in tail in adults is 6.1 to 6.4 meters, the head is about one-fourth of this. An adult female measured as follows: flipper length, outer edge, 66 cm., inner edge, 56 cm.; height of the dorsal fin, 25 cm.; and width of the tail flukes, 181 cm. The normal color is black with gray markings that are variable in position and extent. In sharp contrast to the body color is the pure white of the tongue and interior of the mouth. This feature, together with the ivory-colored, dark margined baleen, gives the pygmy right whale a distinctive appearance. Besides size, this whale differs externally from the genera *Balaena* and *Eubalaena* by its small recurved dorsal fin.

Caperea has a greater number of ribs than any other whale, and the 34 ribs extend farther posteriorly than in any similar species so that only two vertebrae without ribs intervene between those with ribs and the tail. The ribs become increasingly widened and flattened toward the tail and thereby probably provide additional protection to the internal organs.

The absence of sight records at sea suggests that this whale does not form schools and undergo long-range migrations. Perhaps it has simply been overlooked, but it seems more likely from its anatomy and from the general circumstances of its occurrence that it spends an unusual amount of time below the surface. Remington Kellogg (*Quarterly Review of Biology*, 1928, 3:29) remarks that it "seems to be an offshoot of some early stock that passed through its development in the Southern Hemisphere, following a somewhat different path from the balaenids and acquiring peculiarities in the form of the ribs, the vertebral column and the hand."

The records of occurrence off southern Australia and New Zealand suggest this whale is present here all year and that it moves into shallow coastal waters in spring and early summer. Such a movement, if it actually does take place, may be associated with the breeding cycle.

The name *Neobalaena* has also been used for this group.

DOGS, FOXES, WOLVES, JACKALS, BEARS, CACO-MISTLES, RACCOONS, COATIS, KINKAJOUS, OLIN-GOS, PANDAS, WEASELS, FERRETS, MINK, STOATS, WEASELS, MARTENS, FISHERS, TAYRAS, GRISONS, POLECATS, WOLVERINES, BADGERS, SKUNKS, OT-TERS, LINSANGS, GENETS, CIVETS, MONGOOSES, FOSSAS, AARDWOLVES, HYENAS, LYNXES AND BOBCATS, CARACALS, CATS; PODROSSEN, ZORROS, VOSSEN, FUCHSE, RENARD, GATOS DE MONTE, KORAI-TANUKI, USSURI-TANUKI, BOROCHI, PES HYENOVITY, BAKOORJAKKALS OR DRAAIJAKKALS, OSOS ANDINOS, USSURI-KUROKOMA, OSOS NEGROS, IJSBEREN, EISBAREN, ASWAIL, IRARA, WAITI-AIRA, GLUTONS, VEELVARAAT, JEZEVEC LESNI, LOUPS, LOUP-CERVIERS, MUSKEJAATKATTE, FUNGO, URA-LAWA, TENGAALONG, MUSANGS, GATOS, TIGRINA, KATTE, CHATS, FAHED. (Included are vernaculars that are used in other countries.)

THIS ORDER OF seven families and 101 genera has a worldwide distribution, except for the Antarctic and some oceanic islands.

The smallest living carnivore is the least weasel, *Mustela rixosa*, of the family Mustelidae, it has a head and body length of 135 to 185 mm.; the length of the tail is 30 to 40 mm.; and adult specimens weigh from 35 to 70 grams. The largest carnivores are the big brown bears of Alaska, with a length of 3 meters or more and a weight of up to 780 kg. Carnivores have at least four digits on each foot, the first digit is sometimes reduced and not opposable or is absent. The digits are clawed and in the cats, except the cheetah, can be retracted into a sheath. Some members of the order Carnivora such as the dogs and their allies and the cats, walk only on their toes, and others such as the bears, walk on their soles with the heel touching the ground, with intermediate conditions occurring.

A baculum is present. The mammae are variable in number, located on the abdomen, except in Ursidae, in which they are abdominal and pectoral.

The brain has well-developed cerebral hemispheres, and the skull is heavy, with strong facial musculature. The articulation of the lower jaw is such as to permit only open and shut movements. The teeth are rooted. The small, weak, and pointed incisors number 3/3 (3/2 in one genus, *Enhydra*), the first is the smallest and the third the largest. This difference in size is most marked in the upper jaw. The canine teeth are strong, recurved, pointed, elongate, and round to oval in section. The premolars are usually adapted for cutting, and the molars usually have four or more cusps which are sharp and pointed. A pair of cheek teeth (the last upper premolar and the first lower molar) are often developed as specialized shearing teeth and are called the carnassials. They are most highly developed in the cats (Felidae) and least developed in those carnivores that have an omnivorous diet (Ursidae and Procyonidae).

The Carnivora include mainly terrestrial and climbing animals, but there are several genera of aquatic or semiaquatic mammals in this order. Most forms are good climbers. Two genera (*Potos* in the Procyonidae and *Arctictis* in the Viverridae) have prehensile tails. Apparently all forms can swim if necessary, but the polar bear (Thalarctos) and the river otter are regularly semiaquatic, and sea otters are entirely aquatic. The sea otter lives practically its entire life in water, only frequenting the land during storms. Carnivores are nocturnal or diurnal; they shelter in caves, crevices, burrows, and trees. The winter sleep of bears and some other members of the order is claimed by some authorities as not a true hibernation because certain physiological changes do not take place and thus they can be awakened, whereas in true hibernation the animals cannot be awakened due to reduction of their metabolic rate. These mammals are solitary or associate in pairs, family groups, or bands.

The Felidae, and to a lesser extent, Canidae, Mustelidae, and Viverridae live solely or mainly on freshly-killed prey. Their whole body organization and manner of living is adapted to a predaceous way of life. Their diet of flesh varies with the season and the locality. Carnivores hunt largely by scent and catch their prey by stalking or by unexpected pouncing, sometimes with a swift rush (Felidae and Viverridae), a swift chase (Canidae), or a scampering and bounding gait in the smaller forms and a bear-like shuffling gait in the larger forms (Mustelidae). Bears, with the exception of the carnivorous polar bear (*Thalarctos*), eat considerable plant material, as well as a wide variety of animal life. The members of the family Procyonidae are omnivorous; jackals of the family Canidae feed to a large extent on carrion; the aardwolf (*Proteles*) is insectivorous, almost herbivorous in some species; and hyenas (Hyaenidae) are mainly scavengers.

Carnivores generally have one or two litters per year (some Mustelidae have three litters). Most genera have gestation periods of 49 to 113 days. Delayed implantation of the fertilized egg occurs in bears (Ursidae) and some mustelids (Mustelidae) so that their gestation period is considerably longer than the average. The litter size ranges from 1 to 13, and the offspring are usually born blind and helpless but with a covering of hair. The young are cared for solicitously by the mother or, in some forms, by both parents. Most carnivores attain sexual maturity at one to two years and have lived over 30 years in captivity.

Creodonts are primitive carnivores which are believed to have given rise to the carnivores of today. It is thought that the Creodonts preyed upon the primitive, slow-moving ungulates, and were replaced by the more efficient, larger-brained carnivores when the higher ungulates evolved. The geological range of Carnivora is the early Paleocene to the Recent in North America, Europe, and Asia.

Many people think of carnivores as being exclusively or primarily meat eaters. However, there are many that have a widely varied diet and some that eat very little meat or fish. Bears are almost omnivorous. When they come out of hibernation in the spring, they probably consume more vegetable material such as grasses, leaves, and roots or tubers than meat. When berries are ripe, they usually eat them. They are fond of some insects and ants and their fondness for honey is proverbial. By turning over stones and moving small logs or masses of vegetation, they catch small mammals such as mice. Those that are near streams where fish are to be had search diligently for food along the shore and they catch fish, especially salmon where available. Carrion is often eaten. Binturongs (*Arctictis*) feed largely on fruit, and other relatives of the civet group also eat fruit as well as other foods. The large carnivores such as lions and leopards (*Panthera*) often disembowl animals that they have killed and eat the viscera including the intestines even before they eat any of the red meat of the animal. By doing this they obtain valuable vitamins that are present in the digestive tract.

The seals and walruses, order Pinnipedia, have at times been included with the Carnivores, and are so closely related that some authorities still group them together, with the Pinnipeds treated as a suborder.

DOGS, DINGOS, JACKALS, WOLVES, COYOTES, FOXES; PODROSSEN, ZORROS, VOSSEN, FUSCHSE, RENARDS, LOUPS, GATOS DE MONTE, KORAI-TANUKI, USSURI-TANUKI, BOROCHI, PES HYENO-VITY, BAKOORJAKKALS OR DRAAIJAKKALS. (Included are vernaculars used in other countries.)

THIS FAMILY OF 14 genera and about 35 species has a worldwide distribution, except for New Zealand, New Guinea, Melanesia, Polynesia, the Moluccas, Celebes, Formosa, Madagascar, the West Indies, and some other oceanic islands. The dingo (*Canis dingo* or *Canis familiaris dingo*) was probably introduced to Australia by the aboriginal immigrants. The habitats include arctic regions (*Alopex*) and deserts (*Fennecus*).

The members of the family Canidae have lithe, muscular, deep-chested bodies, with long, slender limbs and bushy tails. The muzzle is long and slender, and the ears are large and erect. The first digit on the fore foot and the hind foot is reduced, the digital formula (for the fore foot and hind foot, in that order) being 5/4 (except in the African hunting dogs, *Lycaon*, in which it is 4/4). The claws are blunt. The male animal averages larger than the female in size, the fennec foxes (*Fennecus*) are the smallest members of the family and the gray or timber wolves (*Canis lupus*) are the largest. The length of the head and body is 340 to 1,350 mm., and the length of the tail is 110 to 540 mm. Adult canids weigh from 1 to 75 kg. Most forms are uniformly colored or speckled, but one species of jackal (*Canis adustus*) has stripes on the side of its body and African hunting dogs have blotches over their bodies.

Females of this family generally have three to seven pairs of mammae. A well-developed baculum is present in the males.

The skull is elongate, and the bullae are typically swollen. The incisors are normal, the sharp-pointed canines are elongate, the premolars are sharp and not in contact (with the exception of the last upper premolar and the molars), the carnassial teeth are well developed, and the molars posterior to the carnassials have grinding surfaces. The dental formula in all but three genera is as follows: 3/3, 1/1, 4/4, 2/3 = 42; in *Speothos* it is 3/3, 1/1, 4/4, 1/2 = 38, in *Cuon* it is 3/3, 1/1, 4/4, 2/2 = 40, and in *Otocyon* it is 3/3, 1/1, 4/4, 4/4 = 48.

When not disturbed by man, these alert, cunning animals tend to be active both night and day in the temperate zones, but they are more active at dusk and dawn in the tropics. They use burrows, caves, crevices, or hollow trees for dens. With the exception of *Nyctereutes* from eastern Asia and Japan, members of the family Canidae are active all year (the raccoon-dog sleeps through most of the winter). They walk, trot tirelessly, amble, or canter on their digits or partly on their digits and partly on more of the foot. At full speed they gallop. The coyote (*Canis latrans*) is apparently the fastest member of the family; this canid can run at speeds of 65 km. per hour. Gray foxes (*Urocyon*) often climb trees, an unusual habit for the members of this family, and a captive female bush-dog (*Speothos*) exhibited considerable swimming and diving ability.

Wolves (*Canis lupus* and *C. rufus*), Indian dholes (*Cuon*), and African hunting dogs (*Lycaon*) travel in

A view of the Seattle Fur Exchange in 1929 during the height of commercial fox fur farming. Most of the furs shown are the skins of blue foxes, a color phase of the Arctic fox (*Alopex*). There are also skins of coyotes and probably some of other furbearers. Photo from Seattle Fur Exchange.

bands that arise from family groups and number up to about 30 individuals in most cases (in *Lycaon*, uncommonly up to 60 animals). Other members of the family hunt singly or in relays, with a band of animals sometimes forming a relay system for bringing down its prey. Wolves may have home ranges nearly 80 km. in diameter. Canids have acute hearing and sight, but they hunt mainly by scent and usually obtain their prey by a swift and open chase.

Those canid forms which run in packs, made bold by their numbers, will often run down large, hoofed animals, whereas those that hunt singly or in relays generally prey on small rodents, ground birds, and insects. Jackals feed heavily on carrion, and plant matter is a part of the diet of a number of canids. Gray foxes may feed extensively on vegetable matter at certain seasons and in certain areas. The food and feeding habits vary with the season and the locality. The size of the population of canids may number one-tenth that of its principal prey but will fluctuate with the increased or decreased supply of game.

One litter (sometimes two) of 2 to 13 offspring is reared each year usually in a burrow. In several genera more than one female may raise their young in the same den. In most genera the gestation period is 49 to 70 days, with an average of 63 days; a gestation period of 79 days has been reported for *Nyctereutes* and an 80-day period for *Lycaon*. The offspring at birth are blind and helpless but are covered with hair. They are cared for solicitously by the mother until they are strong enough to outrun their enemies. They are suckled for six weeks (*Canis*) or about ten weeks for certain foxes. The members of this family are sexually mature in one to two years and live from 10 to approximately 18 years in the wild.

The pelts of most genera are used in various ways. Although canids sometimes prey on poultry and livestock, they also reduce the rodent and rabbit population. The howl of the wolf and coyote, which to some people is of more enduring significance than superhighways and skyscrapers, should always remain a part of our heritage. One species of this family, the Falkland Island dog (*Dusicyon australis*), has already been exterminated within historic times. When Dom, Pernetty, and other early explorers landed on the islands, these friendly dogs met the landing parties at the water's edge. Later, they came into the camps in groups, carried away articles, pulled meat from under the heads of sleeping men, and stood about while their fellow animals were being killed. The dogs were often killed by a man holding a piece of meat as bait in one hand then stabbing it with a knife in the other hand. This is a brutal but fairly typical example of human behavior. The extermination of the Falkland Island dog resulted mainly from the activity of the fur traders and by poisoning by the settlers in an effort to protect their sheep.

The geological range of this family is the upper Eocene to the Recent in North America and Europe, the lower Oligocene to the Recent in Asia, the Pleistocene to the Recent in Africa and South America, and the Recent in Australia. A Pleistocene genus (*Sivacyon*) is known from the Siwalik Hills of India; the skull resembles that of the living big-eared fox of Africa (*Otocyon*).

(1) A. Coyote (*Canis latrans*), photo from U.S. Fish & Wildlife Service. B. Wolf (*C. lupus*), photo from New York Zoological Society.

(2) A. Black-backed Jackal (*Canis mesomelas*), photo by Ernest P. Walker. B. Indian Jackal (*C. aureus*); C. Dingo (*C. dingo*); photos from New York Zoological Society.

C. familiaris: DOMESTIC DOGS, HUNDE, CHIENS, PERROS, KELB; *C. lupus:* WOLVES, WOLF, LOUPS, LOBOS, DEEB; *C. dingo:* DINGOS, DINGO; *C. latrans:* COYOTES, KOGOTE; *C. aureus:* GOLDEN JACKALS, WAWI, NKANDWE, DOWAO, KABARRO; *C. mesomelas* and *C. adustus:* JACKALS, BWEHA, JAKKALS, PUKUYE, GIDAR, KOLA, MUBUA-BUA. (Included are vernaculars used in other countries.)

THE EIGHT SPECIES are discussed separately.

Domestic dogs have generally been referred to as *Canis familiaris*, as though they were a distinct species. It is much more likely that they are descended from many of the species of *Canis* with which humans have come in contact for many thousands of years. The aborigines undoubtedly raised young which they found entertaining and useful as hunting companions. As the humans shifted about, they undoubtedly took their dogs with them. These dogs were bred with dogs of different species that had been domesticated by other tribes of humans. Also some were bred with the wild stock as is still done. Thus the domestic dog is almost certainly composed of several strains which probably explains the readiness with which they have developed into the numerous breeds through selective breeding or by accident. There are several excellent books regarding the various breeds of domestic dogs. The dingo (*C. dingo*) was present in Australia when this country was discovered by Europeans, but it is probable that these yellowish-brown dogs were introduced there by aboriginal immigrants.

Two species of wolves are recognized: *C. lupus*, the gray or timber wolf, and *C. rufus*, the red wolf. The gray wolf originally was widely distributed in North America, Europe, and Asia, but it is now eliminated from nearly all settled areas, and the red wolf is now apparently restricted to eastern Texas. The timber wolf has the following measurements: Length of head and body from 1,070 to 1,375 mm., length of tail from 300 to 560 mm., height at the shoulders to 970 mm., and weight from 27 to 79 kg. Coloration is usually gray, sprinkled with black; the legs and under parts are yellowish white, but black and light-colored phases also occur. The wolves of the Arctic coast of Alaska and western Canada are almost white throughout the year. With an average weight of about 15 kg., the red wolf is generally smaller and more slender than the gray wolf and also is more tawny in color. Wolves differ from coyotes in their wider nose-pad and usually in larger and heavier build; while running, wolves usually carry the tail high, whereas coyotes usually carry the tail below the level of the back.

These animals are intelligent and faithful and are definitely social creatures. The social units, that is, the packs, hunt together, although one large wolf is capable of bringing down and killing a large steer. One *C. rufus* had an entire newborn goat in its stomach. Animals as large as deer and sometimes elk and moose are killed by the pack, which consists of three or four to two dozen animals working together and running at speeds up to 45 km. per hour. Much of their food, however, consists of small animals, including mice, fish, crabs, and carrion. Wolves are believed to mate for life. The breeding season is January to March, and after a gestation period of about 63 days, 3 to 13 young are born in a den prepared by the mother. As in the other members of this genus, the life expectancy is usually 14 to 16 years.

The coyote, *C. latrans*, is now found in open country from Alaska to Central America and east to New York. The length of the head and body is about 900 mm.; the length of the tail is about 300 mm.; and the weight is 9 to 12.7 kg. Coloration is brown, sprinkled with black and gray.

Coyotes can run as fast as 64 km. per hour and usually hunt singly or in relays rather than in packs. The greater part of their diet, as shown by the analysis of over 10,000 stomachs, consists of jack-rabbits and rabbits, rodents, and carrion. Sheep and goats are killed on occasion. An individual coyote sometimes forms a "hunting partnership" with a badger (*Taxidea*), an association not well understood. Mating is probably for life. Breeding usually takes place in January and 5 to 10 pups are born in a den 60 to 65 days later. Coyotes are adaptable and intelligent. They have greatly extended their range in recent years, while many other mammals have lost territory.

The three species of jackals are distributed as follows: *C. aureus*, the golden or Asiatic jackal, ranges from Central Africa through the Middle East to Russian Turkestan; *C. mesomelas*, the black-backed jackal, and *C. adustus*, the side-striped jackal, inhabit eastern and southern Africa. All three species occur together in parts of northeastern Africa. The length of the head and body is 560 to 740 mm., the length of the tail is 230 to 355 mm., and the weight is 6.8 to 11 kg. The species can be distinguished by coloration: *C. aureus* is a pale dirty yellow mixed with reds and blacks and has a reddish-brown tail with a black tip; *C. adustus* has a pair of light and dark stripes on each side from the shoulder to the hip, and the tail has a white tip; *C. mesomelas* has a black "saddle" or "blanket" on the back and the tail has a black tip.

Jackals usually spend the day in thickets and clumps of vegetation, and occasionally in deep forests. *C. mesomelas* lives permanently in pairs which hunt together all year round. Maximum running speed is about 56 km. per hour. Jackals usually travel singly, in pairs, or in small groups through the open savannah country, feeding on any small animals they can catch, also on carrion, insects, and plant material. They often follow lions and leopards to obtain scraps from their kills. Poultry is taken at times, and the black-backed jackal is a pest in southern Africa where it preys on small livestock when extremely hungry.

The young usually are born in a burrow that the mother has found unoccupied, or she sometimes digs a burrow. Gestation period is 57 to 70 days, and litter size is two to seven. Pups are able to hunt and kill at eight months but up to this time usually accompany parents on hunting trips after the age of six to eight weeks.

The relatively close relationship between the forms of *Canis* is evidenced by the successful breeding between all the wild forms and the domestic dog.

The type species of the genus is *C. familiaris*, Linnaeus.

Arctic Foxes (*Alopex lagopus*), A. White and blue phases; B. Blue phase; C. Summer coat; photos by Alwin Pedersen. D. Winter coat, photo by Ernest P. Walker.

ARCTIC OR POLAR FOXES, WHITE AND BLUE FOXES; ISATIS, POLARFUCHSE, PODROSSEN.

THE SINGLE SPECIES, *A. lagopus*, inhabits the arctic regions of both the New World and the Old World. In general, *Alopex* lives above timberline and near the seacoast, but in winter it has been noted on ice floes 32 km. from shore. Individuals occasionally wander hundreds of kilometers inland into the forests.

The head and body length is 458 to 675 mm., the tail ranges in length from 255 to 425 mm., shoulder height is about 280 mm., and weight is 2.5 to 9 kg. The dense, woolly coat gives the animal a heavy appearance. There are two color phases: the "white"

form which is brown in summer and white in winter, and the "blue" form which is a dark bluish gray in summer and pale bluish gray in winter. However, in areas within its range where the climate is less severe, such as Iceland and the Pribilofs, the white form may remain fairly dark throughout the year. Blue foxes constitute less than 1 per cent of the total arctic fox population on the Canadian mainland, and less than 5 per cent in Baffin Land, whereas they make up as high as 50 per cent of the fox population in western Greenland. The winter pelage develops in October and is shed in April. The small, rounded ears are well furred, and long hairs are present on the soles of the feet.

Arctic foxes live in burrows, usually in the side of a hill or cliff. At times several foxes come together, particularly near baby seals, the carcass of a stranded whale, or other carrion where the food supply is plentiful. They regularly take advantage of the remains of kills made by polar bears. During blizzards they shelter in burrows dug in the snow. Several polar foxes have been noted in winter on the Greenland icecap more than 450 km. from the nearest ice-free land, with the temperature below −50 degrees C., and these animals have survived experimental temperatures as low as −80 degrees C. Arctic foxes do not hibernate. The Arctic fox may be active at any hour and frequently displays little fear of man.

Except in western Greenland, where lemmings are absent, arctic foxes exhibit fluctuations in population which tend to parallel those of the lemmings. *Alopex* feeds on any available animal life, alive or dead, and may store food. Arctic fox dens frequently have partially eaten or uneaten carcasses of birds and small mammals scattered about the entrance. During the fall these animals become fat, but by spring they are leaner due to the meager food supply.

The season of birth usually is May and June, when 4 to 11 young are born in a den after a gestation period of 51 to 57 days. The pups at birth weigh 60 grams, and both parents care for the young until the family breaks up in the fall. The adult *Alopex* utters a short bark as a warning note to the young. A life span of 14 years has been recorded for captive animals. The average is probably nearer one half that for animals in the wild.

The raising of blue foxes has been an important industry as the undressed skins have sold for $15 to $300 apiece. Falling prices for long-haired furs have forced most fox ranchers out of business since recent prices have fallen below $10. White fox skins are quite beautiful and may be left the natural white or dyed in many colors, particularly "platinum" and imitations of the "blue." The fur farms are of two types, namely, those on small islands on which the animals run at liberty, and those having pens where selective breeding is practiced. The arctic fox has long been an important item in the economy of the native people living within its range. Arctic foxes are rarely abundant because of limited food supplies. The fluctuation in population and fluctuation in prices paid for raw pelts have frequently combined to create serious hardships for those natives who rely on selling pelts for a livelihood.

Red Foxes (*Vulpes fulva*): A. Photo from New York Zoological Society. B. Silver Fox, photo from Fromm Brothers, Inc. C. Platinum Fox Pups, photo from *American Fur Breeder*. D. Cross Fox, photo by Howard E. Uible of mounted specimen in U.S. National Museum.

RED FOXES, KIT OR SWIFT FOXES; RENARDS, FUCHSE, VOSSEN, ZORROS. (Included are vernaculars used in other countries.)

NINE SPECIES compose this genus. The total range of the seven species of red foxes includes most of North America north of Mexico; Europe, including the British Isles; most of Africa, north and south of the Sahara; and most of Asia. A variety of habitats, including brushy and wooded areas and deserts, are frequented. The kit or swift foxes, *V. velox* and *V. macrotis*, inhabit the western half of the Great Plains from southwestern Canada into Texas and the west-central and southwestern United States into northern Mexico.

The head and body length of the red fox is 455 to 865 mm.; tail length is 305 to 555 mm.; and weight is about 9 kg. The usual coloration of red foxes, *V. fulva*, ranges from pale yellowish red to deep reddish brown above, with white, ashy, or slaty under parts. The lower part of the legs is usually black, and the tails generally are tipped with white or black. The desert foxes, however, are quite pale in color, and some of the foxes of India and nearby parts of Asia are grayish with little red or black coloration. In addition, silver or black color phases may occur in some of the species of the red fox group. Another member of the red fox group, the cross fox, is reddish brown in color, and gets its name from the black cross formed by a line down the middle of the back and another dark line across the shoulders. The color of the silver fox, most highly prized of the foxes for its fur, ranges from strong silver to nearly black, the general effect depending upon the proportion of white or silver tipped to black hairs. The so-called black fox (in reality a silver fox) has only a small number of white hairs. Kit foxes have a head and body length of 375 to 500 mm.; a tail length of 225 to 300 mm.; a shoulder height of about 30 cm.; and a weight of up to 3 kg. They are buffy yellow in color with a black-tipped tail.

The genus *Vulpes* may be characterized by small to medium size for the family (Canidae), large and pointed ears, sharp and elongated muzzle, round and bushy tail, which is usually as long as the head and body. It usually has six mammae. Most if not all foxes have a definite "foxy" odor arising from sub-caudal glands, and their pupils generally are elliptical in strong light. Members of the true wolves genus *Canis*, in contrast, lack the "foxy" scent, usually show a round pupil in strong light, and the number of mammae is 8 to 10.

Red foxes are not naturally wary, but they are intelligent creatures. As a result of contact with man, they have developed a cunning that now connotes the name fox with the acme of cleverness. These animals have considerable endurance; they can run at speeds of up to 48 km. per hour; they have a keen sense of sight, smell, and hearing; and, at times, they exhibit what almost seems to be a sense of humor. They generally rest during the day in some sheltered spot, the desert species uses burrows in the sand. The diet is omnivorous; red foxes eat such varied items as small animals, grass, fruits, eggs, and insects. Although they are sometimes a threat to poultrymen, they are one of the principal predators of voles and mice. Some years ago, foxes were largely removed from Door County, Wisconsin, only to be returned because of the alarming increase in the number of mice during their banishment.

Over most of its range the red fox group breeds in late winter. From 49 to 56 days later, 4 to 10 young (an average of 5) are born in a den. The cubs open their eyes in about 9 days and emerge from the den when about 5 weeks old. They are independent at about 5 months of age when they scatter about to seek a hunting ground; they can breed during the following winter. All foxes seem to be monogamous, and both parents care for the young. Their life span is about 12 years.

Kit foxes are quite shy and almost completely nocturnal in contrast to the somewhat bolder, more inquisitive, and occasionally diurnal red foxes. Poisoned baits are taken quite readily by swift foxes and, as a result, this fox population is low in some areas. They dig burrows of their own or use the deserted burrows of badgers (*Taxidea*) or prairie dogs (*Cynomys*). Their tunnels may be 3.5 meters long and 1.5 meters below the surface, with anywhere from one to seven or more entrances. Kit foxes feed on rabbits, rodents, and insects. The four to seven young, born in February or somewhat later, are cared for by both parents. The pups nurse for about ten weeks and remain with the parents until late summer or early fall.

From 1900 to 1920 in North America and, to some extent, in other parts of the world, catching wild foxes and raising them in captivity became an important industry. In the early stages of the breeding industry, choice animals often sold for more than a thousand dollars each. Through selective breeding the silver strains now breed true. The fur of the kit foxes sells for much less than that of red foxes. With the possible exception of the mink, the number of foxes raised today for their fur exceeds that of any other wild animal. One fox farm permanently employed about 400 people and sold pelts worth more than $18 million. The pelts of foxes are used mainly for scarves and trimming on women's apparel. Likewise, platinum and white fox stoles have been popular. Foxes also have furnished sport for hunters through the years. There is no more engaging sight than a litter of fox cubs tumbling and playing about the den, while being watched over by a parent, nor is there a more picturesque animal than a red fox hunting in a stubble-field covered with snow.

The type species of the genus is *V. vulpes* (Linnaeus).

Fennecs (*Fennecus zerda*), photo from New York Zoological Society.

FENNECS OR FENNEC FOXES.

THE SINGLE SPECIES, *F. zerda*, inhabits the arid and desert regions in northern Africa and the Sinai and Arabian Peninsulas. It could be regarded as the Old World counterpart of the North American kit fox.

This animal is the smallest and palest-colored of any of the foxes. The head and body length is 357 to 407 mm.; tail length is 178 to 305 mm.; and weight is about 1.5 kg. The ears are 15 cm. or more long, relatively the largest among all foxes. The coloration above is reddish cream, pale fawn, or almost white; the under parts are white, and the tip of the tail is black. The thick furry coat is soft and long, and the tail is heavily furred.

This desert fox usually lives in burrows in the sand. It digs so rapidly that it has the reputation of "sinking into the ground." Fennecs are active at night, and are quite agile; a captive animal has been known to spring 60 to 70 cm. upward from a standing position and to jump horizontally about 120 cm.

Fennecs apparently obtain some of their food by digging it out of the ground, as evidenced by the pronounced scratching or raking habit in captive animals. They eat various foods, including plant material, small rodents, birds, birds' eggs, lizards, and insects, such as the noxious migratory locusts. These desert foxes can subsist without free water for considerable periods of time; travelers report fox tracks in the desert far from oases, so that these animals evidently do not make frequent trips for water. An abundance of tracks about some waterholes indicates that the desert fox drinks freely when the opportunity presents itself.

The young, usually two to five per litter, are born in March and April after a gestation period of 50 to 51 days. The life span of *Fennecus* seems to be 10 to 12 years.

Eastern Gray Fox (*Urocyon cinereoargenteus*), photo by Ernest P. Walker.

GRAY FOXES; LOS CHACALILLOS, ZORROS GRISEN, GATO DE MONTE (Central and South American names).

THE TWO SPECIES of *Urocyon* are distributed as follows: *U. cinereoargenteus*, from southern Canada and eastern, southwestern, and extreme western United States through Mexico and Central America to northern South America; and *U. littoralis*, certain islands off the coast of southern California. Gray foxes frequent wooded and brushy country, often in rocky areas, and are possibly most common in the arid regions of the southwestern United States and western Mexico

The species *U. cinereoargenteus* has a head and body length of 525 to 685 mm., and a tail length of 275 to 445 mm., whereas the island gray fox measures 480 to 500 mm. in head and body length and 110 to 290 mm. in tail length. Gray foxes usually weigh from 2.5 to 7 kg. The face, upper part of the head, back, sides, and most of the tail are gray; the throat, insides of the legs, and under parts are white; and the sides of the neck, lower flanks, and under parts of the tail are rusty. The hairs along the middle of the back and the top of the tail are heavily tipped with black, which gives the effect of a black mane, and black lines also occur on the legs and face in most individuals. A concealed mane of stiff hairs occurs on the top of the tail. The pelage is coarse.

Urocyon is sometimes called a tree fox because it frequently climbs trees, a rather unusual habit for the family (Canidae). A gray fox when pursued often will seek refuge in a tree, but it also climbs without provocation. Gray foxes do not regularly dig a den but occupy cavities and crevices in rocks, caves, and even hollow trees. They are mainly nocturnal, resting during the day in thick vegetation or among rocks.

These carnivores eat many kinds of small animals as well as insects and plant products. Those living near poultry yards sometimes prey on chickens. Gray foxes seem to prefer more plant products than do the other foxes, and fruits and grains may form the majority of the diet at certain seasons and in certain areas.

The two to seven, usually three or four, young are born in spring after a gestation period averaging 63 days (the den usually is a cave). The pups weigh about 115 grams each at birth, are blackish in color, and begin to take solid food in six weeks. The family breaks up in late summer or early fall, although the parents may stay together through the year. If captured when small, gray foxes (*Urocyon*) tame readily, are as affectionate and playful as dogs, and make much more satisfactory pets than the red foxes (*Vulpes*).

The attractive skins are commonly sold for furs but are not classed as fine furs.

The type species of the genus is *U. cinereoargenteus* (Schreber).

Raccoon Dog (*Nyctereutes procyonoides*), photo by Ernest P. Walker.

RACCOON DOGS; CHIENSRIVERRINGS, MARDER-HUNDE, USSURI-TANUKI, KORAI-TANUKI (local vernaculars).

THE SINGLE SPECIES, *N. procyonoides*, occurs in eastern Siberia, Manchuria, Japan, parts of China, and northern Indo-China. It is now quite rare in Japan largely because it has been hunted for its highly-valued fur. Raccoon dogs inhabit rocky banks and forests in river valleys and near lakes. They have been introduced into parts of Russia and are now also found in Poland and Finland.

The head and body length is 500 to 550 mm., and tail length is 130 to 180 mm. A well-fed raccoon dog in autumn weighs as much as 7.5 kg. The general color is yellowish brown; the hairs of the shoulder, back, and tail are tipped with black. There is a large dark spot on each side of the face, beneath and behind the eye, and the limbs are blackish brown. The hairs are long, especially in winter. Raccoon dogs resemble raccoons in the facial markings, otherwise they are somewhat fox-like but with proportionately shorter legs and tail than foxes.

In general these animals are nocturnal; they live singly or in family groups of five or six and shelter in dens among rocks, in thickets, and in hollow trees.

They use deserted burrows of other animals or dig their own dens, and they have been known to establish themselves beneath occupied houses. Individual *Nyctereutes* in the colder areas of the range usually sleep through most of the winter, emerging on warm days. Raccoon dogs growl and whine but do not bark.

The diet is varied; small rodents, fish, and acorns are especially preferred. Raccoon dogs feed heavily on various berries and fruits in late summer and fall. Carrion is also consumed, and these canids sometimes approach human habitation to obtain refuse. These canids do not prey on chickens.

The breeding season begins in February or March. Gestation periods of 52 days, 60 to 63 days, and 79 days have been reported, and most births occur in May. The number of young is 5 to 12 (usually 6 to 8). The pups are independent by the fall of their first year.

In the Japanese Islands the inhabitants enjoy the flesh of raccoon dogs and use their bones in medicine. Their skins are used throughout the range for various purposes, including the making of bellows, the decoration of drums, and winter head covering. Raccoon dogs have been successfully bred in cages and are known as "ussurian raccoon" in the fur trade.

South American "Fox" (*Dusicyon culpaeus*), photo by Ernest P. Walker.

SOUTH AMERICAN "FOXES"; ZORRA, CULPEU, CHILLA, PAINEGURU, GUARACHAIM (local vernaculars).

ABOUT SIX SPECIES inhabit South America; the extinct Falkland Island dogs belonged to this genus. *Pseudalopex* is herein regarded as a synomym of *Dusicyon* and *Lycalopex*, Burmeister, 1854, as a subgenus of *Dusicyon* for the species *D. vetulus*.

The head and body length is 0.6 to 1 meter, and the tail length is usually 30 to 35 cm. The general coloration is reddish, brownish, or blackish, usually with yellowish tints. The head, ears, and neck are often reddish. The tail is bushy and the coat is usually heavy with a dense underfur and long guard hairs. Most of the species look somewhat like small coyotes (*Canis latrans*), but *Dusicyon* differs structurally from other canids.

The animals inhabit flat, open areas or live in wooded, hilly country; they are found up to 4,000 meters in elevation in the Andes. They usually den among rocks, under bases of trees, and in burrows made by other animals, such as those of the viscachas. Most species are nocturnal, but some individuals are occasionally active during the day. The species *D. gymnocercus* has some interesting habits: It sometimes collects and stores objects such as strips of leather and cloth, and it may freeze and remain motionless upon the appearance of a human being. There is an account of such a "frozen" animal being approached by a man and struck with a whip-handle, yet it remained motionless. Perhaps the animal behaves this way because it cannot run swiftly.

The diet is omnivorous; rodents, rabbits, birds (including chickens and ducks), insects, especially locusts, fruits, sugar cane, frogs and lizards are consumed. The species *D. culpaeus* occasionally preys on sheep. *Dusicyon* howls when abroad at night, especially during the mating season. From three to six young are born in the spring (October and November), and the male helps in the feeding of the young. The mother has been known to defend her pups courageously, and within two to three months the young are hunting with the parents.

These canids are hunted because they prey on fowl and sheep and their fur is desirable, thus the *Dusicyon* population has been greatly reduced in some areas. As a result, rodents and birds have increased to such an extent that they harm crops. The Falkland Island dog (*D. australis*) was exterminated about 1876.

The genotype is *D. australis* (Kerr).

Small-eared Dog (*Atelocynus microtis*), photo from Field Museum of Natural History.

SMALL-EARED DOGS, SMALL-EARED ZORROS; ZOR-
RO NEGRO, ZORRO DE OREJAS CORTAS.

THE SINGLE SPECIES, *A. microtis*, inhabits the tropical wooded areas of the Amazonian basin in Brazil,
Peru, Ecuador, and Colombia, and into the upper
Rio Orinoco basin in Colombia and probably Venezuela. This genus has also been recorded from the
upper Rio Parana basin in Brazil. The elevational
range is from near sea level to approximately 1,000
meters.

The height at the shoulders is about 356 mm.; the
length of the head and body is 720 to 1,000 mm.; the
length of the tail is 250 to 350 mm.; and the weight
is approximately 9 kg. The ears are relatively shorter
than those in any other species of wild dog, only 34
to 52 mm. long. The color is among the darkest of
South American canids. The upper parts are dark
gray to black, and the under parts are rufous mixed
with gray and black. The thickly haired tail sweeps
the ground when hanging perpendicularly as the animal stands. It is black except for the paler basal part
on the underside.

The characteristic external features of *Atelocynus*
are the short and rounded ears and the dark coloration. Features of the skull and teeth also distinguish
this genus from the other South American Canidae.

Small-eared zorros move with a cat-like grace and
lightness not observed in any other member of the
family Canidae. At the present time a pair is in captivity at the Brookfield Zoo in Chicago. These two
animals are completely different in temperament; the
male is exceedingly friendly and docile and the female
exhibits constant hostility. Although the male was
shy in captivity before being sent to Brookfield and
growled and snarled when angry or frightened, it has
not shown any unfriendly actions at the Chicago zoo
and has, in fact, become very tame. It permits itself
to be hand fed and petted by persons it recognizes,
responding to petting by rolling over on its back and
squealing. This male *Atelocynus* now reacts to atten-
tions from familiar people by a weak but noticeable
wagging of the back part of its tail. The female, on
the other hand, when under direct observation, emits
a continuous growling sound without opening her
mouth or baring her teeth.

The odor from the anal glands of the male is strong
and musky, but it is scarcely detectable in the female.
In both sexes the eyes glow remarkably in dim light.
The male, although smaller, is dominant in most activities. Although some snapping has been observed
between these two animals, no biting or fighting has
been noted, and they occupy a common sleeping box
when not active. In the standing posture the tail is
curved forward and upward against the outer side of
a hind leg so that the terminal hairs do not drag on
the ground.

The male, when in captivity at Bogota, ate raw
meat, shoots of a grass, and the common foods that
people eat.

Crab-eating Fox (*Cerdocyon thous*), photo from San Diego Zoological Garden.

SAVANNA FOXES, CRAB-EATING FOXES; ZORROS DE MONTE, ZORROS PERROS, CACHORRO DO MATO (local vernaculars).

THE SINGLE SPECIES, *C. thous*, lives in open woodlands and in grasslands of South America as far south as southern Brazil, southeastern Bolivia, Paraguay, northern Argentina, and Uruguay. It is the common fox of Colombia and Venezuela.

The head and body length is 60 to 70 cm., and tail length is about 30 cm. The coloration is quite variable among individuals, but it is usually pale grayish to brownish, often with yellowish tints. The ears have a dark tip. This species differs from the other canids of South America in characteristics of the skull, teeth, and feet.

The stomachs of 19 specimens of *C. thous* have been examined by E. Mondolfi in Venezuela. In order of abundance, the stomachs contained: small rodents (field mice and rats), insects (mostly grasshoppers), fruits (figs, small berries, bananas, guasimo, and mangos), lizards (two different genera), frogs, and crabs. In just one case were a few bird feathers found. These foxes dig for turtle eggs of a species of *Podocnemys* called "galapago," who bury their eggs in small holes on the savanna. They also eat ducks and chickens. *Cerdocyon* usually hunts singly or in pairs and is mainly nocturnal. The daytime retreat is usually a burrow dug by some other animal.

The litter numbers from two to five. Pregnant females have been taken in April and August. The Zoological Park of Maracay reported births in March and August. Five cubs with their eyes still closed were found in a rice field in September.

The savanna fox can be domesticated quite easily. It has definitely been established that during the dry season, in the llanos, these foxes may develop rabies. The short-haired fur of this species is not so popular for clothing as that of some of the other South American canids.

CARNIVORA; CANIDAE; **Genus: CHRYSOCYON, H. Smith, 1839**

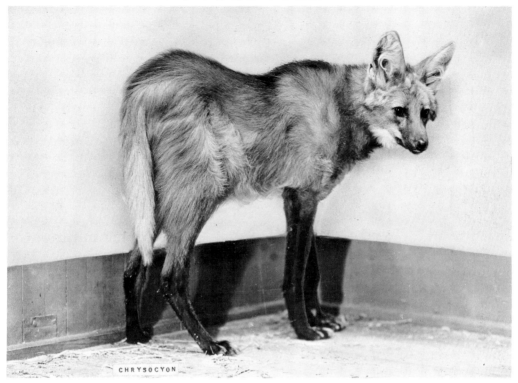

Maned Wolf (*Chrysocyon brachyurus*), photo from U.S. National Zoological Park.

MANED WOLVES; AZUARA-GUASUS OR LOS LOBOS DE CRIN, BOROCH, GUARÁ (local vernaculars).

THE SINGLE SPECIES, *C. brachyurus*, inhabits Brazil, Paraguay, eastern Bolivia, Uruguay, and northern Argentina. It has been observed at the edges of swamps and on the pampas.

In general appearance these large, long-legged animals are much like red foxes (*Vulpes*). The head and body length is about 125 cm.; tail length averages about 30 cm.; and the shoulder height is about 75 cm. Weight is about 23 kg. The coloration is generally a yellowish red; usually the lower part of the legs is darker than the body (almost black). Occasionally there is black about the mouth and black on the back and tail. The tip of the tail and the chin occasionally are white. The coat is fairly long and somewhat softer than that of the true wolves (*Canis*), with an erectile mane on the back of the neck and the top of the shoulders. The pupils of the eyes are round.

Because maned wolves are wary and live in remote areas, little is known of their habits in the wild. They are usually solitary and nocturnal, and, to judge from their build, swift-running and wide-ranging animals. They utter a strange, weird cry at dusk. Captive specimens have shown intelligence, playfulness, and some friendliness. One in the U.S. National Zoological Park about 30 years ago was fairly tame and had a good disposition. If annoyed, however, it lowered its ears and laid them back, producing a striking change in appearance.

Maned wolves eat such mammals as pacas (*Cuniculus*) and agoutis (*Dasyprocta*), birds, reptiles, insects, fruits, and perhaps some other plant material. They have been known to kill sheep, but usually they avoid man and his activities. *Chrysocyon* does not threaten man as do true wolves.

The number of young is usually two, and the pups are generally born in the winter. A litter of three was born at the San Diego Zoo. The pups were dark brown, nearly black, with white-tipped tails. The Antwerp Zoo has successfully kept maned wolves alive on a diet of two kg. of bananas and two pigeons per day per animal.

Some South Americans make a "tea" from bone shavings of the maned wolf. This concoction is given to pregnant women and is said to ease delivery. The same effect is ascribed by these natives to a concoction made from the antlers of swamp deer (*Blastocerus*).

Bush Dog (*Speothos venaticus*), photo from San Diego Zoological Garden.

BUSH DOGS, SAVANNAH DOGS; ZORROS VINAGRE, CACHORRO VINAGRE, CACHORRO DO MATO VINAGRE (local vernaculars).

THE SINGLE SPECIES, *S. venaticus*, inhabits Panama, eastern Colombia, the Guianas, Brazil, Paraguay, eastern Peru, and northern Bolivia. Wooded and savannah areas, often in sandy soil, are frequented.

The head and body length is 575 to 750 mm., and the tail is 125 to 150 mm. long. A male weighed 5.0 kg. and another weighed 7.0 kg. The general color is brown, with orange, tawny, or whitish fore parts. The hindquarters, bell, and tail are darker than the general coloration, sometimes almost black. Pale patches or bands often occur on the upper and under parts. The form of the bush dog is in marked contrast to that of the maned wolf (*Chrysocyon*). The bush dog is stocky with short legs and tail, the hair is long, and the tail is well haired but not bushy. The genus *Speothos* was first described from fossils collected in caves in Brazil.

Little is known of these animals in the wild, and living specimens are rare in collections. Bush dogs apparently are nocturnal and are said to hunt in packs. A female bush dog adapted herself to captivity and exhibited behavior patterns much like those of domestic dogs. Her greatest departure from normal dog behavior was in her ability to swim and dive, and she swam well under water. It has been reported that *Speothos* will pursue pacas (*Cuniculus*) into water. The diet probably is a varied one, but it may consist mainly of rodents.

Whines and squeals, almost bird-like, and "short dog-like barks" have been noted. The latter type of call once drew attention to a female and her three nearly full-grown offspring. These pups had been raised in a hillside burrow in tall forest. Bush dogs are reported to spend the day in the abandoned burrows of armadillos.

One female with two juvenile offspring was found swimming across Rio Negro in the month of July. The female was pregnant. Litters of four and five pups have been recorded in the San Diego Zoo.

Dhole (*Cuon alpinus*), photo from New York Zoological Society.

INDIAN DHOLES, RED "DOGS"; SERIGALA, ADJAG.

THE SINGLE SPECIES, *C. alpinus*, inhabits parts of Russia and Siberia, Korea, parts of China, India, southeastern Asia, Sumatra, and Java, but not Ceylon. This species usually lives in wooded regions.

The head and body length is 760 to 1,000 mm.; tail length is 280 to 482 mm.; and weight is 14 to 21 kg. The northern animals have heavy coats with thick underfur and are colored yellowish to brownish gray in winter and more brownish in summer; the southern animals are not so heavily furred and bear different shades of yellowish brown throughout the year, although usually lighter on the under parts. Indian wild dog, the name applied to these animals by Anglo-Saxons in India, is a misnomer inasmuch as these canids are not of the same genus as dogs. *Cuon* resembles *Canis* in general external features, but the ears are more rounded and the female *Cuon* typically has six or seven pairs of mammae; internally, dholes differ from *Canis* in dental and skull features.

Dholes are gregarious, usually associating in groups of 3 or 4 up to packs of 30. The larger groups probably represent different families, as several females often raise their young together. Dholes are active both day and night but are mainly diurnal. Hunting is carried on by the pack, and the prey is trailed by scent. Dholes usually are silent when running game, but they utter a peculiar call when a tiger is located. They are not fast runners but are seemingly tireless.

A pack will slaughter a wide variety of prey, and with the courage of their numbers, may attack such formidable carnivores as tigers, leopards, Himalayan black bears, and sloth bears. However, the more common kills are deer and musk deer, ibex, wild pigs, wild sheep, antelopes, water buffalos, gaurs, and bantengs. There are no records of attacks on man, except perhaps at one place on Java; but this has never been proved. The attack may have been made by feral dogs. If their depredations remove most of the game from an area, they will hunt elsewhere.

Dholes howl but do not bark, and they have a mating call. Young are born at all seasons in India, but mostly during January and February. The gestation period is about nine weeks, and there are usually two to six young. Holes in banks and among rocks are utilized as dens, as dholes rarely dig burrows of their own.

African Hunting Dog (*Lycaon pictus*), photo by Bernhard Grzimek.

AFRICAN HUNTING DOGS; WILDEHONDE, CHIENS CHASSEURS, LOUPS AFRICAINS, PES HYENOVITY, MBWA MWITU (local vernaculars and native names).

THE SINGLE SPECIES, *L. pictus*, inhabits most of Africa south of the Sahara and occurs from sea level to above the tree line on east African mountains.

The head and body length is 762 to 1,015 mm.; tail length is 305 to 409 mm.; shoulder height is about 610 mm.; and weight is 16 to 23 kg. There is great variation in color, the mottled black, yellow, and white occurring in almost every conceivable arrangement and proportion of color. In most individuals, however, the head is dark and the tail has a white tip or brush. The fur is short and scant, sometimes so sparse that the blackish skin is plainly visible. The long, rounded ears are covered with short hairs. The legs are long and slender, and there are only four toes on each foot. The jaws are broad and powerful; although the hunting dog somewhat resembles the hyenas (*Crocuta* and *Hyaena*), it is not closely related to them. *Lycaon* has a strong musky odor.

These animals, active both day and night, range widely in packs of about 4 to 60 (usually about a dozen) preying on any animal they can overpower after running it down or surprising it. They kill more than they can consume and often kill for the mere

sake of killing. They hunt systematically and when game is flushed, hunting dogs usually capture their quarry. Their speed is not great, but they are seemingly tireless and often run in relays. They are bold, have little fear of man, and, on occasion, have threatened man. The rallying cry of the pack is a wild, eerie call, somewhat like a whinny. Lions seem to be their greatest enemies, but they will even attack lions if in sufficiently large packs.

They bite at prey, snapping out pieces of flesh until the animal falls from loss of blood and exhaustion; and then they literally eat it alive. A pack of about a dozen animals will entirely consume a medium-sized animal in about 15 minutes. Hunting dogs are great scourges to wildlife, mainly the antelopes, and may be quite destructive to livestock, particularly the smaller varieties such as sheep and goats. In the absence of large game, they sometimes hunt for small mammals, such as the cane rats (*Thryonomys*) and birds. When the food supply is exhausted, they wander off to another area.

There seems to be no regular breeding season for *Lycaon*, although those members inhabiting temperate climates breed mainly in the spring and fall. The gestation period has been reported as 63 days and as 80 days. The number of young is usually six to eight, and the life span is about ten years.

African Big-eared Fox (*Otocyon megalotis*), photo by Ernest P. Walker.

BIG-EARED OR BAT-EARED FOXES; BAKOORJAKKALS OR DRAAIJAKKALS.

THE SINGLE SPECIES, *O. megalotis*, lives in arid regions of eastern and southern Africa.

The head and body length is 460 to 580 mm.; tail length is 240 to 340 mm.; shoulder height is 350 to 400 mm.; and weight is 3 to 4.5 kg. The ears are 114 to 135 mm. long. The general color is yellowish brown or yellowish; the mask, lower legs, feet, and tip of the tail are black. This animal may be distinguished by the very large black-tipped ears, black feet, short legs, skull characteristics, and dentition. *Otocyon* has more teeth than any other placental mammal with teeth differentiated in form (heterodont); the full dentition of 46 teeth consists of 3 incisors, 1 canine, 4 premolars, and 3 upper and 4 lower molars on each side of each jaw. The teeth, however, are very weak.

Big-eared foxes sometimes approach human habitations; they are curious and often watch human activities but are difficult to pursue. When slightly alarmed, they are reported to crouch, lower the head, and flatten the ears and project them outward. They are somewhat nocturnal but often come out during the day; they travel singly, in pairs, and in groups of up to six individuals. Bushes, high grass, rocks, and burrows are used as shelters.

The diet is mainly insects, termites being the favorite type. They will also eat vegetable matter, including fruits and tuberous roots, small mammals, and occasionally carrion. Tame animals have taken kitchen scraps and one had a great liking for ground nuts. Rodents such as the gerbilles are run down, and a big-eared fox can skillfully double back on its tracks in a manner similar to that of its prey. *Otocyon* rarely or never molests domestic animals; its diet (particularly termites) is actually beneficial to man's welfare.

Births are said to occur from December through April but may take place throughout the year over the entire range of *Otocyon*. Gestation period is 60 to 70 days, and the number of young is two to five. Owing to the absence of rufous coloration, the cubs of *Otocyon* cannot be mistaken for those of jackals. The parents call to the young with a whistling call.

BEARS; OSOS ANDINOS, USSURI-KUROKOMA, OSOS NEGROS, IJSBEREN, EISBAREN, ASWAIL. (Included are vernaculars used in other countries.)

THIS FAMILY of seven genera and approximately nine species inhabits the Northern Hemisphere and northern South America; bears do not occur in Africa, Madagascar, Australia, various oceanic islands, and the Antarctic. With the exception of the polar bear (*Thalarctos*), which inhabits the Arctic, the members of this family live in temperate and tropical regions.

Bears are big-headed mammals with large, heavily built bodies, short powerful limbs, and short tails. The eyes and ears are small—the ears are rounded and erect. The lips are free from the gums. Those bears that are mainly terrestrial have hairy soles, but the soles are naked in those that climb considerably, such as *Helarctos*. Bears have a plantigrade walk. All the limbs have five digits, and the claws are strong, recurved, and used for tearing and digging. Male bears average about a fifth larger in size than the females. The Malayan sun bears (*Helarctos*) are the smallest members of the family and the Alaskan big brown bears are the largest. The length of the head and body is 1 to approximately 3 meters, and the length of the tail is 70 to 125 mm. Adult bears weigh from 27 to 780 kg. The coat is long and shaggy, and the fur generally is unicolored, usually some shade of brown, black, or white. Black, bluish, cinnamon, and nearly white color phases occur in one genus (*Euarctos*). Some genera have white or buffy crescents or semicircles on the chest. *Tremarctos*, the spectacled bear of South America, typically has a patch of white hairs encircling the eyes. Males have a baculum.

The incisors are not specialized, the canines are elongate, the first three premolars are reduced or absent, and the molars have broad, flat, and tubercular crowns. The carnassials are not developed as such. The tympanic bullae of the skull are not inflated.

Bears are active in the evening and during the night in the tropical and temperate regions, but the polar bear (*Thalarctos*) tends to be diurnal. Those forms

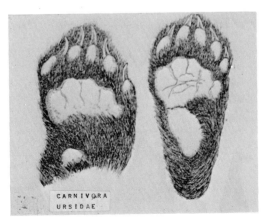

American Black Bear (*Euarctos americanus*), right forepaw and right hind foot, photo from *Proc. Zool. Soc. London.*

that occur on steppes and barren areas often dig dens in hillsides, but the usual shelter is a cave, hollow log, or plant cover.

Bears have a characteristic shuffling gait in which they walk on the sole of the foot with the heel touching the ground. They can walk on their hind legs and are surprisingly agile and careful in their movements when need be. These mammals wander extensively, especially polar bears, which are also aquatic. With the exception of *Thalarctos*, bears are active mainly on the ground or in trees.

The members of this family are sometimes fairly numerous in areas that are distant from civilization. They usually live alone, except when breeding or where females are accompanied by their young.

Bears are usually peaceful, inoffensive animals that try to avoid conflict; but if they think they must defend themselves or their young, food supply, or home territory, they are formidable and dangerous adversaries. Only a small proportion of the alleged unprovoked attacks of bears on man are true. When carefully investigated, it is usually found that the bear was provoked by some thoughtless misdeed.

With the approach of winter, bears in temperate and colder regions become fat, and at the approach of cold weather cease eating and go into a den that they have prepared in a location protected from the worst of the weather. Here they sleep through the winter in "hibernation," although physiologists prefer not to call it hibernation as the body temperature is not reduced and the body functions continue to some degree. Bears can be easily awakened, which is not the case with some other creatures that hibernate. Sometimes mild weather arouses them. Polar bears do not "hibernate," except for pregnant females.

Bears are omnivorous, except the polar bear which eats mainly fish, seals, and food it finds on the beaches. Most bears eat such plant material as grass, leaves, roots, fruits, and any animal material they can obtain such as ants, insects, small or large mammals and sometimes carrion. They often wade in streams to catch fish. They kill much of their food with a blow made by their powerful hands. After emerging from the winter sleep they eat such laxative materials as grass, roots, moss, and ants.

Their eyesight and hearing are not particularly good, but their sense of smell is excellent.

A single litter of one to four young is born each year. Most of them are born while the mother is in hibernation, although the dates range from October to March. The young are very small at birth, ranging from 228 to 453 grams. Polar bears dig dens in the snow when ready to reproduce. The gestation period ranges from six to nine months in most genera as a result of delayed fertilization and implantation of the ova. The young remain with the mother through the first fall and sometimes longer. They become sexually mature at 2.5 to 6 years and usually live for 15 to 30 years in the wild. In captivity a polar bear has lived 34 years and a brown bear (*Ursus arctos*) 47 years.

Bears are related to the dogs and wolves, but the exact line of descent is uncertain. The geological range of this family is the middle Miocene to the Recent of Europe, the middle Pliocene to the Recent of Asia, the upper Pliocene to the Recent of North America, and the Pleistocene to the Recent of South America.

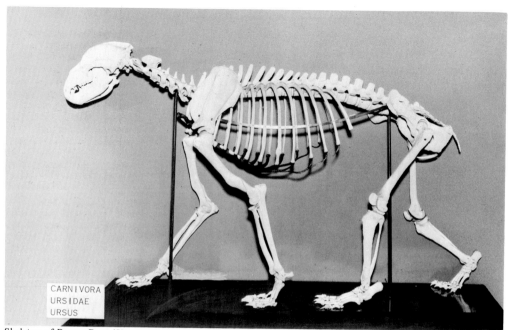

CARNIVORA
URSIDAE
URSUS

Skeleton of Brown Bear (*Ursus arctos*), photo from U.S. National Museum.

SPECTACLED BEARS; OSOS ANDINOS, UCUMARI, OSOS DE ANTEOJOS (local vernaculars).

THE SINGLE SPECIES, *T. ornatus*, inhabits the mountainous regions of western Venezuela, Colombia, Ecuador, Peru, and western Bolivia to 3,000 meters in elevation and may possibly occur in Panama. *Tremarctos* is mainly a forest animal but often ranges into the higher clearings or into the lower savannahs and scrublands.

The head and body length is 1.5 to 1.8 meters; tail length is about 70 mm.; and shoulder height is about 762 mm. One individual, not quite full-grown, weighed about 70 kg. One male, 1.74 meters in length, weighed 140 kg. The entire body is uniformly black or blackish-brown, except for the large circles or semicircles of white around the eyes and a white semicircle on the lower side of the neck from which lines of white extend onto the chest. The English common name is derived from the white around the eyes. These head and chest markings are quite variable, however, and may be completely lacking in some animals. *Tremarctos* is the only South American bear.

Its habits and biology are little known. It is said to be one of the most herbivorous of bears, feeding largely on leaves, fruits, and roots. In Ecuador it is reported to feed on the "pambili" palm, a tree from 24 to 30 meters high. The bear climbs the palm and tears off branches and later descends to the ground to eat them. Food also is obtained in this forested area by tearing open the green stalks of young palms and eating the unopened inner leaves. In an arid area in northern Peru the spectacled bear has been seen feeding on the fruits of a species of *Capparis*. However, these bears eat meat in the zoo as well as plant material, and animals in the wild have been reported to prey on deer, guanacoes, and vicunas.

The report that these bears make large nests of sticks in trees is possible but requires confirmation.

A spectacled bear lived for 20 years in the San Diego Zoo. A female in the Berlin Zoo gave birth to one cub.

Spectacled Bear (*Tremarctos ornatus*), photo from San Diego Zoological Garden.

Asiatic Black Bear (*Selenarctos thibetanus*), photo from New York Zoological Society.

ASIATIC BLACK BEARS; CHOSEN KUROKANA, USSMI KUROKANA, KRAGENBÄR (local vernaculars).

THE SINGLE SPECIES, *S. thibetanus*, occurs in southern and eastern Asia from Baluchistan and Afghanistan through the Himalayas east to Indo-China and north through most of China to Japan, Korea, Manchuria, Siberia, and the islands of Hainan and Formosa. These bears frequent deciduous forests and brushy areas to the upper limit of timber.

The head and body length is 1.3 to 1.6 meters; tail length is 76 to 106 mm.; and the weight ranges up to 120 kg., depending upon the locality and the season. They become fat in late summer and early fall before "hibernation." The coloration usually is black, with some white on the chin and a white crescent-shaped mark on the chest; some animals are reddish brown or rich brown. The generic name means "moon bear."

Their habits are similar to those of the bears of the genera *Ursus* and *Euarctos* except many of them do not hibernate at all or only for short periods when the weather is most inclement. In the mountains they range as high as 3,600 meters elevation in summer and in winter descend to about 1,500 meters, or lower. These bears make a bed of fresh twigs on the snow where they can dry themselves or take a sunbath, and in the summer they make nests of sticks in trees where they sleep. They are more aggressive than *Euarctos* or *Ursus arctos* of the Old World, sometimes killing sheep, goats, cattle, and ponies, raiding bee hives, committing other depredations, and occasionally killing men.

In India the usual size of the litter is two. At birth they are very small like all bear cubs and their eyes are closed. After leaving the den, they follow the mother until nearly grown, sometimes until after a later litter has been born and begun to follow her. Like other bears they swim readily.

The Chinese prize them for the supposed medicinal properties of the flesh and bones and the "dainty dish afforded by its paws."

Alaskan Brown Bear (*Ursus arctos*), photo by Ernest P. Walker.

BROWN AND GRIZZLY BEARS; OURS, BAR.

IN THE Americas the genus *Ursus* is represented by the big brown bears of Alaska that inhabit the Alaskan Peninsula, Kodiak and Afognak Islands, Montague Island in Prince William Sound and Baranoff, Chichagof, and Admiralty Islands in southeastern Alaska; and the grizzly bears that formerly ranged over much of the western half of North America from northern Mexico to the barren lands of Alaska and Canada. The brown bears of the Old World originally inhabited most of Europe, Asia, and probably the Atlas Mountains in North Africa. A recent study (Dirk Pieter, *A Review of Fossil and Recent Bears of the Old World with Remarks on Their Phylogeny Based upon their Dentition* [Netherlands, 1953]) refers all these Old and New World bears to a single species *U. arctos*. Grizzlies now are rare except in Yellowstone and Glacier National Parks (under protection) and in Canada and Alaska (in the wild); the Alaska browns are fairly common over most of their range; but the population of the Old World brown bears has been greatly reduced.

The largest animals of the genus *Ursus*, the Alaska brown bears are the largest living carnivores. They attain a length of 2.8 meters or more and weight of up to 780 kg.. Grizzlies 2.5 meters in length and 360 kg. in weight have been recorded, and the Old World browns usually are about 2 meters in length and from 150 to 250 kg. in weight. Shoulder height of *Ursus* is up to 1.5 meters. The coloration usually is dark brown, but there are variations ranging from cream color to almost black.

It seems likely that a brown bear will attack a human being only when it is assailed or the young are in danger; its usual reaction on seeing a person is to flee. Of all the senses, vision is the least acute. The strength of these bears has been indicated by many examples such as the killing and dragging of a 450-kg. bison by a 360-kg. grizzly. The home range of an individual grizzly has been known to cover an area 72 km. in diameter. Larger animals (adult *Ursus*) do not climb trees because of their weight. They become fat toward fall when they go into "hibernation" and sleep through the winter in natural shelters or, in the steppes and barren areas, they may dig dens in hillsides. After emerging from the winter sleep, they feed on roots, moss, and ants, which have a laxative effect.

Some bears feed solely on plant matter, others eat vegetable and animal material, and some exist solely on flesh. They are not quick enough to prey extensively on wild, hoofed mammals, except for bison, but they sometimes kill domestic livestock.

The gestation period is 180 to 250 days, and the number of young is usually one to three. The cubs are born during the winter "hibernation," and weigh only about 0.5 kg. at birth. They gain about 90 kg. during the first year of life and are cared for by the mother for a year or more. Female bears may breed at 3 years of age, and the usual life span in the wild probably is 15 to 34 years.

A. American Black Bear (*Euarctos americanus*), photo from San Diego Zoological Garden. B. Kermode Bears (*E. americanus*), photo from Provincial Museum of Natural History, Victoria, B.C.

AMERICAN BLACK BEARS; OSOS NEGROS.

THE SINGLE SPECIES, *E. americanus*, originally inhabited practically all the wooded areas of North America north of central Mexico. It now lives mainly in the less settled regions, but sometimes it lives surprisingly close to centers of human population; its ability to avoid man has enabled it to survive. Under the protection of National Parks in the United States and Canada, these bears have greatly increased in number. Having become accustomed to people, black bears are often seen in the parks and have become a great attraction. The bears of this genus were formerly in the genus *Ursus*, and much information has been written about them under this name.

The head and body length is 1.5 to 1.8 meters; tail length is about 12 cm.; shoulder height is up to 91 cm.; and weight usually is 120 kg. to 150 kg. This species has a number of color phases—black, chocolate-brown, cinnamon-brown, blue-black, and white. White individuals seem to be more common on the North American Pacific coast than elsewhere but are never in the majority, and the blue-black phase is known from the St. Elias range in Alaska. Different color phases may occur in the same litter. In contrast to *Ursus*, the genus *Euarctos* has shorter, more uniform hair, shorter claws, and shorter hind feet.

When startled, the voice ordinarily is a "woof," although cubs when lonesome or frightened utter shrill howls. Black bears are good tree-climbers, and like other bears they may be great wanderers. They are quick and powerful but are generally harmless unless badly injured or cornered or when a mother is protecting her cubs. Like other bears that sleep through the winter, they become fat with the approach of cold weather, finally cease eating, and go into a den, hollow tree, or other protected location. The black bear may burrow into snow in the Hudson Bay area for its winter den. This winter sleep is interrupted by excursions outside during periods of relatively warm weather; these excursions are more numerous in southern latitudes than in the northern parts of its range.

The diet consists of vegetation, flesh, fish, and carrion. Occasionally domestic livestock is killed.

Black bears usually are solitary except during the breeding season in June or sometimes later in the year. The sexes separate after the mating, and the female may breed every other year. The gestation period is 100 to 210 days, and the one to four young (usually two or three) are born while the mother is in hibernation, usually in January or February. The cubs weigh about 22 grams at birth and remain with the mother at least through the first fall. The life span is up to 25 years.

The young bears are entertaining animals and can be taught many tricks. Black bears are game animals in some areas, and the meat is eaten to some extent.

Polar Bear (*Thalarctos maritimus*), photo from New York Zoological Society. Insets: A. Fore foot; B. Hind foot; photos from *Proc. Zool. Soc. London.* C. Young, 24 hours old, photo by Ernest P. Walker.

POLAR BEARS; OURS BLANCS, EISBÄREN, OSOS BLANCOS, YSBEREN. (Included are vernaculars used in other countries.)

THE SINGLE SPECIES, *T. maritimus*, is distributed around the North Pole; its presence is correlated with the presence of seals and open water. Its distribution roughly follows the southernmost limit of ice floes.

Head and body length is usually 2.2 to 2.5 meters; tail length is 76 to 127 mm.; and shoulder height is up to 1.6 meters. The maximum recorded weight is about 720 kg., but males average about 410 kg. and females about 320 kg. Coloration is white or creamy white throughout the year. The neck is long, the head is relatively small and flat, and the soles are haired. The fur on the feet probably is of great assistance in maintaining a footing on ice, as well as being a valuable insulation against cold.

Polar bears are the greatest wanderers of all the bears, sometimes traveling great distances. They are swifter than most people think, as they can outrun a reindeer over short distances on land and can attain a swimming speed of about 4 km. per hour. They swim rather high with head and shoulders above the water. If killed in the water, they will not immediately sink. During the winter an animal occasionally may stalk and attack a human, but only when extremely hungry or enraged is this bear particularly vicious. Some authorities claim that the walrus, with its huge canines, is the polar bear's greatest enemy next to man. Normally polar bears do not hibernate; however, pregnant females appear to dig a den in the snow some time before birth of the cubs, where they rest in a lethargic state.

Polar bears often are found hundreds of kilometers from land on drifting ice floes, where they lead a nomadic life. They usually remain at sea and do not venture far inland. In summer they may eat the berries and leaves of tundra plants, and they also may feed on algae, but the diet consists mostly of flesh, fish, and fowl, including carrion. Seals and fish are the main food items, and seabirds and such land mammals as reindeer, musk-ox, and arctic hares also are eaten.

Except for the mid-summer mating, the sexes are apart for most of the year. From one to four young are born in March (eastern Greenland) or April (western Greenland) after a gestation period of about nine months. The eyes are reported as opening at four weeks after birth, and the young stay with the mother for one to two years. Polar bears thus are believed to breed every other year, and they may begin breeding when two and one-half to four years of age. The maximum life span is about 34 years.

Eskimos hunt polar bears for fat, tendons, and fur. The livers contain large amounts of vitamin A and are therefore poisonous. Polar bears are also host to the parasite *Trichinella*, so the meat should be thoroughly cooked before eating.

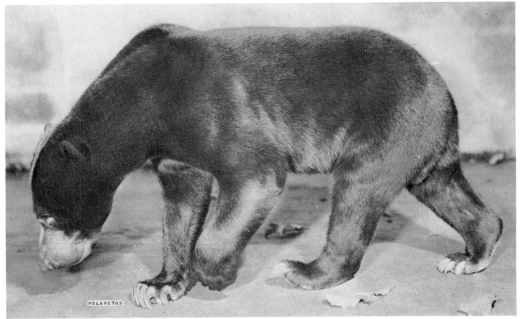

Malayan Sun Bear (*Helarctos malayanus*), photo by Ernest P. Walker.

MALAYAN SUN BEARS; BROEANG.

THE SINGLE SPECIES, *H. malayanus*, is found in forests in Burma, Indo-China, Thailand, the Malay Peninsula, Sumatra, and Borneo, and possibly in part of southern China. It inhabits mountains and lowlands within its tropical and subtropical range.

This is the smallest bear: head and body length is 1.1 to 1.4 meters, shoulder height is about 70 cm., and weight is 27 to 65 kg. Coloration is black, with a whitish or orange breast mark, a grayish or orange muzzle, and sometimes light-colored feet.

The breast mark is variable in form and sometimes is wholly lacking. The sun bear is a stocky, strong animal, with a shortened muzzle, large paws, and strongly-curved and pointed claws. *Helarctos* has naked soles in contrast to terrestrial bears, which have hairy soles.

It is active at night, usually sleeping and sunbathing during the day in a tree, 2 to 7 meters above the ground. Tree branches are broken or bent to form a nest and lookout-post, similar to the nest reported to be made by the Asiatic black bear (*Selenarctos*). Sun bears are adept tree-climbers and are cautious, wary, and intelligent—in fact, very intelligent, as the following examples of behavior illustrate. A young captive observed the way in which a cupboard, containing a sugar pot, was locked with a key. It then later opened the cupboard by inserting a claw into the eye of the key and turning it. Another captive scattered rice from its feeding bowl in the vicinity of its cage, thus attracting chickens which were then captured and eaten.

The diet is omnivorous, and the front paws are used for most of the feeding activity. Trees are torn open in search of nests of wild bees and for insects and their larvae. The soft growing point of the coconut-palm, known as palmite, is ripped apart and consumed. After digging up termite colonies, the forepaws are placed alternately in the nest and the termites licked off. Jungle fowl, small rodents, and fruit juices also are included in the diet.

The sun bear has a curious gait in that all the legs are turned inward while walking. It is usually shy and retiring. This bear does not "hibernate."

The number of young per litter is usually two. The cubs are born on the ground in a secluded spot and remain with the parents for some time. This species is believed to be monogamous.

Young animals make interesting pets, but they become unruly and dangerous within a few years.

In captivity the sun bear has the curious habit of sucking one of its hind feet while making a whimpering sound.

Sloth Bear (*Melursus ursinus*), A. Photo by Hans Jurg Kuhn. B. Photo from New York Zoological Society.

SLOTH BEARS, INDIAN BEARS; ASWAIL, RINCH, RIKSHA, LIPPENBEER (local vernaculars).

THE SINGLE SPECIES, *M. ursinus*, inhabits forested areas of India and Ceylon; the northern boundary of its range is the Indian Desert and the foothills of the Himalayas.

The length of the head and body is 1.4 to 1.8 m.; the length of the tail is 100 to 125 mm.; the height at the shoulder is 610 to 915 mm.; and weight is 54.5 to 136 kg. (usually 91 to 113 kg.). The shaggy black hairs are longest between the shoulders. The overall black coloration is often mixed with brown and gray, but cinnamon and red individuals have also been noted. The chest mark, typically V- or Y-shaped, varies from white or yellow to chestnut-brown.

Sloth bears are mainly nocturnal and do not "hibernate." During cool weather they spend the day in grassy or shrubby cover or in shallow caves. The sense of smell is well developed, but sight and hearing are relatively poor. These factors sometimes cause an animal to find itself in close proximity to a human. If the bear panics, it may rush blindly at the person and maul him. Under normal conditions, however, sloth bears are not aggressive, although they are held in great respect and fear by the natives. Sloth bears sleep anywhere and snore loudly, but they dislike cars and people and thus flee from human settlements to find an undisturbed spot to sleep.

These animals feed on insects, grubs, honey, eggs, carrion, and a variety of plant matter. Sloth bears have a number of structural modifications which are connected with a rather different method of feeding, namely, that of sucking and blowing. These modifications are as follows: the lips are protrusible, mobile, and naked; the snout is mobile; the nostrils can be closed at will; the inner pair of upper incisors is absent, thus forming a gap in the front teeth; and the palate is hollowed. These features enable the bear to feed on termites (white ants) in the following manner: the nest is dug up, the dust and dirt blown off, and the occupants sucked up in a "vacuum-cleaner" action. The resulting noises can be heard for over 185 meters and often lead to the bear's detection by hunters.

Breeding usually takes place in June (India) or over most of the year (Ceylon). About seven months later, one or two, seldom three, young are born in a ground shelter. The cubs leave the den at the age of two to three months and often ride on the mother's back. They remain with the mother until they are almost full-grown, possibly two to three years. *Melursus* is said to be monogamous, both parents caring for the cubs. Sloth bears have lived in captivity for 40 years.

CACOMISTLES, RACCOONS, COATIMUNDIS, KINKA-
JOUS, OLINGOS, GREATER AND LESSER PANDAS;
GUAYANOCHA, RATOUS LAVEURS, MAPACHES, WAS-
BEREN (local vernaculars).

THIS FAMILY of 9 genera (some authors refer *Jen-tinkia* to *Bassariscus* for a total of 8 genera) and about 18 species lives in tropical and temperate regions of the Americas and eastern Asia. These animals live in terrestrial and arboreal habitats, often near water. Considerable disagreement exists over the classification of pandas. The lesser or red panda (*Ailurus*) is usually regarded as a procyonid, but the giant panda has been treated as a member of the family Ursidae, as the sole living representative of a distinct family (Ailuropodidae), and as a procyonid. In external appearance, size, and some other features of their anatomy the giant pandas closely resemble bears except in color pattern. They are very unlike any members of the Procyonidae in either respect. We have included them with the Procyonidae because most zoologists believe they should be in this group.

The length of the head and body of the giant panda is 1.2 to 1.5 meters; the length of the tail is about 120 mm.; and the weight is 70 to 135 kg. Other members of the Procyonidae are small to medium-sized carnivores with medium or long tails. The length of the head and body is 305 to 670 mm., and the length of the tail is 200 to 690 mm. Adults weigh from 0.8 to 22 kg.; the males are about one-fifth larger and heavier than the females. The pelage varies from gray to rich reddish brown. Facial markings are often present, and the tail is usually ringed with light and dark bands. The face is short and broad, and the ears are short, rounded or pointed, furred, and erect. The tail is prehensile in the arboreal kinkajous (*Potos*) and is used as a balancing and semiprehensile organ in the coatis (*Nasua*). Each limb bears five digits; the third digit is the longest. The claws are short, compressed, recurved, and, in some genera, semiretractile. The soles are haired in several genera. The males have a baculum. Glandular sacs lie in the anal region of pandas (*Ailurus* and *Ailuropoda*).

The incisors are not specialized, the canines are elongate, the premolars are small and sharp, and the molars are broad and low crowned. The carnassials are developed only in the cacomistles (*Bassariscus* and *Jentinkia*). The dental formula is: 3/3, 1/1, 3-4/3-4, 2/2-3 = 36 to 42.

Most forms of the family Procyonidae become active in the evening, but coatis (*Nasua*) are active day or night, perhaps most active during the day. Most procyonids shelter in hollow trees, on large branches of trees, or in rock crevices; raccoons (*Procyon lotor*) occupy dens in the ground in treeless parts of their range, and giant pandas sometimes seek refuge in caves. A ring-tailed cat (*Bassariscus*) sometimes shelters in the upper part of a cabin. Raccoons sleep considerably during the winter in the northern parts of their range, but the winter sleep of raccoons is not continuous and they go outside the den during periods of relatively warm weather.

Procyonids walk on the sole of the foot, with the heel touching the ground, or partly on the sole and partly on the digits; the gait is usually bear-like. The members of this family are good climbers, with one genus (*Potos*) spending nearly all its life in trees. Procyonids climb trees to escape danger, but they will fight if cornered. The members of at least one genus (*Procyon*) are good swimmers.

Most procyonids travel in pairs or family groups. The giant panda is usually solitary, except during the breeding season and when with young; and coatis (*Nasua*) associate in bands of as many as 200 individuals but more often in groups of 5 to 40. The maximum territorial range of the raccoon (*Procyon lotor*) is approximately 800 hectares, but the cacomistle (*Bassariscus*) seldom ventures far from its den.

Kinkajous (*Potos*) are believed to eat insects and small animals, but fruit is the main item in the diet (apparently this is also true for the olingos, *Bassaricyon*). Pandas eat mostly vegetable material, and the lesser panda is very fond of bamboo shoots and leaves. With these exceptions, procyonids are markedly omnivorous. Raccoons like to wash their food when water is available. The sense of smell is acute, and hearing and vision are well developed.

The gestation period is 60 to 77 days, except in *Ailurus*, in which it is approximately 90 days, and *Ailuropoda*, in which it is apparently 7 to 9 months with apparently delayed implantation. The litter size is one to six. The young are born in the spring and generally weigh 30 grams or more at birth. The young of the giant panda at birth weigh .9 to 1.9 kg. Raccoons sometimes have two litters in a year. Female raccoons often defend their young ferociously. Giant pandas are sexually mature at four to ten years, whereas the females of the other genera begin to breed in their first year or shortly thereafter, and the males at about two years of age. With the exception of the presumably longer lived giant panda, these carnivores live about ten years in the wild.

Some procyonids, such as *Procyon* and *Nasua*, occasionally damage cultivated crops. Some members of this family are hunted as a source of food or for their pelts.

Procyonids are close to the primitive canid-ursid stock. The geological range of this family is the lower Miocene to the Recent of North America, the upper Miocene to the lower Pliocene of Europe, the lower Pliocene to the Recent of Asia, and the Pliocene to the Recent of South America.

Ring-tailed "Cat" or Cacomistle (*Bassariscus astutus*), photo by Ernest P. Walker.

RING-TAILED "CATS," RINGTAILS, CACOMISTLES, BASSARISES.

THE SINGLE SPECIES, *B. astutus*, ranges from Oregon, Colorado, and Texas to southern Mexico. It is found in a variety of habitats but seems to prefer rocky, broken areas, often near water.

Head and body length is 305 to 375 mm.; tail length is 310 to 440 mm.; shoulder height is about 16 mm.; and weight is 870 to 1,100 grams. The upper parts are buffy with a black or dark-brown wash, and the under parts are white or white washed with buff. The eye is ringed by black or dark brown, and the head has white to pinkish-buff patches. The tail is banded black and white for its entire length, is longer than the body, and bushy.

This animal is a good climber, although generally it is not as arboreal as the cacomistle of Mexico and Central America (*Jentinkia*). *Bassariscus* differs from *Jentinkia* in the following structural features: ears rounded, not pointed; tail shorter; soles hairy, not naked; claws semiretractile; and dental characters.

B. astutus is nocturnal and omnivorous, feeding on plants, mammals, birds, and invertebrates. It travels quickly and with agility among cliffs and along ledges. Dens are situated in rock crevices, hollow trees, the ruins of old Indian dwellings, and old cabins. This species may be somewhat gregarious at certain times of the year. Adults emit an explosive bark and a piercing scream, as well as a plaintive, long, high-pitched call.

The diet of ring-tailed cats includes insects, plant material, rodents, and birds. In summer and fall insects form the major portion of the diet, whereas in winter and spring rodents are the leading food item.

The season of birth is usually May and June. Litter size is one to five (usually three or four). The young weigh about 28 grams each at birth and are at first cared for by the female only. When they are three weeks old, either parent may bring food. At 34 to 35 days of age, the coat takes on the appearance of that of an adult. The young forage with the parents at two months, are weaned at four months, and are nearly adult size at four and one-half months. A ringtail has lived eight years in captivity.

The coat is not of high quality nor particularly popular for fur; it is known in the trade as "California mink" or "civet cat." (There is no scientific basis for either name.) Ring-tailed "cats" make charming pets, particularly females that have been obtained when young. Early settlers of the southwestern United States sometimes had them about the home as house cats to catch mice, and as companions.

Central American Cacomistle (*Jentinkia sumichrasti*), immature, photo from Jorge A. Ibarra through the Museo Nacional de Historia Natural, Guatemala City.

MEXICAN AND CENTRAL AMERICAN CACOMISTLES, RING-TAILED CATS; GUAYANOCHE.

THE SINGLE SPECIES, *J. sumichrasti*, is found in the tropical forests of southern Mexico and Central America. Its range meets that of *Bassariscus* on the eastern slopes of the Mexican highlands. *Jentinkia* seems to be uncommon over most of its range, and only about 30 specimens are in study collections.

Head and body length is 380 to 470 mm. and tail length is 390 to 530 mm. One individual weighed 900 grams. Color is usually buffy gray to brownish, with black-tipped hairs. The tail is ringed with buff and black. *Jentinkia* differs structurally from *Bassariscus* in the following features: ears pointed, not rounded; tail longer; soles naked, not hairy; claws non-retractile, not semiretractile; and dental characters.

The habits of *Jentinkia* are not well known. It appears to be more arboreal than *Bassariscus*, and it feeds on rodents, birds, insects, and fruit. A barking cry has been noted.

Breeding usually takes place in January. The nest is usually located in a hollow tree or rock crevice. From two to four young comprise a litter.

Raccoon (*Procyon lotor*), photo from Zoological Society of Philadelphia.

RACCOONS OR "COONS"; MAPACHES, OSITOS LAVATUMAROX, OSITOS LAVADORES, GUAXINI, MAPACHINS, WASBEREN, RATONS LAVEUR, WASCHBÄREN. (Included are vernaculars used in other countries.)

SEVEN SPECIES are currently recognized. The species *P. lotor* is found from southern Canada through most of the United States into Central America. The species *P. cancrivorus* inhabits southern Costa Rica, Panama, and northern South America. The five other species are found on various islands. "Coons" frequent timbered and brushy areas, usually near water.

Head and body length is 415 to 600 mm.; tail length is 200 to 405 mm.; shoulder height is 228 to 304 mm.; and weight is 1.5 to 22 kg. The prevailing color is gray to almost black. There are five to ten black rings on the rather well-furred tail, and a black "bandit" streak across the face. The head is broad behind with a pointed muzzle. The toes are not webbed and the claws are not retractile; the front toes are rather long, can be widely spread, and the hands are regularly used almost as skillfully as monkeys use theirs. Their footprints resemble those of man.

Raccoons are more nocturnal than diurnal and are good climbers and swimmers. Their dens are usually to be found in hollow trees or in rock crevices. In the southern United States and southward, "coons" are active all year, whereas in the northern part of their range they pass most of the winter in sleep after fattening up in the fall. They are not gregarious. The length of the home range is up to 2.5 km.; one animal per 4 hectares perhaps is a normal population in most areas. A variety of sounds with little carrying power is produced, and the sense of touch, particularly in the forepaws and nose, is well developed.

These animals are omnivorous, but they prefer aquatic life, such as frogs and fish, small land animals, and various nuts, seeds, fruits, corn, and acorns. The raccoon in captivity regularly washes its food in water, but this habit may be more common in captive than in wild animals. Washing the food caught along a stream removes sand and grit, as well as perhaps certain skin secretions of the prey.

Breeding takes place from January through June. The gestation period is 60 to 73 days, averaging 63; and the number of young is one to seven (usually three or four). (Captives in New York weighed 71 grams each at birth. When 50 days of age and 0.9 kg. in weight, they could leave the den under their own strength.) In the wild, the young travel with the mother at ten weeks of age and go out on their own when about one year old. Females may breed when one year old, but males do not usually breed until their second year. The life span is ten or more years.

The type species of the genus is *P. lotor* (Linnaeus). The crab-eating raccoon, *P. cancrivorus*, is often separated subgenerically under the name *Euprocyon*, Gray, 1865.

Coatimundi (*Nasua nasua solitaria*), photo from New York Zoological Society.

COATIS; COATIMUNDIS; PIZOTE, PISTOLE, PISOTE (local vernaculars).

THREE SPECIES are distributed as follows: *N. narica*, from the southwestern United States to South America; *N. nelsoni*, known only from Cozumel Island off the Yucatan Peninsula; *N. nasua*, throughout most of South America. The first species listed seems to be extending its range northward at the present time. Coatis are usually found in wooded areas.

Head and body length is 410 to 670 mm.; tail length is 320 to 690 mm.; shoulder height is up to 305 mm.; and weight is about 11.3 kg. The species *N. nelsoni* has short, fairly soft, silky hair, but in the other species the fur is longer and somewhat harsh. In all species the general color is reddish brown or reddish brown-gray to black above, and yellowish to dark brown below. The muzzle, chin, and throat are usually whitish, and the feet blackish. Black and gray markings are present on the face, and the tail is banded. The muzzle is long and pointed and the tip is very mobile; the fore legs are short; the hind legs are long; and the tapering tail is longer than the head and body.

Males or females, particularly old animals, often are solitary, but coatis usually live in bands of 5 or 6 to 40 individuals. (The solitary individuals are thought to represent a distinct species by natives, who call these coatis *Tejon solo*.) Coatis are active day and night, perhaps most active during the day, and they rest during the heat of the day in ground shelters or in trees. Dens may be located in rocky areas. Coatis are omnivorous, feeding on available plant and animal matter and overlooking little. The highly mobile snout is well adapted to investigate crevices and holes. Coatis forage in trees as well as on the ground, using the tail as a balancing and semiprehensile organ.

A troop of coatis feeding in a ravine or along a hillside presents a rather amusing sight. Usually carrying their tails erect except for the curled tip, the animals move along while pawing at the ground or poking into likely places with their long snouts, then hurrying on to catch up with the more advanced members of the band.

From two to six young are born in spring or early summer after a gestation period of about 77 days.

Coatis rarely damage crops and only infrequently take chickens. They are hunted for their meat by natives, who sometimes have dogs trained for this purpose. If cornered by a dog on the ground, a coati can inflict serious wounds with its large and sharp canines. Coatis can be tamed and make interesting and inquisitive pets.

The type species of the genus is *N. nasua* (Linnaeus).

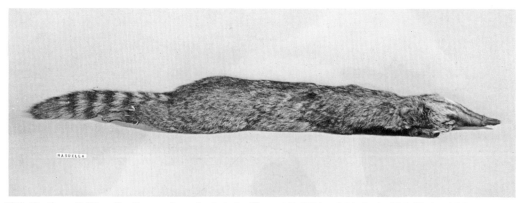

Little Coatimundi (*Nasuella olivacea olivacea*), photo by Howard E. Uible of skin in the U.S. National Museum.

LITTLE COATIMUNDIS OR MOUNTAIN COATIS; COATI OLIVA.

THE SINGLE SPECIES, *N. olivacea*, is known from the Andes of Venezuela, Colombia, and Ecuador. In 1915 Ned Hollister established this genus for *Nasua olivacea meridensis*. The type specimen is in the U.S. National Museum.

Animals of this genus are like small *Nasua* with shorter tails. The general color is grayish sooty brown; the tail is ringed with alternating yellowish-gray and dark-brown bands.

The differences between the genus *Nasuella* and the genus *Nasua* are quite pronounced in the skulls: that of *Nasuella* is smaller and more slender, the middle part of the facial portion is greatly constricted laterally, and the palate extends farther posteriorly.

Habits of the little coatimundi are not known; like *Nasua*, it probably feeds on insects, small animals, and fruit.

Kinkajou (*Potos flavus*), photo from New York Zoological Society.

KINKAJOUS; JUPARA, CUCHUMBIS, CUCHICUCHIS, MARTUCHAS, MICO LEON (local vernaculars).

THE SINGLE SPECIES, *P. flavus*, is found in forests of southern Mexico, Central America, and south at least to Matto Grosso in Brazil.

The length of the head and body is 415 to 575 mm.; the length of the tail is 395 to 555 mm.; shoulder height is up to 254 mm.; and weight is usually 1.4 to 2.7 kg. The upper parts and upper surface of the tail are tawny-olive, yellow-tawny, or brownish, with some individuals having a black mid-dorsal line. The under parts and undersurface of the tail are tawny-yellow, buff, or brownish yellow. The muzzle is dark brown to blackish, and the hair is soft and woolly.

Kinkajous have rounded heads, short faces, long prehensile tails, and short, sharp claws. The hind feet are longer than the fore feet. Animals of the genus *Potos* are very similar to animals of the genus *Bassaricyon*, kinkajous differing from olingos in their round, tapering, short-haired, prehensile tails; in their stockier body forms; and in the fact that their faces are not grayish.

Kinkajous spend almost their entire lives in trees. They spend the day in tree hollows, sometimes emerging on hot, humid days to lie out on limbs or in vine tangles. They travel about at night in pairs or singly. When found in groups, it is usually because they have been attracted to a tree bearing fruit. Although they move rapidly in trees, progress from one tree to an-other is made cautiously and relatively slowly. A variety of calls is given, including barks when disturbed, but the usual call when feeding during the night seems to be "a rather shrill, quavering scream that may be heard for nearly a mile" (Walter W. Dalquest, *Mammals of the Mexican State of San Luis Potosi*, Louisiana State Univ. Studies, Biol. Sci. Ser., No. 1, Dec., 1953, pg. 182).

The long tongue is an adaptation for a frugivorous diet, but kinkajous do little damage to cultivated fruit. They are believed to feed on insects and probably small animals, although fruit is the main item of diet. Individuals probably return to the same trees night after night.

One, seldom two, young are usually born in spring or summer. (A pair which had lived together for 9 years had their first litter at 12½ years of age.) The eyes of the young open at ten days, and they can hang by their tails at seven weeks. An individual lived for 23 years and 7 months in the Amsterdam Zoological Gardens, although about 19 years is probably the usual life span.

If captured when young and kindly treated, kinkajous become good pets. They are sold in pet stores often under the name "honey bear." Their pelage is used in furred wallets and belts.

Some South American natives give this animal the common name "potto," but *P. flavus* should not be confused with the African *Perodicticus*, also called "potto" in English vernacular.

Olingo (*Bassaricyon gabbii*), photo from New York Zoological Society. Inset: Olingo (*B. pauli*), photo by Hans Jurg Kuhn.

OLINGOS.

TWO OR THREE named species, which are probably all races of *B. gabbii*, are found in Central America and northern South America. They prefer a tropical jungle habitat and are found from sea level to elevations of 2,000 meters.

Head and body length is 350 to 475 mm., and the tail length is 400 to 480 mm. The body is covered with thick, soft fur which is pinkish buff to golden, mixed with black or grayish above, and pale yellowish below. The tail is somewhat flattened and more or less distinctly annulated along the median portion. The general body form is elongate with a flattened head, pointed snout, and small round ears. The soles are partly furred and the limbs are short with sharply curved claws.

Olingos are similar externally to *Potos*, differing from kinkajous in their long-haired, non-prehensile tails, more slender body forms, and grayish faces.

These little animals are often gregarious and move about in small parties of their own kind and also with kinkajous. Many, however, apparently travel singly. Olingos are nocturnal and are more at home in the trees than on the ground. It is believed that nests of dry leaves are constructed in hollow trees. Fruit makes up the greater part of their diet.

The little information available seems to indicate that they give birth to only one offspring. A female collected in April had a fetus 195 mm. long which was about to be born. The females of this genus have one pair of inguinal teats.

Few specimens have been collected and little is known about them at the present time. Since they travel with kinkajous, which they resemble in appearance, they may be of much more frequent occurrence than records indicate. Natives usually do not distinguish between olingos and kinkajous.

Lesser Panda (*Ailurus fulgens*), photo by Arthur Ellis, Washington Post Newspaper.

LESSER PANDAS, RED PANDAS, RED CAT-BEARS, HIMALAYAN RACCOONS; WAH, YE, THOKYA, SANKAM, KATZENBÄR (native names).

THE SINGLE SPECIES, *A. fulgens*, is found in Yunnan and Szechuan, China; northern Burma; Sikkim; and Nepal. It inhabits bamboo forests, usually at the higher elevations, and seems to prefer a colder climate than the giant panda (*Ailuropoda*).

Head and body length is 510 to 635 mm.; tail length is 280 to 485 mm.; and weight is usually 3 to 4.5 kg. The coat is long and soft, and the tail is bushy. The upper parts are rusty to deep chestnut, darkest along the middle of the back. The tail is inconspicuously ringed. Small dark-colored eye patches are present, and the muzzle, lips, cheeks, and edges of the ears are white. The back of the ears, the limbs, and the under parts are dark reddish brown to black. The head is rather round, the ears large and pointed, the feet have hairy soles, and the claws are semi-retractile; the tail is non-prehensile, and about two-thirds of the head and body length.

The lesser panda is somewhat nocturnal; it usually sleeps during the day in trees. While sleeping, it generally curls up like a cat or a dog with the tail over the head, but it also sleeps while sitting on top of a limb with the head tucked under the chest and be-tween the fore legs, like the American raccoon (*Procyon*) does at times. Its disposition is mild; when captured it does not fight, tames readily, and is gentle, curious, and generally quiet. The usual call is a series of short whistles or squeaking notes; when provoked, it utters a sharp, spitting hiss or a series of snorts while standing on its hind legs. A "musky" odor is emitted from the anus when excited.

Most of the feeding seems to be done on the ground. Vegetable materials such as bamboo sprouts, grass, roots, fruits, and acorns comprise the principal diet. The lesser panda also at times eats eggs and perhaps birds or mice. Apparently meat is eaten only rarely.

In the wild, lesser pandas commonly travel in pairs or in family groups. The usual number of young per litter is one or two, seldom four. The young are born in the spring in a hollow tree or rock crevice after a gestation period of from 90 to 150 days probably because there is sometimes delayed implantation. Their coloring is not as intense as that of the adults and the tail lacks rings. They are blind for 21 to 30 days, remaining dependent upon the mother for some time, as they seem to stay with her or with both parents for about a year, until the next litter is about to be born.

In captivity they usually eat fruits, vegetables, and bamboo leaves. Only a few adapt themselves sufficiently to survive long in captivity.

Giant Panda (*Ailuropoda melanoleuca*), photo from New York Zoological Society. Insets: A. Right hind foot; B. Right fore foot; photo from *Proc. Zool. Soc. London.* C. Skull showing dentition, photo. by P. F. Wright of specimen in U.S. National Museum.

GIANT PANDAS, RENSEN PANDA; PEI-HSIUNG.

THE SINGLE SPECIES, *A. melanoleuca*, is known from mountain forests in the Chinese provinces of Szechuan, Sikang, Shenshan, and Kansu, and from the Tibetan plateau in the province of Chinghai. It probably frequents the plateau only in summer.

Head and body length is 1.2 to 1.5 meters; tail length is about 127 mm.; and weight is 75 to 160 kg. The coat is thick and woolly, and typically black and white or reddish. The black often has a brownish tinge and the white becomes soiled in an old coat. The eye patches, the ears, legs, and a band around the shoulders are black; the remainder of the body is whitish. This animal can be recognized readily by its bear-like form and striking coloration.

The giant panda has been referred to as an "aberrant bear," although it is thought by others to be more closely related to the raccoons and their allies (*Procyonidae*). The head is relatively massive, due to the expanded zygomatic arches of the skull and the well-developed muscles of mastication. It has an unusual modification of the forepaw which is believed to aid in the grasping of bamboo stems: the pad on the sole of each forepaw has an accessory lobe, and the pad of the first digit—and, to a lesser extent, that of the second digit—can be flexed onto the summit of this accessory lobe and its supporting bone.

There are scent glands under the tail.

Giant pandas are usually solitary, except during the breeding season and when with young. Evidence indicates that they do not hibernate, remaining active all year. When pursued by dogs, they will climb trees, but they live mainly on the ground. Hollow trees, rock crevices, and caves sometimes are used for shelter.

They spend 10 to 12 hours a day feeding. Although bamboo shoots up to 13 mm. in diameter and bamboo roots generally are the major items of their diet, giant pandas also feed on other plants, such as gentians, irises, crocuses, and tufted grasses, and even on animals. They occasionally hunt for fishes, mouse-hares (*Ochotona*), and small rodents, at least on the Tibetan plateau.

Breeding probably occurs in spring, and the one or two cubs are born the following January. They weigh about 2 kg. each at birth, and gain an average of 2.5 kg. per month during the first year of their lives. Sexual maturity is attained between four and ten years of age.

In captivity giant pandas are fed bamboo, vegetables, rolled oats and milk, and cod-liver oil. Their teddy-bear appearance and amusing antics as cubs make them among the most popular of zoo animals. In 1959 there were nine specimens in captivity, five of which were in Peking.

WEASELS AND STOATS, POLECATS AND FERRETS, MINKS, MARTENS AND FISHERS, TAYRAS, GRISONS, WOLVERINES, BADGERS, SKUNKS, AND RIVER AND SEA OTTERS; COMADREJA, IRARA, WAITI-AI'RA, GLUTONS, VEELVARAAT, JEZEVEC LESNI. (Included are vernaculars used in other countries.)

THIS FAMILY of 25 genera and nearly 70 species occupies terrestrial and aquatic habitats (both fresh and salt water) throughout the world, except for Australia, Madagascar, the Antarctic, and most oceanic islands.

The smallest member of this family is the least weasel (*Mustela rixosa*). The length of the head and body in this species is 135 to 175 mm.; the length of the tail is 30 to 40 mm.; and adults weigh from 35 to 70 grams. The largest members of this family are certain otters (*Pteronura* and *Enhydra*), in which the length of the head and body ranges from 1 to 1.5 meters. The males of *Enhydra* (sea otters) weigh up to 36 kg. and the females weigh about 27 kg. Male mustelids are about one-fourth larger than the females. The pelage is uniformly colored, spotted, or striped, and some species of *Mustela* turn white in winter in the northern parts of their range. The body is long and slender in most genera (stocky in the wolverines, *Gulo;* and in badgers). The ears are short and rounded or pointed. The short limbs bear five digits. The claws are not retractile and are compressed and curved. The claws of the badgers are large and heavy for burrowing. The hands and feet of the otters are webbed for swimming.

Well-developed anal scent glands are usually present; male mustelids have a baculum.

The skull is usually sturdy, with a short frontal region. The incisors are normal, i.e., not specialized; the canines are elongate; the premolars may be reduced in numbers; and a "waist" or constriction is usually present between the lateral and medial halves of each upper molar. The carnassials are developed. The second lower molar, if present, is reduced to a simple peg. The dental formula is as follows: 3/3 (3/2 in *Enhydra*), 1/1, 2-4/2-4, 1/1-2 = 28 to 38.

Mustelids are nocturnal or diurnal and shelter in crevices, burrows, and trees. Badgers often dig elaborate burrows. Winter sleep (not true hibernation in that the body processes and temperature are not reduced) occurs in American badgers (*Taxidea*), Old World badgers (*Meles*), and striped skunks (*Mephitis mephitis*) in the northern parts of their ranges. This dormancy is interrupted by trips outside the shelter when warm weather occurs. The members of this family move about on their digits, or partly on their digits and partly on their soles. Their movements differ: the smaller, slender forms usually travel by means of a scampering gait, interspersed with a series of bounds; whereas the larger, stocky forms proceed in a slow, rolling, bear-like shuffle. Mustelids often sit on their haunches to look around. Many genera

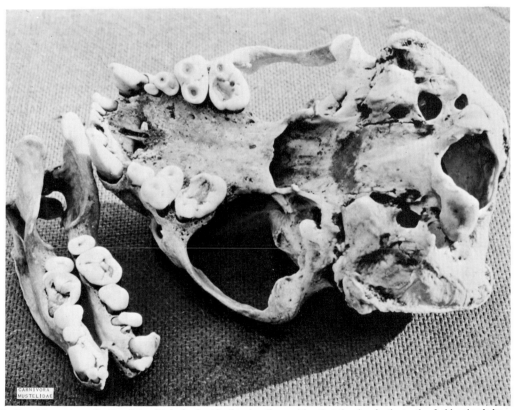

Skull and lower jaw of a Sea Otter (*Enhydra lutris*), showing the cavities that develop in the teeth of old animals because of the hard, rough materials that they eat, photo by H. Robert Krear.

are agile climbers, and otters and minks are skillful swimmers. The members of this family travel singly, in pairs, and in family groups. Others move in bands of up to 30 individuals, which represent several family groups. The least weasel generally confines its territorial activities to about two acres, but the male wolverine has a vast territory (up to a half-million acres) which he shares with two or three females. Sea otters, which seldom leave the water, range over an area of about 48 kilometers. Minks are reported to emigrate when food is scarce. Some genera, particularly *Meles* and otters, are extremely playful, especially when young.

Wolverines fight ferociously if the occasion arises. Many mustelids use the secretion of their anal glands as a defensive measure, and they also flee to their dens. Some genera in this family have a contrasting pattern of body colors, for example, skunks with their black and white stripes. This pattern is thought to be a form of warning coloration associated with the fetid anal gland secretion and is a reminder that the animal is better left alone. Some of the forms with contrasting body colors (such as marbled polecats, *Vormela*, and certain skunks) expose and emphasize this contrasting pattern by means of bodily movements when they are alarmed.

Mustelids are mainly flesh eaters. They hunt by scent, although the senses of hearing and sight are also well developed. Weasels are carnivorous. Some forms occasionally feed on plant material, a few

genera are omnivorous, wolverines prefer carrion, and otters exist mainly on aquatic life. Food is sometimes stored (reported in *Mustela*, *Poecilogale*, *Gulo*, and certain badgers).

Delayed implantation of the embryos occurs in many genera. The gestation period is 39 to about 65 days; with delayed implantation, births are delayed for as long as 12½ months (in *Lutra canadensis*, a species of otter from the New World). There is usually one litter per year, but a species of weasel (*Mustela nivalis*) bears up to three litters (delayed implantation apparently does not occur). The litter size is 1 to 13, and the offspring are tiny and blind at birth, except in the sea otter. The young of *Enhydra* are born with their eyes open and in a more advanced stage than the offspring of other mustelids. The young of most genera can care for themselves at about two months of age and are sexually mature in a year or two. The life span in the wild for most mustelids is from 5 to 20 years.

Mustelids sometimes kill poultry, but they also keep rodents in check. Many genera are sought for their furs.

The geological range of this family is the early Oligocene to the Recent in North America, Europe, and Asia, the middle Pliocene to the Recent in Africa, and the Pleistocene to the Recent in South America. Two genera of otters, now extinct, are known from the Pleistocene; these are *Nesolutra*, from Malta, and *Cyraonys*, from Eurasia.

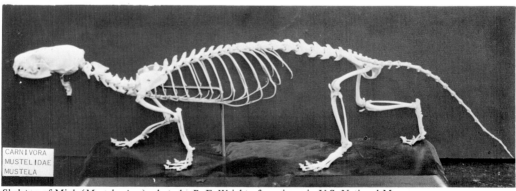

Skeleton of Mink (*Mustela vison*), photo by P. F. Wright of specimen in U.S. National Museum.

(1) A. European Polecat (*Mustela putorius*), photo from Zoological Society of London. B. Polecat (*M. putorius eversmanni*); C. Immature Long-tailed Weasel (*M. frenata*); photos by Ernest P. Walker.

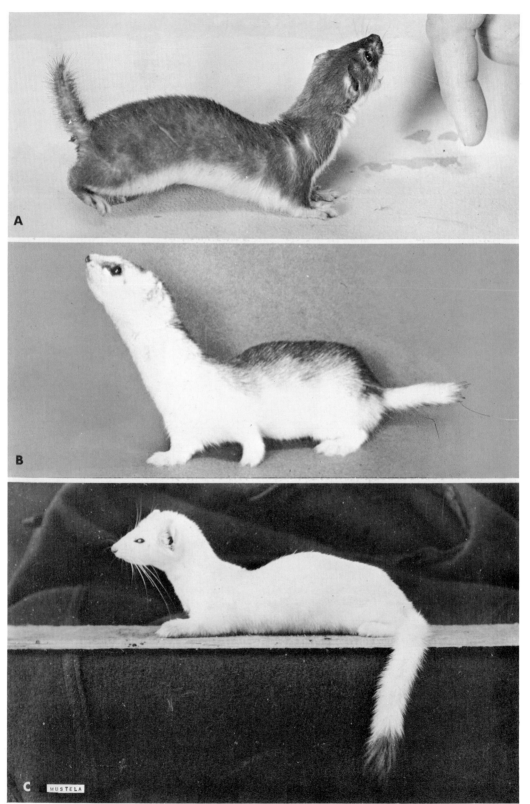

(2) A. Dwarf Weasel (*Mustela rixosa*); B. Dwarf Weasel (*M. rixosa*) changing into winter coat; photos by Ernest P. Walker. C. Weasel or Ermine (*M. erminea*) in winter coat, photo from U.S. Forest Service.

(3) A. Eastern Mink (*Mustela vison*), photo by Ernest P. Walker. B. Black-footed Ferret (*M. nigripes*), photo from New York Zoological Society. C. Weasel (*M.* sp.), photo by Ernest P. Walker.

WEASELS, ERMINES, STOATS; HERMELINE, WIESEL, WEZELS, SAKBIN, BAJLAK XUL, ZABIN, CUX, COMADREJA, for the subgenus *Mustela*. LAS MUSTELAS AMAZONICAS, for the subgenus *Grammogale*, Cabrera, 1940. FERRETS, ILTISSE, POLECATS in Europe (FITCH in the fur trade), for the subgenus *Putorius*, Cuvier, 1817. MINKS, NERZE, for the subgenus *Lutreola*, Wagner, 1841. (Included are vernaculars used in other countries.)

THE COMBINED range of about 15 species is North America, northern South America, northern Africa, Europe, Asia, Java, Sumatra, and Borneo. There is considerable range in size. Members of this genus are usually lithe and slender and have long bodies and short legs; they are carnivorous in the strict sense of that term. All are terrestrial except the mink, which is almost as much at home in the water as on land. Four subgenera are usually recognized.

The subgenus *Mustela* includes about ten species of weasels, with an aggregate range the same as that of the genus. Head and body length is 125 mm. to 250 mm.; tail length is 25 mm. to 150 mm.; and weight is usually 42 to 280 grams. The species *M. rixosa* is the smallest living carnivore. In summer weasels are generally brown above and whitish or yellowish below; in winter they usually become white in the northern and temperate regions. The winter pelage is used for the ermine coat.

Weasels are generally solitary and tend to be nocturnal, although they may be active day or night. Some species that climb well pursue chipmunks and squirrels in trees. Weasels usually kill by biting at the base of the skull; they do not suck blood.

These are remarkably fast animals. They kill with speed and with strength a wide variety of prey from mouse-size to squirrel- and rabbit-size animals. They have been known to attack even a man when he stands between them and their intended prey. Weasels are carnivorous. The slender body enables them to enter any burrow or hole into which they can thrust their heads. In this way, a weasel can follow a mouse to the end of its burrow or enter a chicken coop through a knothole. Cases are known where an individual weasel has killed dozens of chickens in this manner. However, a given weasel can be eliminated if it becomes destructive, and it should be realized that these small carnivores are excellent mousers. A weasel may reside in a den until practically all the rodents in the neighborhood are eliminated in an area from 180 to 275 meters across. It then moves to another area.

Three to 13 young are born in a nest in a burrow. Some species, such as the New World *M. frenata* and the circumboreal *M. erminea*, known as the stoat in the Old World, have delayed implantation, in that the embryos lie dormant in the uterus for some time after fertilization and are not implanted until three to four weeks before birth. Each of these species has only one litter per year, with the long gestation period varying from about 200 to 340 days. These species breed in summer, and the litter is born the following year. On the other hand, in the species *M. nivalis* delayed implantation does not occur and females have more than one litter per year. Male weasels may bring food to the young. Weaning occurs at about five weeks, and the young probably are able to hunt in seven to eight weeks. Captive weasels have lived at least five years.

The subgenus *Grammogale* contains only the tropical weasel *M. africana* of northern South America. This relatively large weasel measures from 250 to 330 mm. in head and body length and 190 to 210 mm. in tail length. The upper parts are reddish to chocolate, and the under parts are light with a longitudinal median abdominal stripe of the same color as the upper parts. Habits are little known, but the animal apparently is a good climber and swimmer. The manner of reproduction is not known.

The subgenus *Putorius* contains two species: *M. nigripes*, the black-footed ferret of western North America; and *M. putorius*, the polecat of Northern Africa, Europe, and Asia, whose skins are sold in the fur trade under the name "fitch."

The former species has buffy yellow upper parts and somewhat paler under parts. A patch across the eyes, the feet, and the tip of the tail are black. Males have a head and body length of 380 to 410 mm., a tail length of 110 to 130 mm., and weight of about 0.7 kg.; females are somewhat smaller. The geographical range of this animal nearly coincides with the range of prairie dogs (*Cynomys*), which are believed to be the main prey of *M. nigripes* and also to supply it with burrows for shelter. Decreases in the number and range of prairie dogs probably resulted in bringing the black-footed ferret population to its present stage of near extinction.

The polecat is dark brown to black in color and has a yellowish patch on each side between the eye and the ear. Head and body length is 350 to 510 mm.; tail length is 125 to 190 mm.; and weight is 0.7 to 1.4 kg.

In the wild, this species may breed twice a year, as delayed implantation does not occur. The gestation period is 40 to 43 days, and the five to eight young are usually cared for only by the mother.

The domestic form, known as the ferret, is largely albino. It is domesticated for use as a rat destroyer and in driving rabbits from their burrows.

The subgenus *Lutreola* consists of *M. vison*, the New World mink of Alaska, Canada, and the United States; and *M. lutreola*, the Old World mink of Europe and Asia. Head and body length is usually 300 to 530 mm.; tail length is 130 to 200 mm.; and weight is up to 1.6 kg. Minks are dark brown in color, with white spots on the throat, chest, or belly, and the fur is modified for an aquatic life.

They are mainly nocturnal, and an individual animal has a home range of about 8 hectares. They shelter and nest in natural cavities in stream banks, in rocks and debris, or in muskrat houses.

Breeding takes place in February and March; the male mates with more than one female but usually stays with one female after the four to ten young are born. Delayed implantation may occur under certain conditions; the gestation period is 39 to 78 days. The young leave the den at six to eight weeks of age, after having been weaned at five weeks. Both sexes breed at one year of age, and minks have lived up to ten years in captivity.

The preferred breeding stock in North American mink ranches is a cross between the large Alaskan and dark Labrador forms. Through selective breeding, platinum and other ranch strains have been propagated. About two-fifths of the marketable pelts come from ranches.

The type species of the genus is *M. erminea*, Linnaeus.

Marbled Polecat (*Vormela peregusna*), photo by Bernhard Grzimek.

MARBLED POLECATS.

THE SINGLE SPECIES, *V. peregusna*, ranges from southeastern Europe and southwestern Asia across the Russian steppes into the Gobi Desert of Mongolia. It seems to prefer steppe and foothill country.

Head and body length is usually 330 to 350 mm., and tail length is usually 200 to 215 mm. Weight is about 0.75 kg. This animal is similar in size and form to the polecat of northern Africa, Europe, and Asia (*Mustela putorius*), differing in its broken and mottled color pattern on the upper parts and in its long claws. The mottling on the back is reddish brown and white or yellowish, and the tail is usually whitish with a dark tip; otherwise the coloration resembles that of *M. putorius* in the blackish or dark-brown under parts and the dark brown facial mask.

Like most members of this family (Mustelidae), marbled polecats possess anal scent glands from which a noxious-smelling substance is emitted. When these animals are threatened, they throw the head back, bare the teeth, erect the body hairs, and bristle and curve the tail over the back. This behavior results in the fullest display of the contrasting body colors, and the pattern thus exposed is thought to be a form of warning coloration, associated with the fetid anal-gland secretion. Marbled polecats show relatively little concern for the presence of man and other animals. Captives exhibit boldness and curiosity.

With their strong paws and long claws they excavate deep, roomy burrows, and also shelter in the burrows of other animals. They usually rest during the day, although captives were most active during the daytime and wild animals occasionally hunt during daylight hours. Marbled polecats are good climbers but mainly ground feeders. They prey on a variety of animal life, such as rodents, birds, and reptiles.

They are solitary, except during breeding seasons. The young are usually born in March or April, after a reported gestation period of nine weeks. Only the mother cares for the young, which are reared in a grass and leaf nest within a burrow.

Marbled polecats sometimes prey on poultry and as a result have been eliminated in some areas. The pelt is valued in certain areas.

Martens (*Martes*), A. Fisher (*Martes pennanti*), photo from San Diego Zoological Garden. B. Yellow-throated Marten (*M. flavigula*), photo by Ernest P. Walker. C. American Marten (*M. americana*), photo by Howard E. Uible.

MARTENS, FISHERS, SABLES; MARTES, MARDER, PEKAN, ZOBEL, ANGA PRAO, DALLA KAFAK. (Included are vernaculars used in other countries.)

THIS GENUS is represented by two species in the New World: *M. pennanti*, the fisher, and *M. ameri-*

cana, the American marten; and by about six other species, all martens, in the Old World. The genus is found in Alaska, Canada, and parts of the United States and in the Old World, from the limits of tree growth south to the Mediterranean and across Europe and Asia into the Malay Archipelago. Fishers and martens inhabit wooded areas, often coniferous forests. They are herein discussed separately. The type species of the genus is *M. foina* (Erxleben). This genus has been divided into two subgenera: *Pekania*, Gray, 1865, for the fisher, and *Charronia*, Gray, 1865, for the yellow-throated Asiatic martens (*M. flavigula* and *M. gwatkinsi*). *Lamprogale*, Ognev, 1928, is considered a synonym of *Charronia*.

Martens have a head and body length of 340 to 610 mm., a tail length of 150 to 300 mm., and a weight of 680 grams to 2 kg. They are golden brown to almost blackish, usually darker on the feet and the tip of the tail, and there is orange, yellow, or white on the throat or chest.

Martens are generally solitary and are active day or night. They are active all winter, although they may stay in their dens for a day or two in unfavorable weather, or descend to lower elevations in mountainous regions. They are largely arboreal and tend to travel in an overlapping series of small areas but may travel as far as 16 km. in a night. These mammals are agile and graceful and feed on a variety of life, including carrion, insects, and fruit. Squirrels are the main prey in many areas.

Breeding usually takes place in the summer, and from one to five young are born the following March or April after a gestation period of 220 to 290 days. Delayed implantation occurs in most species. The den is usually a hollow tree or log. The young at birth weigh about 28 grams each, are weaned at about seven weeks of age, and become solitary after attaining adult weight after about three months. Females probably breed in the summer of the year following their birth. The American marten (*M. americana*) lives from 5 to 17 years in captivity.

In Europe and Asia both private individuals and governmental agencies have tried to breed martens in captivity, but with little success. Martens are nervous, high strung animals, and it will probably require long, patient taming, an abundance of exercise, and proper food to get a few breeding regularly. From these it might then be possible to develop breeding colonies, as was done with silver foxes.

Martens became best known under the name of "sable," when skins from a dark form inhabiting northern Europe and Asia were popular with royalty and sold for very high prices. The darker skins of the American species were sometimes sold as sables, but for many years most of the skins of the American species sold readily under the name of "marten" or "American sable." Stone martens (*M. foina*) of Europe have light color underfur which shows through the guard hairs. Stone marten skins are seen most commonly in the United States. As a result of trapping, the population of these mammals has become drastically reduced over most of their range. The wild stock in Alaska and Canada was badly depleted before 1910. Rigid protection in Alaska for many years resulted in partially restoring breeding stock.

The fisher has a head and body length of 490 to 615 mm., a tail length of 340 to 425 mm., and a weight of about 6.8 or perhaps up to 8.16 kg. It is dark brown with grayish fore parts and blackish rump, tail, and legs. One to five young are born in the spring after a gestation period of 338 to 358 days.

Fishers are less arboreal than martens and their diet is different. Porcupines seem to be a favorite prey. After rather elaborate maneuvers, the fisher suddenly bowls the porcupine over and rips open its belly. Deer are sometimes killed, especially when they flounder in deep snow.

Fishers have been exterminated over most of their range, but rigid protection in recent years has permitted a slight increase in a few areas. They are now quite abundant in New England and New York state. The fur of female fishers is finer and more prized for furs than that of the males. Fishers do not breed readily in captivity so that commercial raising of them has not been developed.

Gray-headed Tayra (*Tayra barbara senilis*), photo by Ernest P. Walker.

TAYRAS; HURONES MAYORES, IRARA, PERRITOS LIGEROS, CABEZA DE VIEJO, GUACHE, GUANAICO, MELERO, COMADREJA GRANDE (local vernaculars).

THE SINGLE SPECIES, *T. barbara*, is found in forests of southern Mexico, Central America, and South America to Paraguay and Argentina. It also inhabits the island of Trinidad.

Head and body length is 600 to 680 mm., and tail length is 380 to 470 mm. A female weighed 4.4 kg. The short, coarse pelage is gray, brown, or black on the head and neck, with a yellow or white spot on the chest, and black or dark brown on the body. There also is a rare light-colored form which is pale buffy with a darker head. Two specimens were in the National Zoological Park, Washington, D.C., in 1934 and 1935. Tayras have a long and slender body with short limbs and a long tail. The head is broad, the ears are short and rounded, and the neck is long. The soles are naked, and the strong claws are non-retractile.

Tayras are often noted in pairs or family groups. They are active both at night and, particularly on overcast days, in the morning. Tayras can climb, run, and swim well. When hunted by dogs, the tayra may climb a tree after running on the ground for some time and then leap through trees for several hundred feet before descending to the ground again, thus gaining distance while the dogs are trying to pick up the trail. Tayras are said to shelter in hollow trees, although young have been found in a nest in tall grass in Panama. They emit a substance which has been reported as having both a pleasant and a rank odor.

Tayras feed on a variety of small mammals and birds, including an occasional chicken. Stomach investigations of tayras in the Matto Grosso yielded small cricetid rodents, agoutis (*Dasyprocta*), and rabbits (*Sylvilagus*). Natives say that tayras kill many tree squirrels and often pull down small deer (*Mazama*). Fruits and honey are included in the diet. Stomach contents of tayras collected at the National Park of Rancho Grande consisted entirely of fruit. The stomach of one taken in the Amazon Territory contained a marsupial. Tayras like bananas and when the ripe fruit is abundant, they may destroy banana crops on plantations.

Breeding habits and reproductive biology are not well known, but the usual litter size is believed to be two to four. A female with three small (head and body length of 12.8 mm.) embryos was collected in April near Auyan-tepui. Captives have lived for at least 12 years.

Natives of Mexico refer to this animal as "cabeza de viejo," meaning "head of an old man." In most of Guatemala it is known to the natives as "perrito ligero," meaning "little swift dog." The baculum is reputed to have aphrodisiacal properties; the shavings of the bone are taken in liquor.

Hurone or Grison (*Grison vittatus*), photo by Ernest P. Walker.

G. vittatus: GRISONS; FURÃO, HURONCITO, HURO-
NES, WAITI-AI'RA, ZORROS CAÑEROS, ZORROS
CAMASITOS (local vernaculars). *G. cuja:* LITTLE
GRISONS, LA CUJA, QUIQUE (local vernaculars).

THE TWO SPECIES are distributed as follows: *G.
vittatus*, from southern Mexico to Peru and Brazil,
and from sea level to about 1,200 meters elevation;
G. cuja, central and southern South America, and
usually at the higher elevations. The little grison has
been recorded from 1,000 meters on the altiplano of
Peru. The genus *Grison* has also been referred to as
Galictis, Bell, 1826, and *Grison cuja* has also been
called *Grisonella*, Thomas, 1912.

In *G. vittatus* the head and body length is 475 to
550 mm., the tail length is about 160 mm., and the
weight is 1.4 to 3.2 kg.; in *G. cuja* the head and body
length is 400 to 450 mm., the tail length is 150 to 190
mm., and the weight is about 1 kg. The color pattern
is striking: In both species the black face, sides, and
under parts, including the legs and feet, are sharply
set off from the back. The back is smoky-gray in
G. vittatus and yellowish-gray or brownish in *G. cuja*.
A white stripe extends across the forehead and down
the sides of the neck in both species, separating the
black of the face from the gray or brown of the back.
Short legs and slender bodies give the animals of this
genus somewhat the appearance of a weasel or ferret,
but the color pattern immediately distinguishes them.

Members of the genus *Grison* are found in open
land and in forests. They live in the burrows of other
animals (such as those of viscachas in South America)
and under tree roots and rocks. These mustelids are
sociable animals, usually noted in groups and often
playing together. They utter a series of barks and
cries, including sharp, growling barks when threatened. They are agile and quick in their movements,
are good climbers and swimmers, and are probably
capable burrowers. Grisons may be active during
both day and night.

They eat a variety of food, but are mainly carnivorous. Two captives, both young animals, reportedly
preferred mice and birds. These individuals also accepted cold-blooded vertebrates, invertebrates, and
fruit. Animals in the wild occasionally prey on
chickens. From two to four young are born.

Young *Grison* tame readily and make affectionate
pets. In 1846 Thomas Bridges reported (in Wilfred H.
Osgood, *Mammals of Chile* [Chicago, 1943], p. 93):
"The native hunters of . . . [the chinchilla] domesticate the quique of Molina which they term here
'huron'—Spanish for 'ferret'; the huron enters the
crevices and holes made by chinchillas and drives
them out, upon which [the chinchillas] are either
killed with sticks by the hunters or taken by dogs
trained for that purpose." It is apparently no longer
legal to keep trained grisons.

The type species of the genus is *G. vittatus* (Schreber).

Patagonian Weasel (*Lyncodon patagonicus*), photo by Tom Scott of mounted specimen in Royal Scottish Museum.

PATAGONIAN WEASELS; HURONCITOS PATAGÓNI-COS.

FOUND IN ARGENTINA and Chile, the single species, *L. patagonicus*, is an animal of the pampas. It is known from scattered localities, mainly in western Argentina and in Chile along the southern Argentine border.

Head and body length is usually 300 to 350 mm., and tail length is 60 to 90 mm. The coloration on the back is grayish brown with a whitish tinge. The top of the head is creamy or white, with this color extending as a broad stripe on either side to each shoulder. The nape, throat, chest, and limbs are dark brown; and the rest of the lower surface is lighter brown varied with gray. The color pattern is quite attractive and is characteristic. This animal is somewhat similar externally to the grisons (*Grison*), differing from that genus in such external features as the peculiar pattern of coloration and the shorter tail. Internally, *Lyncodon* differs from *Grison* in that there are fewer teeth. Like most of the members of this family (Mustelidae), the Patagonian weasel is a slender-bodied and short-legged animal.

Habits and biology are little known. It was reported that these animals were occasionally kept in the houses of ranchmen for the purpose of destroying rats.

ZORILLES, AFRICAN OR STRIPED POLECATS; STINK-MUISHOND.

THE SINGLE SPECIES, *I. striatus*, inhabits Africa from Senegal, northern Nigeria, the Sudan, and Abyssinia to southern Africa. It frequents a variety of habitats.

Head and body length is usually 285 to 385 mm., and tail length is usually 205 to 305 mm. The pattern of coloration is black and white: the body is black with white dorsal stripes, the tail is more or less white, and the face has white markings. The appearance is somewhat that of the spotted skunks (*Spilogale*) of the Americas, and early writers have confused the two. The smaller and more slender-striped weasel (*Poecilogale*) and, to a lesser extent, the smaller banded and spotted weasels (*Poecilictis*), are the only similar-appearing animals in Africa. *Ictonyx* may be recognized by the long hair, bushy tail, and the color pattern.

Zorilles are generally nocturnal and solitary. They rest during the day in rock crevices or in burrows excavated by themselves or by some other animal. Occasionally they shelter under buildings and in outhouses in farming areas. These animals are mainly terrestrial but can climb and swim well. The usual pace is an easy trot, slower than that of a mongoose, and with the back slightly hunched. The fluid ejected from the anal glands may vary in potency with the individual animal, and perhaps with age and the time of year, as well. Some writers remark that the fluid is much less pungent than that of the American skunks, while others state that it is "most repulsive, acrid, and persistent."

At the sight of an enemy, such as a dog, a zorille may erect its hair and tail and perhaps emit its anal-gland secretion as well. Such behavior would seem to make the zorille more formidable than it really is. When actually attacked by an enemy, it usually emits fluid into the face of the attacker and then feigns death. Such action often protects the zorille from being mauled or killed.

Mice and large insects are the main items in the zorille's diet, although it feeds on a variety of animal

Zorille (*Ictonyx striatus*), photo by Lloyd G. Ingles.

life, including eggs and snakes. It may take a chicken on occasion, but it is often useful in eliminating rodents from houses and stables.

Litter size is usually two or three, and the young are born in burrows. When taken young, zorilles are usually docile and friendly, emitting fluid only when they are frightened or annoyed.

This genus is also known in the literature as *Zorilla*, I. Geoffroy, 1826.

North African Striped Weasel (*Poecilictis libyca*), photo by Robert E. Kuntz.

NORTH AFRICAN BANDED AND SPOTTED WEASELS.

THE SINGLE SPECIES, *P. libyca*, is found in northern Africa. It is usually noted in cultivated areas at the edge of deserts. In northern Nigeria and the Sudan, the range of this genus overlaps that of *Ictonyx*, with which it is sometimes confused.

Head and body length is 225 to 285 mm., and tail length is 130 to 180 mm. (Three males weighed 0.2 to 0.25 kg. each.) This mustelid is marked with black and white on the upper parts. The snout is black, the forehead is white, and the top of the head is black, while a variable pattern of black bands and spots is present on the white back. The tail is white, becoming darker toward the tip, and the limbs and under parts are black. This species differs from *Ictonyx* in the banded and spotted color pattern, in its smaller size, skull features, and in having hairy soles except for the pads.

The diet is probably similar to that of the related genera. One individual was caught in a melon field.

The number of young per litter is usually one to three. This species gives birth in January, February, and March, and the young are "as bald and blind as newborn rats."

Individuals of this species become tame and make interesting pets in captivity.

African Striped Weasel (*Poecilogale albinucha*), photo of mounted specimen from Field Museum of Natural History.

AFRICAN STRIPED WEASELS, CAPE WEASELS, WHITE-NAPED WEASELS; SLANGMUISHOND, KAN-GAMBA, KAMPANDWE, NAKHERI OF THE SIKOLOLO (native names).

THE SINGLE SPECIES, *P. albinucha*, is found in southern and central Africa north to the Congo and Uganda.

Head and body length is usually 250 to 350 mm., and tail length is 150 to 230 mm. From the white on the head and nape, four whitish to orangish-yellow stripes and three black stripes extend on the black back toward the tail, which is white. The legs and under parts are black. There is little variation in pattern.

The African weasel differs externally from the African polecat (*Ictonyx*) in its more slender and generally smaller body, and its narrower back stripes and other features of the color pattern. The members of the genus resemble weasels (*Mustela*) in their slender and elongate body and short legs. The body shape is suited to squeezing into the burrows of rodents. Like other weasels, they can enter any burrow or hole they can get their heads into.

These animals frequent a variety of habitats and live in burrows.

Their habits are similar to those of *Mustela*. African striped weasels are active at any time during the day or night. They often travel in pairs or in family groups and spend most of their time on the ground; however, they can climb fairly well. When attacked or under stress, they emit from the anal glands a noxious odor which is not as strong or as persistent as that of the skunks or of the African *Ictonyx*, but it is nauseating.

Normally, African weasels are silent, but when alarmed they emit a loud sound. This sound is diffi-cult to describe; it is between a growl and a shriek.

They feed mainly on small mammals and birds captured on the ground, but also on snakes, insects, and insect larvae. They also prey on blesmols (*Cryptomys*).

They cannot run rapidly but patiently trail their prey by scent. Like most weasels, they grab the throat or nape, hanging on and chewing until the victim is dead. When they attach themselves to the throat of the springhare or another fair-sized animal, the victim often runs some distance with the weasel retaining its hold until the victim is exhausted. They kill far more than they need for food, and, like other weasels, they often suck the blood or eat the brains of their victims. Their method of killing snakes is much like that of the mongoose (*Herpestes*). They repeatedly provoke venomous snakes to strike, eluding the stroke until the snake is tired and slower in recovery. Then, awaiting their opportunity, they seize the snake in back of the head.

Although they kill poultry when they live in close proximity, they are not considered pests because of the great number of rats, mice, and springhares that they destroy. When locusts are about, these insects are eaten in quantity along with their larvae which are dug out of the ground.

They are rather rare over most of their range and relatively little is known of their reproductive biology. The gestation period is not known. Two seems to be the usual number of young, and an approximately half-grown juvenile has been noted in March in Northern Rhodesia. When taken young, they usually become quite tame and make interesting pets.

Some of the African natives use the skins in ceremonial costumes or as ornaments and it is said that some of the medicine men use parts of these animals in their rituals.

Wolverine (*Gulo gulo*), photo by James K. Drake.

WOLVERINES, GLUTTONS; GLUTONS; VIELFRASS, VEELVARAAT.

THE SINGLE SPECIES, *G. gulo*, inhabits taiga and forest-tundra across the high northern latitudes of the world. Wolverines are still found in the western United States.

The length of the head and body is 650 to 870 mm.; the length of the tail is 170 to 260 mm.; the height at the shoulders is about 355 to 432 mm.; and the weight is usually 14 to 27.5 kg. Females are smaller and lighter than males. The fur is long and quite dense. Coloration is blackish brown. A light-brown band extends from the shoulder to the rump along each side of the body, joining its mate over and across the base of the tail.

Wolverines are usually solitary and are active all year. They tend to have a cycle of activity for three or four hours and then rest for about the same length of time. They are not nomadic; each animal inhabits a definite, although vast, area. A male shares his realm, which may be about 300,000 hectares, with two or three females. Wolverines use trails about 0.8 km. in width within their territories. They are mainly terrestrial and the usual gait is a sort of loping gallop; but they can climb trees with considerable speed.

They love to play, and this may be disastrous to a trapper's cabin and belongings. Their ability to learn and their strength are important factors in their survival. Wolverines soon learn what to avoid, and they seem to be unexcelled in strength among mammals of their size. They have been known to drive bears and mountain lions from their kills, and are powerful enough to kill elk and moose that are hampered by snow.

Although carrion is preferred, wolverines are likely to feed on the eggs of ground-nesting birds in early summer, the larvae of wasps in late summer, and berries for several weeks in the fall. Living animals are preyed on mainly in winter, when the snow cover enables the wolverine to travel faster than its prey. Caches of prey or carrion are covered with ground or snow, or sometimes wedged in the forks of trees.

Delayed implantation occurs in the wolverine; the gestation period is not known. The young—usually two or three, but as many as five—are born from February through May. They nurse for eight to ten weeks and remain with the mother for about two years, when they are driven from the territory. Wolverines are sexually mature at four years of age and have lived 16 years in captivity.

Eskimos and other northern natives like to use wolverine fur as trimming about the hoods of parkas, as it retains less frozen moisture from the breath than any other fur.

Honey Badger or Ratel (*Mellivora capensis*), photo by Bernhard Grzimek.

HONEY BADGERS OR RATELS; BIJU, BHARSIA, ICELESI, OUS, CHIRBO, CHUULI (native names).

THE SINGLE SPECIES, *M. capensis*, is found over most of Africa from Senegal, Sudan, Ethiopia and Somalia south. In Asia it ranges from Arabia to Russian Turkestan and eastward to Nepal and India, west of the Bay of Bengal.

Head and body length is 600 to 770 mm.; tail length is usually 200 to 300 mm.; and shoulder height is usually 250 to 300 mm. They are heavy bodied animals. The upper parts from the top of the head to the base of the tail vary from gray to pale yellow or whitish, and contrast sharply with the dark brown or black of the under parts. Completely black individuals, however, have been found in Africa, particularly in the Ituri forest. The color pattern of the honey badger has been interpreted as a warning coloration because it makes the animal easily recognizable.

The hair is coarse and quite scant on the under parts. The skin is exceedingly loose on the body and extremely tough.

Honey badgers have short legs and a relatively short tail. The ears are small and the muzzle is not snout-like. The fore feet are large and armed with very large and strong claws for digging.

They occur in a variety of habitats, living in holes in the ground, among rocks, or in hollow trees, logs, or stumps. They may travel singly but often go in pairs. They are at least partly diurnal as well as nocturnal; and, while primarily terrestrial, they can climb. If there is honey to be obtained, they prove to be successful climbers. They are almost omnivorous but are particularly fond of insects, regularly dig small mammals out of their burrows, and eat lizards, tortoises, and many snakes, including such venomous forms as cobras. They also feed on carrion and plant matter, and their fondness for honey accounts for the common name. The honey badger will attack sheep, eating the tongue, windpipe, and eyes, then the brain. Later it tears open the shoulder and feeds on the contents of thoracic and abdominal cavities.

The structural peculiarities—the thick, loose hide, strong claws, and fairly strong teeth—are effective weapons against attack. The anal gland secretes a vile-smelling liquid which is a deterrent to enemies.

Honey badgers are courageous animals; they may rush out from their burrows and charge an intruder, especially during the breeding season. Horses, cattle, antelope, and even buffalo have been attacked and severely wounded in this manner.

They are extremely difficult to kill; the skin is so tough that a dog can make but little impression on it, except on the belly. The honey badgers can twist about in their skin so that they can even bite an adversary that has seized them by the back of the neck. Porcupine quills and bee stings have little effect on them and snake fangs are rarely able to penetrate their skin.

They seem to be devoid of fear, and it is doubtful that any animal of similar size can regularly kill them in contest. They travel by a jog-trot, but they are tireless and trail their victims until they run them to ground. When annoyed, they can utter a very harsh, grating growl, but they generally remain silent.

A rather remarkable association has developed, at least in tropical Africa, between a bird—the honey guide (*Indicator indicator*)—and these animals. The association is mutually beneficial in the common exploitation of wild bees' nests. In the presence of any mammal, even man, this bird has the unusual habit of uttering a series of characteristic calls. If a honey badger hears these calls, it follows the bird, which invariably leads it into the vicinity of a bee's nest. The badger breaks open the nest to obtain the honey, and the bird obtains enough crumbs of the meal to pay it for its work.

If captured before they are half grown, honey badgers can become very satisfactory pets, as they are docile, affectionate, and active; but they have incredible strength and energy, and can wreck cages and damage property in their explorations.

Two appear to be the usual number of young per birth. Females have two pairs of abdominal mammae. The gestation period has been reported as six months, and the life span in captivity can be 24 years.

Old World Badger (*Meles meles*), photo from Paignton Zoo.

OLD WORLD BADGERS; BLAIREAUX, DÄCHSE, DASSEN, TEJONES, JEZEVEC LESNI, CHÔSEN-ANA-KUMA. (Included are vernaculars used in other countries.)

THE ONE SPECIES, *M. meles*, originally occurred throughout Europe and is found in Asia southward to Tibet, northern Burma, and southern China. It usually inhabits wooded regions.

Head and body length is 560 to 812 mm.; tail length is 115 to 202 mm.; and the weight is usually 10 to 16 kg., with a 20 kg. maximum. The upper parts are grayish, and the under parts, legs, and feet are black. A dark stripe on each side of the face extends from the tip of the snout back to the ear and encloses the eyes; white stripes border the dark stripes. Like the other badgers, *Meles* has a stocky body form with short legs and a short tail. It may be distinguished from the hog badger (*Arctonyx*), which also occurs in China, by its black throat (white in the hog badger) and by its shorter tail that is the same color as the back. (The tail of the hog badger is longer and usually white for the most part.)

Old World badgers usually do not emerge from their burrow until after sundown. They are gregarious in that successive generations may live together in the same enormous (.25 ha.), network of burrows; such a burrow system becomes more complex with each new family. The boar lives in a more simple burrow in the same neighborhood most of the year. After living for several months in one nest, these animals may suddenly move to another part of the burrow. The living quarters are kept quite clean. Bedding material, in the form of dry grass, brackens, moss, or leaves, is dragged backward into the den. Occasionally the bedding material is brought up and strewn around the entrance to air for an hour or so in the early morning. Around the burrows there are dung pits, sunning grounds, and areas for play. Badgers play all sorts of games, including leapfrog.

They hibernate in Scandinavia, Poland, and northern Russia, but they remain active all winter in western Europe. Badgers are omnivorous, feeding on a variety of small prey such as beetles, larvae, worms, slugs, occasionally voles, young rabbits, the combs and larvae of bees and wasps, and in winter on carrion. Suckling females feed entirely on worms. From plants and different kinds of tubers and roots, berries and seeds are eaten. In autumn large amounts of beech mast and acorns are consumed. Sometimes they damage ripening grapes, corn, and oats.

Breeding usually takes place in the summer, although implantation in the uterus does not occur until the end of the year and birth takes place from February through April. The number of young is usually two to four. There are instances of females giving birth to young after having lived alone in captivity for nearly a year. The survival rate in the first year is very low (one out of five); they can, however, reach the age of 15.

The hairs of badgers are used to make different kinds of brushes, such as shaving brushes; their skins, at least formerly, were used in North China to make rugs.

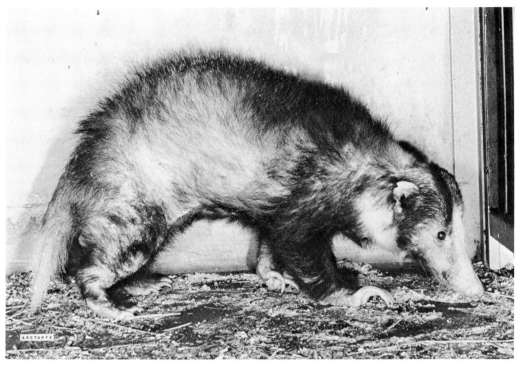

Hog-Badger (*Arctonyx collaris*), photo by Ernest P. Walker.

HOG-BADGERS.

THE SINGLE SPECIES, *A. collaris*, inhabits most of China, northeastern India, Assam, Burma, Indochina, Thailand, and Sumatra, frequenting both lowlands and mountains.

The length of the head and body is 550 to 700 mm.; the length of the tail is 120 to 170 mm.; and the weight is usually 7 to 14 kg. The back is yellowish, grayish, or blackish, and there is a pattern of white and black stripes on the head. The dark stripes run through the eyes and are bordered by white stripes which merge with the nape and with the white of the throat. The ears and tail also are white, and the feet and belly are black. The body form is stocky. This badger is distinguished from the Old World badger (*Meles*) by its white, rather than black, throat; and by its long and mostly white tail, as distinct from the short tail, colored the same as the back, as in *Meles*. Another external difference is that in *Arctonyx* the claws are pale-colored, whereas in *Meles* they are dark.

Hog-badgers are difficult to catch but are fairly common over most of their range. They are nocturnal and spend the day in natural shelters such as rock crevices or in deep burrows they dig for themselves. The snout is believed to be used in rooting for the animal and plant foods they eat.

Their general habits probably resemble those of the Old World badger *Meles*. As in *Meles*, the color pattern has been interpreted as warning coloration because it acts as a warning to a possible enemy that the animal so marked is better left alone. Badgers (and the ratel, *Mellivora*) are savage and formidable antagonists when attacked; they are equipped with a thick, flexible, and loose skin, powerful jaws, fairly strong teeth, and well-developed claws. A badger is generally more than a match for another animal of the same size. Hog-badgers, like the other badgers, also are equipped with a potent anal-gland secretion.

Reproductive biology is not well known. A female hog-badger from northern China had four newly-born young in April.

The common name refers to the long, truncate, mobile, and naked snout, which is often compared to a pig (*Sus*) snout.

Malayan Stink Badger (*Mydaus javanensis*), photo of mounted specimen from National Museum of Ireland.

MALAYAN STINK BADGERS, SKUNK BADGERS; STINKDACHS, TELEDUS, BÓBOT, KALINSÍDA (native names).

THE SINGLE SPECIES, *M. javanensis*, is found in Sumatra, Java, Borneo, and the North Natuna Islands. It is not known from the mainland.

The length of the head and body is 375 to 510 mm.; the length of the tail is usually 50 to 75 mm.; and weight is usually 1.4 to 3.6 kg. This animal is blackish except for a white crown and a complete or incomplete narrow white stripe down the back onto the tail. As in *Suillotaxus*, the face is pointed, the snout is somewhat elongate and mobile, and the legs are short and stout. This genus differs from *Suillotaxus* in its larger ears, a longer tail, and smaller teeth, and in the presence of white stripes or patches on the back.

Stink badgers of the genus *Mydaus* are nocturnal, residing by day in holes in the ground dug by themselves or by porcupines with which they sometimes live. The burrows are usually not more than 600 mm. deep. Captives consume worms, insects, and the entrails of chickens.

They may growl and attempt to bite when handled. When they are molested or threatened, they raise the tail and eject a pale greenish fluid to a distance of 150 mm. or more. This vile smelling fluid is reported by natives to sometimes asphyxiate dogs or even blind them if they are struck in the eye. The old Javanese Sultans used this fluid in suitable dilution in the making of perfumes.

Some natives eat the flesh, removing the scent glands immediately after the animals are killed, and others mix shavings of the skin with water and drink the mixture as a cure for fever or rheumatism.

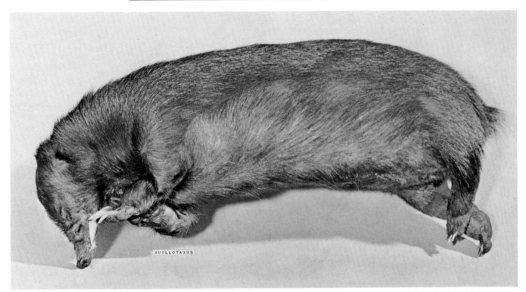

Palawan or Calamian Stink Badger (*Suillotaxus marchei*), photo by Howard E. Uible of skin in U.S. National Museum.

PALAWAN OR CALAMIAN STINK BADGERS.

THE SINGLE SPECIES, *S. marchei*, is found on Palawan and the Calamian islands north and east of Borneo. This genus was established for the animal previously known as *Mydaus marchei*.

Head and body length is 320 to 460 mm., and tail length is 15 to 45 mm. The coloration above is dark brown to black, with a scattering of white or silvery hairs on the back and sometimes on the head; the animal is brown below.

The stink badgers can be arranged in two groups: the small-toothed, long-tailed, and large-eared form from Java, Sumatra, and Borneo, referable to the genus *Mydaus;* and the heavier-toothed, shorter-tailed, and smaller-eared form from the Calamians and Palawan, referable to *Suillotaxus*. These two genera are also distinguishable by the pattern of coloration: *Suillotaxus* lacks the dorsal patches of *Mydaus*.

Little is known of the habits and life history of this badger. The capture of two individuals on a farm may indicate that they frequent cultivated areas. The anal glands are well developed, and their secretion has an extremely offensive odor. Among specimens in study collections are the following: ten in the Field Museum of Natural History, one at the U.S. National Museum, one at Harvard, and one in the Leyden Museum in the Netherlands.

American Badger (*Taxidea taxus*), photo by E. P. Haddon from U.S. Fish & Wildlife Service.

AMERICAN BADGERS; TEJONES, TLALCOYOTES.

THE SINGLE SPECIES, *T. taxus*, is found on the American mainland, from southwestern Canada and the north-central United States south through the western United States into central Mexico. It usually inhabits dry, open country.

The length of the head and body is 420 to 720 mm.; the length of the tail is 100 to 155 mm.; and weight is 3.5 to 10 kg. The upper parts are grayish to reddish, and there is a white stripe extending from the nose at least to the shoulders. Black patches are present on the face and cheeks, and the chin, throat, and mid-ventral region are whitish. The under parts are buffy, and the feet are dark brown to black. The hairs are longest on the sides. This mammal can be recognized by the flattened, stocky form, the distinctive black and white head pattern, the long fur, and the short bushy tail. It is the only New World badger. Anal scent glands are present.

It is usually solitary. If not in close proximity to the activities of man, it is active at almost any hour, usually afternoon and evening. Most American badgers, however, now limit their activites mainly to the night. They are remarkable burrowers and can quickly dig themselves out of sight; the usual signs of their presence are the large holes they dig when after rodents. The diet consists of various rodents, which they dig out, and other animals and carrion. Badgers sometimes store food by burying it. If a sizable meal, such as a rabbit, is obtained, the badger may dig a hole, carry in the prey, and remain below ground with it for several days. Like the Old World badger (*Meles*), the American badger digs holes to bury its feces. It is said that an individual badger sometimes forms a "hunting partnership" with a coyote (*Canis latrans*), but if true, this association is not well understood.

In the northern and more elevated parts of its range, the badger sleeps during most of the time that the ground is frozen. The burrows made by badgers constitute a hazard for cattle and horses. Ranchers often destroy badgers for this reason. The badger destroys many rodents, and the burrows it makes serve as shelters for many other animals, including cottontail rabbits.

Badgers breed in August and September, although implantation does not occur until February; the actual gestation period is about six weeks. (The only hole that is occupied for any length of time is the rearing den.) The one to five young (usually two) are born and raised in a nest of dry grass in a burrow. The young are weaned at about six weeks of age, and the family breaks up in late summer. Badgers have lived 13 years in captivity.

Badger fur is still used to trim garments, and for many years was used for shaving brushes, but synthetic substitutes have largely replaced badger hair in high-quality brushes.

Bornean Ferret Badger (*Melogale orientalis*), photo by Ernest P. Walker.

FERRET BADGERS; OKER, NYENTEK, KYOUNG-U-GYI, KYOUNG-PYAN (local vernaculars).

THE THREE SPECIES are distributed as follows: *M. personata* from Nepal, Assam, Burma, Siam, and Indochina; *M. moschata* from China, Formosa, Assam, Burma, and Indochina; and *M. orientalis* from Java and Borneo. This genus has also been referred to as *Helictis*.

Head and body length is 330 to 430 mm., and tail length is 152 to 230 mm. The weight of one individual was 1.75 kg.

This genus is distinguished from the other Oriental mustelids by the mask in the head region formed by a black and whitish or black and yellowish pattern. A dorsal stripe, white or reddish in color, is usually present on the pale to dark-brown back. The color is somewhat paler below. The tail is bushy.

These animals are found in wooded and grassland country; they reside in burrows and natural shelters during the day and are active at dusk and during the night. They climb on occasion. *M. moschata*, in Formosa, is reported to be a good climber and often sleeps on the branches of trees. These animals are savage and fearless when provoked or pressed and are believed to have an offensive odor. The conspicuous markings on the head have been interpreted as warning coloration. The diet is omnivorous. They are known to feed on small animals, insects, earthworms, and fruit. A ferret badger is welcome to enter a native hut because of its destruction of insect pests.

The young, usually one to three per litter, are born in a burrow in May and June. They apparently are dependent on the milk of the mother for some time, as two nearly full-grown suckling animals and their mother have been dug out of a burrow.

The type species of the genus is *M. personata*, I. Geoffroy.

Striped Skunk (*Mephitis mephitis*), A. Facing danger that does not appear to be imminent; B. Aimed towards the enemy ready to spray its scent; photos by Ernest P. Walker.

STRIPED AND HOODED SKUNKS; ZORRINOS, MA-PURITES.

THE TWO SPECIES are distributed as follows: *M. mephitis*, the striped skunk, from southern Canada, the United States, and northern Mexico; *M. macroura*, the hooded skunk, from southwestern United States to Central America. Skunks are found in a variety of habitats, including woods, plains, and desert areas.

The length of the head and body is 280 to 380 mm.; the length of the tail is 185 to 435 mm.; and weight is usually 0.75 to 2.5 kg. Both species have black and white color patterns, but with considerable variation. The striped skunk usually has white on the top of the head and on the nape extended posteriorly and separated into two stripes. In some individuals of this species the top and sides of the tail are white, while in others the white is limited to a small spot on the forehead. The white areas are entirely of white hair, not mixed with black hairs. The hooded skunk has a white-backed color phase and a black-backed color phase. In the former, there are some black hairs mixed with the white hairs of the back; in the latter, the two white stripes are widely separated and are situated on the sides of the animal, instead of being narrowly separated and situated on the back of the animal as in the striped skunk.

Although probably similar to those of the better known striped skunk, the habits of the hooded skunk are little known. Adult male striped skunks are usually solitary in the summer. In the winter several females may share a den, often in company with a male who probably keeps out other males. In the northern parts of its range, the striped skunk sleeps through the winter, with an occasional foray outdoors. Skunks live in burrows and under buildings—in fact, in almost any dry place. They are active at dusk and through the night; the diet is omnivorous.

Breeding takes place in the late winter or early spring. The gestation period is about 63 days, and the number of young is four to ten (usually four or five). They are born in a den lined with vegetation, weigh about 1 ounce each at birth, and nurse for six to seven weeks. The family breaks up in August or September. Striped skunks breed when a year old and have lived ten years in captivity.

The type species of the genus is *M. mephitis* (Schreber).

Spotted Skunk (*Spilogale putorius*), photo by Ernest P. Walker.

SPOTTED SKUNKS; ZORRINOS, MAPURITES.

THE TWO SPECIES are distributed as follows: *S. putorius* from British Columbia and most of the United States south through Mexico into Central America; *S. pygmaea* from the Pacific coast of Mexico. The latter species is known from only four specimens. Spotted skunks occupy a variety of habitats but are most common in Sonoran and Transition zones.

The length of the head and body is 115 to 345 mm.; the length of the tail is 70 to 220 mm.; and the weight is usually 200 to 1,000 grams. Of the three genera of skunks, *Spilogale* has the finest fur—the hairs are longest on the tail and shortest on the face. The basic color pattern consists of six white stripes which extend along the back and sides, and these are broken into smaller stripes and spots on the rump. There is a triangular white patch in the middle of the forehead, and the tail is usually tipped with white. The variations on this basic pattern are infinite, as no two individuals have ever been found with exactly the same pattern. This genus may be distinguished from the other two genera of skunks by its small size, forehead patch, and pattern of white stripes and spots, the white never being massed.

The habits of *S. pygmaea* are not known; the following remarks apply specifically to *S. putorius*. Spotted skunks are nocturnal and active all year.

They are very playful with one another, and generally remain under cover more than the striped skunks (*Mephitis*). The white-plumed tail is used as a warning signal to other animals; if the sudden erection of the tail does not deter an enemy, the animal may stand on its hands and sometimes even advance toward the enemy. The anal-gland secretion is very strongly scented and is irritating to the eyes.

The feeding habits of spotted skunks are similar to those of striped skunks; the diet consists of vegetable matter and insects in the summer and rodents and small animals in the winter.

Spotted skunks usually den underground but can climb well and sometimes shelter in trees. The dens are lined with dry vegetation. Sometimes as many as seven or eight individuals spend the day in a single den, except during the breeding season.

The young are usually born in the spring, but they may be born at any time in the southern parts of the range, where two litters may be raised in one year. (One record for *S. putorius* indicates a gestation period of at least 120 days.) Litter size is two to six, usually four or five, and the young weigh about 9.4 grams each at birth. Apparently only the mother cares for the young, which are weaned at about eight weeks and attain adult size at about 15 weeks.

The type species of the genus is *S. interrupta*, Rafinesque = *S. putorius interrupta* as currently arranged.

Hog-nosed Skunk (*Conepatus mesoleucus?*), photo by Lloyd G. Ingles.

HOG-NOSED SKUNKS; ZORRINOS, MAPURITES, MA-RITATACA, CANGAMBA (South American names).

THIS GENUS of about six species is found from the southwestern United States to the Strait of Magellan. It is the only genus of skunks in South America. Wooded and open areas are inhabited, and one species (*C. rex*) is found on the altiplano of South America.

The length of the head and body is 300 to 490 mm.; the length of the tail is 160 to 410 mm.; and the weight is usually 2.3 to 4.5 kg. These animals have the coarsest fur of all the skunks. The color pattern is black and white, as in the other skunks. There are two main patterns, with variations: solid white above and black below; or two white stripes which begin at the nape and end on the hips. The latter pattern, which resembles that of the striped skunk (*Mephitis mephitis*), seems to be most common in areas where the hog-nosed is the only skunk present. The former pattern occurs most commonly in those areas where the ranges of *Conepatus* and *Mephitis* overlap. In all cases, the hog-nosed skunk lacks the thin white stripe down the center of the face that is present in *Mephitis*. *Conepatus* may be distinguished from the other two genera of skunks by its nose, which is bare, broad, and projecting. The nose resembles that of a hog somewhat, hence the common name.

Hog-nosed skunks are not as well known as the other skunks. They are nocturnal, somewhat solitary, and generally slow-moving in their actions, like *Mephitis*. Dens are located in rocky places or in burrows made by other animals. This genus, like *Mephitis* and unlike *Spilogale*, does not ordinarily climb. It has the usual skunk odor and defense method of musk secretion.

The principal food may be insects and grubs, although small vertebrates, including snakes, and fruits probably are eaten as well. With their bare snouts and their claws, hog-nosed skunks may turn over the soil in a considerable area in search of food; like *Mephitis*, they also pounce on insects. At least in the Andes, hog-nosed skunks are resistant to the venom of pit vipers. There is some evidence that the spotted skunks (*Spilogale*) also are resistant to rattlesnake venom. Since the musk of skunks produces an alarm reaction in rattlers, the same reaction which the snakes exhibit in the presence of king snakes which prey on them, it may well be that skunks feed on rattlers quite extensively.

The gestation period of one South American species is 42 days, and litter size is usually two to five.

Some natives regard the meat to have curative properties, and others use the skins for capes or blankets.

The type species of the genus is *C. humboldtii*, Gray.

Canadian Otters (*Lutra canadensis*), photos by Ernest P. Walker.

RIVER OTTERS; LOUTRES, FISCHOTTER, NUTRIOS, LONTRA, PERROSDA AQUA, KAWAWOSO KAWAUSO, BERANG-BERANG, VISOTTERS. (Included are vernaculars used in other countries.)

ABOUT 12 SPECIES inhabit streams, lakes, and coastal waters over most of North and South America, most of Africa, through Europe and Asia, and the larger Malayan islands. They are found in all types of inland waterways, as well as estuaries and marine coves.

The length of the head and body is 550 to 800 mm.; the length of the tail is 300 to 500 mm.; and the weight ranges from 4.5 to 14 kg. The upper parts are brownish and the under parts are paler; the lower jaw and throat may be whitish. The fur is short and dense. The head is flattened and rounded; the neck is about as wide as the skull, and short; the trunk is cylindrical; the tail is thick at the base, muscular, flexible, and tapering; the legs are short; and the toes are webbed. The small ears and the nostrils can be closed when the animal is in the water.

River otters are excellent swimmers and divers and are active day and night, although they are more active at night. They hunt singly or sometimes in pairs. The diet consists of crayfish, frogs, turtles, fish, and aquatic invertebrates. Birds and land mammals such as rodents and rabbits also are preyed on. Studies indicate that the fish consumed are mainly non-game species.

With the possible exception of the Old World badger (*Meles*), river otters are probably the most playful of the *Mustelidae*. Some species engage in the year-round activity of sliding down mud and snow banks, and individuals of all ages participate. Sometimes they tunnel under snow to emerge some distance beyond. A combination of running and sliding may be used in traveling overland or over snow and ice. The dens are lined with dry vegetation.

They are docile and sociable for most of the year, but during the breeding season the males may fight one another. Delayed implantation is believed to occur in the New World *L. canadensis*, whose gestation period is 9½ to 12½ months. In the Old World

L. lutra, on the other hand, the gestation period is reported to be about two months. In general, litter size is one to five, usually two or three. The young nurse for about four months, the family remains together for about eight months. River otters have lived 19 years in captivity.

The beautiful and durable fur is used for coat collars and trimmings. River otters become delightful pets if captured when young and then properly cared for.

The type species of the genus is *L. lutra* (Linnaeus). Two subgenera are currently recognized: *Lutrogale*, Gray, 1865, for the smooth-coated Indian otters (*L. perspicillata*) and *Hydrictis*, Pocock, 1921, for the small West African otters with white throat spots (*L. maculicollis*, Lichtenstein).

Flat-tailed or Giant Otter (*Pteronura brasiliensis brasiliensis*), photo from New York Zoological Society.

FLAT-TAILED OR MARGIN-TAILED OTTERS, GIANT OTTERS; EL ARIRAI, NUTRIAS GRANDES, ARI-RANHAS, HWANA-DAGU, PERROS DE AGUA (South American names).

THE SINGLE SPECIES, *P. brasiliensis*, inhabits streams of South America from Venezuela and the Guianas to Uruguay and Argentina. It is usually found in streams with relatively slow currents and in calm tributaries.

Head and body length is 1 to 1.5 meters, and tail length is about 0.7 meter. Their weights have been recorded from about 24 to 34 kg. Coloration is chocolate-brown, with a whitish or creamy chest patch. This otter is similar in general appearance to the otters of the genus *Lutra* except that it is larger, usually has a larger patch on the chest, and the long, flattened tail has flanged or corded margins on either side.

The presence of this animal in a given area is often evidenced by a high-pitched, shrieking call. The calls of the giant otter may be accompanied by the raising of the fore part of the body steeply out of the water. *Pteronura* is active during the daytime and is found usually in small groups. The habits of giant otters are not well known, but they probably do not differ much from those of *Lutra*. As far as is known, the number of young is one or two. Their dens are holes in the river banks or under the roots of trees along the river.

Fish are usually taken to land and consumed there. Eggs and aquatic mammals and birds are also eaten. There is a record that two geese were killed by a margin-tailed otter. The anal-gland secretion can be forcibly ejected.

The hide is sought after by natives as a source of leather, but *Pteronura* is difficult to hunt because of its habit of diving under water when hit and swimming to a secluded spot. In areas where they have not been disturbed, they are relatively easy to approach, at least when they are playing.

Oriental Small-clawed Otter (*Amblonyx cinerea*), photo by Lim Boo Liat.

ORIENTAL SMALL-CLAWED OTTERS.

THE SINGLE SPECIES, *A. cinerea*, is found in southern India, the lower elevations of the Himalayas, southern China, southeastern Asia, Sumatra, Java, Borneo, and Palawan. Some mammalogists include this species in the genus *Aonyx*. This genus was formerly known under the generic name *Micraonyx*, Allen, 1919, which was the new name given to *Leptonyx*, Lesson, 1842, which was preoccupied by *Leptonyx*, Swainson, 1821, a bird, and by *Leptonyx*, Gray, 1837, a seal; *Micraonyx*, however, was antedated by *Amblonyx*.

Head and body length is about 610 mm., and tail length is about 305 mm. Weight is usually 2.7 to 5.4 kg. The color is usually dark brown, only occasionally having the gray or ashy tint which suggested the trivial name (*cinerea*). The under parts are usually paler brown, and the throat may be grayish or whitish. The claws in the adults are only minute spikes which do not project beyond the ends of the digital pads. The webbing on the feet does not extend along the digital pads, as in the river otters (*Lutra*). Other distinguishing structural features of this genus are present in the skull and teeth.

Amblonyx seems to be a hill-otter in southern India, but in the East Indies it seems to be equally common in estuaries and along the coast. Like most otters, these are usually noted in groups.

"The abbreviation of the claws of the front foot is accompanied in this otter by extreme delicacy of the sense of touch in this extremity. I have seen one of these animals manipulating and playing with a marble in a manner recalling that of a conjuror juggling with a cricket-ball" (R. I. Pocock, "On the External Characters of Some Species of Lutrinae (Otters)," *Proc. Zool. Soc. London*, 1921).

The paws are probably used in locating and feeling prey in mud or under stones. There is some indication that this species feeds more extensively on mussels, snails, and crabs than does *Lutra lutra*. In areas where they occur together, direct competition for food between the two species may be thus avoided.

The Oriental small-clawed otter has been noted breeding in banks of paddy fields on Java. Two animals in captivity weighed about 0.5 kg., each at about three weeks of age, and began to accept solid food at about seven weeks of age. The high, bird-like squeaks in the newborn and blind stage of development were gradually replaced by various calls of "contentment," "displeasure," and alarm.

Various species of otters have been trained by some of the Asian peoples to catch and bring fish to them; this species is reported to be kept tame and employed by fishermen in Malacca.

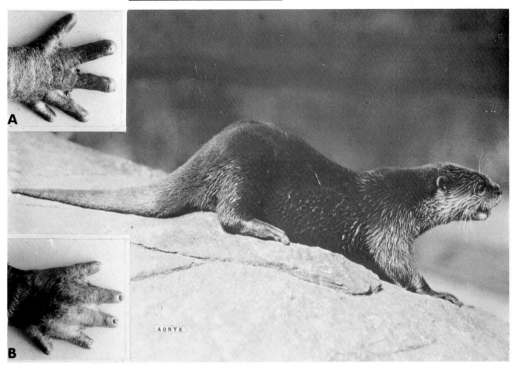

African Clawless Otter (*Aonyx capensis*), photo from the Zoological Society of London. Insets: A. Fore foot; B. Hind foot; photos by U. Rahm.

CAPE OR AFRICAN CLAWLESS OTTERS; GROOT OTTERS, KAAPSE OTTERS, INTINI, ITINI, AKOSTA, KABAO (native names).

THE SINGLE SPECIES, *A. capensis*, inhabits the greater part of Africa, from the Cape region of South Africa north to Ethiopia, the Congo Basin, and Liberia. The habitat ranges from open coastal plains and semiarid country to dense rain forests, but these otters are rarely, if ever, found away from permanent, running water. They prefer the quiet pools and more sluggish streams, in contrast to *Lutra*, which also occurs in parts of the same range.

The length of the head and body is 950 to 1,000 mm.; the length of the tail is about 550 mm.; and the weight of adults ranges from 14 to 23 kg. The coloration is a dull brown, with variable white markings on the cheeks, throat, and chest. The cheek teeth are large, broad, and strong, adapted for crushing crab and mollusk shells, in contrast to those of *Paraonyx*, which are lighter and sharper, more adapted to cutting flesh. The underfur is short and somewhat woolly and the guard hairs are scant; thus, fortunately, the fur is of slight commercial value. The toes of the fore feet have only a small connecting web at the base and lack nails. The hind feet are webbed to the last joint of the toes and also lack nails except on the third and fourth toes, each of which possesses a tiny claw. They swim and dive as well as other otters.

These otters are solitary or associate in pairs and family parties. They are mainly nocturnal, but in wilder areas they may be active by day. Their dens are under boulders, driftwood, in crannies under ledges, or in tangles of vegetation. These otters apparently do not dig their own burrows as do some others. At times they may roam for considerable distances from the river or lake shore and have been known to raid poultry flocks.

Members of this genus seem to be mainly crab-eaters, but they also prey on mollusks, turtles, fish, frogs, lizards, aquatic birds, and small mammals. In captivity these otters will accept a wide variety of food, including pork, milk, biscuits, cake and cheese. Food is usually taken with the hands and never eaten directly off the ground. Like most otters, they habitually come ashore to devour their catch. There is apparently little direct competition for food between *Aonyx* and *Lutra*: *Aonyx* feeds mainly on crabs and other crustaceans, although other animal food is taken as available; *Lutra* feeds mainly on fish. It has been suggested that the African small-clawed otters of the genus *Paraonyx*, with their relatively small, weak teeth and supposed terrestrial habits, feed mainly on relatively soft matter such as small land vertebrates and eggs. If these suppositions be correct, *Aonyx* and *Paraonyx* do not compete with one another for food in those areas where they occur together.

The tracks of these otters in the mud are similar to those of monkeys. Other signs of their presence are piles of cracked crab and mollusk shells. These otters emit powerful, high-pitched shrieks when disturbed or when wishing to attract attention.

Their powerful jaws, great strength, and agility make them formidable adversaries for dogs in the water. Crocodiles are probably their most dangerous enemies. Otters have been known to attack larger mammals such as sheep, but it is thought that this occurs only when drought prevails. Otters travel considerable distances overland between rivers, dams and lakes, especially during droughts.

Two to five young are born after a gestation period of 63 days. Most births apparently occur in the spring. The young remain with the parents for at least a year. If captured when young, these otters make intelligent and charming pets.

Most, if not all, otters use their hands with great skill and probably more than any other mammal when playing with objects that interest them. Apparently the otters of this genus are the most skillful and adept.

The fur of *Aonyx* is not as good as that of *Lutra*, therefore they have not been so extensively hunted for their skins.

AFRICAN SMALL-CLAWED OTTERS, LIBERIAN OT-
TERS.

THE THREE SPECIES, *P. microdon*, *P. congica*, and *P. philippsi*, are still very imperfectly known. The range, as known at present, is Liberia, part of Nigeria, the Cameroons, and a portion of the Congo Basin. *Paraonyx* seemingly occurs only in heavy rain forest, in small, torrential mountain streams.

The length of the head and body is about 600 mm.; the length of the tail is about 350 mm.; and the weight of adults is up to 34 kg. The coloration is uniformly dark, lustrous brown, with scattered black guard hairs and obscure, grayish to whitish facial and throat markings. The toes of the fore feet are only partially webbed (to the last toe-joint), while the hind feet are fully webbed. All the toes bear small, blunt claws. The dentition is weak and brachyodent, with no trace of specialization for crushing crustaceans and mollusks as in *Aonyx* or for fish as in *Lutra*. The skull is similar to that of *Aonyx*, but shorter and broader, especially in the palatal region. The mandible is less robust than in *Aonyx*.

Little has been recorded about the life history of these interesting otters. Because of the scanty hair, the weakly developed facial vibrissae, the structure of the digits, and the features of the teeth, it has been speculated that *Paraonyx* is even more terrestrial in its habits than *Aonyx*. These otters are believed to feed mainly on relatively soft matter, such as small land vertebrates, eggs, and frogs rather than on fish. If this is true, there would seem to be little direct competition among the three genera of otters which, in some few areas, inhabit the same river systems together.

Little is known of the breeding habits of *Paraonyx*, but they probably reach sexual maturity at about one year of age. After a gestation period of approximately two months, two or three young are born.

Certain African tribes believe that a piece of otter skin applied to a stiff neck will cure it. Formerly, only chiefs were allowed to wear otter skins; if anyone else was found wearing one, it was taken from him and he was fined an ox.

The type species of the genus is *P. philippsi*, Hinton.

Sea Otters (*Enhydra lutris*), A. Photo of mounted specimen from U.S. National Museum. B. Floating on its back while it breaks clam shells and eats the clams, photo by Stuart B. Hertz through Woodland Park Zoo, Seattle. C. Mother floating on her back with newborn pup, photo by Karl W. Kenyon.

Sea Otters; Nutrias Marinas.

WITHIN HISTORIC times the range of the single species, *E. lutris*, has extended from Lower California northward along the west coast of North America, adjacent islands, the Aleutian Islands, among the Kurile and Commander Islands, and along the coast of Kamchatka in Asiatic waters.

Sea otters frequent rocky mainland or island shores, often but not necessarily in the vicinity of kelp beds. They are exclusively marine animals that rarely venture more than a kilometer out to sea where the water is not too deep for them to find their food. They prefer depths of 3 to 20 meters. They spend relatively little time on shore and seldom go more than a few meters from the water. Excessive hunting for their skins for 170 years almost exterminated them by 1910; only a few remained in some of the most isolated regions. Being too scarce for profitable hunting, and benefiting from international treaty and absolute protection, they have gradually increased and reestablished colonies in central California, western Alaska, and in the Commander and Kurile Islands, but after more than 50 years of full protection, they have reoccupied only one-fifth of their former range.

The length of the head and body is usually 1 meter to 1.2 meters; the length of the tail is 250 to 370 mm.; and males weigh between 27 and 37 kg. and females, from 16 to 29 kg. The color varies from black to dark brown except for the grayish or creamy head, throat, and chest. Albinistic individuals are rare. The head is large and blunt; the neck is short and thick; the ears are short, thickened, valve-like, and pointed; and the legs and tail are short. The hind feet are webbed and flattened into broad flippers, and the fore feet are small. The sea otter is the only carnivore with four incisor teeth in its lower jaw; it also has unique cheek teeth. The molars are broad, flat, and well adapted to crushing shells of crustaceans, snails, sea urchins, and mussels.

Sea otters are active during the daytime and are sometimes gregarious, but not migratory. Generally they swim and float on their backs within a kilometer of land, swimming belly down only when in a hurry. Sea otters usually spend the night in kelp beds and lie under strands of kelp to avoid drifting while sleeping. Sometimes they sleep with their hands over their eyes. No territorial aggressiveness has ever been noted even during the breeding season.

Sea urchins, mollusks, crabs, and fish are obtained by diving to depths seldom more than 40 meters. The sea otter floats on its back while eating and uses its chest as a "lunch counter." This is one of the few mammals that makes use of a tool: while floating on its back, it places a rock on its chest; it then uses the rock as an anvil for breaking the shells of mussels, clams, and large sea snails in order to obtain the soft internal parts. Sea otters require a great deal of food and must eat about one-fourth their body weight every day.

Sea otters apparently begin to breed when about three years old, and females breed approximately every other year. Courtship and mating take place in the water. The gestation period is eight to nine months as far as is known, and the single pup may be born at any season. Compared to most carnivores, the sea otter pup is born in an advanced stage of development, as its eyes are open and it has a complete set of milk teeth at birth. The pup weighs from 1.4 to 2.3 kg. at birth and nurses for about a year, although it begins to take soft food from the mother a few weeks after birth. The young is carried, nursed, and groomed on its mother's chest as she swims on her back.

Sea otters differ from most marine animals in that they lack an insulating subcutaneous layer of fat. For protection against the cold water, they depend entirely on a layer of air trapped among their long, soft fibers of hair. If the hair becomes soiled, it loses its insulating qualities. The underfur is very dense and about 25 mm. long. It is protected by a scant coat of guard hairs, which are usually plucked when the fur is made ready for sale. Sea otter skins have usually been the most expensive of all furs and were often used by royalty.

CIVETS, GENETS, LINSANGS, MONGOOSES, AND FOSSAS; MUSKEJAATKATTE, FUNGO, URALAWA, TENGGALONG, MUSANGS (native names).

THIS FAMILY of 37 genera and approximately 75 species occurs in southern Europe (*Genetta genetta*), Africa, Madagascar, and Asia, including Indonesia and the Philippines. Mongooses are essentially African in distribution. *Herpestes* is the only genus occurring naturally in Asia, whereas civets (including palm civets) are widely distributed throughout the range of the family. Certain members of the family Viverridae have been introduced in various areas—*Paguma* in Japan and *Herpestes* in Hawaii and the West Indies. Viverrids are essentially forest inhabitants, but they also live in dense brush and thick grass.

These are the characteristic small and medium-sized carnivores of the Old World. The length of the head and body is 170 to almost 975 mm.; the length of the tail is 120 to 900 mm.; and adult specimens weigh less than 0.5 kg. to approximately 13 kg. Dwarf mongooses (*Helogale*) are the smallest members of the family and binturongs (*Arctictis*) are the largest. Viverrids have a variety of striped, spotted, and uniform color patterns, and the tail is banded or ringed in a number of genera. One genus (*Arctictis*) has a truly prehensile tail. Considerable structural variation appears in this family; some, particularly the fossa (*Cryptoprocta*) of Madagascar, are so cat-like that they have been placed in the family Felidae by some authors. The body is long and sinewy, with short legs and generally a long, bushy tail. The head is elongate and the muzzle is pointed. The first digit on the fore foot and hind foot may be reduced or lacking; the digital formula (the number of digits on the fore foot followed by the number of digits on the hind foot) is 5/5, 5/4, or 4/4. The claws are retractile or non-retractile.

Female viverrids generally have one, two, or three pairs of mammae (usually two or three pairs) located on the abdomen. A baculum is present in males. Most viverrids have scent glands in the anal region which secrete a strong-smelling fluid; in mongooses and some other members of this family, these glands open into a pouch or sac-like depression outside the anus proper in which the secretion is stored.

The second lower incisor is raised above the level of the first and third, the canines are elongate, the premolars number 3/3 or 4/4, and the molars number 1/1 or 2/2. The carnassials are developed. The following dental formula prevails: i 3/3, c 1/1, pm 3-4/3-4, m 1-2/1-2 = 32 (*Cryptoprocta*) to 40 (sometimes 42—*Rhynchogale*). The skull is usually long and flattened.

Many of the 37 genera are not well known. The members of this family are nocturnal or diurnal, and they shelter in any convenient retreat, usually a hole in a tree, a tangle of vines, ground cover, a cave or crevice, or a burrow. A few species dig their own burrows. Those species living near man sometimes seek refuge under the rafters or in the drains of houses. Viverrids are solitary or live in pairs or groups. Several genera (*Cynictis;* perhaps *Paracynictis* to some extent; and *Suricata*) live in colonies in ground burrows, an unusual occurrence among carnivorous or even partly carnivorous mammals. A number of genera of mongooses associate in bands and take refuge as a group in any convenient shelter. Those viverrids that walk on their digits (such as *Genetta*) have a gait described as "a waltzing trot," whereas the members of this family that walk on the sole, with the heel touching the ground (such as *Arctictis*), have a bear-like shuffle. Many genera are agile and extremely graceful in their movements. A number of species are skillful climbers; some viverrids apparently spend most of their lives in trees. Some genera take to water readily and swim well; three genera, *Osbornictis* and *Atilax* from Africa, and *Cynogale* from southeastern Asia, are semiaquatic.

Viverrids may fight when cornered. Nearly all the members of this family discharge a nauseous-smelling fluid from the anal scent glands as a defensive measure. The conspicuous patterns of pelage in some genera have been interpreted as a warning that the fetid anal gland secretion is present. A similar color pattern is associated with certain members of the Mustelidae. The secretion of these glands, when rubbed on various objects, also is recognized by other individuals of the same species.

Viverrids seek their prey in trees and on the ground, either by stalking it or pouncing upon it from a hiding place. These mammals eat small vertebrates and various invertebrates and occasionally consume vegetable matter such as fruits, bulbs, or nuts. Carrion is eaten by some forms. Sight, hearing, and smell are acute.

The breeding season is in the spring, summer, or throughout the year, with a number of genera having two litters in a year. The gestation period is known for only a few forms; in *Herpestes* it is approximately 60 days. From one to six offspring are born blind but haired. The age at which sexual maturity is attained is not known. Most forms probably live from 5 to 15 years in the wild.

The secretion of the scent glands, known as civet, is obtained from several genera (*Civettictis, Viverra,* and *Viverricula*) for both perfumery and medicinal purposes. Viverrids occasionally kill poultry but also prey on rodents. Mongooses, particularly members of the genus *Herpestes*, have been introduced into several areas to check the numbers of rodents and venomous snakes. Such introductions, however, generally have not proven beneficial, as the mongooses quickly multiply and destroy many desirable forms of mammal and bird life. Certain members of the family Viverridae are tamed and kept to extract the musky scent. They may also be kept as pets.

The geological range of this family is the upper Eocene to the Recent in Europe, the lower Pliocene to the Recent in Asia, and the Recent in Africa and Madagascar. Typical viverrids are similar to an extinct group of mammals, the miacids, and early fossil viverrids are difficult to distinguish from the miacids.

African Linsang (*Poiana richardsoni*), photo from *Proc. Zool. Soc. London.*

AFRICAN LINSANGS; OYAN.

THE SINGLE SPECIES, *P. richardsoni*, inhabits West Africa and the island of Fernando Po. It is known from Sierre Leone, Liberia, the French Cameroons, and the Congo. The generic name refers to the last part of the name "Fernando Po."

The length of the head and body is about 330 mm., and the length of the tail is about 380 mm. The general color effect is light brownish gray to rusty yellow; dark brown to black spots and rings are present. Some individuals have alternating broad and narrow black bands on the tail, whereas others have only the broad bands. This genus differs from the Asiatic linsangs in that the spots are smaller and show no tendency to run into bands or stripes, except in the region of the head and shoulder. It also differs from them and resembles the genets (*Genetta*) in having a narrow bare line on the sole of each hind foot. *Poiana* is distinguished from *Genetta* by dental features.

The linsang of Africa is a forest animal, resting during the day in clumps of thick tangled vines and moving about and feeding at night. The diet is assumed to be omnivorous.

A lactating female has been noted in October. The number of young per litter is usually two or three, and, like many other members of the family Viverridae, the African linsang may have two litters per year. Practically nothing has been published regarding the specific habits and biology of this rare animal.

The following information has been given to us by Dr. Hans Jurg Kuhn. In the Liberian hinterland natives make medicine bags from the skins of these animals. The diet includes cola-nuts, insects, young birds, and plant material. *Poiana* builds round nests of green material in which several animals sleep for a few days, then they move on and build a new nest. The nests are at least 2 meters from the ground, usually higher. Although it is recorded in the literature that these animals sleep in abandoned nests of squirrels, reliable hunters say that the reverse is true, i.e., squirrels sleep in abandoned nests of *Poiana*.

Genet (*Genetta tigrina*), photo by John Markham.

GENETS; MUSKEJAATKATTE, GINSTKATZE, GINE-
TAS, GENETKATTEN.

THIS GENUS of about six species inhabits most of
Africa except the Sahara Desert, Israel and Arabia,
and western Europe. Only one species, *G. genetta*, is
found in the latter areas; the other species are confined to Africa. Genets frequent forests, dense brush,
and thick grass.

The length of the head and body is usually 420 to
580 mm., and the length of the tail is 390 to 530 mm.
The weight is usually 1 to 2 kg. Coloration is variable, but the body color is generally grayish or yellowish with brown or black spots and blotches on the
sides, tending to be arranged in rows. A row of black
erectile hairs is usually present along the middle of
the back, and the lower parts of the legs are gray or
black. The tail has black and white rings of about the
same width. Melanistic individuals seem to be fairly
common. Genets are long-bodied and short-legged
animals with pointed snouts; prominent, rounded
ears; short and curved retractile claws; and soft,
dense hair.

Genets are active at night, usually spending the
day in a rock crevice, in a burrow excavated by some
other animal, in a hollow tree, or on a large branch—
in fact, in any shelter affording sufficient protection
against attack. They seem to return daily to the same
shelter and travel singly or in pairs.

These animals climb trees to prey on nesting and
roosting birds, but much of their prey is caught on
the ground. They are silent and stealthy hunters;
when stalking prey, they crouch until the body and
tail seem to glide along the ground. At the same time,
the body seems to lengthen. Genets can go through
any opening the head can enter because of the slender
and loosely jointed body. The diet consists of any
small animals that can be captured, including rodents,
birds, reptiles, and insects. Genets sometimes destroy game birds and poultry. They have the ability
to emit a musky-smelling fluid from their anal glands.

The litter size is usually two or three, and two litters are born each year, at least in South Africa—
one in the spring and one in the fall. One individual
lived in the London Zoo for 34 years; life span in the
wild is probably ten years or less. Females have two
pairs of abdominal mammae.

The type species of the genus is *G. genetta* (Linnaeus). *Paragenetta*, Kuhn, 1960, was proposed as a
subgenus to contain a remarkable new species, *G.
lehmanni*, from Liberia.

Lesser Oriental Civet (*Viverricula indica*), photo by Ernest P. Walker.

LESSER ORIENTAL CIVETS, RASSES; MASHK-BILLA, URALAWA (native names).

THE SINGLE SPECIES, *V. indica*, is found in India, Ceylon, and through southern China and southeastern Asia, to Sumatra, Java, and Bali. It has been introduced to Socotra, the Comoro Islands, the Philippines, and Madagascar by natives probably for the production of civet.

The length of the head and body is 450 to 630 mm.; the length of the tail is 300 to 430 mm.; and the weight is usually 2 to 4 kg. The fur is harsh, rather coarse, and loose. The body color is buffy, brownish, or grayish, and the feet are black. Small spots are present on the forequarters, and larger spots, tending to run into longitudinal lines, are present on the flanks. There are six to eight dark stripes on the back, and the tail is ringed black and white by six to nine rings of each color.

These civets are distinguished from the Oriental civets (*Viverra*) by their smaller size, by the absence of the dorsal crest of erectile hairs, and by the insertion of the ears, the inner edges of which are set closer together on the forehead than in *Viverra*. The muzzle is also shorter and more pointed. Internally, these two genera differ in skull and dental features.

Rasses are usually solitary but occasionally associate in pairs. They are nocturnal in the more heavily populated areas but may be seen hunting in the daytime in the wilder jungle. These animals usually seek shelter in thick clumps of vegetation. They seldom take refuge in a tree, even when pursued by dogs. Instead they try to escape by dodging and twisting through the underbrush.

Rasses eat small vertebrates, insects and their grubs, and fruits and roots. They are fond of carrion and are often attracted by dead animals.

They breed throughout the year in Ceylon. The two to five young are born in a shelter on the ground.

Rasses are kept in captivity by the natives for the purpose of extracting the civet that is secreted and retained in sacs close to the genitals in both sexes. The removal of this secretion is accomplished by scraping the inside of the sac with a spoon-like implement. In India this secretion is used as a perfume to flavor the tobacco that is smoked by the natives.

The specific names *rasse* and *malaccensis* have been used but are considered to be synonyms of *indica*.

1227

Congo Water Civet (*Osbornictis piscivora*), photo from *Bull. Amer. Mus. Nat. Hist.*

CONGO WATER CIVETS.

THE SINGLE SPECIES, *O. piscivora*, is known only from the Congo of Africa. There are two specimens in the American Museum of Natural History in New York: one taken in a stream that was overflowing through a forest, and another obtained from a native; there are several specimens in the Musée de l'Afrique Centrale, Tervuren, Belgium. This animal has never been captured alive.

The length of the head and body is about 500 mm., and the length of the tail is about 415 mm. This animal is chestnut-red to dull red in body color, with a black tail. There is a pair of elongated white spots between the eyes, and the front and sides of the muzzle and the sides of the head below the eyes are whitish. Black spots and bands are absent, and the tail is not ringed. The pelage is long and dense, especially on the tail. The palms and soles are bare, not furred as in *Genetta* and other related genera. This genus may be distinguished by its color pattern. The skull is long and lightly built, and the teeth are relatively small and weak.

Apparently these animals lead a semiaquatic life and feed upon fish to some extent. Practically nothing is known of them in the wild, but the following characters are believed to be correlated with their habits: small size of the rhinarium and absence of a median partition, naked palms and soles, shortened rostrum, comparatively slender and light bones.

Oriental Civet (*Viverra tangalunga*), photo by Ernest P. Walker.

ORIENTAL CIVETS; CIVET KATTEN, TĚNGGALONG (native name).

THE THREE SPECIES and their distribution are as follows: *V. zibetha*, southern China, Nepal, Assam, and eastward to the Malay Peninsula; *V. megaspila*, parts of India and the Malay Peninsula; *V. tangalunga*, the East Indies and the Philippines. They occur in a variety of habitats.

The length of the head and body is 585 to 838 mm.; the length of the tail is 315 to 482 mm.; and the weight of *V. zibetha*, the largest species of the genus, is usually 7 to 11 kg. The fur is long and loose, particularly the winter coat. It is usually elongated in the median line of the body, forming a low crest or mane. The color pattern of the body is composed of black spots on a grayish or tawny ground color, and the sides of the neck and throat are marked with black and white stripes—usually three black and two white collars. The crest is marked by a black spinal stripe which runs from the shoulders to the tail, and the tail is banded or ringed black and white. The feet are black. In two of the species of this genus (*V. zibetha* and *V. tangalunga*), the third and fourth digits of the fore feet are provided with lobes of skin which act as protective sheaths for the retractile claws.

This genus is distinguished from the lesser Oriental civet (*Viverricula*) by its larger size, by the presence of a dorsal crest of erectile hairs, and by the insertion of the ears, the inner edges of which are set farther apart on the forehead.

Oriental civets are generally solitary, usually nocturnal, and stay in the dense cover of forests, brush, or grassland during the day and come out into the open during the night. Like *Viverricula*, they are often found near villages and are common over most of their range. They are mainly terrestrial and often live in holes in the ground dug by other animals. Apparently they can climb readily but seldom seem to do so. Like most civets, they are easily trapped. They are vigorous hunters, killing small mammals, birds, snakes, frogs, insects, and taking eggs, fruits, and some roots. The species *V. zibetha* has been observed fishing in India, and parts of crabs have been found in the stomachs of two animals in China.

Litter size is one to four, usually two to three. The young are born in holes in the ground or in dense vegetation. The life span is about 13 to 15½ years.

This genus is one of the sources of civet, the substance that is used commercially in producing perfume. Civet is also obtained from the genera *Viverricula* and *Civettictis*.

The type species of the genus is *V. zibetha*, Linnaeus. *Moschothera*, Pocock, 1933, is often used as a subgenus for the species *V. megaspila*.

African Civet (*Civettictis civetta*), photo from New York Zoological Society.

AFRICAN CIVETS; SIWETKATTE, LISISI, MPICA-MADHLOTI, NGAWA (native names).

THE SINGLE SPECIES, *C. civetta*, is found in Africa, from Senegal eastward through the central part of the continent to Somaliland and southward to southern Africa. It usually frequents brushy areas.

Head and body length is 670 to 800 mm., and tail length is about 460 mm. The color is black with white or yellowish spots, stripes, and bands. The hair is long and coarse, and that of the tail is thick. The perineal glands under the tail contain the oily scented matter used commercially in making perfume. All the feet have five claws, and the soles are hairy. This animal is distinguished by certain structural features from *Viverra*, the similar genus of Asia.

The African civet is active at night, frequenting dense brush and burrowing during the day. It usually travels singly or in pairs; it is terrestrial but takes to water readily and swims well. Sometimes it takes refuge in a small tree when hunted. "The ordinary call is a low-pitched cough, but when cornered it gives a low deep growl and all the hair on the body stands out" (Hugh Copley, *Small Mammals of Kenya*, [London, 1950], p. 46). It is not particularly aggressive. The diet is usually animal but also includes such vegetable matter as the soft tops of maize stems, fruits, and tubers. Poultry is often taken.

From two to three young form a litter, and there are usually two litters per year.

In Abyssinia, and to a lesser extent in other parts of Africa, the natives keep civets in captivity and remove the musk from them several times a week, an average animal yielding 3 to 4 grams weekly. However, the natives do not raise civets but merely capture wild stock to replenish the supply. In 1934 Africa produced about 2,475 kg. of musk with a value of $200,000; in this same year the United States imported 200 kg. of musk having a value of $9,871. The production of civet musk is an old industry: King Solomon's supply of civet scent came from east Africa.

BANDED, SPOTTED, OR ORIENTAL LINSANGS, TIGER CIVETS; ZIK-CHUM, SULIYU, NAM-LANIAO (native names).

THERE ARE TWO SPECIES: the banded linsang (*P. linsang*) which inhabits Tenasserim, the Malay States, Sumatra, Java, and Borneo; and the spotted linsang (*P. pardicolor*) which inhabits Nepal, Assam, northern Burma, and Indo-China. Apparently both frequent thick forests and jungle growths. They are extremely slender, graceful, and beautiful mammals. (*Pardictis*, Thomas, 1925, for the spotted linsang, is regarded as a subgenus of *Prionodon*.) The type species of the genus is *P. linsang* (Hardwicke).

The length of the head and body is 376 to 431 mm.; the length of the tail is 304 to 355 mm.; and the weight is usually about .75 kg. The claws are retractile; claw sheaths are present on the forepaws, and protective lobes of skin are present on the hind paws. The skull is long, low, and narrow, and the muzzle is narrow and elongate. The fur is short, dense, soft, and has the appearance of and feels like velvet.

In *P. linsang* the ground color varies from whitish gray to brownish gray and becomes creamy on the under parts. The dark pattern consists of four or five broad, transverse, black, or dark-brown bands across the back; there is one large stripe on each side of the neck. The sides of the body and legs are marked with dark spots, and the tail is banded.

On the average, *P. pardicolor* is slightly smaller. Some individuals have a ground color of orange-buff, whereas others are pale brown. Black spots on the upper parts are more or less arranged in longitudinal rows, and the tail has eight to ten dark rings.

The habits and biology of these animals are not well known. They seem to be active mainly at night and are good climbers. The few observations indicate that they prey on birds, probably small mammals, and insects. They live in hollows of trees but are at home on the ground.

Data on reproduction is meager. Apparently they have two litters of two or three young each year. They are said to breed in February and August.

The banded linsang does not seem to have an odor, and none was detected by the senior author when photographing one.

Banded Linsang (*Prionodon linsang*), photo by Ernest P. Walker.

In a letter, Mr. Lim Boo Liat of Malaya says of the banded linsang: "The local Malayan name is 'Musang belang' or 'choreng.' The words 'belang' and 'choreng' mean 'stripes' or 'streaks.' However, the name 'Musang' is used generally by Malayans for the civets. The banded linsang is said to eat birds' eggs, but it probably takes a wide variety of animal food, and parts of a young squirrel have been found in its stomach. Little is known regarding breeding habits, but the aborigines found three young with the mother in a hole under the roots of a large tree. A nest of dried sticks and leaves was built in the burrow. Banded linsangs are also said to build nests in hollow trees above the ground level.

"A captive female obtained by aborigines at first did not offer much of a fight when handled. Food was no problem. She was fed on meat and fish daily; and for delicacies, birds, eggs, and ox-liver were occasionally offered. It was amazing to watch her breaking the egg. She grasped the egg with her fore legs and rolled it backward under her belly; she then sat for about two minutes like a mother hen sitting on eggs, after which she pushed it forward toward the fore legs, started turning the egg, all of a sudden cracking it with one of her fore legs. This female quickly learned to run a wheel, using it between 10 and 11 o'clock in the morning and between 6 and 7 o'clock in the evening. She would run the wheel for a few minutes, rest a few minutes, then run it again."

African Palm Civet (*Nandinia binotata*), photo by Ernest P. Walker.

AFRICAN PALM CIVETS; PALMSIWET.

THE SINGLE SPECIES, *N. binotata*, is found in central and southern Africa, from Senegal and the southern Sudan south to Angola and Southern Rhodesia. It also inhabits the island of Fernando Po.

The length of the head and body is 440 to 570 mm., and the length of the tail is 460 to 620 mm. Coloration is quite variable but is usually grayish or brownish, tinged with buffy or chestnut. Two creamy spots are often present between the shoulders, and obscure dark brown spots are present on the lower back and top of the tail. The tail is somewhat darker than the body; it is the same color above and below, with a variable pattern of black rings. The throat tends to be grayish, and the under parts are grayish, tinged with yellow.

The genus is characterized by short, woolly, but coarse-tipped hair; dull coloration; short and rounded ears; fairly thick tail; short legs with sharp, curved claws adapted for climbing; and skull and dental features.

This animal is arboreal and terrestrial. It is active at night, usually sheltering by day in vine tangles in trees. One individual has been observed leaping from a high branch, then gliding to the ground with legs and tail outstretched to make a perfect four-point landing. It then climbed another tree and repeated the action. Two animals have been heard calling each other at evening in trees "in a small, faint voice, like a kitten mewing" (G. L. Bates, *Proc. Zool. Soc. Lond.*, 1905, p. 75).

The main item in the diet seems to be fruits, but small mammals and birds are also eaten. African palm civets prey on pottos (*Perodicticus*), and a tree-rat (*Oenomys*) was recovered from one stomach and a swamp-rat (*Otomys*) from another.

There are probably two litters per year, with two or three young in each litter. The gestation period is 64 days.

This palm civet is easily tamed and will drink milk in captivity. It is said to be quite clean and to keep houses free of rats, mice, and cockroaches.

Small-toothed Palm Civet (*Arctogalidia trivirgata*), photo by Lim Boo Liat.

SMALL-TOOTHED PALM CIVETS, THREE-STRIPED PALM CIVETS; MUSANG-AKAR, KYOUNG-NA-RWEK-PHYU (native names).

THE SINGLE SPECIES, *A. trivirgata*, is found in Assam, Burma, Indo-China, Thailand, Malaya, Sumatra and numerous small adjacent islands, Java, and Borneo. It is an inhabitant of dense forests and frequents coconut plantations in some areas.

The length of the head and body is 432 to 532 mm.; the length of the tail is 510 to 660 mm.; and the weight is usually 2 to 2.5 kg. The upper parts, proximal part of the tail, and the outside of the limbs are usually tawny, varying from dusky grayish tawny to bright orangish tawny. The head is usually darker and grayer, and the paws and the distal part of the tail are brownish. There is a median white stripe on the muzzle, and three brown or black longitudinal stripes on the back; the median stripe is usually complete and distinct, whereas the laterals may be broken up into spots or almost absent. The undersides are grayish white or creamy buff, with a whitish patch on the chest.

Only the females of this genus possess the civet gland, which is located near the opening of the urinogenital tract. Members of this genus closely resemble *Paradoxurus* in external form and in the length of the legs and of the tail and differ externally in characters of the feet. Internally, the skull differs from that of *Paradoxurus*, and the back teeth are smaller, hence the common name.

These palm civets are arboreal and active at night. Habits are not well known, but they are active climbers and leap from branch to branch with considerable agility. Three animals, representing both sexes, occupied an empty nest of *Ratufa bicolor* in a tree about 20 meters above the ground. The diet consists of fruits and such animals as squirrels.

The young are probably reared in hollow trees; litter size seems to be two or three, and there are probably two litters a year. Mewing calls and light snarls, accompanied by playful leaps and chases, have been noted in a male and female at night in the wild.

Palm Civet (*Paradoxurus hermaphroditus*), photo by Ernest P. Walker.

PALM CIVETS, MUSANGS, TODDY CATS.

THE THREE SPECIES are distributed as follows: *P. hermaphroditus* from Ceylon and India through southern China, southeastern Asia, and the East Indies to the Philippines; *P. jerdoni* from southern India; and *P. zeylonensis* from Ceylon.

The length of the head and body is 432 to 710 mm.; the length of the tail is 406 to 660 mm.; and the weight is 1.5 to 4.5 kg., averaging about 2.5 kg. The ground color is grayish to brownish but is often almost entirely masked by the black tips of the guard hairs. There is a definite pattern of dorsal stripes and lateral spots, at least in the new coat, but this is some-times concealed by the long black hairs. The pattern is most plainly shown in the species *P. hermaphroditus*, where it consists of longitudinal stripes on the back and spots on the shoulders, sides, thighs, and sometimes on the base of the tail. A pattern may also be present on the head of this species; it consists of white patches with a white band across the forehead.

The species *P. hermaphroditus* can always be distinguished from *P. jerdoni* and *P. zeylonensis* by the backward direction of the hairs on the neck. In the other species the hairs on the neck grow forward from the shoulders to the head. The genus *Paradoxurus* differs from *Arctogalidia* in characters of the feet, skull, and teeth; and from *Paguma* in its pattern of stripes and spots and characters of the skull and teeth.

Musangs are nocturnal; they are expert climbers and spend most of their time in trees, where they utilize cavities or secluded nooks. They are often found about human habitations, probably because of the rats and mice around dwellings. Under such conditions they shelter in thatched roofs and in dry drain tiles and pipes. Small vertebrates, insects, fruits, and seeds are eaten. They are fond of the palm juice or "toddy" collected by the natives—thus one of the vernacular names.

At least one species (*P. hermaphroditus*) emits an extremely potent discharge from its anal glands, which is used only as a last resort when threatened by a predator.

Litters of two to four young are born throughout the year, and the female probably gives birth to more than one litter a year.

The type species of the genus is *P. hermaphroditus* (Pallas).

Masked Palm Civet (*Paguma larvata*), photo from New York Zoological Society.

MASKED PALM CIVETS, HIMALAYAN PALM CIVETS.

THERE SEEMS TO BE just one species, *P. larvata*, which is found in China and from Kashmir eastward to Burma, southeastern Asia, Sumatra, and Borneo. It is also found on Formosa, Hainan, and the Andaman Islands and has been introduced in Japan. This species frequents forests and brush.

The length of the head and body is 508 to 762 mm.; the length of the tail is usually 508 to 636 mm.; and the weight is usually 3.6 to 5 kg. In the facial region there is generally a mask which consists of a median white stripe from the top of the head to the nose, a white mark below each eye, and a white mark above each eye extending to the base of the ear and below. The general color is gray, gray tinged with buff, orange, or yellowish red. There are no stripes or spots on the body, and no spots or bands on the tail. The distal part of the tail may be darker than the basal part, and the feet are blackish. This genus differs externally from *Paradoxurus* and *Arctogalidia* in the absence of the striping and spotting.

This is another viverrid whose habits are not well known. It is arboreal and omnivorous, feeding on small vertebrates, probably insects, and fruits and roots. In Tenasserim it is reported to be a great ratter and does not destroy poultry. Like the palm civets of the genus *Paradoxurus*, this animal has an extremely potent anal-gland secretion which it uses to ward off predators. The conspicuously marked head has been interpreted as warning coloration.

It is reported to raise its young in tree holes, at least in Nepal, and to have litters of three or four young. Young animals born and raised in captivity differed from their parents in having the facial pattern less emphasized, and in having a grayer general body color, with white undersides. They also exhibited on the back and sides faint traces of the pattern characteristic of *Paradoxurus*. These young almost equaled their parents in size at the age of three months.

Celebes Palm Civet (*Macrogalidia musschenbroeki*), photo by Edgar Wenzel of mounted specimen in Natural History Museum, Leiden, Holland.

CELEBES PALM CIVETS.

THE SINGLE SPECIES, *M. musschenbroecki*, is known only from the island of Celebes. It formerly occurred throughout the island but is now confined to the northeastern part. Apparently this is either a rare animal or its principal haunts have not been found. Specimens have been collected in wooded areas and are in the Netherlands Academy of Science at Amsterdam, the Leyden Museum, the Dresden Museum, and the British Museum (Natural History).

Head and body length is about 1 meter, and tail length is about 0.6 meter. The color of the upper parts is light brownish chestnut to dark brown; the cheeks and a patch above the eye are usually buffy or grayish. The under parts range from fulvous to whitish, with a reddish breast. Faint brown spots and bands are usually present on the sides and lower back, and the tail is ringed with dark and pale brown. The tail has more bands than *Arctogalidia* or *Paradoxurus*. Other distinguishing characters are short, close fur; a whorl in the neck with the hairs directed forward; and features of the teeth and skull.

The natural history and habits of this animal are not well known. It feeds on rats and such fruits as papayas, and probably on other small animals and vegetable matter. Subfossil remains of this species found in southern Celebes indicates that it formerly ranged throughout most of the island.

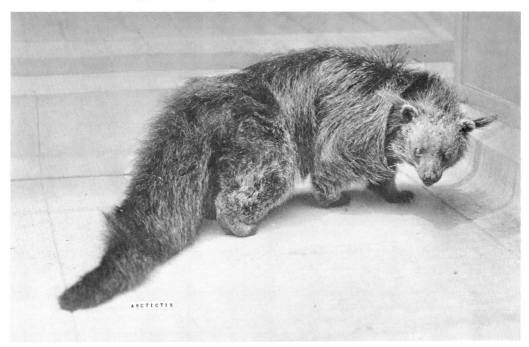

Binturong (*Arctictis binturong*), photo from New York Zoological Society.

BINTURONGS.

THE SINGLE SPECIES, *A. binturong*, is found in Burma, Indochina, Thailand, the Malay States, Sumatra, Java, Borneo, and Palawan, and also may possibly occur in Assam, Bhutan, Nepal, and Sikkim. It lives in dense forests and is nowhere abundant.

The length of the head and body is 610 to 965 mm.; the length of the tail is 560 to 890 mm.; and the weight is usually 9 to 14 kg. The fur is long and coarse, that on the tail is longer than on the body. The hairs are black and lustrous, often with gray, fulvous, or buff tips. The head is finely speckled with gray and buff, and the edges of the ears and whiskers are white. The ears have long hairs on the backs that project beyond the tips and produce a fringed or tufted effect. The tail is particularly muscular at the base and prehensile at the tip. The only other carnivore with a truly prehensile tail is the kinkajou (*Potos flavus*), which the binturong resembles somewhat in habits.

This genus can be distinguished from all other members of its family (*Viverridae*) by the long ear tufts and by the prehensile nature of the long, bushy tail. Casual observation of this animal may fail to reveal its relationships with other *Viverridae*, but study of its anatomy discloses that it possesses essentially the same structure and is merely a peculiarly specialized form.

When resting, the binturong usually lies curled up with the head tucked under the tail. It is mainly arboreal and nocturnal. It has never been observed to leap; rather, it progresses slowly but skillfully, using the tail as an extra hand. Its movements, at least during daylight hours, are rather slow and cautious, the tail slowly uncoiling from the last support as the animal moves carefully forward. When moving about, it may periodically utter a series of low grunts or a hissing noise, and it growls fiercely when irritated.

The diet probably consists mainly of fruits and other plant matter, but carrion is also consumed.

Breeding habits and gestation period are not known. Females have two pairs of mammae.

The binturong is sometimes kept as a pet. It is said to be easily domesticated, to become quite affectionate, and to follow its master like a dog. The Chinese use this animal for medicinal purposes. It is the only mammal in the Old World that has a prehensile tail, but it does not use it as efficiently as many of the American mammals that have such tails.

Fanaloka (*Fossa fossa*), photo from U.S. National Zoological Park.

FANALOKAS, FOSSANES, MALAGASY CIVETS.

THE SINGLE SPECIES, *F. fossa*, is found only on the island of Madagascar. It is given special protection under the London Convention of 1933.

The length of the head and body is about 407 mm., and the length of the tail is about 206 mm. The ground color is grayish, washed with reddish; there are four rows of black spots on each side of the back and a few black spots on the backs of the thighs. These spots may merge to form stripes, and the gray tail is banded with brown. The under parts are grayish or whitish and more or less obscurely spotted.

The limbs are slender, perhaps adapted for running, and scent pouches are lacking; it is completely digitigrade. The voice ranges from a "reedy" growl to a loud shriek.

The fact that the generic name of this animal is the same as the vernacular name of another Madagascar mammal, the fossa (*Cryptoprocta*), should not lead to confusion, as they are distinctly different animals.

The fanaloka is not well known. It eats flesh and fruit in captivity, being especially fond of bananas, and is known to feed on insects, lizards, birds, mice, and small tenrecs in the wild. It is strictly nocturnal.

Thirteen specimens were obtained by the Franco-Anglo-American Zoological Mission of 1929 to 1931.

Banded Palm Civet (*Hemigalus derbyanus*), photo of mounted specimen in the Field Museum of Natural History. Insets: Bottom of left hind foot and fore foot, photos from *Proc. Zool. Soc. London.*

Banded Palm Civets; Hardwick's Civets.

The single species, *H. derbyanus*, inhabits Tenasserim, the Malay Peninsula, Sumatra, some of the islands west of Sumatra, and Borneo.

The length of the head and body is 410 to 510 mm., and the length of the tail is 255 to 383 mm. Weight is usually 1.75 to 3 kg. On the head there is a narrow, median dark streak extending from the nose to the nape, and on each side of this there is a broader dark stripe which encircles the eye and passes backward over the base of the ear. Two broad stripes, sometimes more or less broken into shorter stripes or spots, run backward from the neck and curve downward to the elbow. Behind these are two shorter stripes. The back behind the shoulders is marked with four or five broad transverse stripes separated by pale, usually narrower spaces, and there are two imperfect stripes at the base of the tail. The ground color is whitish to orange-buff, usually lighter and more buffy below, and the tail is usually black.

The hair on the back of the neck is reversed in that the tips of the hairs point forward. The five-toed feet have strongly curved claws that are retractile like those of cats. Small scent glands are present. This genus differs externally from *Diplogale* in the color pattern, and from *Chrotogale* by the reversed direction of the hairs of the neck. It differs internally from both genera in skull and dental features.

The stomach contents of an individual collected in Borneo consisted of the remains of worms and some ants. A female pregnant with one embryo has been noted in February in Borneo.

Although almost nothing has been recorded regarding their habits, they are supposed to be similar to those of the palm civets or toddy cats (*Paradoxurus* and *Paguma*). (Also see *Diplogale*.)

Owston's Civet (*Chrotogale owstoni*), photo from *Field Mus. Nat. Hist. Pub.*, "Mammals of the Kelley-Roosevelt and Delacour Asiatic Expeditions," W. H. Osgood.

OWSTON'S PALM CIVETS.

THE SINGLE SPECIES, *C. owstoni*, is known from only about 15 specimens taken in Tonkin and Laos in Indo-China.

Head and body length is 508 to 635 mm., and the length of the tail is 381 to 482 mm. The body and base of the tail have alternating and sharply contrasting dark and light transverse bands, and longitudinal stripes are present on the neck. The pattern of stripes and bands resembles that of *Hemigalus*, but it is supplemented by black spots on the sides of the neck, the forelimbs and thighs, and the flanks. Four seems to be the maximum number of dorsal bands. It has been suggested that this striking pattern serves as warning coloration, as this species is believed to possess a particularly foul-smelling anal-gland secretion. The under parts are pale buffy, and a narrow orange mid-ventral line runs from the chest to the inguinal region. The terminal two-thirds of the tail are completely black. *Chrotogale* is distinguished structurally from similar genera by dental and skull characters.

Form and markings are strikingly like those of *Hemigalus*, but the considerable difference in the skulls of the two indicates a greater difference than might at first be suspected from external appearance.

The incisor teeth are remarkable in that they are broad, close set, and arranged in practically a semicircle, a type unique among carnivores and only approached in certain of the marsupials. The other teeth and the skull are also peculiar and certainly indicate habits and a mode of life different from that of other genera in the family *Viverridae*.

Notes on habits and natural history are meager. (One investigator found the stomachs of two specimens to contain earthworms.)

The 15 specimens are preserved in the following museums: the Paris Museum, the British Museum of Natural History, and the Field Museum of Natural History.

Bornean Mongoose (*Diplogale hosei*), photo from *Proc. Zool. Soc. London.*

BORNEAN MONGOOSES, HOSE'S PALM CIVETS.

THE SINGLE SPECIES, *D. hosei*, is known only from Borneo. It seems to be an inhabitant of mountains, as all the records are from elevations of 600 to 1,200 meters.

The length of the head and body is about 0.6 meter, and the length of the tail is about 0.3 meter. Coloration is dark brown or black above, and grayish, yellowish white, or slightly rufescent below. The ears are thinly haired and white inside. A buffy-gray patch extends from above the eye to the cheek and terminates where it meets the white of the lips and throat. The inner sides of the limbs near the body are grayish, while the remainder of each limb is black. The tail is not banded; it is dark throughout.

This animal was originally described as *Hemigalus hosei*. Because of differences in the skull and teeth and the essential difference in the pattern of coloration between this species and the type species of the genus *Hemigalus*, *H. derbyanus*, the genus *Diplogale* was formed for the species *hosei*.

It is assumed that Hose's palm civet climbs readily and is omnivorous. This is another viverrid whose natural history and habits are practically unknown. Only a few specimens have been collected. These are in the Sarawak Museum, the British Museum (Natural History), and the Field Museum of Natural History.

Otter Civet (*Cynogale bennetti*), photo of mounted specimen in Ipswich Museum.

OTTER CIVETS.

THE SINGLE SPECIES, *C. bennetti*, is found in Indo-China, the Malay States, Sumatra, and Borneo, usually near rivers and swampy areas.

The length of the head and body is 575 to 675 mm., and the length of the tail is 130 to 205 mm. The weight is usually 3 to 5 kg. The form is somewhat like that of the otter (*Lutra*). The underfur is close, soft, and short, pale buff near the skin, shading to dark brown or almost black at the tips. The longer, coarser guard hairs usually are partially gray which gives a frosted or speckled effect on the head and body. The lower side of the body is lighter brown and not speckled with gray. The whiskers are remarkably long and plentiful; those on the snout are fairly long, but those on a patch under the ear are the longest. The newly born young lack dorsal speckling; they have some gray on the forehead and ears, and two longitudinal stripes down the sides of the neck extending under the throat.

Because of the deepening and expansion of the upper lip, the rhinarium occupies a horizontal position with the nostrils opening upward on top of the muzzle. The nostrils can be closed by flaps, an adaptation for aquatic life. The ears can also be closed. Although the webs on the feet do not extend farther toward the tips of the digits than in such genera as *Paradoxurus*, they are quite broad, and the fingers are capable of considerable flexion. A glandular area, merely three pores in the skin, is located near the genitals and secretes a mild scent material. The premolar teeth are elongated and sharp, adapted for capturing and holding prey, while the molars are broad and flat for crushing.

This animal feeds on fish, crustacea, perhaps mollusks, small mammals, birds, and fruits. The shortness and absence of special muscular power in the tail, and the scant development of the webs between the fingers and toes suggest that the otter civet is probably a slow swimmer and cannot turn quickly in the water. It probably captures aquatic prey after they have taken shelter from the chase, and some mammals and birds as they come to drink. It cannot be seen by its prey because it is submerged with only the tip of the nose exposed above the surface of the water. The otter civet can climb well and, when chased by dogs, often takes refuge in a tree rather than in water. It usually carries its head and tail low and arches its back while walking.

The females possess four mammae. There are records of pregnant females with two and three embryos. Young still with the mother have been noted in May in Borneo.

Falanouc (*Eupleres goudotii*), photo of mounted specimen in Field Museum of Natural History.

SMALL-TOOTHED MONGOOSES, FALANOUCS; AM-BOA-LAOLO, FANALOKA (native names).

TWO SPECIES, differing externally in size and color, are found on Madagascar.

E. goudotii has a head and body length of 600 to 700 mm., and is fawn-colored above and lighter below; the other species, *E. major*, has a head and body length of 800 to 900 mm., a tail length of 200 to 300 mm., and the males are brownish and the females grayish. The young have black stripes across the shoulders. The fur is woolly and soft, made up of a dense underfur and longer guard hairs. In both species the tail is covered by rather long hairs that give it almost a bushy appearance.

Falanoucs have pointed muzzles, narrow and elongate heads, and short, conical teeth. They resemble civets in some structural features and mongooses in others. The small teeth are similar to each other and resemble those of insectivores rather than carnivores. Indeed, for some time the animal was classified with the insectivores before its somewhat obscure relationship with the mongooses was detected. This genus does not possess a perineal scent-pouch or an anal sac. The claws are relatively long and not retractile, or only imperfectly so. The feet are peculiar in the comparatively large size and low position of the great toe and thumb.

Little has been recorded regarding the habits of these animals. They rest during the daytime in rock crevices and in burrows, according to natives, and are active at dusk and through the night. A skipping gait has been reported for *E. goudotii*. Falanoucs apparently dig for some of their food, which consists of such items as adult and larval insects and other invertebrates, lizards, and frogs, and probably birds and small mammals.

Certain natives claim that they can capture *E. goudotii* by placing rice on a piece of white cloth in which the nails of the animal will become entangled. The hair of the tail of this species is used by the southeastern tribes for ornaments.

The type species of the genus is *E. goudotii*, Doyère.

Madagascar Ring-tailed Mongoose (*Galidia elegans*), photo by Howard E. Uible.

MADAGASCAR RING-TAILED MONGOOSES; VONTSIRA AND HALAZA (native names).

THE SINGLE SPECIES, *G. elegans*, is found on the island of Madagascar.

Head and body length is about 380 mm., and tail length is about 305 mm.

Coloration is dark chestnut brown, and the tail is ringed with dark brown and black.

These animals have some structural features of civets and some of mongooses. The feet differ from those of *Galidictis* in having shorter digits that are more fully webbed and shorter claws. The soles of the feet are more hairy and the lower canine teeth are smaller. The second upper premolar is very small, which, with the rings on the tail, distinguishes *Galidia* from *Salanoia*. A scent gland closely associated with the external genitalia has been found in the females but has not been detected in the males. This is based on only two dissections, however.

Little appears to be recorded on the habits of members of this genus. They are active during the day, are graceful, and able to climb readily. They are usually solitary or sometimes travel in pairs. They seek ground cover when surprised in a tree. They make a plaintive, whining sound that appears to be a call of fright or alarm.

Their food consists of a variety of prey including insects, lizards and other reptiles, birds, and probably small mammals.

They are either very rare or the center of their abundance has not been found.

The tribes of the Southeast and extreme South (Antaisaka, Antanosy, Antandroy) use the hair of the tails in a body ornament called "Kelibotsike" or "Volombotsira."

Madagascar Broad-striped Mongoose (*Galidictis striata*), photo from *Zoologie de Madagascar*, Grandidier et Petit.

MADAGASCAR BROAD-STRIPED MONGOOSES; VONT-SIRAFOTSY (*G. striata*), BAKIAKA BETANIMENA OR BAKIAKA BELEMBOKA (*G. fasciata*) (native names).

THE TWO SPECIES, *G. striata* and *G. fasciata*, inhabit Madagascar.

Head and body length is about 355 mm., and the tail length is about 330 mm. The body color is pale brown or grayish. In *G. striata* there are usually five longitudinal black bands or stripes on the back and sides, and the tail is whitish; in *G. fasciata* there are usually eight to ten stripes and the tail is bay-colored and somewhat bushy.

This genus differs from the other viverrids in the color pattern, skull features, and dental characters. The feet differ from those of *Galidia* in having longer digits, not as fully webbed, and in the longer claws.

A scent-pouch is present in *Galidictis* females.

Beddard, in reporting upon his dissection of *Galidictis striata*, mentions finding a complete double uterus in the one female he examined. This is unique among the carnivores. He also found an area of considerably enlarged papillae near the tip of the tongue in this species.

Little is known about these endemic Madagascar carnivores. The tail is bristled when the animals are angry. The diet is assumed to be omnivorous. One individual of the species *G. striata* was encountered at night in a dry forest while it was digging up the bodies of skinned birds buried near a camp.

Young *G. vittata* are said to tame readily, to follow their master, and even to sleep in his lap.

The type species of the genus is *G. striata*, I. Geoffroy.

Madagascar Narrow-striped Mongoose (*Mungotictis substriatus*); Inset: Head (*M. substriatus*); photos by Don Davis.

MADAGASCAR NARROW-STRIPED MONGOOSES.

THE TWO SPECIES, *M. lineatus* and *M. substriatus*, inhabit Madagascar.

T. Haltenorth tells us (in correspondence) that *M. substriatus* has a head and body length of about 350 mm., and a tail length about the same. The species *M. lineatus* has a pale gray ground color on the back and sides; the head is darker; the legs, throat, and belly are yellowish buff; and the tail is grayish to black. There are eight narrow but conspicuous blackish-brown stripes, six of which extend to the head, and in addition a faint mid-dorsal stripe and a faint stripe on each side below the fourth prominent stripe, or 11 stripes in all. In *M. substriatus* the ground color is dark olive-gray and the legs, feet, and under parts are yellowish buff. There are also narrow reddish-brown stripes, longitudinal as in *M. lineatus*, but only ten in number. These are inconspicuous and none extend in front of the shoulder, and the third from the top is short. The feet are similar to those of *Galidictis*, except that the heel is naked and not hairy. It is not known if a scent-pouch is present or absent.

In 1848 Gray ("Description of a New Species of *Galidictis* from Madagascar," *Proc. Zool. Soc. London*, pt. 16, pg. 22) described the habits of *Galidictis vittatus* (= *Mungotictis lineatus*) in captivity in the following manner: "Its chief food was uncooked meat, but it preferred raw eggs above all other articles when they could be procured. Its method of breaking them was not a little amusing: On receiving one it would roll it towards a projecting timber or gun-slide; then, laying down on its side, the little creature would grasp the egg with all its feet and throw it by a sudden jerk, repeating the attempt until the contents were obtained. Turtles' eggs being so soft and rich were always eagerly sought by it. It was very irascible while feeding, and would attack those who interfered with it at such a time, although at others it delighted in being fondled, and would play like a kitten with those it knew. The habits of this interesting animal were not nocturnal."

The type species of the genus is *M. lineatus*, Pocock.

Madagascar Brown-tailed Mongoose (*Salanoia unicolor*), photo of mounted specimen in Field Museum of Natural History.

MADAGASCAR BROWN-TAILED MONGOOSES; SALANO AND TABIBOALA (native names).

THE TWO SPECIES, *S. unicolor* and *S. olivacea*, are known from Madagascar.

The length of the head and body is about 336 mm., and the length of the tail is about 280 mm. The species *S. unicolor* is reddish brown in color and has black spots; *S. olivacea* is olive-brown and has yellow spots.

In both species the tail is the same color as the body and is not ringed. It is not known whether a scent pouch is present. The claws are not strongly curved, the ears are broad and short, and the muzzle is pointed.

No published accounts of habits have been found.

The type species of the genus is *S. olivacea*, Geoffroy.

Suricates (*Suricata suricatta*), photo by Bernhard Grzimek.

SURICATES, MIERKATS, SLENDER-TAILED MEERKATS.

THERE IS only one species, *S. suricatta*, that inhabits southern Africa, mostly south of the Orange river.

The head and body length is 250 to 350 mm., and the tapering tail is 175 to 250 mm. in length. The coloration is a light grizzled gray; the rear portion of the back is marked with black transverse bars. The bars are caused by the alternate light and black bands of individual hairs coinciding with similar markings of adjacent hairs. The head is almost white, the ears black, and the tail is yellowish with a black tip. The coat is long and soft, and the underfur is dark rufous in color. The body is quite slender, although difficult to see because of the long fur.

Suricates generally live in colonies; those of the plains areas dig their own burrows, while those of the rocky regions live in crevices among the rocks. Their activities are almost entirely limited to the daytime and they enjoy basking in the sun, lying in many different positions or sitting up on their haunches.

They are often in association with the yellow mongoose (*Cynictis*), perhaps in search of ground squirrels (*Geosciurus*), in addition to mice and gerbilles.

Bulbous roots constitute a considerable portion of their diet but they also dig up grubs, catch locusts and other insects, termites, and particularly seek moderate-sized snakes and their eggs, lizards, and small mammals, birds and their eggs.

Pregnant individuals have been noted in November and February, and the litter size is two to four.

The slender-tailed meerkat is altogether too fearless for its own good, and it stays about its burrows, often sitting up like the prairie dog (*Cynomys*) or marmot (*Marmota*).

They tame readily and are affectionate, especially enjoying snuggling close to their masters, as they enjoy the warmth. They are often kept about homes in South Africa to kill mice and rats. They are sensitive to cold. They have a large vocabulary of chatters and whines for all occasions and barks for alarm.

These animals should not be confused with thick-tailed meerkats (*Cynictis*), which inhabit some of the same range but are not so winning in their ways or so pleasing as pets.

A. African Mongoose (*Herpestes ichneumon*), photo by Ernest P. Walker. **B.** Crab-eating Mongoose (*H. urva*), photo by Robert E. Kuntz.

MONGOOSES; DITO AND RAM-MUGATA, MUI-SHOND, MRUNTI, ZERDI, ICHNEUMONS; MAN-GOUSTES; GROOTGRYSMUISHONDE; MANGOESTEN (local vernaculars).

ABOUT NINE SPECIES have a combined range covering southern Spain, southern Europe, southern Asia Minor, the continent of Africa, Arabia, India, the Malay Peninsula, and adjacent islands. They have been introduced in the West Indies and the Hawaiian Islands. *Galerella*, Gray, 1864, and *Myonax*, Thomas, 1865, are regarded as subgenera.

The length of the head and body is about 230 to 640 mm.; the length of the tail is 230 to 510 mm.; and the weight ranges from about one half to 3.2 kg. There is considerable range in size within this genus, although the Asiatic species are the largest.

Coloration and patterns vary considerably. Some forms are a greenish gray, yellowish brown, or grayish brown, while other forms are finely speckled with white or buff, because the hairs have bands of these colors. The under parts are generally somewhat lighter than the back and sides. In some species the underside is white. Some species have fur that is short and soft, while in others it is rather long and coarse.

This genus is characterized by the typical mongoose body form: long tail, five toes on the fore and hind feet, hind foot naked to the heel, sharp, curved foreclaws, and 40 teeth in all. Small scent glands are situated near the anus, and some species can eject for some distance a vile-smelling secretion, much like skunks.

The members of this genus occupy a wide variety of habitats ranging from dense hill-forest vegetation to arid, open sandy country.

They are active either night or day in their wanderings and search for food. They usually travel alone but sometimes roam in small parties of from four to a dozen individuals. These animals seek refuge in hollow logs, holes in the ground, and crevices. During the morning they frequently stretch out in an exposed area to sun themselves.

Some members of this genus kill cobras and other venomous snakes. They are not immune to the bites of these reptiles, as is erroneously believed. Rather, they are so skillful and quick in their movements that they avoid being struck by the snake, almost invariably succeeding in seizing it behind the head. The battle usually ends with the animal eating the snake. The diet includes snakes, small mammals, frogs, fish, crabs, insects and birds. Some species eat fruit and vegetation.

The mating season for some species continues throughout the year. The gestation period is about 60 days. The normal litter consists of from 2 to 4 young, the life span is 7 to 12½ years, and the female has 4 to 6 mammae.

They were introduced in the West Indies and Hawaiian Islands to control rats and snakes, but mongooses kill many other small mammals and birds; they are so destructive that they usually soon become pests when introduced into a climate in which they can exist. Because of this the importation or possession of some species of this genus is forbidden in the United States by federal statute.

They tame readily but will almost invariably kill birds and small mammals in spite of the owners' utmost precautions.

Several of the species included herein have been treated under the generic names *Galerella*, *Ichneumia*, *Myonax* and *Xenogale*.

The type species of the genus is *H. ichneumon* (Gmelin).

Dwarf Mongoose (*Helogale parvula*), photo by Bernhard Grzimek.

DWARF MONGOOSES, PIGMY MONGOOSES; DWERG-
MUISHOND, DWERG KOMMETJE KAT, SALA, LISI-
CHERERE, BIMUIVES (native names).

THE SINGLE SPECIES, *H. parvula*, inhabits Africa from Ethiopia and Somaliland southward to the Orange River. It is found most frequently in areas of dry acacia brush, mountain scrub, woodlands, and thick forests from sea level to about 1,800 meters elevation.

The length of the head and body is 170 to 235 mm.; the length of the tail is 150 to 195 mm.; and the weight is about 680 grams. This is the smallest of the mongooses. The coloration is speckled brown to grayish above, the tail and lower parts of the legs are dark, and the under parts are only slightly lighter than the upper parts. Coloration is somewhat variable, however, as some individuals have a rufous patch on the throat and breast, and the basal portion of the lower side of the tail is reddish brown; other individuals are entirely black.

The dwarf mongoose is gregarious, usually associating in bands of 4 to 12 individuals. Apparently it has no fixed place of abode and never establishes large colonies. Dwarf mongooses roam throughout the daylight hours and seek shelter at dusk in deserted ant and termite mounds, among gnarled roots of trees, and in crevices, their slender bodies enabling them to squeeze into quite small openings. They also make their own burrows at times. They are active and spend much time searching noisily through dry leaves and brush. They are not especially shy and most of the time seem to be intent in their quest for food. Like other mongooses, these animals feed on a wide variety of plant and animal life; they eat insects, mice, small birds, reptiles, fruit, berries, and eggs. Several may join forces in killing a snake.

Information regarding their breeding habits is meager, but half-grown individuals have been collected between April and July. It appears that the young, numbering two to four per litter, are born either in a den or in a nest constructed of grass. Young born in a zoo were playful when about the size of mice.

The dwarf mongoose is said to be exceptionally tame in captivity and makes an interesting pet.

Carnivorous mammals that remain together in groups must necessarily roam over a considerable area in order to find enough food. Indeed, the need for a fairly large area to produce enough food for a carnivore is probably the reason so few of them remain in groups longer than is required for the young to become self-supporting.

African Tropical Savannah Mongoose (*Dologale dybowskii*), photo by F. Petter of mounted specimen in Museum National d'Histoire Naturelle.

AFRICAN TROPICAL SAVANNAH MONGOOSES.

THE SINGLE SPECIES, *D. dybowskii*, inhabits savannah country in the Sudan, Uganda, and the Congo. This animal was originally described as *Crossarchus dybowskii*.

The length of the head and body is about 250 to 330 mm., and the length of the tail is 160 to 230 mm. Stripes are lacking. The head and neck are black, grizzled with grayish white; the back, tail, and limbs are lighter in color with brownish spots; and the under parts are reddish-gray. The fur is short, even, and fine, in contrast to the loose and coarse fur of *Crossarchus*.

Other features separating *Dologale* from *Crossarchus* are the nature of the snout (normal in *Dologale*, lengthened in *Crossarchus*), characters of the skull and the teeth. The habits and biology of *Dologale* have apparently not been recorded.

West African Water Mongoose (*Atilax paludinosus*), photo by Ernest P. Walker.

MARSH OR WATER MONGOOSES; KHANANGA, NGOGO, ZWARTE MUISHOND, IVUSI (native names).

THE SINGLE SPECIES, *A. paludinosus*, is found in Africa, from the southern part of the continent north to the Congo and Sierra Leone in the west, and to the Sudan and Ethiopia in the east. Favored haunts are marshes, reed-grown stream beds, and tidal estuaries.

The length of the head and body is 450 to 600 mm., the length of the tail is usually 300 to 400 mm., and they are fairly heavily built. Coloration is brownish with a sprinkling of black guard hairs that often gives a dark effect, or in some individuals light rings on the hairs prevail and impart a grayish tinge. The head is usually distinctly lighter than the back, and the under parts are still lighter.

Although more aquatic than any other mongoose, water mongooses are the only ones with toes that completely lack webs. This may be related to their feeding habit of feeling for aquatic prey in mud or under stones. They are characterized by the nearly uniform dark coloration; long, coarse hair; large, naked anal area; naked soles; five toes on the fore feet and hind feet; short, blunt claws; and a narrow, naked slit between the nose and the upper lip. Females have two pairs of mammae.

They are usually alone or in pairs. They are excellent swimmers and divers. When hard pressed they submerge under the water, leaving only the tip of the nose exposed for breathing. The water mongooses usually expose part of the back, in addition to the head, when swimming. They dive in search of food

and have regular pathways along the borders of streams and marshes which they travel at night in search of food. Almost any living thing that can be caught and killed is eaten, and when food is scarce along or in the water, marsh mongooses search the adjacent lands for rodents and birds. Their usual diet consists of frogs, crabs, fish, snakes, aquatic insects, and eggs. Apparently they throw creatures such as snails and perhaps crabs against hard surfaces to break the shell, as a captive was seen to take a piece of beef rib between its hands, rear onto its feet with its hands held high, then forcefully throw the bone to the floor of the cage, in an effort to break it. Like other mongooses, this species does little or no climbing but does run up leaning tree trunks or other inclines easy of access. Grassy patches and floating masses of vegetation often serve as feeding places and as dry resting spots.

The animals of this genus occasionally kill snakes. One case is reported in which a water mongoose killed a puff adder, consumed the head, and soon died. Examination disclosed that the fangs had pierced the walls of the stomach introducing the poison into the blood stream. The snake venom can ordinarily be eaten and digested by animals without harm.

Marsh mongooses are said to give birth to their young in burrows or on masses of vegetation gathered into heaps among reed beds. The usual litter size is two or three. One litter has been born in August in South Africa and a full-term fetus was recorded in Northern Rhodesia in October. Litters of two have been born in the U.S. National Zoological Park.

Banded Mongoose (*Mungos mungo*), photo from Zoological Garden Berlin-West through Ernst von Roy.

STRIPED MONGOOSES, BANDED MONGOOSES; GE-
STREEPTE MUIHOND, STINK MEERKAT, GEBANDE
MUISHOND, NKALA, MFUKI, MFWENGE, NENGA,
CHISAKANENGA, LIKONGE, NYANGA, O'ORO, GE-
BANDE MUISHONDE (native names).

THE SINGLE SPECIES, *M. mungo*, is found in Africa
from Portuguese Guinea eastward to Nigeria, the
Sudan, and Somaliland, and southward to about the
Orange River. It is usually found in the neighborhood
of rocky or tree-fringed water courses or thorn
thickets.

The length of the head and body is 300 to 450 mm.,
and the length of the tail is 230 to 290 mm. The hair
is coarse and, compared with other mongooses, there
is little underfur. Coloration is brownish gray with
dark brown and well-defined yellowish or whitish
bands across the rump. The banded pattern is produced by hair markings of the same type that produce the ground color of the remainder of the body.
The hairs are alternately ringed with dark and light
bands; the color rings on the individual hairs coincide
with like colors on adjacent hairs.

Although the tail is not bushy, it is covered with
coarse hair and is tapered toward the tip. These
animals have elongated foreclaws, soles that are naked
to the wrist and heel, and five toes on all feet. There
is no naked grooved line from the tip of the nose to the
upper lip. The females have six mammae.

When pleased or to attract attention, they have a
pleasant twittering call, but when alarmed they bark.

The members of this genus are gregarious, roving
about in parties of 6 to 20 individuals. When traveling
from one location to another, they maintain a fairly
compact formation, and at times an entire colony
will take refuge in a common shelter. They do not
remain long in any locality and apparently do not
stay longer than a day or two in any one "nest."
Since they are such travelers, they take up a temporary
abode in any nest of burrows which they may find
convenient. These mongooses usually work in a
circular course, returning over the same general
ground from time to time.

Banded mongooses are most frequently observed
during the morning and evening; they are usually so
occupied scratching among dead vegetation or ex-
ploring crevices in search of food that they may be
easily watched. While engaged in these activities,
they chatter continually. Occasionally several individuals may crowd together in a friendly fashion to
investigate or to share in the discovery of a choice
morsel of food. The diet of these animals consists of
insects (particularly larvae, which they dig from the
ground), snails, mice, small reptiles, eggs, wild fruit,
and berries which they find among dead leaves and
rotten wood.

In the vicinity of Lake Victoria newly-born young
have been found in May and early June, and elsewhere
others have been found in November and December.
A banded mongoose lived in the Giza Zoo for about
eight and one half years.

These animals become tame in captivity and make
interesting pets. It should be pointed out that the
generic name *Mungos* has been applied to many
different groups of mongooses with resulting confusion in names.

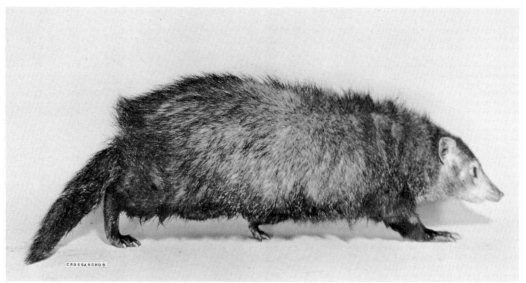

Cusimanse (*Crossarchus obscurus*), photo by Ernest P. Walker.

CUSIMANSES, ANGOLAN KUSIMANSES; CHIPULWE, NDEMBO (native names).

THIS GENUS of four species (?) is found in western and central Africa, where they prefer forests.

The length of the head and body is 305 to 410 mm.; the length of the tail is 150 to 255 mm.; and the weight is 450 to 1350 grams. The body is covered by relatively long, coarse hair which is a mixture of browns, grays, and yellows. The head is usually lighter-colored than the remainder of the body, while the feet and legs are usually the darkest. The legs are short, the tail is tapering, the ears are small, and the face is sharp.

They are gregarious, traveling in bands of 10 to 24 individuals, seldom remaining longer than two days in any locality. Such roving is very rare among small mammals and when larger carnivores follow the practice they usually work in a circular course, returning over the same general ground from time to time. Due to this vagrant life, they take up a temporary abode in any place that they find convenient. Cusimanses are diurnal. During the morning they frequently sit up to enjoy the warmth of the early sunshine and to view distant objects. Whether they are on the move, hiding, or searching for food, they are noisy, doing much grunting and high-pitched chattering. They have pleasant twittering calls when pleased or desiring to attract attention.

While seeking food they scratch and dig in dead vegetation and in the soil. The diet consists principally of insects, larvae, small reptiles, crabs, tender fruits, and berries. It is said that the shells of snails and eggs are cracked by hurling them with the forepaws back between the hind feet against some hard object.

Little has been recorded regarding breeding habits, but they are probably similar to those of other mongooses in central Africa. They are said to tame easily and make good pets. One lived in captivity six years in the London Zoo, and no doubt their life span is usually longer.

There has been much confusion in written articles regarding members of this and related genera. Under the name *Crossarchus*, information has been given that relates to *Mungos* and perhaps other genera, and information relating to *Crossarchus* has been published under *Mungos* and perhaps other genera.

The type species of the genus is *C. obscurus*, Cuvier.

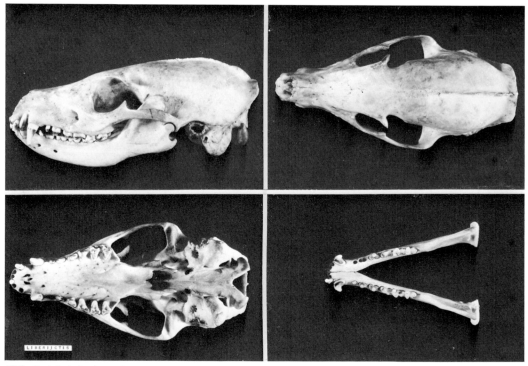

(*Liberiictis kuhni*), photos by Hans-Jurg Kuhn.

THE SINGLE SPECIES, *L. kuhni*, is known only from eight skulls from forested areas in northeastern Liberia which were named and described in 1958. The external characters are not known at the present time.

These mongooses are similar to *Crossarchus* in skull and dental features, but they have four premolar teeth above and below on each side instead of three as in *Crossarchus*. The skull is also larger and the teeth are proportionately smaller and weaker than in any species of *Crossarchus*. The rostrum and nasals are more elongated than those of *Crossarchus*.

The history of the discovery of these animals is as follows: Dr. Hans Himmelheber of Heidelberg, Germany, recieved a number of mammal skulls from native villages in northeast Liberia. Herr Hans-Jurg Kuhn, also of Heidelberg, examined these skulls but could not identify eight of them with certainty. He took one complete skull to the British Museum (Natural History), where the distinctness of this animal was recognized. The new mongoose was then named and described by R. W. Hayman of the British Museum. One skull is at the British Museum (Natural

History), six are in the Bonn Museum, and one is in the Zoological Institute of the University of Saarbrucken.

Dr. Hans-Jurg Kuhn has made another trip into the Liberian region and has tried to obtain additional specimens of *Liberiictis* or information regarding the genus. A personal communication to the senior author dated June 26, 1963, contains the following section:

The Krahn [or Kran] people in the Eastern Province have only one name for *Crossarchus* and *Liberiictis:* Senna. But they distinguish between "quiqui-senna" and "boire-senna." Quiqui-senna is *Crossarchus*, as I know from dozens of animals that they have brought to me alive and dead. "Quiqui is the way it talks." It lives in groups of 20-30, mostly in the secondary forest. "Boire-senna" has its name from "boire," the black hog (*Hylochoerus*). It is said to be of the size of *Atilax paludinosus*, and to live in groups of 3-5 in the high forest. It is usually found in tree-holes. It is said to be completely black. I am sure it will show up one day.

White-tailed Mongoose (*Ichneumia albicauda*), photo by Ernest P. Walker.

WHITE-TAILED MONGOOSES; WITSTERTMUISHOND, SAKA, KANANGA, NYERETZI, GOROMATUTU, WEL (when tail is white) and LOINYAR (when tail is black) (native names).

THE SINGLE SPECIES, *I. albicauda*, is found in Africa from Ghana, Nigeria, the Sudan, and Somaliland southward to southern Africa; it also inhabits southern Arabia. It prefers thick cover, the edges of forests, and bush-fringed streams.

The length of the head and body is 533 to 609 mm.; the length of the tail is 420 to 470 mm.; and the weight is about 4.5 kg. Long, coarse, black guard hairs protrude from a yellowish or whitish close, woolly underfur, producing a grayish general body color. The four extremities from the elbows and knees are black. The basal half of the tail is of the general body color, while the terminal portion is usually white. The white-tailed mongoose is characterized by its large size; bushy, tapering tail; soles of the fore feet naked to the wrist; and the upper lip which is divided by a naked slit from the nose to the mouth.

These mammals are generally solitary, although occasionally they travel in pairs. During the day they take shelter in porcupine or aardvark burrows, cavities under tree roots, or under rocks. They are said to utter a bark similar to that of a small dog. They are shy and little has been recorded of their habits. In secluded localities they frequently begin searching for food in the afternoon, but elsewhere they are nocturnal. In the wild they feed on rats, mice, rock dassies (*Procavia*), cane rats (*Thryonomys*), young hares, reptiles, birds, birds' eggs, and insects. They consume quantities of the migratory locust larvae and adults. Heller's examination of the stomachs of five individuals revealed one with a small cobra and large beetles; two with large beetles; one with termites; and one with termites and rodents.

The usual litter size appears to be two, although the female has four mammae. A white-tailed mongoose lived in the London Zoo for a little over ten years. The young have a browner body than the adults with no trace of the longer annulated hairs.

Most mongooses do not climb trees, but Theodore Roosevelt (*African Game Trails* [London, 1910], pg. 420) says, "They [tree hyraxes] are preyed on . . . and the white-tailed mongoose is their especial foe, following them everywhere among the tree tops. This mongoose is both terrestrial and arboreal in habits, and is hated by the Ndorobo because it robs their honey buckets."

When the white-tailed mongoose lives near a poultry raiser, it usually proves a pest. In captivity it is the shyest of the mongooses, but if captured young it is said to become a pleasing pet.

Black-legged Mongoose (*Bdeogale* sp.), photo by Don Davis.

BLACK-LEGGED MONGOOSES, DOG MONGOOSES; DIKSTERT-MUISHOND, KARASA, NGOGO (native names).

THIS GENUS of three or four species is found in eastern Africa, from Kenya south to Northern Rhodesia, Nyasaland, and Mozambique, and is also known from Gabon on the west coast. It may also occur in northern Angola. *Galeriscus*, Thomas, 1894, is herein regarded as a subgenus of *Bdeogale*.

The length of the head and body is 375 to about 600 mm., and the length of the tail is 175 to 375 mm. There is considerable variation in color within some of the species as well as between species. Black legs and grays and browns predominate. The fur of the adults is rather close, dense, and short, while that of the young animals is nearly twice as long and lighter in color. This genus resembles *Ichneumia* in its black feet, soft underfur and long, coarse hair over the upper parts of the body; it differs in lacking the first or inner toe on each foot and in having larger premolar teeth. *Bdeogale* differs from *Rhynchogale* in having a naked groove from the nose to the upper lip. The fore parts of the feet of *Bdeogale* are naked, but the hind parts are well haired.

Beetles and mice remains have been found in the stomach of one individual. Droppings, consisting chiefly of crab remains and thought to belong to *B. crassicauda*, have been found in trails.

This mongoose is known to have died after eating a poisonous snake whose fang pierced the interior of its digestive tract, introducing poison into its tissues. The poison is harmless in the digestive tract and dangerous only when it gets into the tissues. The remains of a rhinoceros viper were removed from the stomach of one mongoose. The habit of killing and eating snakes is common to several kinds of mongooses.

A female taken in December at Mazeras, East Africa, was pregnant with one large embryo, and another animal taken a week later was nursing a quarter-grown young. Like many of the other mongooses, little has been recorded of their habits.

The type species of the genus is *B. crassicauda*, Peters.

Meller's Mongoose (*Rhynchogale melleri*), photo from *Proc. Zool. Soc. London.*

MELLER'S MONGOOSES; UMBI, MELLERSE MUIS-HONDE, CHIMPUMPI, KAFUNDI (native names).

THERE IS ONE SPECIES, *R. melleri*, found in Africa from Tanganyika, Northern Rhodesia, Nyasaland, and Mozambique to southern Africa and possibly extreme northeastern Angola. *R. caniceps* of Tanganyika is conspecific and perhaps not even deserving of sub-specific recognition.

The length of the head and body is 440 to 485 mm., and the length of the tail is usually 300 to 400 mm. The color is grayish or pale brown, the head and undersides are paler, and the feet and tail are usually darker.

The genus resembles *Ichneumia* in the coarse guard hairs protruding from the close underfur, rather solid back teeth, and the same number of teeth. *Rhynchogale* differs from *Ichneumia* in the frequent reduction of the hallux and the lack of a naked crease from the nose to the upper lip. *Rhynchogale* has hind soles that are hairy to the roots of the toes.

This genus is not well represented in study collections. Practically nothing has been recorded on its habits and life history. It is solitary and terrestrial and may be partly diurnal, although it is probably mainly nocturnal. Wild fruits and termites have been found in the stomach of *Rhynchogale*. Small vertebrates are probably also eaten.

The only breeding records are of some specimens recently obtained in the Fort Jameson District, Northern Rhodesia, by V. J. Wilson. These were recently-born young, with eyes still unopened, found in a small cave on a rocky hill in December, 1960; and a female which contained fetuses averaging 60 mm. from crown to rump and which was taken in December, 1961. In each case the litter consisted of two, one male and one female. There are two abdominal pairs of mammae.

YELLOW MONGOOSES; MIERKATS, ROOIMEERKAT, GEELMEERKAT, IGALA (native names).

Yellow Mongoose (*Cynictis penicillata*), photo by Hans-Jurg Kuhn.

THE SINGLE SPECIES, *C. penicillata*, is found in southern Africa. It frequents well drained or arid open regions, preferably those with loose soil, but when disturbed may take refuge in brush along the banks of streams and among rocks.

The length of the head and body is 270 to 380 mm., and the length of the tail is 180 to 280 mm. The hair is fairly long, particularly on the tail, which is some-what bushy. The general color is dark orange-yellow to light yellowish gray. The underfur is rich yellow, the chin is white, the under parts and limbs are lighter than the back, and the tail is tipped with white. The individual guard hairs are usually yellowish in the basal half, followed by a black band and a white tip. There is a seasonal color change in the coats. The summer coat, typical in January and February, is reddish, short, and thin. The winter coat, typical from June to August, is yellowish, long, and thick. The transitional coat, typical in November and December, is pale yellow. The hands have five fingers and the feet four toes. The first or inner finger on the hand is small and is above the level of the other four so that it does not touch the ground.

Yellow mongooses live in colonies, one of the few instances of carnivorous mammals living in such a manner. These colonies may number 50 or more individuals and cover 50 or more square meters. Sometimes they use the deserted burrows of other animals or the burrows of the springhaas (*Pedetes*) or other mammals that they have killed, but they usually dig their own tunnels. This species is an energetic burrower and constructs underground tunnels and chambers with a number of entrances and exits. Certain definite areas in the colonies are used for the deposit of body wastes. Although social at the burrows, they usually hunt for food alone or in pairs.

They seldom wander more than a kilometer from the burrows. Daylight hours are their favorite period of activity, but those in close contact with man often become nocturnal. The yellow mongoose basks in the sun and sits up on its haunches to obtain a better view of the surroundings. It is agile and capable of traveling at considerable speed.

Small rodents or even mammals as large as itself, birds, birds' eggs, snakes, lizards, turtle eggs, insects, and termites are all included in the diet. It appears that pairs or perhaps the entire colony seeks new homes when food becomes scarce near the old home.

The number of young is usually two to four. The gestation period and seasons of birth have apparently not been recorded.

Selous' Mongoose (*Paracynictis selousi*), photo by Don Carter.

GRAY MEERKATS, SELOUS' MONGOOSES; KLEIN-WITSTERTMUISHONDE.

THE SINGLE SPECIES, *P. selousi*, is found in southern Africa. This animal was originally described as *Cynictis selousi*.

Head and body length is 390 to 470 mm., and tail length is 280 to 400 mm. The upper parts are dull buff-gray, the belly is buffy, and the fore feet and hind feet are black. The tail is white-tipped. There is no rufous in the coloring, nor are there any spots or stripes in the color pattern. This animal has only four toes on each foot, and the claws are long and slightly curved. This genus differs from *Cynictis* in the number of digits. *Paracynictis* is distinguished structurally from *Bdeogale*, which also has only four digits on each foot, by features of the skull and teeth. *Paracynictis*, some species of *Bdeogale*, and *Ichneumia* are similar in coloration, and all have whitish or white-tipped tails which make these animals visible at night. These viverrids have strong anal-gland secretions and the tail color may thus act as "warning coloration."

Paracynictis resides in labyrinthine chambers of its own construction. The suppression of the first toe on each digit and the long and curved claws are related to the burrowing habit. The burrows are located in sandy soil and contain numerous entrances facing in several directions. Apparently each individual constructs its own burrow system, but it is not definitely known whether several animals inhabit the same labyrinth or whether this species is usually solitary. *Paracynictis* is active at night but has been seen outside its burrow during the daytime. It is described as shy and retiring. It is terrestrial and eats locusts and small vertebrates. The skull of one individual was found under a tree, probably killed and eaten by an eagle.

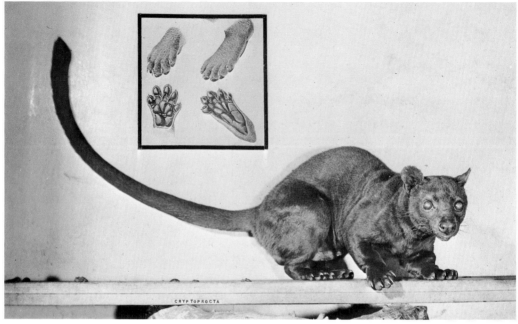

Fossa (*Cryptoprocta ferox*), photo by Ernest P. Walker. Inset: Fore feet and hind feet, top and bottom, photos from *Zoologie de Madagascar*, Grandidier et Petit.

FOSSAS, FOSSA CATS.

THE SINGLE SPECIES, *C. ferox*, inhabits the forested regions of the island of Madagascar.

The length of the head and body is about 610 to 760 mm., tail length is about 660 mm., and height at the shoulders is about 370 mm. These are the largest carnivores of Madagascar and are quite powerful. The fur is short, smooth, soft, thick, and reddish brown in color. Black individuals, however, have been captured in the interior and in the rain forests on the east coast. The mustache hairs are as long as the head. The curved claws are short, sharp, and retractile like those of a cat, but the head is relatively longer than in the cats. The general appearance is much like that of a gigantic jaguarondi (*Felis yagouaroundi*) or a small long-headed puma (*Felis concolor*) of the Americas. Like some of the other viverrids, fossas possess scent glands in the region of the anus and external genitals which discharge a strong, disagreeable odor when the animal is irritated.

Fossas walk in a flat-footed manner on the soles of their feet like bears, instead of on their toes like cats.

They are active at night and are said to eat lemurs and to pursue them in trees. They prey on poultry, young pigs, and other domestic animals. They may possibly, on occasion, attack wild hogs and even oxen, as some accounts claim, but smaller creatures are certainly the preferred prey.

During the mating season fossas are often seen in groups of four to eight individuals. They normally flee on sight of man but may be dangerous when wounded or when encountered during the mating period. The usual number of young is two or three. The life span is probably about 17 years.

Formerly classified in the cat family (Felidae), fossas are now placed in a separate subfamily of the family Viverridae. The fact that the common name of this animal is the same as the generic name of the Madagascar civet (*Fossa*) should not cause confusion, as they are quite distinct.

Most of the meager accounts on this animal mention its savagery, blood lust, and agility, probably in an exaggerated manner, largely based on natives' accounts.

The Madagascar natives dislike fossas because they often feed on their chickens and ducks. A farmer recently reported that one night one of these animals killed 25 of his chickens by biting into their necks. According to one native source, these animals will dig out human corpses and feed on them. Sometimes, but very rarely, the natives have been able to train them to aid in hunting the water hog (*Potamochoerus*).

Natives report that fossas are not rare. A few have been kept in zoos. It is surprising how little factual information has been collected about such a large mammal that has been known so long. Of the statements made regarding this animal, it is very difficult to separate facts from native superstitions, beliefs, and the unfounded tales of other people. The Madagascar natives have many fabulous stories about them; they claim that their scent kills poultry and that they can retract (or contract) their eye pupils so that they disappear completely.

HYENAS AND AARDWOLVES; DEDAR OR WERRA.

THIS FAMILY consists of two genera (*Hyaena* and *Crocuta*) and three species of hyenas from Africa, Asia Minor, and southwestern Asia, and the single genus and species of aardwolf (*Proteles cristatus*) from Africa. These animals generally inhabit plains and bushland and also occur in open forests at times.

The members of this family have a large head and forequarters, but the hindquarters are rather weak. The forelimbs, which are slender in the aardwolf but powerfully built in the hyenas, are longer than the hind limbs. The digital formula (the number of digits on the fore foot, followed by the number of digits on the hind foot) is 5/4 in the aardvark and 4/4 in the hyenas. The blunt claws are not retractile. *Proteles* is the smallest genus and *Crocuta* the largest; in the latter the length of the head and body is 550 to approximately 1,600 mm., and the length of the tail 200 to about 320 mm. Hyenas weigh from 27 to 80 kg. The aardwolf and the striped hyena (*Hyaena hyaena*) have a striped pattern; the brown hyena (*Hyaena brunnea*), except for its barred feet, has an unmarked pelage; and the spotted hyena (*Crocuta*) has a spotted pattern. The guard hairs are coarse in all genera.

Scent glands are present in the anal region. These glands and their associated pouches indicate a relationship with the family Viverridae. In the female spotted hyena the scent glands are similar to those in the male, the clitoris is penis-like, and there are scrotal pouches, so that the two sexes of *Crocuta* closely resemble each other externally. The males of this family do not have a baculum, and the females have two or three pairs of mammae.

In aardwolves the skull and jaws are weak, and the small cheek teeth are so widely spaced that they are of little value in fighting, holding objects, or chewing. The carnassials are not developed in the genus *Proteles*, although the canines are sharp and fairly powerful. In hyenas, on the other hand, the skull and jaws are strong, and the teeth, including the carnassials, are powerfully developed for crushing bone. The muscles used in chewing and those of the neck are well developed in hyenas. The dental formula in the family Hyaenidae is as follows: 3/3, 1/1, 3-4/3, 1/1 = 32 or 34. The incisors are not specialized, and the canines are elongate.

Hyenas and aardwolves live in the abandoned burrows of other animals or in caves and dense vegetation. They are mainly nocturnal but may be active during the day in remote areas. These mammals progress on their digits and seem to trot and even run tirelessly. Hyenas are great wanderers, and when moving about they utter a melancholy "whoo-oof." A number of other calls are emitted, including (in *Crocuta*) a laughing cry. The members of this family move alone or in pairs, except when there are young, devouring a carcass, or hunting in packs.

The main defense of the aardwolf, other than flight, is the ejection of a musky fluid from its anal glands and use of its canine teeth to bite. Hyenas combine cowardice with boldness (when hungry) and, particularly in the spotted hyena, with ferocity.

Aardwolves feed primarily on insects, whereas hyenas are scavengers. Hyenas also hunt in packs and kill animals by ripping out their entrails in a sudden and savage attack. Spotted hyenas can be extremely ferocious in their assaults while hunting and have been known to kill old crippled lions and even a half-grown rhinoceros. Hyenas share carrion with vultures and jackals. The members of the family Hyaenidae hunt by scent. Almost anything bearing an animal smell may be chewed or dragged off by hyenas, including harnesses and boots.

The gestation period ranges from 90 to 110 days, and the litter size is one to six (usually one to four). In the aardwolf several females may raise their young together so that a reported litter of six may have been the offspring of two females. There is normally only one litter per year, and the young are blind at birth. Members of this family have lived as long as 25 years in captivity.

The Convention for the Protection of the Fauna and Flora of Africa, held in London in 1933 at the invitation of the British government and attended by representatives of the nine countries having territories in Africa at that time, designated the aardwolf as a class A animal and thus gave it rigid protection, at least theoretically (class B animals are those which can be taken only by means of a special license). Although hyenas sometimes attack livestock (and man), they make valuable scavengers. Their jaws and teeth are powerful enough to twist or bite off the tongue of an iron trap, and they will not touch bait if scraps of paper, cartridge-cases, or other articles are left lying around. Young hyenas are said to be easily tamed and to remain docile and trustworthy, even when full grown.

Hyenas are believed to represent a side branch of the Viverridae, and the aardwolf is generally regarded as a close relative which has adopted different feeding habits. The geological range of this family is the Miocene to the Recent in Asia, the Recent in Africa, and the Pliocene to the Pleistocene in Europe and North America.

Aardwolf (*Proteles cristatus*), photo by R. Pucholt.

AARDWOLVES, EARTH WOLVES; ERDWOLVES, MAANHAARJAKKALS, GREY JACKALS, INCI, ISINGCI, TUKU (native names).

THE SINGLE SPECIES, *P. cristatus*, is found in southern and eastern Africa, from the Cape of Good Hope and Natal north to Angola, Northern Rhodesia, and the Sudan, but the distribution is broken between extreme southwestern Northern Rhodesia and Tanganyika. It is most common in open sand-plains or bush country.

The length of the head and body is 550 to 800 mm.; the length of the tail is usually 200 to 300 mm.; and the height at the shoulder is usually 450 to 500 mm. The underfur is long, loose, soft, and wavy and is interspersed with longer, coarser guard hairs. The body is yellow-gray with black stripes. The legs are banded with black, and the part below the knee and hock is entirely black. The tail is bushy and tipped with black, and the hair along the back is long and crest-like, as evidenced in the Boer vernacular of "manhaarjakkal" or maned jackal.

The jaws are weak and the cheek teeth are vestigial and widely spaced, but the canine teeth are sharp and reasonably powerful. The general build is not as stocky as in the true hyena, and the aardwolf has five toes on the fore feet and four on the hind feet, in contrast to the hyenas which have four toes on all feet.

The aardwolf is perhaps best considered as a hyena-like animal that has adopted an entirely different diet. Its food consists almost entirely of termites and insect larvae that it digs out of the ground. Some aardwolves apparently catch mice and small birds and they may, at times, eat the eggs of small birds that nest on the ground. They have been accused of killing lambs and chickens. Perhaps hungry individuals have done this on occasions but evidence to the contrary is overwhelming, and it is known that they can scarcely be induced to eat meat unless it is finely ground or cooked. When seen near carrion, they are usually there to pick up carrion beetles, maggots, and other insects. If attacked by dogs, the aardwolf ejects a musky fluid from its anal glands, and can at times put up a fair fight with its sharp canine teeth.

The aardwolf is often solitary, but pairs and family groups of five and six are often noted. Aardwolves are nocturnal and den in holes in the ground, usually old burrows of the aard-vark (*Orycteropus*).

In the southern part of their range aardwolves give birth in November and December. The litter size is usually two to four.

Under the provisions of the International Convention at London in 1933, these animals were recommended for class A protection, i.e., a high degree of protection.

Spotted Hyena (*Crocuta crocuta*), photo from New York Zoological Society.

SPOTTED OR LAUGHING HYENAS; GEVLEKTE WOLVES, TIGER WOLVES; ISADAWANE, IMPISI, WARABA, TIKA, PALA (native names).

THE SINGLE SPECIES, *C. crocuta*, inhabits most of Africa south of the Sahara Desert.

The length of the head and body is usually 1,275 mm. to 1,658 mm.; the length of the tail is 255 mm. to 330 mm.; the height at the shoulder is 762 mm. to 915 mm.; and the weight is 59 to 82 kg. The hair is coarse and woolly. The ground color is yellowish gray and the round markings on the body are dark brown to black. There is no mane or only a slight one. The jaws are probably the most powerful in proportion to size of any living mammal. This genus differs from the striped hyena (*Hyaena*) in its shorter ears, the hair and bristles on the face, more robust size, lighter color with spotting, larger and more swollen brain case, and features of the teeth.

Spotted hyenas are nocturnal and live in holes in the ground, in caves, or in lairs or shelters in dense vegetation. These are the largest and most aggressive of the hyenas. They frequently form packs but do not limit their diet to carrion and small prey as the striped and brown hyenas do. If their usual food supply is scarce, spotted hyenas kill sheep, goats, calves, and any other animal they can catch and over-power, but they are cowardly and will not fight if their prospective victim defends itself. They sometimes carry off sleeping children and attack adults who are asleep. In consuming carrion they crush the largest bones of such animals as cattle (*Bos*) and cape buffalo (*Syncerus*). Hyenas are scavengers. The dead from battles between tribes in central and northern Africa are often left for hyenas to eat. They have powerful necks and it is reported that they can carry a man's body or that of an ass (*Equus*). They also consume large numbers of the migratory locust.

Their maximum running speed is about 65 km. per hour. Spotted hyenas are quite noisy. When in the presence of food in the evening, they utter a remarkable howl with the head held close to the ground. This begins low and deep and increases in volume as it runs to higher pitches. Another call is the so-called "laugh," uttered during the breeding season or when the animals are otherwise excited.

Female spotted hyenas are polyestrous all year, with a cycle of about 14 days, whereas males lack seasonal sexual activity. The resemblance of the external reproductive organs in the sexes is so great that the ancients regarded these animals as hermaphroditic. The gestation period is about 110 days, and the number of young is usually one or two. The life span is about 25 years.

A. Striped Hyena (*Hyaena hyaena*), photo from San Diego Zoological Garden. B. Brown Hyena (*H. brunnea*); this specimen has a tumor near the left eye; photo from U.S. National Zoological Park. Inset: Young Striped Hyena (*H. hyaena*), photo by Reginald Bloom.

STRIPED AND BROWN HYENAS, STRAND WOLVES; INCUKA, DEBAÂ, DEDAR OR WERRA (native names).

THE TWO SPECIES are readily distinguishable and have fairly well separated ranges. The striped hyena (*H. hyaena*) inhabits India, North and Northeast Africa and Kenya, West Pakistan, Afghanistan, Transcaucasia, southern Russian Turkestan, and is found over Asia Minor. The brown hyena (*H. brunnea*) is found in southern Africa north to Rhodesia and Mozambique.

The length of the head and body is from 910 mm. to 1200 mm.; the length of the tail is about 310 mm.; and body weight is usually 27 to 54 kg.

The hair of these animals is rather coarse. The striped hyena has a grayish to light yellowish-brown ground color with dark brown to black markings across the neck and around the legs, and with the lower legs and feet almost or quite black. The brown hyena has a grayish head and grayish lower legs and feet with dark brown bars.

Both species have erectile manes of long hairs along the neck and back. These hairs are up to 305 mm. long.

Each front and hind foot has four toes. Hyena tracks can readily be distinguished from those of dogs, as the tracks of the front feet are decidedly larger than those of the hind feet. Both species possess a large glandular pouch below the tail which largely obscures the external genitalia and indicates their relationship to the Viverridae. Although they have much the appearance of dogs (*Canis*), they are not closely related.

Holes in banks or among rocks are their favorite dens. They do not appear to be found above 1,525 meters elevation.

Like the spotted hyena (*Crocuta*), the members of this genus are mainly nocturnal, but they are not as noisy or as aggressive. When threatened, they growl and erect the mane but will rarely fight. They often allow dogs to attack them without attempting to defend themselves. However, there are rare instances reporting that they attack larger animals and carry off children.

Their principal food is carrion. If the meat has been picked from carcasses by vultures and other animals, they can still obtain a meal by eating the bones. The largest bones of cattle are crushed by means of their powerful jaws and teeth. The brown hyena particularly frequents ocean beaches, where it feeds on marine life and sea refuse from crabs to whales. When the supply of carrion is inadequate, these animals sometimes kill goats, sheep, and small animals. Although hyenas may be infected with rabies, they do not normally display a strong desire to attack, as do most rabid animals.

From two to six young (usually two to four) are born and raised in a cave or hole in the ground. The gestation period for *H. brunnea* is three months, and the life span is up to 24 years.

Hyenas are scavengers. In the walls surrounding some of the native villages in Africa, holes are left for the hyenas to enter. In the evening the villagers place all domestic refuse outside the homes to be eaten by these animals during the night. Some natives even place their dead outside the villages for the same purpose. Not a trace remains the following morning except for perhaps a few splinters of bone.

The type species of the genus is *H. hyaena* (Linnaeus).

CATS, including LYNXES, BOBCATS, CARACALS, PUMAS, JAGUARS, LIONS, TIGERS, LEOPARDS, AND CHEETAHS; GATOS, TIGRINA, KATTE, CHATS, FAHED. (Included are vernaculars used in other countries.)

THERE IS so great a variation in the cat family that zoologists have used many names and made many groupings in classifying them. The genera used in this publication are those that recognize the major differences; the selected names have the approval of as many mammalogists as any other combination of names we might choose.

This family of 6 genera and 36 species (and the domestic cat *Felis catus*) has almost a worldwide distribution except for Antarctica, the Australian area, Madagascar, the West Indies, and some oceanic islands. Considerable disagreement exists on the number of genera that should be recognized, some mammalogists referring all the cats, except the cheetah (*Acinonyx*), to the genus *Felis*.

Cats exhibit a variety of external forms but all are readily recognizable as cats. The general cat type, once established, probably did not undergo much structural modification. The differences in size and color pattern seem to have arisen mainly from the influence of the size of the prey and the local habitat. These animals have lithe, muscular, compact, and deep-chested bodies, with rounded and shortened heads. The eyes have pupils that contract vertically, and the ears range from rounded to pointed. The whiskers are well developed. The length of the head and body is 0.5 to 3.75 meters. Certain species of the genus *Felis* (as herein defined) are the smallest members of the family and the tiger (*Panthera tigris*) is the largest. Adults of the cat family weigh from approximately 2.5 to 275 kg. The tail is 10 to about 114 cm. long; it is well haired but not bushy (with a bushy tip in the lion, *Panthera leo*). The pelage is soft and woolly; its beautiful and glossy appearance is maintained by frequent licking and cleaning with the tongue and paws. The color varies from gray to reddish and yellowish brown, generally with stripes, spots, or rosettes.

The limbs in the cat family range from short to long and sinewy; the fore foot has five digits and the hind foot four. The claws are retractile (to prevent them from becoming blunted), large, compressed, strongly curved (to aid in holding living prey), and sharp, or (in the cheetah) semiretractile and somewhat poorly developed. Except for the naked pads, the feet are well haired to aid in the silent stalking of prey.

A baculum is vestigial or absent, and the females have two to four pairs of mammae.

The incisors are small, unspecialized, and placed in a horizontal line; the canines are elongate, sharp, and slightly recurved; and the carnassials, which cut the food, are large and well developed. The dental formula is 3/3, 1/1, 2-3/2, 1/1 = 28 or 30. The tongue is suited for laceration and retaining food within the mouth, its surface being covered with sharp-pointed, recurved, horny papillae. The skull is short and rounded.

The members of the family Felidae walk or trot on their digits, often placing the hind feet in the tracks of the fore feet. They stalk their prey or lie in wait and then seize their quarry with a short rush. The cheetah is the exception, as this cat obtains most of its prey by racing 600 meters at speeds of up to about 112 kilometers per hour, after having stalked the game for awhile. At high speed, cats bound in long leaps (up to about 6.5 meters for the lion). Some cats, particularly the larger species, range over large areas; the mountain lion (*Felis concolor*), for example, has a home range up to 80 kilometers in diameter. These animals are agile climbers and good swimmers. They travel singly, in pairs, in family groups, or (the lion) in "prides" of about 23 individuals. Some cats are nocturnal whereas others are active mainly during the day. Felids shelter in trees, hollow logs, caves, crevices, the abandoned burrows of other animals, and ground vegetation. Cats defend themselves with tooth and claw or they flee, sometimes seeking refuge in trees. The normal facial expression of nearly all cats is quite unlike the savage expression usually pictured when they are on the offensive or defensive.

Felids have acute scent, hearing, and sight. They prey on almost any mammal they can overpower or on birds, fish, and occasionally reptiles. The big or great cats (four species in the genus *Panthera*) are especially powerful. The leopard, for example, often stores some of its prey in a tree; a single piece of flesh, part of a young buffalo that weighed about 45 kg., was found in an acacia tree nearly 3.5 meters above the ground. The great strength of a mature tiger is well known, a typical example is the shifting of a buffalo for 15 meters which 13 men could not drag.

Most cats have one or two litters a year, the larger species sometimes breed only every two or three years. The gestation period is 55 to 113 days (a gestation period of 9 months has been reported for the jaguarundi, *Felis yagouaroundi*), and the litter size is one to six (the domestic cat may have more than six young. The young at birth are usually blind and helpless, but they are haired and often spotted. They remain with their mother until they can hunt for themselves. The females of most species of *Felis* and of *Lynx* attain puberty in 12 to 15 months, whereas female mountain lions (pumas) do not breed until their third year. Felids may live as long as 30 years.

The larger cats (*Panthera*) prey on livestock and in some cases on human beings. As a result they have been hunted extensively and are rare to uncommon over much of their range.

The geological range of this family is the upper Eocene or lower Oligocene to the Recent in North America and Eurasia, the Miocene to the Recent in Africa, and the Pleistocene to the Recent in South America. The saber-toothed cats represent a specialized line that became extinct in the Pleistocene. Two genera of Old World cats, known from the Pleistocene and now extinct, are *Sivapanthera* from Asia and *Homotherium* from Europe. The latter genus had a large saber-like tooth.

Much of the classification of mammals is based on the shapes and relative proportions of the different parts of the skulls of different mammals, but the cats have a remarkable uniformity of proportions between the various parts of the skulls in spite of the great variation in sizes of the animals and the proportions of the limbs and tail, and the wide variation in markings. The latter range from almost the same color over the entire animal through spots, stripes, and blotches of various colors, sizes, shapes, and arrangement. This peculiar combination of characters has led to great diversity of opinion as to how the cats should be classified, with resultant multiplicity of names and groupings. One author used as many as twenty-three generic names for the cats, and other authors have taken the other extreme and recognized only two or three genera. Fortunately the cats are not as badly confused as the mammalogists. We have followed a median line that appears to be as nearly generally acceptable as any of the other groupings, as the five drafts of our checklists have been examined and passed upon by many capable mammalogists.

A. Canada Lynx (*Lynx canadensis*), photo from San Diego Zoological Garden. B. Caracal (*Lynx caracal*), photo by Bernhard Grzimek.

Lynxes, Bobcats, Wildcats; Luchs, Los, Caracals.

This genus is comprised of four species. *L. canadensis*, the lynx, is distributed over Alaska, Canada, and the northern part of the United States. *L. lynx*, the European lynx, was formerly native to forested areas throughout Europe but is now greatly restricted in range, although common in some areas. *L. rufus*, the bobcat, is distributed over southern Canada, the entire United States (except the midwestern corn belt), and southward into Mexico. *Caracal*, Gray, 1843, with the single species *L. caracal*, the caracal, of Africa and southern Asia, is considered a subgenus. It is possible that the European and American lynxes comprise only one species, in which event *L. canadensis* is a synonym of *L. lynx*. The type species of the genus is *L. lynx* (Linnaeus).

The length of the head and body is 762 mm. to 1 meter; the length of the tail is 102 to 165 mm. in lynxes and bobcats, and 200 to 300 mm. in the caracal. The shoulder height is 510 to 610 mm., and the weight is generally 5.4 to 11.3 kg., although some individuals weigh as much as 18 kg. On the average, lynxes are larger than bobcats. The caracal may be distinguished by its smooth, short fur, reddish color, and pointed and tufted ears.

Animals of the genus *Lynx*, except the caracal, have rather long, soft fur, especially on the lower cheeks, which appears as a ruff about the neck. The lynx is gray-buff with brown mottlings, while the bobcat has a general coloration of pale brown to reddish brown streaked with blackish, usually with dark spots on a white belly.

Lynxes are distinguished from bobcats in the prominent ear tufts and a completely black-tipped tail, whereas bobcats have smaller ear tufts and the terminal end of the tail has black bars. These animals have relatively short bodies; long, heavy legs; and furred feet, an adaptation to aid the northern individuals in walking over snow. The pupil of the eye of all these animals is vertical.

While the lynx seldom ventures far from the shelter of forests, the bobcat is found in a variety of habitats. The caracal is found in both hilly country and in scrub- or tree-covered plains.

Members of this genus usually travel alone; however, several individuals have been reported roaming as a group. They are expert tree climbers, swimmers, and powerful fighters, using both their teeth and claws as savage weapons. They are most active after dark, hunting by sight and smell over an irregular route of perhaps 40 km. in one night.

Lynxes, whose principal item of food is the snowshoe hare, have a population that fluctuates with the food supply. When these hares are scarce, lynxes sometimes roam far beyond their normal range. On the other hand, bobcats, whose varied diet of numerous mammals, birds, etc., does not vary greatly in numbers, do not encounter food shortages; thus they do not roam beyond their normal range. All of these animals eat almost any bird or mammal they can kill, and their habits are much like those of other cats.

Mating in lynxes and bobcats takes place in late winter. After a gestation period of about 60 days, one to four young are born in a natural cavity on a rocky ledge or in a thicket. The young weigh about 340 grams at birth, and their eyes open in nine to ten days. They are weaned at two months. The females breed after one year, and the litter disbands in about six to nine months. The life span is 10 to 20 years.

The pelts of these animals are used for fur and garment trimming. Their meat is edible but should be well cooked. Although they occasionally kill livestock and poultry, they are useful to the farmer because they kill rodents. Some individuals have been tamed as pets, but they are not as readily domesticated as other mammals.

The caracal was formerly placed in a separate genus, *Urolynchus*.

A. Marbled Cat (*Felis marmorata*), photo from *Jour. Bombay Nat. Hist. Soc.* B. Serval (*F. serval*), photo by Bernhard Grzimek. C. Golden Cat (*F. temmincki*), photo by Ernest P. Walker. D. Pallas' Cat (*F. manul*), photo by Howard E. Uible. E. Pumas (*F. concolor*), photo by Ernest P. Walker.

A. African Black Footed Cat (*Felis nigripes*), photo of mounted specimen by James A. Bateman. B. Little Spotted Cat (*F. tigrina*); C. Jungle Cat (*F. chaus*); photos by Ernest P. Walker. D. European Wild Cat (*F. sylvestris*), photo from the Zoological Society of London. E. Jaguarundi (*F. yagouaroundi*), photo by Ernest P. Walker.

CATS, PUMAS, MOUNTAIN LIONS, AMERICAN LIONS, COUGARS; GATOS, TIGRINA, KATTE, CHATS, KATZE. (Included are vernaculars used in other countries.)

THE COMBINED RANGES of about 25 species cover most of the world, except the Australian region, Madagascar, the West Indies, and some other islands. Although the species differ in general form, size, and color, they are similar enough in the proportions of their anatomy to warrant their inclusion in the single genus *Felis*. In fact, some mammalogists refer all the cats, except the cheetah (*Acinonyx*), to the genus *Felis*.

The genus *Felis* as herein treated, ranges in size from the mountain lion or puma to wild cats that are smaller than the average domestic cat. The prevailing colors are browns, grays, and blacks. Most species of *Felis* have stripes, spots, or mottled patterns of dark brown or black on a gray or brown ground color; however, some lack markings. A given species usually varies considerably in its pattern of stripes or spots. This genus may be characterized as follows: It consists of medium to large carnivores that walk on their toes instead of their soles; the tail is usually long; the feet are large; the fore feet have five digits, the hind feet have four; the claws are sharp, recurved, and retractile; the eyes are large and the ears well developed; the coat is tawny, spotted, or striped; the skull is highly arched in the frontal region with a flattened face and a short rostrum.

These animals are generally nocturnal. They shelter in rock crevices, hollow trees or logs, holes in banks, in the ground, or in tall grass or underbrush. They are much alike in habits, preying on almost any mammals they can overcome, as well as birds and, on occasion, reptiles. Cats are usually fond of fish and a few catch fish regularly. Practically all of the cats are excited by the odor of the catnip plant, and, like the domestic cat (*Felis catus*), they endeavor to obtain possession of the source of the scent, rolling on it, rubbing themselves on it, purring, and showing every evidence of pleasure. The facial expression of nearly all cats is normally mild, pleasant, and full of character. These cats almost never attack men.

The females of most species are seasonally polyestrous, that is, they come into heat several times in one year. Puberty in the female is usually reached at an age of 12 to 15 months. At least in the domestic cat, ovulation is induced by the reproductive act and only rarely occurs in its absence. Litter size for the genus is one to six, usually two to four (the domestic cat may have more than six young). The gestation period for most species is 55 to 80 days. The mountain lion (*Felis concolor*) has a gestation period of 90 to 96 days, and a gestation period of 9 months has been reported for the jaguarondi (*F. yagouaroundi*). The mother carries food to the young until they are able to follow her and learn to hunt for themselves. The smaller species may have more than one litter per year, whereas the larger species may breed only every two or three years. The life span ranges from 16 to 22½ years.

Separate accounts of the species follow. Most of the species have ground colors of gray to pale brown with spots, longitudinal stripes on the head and back, and bars across the back. The pattern and range of color is fairly uniform for these relatively short-legged cats.

They are: *F. silvestris*, the European wild cat of Europe and Asia Minor; *F. libyca*, the African wild cat which ranges from Africa across Asia Minor into southern Asia; *F. nigripes*, the black-footed cat of southern Africa; *F. margarita*, the sand cat of northern Africa, Arabia, and southern Russian Turkestan; *F. chaus*, the jungle cat, which ranges from Egypt east to China, India, Ceylon, and Indo-china; *F. bieti*, the Chinese desert cat of Mongolia and the Chinese provinces of Kansu and Szechuan; and *F. minuta*, of the Philippines. The head and body measures 0.5 to 1 meter in length, and the tail is about 0.3 meters long. Nearly all these species are larger than the domestic cat which traces its ancestry to many parts of the world. Early men captured and domesticated the species of wild cats native to their respective regions, transported them as pets, and permitted them to breed with tame cats of other species from other regions. Thus the breed has become a mixture beyond definite determination. Although some records indicate 2400 B.C. as the earliest domestication of the cat, 1300 B.C. (in Egypt) seems a more valid date. Cats were venerated in Egypt, where a city, Bubastis, was dedicated to cat worship. The cat goddess, Bast, was goddess of the hunt, of love, and of pleasure. In medieval Europe, on the other hand, cats were feared and hated and associated with the devil and witches.

The pallas or steppe cat, *F. manul*, is thought by some authorities to be the ancestor of the domesticated Persian cat. The steppe cat is an inhabitant of rocky, arid areas of little vegetation in central Asia. It is about the size of a large domestic cat; the head and body measuring about 51 cm., and the tail about 25 cm. The fur is especially long near the end of the tail; on the under parts of the body it is almost twice as long as on the back and sides. Such an arrangement provides good insulation for an animal that spends much time lying on the frozen ground and snows of the north. The color is pale yellowish gray to almost white and the few indistinct markings are black. The tips of the ears are only about as high as the top of the head, giving the appearance that the animal has its ears laid back.

The serval, *F. serval*, of Africa is a long-legged, short-tailed, large-eared cat of slender build. The length of the head and body is about 1 meter and the length of the tail is about 41 cm. The ground color is yellowish brown on the back and sides, shading to almost white beneath, and the spots are dark brown or black. This cat has great speed for short distances, and in high grass it progresses by long, high leaps. It charges prey for short distances, and, by making remarkable leaps, often catches birds that it has flushed into the air or that are perched within 3 meters of the ground. The serval is a rapid and skillful climber and can capture fleeing hyraxes (*Dendrohyrax*) in the trees. It is a vigorous fighter and often kills dogs. Serval skins are used in making the mantles worn by the chiefs and high officials of native tribes.

Three species of relatively long-legged, spotted, and striped cats are found in Asia: *F. bengalensis*, the leopard cat of eastern Asia, including the Philippines; *F. rubiginosa*, the rusty-spotted cat, of southern India and Ceylon; and *F. viverrina*, the fishing cat, of Ceylon, India, Indo-China, Thailand, Sumatra, and Java. They are inhabitants of forests and grasslands. The length of the head and body is 46 to 76 cm. and

A. Leopard Cat (*Felis bengalensis*), photo by Lim Boo Liat. B. Margay Cat (*F. wiedii*), photo by Ernest P. Walker. C. Pampas Cat (*F. pajeros*), photo from San Diego Zoological Garden. D. Fishing Cat (*F. viverrina*), photo from New York Zoological Society. E. Geoffroy's Cat (*F. geoffroyi*), photo by Ernest P. Walker. F. African Wild Cat (*F. libyca*), photo by Bernhard Grzimek.

the length of the tail is about 31 cm. The fishing cat is of particular interest, as it frequents the vicinity of streams where it catches and eats fish. However, a variety of other prey is consumed as well, so that the common name may be somewhat misleading.

Another Asian cat with a striped and spotted pattern is the flat-headed cat, *F. planiceps*, of the Malay Peninsula, Sumatra, and Borneo. The length of the head and body is about 61 cm.; the tail is rather short (from 15 to 20 cm. in length) and thickly furred.

There are two species of marbled cats: *F. marmorata*, the marbled cat of Nepal through Burma to Indo-China, Sumatra, and Borneo; and *F. badia*, the marbled cat of Borneo. These animals might be thought of as small replicas of the clouded leopard (*Neofelis*). The upper and posterior edges of the large, irregular blotches are often the darkest parts of the markings. Although their habits are not well known, marbled cats are generally thought to be arboreal.

Still another Old World cat is the golden cat, *F. temmincki*, of southern China, Nepal, Burma, Indo-China, and Sumatra, and *F. aurata* of western and central Africa. The length of the head and body is about 76 cm., and the length of the tail is about 48 cm. The face has a banded and striped pattern, but the body is without stripes or spots for the most part. The color is chestnut or ferruginous, darkest above, paler on the sides, and still paler below. Melanistic individuals are fairly common. Little is known about this animal. A few specimens have been exhibited in zoological parks and from these it appears that the species is not readily tamed.

As herein treated, there are nine species of *Felis* in the New World. Three of these species are quite similar in appearance and perhaps in habits. These are the ocelot, *F. pardalis*; the margay, *F. wiedii*; and the little spotted cat, *F. tigrina*. The first two species are known from the United States, but all three are most common farther south and are found in South America. They are pale gray to grayish yellow or deep, warm brown, with brownish stripes and large, black-bordered spots and blotches. The length of the head and body is usually 50 to 97 cm., and the length of the tail is 30 to 50 cm. The margay resembles a small, long-tailed ocelot. Ocelots are expert climbers and hunt for food both in trees and on the ground. These species live in forested or brushy areas.

As its common name indicates, the pampas cat, *F. pajeros*, of South America is an inhabitant of open country. The length of the head and body is about 76 cm., and the length of the tail is about 25 cm. The ground color is yellowish gray and the markings are brownish or straw-colored. The fur is coarse and long, and the hairs are slightly longer along the mid-dorsal line, producing a slight but distinct crest which is usually darker than the remainder of the back. Also found only in South America are the species *F. geoffroyi*, *F. guigna*, and *F. jacobita*.

The jaguarundi, *F. yagouaroundi*, is an elongate, long-tailed, short-legged cat without stripes or spots whose range enters the United States as far as parts of Texas and Arizona. The limits of its southernmost range are in South America. This animal inhabits chaparral and dense forests, having a preference for localities near streams. The length of the head and body is 55 to 67 cm., and the length of the tail is 33 to 61 cm. There are three color phases, and they may occur in the same litter. These phases are a black, a brownish red and a gray. Jaguarundis are active day or night and seem to be more cursorial and less arboreal than are the smaller spotted cats of Mexico and South America.

The mountain lion or puma, *F. concolor*, has the largest range of any species of native mammal in the New World. It occurs from British Columbia in Canada to Patagonia in South America. The length of the head and body is 103 to 197 cm., and the length of the tail is 53 to 82 cm. The weight of this cat, the the largest species of *Felis*, is 35 to 105 kg. Coloration is yellowish brown above and whitish below. With the exception of the jaguarundi, this is the only unmarked cat in the Americas. Young pumas are spotted with darker brown and the tail is ringed, but these markings generally disappear before the animal is half grown. Mountain lions feed on a variety of animals and usually do not go back to an old kill. Their attacks on domestic livestock and game have resulted in persistent efforts to reduce their numbers throughout their range.

Females probably do not breed until three years of age. Mountain lions have a life expectancy of up to 20 years.

The type species of the genus is *F. catus*, Linnaeus.

A. Lion (*Panthera leo*), photo from P. D. Swanepoel. B. Lioness and Cub (*P. leo*), photo by Ernest P. Walker. C. Lion Cubs (*P. leo*), photo from San Diego Zoological Garden. D. Leopard (*P. pardus*), photo from the U.S. National Zoological Park.

A. Tiger (*Panthera tigris*), photo from San Diego Zoological Garden. B. Black Jaguar (*P. onca*); C. Jaguar (*P. onca*); photos from the U.S. National Zoological Park.

JAGUAR (TIGRE, YAGUARES), LEOPARD (NKA-SHAMA, PANTHER, LUIPERDE, LUIPAARD, PANTER, TENDWA), TIGER (BAGH, SHER, RIMAU, HARI-MAU TIJGERS), AND LION (LEEUE, LEEUWEN, NTAMBWE, SHER, BABAR-SHER, SIMBA).*

THESE ANIMALS, the so-called big or great cats, have been treated under a variety of scientific names; they are all herein discussed separately under the genus *Panthera*.

The jaguar or tigre Americano, *P. onca*, ranges from the southwestern United States south to about 40 degrees South latitude. Head and body length is 1.5 to 1.8 meters; tail length is 70 to 91 cm.; and weights are usually 68 to 136 kg. The coloration is cinnamon-buff, with black spots in the center of rosettes. The leopard, *P. pardus*, has a similar pattern but lacks the central spots; *P. onca* is also a stockier animal than *P. pardus*. The jaguar inhabits thick wooded country and arid shrubby areas and feeds on peccaries, capybaras, turtles, large fresh water fish, alligators, smaller animals, and domestic stock. The South American Indian name for this animal, "jaguara," is said to mean the "carnivore that overcomes its prey in a single bound." One to three young are born after a gestation period of 100 to 110 days.

The leopard, *P. pardus*, has the greatest range in area of any felid; it is found throughout most of Africa and Asia. It inhabits a variety of regions, from tropical forest and rocky areas with heavy or scattered vegetation to the high, cold regions of the Himalayas. Head and body length is 91.4 cm. to 1.5 meters; tail length is about 91.4 cm.; and weight is about 91 kg. Coloration is cinnamon-buff with a rosette pattern; the "black panther" is a color phase of the leopard. In rocky areas the leopard lives in caves, but in forested regions it lives in thick vegetation. This animal is active and agile in trees, often springing on its prey from an overhanging bough. It usually travels singly or in pairs, but sometimes family groups of four to six are noted. The leopard is more silent than the lion or the tiger and is a wary and cunning animal. It feeds on almost any animal it can overpower and, when it cannot consume its prey in a single meal, caches the remainder in a tree. The leopard breeds throughout the year.

The tiger (*P. tigris*) is found sparingly through China and is common in the jungles of India, southern China, the Malay Peninsula, Sumatra, Java, and Bali. Head and body length is usually 1.8 to 2.8 meters; tail length is about 91.4 cm.; and weight is from 227 to 272 kg. The beautifully striped pattern of the tiger is familiar to everyone. The Siberian tiger (*P. tigris longipilis*) is found in the cold forests of Manchuria and Siberia. Until within striking distance, tigers usually stalk their prey with a silent, stealthy crawl. They feed upon animals of all kinds, leopards and other tigers sometimes are included among the prey of a given individual. Tigers have even been known to consume crocodiles, turtles, and fish during floods. They bathe and take to the water freely. Tigers in captivity have lived 12 to 19 years.

The lion, *P. leo*, formerly ranged from Africa eastward to India but is now mainly confined to the more protected areas of Africa and the Gir forest in India. This great cat prefers open country, i.e., savannahs and plains. Head and body length is 1.8 to 2.4 meters; tail length is 61 to 91 cm.; and weight is 181 to 227 kg. The coloration is tawny yellow, and the males have a ruff of hair—the mane—around the neck and shoulders. Lions prey mostly on hoofed mammals and charge by a series of bounds or leaps. The tremendous initial spurt soon tires a lion. It hunts singly, in pairs, and in bands or "prides," consisting of animals of both sexes and all ages. The lion is polygamous and breeds throughout the year.

The roars and other calls of the big cats are associated with the hyoid structure; the hyoid in these animals is supplied with an elastic ligament. In those cats which "purr" but do not "roar" the hyoid is not supplied with this ligament. Species of *Panthera* are active mainly at night. Most of the big cats seem to have a hunting territory or "beat"; when hunting in pairs, one animal often drives the victim downwind to the other animal. Depredations on livestock are often extensive, and both carrion and fresh meat are consumed. The big cats usually gorge themselves on their kill; a pair of lions, for example, will consume most of a wildebeest at one meal. After feeding, these cats usually drink quantities of water in the early morning and then retire to a secluded spot to spend the day. All the great cats, with the possible exception of the jaguar, sometimes become man-eaters. Most big cats take readily to water and are strong swimmers. The gestation period for the genus is 92 to 113 days, and the number of young is one to six, usually two or three. Longevity in the wild seems to be 15 to 30 years.

The type species of the genus is *P. pardus* (Linnaeus).

---

* Local vernaculars are in parentheses.

Clouded Leopard (*Neofelis nebulosa*), photo from San Diego Zoological Garden.

CLOUDED LEOPARD; PUNGMAR, LAMCHITIA, THIT-KYOUNG, RIMAU-DAHAN, DAHAN, BANDER BAGH (local vernaculars).

THE SINGLE SPECIES, *N. nebulosa*, inhabits Nepal and Sikkim eastward to southern China, Hainan, and Formosa, and south to Sumatra, the Malay States, and Borneo. It frequents jungles and shrub, including swampy areas.

The length of the head and body ranges from about 616 to 1,066 mm., the length of the tail is 608 to 912 mm., and the height at the shoulder is about 803 mm. The weight is usually 16 to 23 kg. The adults are grayish or yellowish with black markings in the form of circles, rosettes, ovals, and other shapes. The blotches on the shoulders and back are darker on their posterior margins than on their front margins, which probably suggests that stripes can be evolved from blotches or spots. The young animals lack these markings. This is a long animal with short, stout legs and broad paws. The pads are quite hard, in spite of arboreal habits. The canine teeth are exceptionally long; the upper canines are about three times as long as the basal width at the socket. Other dental and cranial features are also characteristic.

Many of the clouded leopards that have been in captivity have been gentle, playful, and like to be petted by their custodians. Some play by the hour with articles to toss and cuff. Some have been active in their cages, while others have spent most of their time sleeping.

The native names for this animal usually refer to its arboreal habits. The clouded leopard hunts in trees and springs on ground prey from overhanging branches, but it also hunts on the ground. It feeds on a variety of animals, including monkeys, birds, pigs, deer, cattle, young buffaloes, goats, and even porcupines. It is not known to attack people.

The young are said to be born in a tree hollow. The litter size is usually two, and the young animals "chuckle, purr, and growl." The gestation period is not known. In fact, little is known of these animals in the wild state.

The canine teeth are used by certain Bornean natives as ear ornaments; the skins are employed in the making of seating-mats, and parts of the body are used by the Chinese for making medicines.

Clouded leopards have bred and reared young in the Cheyenne Mountain Zoo near Colorado Springs, Colorado, and at the U.S. National Zoological Park, Washington, D. C.

Snow Leopard (*Uncia uncia*), photo by Ernest P. Walker.

OUNCES OR SNOW LEOPARDS; IKAR, ZIG, SACHAK, SÂH, BHARAL HE, THURWÁGH, STIAN AND SAFED CHEETAH, BURHEL HAYE, OR "BURHEL KILLER," SCHNEELEOPARD.

THE SINGLE SPECIES, *U. uncia*, inhabits the highlands of central Asia; it is found in Eastern Russian Turkestan, north to the Altai Mountains, in the Pamirs, Kashmir, the Tian Shan system and adjacent ranges, the Astin Tagh in Chinese Turkestan, and in Tibet eastward to about Lhasa. The ounce is not a scrub or jungle cat; it is found on rocky mountainsides above the tree line.

The head and body length is usually 1.2 to 1.5 meters, and the tail length is about three-fourths of the head and body length. The weight is usually 23 to 41 kg. This is a beautiful cat, with thick, long hair and dense, woolly underfur. The color above is whitish or grayish (sometimes with a creamy or yellowish cast) and whitish below. A pattern of dark and indistinct rosettes or rings is present on the upper parts.

In the summer snow leopards live at or near the snow line at about 3,660 to 3,965 meters elevation. However, in winter some descend to about 1,830 meters. They rest during the day and become active toward evening, searching for food—wild sheep, musk deer, hares and rodents, goats and other domestic stock, and birds such as the monal pheasant.

The gestation period is about 93 days, and the number of young is usually two to four.

Snow leopards are seldom seen by man in the wild because of the inaccessibility of their haunts and their nocturnal habits. Their skins are popular in the fur trade. Most animals are trapped in pits wider at the bottom than at the top and baited with young sheep or goats. Many are also captured in iron traps, so that a great many of the animals offered to zoos are missing one or more toes, or even a foot or part of the leg.

Cheetah or Hunting Leopard (*Acinonyx jubatus*), photo from New York Zoological Society.

CHEETAHS, CHITAS, HUNTING LEOPARDS; JAG-
LUIPERDE, GUÉPARD, JACHTLUIPAARDEN, DHAM-
BANYIKA, KAMBULUMBULU, FAHED, YUZ, SHABEL,
KILLI (native names).

THERE ARE two species, *A. jubatus* and *A. rex*. *A. jubatus* is found in India westward to Egypt, Libya, Morocco, and Rio de Oro. In tropical Africa it occurs from Nigeria, the Sudan, and Somaliland south into southern Africa. It prefers open country but is usually found in denser savannahs where it is persecuted by man.

The length of the head and body is 1.4 to 1.5 meters, the length of the tail is 0.6 to 0.75 meters, the height at the shoulder is about 1.0 meter, and the weight is usually 50 to 65 kg. The ground color of the upper parts is tawny to pale buff or grayish white, and the under parts are white. Also there is a black stripe that extends from the eye to the mouth on each side. Normally the pattern consists of solid black spots set quite close together over the body. The hair of the neck is erect and forms a slight ruff. The mat-like growth of long hair covering the upper side of the young is represented in the adult by the short mane. Cheetahs are extremely long-legged cats, with a rounded head and short ears. The pupil of the eye is round. The feet look much like those of dogs, as the claws are blunt, only slightly curved, lack sheaths, and are only partially retractile. They are handsome cats of gentle disposition and are the swiftest of the mammals.

Although other cats capture their prey mainly in a single leap or in a short rush after waiting until the victim is within springing distance, cheetahs catch their prey by racing as far as 550 meters, after having stalked the game to some extent. Small antelopes are the main prey, but smaller mammals (such as hares) and birds are probably taken as well. Chee-tahs hunt by sight rather than by scent; they usually hunt in daylight but have been said to be active also on moonlight nights. They are solitary or associate in small groups, and at times utter a wild cry that resembles a "barking howl."

The maximum speed for short distances is about 110 km. per hour. In India they are often trained to aid in running down large game. They are usually hooded like falcons when taken out for the chase and freed when the game is in sight. The cheetah is re-warded for a successful hunt with some blood and meat of the victim.

Like some other cats, cheetahs have regular scratch-ing posts which they frequent. They are often cap-tured at these posts with set nooses.

The gestation period is from 84 to 95 days, and the number of young is two to four. Tame cheetahs are playful, affectionate, and utter a deep, low, broken purr when contented. They also utter a robin-like chirp when alarmed. This bird-like call is sometimes given when they eat.

A. rex, described in 1927, is known from only a few specimens from east central Rhodesia. The ground color is similar to that of *A. jubatus*, but black stripes—longitudinal on the back and tail and diago-nal on the flanks—largely replace the spots. Perhaps these are aberrant specimens and not a valid species.

Order: PINNIPEDIA—Pinnipeds

SEALS, SEA LIONS, WALRUSES; ZEELEEUWEN, LOBOS MARINOS, TODO, MORSAS, MORSES, WALROSS, KOMINI-AZARASI, NERPA, STEENKOBBE, ZEEHONDEN, BARTROBBE, FOCAS FRAILES. (Included are vernaculars used in other countries.)

THIS ORDER of "aquatic carnivores" consists of three Recent families including 20 genera and 31 species. Pinnipeds occur along most of the coasts of the world and some ascend rivers or live in inland lakes; these animals are most numerous in polar and temperate waters. The monk seals (*Monachus*) are the only tropical pinnipeds. The world population of this order is estimated at 15 to 25 million individuals.

Pinipeds have a streamlined, torpedo-shaped body and all four limbs are modified into flippers. The arm and leg bones are similar to those in the order Carnivora, but the bases of the limbs to or beyond the elbows and the knees are deeply enclosed within the body. The hand and foot are long and flattened (hence the name "pinnipedia," meaning "feather-footed"). Each limb has five broadly webbed, oar-like digits for propulsion in the water. The head is flattened and the face is shortened except in the hooded seals (*Cystophora*) and the elephant seals (*Mirounga*). The external ears are reduced or absent, and the nostrils are slit-like; the ears and the nostrils are closed when the animal is beneath the water. The eyes, which rest in a deep protective cushion of fat, are adapted for use under water; the cornea is flattened and the pupil is capable of great enlargement. The neck of a pinniped is thickened and muscular, yet quite flexible. An upward bending of the vertebral column is possible because of the reduction in the interlocking processes of the vertebrae.

These animals vary in length from 140 to 650 cm.; the length is measured by a straight line from the tip of the nose to the tip of the tail. The tail in pinnipeds is short or vestigial and grows very little after birth. Adult specimens weigh from 90 kg. to about 3.5 metric tons; ringed seals (*Pusa hispida*) are the smallest members of the order Pinnipedia and elephant seals are the largest. The males are larger than the females, except certain members of the family Phocidae where the male may be about the same size or slightly smaller than the female. Pinnipeds are usually well covered with hair, although adult walruses (*Odobenus*) may be almost naked. The coat of fur seals, *Callorhinus* and *Arctocephalus*, consists of a very dense growth of fine short hairs, which are valuable as insulation, and between them grow longer, coarser guard hairs that protect the fine undercoat by receiving most of the wear. When fur seal skins are prepared for sale as furs, the guard hairs are removed so that the fur garments we usually see consist of only the underfur. The young of most true seals (Phocidae) are covered with dense, soft, woolly, often white coats at birth; some pups shed this covering within a few hours after birth, but others retain the coat for several weeks. Most living pinnipeds are wet when seen and therefore appear much darker than when dry. These animals have a thick layer of oily fat or blubber between the thick, tough epidermis and the muscles of the body. This protective layer enables them to endure the chilly waters and provides a form of reserve energy as well as buoyancy and padding.

The external genitalia and the mammary teats are withdrawn beneath the surface of the body at nearly all times. Female pinnipeds have two or four mammae, and males have a baculum.

The dental formula varies widely, is not always diagnostic and is often perplexing. Carnassials are not developed. The skull is usually greatly compressed interorbitally, and the orbits are large. The mouth, jaws, and teeth are adapted for grasping and tearing flesh rather than for chewing.

Pinnipeds are quite clumsy on land, but in the water they are skillful swimmers and divers. They swim by means of the flippers and the entire sinuous trunk. In the Otariidae and the Odobenidae locomotion is accomplished mainly by the use of the forelimbs, whereas in Phocidae the hind limbs supply most of the thrust. The northern fur seal can swim 15 miles per hour when pressed, and many pinnipeds often leap clear of the water. Diving ability is now known to be at least 600 meters, and submergence time 43 minutes, 20 seconds. Much the same respiratory mechanisms are operative in the diving of pinnipeds as in cetaceans. This process allows for efficient use and availability of oxygen when the animal is submerged. Some species of pinnipeds migrate to seek an adequate food supply or more favorable temperatures. Some species, such as the harbor seal (*Phoca*), remain on land much of the time, and others, such as the northern fur seal (*Callorhinus*), may spend about eight months at sea.

Some pinnipeds apparently seek food at night, and certain polar seals feed in total darkness for four months out of a year. The diet differs with the species but consists of flesh at all times. The seaweed fragments occasionally found in the stomachs of pinnipeds probably are not deliberately ingested. A 100-kg. seal eats approximately 5 to 7 kg. of food a day when not fasting.

Some species, such as the Ross seal (*Ommatophoca*), live alone during the winter, but pinnipeds are much more gregarious than the land carnivores. A breeding colony of pinnipeds ranges from a few individuals to more than a million animals within a radius of 50 km. (the northern fur seal). These mammals tend to frequent small, isolated breeding grounds and are polygamous (Otariidae and Odobenidae) or mostly monogamous (Phocidae). All give birth ashore, on land or ice, and mate once a year. The gestation period is 8 to 12 months, with delayed implantation occurring in many, perhaps most, species. Delayed implantation may represent an adaptation that allows the births to take place at approximately the same time of the year, an important feature for colonial and, in some cases, migratory species. Single births are the rule, twins the exception. Newborn pinnipeds can swim, but the pups of some species do not have enough blubber to provide buoyancy and insulation until they are several weeks old. Growth during the nursing period is rapid, for the mother's milk is particularly rich, about 50 per cent fat. The adult pelage is usually acquired near the end of the first summer. Pinnipeds are sexually mature at two to five years and may live 40 years in the wild. Predators include large sharks, killer whales (*Orcinus*), leopard seals (*Hydrurga*), walruses (known to kill and eat ringed seals and bearded seals—*Erignathus*), and polar bears (also an enemy of walrus).

Sea lions along the South American coast are killed in limited numbers for their hides, oil, and meat for food or fertilizer. However, most of the islands on which they haul out are so rugged and exposed to the ocean seas and swells that it is very difficult and dangerous for small boats to approach close enough for successful operations. It has been estimated that about 75,000 skins were taken annually along the Peruvian coast prior to 1942.

When either sea lions or walruses are shot, many are lost in the ocean when they struggle from the rocks or ice into the water. This results in a much higher mortality rate than is represented by the reports of the numbers of animals taken.

The known geological range of the Pinnipedia is the lower Miocene to the Recent of North America, the Pliocene to the Recent of South America and Europe, the upper Pliocene of Egypt, and the Pleistocene of New Zealand, Australia, and Japan.

A young Northern Elephant Seal (*Mirounga angustirostris*) on a sandy beach. The remarkable modification of the hind limbs and body which adapts it for an aquatic existence are well illustrated here. The front flippers are partially hidden by the loose sand. Photo by Julio Berdegue.

1284

SEA LIONS AND FUR SEALS; SEELÖWEN, ZEELEEUWEN, LOBOS MARINOS, TODO. (Included are vernaculars used in other countries).

THIS FAMILY of 6 genera and 12 species occurs in the Pacific, South Atlantic, and southern Indian oceans, i.e., the coastlines of western North America and South America, southern Africa, Australia, New Zealand, and some oceanic islands. These pinnipeds inhabit arctic, temperate, and subtropical waters. Their estimated world population probably numbers from 2,850,000 to 4,175,000.

The body form of these pinnipeds is slender and elongated, with oar-like fore flippers measuring more than one-fourth the body length. All the flippers are thick and cartilaginous, thickest at the leading (forward) edge, and their surfaces are naked, smooth, and leathery. The claws are small. The external ear is small and cartilaginous. In the family Otariidae, as well as in the Odobenidae, the hind limbs can be turned forward to help support the body so that all four limbs can be used in traveling on land. The members of these two families walk or run in a somewhat dog-like position. In the other family of pinnipeds, the Phocidae, the hind limbs cannot be moved ahead and these animals must wriggle and hunch to travel on land.

These pinnipeds range in length from 150 to 350 cm., and weigh from 34 to 1,100 kg., the males being much larger than the females. The tail is short but distinct. In sea lions (four genera) the pelage consists essentially of one layer of coarse hair, although fine underhairs are present, whereas in fur seals (two genera) the underfur is distinct and important. The pelage of the newborn is hairy, never woolly. The coloration varies from yellowish or reddish brown to black; there are no stripes or sharp markings.

The females have four mammae.

The normal dental formula is: i 3/2, c 1/1, pm 4/4, m 1, 2, or 3/1 = 34 to 38. The first and second upper incisors are small and divided by a deep groove into two cusps, and the third (outer) upper incisor is canine-like. The canine teeth are large, conical, pointed, and recurved, and the premolars and molars are similar, with one main cusp. The number of upper molars varies within and among genera. The skull is somewhat elongate and rounded, though quite bear-like.

Animals of this family are highly gregarious, especially during the breeding season. They shelter in quiet bays, on rocky isolated islands, and along sea coasts. In this family (and the Odobenidae) the swimming mechanism is centered near the fore part of the body and locomotion in the water is accomplished mainly by the use of the forelimbs. A California sea lion (*Zalophus*) swimming underwater has been clocked at 17 kilometers per hour, and northern fur seals (*Callorhinus*) can swim as fast as 26 kilometers per hour when pressed. Extensive migrations are undertaken by two genera, *Callorhinus* and the South Georgian population of *Arctocephalus*, with the females and older males usually returning to the same beach that they left when they began their journey. The members of this family are nocturnal and diurnal, and have acute sight but poorly developed sense of smell and hearing. They defend themselves by tearing an adversary with their canine teeth, by hurling their weight against their adversary, or by swimming and diving.

Sea lions and fur seals live mainly on fish but also eat cephalopods and crustaceans. Penguins are sometimes taken by one genus of sea lions (*Neophoca*). Harem bulls, except perhaps in *Neophoca*, fast during the breeding season.

The breeding habitat is exclusively marine, never fresh water. The males arrive first on the breeding grounds, where they establish definite territories. The females come somewhat later and give birth shortly after arrival. The members of this family are polygamous, each bull having from 3 to more than 40 females in his harem; the size of the harem depends on the kind of species and the strength and ferocity of the bull. The bulls mate with their females on land soon after the females have given birth to the young. The gestation period is about 250 to 365 days, with delayed implantation known to occur in the two genera of fur seals. Only the mother cares for the pups. The young usually do not swim for at least two weeks; they are generally weaned in three to four months, although the offspring of *Arctocephalus pusillus* are reported to suckle for nearly a year. Sea lions (*Zalophus*) have lived for 23 years, and the average life span of the northern fur seal, that is, for females one year and older, is more than seven years.

Fur seals supply man with fur and blubber. The pelt of a sea lion, since it has only limited amounts of underfur, is valuable mainly for leather. Steller sea lions (*Eumetopias*) sometimes steal fish from nets and traps; they gather near estuaries to feed during salmon and herring runs.

The known geological range of this family is the late Miocene to the Recent in Pacific North America, the Pliocene to the Recent in South America, the Pleistocene to the Recent in Australia, New Zealand, and Japan, and the Recent in the Pacific and the Antarctic.

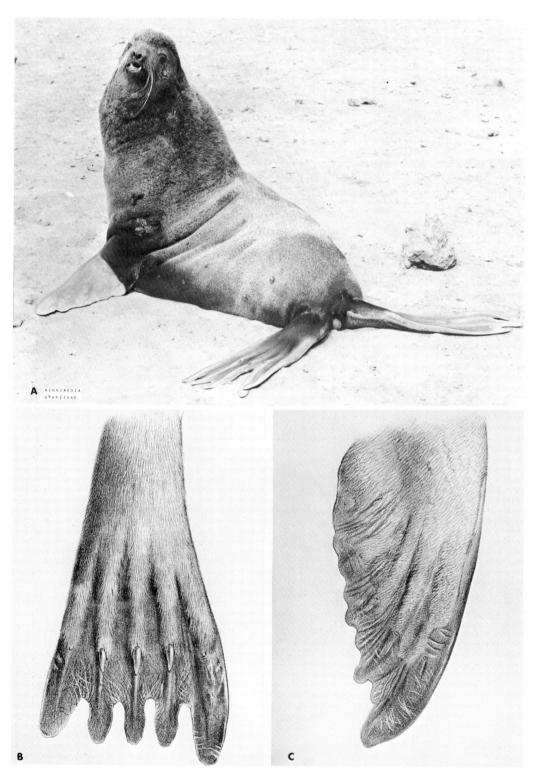

A. A Northern Fur Seal (*Callorhinus ursinus*), member of the family Otariidae which, together with the Odobenidae, are able to move their foreflippers with great freedom and can turn their hind limbs forward thus enabling them to assume an erect posture. Photo by Victor B. Scheffer through U.S. Fish and Wildlife Service. B. Right rear flipper and C. Right front flipper of South American Sea Lion (*Otaria byronia*), photos from *Proc. Zool. Soc. London*.

Patagonian or South American Sea Lions (*Otaria byronia*), photo of mounted group in Denver Museum of Natural History.

SOUTH AMERICAN SEA LIONS; LOBOS MARINOS, ZEELEEUWEN, OTARIES, SEELÖWEN. (Included are vernaculars used in other countries.)

THE SINGLE SPECIES, *O. byronia*, is found from Brazil to the Strait of Magellan and Peru. It also inhabits the Falkland Islands but has not been recorded from the Galapagos Islands. *Otaria's* geographic distribution includes about 10,000 km. along the South American coast. The estimated world population is 700,000 to 1,000,000.

Large males are about 245 cm. in length and weigh about 520 kg., whereas large females measure about 195 cm. in length. In the adults the darker colors predominate, although some individuals are gray, pale gold, or dull yellow. After the third year the males become darker and browner, whereas the females become grayer in color. The belly is dark yellow in most of these phases. The newborn young of all sea lions are brown to dark brown in color. As in the other sea lions, the pelage consists of only one layer of coarse hair, although fine underhairs are present. Males have a mane on the neck which reaches the shoulders.

Sea lions are usually found only around salt water, but they occasionally ascend rivers. South American sea lions have been noted 300 km. up the Rio de la Plata. In the water only the front flippers are used at slow speeds, in a rowing manner. Swimming speed is increased by bringing the hind flippers into use. All four limbs are also used in progessing on land, but with each step the hindquarters must be thrown forward because the soft tissues and tail extend so far toward the ankle joints. On a pebbly beach this clumsy gait can be increased to a speed almost as fast as a man can run. These animals are inquisitive, but they become frightened and panic quite easily.

Although southward movements have been reported for certain areas, these sea lions are not believed to be migratory in the true sense. Their diet consists of cuttlefish, crustaceans (*Mundia* sp.), and fish (around the Falkland Islands).

When not reproducing they live in large, apparently unorganized herds. As the Antarctic summer approaches, however, the breeding and non-breeding animals separate. The breeding herds consist of harem bulls, sexually mature cows, and newborn pups. The female becomes sexually active about the end of the fourth year. Studies in the Falkland Islands revealed an average harem size of nine females. The harem bull guards his females against the sexual approaches of other males and breeds them soon after the young of the preceding year are born. The gestation period is about 330 days, and the number of newborn young is one, rarely two. The harems break up after the bull has bred all the females. Then male aggressiveness decreases and they may be seen guarding the young. Two females have lived in a zoological park for 16½ and 17½ years respectively.

These and other sea lions have never been exploited commercially on an important scale, mainly because the rocky, exposed places they inhabit are difficult for boats to land on.

Steller Sea Lions (*Eumetopias jubatus*), A. Rookery, photo by Victor B. Scheffer. B. & C. Male, female, and pup, photos by Karl W. Kenyon.

NORTHERN OR STELLER SEA LIONS; TODO.

THE SINGLE SPECIES, *E. jubatus,* breeds from northeastern Bering Sea, the Aleutian Islands, and the west coast of North America, southward to southern California, and westward to the Commander Islands, Kamchatka, and Japan. This is a subarctic to cool temperate species. Northern sea lions move along the coast when not breeding, but little is known of their movements. Like other sea lions, they occasionally ascend rivers; one was captured 150 km. from the ocean in the Columbia River. The estimated world population is 60,000 to 150,000.

These are the largest of the Otariidae. Males measure about 350 cm. in length and weigh as much as 1,100 kg.; females attain 270 cm. in length and 350 kg. in weight. The tail length is usually 7.7 to 17.8 cm. Young animals are dark brown in color, and adults are buffy or yellowish tan. These seals are practically hairless. Characteristics include the large size, light color, and heavy muzzle and head. Young less than a year old may be confused with the fur seals and *Zalophus.*

Steller sea lions are seldom seen in zoos. Adults utter a prolonged, deep-throated, bellowing roar, as well as coughing and grunting sounds. They may descend from 110 to 146 meters below the surface and sometimes reach a depth of 183 meters. The diet seems to consist mainly of fish but also includes squid.

The harem masters of most members of this family (Otariidae) do not feed during the breeding season.

This species congregates in colonies along the ocean coasts where the animals clamber above the water on ledges and rocks. The single pup is born in such areas less than a week after the mother comes ashore. The young are born in late May and June, and soon after giving birth the female breeds again, although there is some evidence that the female is not bred every year. The harems usually contain from 10 to 20 females, and the bulls fight savagely with rivals to hold their favorite ground and harems. The necks of old males are usually scarred from bites received in such battles. The harems gradually break up during July, and by August most of the bulls have left the breeding grounds.

The pups weigh 16 to 23 kg. at birth. They live on milk for at least three months. Some still may be seen with their mother a year after birth. Although the young are capable of swimming immediately after birth, they lack sufficient body fat to survive long in cold water. By the time they are several weeks old, they spend much of their time swimming and playing in tide pools. Mortality is high among the young. Many drown as a result of exhaustion after falling into the sea and inability to climb back onto the rookery reefs. Others are crushed by bulls, especially when the latter are fighting. The sounds made by the young very much resemble the bleat of a lamb.

California Sea Lion (*Zalophus californianus*), photo by Victor B. Scheffer.

CALIFORNIAN AND JAPANESE SEA LIONS; LOBOS MARINOS.

THREE ISOLATED POPULATIONS of the single species, *Z. californianus*, inhabit the west coast of North America, the Galapagos Islands, and perhaps the Southern Sea of Japan. This is a subtropic to temperate species. The estimated world population is 70,000 to 150,000; the population in Japanese waters may have become extinct in the 1950's.

Large males measure 236 cm. in length and weigh about 280 kg., and large females attain lengths of about 180 cm. and weights of about 90 kg. These animals appear to be black when wet; when dry, the true brown color ranges from shades of light buff to deep sepia. The adult male may be recognized by the crest on the top of the head which becomes lighter in color with age. Both sexes have broader, heavier muzzles than the fur seals.

These are the trained seals of circuses and vaudeville. With rare exceptions, they are the only pinnipeds that have been trained to perform. They are playful, even in the wild, and are gregarious through-out the year. The sounds made are sharp barks or honks. The other members of this family (Otariidae) have more prolonged roaring calls.

These sea lions feed on squid, octopus, herring, rockfish, hake, and rat fish, which they catch by means of their agility in swimming and turning in the water. On land they progress by "walking" with the flippers and "hitching" with the body. Like other Otariidae, they can travel more rapidly and farther on land than members of Phocidae. California sea lions tend to frequent sandy or rocky beaches as well as inner reefs on coastal islands.

The cows apparently begin to breed at three years of age and the bulls when five or more years old. The bulls arrive on the breeding grounds in early June and take up their stations, then the cows come ashore. The more powerful males have harems of 5 to 20 females, but the harems are not closely organized. After the single pup is born, the females are bred again. The gestation period is 342 to 365 days. The pups swim in tide pools and later go to sea with their mothers. They remain together for nearly a year. Captive individuals have lived 23 years.

A. Australian Sea Lions (*Neophoca cinerea*), photo by Vincent Serventy. B. White-Capped Hair Seals (*N. cinerea*), photo by Eric Lindgren.

AUSTRALIAN AND NEW ZEALAND SEA LIONS, WHITE-CAPPED HAIR SEALS; TASMAN SEA LIONS.

As PRESENTLY UNDERSTOOD, this genus is confined to the southern hemisphere. The population from the south coast of Australia is known as *N. cinerea*, and the population from extreme southern New Zealand is referred to as *N. hookeri*. The genus is not well known. Australian sea lions have been exterminated in southeastern Australia and Tasmania and are now confined to waters west of Adelaide.

The length of the large males is up to 240 cm.; the females are smaller and more gracefully built than the males. Large males weigh as much as 410 kg., and large females, about 230 kg. Old bulls have a yellowish mane and a dark-brown head and body; in younger males the mane and the thickening of the neck and shoulders are less pronounced; females are dark brown above and yellowish below. Morphologically, this genus differs in skull features from the other genera of Otariidae. As in the other sea lions, there are only small amounts of underfur and the pelt is valuable for leather.

The following remarks apply to *N. cinerea*. This pinniped is quite sedentary and may live its entire life around the beach on which it was born. Pupping and breeding take place from October to December, at which time the entire community is ashore, usually on a sandy beach flanked by granite outcrops. Although one bull may be associated with only one female, a given bull usually has a harem of three or more females which he defends against intruders. The single young is carefully guarded. *N. cinerea* does not fast during the breeding season. It feeds during this time, mainly on penguins which it catches as they come out of their shelters or as they waddle across the beach.

In recent studies on *N. hookeri* on Campbell Island, it was noted that these animals liked to play. They would entice some of the island dogs into the water by splashing and then would play "ring-around-a-rosy." The sea lions swam in circles around the dogs and the dogs barked and tried to nip the sea lions.

Neophoca has remarkable running and climbing abilities. Occasionally it wanders inland, and there is a record of an individual *N. cinerea* being found 9.7 km. from the coast.

These pinnipeds have been considerably reduced in numbers, being slaughtered by man. The estimated world population of the genus at the present time is 12,000 to 60,000.

The type species of the genus is *N. lobata* (Gray) = *N. cinerea*.

New Zealand Fur Seal (*Arctocephalus forsteri*), photo by John Warham.

SOUTHERN FUR SEALS; SEELEEU, OSOS MARINOS, LOBOS DE DOS PELOS, SEELEEUE, ZEEBEREN.

THE SIX SPECIES and their distribution are as follows: *A. pusillus*, the sea and islands along the southern coast of Africa; *A. forsteri*, southern New Zealand and adjacent subantarctic islands; *A. doriferus*, southern Australia and Tasmania; *A. tropicalis*, subantarctic islands in the southern Indian Ocean and the southern Atlantic Ocean; *A. australis*, from Brazil to the Strait of Magellan and northward to Peru, also the Galapagos Islands and the Falkland Islands; *A. philippii*, apparently now only around Guadalupe Island off the coast of Lower California. The estimated world population of the genus is about 430,000 to 900,000. The population of the Guadalupe fur seal is estimated at only 200 to 500, the only surviving individuals of this genus in the Northern Hemisphere.

The length is usually 1.5 to 2 meters; the females are considerably smaller than the males. The species *A. pusillus* may be the largest of all fur seals. Males measure up to 257 cm. in length and weigh 295 kg., and females attain 179 cm. in length and weigh 122 kg. The color is usually some shade of brown or black, gray, or yellowish gray. In general external appearance and size these pinnipeds are similar to the northern fur seals (*Callorhinus*), but the shape of the head is different. A fine, dense underfur is present of slightly less commercial value than in *Callorhinus*.

Southern fur seals emit roars, growls, and coughs. They congregate on favorite rocks and beaches. The south Georgia Island population of *A. australis* seems to be the only population of this genus that makes a true migration. On the Galapagos and Guadalupe islands some of the seals stay in caves during the daytime, a habit which has probably saved these colonies from extermination. The diet seems to be mainly small fish, cuttlefish, and crustaceans.

A. pusillus remains near its breeding grounds all year. The mature males of this genus establish harems which formerly consisted of as many as 50 females but now number 5 to 15 cows. The cows are usually bred within a week after giving birth to one, rarely two, young. The gestation period in *A. pusillus* averaged 259 days in a recent study, and the gestation period in *A. australis* has been reported as about 11 months. Delayed implantation is known to occur. Female *A. pusillus* breed after their second winter. The pups of this species suckle for nearly a year. The life span for the genus may be 20 years.

The best known of all the species is *A. pusillus*. This fur seal has been hunted commercially for more than 300 years, and some 30,000 pelts are taken annually. From the fat of fur seals and sea lions (*Otaria*) the Uruguayan government prepares oil which is high in certain vitamins and is distributed to hospitals for tubercular patients.

Seals have had an important part in Antarctic history. The first men to see and set foot upon the continent came there looking for fur seals. They found them on the islands around Antarctica by the thousands, but so greedy were these men that the fur seals almost completely disappeared within less than 10 years.

The type species of the genus is *A. pusillus* (Schreber).

Northern Fur Seals (*Callorhinus ursinus*), A. Harem bull with females and young; B. Courtship between fur seals; photos by Victor B. Scheffer.

NORTHERN FUR SEALS; OTTOSEI.

THE SINGLE SPECIES, *C. ursinus*, breeds in the summer and fall on the Pribilof Islands in the Bering Sea, the Commander Islands beyond the western end of the Aleutians, and Robben Island in the Okhotsk Sea. Small breeding populations are returning to the Kurile Islands. During the winter and spring, northern fur seals are widely dispersed over the southern Bering Sea, the Sea of Okhotsk, the North Pacific Ocean, and the Sea of Japan and are found as far south as

the waters off San Diego, California, and Japan. On rare occasions individuals have also been noted in the Arctic Ocean. The estimated world population is 1,580,000 to 1,920,000.

Adult bulls have a length of 1.9 to 2.1 meters and weigh 180 to 300 kg.; adult cows attain lengths of 1.5 to 1.7 meters and weights of 36 to 68 kg. Pups at birth weigh about 5 kg. and are glossy black in color. The adult males are dark gray to brown above, usually with gray shoulders and foreneck, and with reddish-brown flippers and under parts; adult females have grayish-brown upper parts and reddish-brown or gray under parts. In the males of this genus the forehead descends more abruptly than does that of the southern fur seals (*Arctocephalus*).

Northern fur seals spend most of their life in the water, where they travel singly or in small groups. They are rapid and skillful swimmers and are known to dive to depths of 110 meters. They travel relatively well on land but must rest frequently. These animals roar, bleat, cough, and bark. They feed on at least 30 kinds of marine organisms, mainly squids, fish, and crustaceans. The food habits of this species have been studied extensively because of the allegation by some fishermen that northern seals destroy many salmon. More than 4,900 stomachs have been examined, and the flesh of salmon was found in only 1½ per cent of the stomachs. *Callorhinus* eats about 7 per cent of its own weight each day. As in *Arctocephalus*, the harem bulls do not feed during the breeding season, subsisting on their own blubber during this time.

The bulls arrive first on the breeding grounds, and the mature females follow in June and July. A mature male seven years old may gather a harem of several cows, whereas a bull of twice this age has a harem of 40 cows. The older bulls are able to gather larger harems because of their greater strength and ferocity. The cows give birth to a single pup a few days after they arrive on the breeding grounds and breed again a few days later. The young are born from about June 20 to July 20. Including the period of delayed implantation, the gestation period is thus about one year. The cows may begin to breed when three years old and have reproduced when 21 years of age.

The pups are nursed in the harem. Several times a week the mother swims out to sea, often 80 to 160 kilometers from the breeding grounds, and feeds in order to obtain sufficient nourishment to continue nursing her pup. She then returns to the land, finds her pup among the thousands in the rookery, and nurses it. The pups can swim at six to eight weeks of age and are weaned at four months, when the cows leave on the southward migration between September and December. This is the feeding migration. The pups also leave the rookeries about this time, but they do not travel with the cows. The bulls do not travel as far south as the cows and the juveniles; those of

the Pribilof herd winter in the Gulf of Alaska and off British Columbia. Harem bulls have become so thin by the end of the breeding season that they hardly have the strength to travel down to the water. It was once thought that the three breeding herds of this highly social and mobile species remained distinct in their winter migration, but recoveries of banded and tagged individuals have shown that thousands of seals from Alaskan waters migrate into Japanese waters and mingle there with Asian seals, and that seals born in Alaskan rookeries occasionally return north to Asian breeding grounds as subadults. The homing instinct is quite strong on the return migration, however, and the females and older males usually return to the rookery of their birth. This species undergoes the most extensive migration of any pinniped: distances of up to 10,000 km. may be covered in one year. Fur seals in migration do not travel in herds, but in small groups or even singly.

Exploitation and wanton slaughter reduced the numbers of this species to about 132,000 in 1910. An international treaty abolishing sealing on the high seas for 15 years was signed in 1911 by the United States, Great Britain (representing Canada), Russia, and Japan to help prevent the continued decline of this species. Under this treaty the United States and Russia, as guardians of the seal herds, agreed to pay to both Great Britain and Japan, for their relinquishment of pelagic sealing, 15 per cent of the proceeds from the land sealing conducted by these two nations. Japan, in turn, agreed to pay to the United States, Great Britain, and Russia, respectively, 10 per cent of the land catch of the herd under her jurisdiction. The treaty endured until 1941. Following 16 years of temporary arrangements, a new four-nation treaty was signed in 1957. The Pribilofs are a special government reservation—landings can only be made with government permission or because of bad weather conditions. These measures restored the species to its present numerical status. Each year, at the present time, 80 per cent of the three- and four-year-old idle or bachelor bulls in the Alaskan herds are killed for pelts, oil, and meal. The total annual kill is about 60,000 bachelor males and 30,000 surplus females of various ages. This does not affect the species population adversely; it is supervised by the U. S. Fish and Wildlife Service. The restoration of this species is one of the finest examples of conservation in action.

Walruses (*Odobenus rosmarus divergens*), A. A herd of walruses, photo from U.S. Navy. B. Walruses basking on land, photo by Alwin Pedersen. C. Young walrus, photo from Zoologisk Have, Copenhagen.

WALRUSES, MORSES; WALROSS, MORSAS, MANSE.

THIS FAMILY contains a single Recent genus and species, *Odobenus rosmarus*, the walrus. These pinnipeds inhabit open waters of the Arctic Ocean near the edge of the polar ice; their circular distribution apparently is restricted to the northeastern coast of Siberia, the northwestern coast of Alaska, and north to northwest Greenland and Ellesmere Island. Most animals migrate south in winter, with the advance of the arctic ice, and move north in the spring when the ice retreats. They ride the floes in migration, but their movements are sufficiently directional that they can abandon the ice when it strays from their intended course. Stormy weather may force them to travel on snow as far as 33 km. overland. The estimated world population is 45,000 to 90,000 individuals, and it appears to be decreasing.

These pinnipeds have a thick, swollen body form, a rounded head and muzzle, a short neck, a tough, wrinkled, thinly-haired skin, and large tusks. The eyes are small and pig-like, and the external ears are represented by only a low wrinkle of skin. It has recently been observed (Pedersen, 1962) that the nostrils of *O. r. divergens*, the Pacific walrus, are not visible when viewed from the front. In the Atlantic subspecies, *O. r. rosmarus*, however, the nostrils are visible when viewed from the front. The fore flippers are long and oar-like and about one-fourth the length of the body. All the flippers are thick and cartilaginous, being thickest on the forward (leading) edge. The flippers have five digits, and the palms and soles are bare, rough, and warty for traction on ice. In the family Odobenidae as in the Otariidae the hind limbs can be turned forward to aid the body in maneuvering on all four limbs on land; the members of these two families walk or run with a somewhat upright carriage. In the third family of pinnipeds, the Phocidae, the hind limbs cannot be so manipulated and these animals must twist and move forward jerkily on land.

The length of bulls is 3 to 3.7 meters, the height is as much as 1.5 meters, and the weight is usually more than a metric ton and can be 1,260 kg.; the cows are about one-third smaller. There is no external tail. The skin is 1.5 to 5 cm. thick, with an underlying layer of blubber about 15 cm. in thickness. The wrinkled, yellowish-gray hide, which appears to be bay color when dry, is naked except for a few scattered stiff hairs. There is also a conspicuous mustache, consisting of about 400 thick bristles richly supplied with blood vessels and nerves. The pelage of the newborn walrus is hairy, never woolly.

The baculum, about 63 cm. in length, is occasionally fractured, suggesting that the evolution of body weight may be proceeding faster than the evolution of the supporting framework. The females have four mammae.

The upper canines are the outstanding feature of the adult walrus. These teeth grow throughout life in both sexes, developing into tusks that may attain a length of 100 cm. in the male and 60 cm. in the female, of which about 80 per cent is exposed. A single tusk in an old male may weigh 5.35 kg. The tusks of the female are more curved in the middle and more slender than are those of the male. Walrus skulls with three upper tusks are fairly common. The tusk is peculiar in that it bears enamel only at the tip for a short time after it has erupted; the entire crown in the adult consists of dentin (ivory). The permanent dental formula is quite variable, but usually is: i 1/0, c 1/1, pm 3/3, m 0/0 = 18. The bluntly conical or flat cheek teeth are specialized for crushing mollusk shells, although no crushed shells have ever been discovered in a walrus stomach. Another theory is that the shellfish are sucked from their shell attachments. The deciduous or milk dentition is as follows: 3/3, 1/1, 5/4 (some of the postcanine teeth are lost early in life or are vestigial and concealed in the gums). The skull is rounded, and the halves of the lower jaw are solidly fused in the adult.

Walruses generally associate in mixed herds of cows, calves, and bulls, numbering up to a hundred individuals or more. They shelter on isolated rocky coasts, islands, and ice floes. In the families Odobenidae and Otariidae the swimming mechanism is centered near the fore body and progress in the water is made by using the forelimbs. Walruses can swim about 24 km. per hour. They have a bellow that sounds like the voice of a St. Bernard dog and an elephant-like trumpeting sound. They use their tusks to aid them when they haul out on the ice and when threatened, the whole herd joining in the defense of a single member. These pinnipeds are nocturnal and diurnal; they have fair sight but poor senses of smell and hearing. The extremely heavy bristles on the snout are excellent sensory organs and are also believed to act as a filter for food organisms on muddy ocean bottoms.

Members of the genus *Odobenus* live mainly in coastal waters, as they usually forage at depths of less than 90 meters. While feeding, a walrus sinks to the bottom and perhaps, though not certainly, uses its tusks and perhaps the snout bristles to obtain mollusks and other marine life. The shells of its prey seldom are swallowed. The food is worked into the mouth by the muzzle pads. A solitary walrus is reported to feed occasionally on a narwhal (*Monodon*), a beluga (*Delphinapterus*), or a seal, but the stomach will hold only about a gallon of food. It would seem likely that dead cetaceans, rather than live ones, are attacked for food.

The breeding habitat is exclusively marine. Walruses are polygamous. The gestation period is 11 to 12 months (delayed implantation probably does not occur), the births taking place from April to June. The calf at birth is approximately 1.25 meters long, 45 to 68 kg. in weight, gray in color, and capable of swimming. There is no external evidence of teeth. The mother defends and guards her young against danger; a small calf travels on its mother's neck even when she swims and dives. The offspring nurses for 18 to possibly 24 months, by which time its tusks are developed sufficiently for it to dig its own food. As a result of the extended period of nursing, the cow is not bred more often than every other year. The cows are capable of bearing young at four to five years of age and the bulls are sexually mature in about seven years. Walruses probably can live 40 years in their native habitat.

Practically every part of the walrus is used by the Eskimo either for food, material for boats or shelter,

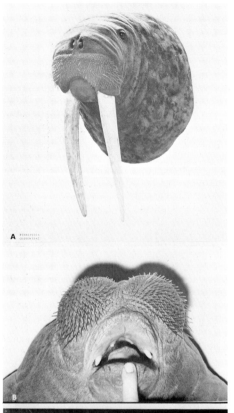

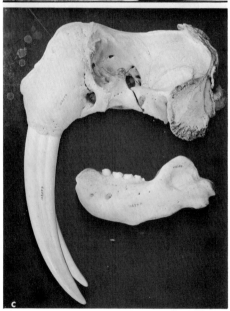

oil, or charms. The Eskimos actually "fish" for walrus, using strong lines baited with chunks of blubber, in addition to hunting them. Today, hunting by certain natives for tusks alone is a threat to the existence of local walrus populations; and there is a high, perhaps excessive, percentage of loss in current Eskimo harvest methods.

The known geological range of the family Odobenidae is the upper Miocene to the Pleistocene in Atlantic North America, the middle Pliocene to Pleistocene in Europe, and the Recent in arctic regions. *Trichecodon* is a genus of walrus known from the Mid-Pliocene to the Pleistocene of Europe; its remains have been taken from fossil beds in England and Russia. This animal had a shortened jaw and a rather typical walrus skull.

A. Mounted head of an adult male walrus from eastern Siberia (*Odobenus rosmarus divergens*), photo by Grancel Fitz through New York Zoological Society. B. Yearling male walrus (*O. rosmarus rosmarus*), photo by Victor B. Scheffer. C. Skull of Pacific Walrus (*O. rosmarus divergens*), photo from U.S. National Museum.

TRUE, EARLESS, OR HAIR SEALS, ELEPHANT SEALS; KOMINI-AZARASI, NERPA, STEENKOBBE, ZEEHONDEN, SEEHUNDE, FOCAS FRAILES. (Included are vernaculars used in other countries.)

THIS FAMILY of 13 genera and 18 species inhabits coastal and oceanic waters in polar, temperate, and tropical regions of the world and is most numerous in colder areas. It also occurs in certain fresh-water lakes. Eight genera live in the Northern Hemisphere, five occur in the Southern Hemisphere, but one of the thirteen (*Mirounga*) occurs in both hemispheres. With the exception of an occasional California sea lion, *Zalophus* (Otariidae), monk seals (*Monachus*) are the only tropical pinnipeds. The world population of phocids is estimated at 10,887,500 to 22,142,500 animals.

The fore flippers, which are placed far forward, are smaller than the hind flippers and are much less than a fourth of the body length. The flippers are flexible, of nearly uniform thickness, and equipped with five digits. These pinnipeds cannot turn their hind limbs forward and therefore wriggle and hunch along in order to travel on land. Such locomotion is rather laborious, so that whenever possible the animal rolls or slides. In phocids the external ear is represented by a faint wrinkling of the skin, as in the Odobenidae there is no supporting cartilage.

Phocids measure from 125 to 650 cm. in length, and weigh approximately 90 kg. to 3.5 metric tons (some individuals of the genera *Phoca* and *Pusa* weigh less than 90 kg.). Ringed seals (*Pusa*) are the smallest pinnipeds, and elephant seals (*Mirounga*) are the largest. In a number of genera the newborn are covered with dense, soft, woolly, often white coats, and some members of this family (the harp seal, *Pagophilus*; and the hooded seal, *Cystophora*) have three distinctive coats: the newborn, subadult, and adult pelages. The fur in adults is stiff and lacks appreciable amounts of underfur (the skin of the adult elephant seal may be almost nude). The eyebrow vibrissae are well developed, and the vibrissae in the mustache are often beaded. A number of genera have a spotted color pattern, and two genera (*Pagophilus* and *Histriophoca*) are the only pinnipeds with a banded pattern and sexual differences in the pattern. As in other pinnipeds, extensive amounts of blubber are present; approximately 113 kg. of blubber were removed from a Weddell seal (*Leptonychotes*), more than one-fourth of the total weight of the animal.

The baculum is well developed. The females have two or four mammae.

The upper incisors have simple pointed crowns, the canines are elongate, and the postcanines usually have three or more distinct cusps. The dental formula is as follows: i 2-3/1-2, c 1/1, pm 4-6/4-5 = 26 to 36.

Phocids shelter on rocky or sandy coasts, islands, and ice floes, with some members of the family, such as *Pusa*, staying on land or ice much of the time. They generally congregate in groups (*Mirounga* is a highly gregarious genus), but a few forms tend to live alone at certain times. The earless seals do not congregate in large rookeries like the eared seals do and there are no large harems. They go onto sandy or rocky beaches singly or in small groups, where ice floes or ledges provide easy access onto the ice.

The members of the family Phocidae propel themselves in water by the hind flippers moving in a vertical plane, as the swimming mechanism is centered near the hind part of the body, and not close to the fore body as in the Otariidae and Odobenidae. Phocids frequently swim on their backs, at least in captivity, and regularly stand upright in water, maintaining their position by "treading" with their fore flippers. Some forms migrate, others make local movements corresponding to the fluctuations of the ice, and long dispersals from the home colony are common in some species. Comparatively little is known regarding the depths to which these seals dive, or the duration of their dives. The Weddell Seal (*Leptonychotes weddelli*) is known to have stayed submerged for 43 minutes and 20 seconds, and to have descended to a depth of at least 600 meters. Weddell seals frequently dive to 300 and 400 meters, and usually remain submerged 6 to 15 minutes. Phocids defend themselves by opening their mouth, uttering menacing cries, and by advancing against the enemy, or they may flee to the water and dive. Despite their hunching and wriggling mode of progression on land, phocids can move fast when necessary. The crab-eater seal (*Lobodon*) may be the fastest pinniped on land and has been known to outrun a man racing with it.

Seals in the polar regions maintain breathing holes in the ice by tearing or sawing new ice with their teeth. Elephant seals, when sleeping on land, breathe regularly for about five minutes (nearly six times a minute) and then stop breathing for an interval of eight minutes or longer (about five minutes on the average).

The members of this family are diurnal and nocturnal, have good sight, and a fair sense of smell, but poor hearing. Most forms eat fish, shellfish, and cephalopods, with some species feeding mainly on invertebrates and the weaned young of other species. *Hydrurga*, the leopard seal, is the only seal that preys regularly on birds and other seals. Some members of this family can fast for long periods; the southern elephant seal, for example, fasts in the wild on land during the rearing of the newborn for more than two months and in captivity (after capture) for almost 100 days, and a monk seal in captivity may fast for about 4 months.

The breeding habitat is usually marine, but often it is at a river mouth. Some species live permanently in fresh-water lakes. The males establish territories on land during the breeding season. Most species live in pairs during the mating season, and polygamy apparently occurs only in the gray seals, *Halichoerus* (average harem, 10) and elephant seals (average harem, 20). The leopard seal breeds approximately four months after the pups are born; some phocids mate soon after the females give birth in the spring. Delayed implantation is definitely known to occur in several genera and is suspected in others. The gestation period is about 270 to 350 days. The pups at birth weigh from 5 to almost 45 kg.; they can swim (*Phoca*), but other species often shun the water for several weeks. Young phocids nurse for at least 10

A. Southern Elephant Seals (*Mirounga leonina*), a non-breeding group assembled on Macquarie Island. In such places they are helpless against human predators, and this group is composed of the descendants of a few that remained after the species was almost exterminated in the Antarctic up to 1918. Photo from Australian News and Information Bureau. B. & C. Weddell Seals (*Leptonychotes weddelli*), about 14 days after the birth of the pup, the mother tries to get it in the water by going in herself and calling him. While the pup gains courage, she saws a ramp in the ice with her teeth so that the pup can slide into the water. Photos from U.S. Navy.

1300

days, usually for several weeks. They are capable of breeding at an age of 2 to 8 years and may live approximately 40 years.

It is doubtful that any newly born mammals undergo such an extreme change in conditions as do the babies of some of the Pinnipeds, particularly those of the earless seals (Phocidae) and the walruses (Odobenidae). Most of them go abruptly from the comfortable temperature of the mother's body to lie on the ice and breathe the cold air which is usually much below freezing. The baby seals of most genera are protected by an insulating coat of short, dense wool-like hair. The woolly coat of baby seals is shed in less than a month and replaced by the adult coat which is better adapted for life in the cold water. Baby walruses and the young of some of the genera of the family Phocidae do not have the dense, woolly white coat when born, but have a soft baby coat at first.

Phocids are hunted for food, clothing, oil, tools, and fur by the Eskimos.

The commercial sealing industry was carried on for many years from both the European and northeastern American coasts. Seals were taken in the North Atlantic where they were usually killed by being hit on the head with a club as they were lying on the ice floes, although some were shot. Both the newly born young in the white woolly coats and adults were taken. Finally, the dwindling population and the increased cost of operations caused the industry to decline, but there is still some commercial sealing in the North Atlantic.

The skins are obtained for leather and for decorative purposes (when the hair is left on). The white, woolly skins of the young are used for ornamental purposes. Seal fat was formerly an important source of oil.

The known geological range of this family is the lower Miocene to the Recent in North America, the upper Pliocene in Egypt, the middle Miocene to the Recent in Europe, and the Recent in nearly all seas and oceans.

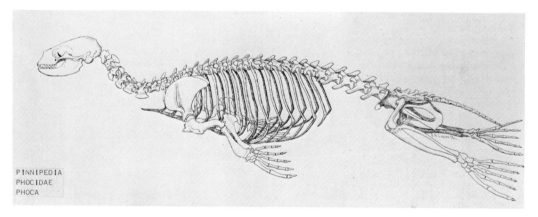

PINNIPEDIA
PHOCIDAE
PHOCA

Skeleton of Harbor Seal (*Phoca vitulina*), photo from the American Museum of Natural History.

Hair or Harbor Seals (*Phoca vitulina*), A. Adult male, photo by Erna Mohr. B. Two females, photo from Miami Seaquarium. C. Immature seals, photo by Alwin Pedersen. D. Head, showing nostrils closed, photo by Erwin Kulzer.

HAIR SEALS, HARBOR SEALS, EARLESS SEALS; SELCHIE, RAWA, NERPA, STEENKOBBE, ZEEHONDEN, PHOGNES, KOMINI-AZARASI, KURUKOKE-AZARANI. (Included are vernaculars used in other countries.)

A SINGLE SPECIES, *P. vitulina*, inhabits the shores of the oceans of the Northern Hemisphere. Although hair seals generally frequent salt water, they often ascend large rivers for hundreds of kilometers, particularly to follow runs of fish. Those in Seal Lake, Ungava, live regularly in fresh water, and there are seals in Lake Iliamna (Alaska) which may be resident or may return to the Bering Sea when they wish to do so. These seals do not make definite migrations, but unusually heavy ice in the north may cause them to be temporarily absent.

They range in head and body length from about 1.3 to 2 meters, and the tail is only 75 to 102 mm. long. There are no external ears, and the eyes are prominent. The hind limbs (flippers) do not bend forward to support the body when out of the water, as in the case of the eared seals.

The late fetal or newborn young are covered by a coat of soft white or yellowish-white wool that is shed before or after birth; it is probably never retained for more than a week or two. The succeeding coats consist of short, stiff, coarse hairs (about 25 mm. long) without underfur. The ground color varies widely through silver, gray, or whitish gray to dark grayish brown or almost black; the color is usually darkest on the back which has slightly dark spots, blotches, or rings. Occasionally the markings are light on a dark ground color.

These seals feed on a wide variety of coastal fish and shellfish. Where they compete with commercial fishing interests, they are threatened with extermination.

These animals are scattered during the summer. The late summer groups contain individuals of all ages, and in September the mature seals swim to secluded areas where they mate in the water. Loosely organized colonies may be formed, but harbor seals do not establish harems. The winter is usually spent away from the mainland, except possibly in the northern parts of the range.

The gestation period is about 280 days, and one or two young are born. Young seals become tame in a few moments or hours at most. They make intelligent, docile, and affectionate pets. Life expectancy is about 19 years.

Eskimos hunt them occasionally (taking far greater numbers of ringed seals), and use practically every portion of the carcass for clothing, food, fuel, tendons for sewing, harness, etc. Limited commercial use has been made of their skins for leather or for ornamental purposes. However, the animals are difficult to obtain and hunting them is not profitable. Killer whales (*Orca*) and polar bears (*Thalarctos*) are the greatest enemies of these seals.

Ringed Seal (*Pusa* sp.), photo from the Zoological Garden Berlin-West through Ernst von Roy.

RINGED, BAIKAL, AND CASPIAN SEALS; ZEEHON-DEN.

THE THREE SPECIES and their distribution are as follows: *P. hispida*, the ringed seal, is circumboreal near the ice edge to the North Pole, also in land-locked lakes of western Europe and in at least one lake on Baffin Island; *P. sibirica* is known only from Lake Baikal in Siberia; *P. caspica* is known only from the Caspian Sea. Members of the genus *Pusa* have an affinity for ice.

Large males and females measure about 140 cm. in length and weigh about 90 kg. These are believed to be the smallest pinnipeds. Coloration in *P. hispida* is highly variable, but the back is streaked and marbled with black; white spots with dark centers, although not always present, are characteristic; the under parts are usually whitish. The species *P. caspica* also has spotted upper parts. In *P. sibirica* the back is uniformly olive brownish or brownish silver-gray, and the sides and under parts are lighter and yellower; spots are lacking. The whitish pelage of the newborn persists for about two weeks after birth in *Pusa*. Besides their affinity for ice, seals of this genus differ from *Phoca* in having more delicate skull structure. Old males have a strong, disagreeable body odor.

The ringed seal is one of the most common and widely distributed seals and is probably the most important pinniped in the economy of Arctic natives. The estimated world population of this species is 2,267,000 to 5,815,000. It is not gregarious and not migratory, although it moves with the movements of the edge of the ice. It feeds mainly on small, free-swimming crustaceans and mollusks, and also on small fish. The young are born on the ice in the spring and remain there for four to six weeks.

The estimated world stock of the Baikal seal is 40,000 to 100,000. Lake Baikal freezes over in the winter, and only pregnant females haul out on the ice during this time. Beginning in April, the rest of the seals come onto the ice and form groups of 100 to 200 individuals. When the ice breaks up in early summer and drifts to the northern part of the lake, the seals follow it and form summer rookeries on rocks projecting from the water. These rookeries break up with the ice formation in the fall.

The Caspian seal has an estimated world population of 800,000 to 1,500,000. Since the Caspian Sea freezes only in its northern part, these seals migrate northward in the autumn and form winter rookeries on the ice. Most pups are born in January, and most breeding takes place in February and March. In May Caspian seals migrate to the cooler waters in the southern part of the sea. As in the Baikal seal, the diet is mainly fish.

The genotype is *P. hispida* (Schreber).

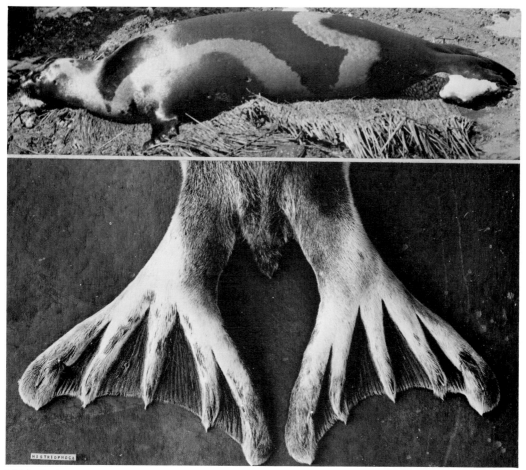

Ribbon Seal (*Histriophoca fasciata*), upper photo by Ford Wilke, lower photo by Victor B. Scheffer.

RIBBON SEALS; KAIGULIK (Eskimo name).

THE SINGLE SPECIES, *H. fasciata*, is known from the Bering Sea, the Siberian Sea, the Sea of Okhotsk, and southward to Hokkaido, Japan. It seems to be most common in the northwestern part of the Bering Sea; the distance from one end of the range to the other, via water, is about 5,000 km. These seals inhabit open marine waters, mainland and insular shores, and sea ice.

Large males are about 170 cm. in length and 95 kg. in weight; large females measure about 165 cm. and weigh about 80 kg. This species may be identified immediately by the banded pelage and the Pacific-Arctic range. The only other seal with a banded coat is the harp seal (*Pagophilus*), which breeds in the Atlantic-Arctic. Male ribbon seals are chocolate-brown in color with a series of ribbon-like bands—one around the neck, one around each fore flipper, and one around the rump. Females and young are pale to dark gray with faint indications of the bands. The white woolly coat of the young is shed in April or May.

The estimated world population is 20,000 to 50,000. Ribbon seals seem to be rare, as there are no histori-cal records that they were ever numerous in any region.

They are usually solitary or found in small groups. Ribbon seals are known to feed on fish and squid.

Movements are not well known. S. P. Naumov (*Pinnipedia of the Okhotsk Sea, Chiefly Southern Part*, Uchenye Zapiski Moskovskogo Gosudarstvennogo Pedagogicheskogo Instituta, Tom 24, no. 2, 1941, p. 74 [In Russian, English summary]) comments: "This species is found in the Okhotsk Sea almost exclusively in the spring and early summer (April–June) on floating blocks of ice. Seals with young are found only in the Tartar strait (Tatar strait). Young, still in their white embryo fur, were found on floating ice in March–May." The gestation period is believed to be about 280 days.

The Alaskan Eskimos capture a few individuals while they are hunting other seals on the pack ice in winter and when at sea in kyaks in the spring and fall. The skin of the male is highly prized by the Eskimos, who remove the skin and tan it, the only opening being a long slit in the abdomen. This is provided with eyelet holes and a lacing string to make a waterproof clothes bag. Japanese sealers take some ribbon seals during the winter for oil, meat, and leather.

Harp Seals (*Pagophilus groenlandicus*), A. Adult female; B. Young, 2 years old; photos by Alwin Pedersen.

HARP SEAL OR SADDLEBACK; PHOQUES DE GROEN-
LAND, SATTELROBBEN, ZADELROBBEN. (Included
are vernaculars used in other countries.)

THE SINGLE SPECIES, *P. groenlandicus*, is a migratory seal that breeds on drifting pack ice in the North
Atlantic and Arctic oceans. Migration limits in the
west and east are the mouth of the Mackenzie River
and Severnaya Zemlya, respectively; 75 to 80 degrees
north latitude represents the northern limit of the
genus, and about 50 degrees north latitude represents
the southern limit.

Large males and females measure up to about 180
cm. in length and weigh up to about 180 kg. The
upper parts are usually tawny gray or tawny yellowish, and the under parts are silvery. A dark band begins between the shoulders and sends a branch downward and backward on each side; the band in the
female is lighter and may be broken. This seal and
the ribbon seal are the only pinnipeds with a banded
pelage, and the only phocids with sexual differences
in pelage.

Toward the end of winter, harp seals migrate to
three breeding grounds in the pack ice: off the coast
of Newfoundland and in the Gulf of St. Lawrence,
in the Greenland Sea between Iceland and Spitzber-
gen, and in the White Sea. Marking experiments
indicate that these three breeding grounds represent
three stocks of harp seals which probably are isolated from each other.

The pups usually are born from March 18 to 20 in
the Greenland Sea and at an earlier date in the other
two breeding areas. Weaning occurs from 10 to 12
days after birth, at which time the bulls swim into
the drifting ice and join the females on the floes.
After mating, the adults leave the breeding grounds;
those in the Greenland Sea stock swim northward
and assemble on ice north of Jan Mayen Island,
where molting occurs. In May these seals disperse to
sea.

The young harp seal gains from 1.75 to 2 kg. in
weight per day during the period of suckling. After
being weaned, it is left on the ice by its mother. During the next 10 to 14 days (20 to 26 days after birth),
the young animal does not feed and undergoes a
molt in which a replacement of the white, woolly
coat occurs. After molting, the young harp seal
begins to feed in the sea, at first mainly on small
crustaceans. These animals gradually collect into
herds and migrate northward. Yearling saddlebacks,
and possibly some older immatures as well, at least
in the Newfoundland stock, remain in the Arctic and
do not migrate south with the main stock in the winter.

Sexual maturity is not attained until eight years of
age in the males and from five to eight years of age
in the females. Individuals over 20 years old are rare.
The adults feed on macroplankton and fish.

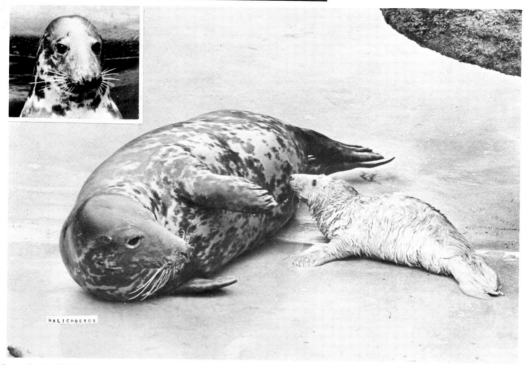

Gray Seals (*Halichoerus grypus*), mother suckling young, photo from North American Newspaper Alliance, Inc. Inset: Young Adult (*H. grypus*), photo by Erna Mohr.

GRAY SEALS; GRYZE ZEEHOND, PHOQUES GRISES, KEGELROBBEN.

THE SINGLE SPECIES, *H. grypus*, inhabits temperate waters in the North Atlantic from Labrador eastward to Novaya Zemlya and southward to the Channel Islands and France. These seals are rare in the southern parts of the range. They prefer turbulent waters near cliffs and about rocks and reefs; they are also found in estuaries and on sand bars. The estimated world population is 25,000 to 50,000.

Males are about 1.8 to 3.1 meters in length and 160 to 290 kg. in weight; females measure 1.75 to 2.25 meters and weigh 120 to 250 kg. The upper parts are light or dark gray, sometimes almost black, and usually have obscure spots or blotches; the under parts are lighter. The young are white and woolly. The snout is long. The forelimbs are flexible and often used for climbing or crawling, and the foreclaws are long, slender, and curved. This genus may be distinguished externally from *Phoca* by the heavy head and, in the adult male, by the stout neck with three or four conspicuous wrinkles.

Gray seals are gregarious and rather deliberate, almost sluggish, in their movements. They are known to dive to depths of at least 128 meters. They feed on fish and to some extent on cuttlefish.

There seem to be three population groups that are separated by geographical gaps and by different breeding times. These groups are found in the West Atlantic, mainly in the Gulf of St. Lawrence; in the East Atlantic, mainly in the British Isles; and in the Baltic Sea. At the present time little is known of the movements in the West Atlantic group. In the East Atlantic and Baltic groups, most of the young seals seem to disperse from the home colony and spend the first two years of their lives at sea. A smaller number of young individuals remain near the breeding grounds. Dispersals of about 644 km. have been established. The movements of this species are made in search of food.

The young are born on the ice in late winter and early spring in the West Atlantic and Baltic populations, whereas the seals of the East Atlantic give birth and breed on shore in the fall. The number of young is one, rarely two. The pups nurse for at least two weeks. The cows are usually bred again within two weeks after giving birth. Polygamy is moderately developed in this species, the average harem consisting of a bull and about ten cows. Gray seals have lived as long as 41 years in captivity.

Bearded Seal (*Erignathus barbatus*), photo from the Zoological Garden Berlin-West.

BEARDED SEALS, SQUARE-FLIPPERS; OGJOOK, OOG-RUK, LACHTAK, BARTROBBE, PHOQUES BARBU. (Included are vernaculars used in other countries.)

THE SINGLE SPECIES, *E. barbatus*, inhabits the edge of the ice along the coasts and islands of North America and northern Eurasia. The southern limits are the Tatar Strait, northern Hokkaido, the eastern Bering Sea, Newfoundland, France, the British Isles, and Norway. Bearded seals are rare along European coasts. They prefer areas of shallow water, 30 to 50 meters deep, and with many bays and creeks. The estimated world population is 75,000 to 150,000.

This and the elephant seal are the largest of the true seals (Phocidae) of the Northern Hemisphere. Males are usually 3 to 3.75 meters long and weigh 225 to 410 kg.; the females are smaller, with a maximum length of about 2.6 meters. Adults have grayish to dull yellowish-brown upper parts, and yellowish or silvery under parts. Darker obscure spotting is present or absent. The pelage of the newborn is dark grayish or brownish. The common name, bearded seal, is derived from the prominent bushy tuft of long, flattened bristles on each side of the muzzle.

Unlike other seals, the third digit of the fore flipper is longer than the other digits. The teeth of the adult are loosely rooted and are often worn down to the surface of the jaw or even lost. There are four mammae.

This species is more or less resident. It moves from one area to another but does not undergo any regular migration. Temporary groups of 1,000 and more are formed, at least in the Sea of Okhotsk, but bearded seals are usually solitary or found in small groups. Up to 50 individuals may congregate on the ice during the breeding season. Like the walrus, the bearded seal is a bottom feeder, perhaps scraping with its claws and heavy whiskers for mollusks and other invertebrates which it obtains by diving to considerable depths. Fish and other aquatic life are eaten less frequently.

The gestation period is said to be 11 months. The pups are born in April and May and are about 1.4 to 1.5 meters in length at birth. Bearded seals are reported to give birth in February and breed in August in the Okhotsk Sea. The young apparently remain with the mother for a long period. Males mature in seven years and females in six. The females breed every other year.

Bearded seals are of great value to the Eskimos for the skins, fat, and flesh. The Alaskan Eskimos prefer to use this leather on the soles of their boots. It is a rough, non-skid, tough leather. North Atlantic sealers take a few each year; the skins are used for leather and the blubber for oil.

Hawaiian Monk Seals (*Monachus schauinslandi*), A. Photo from San Diego Zoological Garden. B. Photo by Karl W. Kenyon.

MONK SEALS, WEST INDIAN SEALS; FOCAS FRAILES, PHOQUES MOINES MÖNCHSROBBE. (Included are vernaculars used in other countries.)

THE THREE SPECIES and their distribution are as follows: *M. monachus*, the Black and Adriatic seas, the Mediterranean Sea (except most of the Mediterranean coast of Africa) southward to Cape Blanc, Spanish West Africa, Madeira and the Canary and other offshore islands; *M. tropicalis*, formerly the shores of small islands off eastern Honduras and Yucatan, West Indies, the Bahamas, and Florida, but now perhaps extinct; *M. schauinslandi*, small isolated islands and reefs of the western half of the Hawaiian Islands between 20 degrees and 30 degrees N. latitude. With the exception of an occasional California sea lion (*Zalophus*), these are the only tropical pinnipeds. The geographical separation of the three species is at least 5,000 km.

The length of the head and body is 2 to 3 meters. A female weighed 302 kg. (without the internal body organs); 225 to 275 kg. is probably an average weight for both sexes. The upper parts are grayish or yellowish with black spots or nearly uniform brown tinged with gray, and the under parts are white or yellowish white. The pelage of *M. monachus* often has a ventral white patch, which is always lacking in the other two species. The pelage of the adults is dry and stiff, and there is no underfur. The pups are jet black at birth.

The unusual form of the skull characterizes this genus among the family Phocidae. The nails of the fore flippers are well developed, whereas those of the hind flippers are small. The first and fifth toes of the hind flippers are longer than the remaining toes, which gives a V-shaped outline to the hind flippers. Females have four mammae.

Columbus found the Caribbean seals plentiful on his second voyage in 1494, at which time the seals were killed for food. They are the first animals described from the New World. In addition to wanton destruction, extensive hunting for oil, hides, and meat brought them to the verge of extinction by 1885. The last record of this species seems to be its occurrence in Jamaican waters in 1952. The estimated world population of the Mediterranean species is 1,000 to 5,000; that of the Hawaiian species is only 1,000 to 1,500.

These seals appear to be sluggish and unsuspicious. These factors, in combination with somewhat gregarious habits and restricted habitats, made them vulnerable. The diet is not known but may include reef fish and mollusks. Living mainly in areas without sharply defined seasons, it is possible that the breeding season is quite prolonged. The pup of the Hawaiian monk seal may be born from December to March and is dependent on its mother for about five weeks.

The type species of the genus is *M. monachus* (Hermann).

A. Crab-eater Seal (*Lobodon carcinophagus*), photo by U.S. Office of Territories through the National Archives. B. Teeth of Crab-eater Seal (*L. carcinophagus*), postcanines 3, 4, and 5, right mandible, lingual aspect, photo by Victor B. Scheffer.

CRAB-EATER SEALS; FOCAS CANGREJERAS.

THE SINGLE SPECIES, *L. carcinophagus*, is associated with the drifting ice of the southern ocean. Most individuals move north with the pack ice in the fall to about 55 to 65 degrees S. latitude, and a few wander as far north as the temperate waters off the coasts of South America and Australia. This species may be the most abundant pinniped, as the estimated world population is 2 to 5 million.

The length is usually 230 to 260 cm. and the weight is usually 200 to 225 kg.; as in the Weddell seal (*Leptonychotes*), the females tend to be larger than the males. The adults molt in late summer from a whitish, almost immaculate pelage into a somewhat mottled gray-brown coat, which weathers to the lighter color as the season progresses. The close-set fur is rigid at the base of the hairs and softens at the tips; there is no underfur. The cheek teeth of crabeaters have remarkably elaborate cusps for straining and filtering macroplankton from the sea.

This gregarious species usually lies out on ice or on snow patches, only rarely occupying rocky islands or beaches. It is perhaps the fastest pinniped on land, obtaining its motive force from powerful blows against hard-packed snow with the hind flippers, and also striking the snow with backward blows of the front flippers. Land speeds of at least 24 km. per hour can be achieved in this manner.

A few individuals may winter beneath the ice, but in most areas there are pronounced local movements. During the winter, spring, and part of the summer, they are usually in the northern part of their range. During the summer, many crabeaters move into Antarctic coastal waters, west of Graham Land, and into the southern part of the Ross Sea. Further study of these movements may reveal the crabeater as a truly migratory seal.

These seals, like leopard seals (*Hydrurga*), feed and breed along the outer edge of the pack ice. The name crabeater is inappropriate, as these seals do not feed on crabs, but mainly on euphausians (krill) and occasionally on a few small fish. The pups are born in early spring on the pack ice. They probably weigh about 25 kg. at birth, and present information indicates that the pup remains with its mother for less than two weeks and then enters the water and is on its own. Breeding occurs about mid-summer, and the period of gestation is about nine months. Females may begin breeding in their second year.

Crabeaters are often cut and scarred by the attacks of killer whales (*Orcinus*).

Ross Seal (*Ommatophoca rossi*), photo by U.S. Office of Territories through the National Archives.

ROSS SEALS.

THE SINGLE SPECIES, *O. rossi*, is the only Antarctic seal that is confined to high latitudes. It seems to be local in distribution and is rare in eastern longitudes. There are no records from island or continental beaches, and few from the vast semicircular edge of Antarctica, including about 155 degrees of angle which fronts the Indian Ocean. Ross seals inhabit the outer edge of the pack ice and probably do not winter under ice. The estimated world population is 20,000 to 50,000.

The length is usually 200 to 230 cm. and the weight is about 150 to 215 kg. The fur is coarse and rough. Coloration has been described as greenish yellow above, with oblique yellow stripes on the sides, and paler under parts. The neck is thick and short and has large folds. The orbits are large; in fact, this seal was formerly referred to as the "big-eyed seal." The teeth are relatively small.

Probably less than 50 Ross seals had been seen prior to 1945. Many more have been noted in recent years with increased Antarctic explorations, but the habits and natural history of this species are still little known. Ross seals usually remain solitary or are found in small groups. J. Perkins "Biology at Little America III, the West Base of the United States Antarctic Service Expedition 1939–1941," *Proc. Amer. Phil. Soc.*, Vol. 89, 1945, p. 280) comments: "Although these seals were sluggish in their movements on the ice, and although they exhibited the usual defenselessness of the other seals, they seemed to resent the presence of man even more than the crabeaters. They gave a little birdlike chirping call similar to that of Weddell's seal; and when disturbed they raised their heads, filled their lungs with air, and exhaled suddenly." It has been suggested that Ross seals are rapid swimmers because of their body shape and short head. Because of rapid swimming and their habit of frequenting the edge of pack ice four seals examined by Perkins lacked scars from attacks by killer whales (*Orcinus*). The diet is mainly cephalopods, fish, and some crustaceans.

An attempt was made to bring an individual back alive to the United States, but it died within a few days, presumably from injuries received during its capture.

LEOPARD SEALS; LEOPARDOS MARINOS, ZEE LUIPAARD.

THE SINGLE SPECIES, *H. leptonyx*, has a scattered distribution around Antarctica and has been recorded occasionally from the southern parts of other southern continents. Leopard seals frequent the pack ice in summer and migrate northward to spend the winter around ice-free islands. The estimated world population is 100,000 to 300,000.

The length of the head and body is usually 250 to 350 cm., and the weight is as much as 380 kg. On the average, adult females are 10 per cent larger than adult males. There are two main types of pelage; one is dark gray to black above and light gray below, and the other is light gray above and below with conspicuous black spots. There is very little hair and no underfur. The body form is long and sinuous, and the head is proportionately longer than that of other seals. The dentition is adapted for seizing and tearing flesh: the cheek teeth are sharply cuspidate and the middle cusp of the three on each tooth is high, pointed, and curved backward.

These are the only seals that regularly prey on warm-blooded creatures. Penguins seem to be the main prey, but other birds and seals are also consumed. In preying on penguins, leopard seals swim rapidly under water, grab the feet and rump of the bird, shake it violently, and then consume it. The feathers and skin are apparently eaten along with the body. Leopard seals generally feed in the water rather than on land.

When at sea, they are usually solitary and nowhere abundant. Regular haul-outs of up to 250 animals occur in some areas. These are influenced by weather

Leopard Seal (*Hydrurga leptonyx*), A. Photo by U.S. Office of Territories through the National Archives. B. Photo by John Warham.

and conditions on the beach. The populations o the various beaches vary seasonally. Leopard seals may be quite ferocious but have never been known to attack man unless provoked.

Mating is reported to take place between September and November, about four months after the birth of young. The pups are born on the pack ice. They are believed to nurse for at least two months. At one year of age, leopard seals have an average length of about 80 cm.; at two years, about 95 cm.; at three years, about 103 cm.; and at four years, about 110 cm. Males are possibly sexually mature in four to six years and females, in three to four years.

Weddell Seals (*Leptonychotes weddelli*), photo from U.S. Navy.

WEDDELL SEALS.

THE SINGLE SPECIES is *L. weddelli*. The main breeding grounds are in Antarctic waters; marginal records are reported from Australia, New Zealand, and southern South America. "The Weddell seal is circumpolar, and its normal habitat is the in-shore waters of the Antarctic continent and adjacent islands. It spends much time in the water, but emerges at intervals to lie out on the beaches or on fast ice. It is not a seal of the Antarctic pack ice, and is rarely found on isolated floes or far from land" (G. C. L. Bertram, "The Biology of the Weddell and Crabeater Seals, With a Study of the Comparative Behavior of the Pinnipedia," *Brit. Mus. (Nat. Hist.) Sci. Repts.*, Brit. Graham Land Exped. 1934–1937, 1940, pp. 5–6). The Weddell seal is not migratory.

Length is about 3 meters and weight is 340 to 450 kg. Coloration above is shiny dark iron-gray; below it is slightly lighter, streaked, and spotted with yellowish white. The young are pale gray with lighter and faintly mottled under parts. The upper incisors are markedly unequal; the outer is about four times longer than the inner and the postcanines are strong and functional.

Weddell seals feed on small fishes and cephalopods along the shore ice. Apparently, according to one source, "They remain below the ice, resting on interior ice shelves and probably making use of the anticlinal domes as places to breathe, for they can be heard calling beneath the ice all winter" (J. Perkins, "Biology at Little America III, the West Base of the United States Antarctic Service Expedition 1939–1941," *Proc. Amer. Phil. Soc.*, Vol. 89, 1945, pp. 278–79). Cracks in the ice also are used for breathing; if new ice has formed in the crack, the seals cut through it with their teeth.

The estimated world population is 200,000 to 500,-000. Weddell seals tend to be solitary or semigregarious and are found in groups of as many as 40 during the pupping time. One or two young are born from September through October after a gestation period of about 310 days. Newborn young are almost half the length of the mother and weigh about 34 kg. They are weaned at about eight weeks of age, at which time they weigh approximately 140 kg. The mother stays on the ice for a week before giving birth and remains on the ice for about a week thereafter. Mother and young go into shallow pools of water on the ice; later the young animal enters the sea to obtain food. The mother loses about 140 kg. before the offspring is weaned, but she regains it during the winter.

Weddell seals are quite tame, often allowing man to approach within a few feet.

Hooded Seals (*Cystophora cristata*), A. Adult Male, photo by Bernhard Grzimek. B. Bladder nose fully inflated while swimming; C. Adult male with hood inflated; D. Young in stage called "blueback"; photos by Erna Mohr.

HOODED SEALS, BLADDERNOSE SEALS; PHOQUES À CAPUCHON, BLASENROBBEN.

THE SINGLE SPECIES, *C. cristata*, is associated with the ice pack in deep waters of the Atlantic and Arctic oceans. Hooded seals are migratory and likely to wander: individuals have been noted in the Yukon, Florida, and Portugal. They rarely haul out on land. The estimated world population is 300,000 to 500,-000.

Males have a length of 2.1 to 3.5 meters and a weight of about 410 kg. Females measure up to nearly 3.1 meters and weigh about 270 kg. The males are usually bluish or dark gray above, and lighter on the sides and below; some have whitish spots on the sides, while others have dark spots or blotches. The face and muzzle of males are blackish. Females are paler in color and have less distinct markings. The white birth coat is replaced by an attractive grayish one, and the young seal, at this stage called a "blueback," is sought for by sealskin hunters. Both sexes have a nasal "hood" or "pouch," which consists of mucous membrane overlaid by muscle fibers in a support of connective tissue and fat that is covered by skin. The hood is largest in the male.

Male hooded seals are reported to have a quarrelsome nature. When annoyed or sufficiently aroused, they inflate one side of the thin nasal septum and the hood which forms a brilliant red "bladder" 15.2 to 17.8 cm. long. It has been suggested that the inflated pouch is used to frighten enemies. The hood is 25 cm. long and when fully extended, it holds about 6.3 liters of water.

Migrations are not well understood. There seem to be two main breeding areas: one to the north of Jan Mayen Island, where the seals breed in the spring and then move northward toward Svalbard; and another south of Greenland near Newfoundland, where the seals breed in the spring and then migrate to ice off the coast of Greenland. Hooded seals travel with harp seals (*Pagophilus*), but the two species tend to remain apart. These two phocids also breed in the same areas, but the hooded seals form separate family groups on the ice floes. These groups usually consist of a bull, cow, and their offspring.

The pup weighs from 11 to 14 kg. at birth and is left on its own after two to three weeks. The adults breed at this time. The young animals tend to remain by themselves until sexually mature; hooded seals can breed at about four years of age. The adult sexes usually remain in separate groups except during the breeding season.

The diet seems to be mainly fish and squids.

Northern Elephant Seals (*Mirounga angustirostris*), A. Male, photo from Allan Hancock Foundation. B. Mother and baby, photo by Julio Berdegué. C. Seal shedding its skin, photo from Colorado Museum of Natural History, through Alfred M. Bailey and R. J. Niedrach. D. Adult male with proboscis turned downward into mouth, photo by Julio Berdegué. E. Young Elephant Seal, photo by Julio Berdegué. F. South Atlantic Elephant Seal (*Mirounga leonina*), photo from the Zoological Garden, Berlin-West.

ELEPHANT SEALS, CALIFORNIA SEA ELEPHANTS; ZEE-OLIFANTE, ZEE-DIFANT, ELEFANTES MARINOS.

THE TWO SPECIES are distributed as follows: *M. angustirostris* during the breeding season ranges from the west coast of Baja, California, to central California; *M. leonina* is found in subantarctic waters, breeding from Gough Island and Argentina to the South Shetland Islands. After the reproductive season, some individuals of the northern species wander considerable distances, quite often as far north as southern British Columbia, and the southern species has been noted from Saint Helena (16 degrees S) to 78 degrees S. The estimated world population of the southern species is 380,000 to 660,000, whereas that of the northern species is only 8,000 to 10,000.

These are the largest pinnipeds. Bulls are 450 to 650 cm. in length and have been reported to weigh as much as 3.5 metric tons; the females usually measure 300 to 350 cm. and weigh up to 900 kg. The adult coloration is nearly uniform and is not spotted. The northern species is yellowish or grayish brown, and the southern form is bluish gray, with lighter under parts in both species. The hair is dry, stiff, and short, and there is no underfur. Newly-born animals are brownish black. The common name is derived from the large size and trunk-like proboscis of these seals. The "trunk" or snout is about 38 cm. long. The lining of the trunk cannot be extruded at will to form a "bladder," as in the hooded seal (*Cystophora*).

Elephant seals dive to several hundred meters to feed upon fish and cuttlefish. After breeding and molting, the southern species disperses to sea and probably spends the winter at the edge of the pack ice.

The northern species seems to be resident and not migratory. These seals feed for only a few months in summer, between the breeding season and the haul-out for molting, and in winter; breeding and molting take place on land or on ice, and the seals fast during these times.

These seals are gregarious, and colonies of the northern species tend to congregate on the beaches of offshore islands where they are frequently found in association with *Zalophus*. They generally show little fear of man and will allow close approach. The males make a deep trumpeting sound. This is most often heard during the breeding season.

These seals are polygamous. A dominant bull in an undisturbed population has a harem of 10 to 30 cows. Both sexes are pugnacious during the breeding season. Breeding takes place from December through March in the northern species, and in spring and summer in the southern form. Bulls are sexually mature at about four years of age, but they do not seem to form harems until five to seven years old. Females usually begin mating in their second year. The gestation period is about 350 days. Twins are rare. At birth the pup is about 1.2 meters long and weighs about 50 kg.; when weaned about three weeks later, it weighs over 175 kg. At about this time, the cow is mated again. Female *M. leonina* live to an average age of 12 years, and male *M. leonina* may live as long as 20 years.

The northern elephant seal was nearly exterminated by commercial sealers but has increased greatly in numbers in recent years. Elephant seals have been found in the stomachs of killer whales.

The type species of the genus is *M. leonina* (Linnaeus).

Order: TUBULIDENTATA; Family: ORYCTEROPODIDAE; Genus: ORYCTEROPUS, E. Geoffroy, 1795

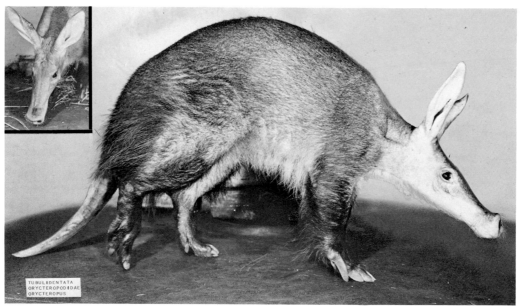

Aardvark (*Orycteropus afer*), photos by Ernest P. Walker.

AARDVARKS, EARTH HOGS, ANT "BEARS;" AARD-VARKE, ERDVARKS, ARDVARKEN, ISAMBANE (native name).

THIS ORDER contains only a single family, Oryctero-podidae, with only one Recent genus, *Orycteropus*, for the single living species of aardvark, *O. afer*. Aardvarks are native to most of the African continent south of the Sahara and Sudan. The presence of sufficient quantities of termites and ants apparently is the main factor determining their local distribution. Dense forests are avoided. They are now greatly reduced in numbers.

Aardvarks have a massive body, with a long head and snout that terminates in a round, blunt, pig-like muzzle that is pierced by circular nostrils, from which grow many curved whitish hairs, 25 to 50 mm. long. The ears are tubular and 150 to 210 mm. in length; they fold back to exclude dirt when the animal is burrowing and can be moved independently of one another. They are waxy and smooth like scalded pig's skin. The tapering tongue often hangs out of the mouth with the end coiled like a clock spring. The neck is short, the forequarters are low, and the back is arched. The strong and muscular tail is thick at the base and tapers to a point. The legs are short and stocky; the fore foot has four digits and the hind foot has five, the digits being webbed at their bases. The long, straight, strong, blunt claws are suited to burrowing. These animals resemble a medium- to large-sized pig. The length of the head and body is 1,000 to 1,580 mm.; the length of the tail is 445 to 610 mm.; and the height at the shoulder is approximately 600 to 650 mm. Adult animals weigh as much as 82 kg., although most individuals weigh from about 50 to 70 kg. The thick skin is scantily covered with bristly hair which varies in color from dull brownish gray to dull yellowish gray. The hair on the legs is often darker than that on the body, and one form has a white tail. Numerous vibrissae occur on the face around the muzzle and about the eyes. The dull pinkish-gray skin is so tough that it sometimes saves the aardvark from the attacks of other animals.

The females have two pairs of inguinal mammae. In the males the penis has a fold of skin which covers scent glands at its base.

The teeth in the embryo are numerous and traversed by a number of parallel vertical pulp canals. The milk teeth do not break through the gums. In the adult the teeth are only in the posterior part of the jaw. The usual dental formula is: i 0/0, c 0/0, pm 2/2 (additional vestigial premolars are sometimes present), m 3/3. These do not grow simultaneously. Those nearest the front of the jaw develop first and fall out about the time the animal reaches maturity; they are succeeded by others further back. Each cheek tooth, which is covered externally by a layer of cement, resembles a flat-crowned column and is composed of numerous hexagonal prisms of dentine surrounding tubular pulp cavities, hence the ordinal name Tubulidentata ("tubule-toothed"). The teeth of aardvarks grow continuously and lack enamel. The skull is elongate, and the lower jaw is straight, blade-like anteriorly, and swollen at the molars.

Aardvark is an Afrikaans word which means "earth-pig," an appropriate name as these animals look somewhat like a pig and are extraordinarily active burrowers. If overtaken away from their den, they dig into the ground with amazing speed; aardvarks can dig faster in soft earth than can several men with shovels, and even the hardest sun-baked ground is no obstacle to their powerful fore feet. An aardvark, when digging, pushes the ground backward under its body while resting on its hind legs and tail. When a sufficient amount of soil has accumulated it is shoved back or to one side with the hind feet, sometimes with the aid of the tail. These animals excavate extensive burrows about 3 meters long. The tunnel ends in a chamber large enough for the aardvark to turn in, as it generally enters and leaves its burrow head-first. A number of aardvarks may burrow in the same area; there is one record of 60 entrances in an area approximately 300 by 100 meters. The burrows, when abandoned, are used by many animals. Aardvarks sometimes use termite nests as temporary shelters; their thick skin seems impervious to insect bites. They are active mainly at night; sometimes they go abroad by day, and occasionally they sun themselves in the early morning at the burrow entrance. Aardvarks sleep during the day curled up in a tight circle, with the snout protected by the hind limbs and tail.

These animals are extremely powerful. A native with a firm grip on the tail of an aardvark in its den was slowly drawn into the burrow up to his waist and finally had to relinquish his hold, despite the additional leverage afforded by two other natives holding onto his legs. Aardvarks' movements are awkward and slow, but it is said that they can escape with surprising rapidity if alarmed. Their hearing is acute, and at the least alarm they seek a burrow. Aardvarks avoid enemies by digging or running, but if cornered they will fight by striking with the tail or shoulders, by rearing on the hind legs and slashing with the fore feet, or by rolling on their backs and slashing with all four feet. Their main enemies are lions, leopards, cheetahs, hunting dogs, pythons, and man.

Aardvarks tend to walk on their claws, and their tails often leave a track on soft ground. Shy and timid, they generally hunt for food alone, wandering 12.5 km. in a night. They obtain termites and ants by tearing into their nests and, at least in some areas,

by seeking out these insects when they are on the march. A marching band of termites may number in the tens of thousands and may be about 40 meters long; it is thought that the aardvark is guided to these columns by picking up the sound of thousands of tiny "footfalls" and by its sense of smell. In Karamoja aardvarks feed largely on the harvester ant (*Pheidole* sp.). Termites, ants, locusts, and other insects are gathered with the sticky tongue, which can be extended for a distance of 30 cm. There is some indication that aardvarks also eat the fruits of a plant which germinates in their buried feces. In captivity they will eat meal worms, boiled rice, meat, eggs, and milk and seem to thrive when some carbohydrate is included in their diet.

The single offspring (occasionally two) is born in October or November (the beginning of the second rainy season) in central Africa. The gestation period is not recorded. The naked and flesh-colored young aardvark remains in the burrow for about two weeks and then begins to accompany its mother on her nightly excursions. For the next several months the mother and her offspring occupy a series of burrows, moving from one place to another; the youngster can dig for itself in about six months. Aardvarks have lived 10 years in captivity.

The flesh is prized by some natives and has the appearance of coarse beef, whereas others report it as strong smelling and tough as leather. In some areas the hide is made into bracelets and the claws are worn as good luck pieces. The skin is also made into straps.

The geological range of this order is the Eocene in North America (*Tubulodon*), the Eocene to the Oligocene and the Pliocene in Europe, the Pleistocene in Madagascar, and the Miocene and Recent in Africa. Some naturalists have included these, along with sloths, anteaters, armadillos, and pangolins in the order Edentata, but this view is now abandoned by most recent zoologists.

Order: PROBOSCIDEA; Family: ELEPHANTIDAE

ELEPHANTS.

THIS ORDER is comprised of six families, five of which are extinct. During the Pleistocene, proboscideans ranged through every continent except Australia; they are now greatly reduced in range and species. The only Recent family, Elephantidae, contains two genera, each with a single species: *Loxodonta africana*, the African elephant, and *Elephas maximus*, the Asiatic elephant. These Recent forms inhabit a variety of terrain, but they generally live in forests, savannahs, and river valleys. The geological range of this order is the late Eocene to the Recent; the geological range of Elephantidae is the late Pliocene to the Recent in Asia, the Pliocene to the Pleistocene in Europe, the Pleistocene to the Recent in Africa, and the Pleistocene in North and South America.

The most conspicuous external feature in proboscideans is the elongated, flexible, and muscular trunk or proboscis, a character reflected by the ordinal name. The trunk is actually a great elongation of the nose, the nostrils being located at the tip. The finger-like extremity of this amazing structure is used to pick up small objects such as peanuts.

The head is huge, the ears are large, especially in *Loxodonta*, and fan-shaped, the neck is short, the body is long and massive, and the tail is of moderate length. The living members of the order Proboscidea have a maximum height of nearly 4 meters and a weight of almost 7,000 kg. (males). The limbs of proboscideans are long, massive, and columnar. The knee joint is located below the body in contrast to most quadrupeds, in which it is concealed. All the limb bones are well developed and separate; lacking marrow-cavities, they are filled with spongy bone through which the marrow is disseminated. The feet are extremely short and broad and columnar in shape. The weight of the animal rests on a pad of elastic tissue. There are five toes on each foot, but the outer pair may be vestigial so that some digits do not have hooves (nails). The Asiatic elephant has four hooves (occasionally five) on the hind foot and five on the fore foot, and the African elephant has three on the hind foot and five on the fore foot.

African Elephant (*Loxodonta africanas*), A. Swimming across a channel in Uganda; B. The same elephant a few moments later in shallow water; photos by P. F. Wright.

In Recent forms the thick skin of adults is sparsely haired. The glands associated with the hair follicles in most mammals (sebaceous glands), which soften and lubricate the hair and skin, are not present in the Elephantidae. The females of the Recent forms have two nipples just behind the front legs; the young nurse with the mouth as in other mammals, and the males retain the testes permanently within the abdomen.

At birth, baby elephants have a coat of widely spaced brown hairs that produce a halo effect as they stand out from the body. As they grow older, the hairy coat becomes less noticeable, until adult elephants appear to be without hair, but throughout life they have a scattered coat of hair.

The following dental formula prevails in Recent forms: i 1/0, c 0/0, pm 3/3, m 3/3 = 26. The single upper incisor grows throughout life into a large tusk (up to 3.3 meters long in the African elephant). The tusk, which is usually absent in females of the Asiatic elephant, has enamel only on the tip, where it is soon worn away (some extinct proboscideans had lower tusks and others had longitudinal bands of enamel on their tusks). The grinding teeth are generally large, high-crowned, and with a complex structure. Each tooth is composed of a large number of transverse plates of dentine covered with enamel; the spaces between the ridges of enamel are filled with cement. Ridges do not show on an unworn tooth as it is thickly covered with cement. The grinding teeth increase in size and in the number of ridges from front to back. These teeth do not succeed one another vertically in the usual mammalian fashion in the Recent forms (some fossil forms had the usual vertical replacement of teeth) but come in successively from behind, the series moving obliquely forward. When the foremost tooth is so worn down as to be of no further use, it is pushed out, mostly in pieces. As these teeth are very large and the jaws are fairly short, only one tooth on each side, above and below, is in use at the same time in the Recent forms (part of a second tooth also may be used).

The skull is huge and often shortened. The premaxillary bones have been converted into sheaths for the tusks, and the nasal bones are extremely shortened. All the bones forming the brain case are greatly thickened and, at the same time, lightened by the development of an extensive system of communicating air cells and cavities. The brain chamber is hidden within the middle of the huge mass of skull. The skeleton of a proboscidean is massive, comprising 12 to 15 per cent of the body weight in the Recent forms.

Some of the extinct species probably were contemporary with man. The mammoths (*Mammuthus*) are known from the Northern Hemisphere of both the Old and New Worlds (several species have been described). In *M. primigenius*, the woolly mammoth, the body was covered with a dense coat of woolly hair and long, coarse outer hair, as a protection against cold. This proboscidean is the species found in the frozen ground in Siberia, complete with hide and hair. Paleolithic man has left drawings of woolly mammoths on the walls of caves. The tusks in *Mammuthus*, although quite variable in form, had a tendency to spiral, first downward and outward, then upward and inward, and the grinding teeth had numerous ridges of enamel. Mammoths stood about 3 meters high at the shoulders. Mastodons, *Mastodon*, became extinct in the Old World before the end of the Pliocene, but the American species, *M. americanum*, is thought to have outlived the now extinct species of elephants in North America, probably persisting until well after the coming of man to this hemisphere. Mastodons were about the same size as mammoths, the distinguishing features of the genus being the low-crowned and fairly small grinding teeth which had three or four prominent transverse ridges of enamel. The tusks in the American species were directed nearly straight forward and were almost parallel with each other; another group of mastodons had fully developed lower tusks.

The following genera represent proboscideans known from the Pleistocene of the Old World and now extinct: *Anacus* is a genus of Proboscidea known from England, France, Germany, Austria, Hungary, and Russia. The generic name refers to the straight upper incisor (tusk) which occurred in some forms. Fossils of *Stegolophodon* have been found in India, Burma, and Borneo. The tusks were straight or slightly curved, and the grinding teeth were large. *Stegodon*, from Asia, had a larger skull and lower-crowned teeth than present-day elephants. The unusual *Deinotherium*, known from the lower Miocene to the middle Pliocene of Europe and Asia, and the lower Miocene to the Pleistocene of Africa, is characterized by its large size, a pair of lower tusks directed downward, relatively small grinding teeth, a long, flattened skull, and probably a proboscis of some sort. This animal may have been aquatic in habits.

All the proboscideans have been vegetarians. The Recent forms may consume 225 kg. or more of forage a day. Present-day elephants are gregarious herd animals, with a life expectancy of about 80 years. The Indian elephant is commonly used as a beast of burden, and the African elephant is used as a draft animal to some extent. Ivory is obtained from the tusks of the African species.

Asiatic Elephant (*Elephas maximus*), photo by Ernest P. Walker. Inset: Tip of trunk (*E. maximus*), photo from Philadelphia Zoological Garden through Roger Conant.

ASIATIC OR INDIAN ELEPHANTS; INDISCHE OLI-
FANTE, GADJAH (local vernaculars).

THE SINGLE SPECIES, *E. maximus*, is native to India,
Assam, Burma, Siam, the Malay States, Sumatra,
and Ceylon. A few occur in Borneo, but their origin
is still a puzzle. Probably they were imported a few
hundred years ago. Asiatic elephants inhabit a variety of terrain, from thick jungle areas to open
grassy plains.

The length of the head and body is 5.5 to 6.4 meters;
the length of the tail is 1.2 to 1.5 meters; the height
of the shoulder is 2.5 to 3 meters; and the weight is
about 5,000 kg. The hair covering is scant; the hairs
are long, stiff, and bristly. There is a tuft of hair at
the tip of the tail. The coloration of the skin is dark
gray to brown, often mottled about the forehead,
ears, base of trunk, and chest with flesh-colored
blotches that are probably due to some skin disease.
True color is often masked by the color of the soil
on which the animals live, as they constantly throw
dirt over their backs and wallow in the mud. *Elephas*
apparently has a heart with a double apex which is
often confused with a "double heart."

E. maximus, with its trunk, its heavy, thick-set
body, its long, stout limbs and sloping hindquarters,
is a familiar sight to almost all circus-goers. The
Asiatic elephant is distinguished from the African
elephant (*Loxodonta*) in that the former genus has
considerably smaller ears, usually four hooves (nails)
on the hind foot, 19 pairs of ribs, and 33 caudal
vertebrae. In the Asiatic species, the forehead is flat
and the top of the head is the highest point. In the

African species the ears are large, there are generally
three hooves on the hind foot, 21 pairs of ribs, and a
maximum of 26 caudal vertebrae. The forehead is
more convex and the back slopes more in *Loxodonta*
and the shoulders are the highest point; the trunk
has two finger-like processes at its tip in contrast to
the one at the tip of the trunk in *Elephas*.

Asiatic elephants are gregarious and roam about
in herds of 15 to 30 individuals led by an old female.
Usually the members within the herd are related to
one another, the herd being composed chiefly of females, immature elephants, and one old bull. In the
jungle the average herd elephant is inoffensive, asking
only to be left in peace, although occasionally individuals are dangerous. They feed in the morning,
evening, and at night, their diet consisting of grass,
vines, leaves, tender shoots, and fruit. They rest
during the middle of the day. When food becomes
scarce or the insects too troublesome, they trek to
another territory, marching in single file. The greatest
enemy of *Elephas* appears to be the tiger.

There seems to be no definite breeding season; the
gestation period is 607 to 641 days and one or sometimes two young are born. At birth the young weigh
about 90 kg., measure about 1 meter at the shoulder.
Maximum growth is attained in 25 years and the life
span is similar to man's. Sexual maturity occurs at
8 to 12 years.

Asiatic elephants have been domesticated for centuries; they are intelligent and docile when well
treated. They are valued in Asia as draft animals
and also are used in transportation and hunting.

For many years Indian elephants have been captured in the wild, tamed, and trained to do work for people. To capture them, a strong fence, made of high posts set close together, is usually built in a circular form, with wings leading outward from the entrance to make a V-shaped entrance to the enclosure. When a group of elephants is in the proper position, they are driven into the V and the corral. Then the entrance is closed, and the process of select-

ing and taming is started. Tame elephants that have been trained are of great assistance in this. Wealthy Indians and royalty owned elephants and rode on them, and elaborate howdahs instead of saddles provided comfortable seats for the occupants. Tame elephants were extensively used in handling such heavy articles as teak logs.

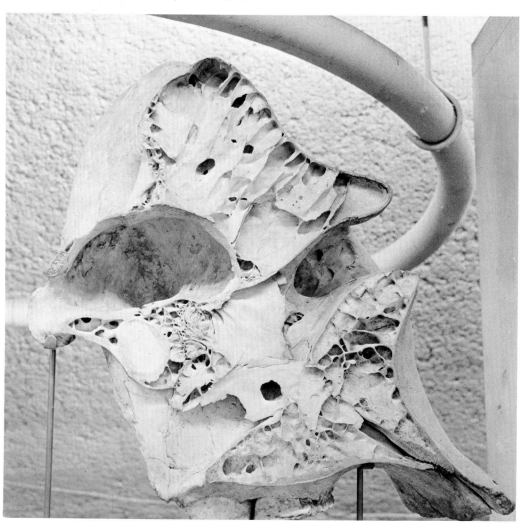

View of vertical median section through skull of Asiatic Elephant (*Elephas maximus*) which shows the great thickness of bone with large cells or sinuses which almost completely surround the brain cavity. Photo by P. F. Wright of specimen in U.S. National Museum.

African Elephant (*Loxodonta africana*), photo by Ernest P. Walker. Inset: Tip of trunk of an East African Bush Elephant, photo from New York Zoological Society.

AFRICAN ELEPHANTS; AFRIKAANSE OLIFANTE, KAFUMBU, DJAMBA, KAPUMBA, NDJOVU, TEMBO, NDOVU (native names).

THE SINGLE SPECIES, *L. africana*, is found throughout most parts of central, eastern, and southern Africa. It thrives in a variety of habitats: savannahs, river valleys, thornbush, dense forest, and desert scrub. There is no species of pygmy elephant; adult individuals of the forest or western race are often small.

The length of the head and body (including the trunk, which is really an elongated nose capable of varied uses) is 6 to 7.5 meters; the length of the tail is 1 to 1.3 meters; the height at the shoulder is 3 to 4 meters; and the weight is from about 5 to 7.5 metric tons. This is the largest living terrestrial mammal.

Sparsely scattered with black bristly hairs, the skin is dull brownish gray in color. The flattened end of the tail has a tuft of coarse, crooked hairs 38 to 76 cm. long. African elephants wallow in streams and pools and toss dirt or mud onto their backs; thus their prevailing color is usually similar to that of the soil they frequent. In both sexes one incisor tooth on each side of the upper jaw is greatly developed to form tusks. The largest known tusk measures about 350 cm. and weighs about 107 kg. The largest female tusk weighs about 18 kg. (the average is about 7 kg.). The end of the long, tubular, muscular, and very sensitive projection of the snout, called the trunk, has a finger-like projection both above and below. These projections are skillfully used to pick up food or other articles and to examine objects. Members of this genus have much larger ears than the Asiatic elephant (*Elephas*), and there is often a hole through the lower portion of the ear lobe caused by injury. The ears are sometimes 1.5 meters from top to bottom.

African elephants associate in herds of various sizes, consisting of both sexes and all ages and often led by a cow. Old bulls sometimes remain solitary. For such huge animals, they can negotiate rough terrain with considerable ease. Members of a herd will assist a wounded comrade. It has been recorded that two uninjured animals leaned on either side of a wounded member to prevent it from falling in its effort to escape from a hunter. African elephants are intelligent and not difficult to tame; however, they have not been used so extensively for motive power and as beasts of burden as have the Asiatic elephants (*Elephas*). A government project was started in 1909 by Belgium in the former Belgian Congo to tame and train them for work.

Such large animals require much food; therefore they must have large areas over which to wander in the wild. They use the trunk to pull branches off trees, uproot grass, pluck fruit, and to place food in their mouth. Water is sucked up into the trunk, then it is blown out into the mouth. These animals may also spray their backs or other objects with water.

One young is generally born in July or August after a gestation period of about 22 months. The herd waits until the young has sufficient strength to roam with them (usually about two days). A female may bear four to five young in a lifetime, and the life expectancy is similar to man's, approximately 50 to 70 years.

African elephants have been extensively slaughtered for their ivory tusks which are used as trophies and are carved by natives and sold as ornaments. These elephants and other large mammals in Africa attract hunters and tourists who bring money into the country and provide employment for the natives. Large areas have been set aside as game preserves where the elephants can live undisturbed by hunters.

African Elephants (*Loxodonta africana*), mounted group in American Museum of Natural History. This shows the large tusks of the male, the large ears characteristic of the genus, and the brush-like tuft of stiff hairs at the end of the tail. Photo appeared in the Annual Report of the American Museum of Natural History, 1921.

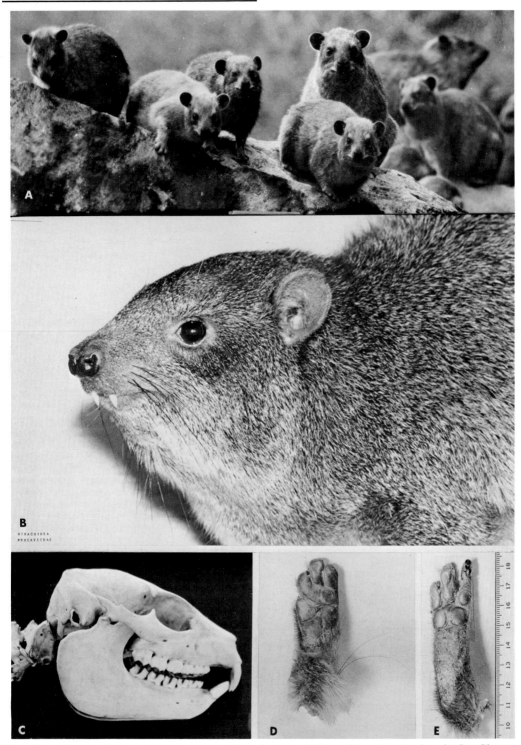

(1) A. Rock Hyraxes (*Heterohyrax* sp.), photo by C. A. Spinage. B. Hyrax (*Procavia* sp.), photo by Roy Pinney. C. Skull of Rock Hyrax (*Procavia capensis*), photo by P. F. Wright of specimen in U.S. National Museum. D. Palmar surface of hand (*P. capensis*); E. Plantar surface of foot (*P. capensis*); photos by Ernest P. Walker.

THIS ORDER contains only one recent family, Procaviidae, with three genera and about nine species. Hyraxes occur in Africa, Sinai, Israel, Syria, and Arabia from sea level to 4,500 meters elevation. The terrestrial genera (*Procavia* and *Heterohyrax*) inhabit rocky areas, arid scrub, and open grassland, whereas tree hyraxes (*Dendrohyrax*) are usually found in forested areas, though in eastern Africa they inhabit lava flows.

These animals are comparable in size and external appearance to rodents and lagomorphs. The length of the head and body is 300 to 600 mm.; the tail is 10 to 30 mm. in length or lacking. Adults sometimes weigh as much as 3 kg. The pelage consists of fine under hairs and coarser guard hairs. Scattered bristles, presumably tactile, are located mainly on the snout. A gland on the back is covered with hair of a different color from that on the rest of the body. The eye is unique in that a portion of the iris above the pupil bulges slightly into the aqueous humor, thus cutting off light from almost directly above the animal. Dassies have a short snout, a cleft upper lip, short ears, and short, sturdy legs. The vertebral column is convex from the neck to the tip of the tail. The fore foot has four digits, with flattened nails resembling hooves. The hind foot has three digits; the inner toe, the second digit, has a long curved claw and the other digits short, flattened, hoof-like nails. The soles have special naked pads for traction; these pads are kept continually moist by a glandular secretion and have a muscle arrangement that retracts the middle of the sole. This forms a hollow, which is a suction cup of considerable clinging power.

The dental formula of the deciduous teeth is i 2/2, c 1/1, pm 4/4 = 28; but the formula for the permanent teeth is i 1/2, c 1/1, pm 4/4, m 3/3 = 38. The single pair of upper incisors grows continuously and is long and curved. The upper incisors are triangular in cross section and semicircular in form; the flattened back surfaces are without enamel and so produce pointed cutting edges. The lower incisors are chisel-shaped; the first pair has three cusps and the second pair only one. There is a wide space between the incisors and the cheek teeth. The milk canines are rarely persistent. The premolars resemble the molars, for they are arranged in a continuous series with the molars that are low-crowned to high-crowned. Each has four roots and the lower ones bear two crescents similar to the corresponding teeth of rhinos and horses. The skull is stout and the roof is flattened.

Although the members of only one genus, *Dendrohyrax*, are arboreal, all the species apparently can climb well; *Heterohyrax*, for example, sometimes suns itself in a tree. Dassies move quickly and are extremely agile on rugged and steep surfaces, running and jumping with skill and gaining traction by means of the specialized foot pads and probably the inner claw on the foot. This claw is apparently also used to groom the hair. Hyraxes travel on the sole of the foot, with the heel touching the ground, or partly on the digits. The terrestrial forms are similar in habits to the pikas, *Ochotona*, sheltering in colonies of 5 to about 50 individuals, usually among rocks. They are active mainly during the daylight hours and are fond of basking in the sun and rolling in the dust. Tree hyraxes shelter singly or in family groups, using tree hollows and dense foliage; they are active during the night. They are less gregarious than the terrestrial forms and are usually more tractable. The terrestrial hyraxes whistle, scream, and chatter; the tree hyraxes utter a series of croaks ending in a loud scream.

Dassies have acute sight and hearing. They feed mainly on vegetation, but most forms also consume insects and grubs. Tree hyraxes feed on the ground as well as in trees. All the species habitually work their jaws in a manner reminiscent of "cud-chewing." Generally these animals are not limited in their distribution by a lack of water to drink. They sometimes travel more than 1.3 km. for food.

There does not seem to be a definite breeding season. The gestation period is seven to seven and one-half months, and the litter size is one to six (usually one to three). The offspring of the terrestrial species are born in a concealed, fur-lined nest. They have open eyes and hair at birth. They become active shortly thereafter. Individuals of *Procavia* bear offspring at the age of two years. Captive dassies have lived seven and one-half years.

The hyraxes are preyed on mainly by rock pythons, eagles, and leopards.

Hyraxes, referred to in the Bible as conies, are in an order that originated in Africa and evolved for some time before the Oligocene. They probably never spread beyond Africa and the Mediterranean regions because of ecological limitations not well understood. The geological range of this order and of the single Recent family is the early Oligocene to the Recent in Africa, the early Pliocene in Europe, and the Recent in southwestern Asia. There are two extinct families. No fossils have been found of the living genera.

(2) Tree Hyrax (*Dendrohyrax dorsalis nigricans*), the light-colored hairs indicate the location of glands that exist on the backs of hyraxes, from color photo by Jean-Luc Perret.

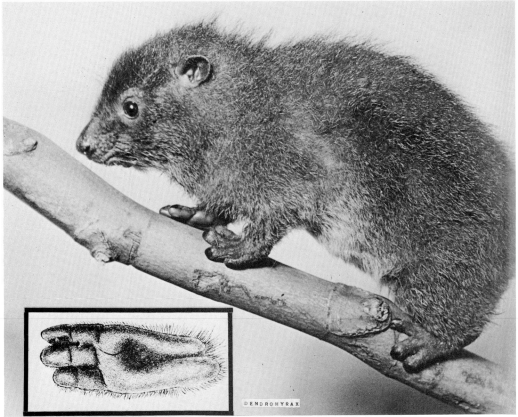

Beecroft's Tree Hyrax (*Dendrohyrax dorsalis*), photo by John Markham. Inset: Underside of right hind foot, photo from *Proc. Zool. Soc. London.*

TREE OR BUSH HYRAXES OR DASSIES; BOOMDASSIES OR BOSDAS, MHA, PERERO, MHELELE (native names).

THIS GENUS consists of three species, *D. dorsalis*, *D. validus*, and *D. arboreus*, and is found in forests of central and southern Africa, including the islands of Fernando Po and Pemba. Tree hyraxes are found at elevations up to 4,500 meters.

Head and body length is 400 to 600 mm.; tail length is 10 to 30 mm.; and weight is usually 1,500 to 2,500 grams. The hair on the upper parts is brown, tipped with gray or yellow; black hairs are also present on the back. Some forms (*D. dorsalis emini*) have two color phases, the darker coat and a yellow pelage. A white patch of hair, marking the location of a gland, is present on the back, and the ears are edged with white hairs. The under parts are usually brownish. The fur is longer and slightly more silky than that of other hyraxes. Tree hyraxes also differ morphologically from the other dassies in the white dorsal patch and in skull and dental features.

In habits, *Dendrohyrax* differs from the other hyraxes: it is less gregarious, more arboreal, and nocturnal. Tree hyraxes spend the day in tree hollows or in dense foliage and feed during the night on leaves, shoots, buds, and insects. They are essentially arboreal, running up and down tree trunks and occasionally leaping from one branch to another, but they also descend to the ground to feed.

Their calls are better known than the animals themselves to most people within the range of this genus. Tree hyraxes begin to call soon after dark in a series of croaks that gradually mount the scale and end in a loud scream.

These animals often assume a characteristic defensive position when threatened by a predator; the back and the rump are turned toward the enemy, and the hairs around the dorsal gland are spread out and separated from each other so that the naked glandular area is exposed. They are said to be less irritable than the other dassies and to tame readily. Their flesh and skin are highly prized by natives.

The one or two, rarely three, young may be born at any time of the year; gestation period is assumed to be about seven months. The young animal is precocial and one individual measured about one-half the length of its mother a few hours after birth.

The type species of the genus is *D. arboreus* (Smith).

1327

Rock Hyrax (*Heterohyrax syriacus*), photo by C. A. Spinage.

Rock or Gray Hyraxes, Yellow Spotted Hyraxes; Ceed Koldasse, Ishkwokwo, Perere, Kira, Okile, Mhelele, Mbira, Bogos, Tubsum (native names).

This genus comprises about half a dozen species which are distributed from Ethiopia and the Congo southward through Southern Rhodesia and southwest Africa. They prefer rocky mountainous areas and range in elevation from sea level to at least 3,800 meters.

The length of the head and body is 305 to 380 mm.; an external tail is absent; the height of the shoulder is 305 mm.; and the weight is 475 grams to 4.5 kg. The body is covered with thick, short, rather coarse hair and the general coloration is brown and whitish, suffused with black; the under parts are white. The general appearance is much like a large guinea pig (*Cavia*). Members of this genus are distinguished by a patch of yellowish or whitish hair in the middle of the back. This patch covers a gland which is exposed when the surrounding hairs are erected in anger. Females have one pair of pectoral mammae and two pairs of inguinal mammae, although the pectoral mammae were absent in one specimen studied.

These animals are semigregarious, living in colonies of hundreds of individuals. They are principally diurnal and enjoy lying on rocky ledges during the afternoon. They like to play and chase one another to and fro among rocks. They are sharp-sighted, keen of hearing, and quite aggressive, bravely prepared to bite anything that molests them. Their presence is often detected by their call, which is similar to a shrill scream. These animals are noted for their wariness; they are ever alert and seek shelter upon the slightest alarm but are extremely curious and will soon show themselves again. They feed in the early morning, late afternoon, and evening and their chief source of food is roots and bulbs. They are particularly fond of locusts.

There appears to be no definite breeding season, although most of the young (three the usual number) are born during the latter half of March. The young are born in a fur-lined nest about 225 days after the parents have mated. Within a few hours after birth they are able to scamper about with the others. The life span probably does not exceed seven years.

Natives and Arabs eat hyrax flesh because other flesh is very scarce, but it is said to be tough, dry, and not particularly desirable if other food is obtainable.

The chief wild foe of hyraxes is the rock python. They are also preyed upon by leopards, birds of prey, probably mongooses, and other small carnivores.

W. L. Sclater (*The Mammals of South Africa* [London, 1900]) says "The soles, which are naked, are covered by a very thick epithelium which is kept constantly moist by the secretion of the sudorific glands there present in extraordinary abundance;

furthermore, a special arrangement of muscles enables the sole to be contracted so as to form a hollow air-tight cup which, when in contact with the rock, gives the animal great clinging power, so much so that even when shot dead it remains attached to almost perpendicular surfaces as if fixed there."

Heterohyrax syriacus of Palestine and Arabia is the "Shapham" of the Bible which has been erroneously interpreted as a coney (Leviticus, 11:5; Deuteronomy, 14:7; Psalms, 104:18; Proverbs, 30:24-28).

The Leviticus reference is in error, as the hyrax does not chew a cud, although its jaws are frequently in motion as though chewing. It really does have a "cloven hoof," however, since the toes are tipped with tiny hoofs.

Hyraxes on islands in Lake Victoria are of a species different from those on the mainland.

The type species of the genus is *H. syriacus* (Schreber).

Rock Hyrax (*Procavia capensis*), photo from San Diego Zoological Garden.

ROCK DASSIES, HYRAXES, CONIES; DASSIES, KLIP-DASSEN, KLIPPSCHLIEFER, IMBILA (local vernaculars).

THIS GENUS of three species is found over much of Africa as well as in parts of Syria, Sinai, and Palestine. Members of this genus frequent rocky, scrub-covered ranges wherever there are suitable shelters in, between, or under rocks, or where they can dig burrows of their own.

The length of the head and body is 305 to 550 mm.; an external tail is lacking; the height of the shoulder is 202 to 305 mm.; and the weight is 14 to 20 kg. The hair is short and rather coarse and the general coloration of the upper parts is brownish gray. The flanks are somewhat lighter, and the under parts are creamy. There is, however, considerable variation in color and intensity. The black whiskers may be as long as 180 mm. In general appearance the rock dassies are similar to a large pika (*Ochotona*) or a tailless woodchuck (*Marmota*). However, the similarities go no further than the superficial appearance. The soles are moist and rubber-like, which gives the animals traction on smooth surfaces and steep slopes. Members of this genus are distinguished from their relatives, members of the genera *Heterohyrax* and *Dendrohyrax*, by a black dorsal patch. This patch covers a gland which is exposed if the surrounding hairs are erected. Erection of these hairs occurs when the animal is angry or frightened.

These animals live in small communities of about six individuals to colonies of about 50 individuals. They are mainly diurnal but also come out on warm, moonlight nights. In spite of their heavy build, rock dassies are active and agile, running up steep, smooth rock surfaces with ease. Their senses are keen and when persecuted they become quite shy. When alarmed, they quickly dash into a rock cranny or their own burrow. Although not large animals, they can put up a vigorous fight in self-defense, biting savagely. Dassies are exclusively vegetarians, preferring grass, leaves, bark, etc.

The usual number of young per litter is two or three; they are born after a gestation period of about 225 days. The young are born fully covered with hair and with open eyes. Birth usually occurs in a crevice. Puberty is reached in two years, and the female has six mammae. One *P. capensis* lived at the London Zoo nearly six years.

The flesh is prized by some natives. The young make interesting pets and will eat practically any vegetable matter. The chief natural enemies of rock dassies are leopards and eagles, but foxes, weasels, and mongooses doubtless prey on them also.

The type species of the genus is *P. capensis*, Pallas.

Order: SIRENIA

DUGONGS, SEA COWS, AND MANATEES.

THIS ORDER of aquatic mammals contains two Recent families: Dugongidae for the genera *Dugong* (dugongs, one species) and *Hydrodamalis* (Steller's sea cow, one species, extinct); and Trichechidae for the single genus *Trichechus* (manatees, three species). Dugongs inhabit coastal regions in the tropical areas of the Old World, but some go into fresh water of estuaries and up rivers. Steller's sea cow occurred in the Bering Sea, the only Recent member of this order adapted to cold waters; and manatees live along the coast and in coastal rivers of the southeastern United States, the West Indies, northern South America, and western Africa.

These massive, fusiform (spindle-shaped) animals have paddle-like forelimbs, no hind limbs or dorsal fin, and a tail in the form of a horizontally flattened fin. The adults of the living forms generally are from 2.5 to 4 meters in length and weigh up to 360 kg. The skin is thick, tough, wrinkled, and nearly hairless; stiff, thickened vibrissae (tactile hairs) are present around the lips. The head is rounded, the mouth is small, and the muzzle is abruptly cut off. The nostrils, which are valvular and separate, are located on the upper surface of the muzzle. The eyelids, although small, are capable of contraction, and a well-developed nictitating membrane is present. An external ear flap is lacking. The neck is short.

The females have two mammae, located in the chest region. The testes in males are abdominal (borne permanently within the abdomen).

The skeleton is dense and heavy; the increased specific gravity is probably an adaptation to remaining submerged in shallow waters. The skull is large in proportion to the size of the body; the nasal opening is located far back on the skull and directed posteriorly. The lower jaws are heavy and united for a considerable distance. The forelimb has a well-developed skeletal support, but there is no trace of the skeletal elements of the hind limb. The pelvis consists of one or two pairs of bones suspended in muscle. The vertebrae are separate and distinct throughout the spinal column; one genus (*Trichechus*) has six neck vertebrae (nearly all other mammals have seven).

The dentition is highly modified and often reduced (functional teeth are lacking in Steller's sea cow).

The tusk-like incisors are reduced or absent, and canines are present only in certain fossil species. When the incisors are present, there is a space between them. The cheek teeth, which are arranged in a continuous series, number from three to ten in each half of each jaw. The anterior part of the palate and the corresponding surface of the lower jaw are covered with rough, horny plates, presumably used as an aid in chewing food; the small, fixed tongue is also supplied with rough plates.

Dugongs and manatees differ in a number of ways. In dugongs (and sea cows) the tail fin is deeply notched, but in manatees the tail fin is more or less evenly rounded. The upper lip is more deeply cleft in manatees than in dugongs (and sea cows). Dugongs have one pair of tusk-like incisors (in the males but concealed in bone in the females) and 3/3 functional cheek teeth; in manatees functional incisors are not present, but the cheek teeth are numerous, but indefinite in number (up to 10 in each half of each jaw). The cheek teeth in manatees are replaced consecutively from the rear as in many proboscideans; an individual cheek tooth is worn down as it moves forward.

Sirenians are solitary, travel in pairs, or associate in groups of three to about six individuals. Generally slow and inoffensive, they spend all their life in the water. They are vegetarians and feed on various water plants. The ordinal name Sirenia is related to the mermaid-like manner of nursing in dugongs (the Sirens of mythology) and manatees. The only reliable observations of nursing in manatees, however, have revealed that the young suckle while the mother is underwater in a horizontal position, belly downward, and dugongs probably nurse in the same position.

These aquatic mammals were apparently more abundant in previous times, that is, during the Miocene and early Pliocene. Their comparative scarcity at the present time is probably due somewhat to their persecution by man for food, hides, and oil, but, perhaps most importantly, to climatic changes in the recent past.

The geological range of the order Sirenia is the Eocene to the Recent. There are two extinct families. Many paleontologists and zoologists think that Sirenia and Proboscidea evolved from a common ancestry.

DUGONGS, SEA COWS; WALIKI, YUANGAN.

THIS FAMILY contains two genera, each with one species: *Dugong*, dugongs, from coastal regions in the tropical areas of the Old World, is confined to marine waters; and *Hydrodamalis*, Steller's sea cow, now extinct, formerly lived in the Bering Sea. The latter genus, which was the only Recent sirenian adapted to cold waters, had a brief and tragic history. Although it was probably represented by less than 5,000 individuals at the time of its discovery, man's greed, not natural causes, resulted in its swift extermination.

Dugongs (the modern sea cow) are generally 2.5 to 3.5 meters in length, whereas Steller's sea cows measured almost 7.5 meters. The flippers in Steller's sea cows were curiously bent and were said to have been used to pull an individual along the bottom of the ocean as it foraged. Members of the family Dugongidae lack nails on their flippers. The deeply notched tail fin has two pointed, lateral lobes (the tail fin in manatees is more or less evenly rounded). The upper lip, which is more deeply cleft in the adult dugong than in the young, is not so deeply cleft as that of the manatees. The nostrils are located more dorsally than in other sirenians. In dugongs (and apparently all sirenians) the eyelids contain a number of glands which produce an oily secretion to protect the eye against water.

The ribs of Steller's sea cow consisted entirely of dense bone; those of dugongs contain some porous bone.

The skull of a dugong has a downwardly-bent rostrum (for holding the incisors), whereas the skull of a Steller's sea cow had a rostrum which was only slightly inclined. Functional teeth were lacking in *Hydrodamalis* but occur in *Dugong*. Dugongs have one pair of tusk-like incisors (in the males but concealed in bone in the females), which are directed downward and forward and are partially covered with enamel, and 3/3 functional cheek teeth (up to 6/6 may be present in an individual's lifetime). The cheek teeth are columnar, covered with cement, lack enamel, and have simple, open roots.

The following information applies only to the genus *Dugong*. These sirenians are solitary, occur in pairs, or associate in groups of three to about six individuals; they are affectionate and fond of one another. Dugongs are frightened by noises above and below water; they have keen hearing. The sense of taste is also well developed, but vision is poor. These animals have a strong and distinct odor. They apparently cannot breathe through the mouth, as Australian aborigines asphyxiate these animals by plugging their nostrils. Dugongs inhale quickly, close the nostrils by means of valves, and sink to the bottom to search for food. They apparently rest in deep water during the day, coming inshore at night to feed.

The local distribution of dugongs depends upon the availability of various algae and grasses. A dugong, while feeding, rips out the entire plant, swishes it back and forth in the water until most of the sand is removed, and then swallows it with little chewing. Brown seaweeds are usually rejected, the green species are favored. Dugongs do not browse haphazardly but feed rather methodically. They often pile whole plants of sea grass in stacks along the shore and eat them later.

Dugongs usually bear a single young. The young is born underwater and must swim to the surface for its first breath of air. These sirenians may have served as the basis for the Sirens of mythology, although their mermaid-like manner of nursing has been largely discredited.

The existing populations of dugongs are nearing extinction in some areas. They are killed with spear, net, and gun and are used for food, oil, leather, and other products. Natives use certain parts for medical purposes. It is said that in areas of northwestern Australia salted dugong flesh and turtle eggs take the place of the customary breakfast of ham and eggs in the Western Hemisphere. There is some indication that the Ark of the Covenant, taken by the Hebrews on their journey through Sinai, was covered with dugong leather. The oily secretion of the eyelid glands collects in the inner eye corner in animals caught and drawn out on land; these "sirenian tears" are valued by the native people as good luck pieces. "Dugong" is apparently a Malayan name.

The geological range of this family is the middle Eocene to the Recent in Africa and Europe, the Eocene to the Recent in North America, and the Recent in Asia.

Dugong (*Dugong dugon*), picture from *Extinct and Vanishing Mammals of the Western Hemisphere*, Glover M. Allen.

DUGONGS OR SEA COWS; WALIKI, YUANGAN.

THE SINGLE SPECIES, *D. dugon*, is found in the Red Sea, along the east coast of Africa, around the islands of the Bay of Bengal, along the Malay Archipelago, and in the Moluccas as far as the Philippines, New Guinea, and to the coast of Australia north of the tropics. These are tropical warm-water mammals, restricted to warm marine waters along the coasts and never ranging far to sea nor into the fresh waters.

The average length for adult animals would appear to be between 2.5 to 3.2 meters. A male, 275 cm. long, weighed 170 kg., and a female, 243 cm. long, weighed about 140 kg. The skin coloration varies somewhat but is generally brownish or grayish. The tail flipper is broadly notched in the mid-line and has two pointed lateral lobes. The forelimbs are flipper-like, more long than broad. There are scattered stiff hairs around the muzzle.

These animals may be the Sirens of mythology, since some of the stories of mermaids are based on dugongs. They were first mentioned in Western literature by Pliny and may have served as the basis for Homer's fanciful tale of Odysseus and the Sirens. The early European seafarers brought back tales of seeing mermaids that lived in the sea and nursed their babies at the breast in human style; these tales were undoubtedly based on encounters with these peaceful browsers of the sea. Dugongs are very inoffensive and do nurse their young at twin mammae, but this probably takes place underwater, as in the manatees.

Dugongs are more strictly confined to marine environments than are manatees, as they have only rarely been reported from river mouths or other fresh-water localities. They usually occur in pairs or in groups of three to six. Dugongs surface to breathe at irregular intervals while grazing; the records for submergence are one to ten minutes. They feed on various marine algae and on marine grasses which grow in shallow water. The grasses are usually swallowed whole. In some coastal areas the distribution of dugongs is dependent on an abundant supply of grass.

The breeding season apparently lasts throughout the year, as young have been seen in different stages of development in every month. Usually a single young is born at a time, after a gestation period of about 11 months. The young is carefully guarded by the mother and sometimes carried on her back.

Throughout their range they are caught for the valuable oil which is rendered from their blubber, for various mystical, superstitious "medicinal" uses, and for the fat and meat of the body. The natives of Madagascar, for example, consider dugong flesh to be delicious and use the powder of the upper incisors in drugs for people who have eaten contaminated food, the fat of the head for headaches, and the tallow as a laxative. (A dugong weighing 200 to 300 kg. will yield 24 to 56 liters of oil.) In many areas they have already declined greatly in numbers, and fears are expressed that they might be exterminated by continuing pressure.

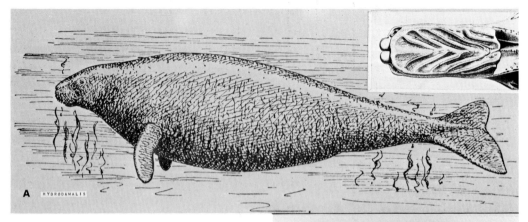

STELLER'S SEA COW.

NOW EXTINCT, this huge, dugong-like creature (*H. gigas = H. stelleri*) had an extremely restricted range; it was confined to the waters around Bering Island and other small islands in the Komandorskie group in the Bering Sea. It was discovered when an expedition led by Captain Vitus Bering in 1742 was stranded on the island with most of the men sick with scurvy. Due to man's subsequent relentless slaughter for food and other purposes, it became extinct about 27 years after its discovery.

This animal was the largest of the Recent sirenians. From notes and data taken from observations of the living animal by Georg Steller, the famous German naturalist of Bering's trip, we can get an idea of the size and appearance of the animal in life. It measured 752 cm. from the tip of the nose to the point of the tail flipper. Its greatest circumference measured 620 cm. Steller estimated an adult female weighed about 4,000 kg. The head was small in proportion to the body. The tail had two pointed lobes forming a caudal flipper. The forelimbs were very small, flipper-like, and somewhat truncated. There were no hind limbs externally, no trace even remaining of the pelvic elements. The skin was naked and was covered with a very thick, bark-like, extremely uneven-appearing epidermis, from which the German name for this animal, "Borkéntier," was derived. The skin was a dark brown to gray-brown color, occasionally spotted or streaked with white. The forelimbs were covered with short, brush-like hairs. Some dried pieces of this skin are still preserved, one in Leningrad and one in Hamburg. These animals were parasitized by two or three species of small crustaceans that burrowed into the rough skin. Steller says that he found some of the holes made by the small crab-like crustacean *Cyamus* to ooze a thin serum.

These giant sirenians, the only Recent members of their order adapted to cold waters, had a brief and tragic history of discovery followed by swift extermination; however, they were probably already reduced by nature to a small relict population of a once widely-dispersed creature, as they were apparently confined in range to a few tiny, bleak islands in the Bering Sea. All that we know about their habits comes from Steller's account. They were quite numerous in the

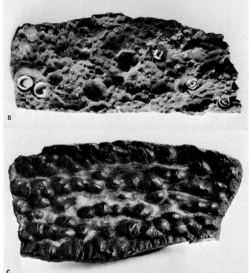

Steller's Sea Cow (*Hydrodamalis stelleri*), A. Photo from *Extinct and Vanishing Mammals of the Western Hemisphere*, Glover M. Allen. Inset: Steller's Sea Cow's palate, from *Symbolae Sirenologicae*, drawing by J. F. Brandt. B. Outer surface of skin; C. Flesh side of skin; photos by Erna Mohr.

shallow bays and inlets around the coast of Bering Island when first discovered. They fed upon the kelp beds and the extensive growths of various marine algae which grew in the shallower waters. They were slow moving, utterly fearless of man, and were said to be affectionate toward each other, as they apparently tried to aid other individuals that were either wounded or in distress.

The following are excerpts from Steller's own account:

Usually entire families keep together, the male with the female, one grown offspring and a little, tender one. To me they appear to be monogamous. They bring forth their young at all seasons, generally however in autumn, judging from the many new-born seen at that time; from the fact that I observed them to mate preferably in the early spring, I conclude that the fetus remains in the uterus more than a year. That they bear not more than one calf I conclude from the shortness of the uterine cornua and the dual number of mammae, nor have I ever seen more than one calf about each cow.

These gluttonous animals eat incessantly, and because of their enormous voracity keep their heads always under water with but slight concern for their life and security, so that one may pass in the very midst of them in a boat even unarmed and safely single out from the herd the one he wishes to hook. All they do while feeding is to lift the nostrils every four or five minutes out of the water, blowing out air and a little water with a noise like that of a horse snorting. While browsing they move slowly forward, one foot after the other, and in this manner half swim, half walk like cattle or sheep grazing. Half the body is always out of water. . . . In winter these animals become so emaciated that not only the ridge of the backbone but every rib shows.

Their capture was effected by a large iron hook, . . . the other end being fastened by means of an iron ring to a very long, stout rope, held by thirty men on shore. . . . The harpooner stood in the bow of the boat with the hook in his hand and struck as soon as he was near enough to do so, whereupon the men on shore grasping the other end of the rope pulled the desperately resisting animal laboriously towards them. Those in the boat, however, made the animal fast by means of another rope and wore it out with continual blows, until, tired and completely motionless, it was attacked with bayonets, knives and other weapons and pulled up on land. Immense slices were cut from the still living animal, but all it did was shake its tail furiously. . . . (Translation by Leonhard Stejneger in his book *Georg Wilhelm Steller* [Cambridge, 1936], pp. 355-56.)

The meat was used for food and the hide for making skin boat covers or for shoe leather.

Manatees (*Trichechus manatus*), photo of mounted specimens from Field Museum of Natural History. Insets: Head (*T. senegalensis*), photo from Societe Royale de Zoologie d'Anvers through Walter Van den Bergh; Tail (*T. senegalensis*), photo from the Jardin Zoologique, Anvers.

MANATEES, AMAZON OX; LOS MANATIS, VACOS MARINOS, PEIXE BOI, ZEE KOEIEN.

THIS FAMILY contains a single genus, *Trichechus*, with three species which are distributed as follows: *T. manatus*, along the coast and coastal rivers of southeastern United States westward to Texas, and the West Indies and the adjacent mainland from Veracruz southeastward to northern South America; *T. inunguis*, the Amazon and Orinoco drainage areas of northeastern South America; and *T. senegalensis*, western Africa, from the Senegal River (16 degrees N. latitude) southward to the Cuanaga River (10 degrees S. latitude) and in the Lake Chad drainage area. Manatees occur in marine bays and sluggish rivers, usually in turbid water.

These animals have a rounded body, a small head, and a squarish snout. The upper lip is deeply split and each half is capable of moving independently of the other. The nostrils are borne at the tip of the muzzle, the eyes are small, and there are no external ears. Vestigial nails occur on the flippers, and the tail fin is more or less evenly rounded (not notched as in dugongs and sea cows). Stout bristles appear on the upper lip, and bristle-like short hairs are scattered singly over the body at intervals of about 1.25 cm. These sirenians attain a maximum length of nearly 4.5 meters and a weight of 680 kg.; most individuals are 2.5 to 4 meters long and 140 to 360 kgs. in weight. Coloration is a uniform dull gray to black. The skin is 5.1 cm. thick.

The stout ribs consist wholly of dense bone. Manatees have only six neck vertebrae, whereas nearly all other mammals have seven. The single pair of mammae are pectoral.

Nasal bones are present in the skull (these bones are absent or vestigial in dugongs and sea cows). Manatees have 2/2 incisors which are concealed beneath the horny plates and are lost before maturity. The cheek teeth number up to 10 in each half of each jaw (although more than 6/6 are rarely present at any one time). They are low-crowned, enameled, divided into cuspidate cross-crests, lack cement, and have closed roots. These teeth are replaced horizontally; they form at the back of the jaw and wear down as they move forward. This may be an adaptation to eating food mixed with sand, as a similar replacement of teeth occurs in many proboscideans and other mammals.

Manatees sometimes gather in groups of 15 to 20 individuals when the young are half-grown, and in Florida may migrate to, and congregate in, warm spots during cold weather, but they usually occur singly or in small herds of family-group size. Their presence is often indicated by a series of upwellings in the water. These sluggish, generally inoffensive creatures can remain submerged for at least 16 minutes; they normally surface for two or three breaths at five to ten minute intervals. Manatees rest at the surface with their backs arched and their tails below the head. In shallow water they recline on their tails, which are then curved ventrally. Occasionally in shallow water they will "walk" on the inturned tips of the flippers. The young swim only with the flippers, whereas the adults usually swim only with the tail, often using their flippers to scull themselves about to the right or left. The adult can surface by means of the tail. A full-grown manatee is incapable of locomotion when completely stranded on land.

These sirenians often greet each other with "muzzle-to-muzzle" play. They are rather deliberate in most of their movements. They are inquisitive and frequently inspect anchored fishing boats at close range as their eyesight is poorly developed. Two captive *T. manatus* learned to perform simple tricks.

Manatees are active at any hour, but seem to feed mainly at night. The flippers are used to direct vegetation toward the mouth, the split lip is used like a forceps in picking up food, and the stout bristles on the upper lip aid in working the food into the mouth. In such places as the Botanic Gardens of British Guiana, they have been tamed and readily snatch food with their protractile lips from the hands of visitors. Manatees are strictly herbivorous; they feed on marine, brackish, and fresh-water plants, and on some terrestrial plants which hang over the water. A captive 4.5-meter animal consumed from 27 to 45 kg. of food a day.

Courtship in *T. manatus* involves, among other maneuvers, a male approaching, nuzzling, "embracing," and presenting its underside to a female Manatees usually mate in shallow water; the gestation period is at least 152 days and may last 180 days. The young (one, sometimes two) are born underwater at any time of the year and are immediately brought to the surface by the mother. The calves at birth are approximately 1 meter in length, 18 to 27 kg. in weight, and pinkish in color; they are cared for by both parents and remain with their mother for more than one year, probably for two years. A young manatee sometimes rides on its mother's back. For 18 months the mother nurses her offspring underwater in a horizontal position with her belly down; the calf is not clasped in the mother's flippers—neither animal's head is above water, nor is either animal in a vertical position. Breeding may begin at three or four years of age; a manatee under 2.5 meters in length is probably sexually immature.

The excellence and fine quality of the meat, hide, and oil has resulted in such persistent hunting of manatees that their number has been greatly reduced in some areas. Today, in an effort to conserve manatees, the state of Florida levies a $500 fine for killing these animals. Man seems to be the only predator of adult manatees; possibly sharks or crocodiles prey on the young. Manatees are sometimes used in British Guiana to clear canals and other waterways of weeds and algae. Good results have been obtained in Georgetown. Manatees are very sensitive to changes in water temperature and are often killed when severe cold spells occur.

The geological range of this family is the Pleistocene to the Recent in North America, the Miocene to the Recent in South America, and the Recent in Africa.

The type species of the genus is *T. manatus*, Linnaeus.

Order: PERISSODACTYLA

ODD-TOED HOOFED MAMMALS—HORSES, TAPIRS, AND RHINOCEROSES.

CONTAINED IN THE ORDER Perissodactyla are three Recent families: the Equidae (the horses), Tapiridae (the tapirs), and Rhinocerotidae (the rhinos), with a total of 6 Recent genera and approximately 17 species. Members of this order occur in central and southern Asia, Sumatra, Java, Borneo, Africa (except the Sahara), and in the New World from southern Mexico to northern Argentina; tapirs are the only living native perissodactyls of the Western Hemisphere. Tapirs usually inhabit humid tropical forests, whereas horses and rhinos live on grassy plains or in open scrub country.

These are medium to large mammals adapted to running (especially the members of the Equidae). All of the Recent families are quite distinct, with tapirs and rhinos resembling one another more than either family resembles the horse. The main character common to these animals is that the weight of the body is borne on the central digits, with the main axis of the foot passing through the third digit, which is the longest on all four feet. In the horses only the third digit of each foot is functional, whereas in tapirs four digits are developed on the fore foot and three on the hind foot, and in rhinos three digits are present on all four feet. The first digit is not present in Recent forms; it was vestigial in certain fossil species. The terminal digital bones are flattened and triangular, with evenly rounded free edges, and are incased by hooves (some members of the extinct family Chalicotheriidae had clawed digits). Perissodactyls progress on their hoofs or on their digits, never on the sole of the foot with the heel touching the ground. The ulna and the fibula are reduced, so that the movement of these bones is reduced or lacking. The ankle bone or astragalus has only a single, deeply-grooved, pulley-like surface for the tibia, and its lower end is nearly flat; the calcaneum, or heel bone, which has a widened lower end, does not articulate with the fibula.

The skin is usually thickened and sparsely to densely haired. The mammae are located in the region of the groin, and the males do not possess a baculum.

The dental formula for the order is as follows: i 0-3/0-3, c 0-1/0-1, pm 2-4/2-4, m 3/3 = 20-44; for the Recent species it is: i 0-3/0-3, c 0-1/0-1, pm 3-4/3-4, m 3/3 = 24-44; and in the Eocene genera it is i 3/3, c 1/1, pm 4/4, m 3/3 = 44. The canines, when present, are never tusk-like in the Recent species. The cheek teeth are arranged in a continuous series; the premolars (at least the rear members of the series) are molar-like in the Recent species; the first cheek tooth is a persistent milk premolar. The grinding teeth are usually complex in structure, massive, and low-crowned to high-crowned; prominent transverse ridges are present in the cheek teeth of tapirs and rhinos, whereas the cheek teeth in horses, which are grazers rather than browsers, develop high crowns with four main columns and various infoldings. Some fossil species in this order had tubercles on the crowns of their grinding teeth. The skull is usually elongate, with an abrupt slope in the back. The nasal bones are expanded posteriorly. Characteristic of the order is the arrangement of openings in the skull by which nerves and blood vessels enter and leave the brain case. The Recent species lack horns with true bony cores, although roughened cushions on the nasal bones of the skull bear horns in rhinos.

The development of the foot is a specialization which, in its highest form, the horses, enables these animals to be swift and strong runners. It is not developed to such an extent in the rhinoceros and tapir. Rhinos, however, can run rapidly for short distances, and tapirs can also run well, although they usually inhabit a type of terrain that permits them to plunge into dense cover or water to escape their enemies. The members of this order eat plants, as they are either browsers or grazers; the structure of their lips and teeth facilitates the obtaining and chewing of coarse vegetable food. Adulthood is attained in four to six years and longevity is five to seven times that long.

Except for horses, which comprise the only group of perissodactyls that was domesticated by man, individual animals of this order are not particularly numerous. Various members of the Equidae, however, are probably second only to the cattle (Bovidae) in the economic life of man.

This order is actually declining in number, it was much more widespread and numerous, with a greater assemblage of forms, in past geologic ages. Nine extinct families are recognized; the geological range of this order is the upper Eocene to the Recent. Four genera, now extinct, are known from the Pleistocene of the Old World.

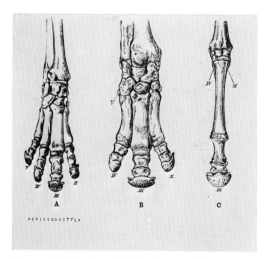

PERISSODACTYLA

Bones of the fore feet; A. Tapir (*Tapirus indicus*); B. Rhinoceros (*Didermoceros sumatrensis*); C. Horse (*Equus caballus*); photos from *Mammalia*, Beddard.

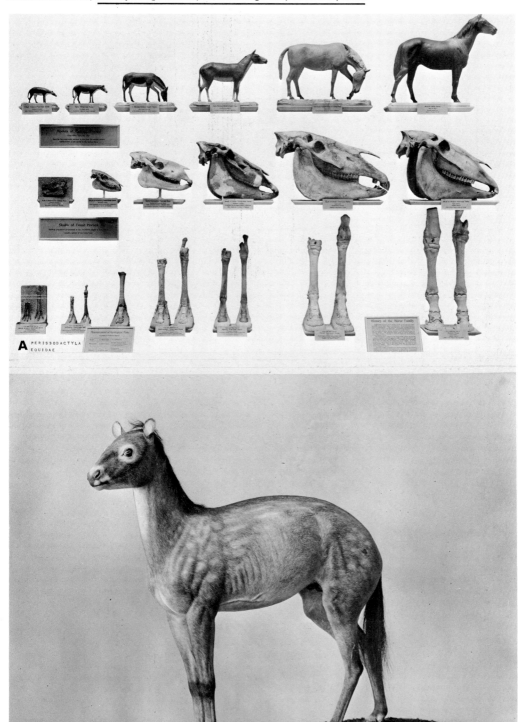

A. Exhibition in the Chicago Natural History Museum showing the evolution of horses. B. A restoration of the primitive three-toed horse (*Mesohippus* sp.) that inhabited western America and other regions, photos from Field Museum of Natural History.

HORSES, ZEBRAS, QUAGGAS, ASSES, ONAGERS, KIANGS, BURROS, JACKASSES, MULES, HINNIES, TARPANS; HASSAN, FARAS, GORKHUR, GHUR, HEMIONE, MBIDAI, MBWETE, HOMAR, AKHDA, GUMBURI, PFERDE, ESEL, CHEVAUX, ANES, EZELS (local and native vernaculars).

THIS FAMILY contains a single Recent genus, *Equus*, for approximately eight species of horses and horse-like animals. The living members of the family Equidae are native to central and eastern Asia and Africa, except the Sahara. The true horse (*E. caballus*) is now nearly cosmopolitan as a result of introduction by man. Equids inhabit grassy or shrubby terrain in temperate and tropical regions, although their range extended into subarctic areas within historic times; most species seem to be limited by the presence or absence of a permanent water supply. The species are grouped into subgenera as follows: *Equus* includes the horses; *Dolichohippus*, Heller, 1912, and *Hippotigris*, H. Smith, 1841, the zebras; and *Asinus*, Gray, 1824, and *Hemionus*, F. Cuvier, 1823, the asses. They all are similar in general body form with relatively long necks and heads, one functional digit on each foot, long tails, and two mammae.

The general body form ranges from thick-headed, short-legged, and stocky (*E. przewalskii*) to slender-headed and graceful-limbed (*E. caballus*). The size is variable and is influenced by the wide range among the domesticated forms. The wild species measure from 1 to 1.5 meters high at the shoulders. The tail is moderately long, with the hairs reaching at least to the middle of the leg. Equids are heavily haired, but the length of the hair is variable. Most species have a mane on the neck and a lock of hair on the fore part of the head, known as the forelock. The females have two mammae in the region of the groin.

The Recent species have only one functional digit, the third. The terminal digital bone on each foot is widened and evenly rounded or spade-shaped; equids walk on the tips of their toes. The radius and ulna are united, although the ulna is greatly reduced in size so that all the weight is borne on the radius. In the hind leg the enlarged tibia supports the weight, and the fibula is reduced and fused to the tibia.

The dental formula in the extinct species is i 3/3, c 1/1, pm 3-4/3-4, m 3/3 = 40 to 44; and in the Recent forms it is i 3/3, c 1/1, pm 3-4/3, m 3/3 = 40 to 42. The incisors are chisel-shaped, the enamel on the tips folding inward to form a pit, or "mark," that is worn off in early life; the first permanent incisors appear at about two and a half to 3 years in domestic horses. The canine teeth are vestigial or absent in female equids. The premolars are molar-like and permanent, except the first which, when present, represents a persistent milk tooth. The first upper premolar is often reduced or absent. The cheek teeth have a complex structure. They are high-crowned with four main columns and various infoldings with much cement; the grinding teeth in certain fossil species had four tubercles and little cement. Age is often estimated by the degree of wear of the surface pattern of the cheek teeth, but the rapidity of wear depends to a considerable extent on the abrasive character of the food. The skull is long, and the nasal bones are long and narrow, freely projecting, pointed ante-riorly, and hornless. The eye socket is behind the teeth thus avoiding pressure on the eye by the long molars.

The single surviving species of the wild horse is *E. przewalskii*. It inhabits the vast plains on either side of the Altai Mountains in Mongolia and is distinguished from domestic horses by its erect mane and the absence of a forelock.

The length of the head and body is 1.8 to 2 meters; the length of the tail is about .9 meters; the height at the shoulder is 1 to 1.2 meters; and adults weigh about 350 kg. The summer pelage is short and smooth, the back and sides are reddish brown, gradually becoming yellowish white on the belly. The winter pelage is somewhat longer and lighter in color. The mane is dark brown, the dorsal stripe is reddish brown, and the inner sides of the legs are gray.

These animals formerly associated in large herds, but they have been almost exterminated by man. They are alert to avoid enemies. The young are born in April and May, and the life span is 25 to 30 years.

Since this is the only true wild horse surviving in the world today, it attracts special interest. Through interbreeding with the ponies of the Mongols it will not be long before it ceases to exist as a pure wild species. This animal was probably tamed about 3000 B.C. in the grasslands of central Asia and was used as a means of transportation.

The tarpan, *E. caballus*, now extinct in the wild, originally inhabited much of Europe and portions of Asia. It was an important source of food for humans before the dawn of history and was probably domesticated quite early. This name is usually used for the domestic horse, but it is possible that the latter is a mixture of two or three species, including *E. przewalskii*.

Horse flesh is occasionally eaten by man and is also important in the manufacture of commercial pet foods.

Through selective breeding under domestication many different strains of horses have been developed. There is much excellent literature regarding the different breeds.

Zebras inhabit eastern, central, and southern Africa, preferring plains, savannahs, and in some cases mountainous regions. The length of the head and body is 2 to 2.4 meters; the length of the tail is 47 to 57 cm.; and the height at the shoulder is 1.2 to 1.4 meters. The weight is about 350 kg. The zebras are unmistakably distinguished by their coloration, which consists of variously arranged dark bands on portions of or over all the body. They have strong upright manes and terminally haired tails. The three living species of zebras are well distinguished by external characters such as large rounded ears or small narrow ears, body size, and the characteristic patterns of striping. The width of the striping on the body, the number of stripes, the presence of "shadow" stripes, and the great reduction in prominence of the striping of the limbs are highly variable in *E. burchelli*.

Zebras are generally gregarious, assembling in herds of 10 to 12 individuals or else mingling in herds of other animals such as wildebeests (*Connochaetes*) or even ostriches (*Struthio*). Old males are occasionally solitary. Seasonal concentrations of *E.*

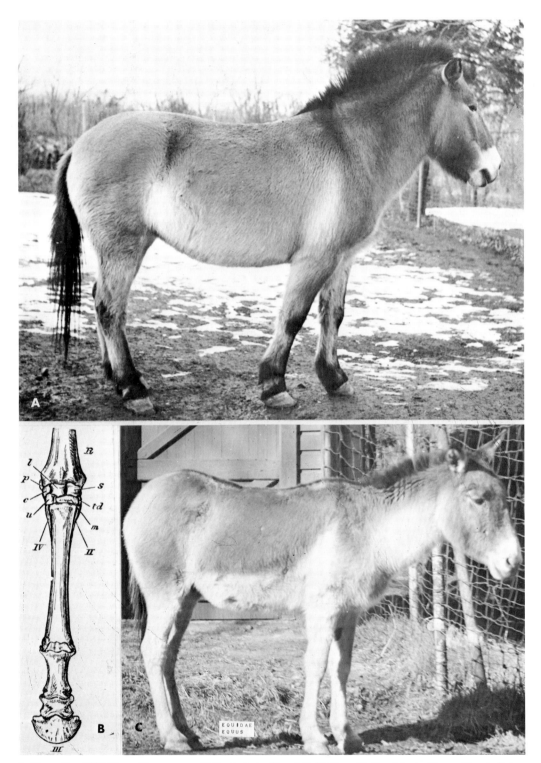

A. Mongolian Wild Horse (*Equus przewalskii*), photo by Ernest P. Walker. B. Front foot of horse (*E. caballus*): c. cuneiform; l. lunar; m. magnum; p. pisiform; r. radius; s. scaphoid; td. trapezoid; u. unciform; II. & IV. rudimentary metacarpals; photo from *Mammalia*, Beddard. C. Kiang (*E. hemionus kiang*), photo by Ernest P. Walker.

burchelli may number in the hundreds. Zebras are inquisitive creatures, and because of this trait they are easily killed. They are, however, capable of running at speeds of up to 64.4 km. per hour. They generally graze on savannah grasses nightly. One young is born in the spring after a gestation period of 345 to 390 days. The life span may be 28 years. Zebras thrive well in captivity and are one of the best known African mammals, as they are found in almost all zoological parks and in circuses. They are favored food for lions, their chief enemy.

The quagga (*E. quagga*), a zebra which inhabited southern Africa, had much less pronounced stripes than most zebras. It was exterminated in the wild before 1860, and the last survivor died in the Artis Zoo in Amsterdam in 1883. The nominate race of Burchell's zebra, which also inhabited southern Africa, was exterminated about 1910.

Zebras are resistant to common African diseases that horses cannot survive. Therefore efforts have been made by government and private agencies to domesticate them or to cross them with horses. They are so resistant to taming that domestication has not been successful, and cross breeding has not been successful either. The U.S. National Zoological Park has exhibited zebra-horse hybrids and zebra-ass hybrids which were produced by the U.S. Department of Agriculture.

Asses are native in Asia from Mongolia and Tibet to Syria, and in Africa in the northern and eastern parts of the continent. They are found most frequently in desert plains sparsely covered with low shrubs.

The length of the head and body is 2 to 2.2 meters; the length of the tail is 42.5 to 49 cm.; the height at the shoulder is 0.9 to 1.5 meters; and the weight is about 260 kg. Asses are variously colored, but they are usually light on the nose, belly, and flanks. The coat is thick and grayish in winter, and in summer it is lighter and reddish or brownish. These animals are characterized by their long ears, tails that are long-haired at the tip, deep-set eyes, coarse, wiry, uneven manes, absence of forelocks, and small feet.

They occur singly, in small groups, and occasionally in herds of up to 100 or more individuals. In Mongolia they frequently associate with gazelles (*Gazella*). The herds of asses break up at the onset of foaling time. Mating occurs in the spring, and the young are born 348 to 377 days later. Females attain puberty in one year.

Asses can go longer periods without water than other members of this genus, and they are remarkably capable of surviving on a minimum of food and working under hot, difficult conditions. Because of their sure-footedness, persistence, and endurance, they are useful as pack animals. They are capable of carrying 113 kg. for days with little food. They have been domesticated for centuries. Their movements are much slower than those of other members of the genus, but in portions of the world where horses do not thrive or where poverty prevents the people from obtaining horses, burros have been extensively used as beasts of burden and for riding. Asses are frequently mentioned in the Bible. They have been used in the western United States by prospectors to pack supplies into regions that were difficult of access.

Mules are the hybrid offspring of a male ass and a female horse. They are usually about the size of a horse, have long ears, small hoofs, and the tail is sparsely haired for about the basal two-thirds and fairly well haired for the terminal third. They are particularly valued for their endurance, sure-footedness and strength. The hinny is also a hybrid, a cross between a male horse and a female ass. It is much less common than mules. Both mules and hinnies are sterile.

Both burros and domestic horses have escaped and live wild in the western portion of North America, where they have multiplied to such an extent as to give the erroneous impression that they were indigenous to the area. In South America horses have also established themselves in the wild from individuals that escaped from captivity.

All members of this genus are relatively swift runners, although the asses are the slowest and domesticated ones are particularly deliberate in their movements. In the wild they are alert for enemies; and since they have no very effective way of fighting, they usually run away and, unless surprised by a large powerful animal that catches them by a quick rush, are ordinarily swift enough to escape. In fighting among themselves or defending themselves, they kick with the hind feet, occasionally strike with the fore feet, and sometimes bite, for their teeth, although not adapted for lacerating or tearing except in male zebras which have pointed canines, can give quite hard pinches. Unfortunately the curiosity of some of the forms has led to their extermination or depletion.

Equids, which have been termed "admirable running machines," are active night and day, but mainly during the evening, and are gregarious. The members of this family travel in herds, numbering from 3 to more than 100 individuals and made up of the young and adults of both sexes. A herd has a leader, usually a male but often a female. The wild species are known to associate and interbreed with domesticated forms. The members of this family are vegetarians, feeding mainly on grass, although some browsing is done. Although most forms drink water daily, they can go three days without water. *E. przewalskii*, however, apparently can go for long periods without free water.

Females come into heat several times a year, with estrus continuing for several months if the mare is not bred. Some species give birth every two years; the number of young is usually one (twin births are generally abortive), and the gestation period is 11 to 12 months. The life span is 25 to 30 years.

The members of this family provide man with many products, including food and leather, and are used for farm labor and recreation.

The geological range of the family Equidae is the early Eocene to the Recent, the early Eocene to the Pleistocene in North America, the early Eocene to the Recent in Europe, the Miocene to the Recent in Asia, the Pliocene to the Recent in Africa, and the Pleistocene in South America. The geological range of the genus *Equus* is the late Pliocene to the Recent. Although horses passed through most of their evolutionary development in North America, none of the Pleistocene species left any descendants; the true horse, *E. caballus*, was not among these species.

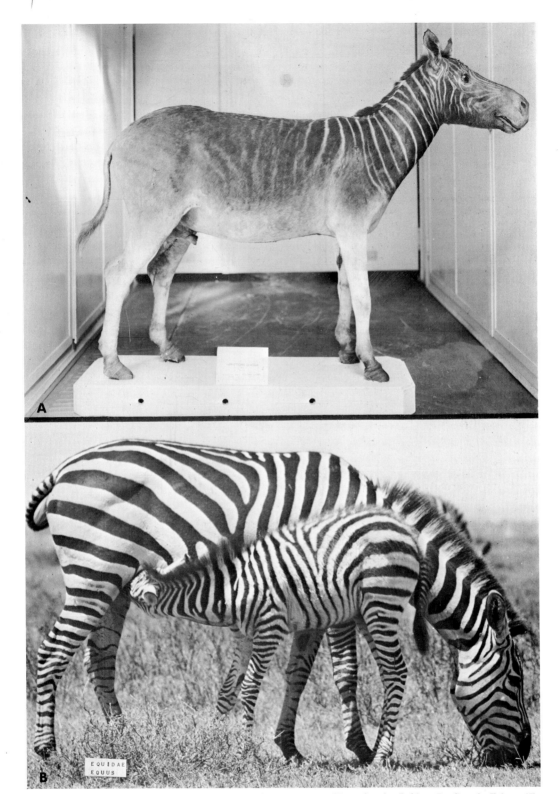

A. Quagga (*Equus quagga*), photo from Rijksmuseum van Natuurlijke Historie, Leiden. B. Grant's Zebras (*E. burchelli*), photo by C. A. Spinage.

Wild horses did not appear again in the Americas until after the Spanish expeditions of De Soto and Coronado in 1541. American Indians probably first acquired horses from the early seventeenth century Spanish stock-raising settlements in the Southwest.

Beginning with such forms as *Eohippus* (from the Eocene) and proceeding through *Mesohippus*, *Protohippus*, and others, culminating in *Equus* at the present time, the following modifications may be noted in the evolution of this line. The early members were browsers and had teeth well suited for the task; the grinding teeth of these animals bore conical cusps and were low-crowned, rooted, and cement-free. When grazing forms replaced the browsers, the teeth became progressively more high-crowned, prismatic, and cement-covered. *Mesohippus*, from the Oligocene of North America, was the first equid in which the "mark" or enamel pit became established (only in the upper incisors in this genus). Other changes took place. The size became larger, the neck was extended, the arched back was straightened, the limbs became elongated, and the feet were lengthened, the third (middle) digit growing and changing shape until it carried all the weight. The first digit was lost initially, then the fifth, and next the second and fourth were reduced to dewclaws, and finally to splints. A long-legged, grazing animal must have a neck long enough to enable the mouth to reach the ground easily; in the history of the horses, the elongation of the head and neck parallel the lengthening of the legs and feet.

The type species of the genus is *E. caballus*, Linnaeus.

A. Onager (*Equus hemionus onager*), photo by R. Pucholt. B. Wild Ass (*E. asinus*), photo from San Diego Zoological Garden.

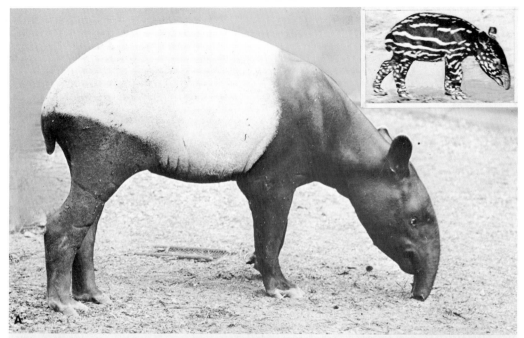

A. Malayan Tapir (*Tapirus indicus*), photo from New York Zoological Society. Inset: Malayan Tapir young (*T. indicus*), photo from Zoological Society of London. B. Brazilian Tapir (*T. terrestris*) and 8 day old young, photo by Ernest P. Walker.

TAPIRS; DANTAS, TAPIRES.

THIS FAMILY contains a single Recent genus, *Tapirus*, with four species which are distributed as follows: *T. terrestris*, the Brazilian tapir: South America, from Colombia and Venezuela southward to the Gran Chaco region of Paraguay and to the State of Rio Grande do Sul, Brazil; *T. roulini*, the woolly, Andean, or mountain tapir: the Andes in Colombia and Ecuador, and possibly in northern Peru and western Venezuela (some of the trails of this species lead above timber line); *T. bairdi*, Baird's tapir: southern Mexico southward through Central America to Colombia, and Ecuador west of the Andes; and *T. indicus*, the Asiatic tapir: Burma, Thailand, the Indo-Chinese peninsula, the Malay States, and Sumatra (there are no definite records of living tapirs from Borneo). The altitudinal range is from sea level to approximately 4,500 meters. Tapirs may live in nearly any wooded or grassy habitat where there is a permanent supply of water; they usually shelter in forests and thickets by day and emerge at night to feed in bordering grassy or shrubby areas. The discontinuous distribution of Recent tapirs suggests that they represent the survivors of a family once widespread; the fossil record shows that tapirs originated in the Northern Hemisphere and at various times occupied the land masses between where the present-day Asiatic and American tapirs exist.

The fact that tapirs are now living in both the American and Asiatic tropics supports the many bits of evidence that the two continents were connected rather recently as measured by geological time, and that during that period the climate was mild to warm in the northern portion of these continents, making conditions favorable for animals to move from one continent to another. Subsequently the continents were separated by Bering Strait or at any other land bridge that may have existed, and the climate changed so that the animals are now prevented from going between the two continents both by the Strait and by climatic conditions.

The general form is rounded in back and tapering in front, well suited for rapid movement through thick underbrush. These animals are about the size of a donkey. The length of the head and body is 1,800 to almost 2,500 mm.; the length of the tail is 50 to 100 mm.; the height at the shoulders is 735 to 1,030 mm.; and the weight is 225 to approximately 300 kg. Short bristly hairs are scattered on the body; they are thickest on the mountain tapir. A low, narrow mane, which is not always conspicuous, is present in *T. bairdi* and *T. terrestris*. The skin is quite thin in the mountain tapir, whereas it is thick in the other three species. The Asiatic tapir is readily distinguished by its color pattern; in this species, the front half of the body and the hind legs are blackish, and the rear half above the legs is white. The other species are dark brown to reddish above, and often paler below. Young tapirs are dark with yellow and white stripes and spots; this pattern is usually lost in six to eight months.

The snout and the upper lip are projected into a short fleshy proboscis; the transverse nostrils are located at its tip. The proboscis is more elongated in the New World species than in the Asiatic tapir. The eyes are small and flush with the side of the head, and the ears are oval, erect, and not very mobile. The legs are rather short and slender. The radius and ulna are separate and about equally developed, and the fibula is complete. The fore foot has three main digits and a smaller one (the fifth) for a total of four; the small digit is functional only on soft ground. The hind foot has three digits. The tail is short and thick.

The female tapir has one pair of mammae in the region of the groin.

The dental formula in the fossil forms is i 3/2-3, c 1/1, pm 3-4/3-4, m 3/3 = 38 to 44, and in the Recent species it is i 3/3, c 1/1, pm 4/3-4, m 3/3 = 42 to 44. The incisors are chisel-shaped; the third upper is canine-like and larger than the canines and the third lower is reduced. The canines are conical and separated from the cheek teeth by a space. The posterior three premolars are molar-like in the Recent species; they were usually simpler than the molars in the extinct species. The cheek teeth lack cement and are low-crowned with a series of transverse ridges and cusps. Horns are absent. The skull is relatively short and laterally compressed, with a high brain case and a convex profile. The nasal bones are short, triangular, tapered toward the front, arched, and freely projecting.

Tapirs generally live alone or in pairs and are agile in closed or open terrain and in or under water. They are good hill-climbers, runners, sliders, waders, divers, and swimmers. They generally walk with their snouts close to the ground and are fond of splashing in water or wallowing in mud. Tapirs are generally shy and docile and seek refuge in water or crash off into the brush when threatened, but they can and will defend themselves by biting. They possess keen powers of hearing and scent. The main predators of tapirs are the larger cats, jaguars in the New World and tigers in the Old World. Bears (*Tremarctos*) sometimes prey on mountain tapirs. All the species of tapirs are heavily parasitized by ticks; the mountain tapir often has a bald and calloused rump, apparently as a result of scratching and rubbing to relieve itching on this part of the body. The Asiatic tapir often has sore eyes. Tapirs sleep on the banks of streams and lakes.

These hoofed mammals wear paths to permanent bodies of water in areas where their population is dense, and human engineers sometimes follow their trails up the sides of mountains in the construction of roads. In northwestern South America, *T. bairdi* and *T. terrestris* may frequent the same feeding and watering places. Tapirs consume aquatic vegetation and the leaves, buds, twigs, and fruits of low-growing terrestrial plants, but in any particular habitat they eat mainly the green shoots of the most common browsing plants. They also graze for food and at times have been known to damage young corn and other grain fields, especially in Mexico and Central America.

Breeding apparently takes place at any time of the year. The gestation period is 390 to 400 days, and the number of offspring is one, rarely two. The life span is about 30 years. Tapirs tame quickly and adjust easily to artificial living conditions in captivity.

In some areas tapirs are hunted extensively both for food and for sport. Some South American Indians do not kill tapirs for religious reasons. In addition, the population of all species, particularly the Asiatic tapir, has declined within historic times, due mainly to the clearing of forests by man for agricultural purposes.

Tapir is a name derived from the same word in the Brazilian Tupi language.

The geological range of this family is from the middle Oligocene to the Recent in North America, the early Oligocene to the Pleistocene in Europe, the Pleistocene to the Recent in South America, and the Miocene to the Recent in Asia. The geological range of the genus *Tapirus* is the late Miocene to the Recent. *Megatapirus* is the only extinct tapir that has been found in Pleistocene deposits of the Old World, known only from Szechwan province of China. It was much larger than any Recent tapir and also differed in skull proportions and dentition. The skull was short and deep.

The type species is *T. terrestris* (Linnaeus). The species have been divided among four subgenera:

1. *Tapirus* for the species *T. terrestris*.
2. *Pinchacus*, Gray, 1873, for the species *T. roulini = T. dowii* of some authors.
3. *Tapirella*, Palmer, 1903, for the species *T. bairdi*.
4. *Acrocodia*, Goldman, 1913, for the species *T. indicus*.

Young Malayan Tapir (*Tapirus indicus*) in a position unusual among perissodactyls, photo by Ernest P. Walker.

RHINOCEROS; BADAK RAYA.

THIS FAMILY of four Recent genera, with five living species, inhabits savannahs, shrubby regions, and dense forests in the tropical and subtropical areas of eastern Asia, including Sumatra, Java, Borneo, and Africa. The African rhinos usually live in more open areas than does the Asiatic species. The Recent range of the family is discontinuous. All species are rare or are approaching rarity or extinction.

These hoofed mammals have a massive body, a large head, one or two horns, a short neck, a broad chest, and short, pillar-like legs. The radius and ulna, and the tibia and fibula are only slightly movable, but well developed and separate. The fore foot has three digits (four in some fossil forms) and the hind foot has three digits; the hooves are distinct and separate for each digit. The upper lip is prehensile in two genera (*Rhinoceros* and *Diceros*). The small eyes are located on the side of the head midway between the nostrils and the ears; the ears are fairly short but prominent and erect. The thick skin, which is scantily haired and often wrinkled, is furrowed or pleated, having the appearance of riveted armor plate in some species. The tail bears stiff bristles.

The length of the head and body is 2 to 4.2 meters; the length of the tail is about 610 to 760 mm.; and the height at the shoulders is 1 to 2 meters. The female rhinoceros is smaller than the male. Adults weigh from 1 to 3.5 metric tons. The coloration is grayish to brownish, but the true color is often concealed by a coating of mud or dust.

The dental formula is as follows: i 1-0/1-0, c 0/1-0,

pm 3-4/3-4, m 3/3 = 24 to 34. The incisors and canines are vestigial. The premolars resemble the molars (except the small first premolar). The cheek teeth, which are high-crowned in the square-lipped or white rhino *Ceratotherium* (the only species of Recent rhino which grazes rather than browses) and fairly low-crowned in the other Recent genera, are marked with transverse ridges of enamel. The skull, which is elongate and elevated posteriorly, has a small brain case. The nasal bones project freely beyond the skull. One or two conical median horns are present in Recent rhinos, although short or obscure in some forms (they were not present in some extinct species). If there is only one horn, it is borne on the nasal bones; if there are two horns, the posterior one is over the frontal bones of the skull. These horns are dermal in origin; although solid, they are composed of solid keratin of a fibrous nature.

Although rhinos in general are solitary except during the breeding season, the square-lipped rhino usually associates in small groups comprised of the adults of both sexes and young animals. These hoofed mammals are active mainly during the evening, through the night, and in the early morning, resting during the day in heavy cover which may be several kilometers from the waterholes. Dense thorn thickets are penetrated by sheer force. Rhinos sleep in both standing and recumbent positions and are fond of wallowing in muddy pools and sandy river beds. They run with a cumbersome motion, reaching their top speed at a canter, that is, at a gait resembling a gallop but with moderate and easy bounds or leaps. The African black rhino (*Diceros*) can attain speeds of up to 45 kilometers per hour for short distances. Rhinos are usually timid but are ferocious at bay. They sometimes charge an enemy, although their attack is often poorly directed. They may grunt or squeal when excited. Vision is poor, but apparently smell and hearing are acute.

These mammals are often accompanied by tick-birds and egrets, which act as sentinels and, in turn, feed on external parasites of the rhinos and on insects stirred up by the feet of these ungulates. The large cats prey on young rhinos, but the adults apparently have no enemies other than man.

Rhinos are generally restricted to areas where daily trips to water are possible. Their paths between the watering and feeding places often pass through tunnels in the brush. These are grazing (*Ceratotherium*) or browsing animals, a variety of vegetation (usually succulents) is included in their diet. Rhinos drop their dung in well-defined piles and often furrow the area around the piles with their horns; these piles may be scattered afterward. They are believed to act as "sign-posts" or "territory markers" (urination spots and rubbing sticks also seem to serve this function).

During the breeding season a pair of rhinos may be together for four months; the members of this family are believed to breed every several years. The gestation period is approximately 510 to 570 days (reported to be seven to eight months in *Didermocerus*). The single offspring is active soon after birth and remains with its mother until the next youngster is born. The mother may guide its baby with her horn. Rhinos have a life span of almost 50 years.

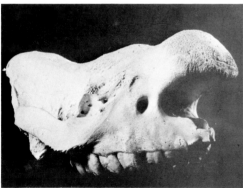

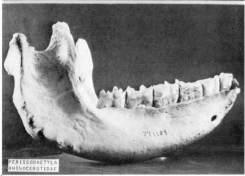

African Black Rhinoceros (*Diceros bicornis*), photos by P. F. Wright of skull in U.S. National Museum.

Man has hunted rhinoceroses extensively because nearly all parts of the animal are used in folk medicine. If they are to be prevented from becoming extinct, it will be necessary to enforce positive and vigorous protective measures.

The geological range of this family is the middle Eocene to the Pleistocene in Europe, the late Eocene to the Recent in Asia, the Miocene to the Recent in Africa, and the late Eocene to Pliocene in North America. The Recent genera are known from at least the Pleistocene; *Didermocerus* is recorded from the lower Oligocene of Europe and Asia. The only genus of extinct rhinoceros known from the Pleistocene of the Old World is *Elasmotherium*, a huge animal from Siberia. This family was more dominant in earlier geologic epochs than it is at present; at least 30 genera referable to this family are known from past epochs, one of them (*Baluchitherium*) being the largest land mammal yet known.

Great Indian One-horned Rhinoceroses (*Rhinoceros unicornis*), photo by Dorothy Y. Mackenzie.

INDIAN RHINOCEROSES, ONE-HORNED RHINOC-EROSES; BADAK RAYA, BADAK SAMBU (native names).

THIS GENUS comprises two species: *R. unicornis*, a large species native to Nepal and northeastern India; and *R. sondaicus*, which formerly inhabited Sikkim, Bengal, Assam, Burma, Thailand, Indo-China, Malaya and Sumatra but may now be restricted entirely to Java, where no more than four dozen individuals survive. These animals seek tall grass and reed beds in swampy jungle areas.

The length of the head and body is 2.1 to 4.2 meters; the length of the tail is 0.6 to 0.75 meters, the height of the shoulder is 1.1 to 2 meters; and the weight is 2,000 to 4,000 kg. *R. unicornis* is very much larger than *R. sondaicus*. The skin is practically naked except for a fringe of stiff hairs around the ears and the tip of the tail. The skin of *R. unicornis* has large convex tubercles, whereas that of *R. sondaicus* is covered with small polygonal scale-like disks. Coloration is from grayish to blackish with a pinkish cast on the undersurface and the margins of the skin folds. Rhinos are large, awkward-looking creatures with large heads, short, stumpy legs, small eyes, and wide nostrils. Each foot has three toes. Members of this genus have a single "horn" on the upper surface of the nose which is composed of agglutinated hairs and has no firm attachment to the bones of the skull.

These animals may be distinguished from their African relatives by their skin, which has a number of loose folds giving the animals the appearance of wearing armor. The African rhinos lack such folds.

R. unicornis has a fold of skin which does not continue across the back of the neck; in *R. sondaicus*, on the other hand, the fold continues across the mid-line of the back.

These rhinos remain more or less solitary; they usually seek to escape rather than to attack an enemy. When wounded or when with a calf, they occasionally charge. In such defensive charges, contrary to popular belief, they use their sharp, pointed lower tusks—not the "horn." They remain near water, in which they bathe daily; they also enjoy wallowing in mud. Mornings and evenings are the chief feeding periods, the remainder of the day is spent in slumber. Their diet consists of grass, reeds, and twigs.

The birth of a single young takes place between the end of February and the end of April, about 19 months for *R. unicornis* and 17 months for *R. sondaicus* after breeding occurs. The young have a head and body length of 1 to 1.2 meters; a shoulder height of about 0.6 meter; and a weight of 34 to 75 kg. The young nurse for two years. The life span may be as much as 50 years or more.

The Chinese believe that the "horn," blood, and urine of these animals have magical medicinal properties. Because of this, these animals have been ruthlessly killed almost to the point of extinction. For the horn the Chinese pay one-half its weight in gold; they pay about two dollars per kilogram for dried blood. These harmless beasts owe their survival to their elusive and retiring habits and their remote haunts.

The type species of the genus is *R. unicornis*, Linnaeus.

Asiatic Two-horned Rhinoceros (*Didermocerus sumatrensis*), photo of mounted specimen in The City Museum, Bristol, England.

ASIATIC TWO-HORNED RHINOCEROSES; BADAK BĚRĚNDAN, BADAK KERBAU (native names).

THE SINGLE SPECIES, *D. sumatrensis*, is found in Assam, Burma, Thailand, Indo-China, the Malay States, Sumatra, and Borneo. It formerly came out of the forests into open country but now is a rare animal over its entire range, found mainly in dense hill forests, usually near streams.

This is the smallest living rhinoceros. Head and body length is usually 2.5 to 2.8 meters; shoulder height is usually 1.1 to 1.5 meters; and weight is about 1 metric ton. It is immediately distinguished from the other Asiatic rhinos by its two horns. In the female the anterior horn is about 150 mm. long and the posterior horn is about 50 mm. long. Horn lengths in the male are about three times longer. Coloration is grayish to blackish. The skin is folded, the ears are fringed with hair, and the body hairs are bristle-like.

This animal is usually solitary, but a male and a female may be seen together. As in other rhinos, sight is poor, but the senses of smell and hearing are good. Mud wallows are frequented, and the day is spent in a wallow or in a sheltered area. This prehensile-lipped browser feeds on leaves, twigs, bamboo shoots, and, occasionally, fruits. It feeds usually in the early morning and evening. One young per birth is the usual number. The gestation period has been reported as seven to eight months.

Extensive hunting by natives and white hunters (particularly with modern firearms and often in violation of the law), indifferent governments, and the slow breeding rate have been the main factors in the numerical decline of this animal. Its extensive hunting has been stimulated by the belief, widespread in the East, that the horn has aphrodisiac properties, and by the use of the horn in carving. There is evidence that there already was extensive trade in rhino horns between Borneo and China more than a thousand years ago. Today this animal is protected over most of its range and may be hunted only with a special license. The danger point may already have been approached, however, and this rhinoceros may be close to extinction.

African Black Rhinoceros (*Diceros bicornis*), photo by Bernhard Grzimek.

AFRICAN BLACK RHINOCEROSES; SWARTRENOSTER,
KIFARU (native names).

THE SINGLE SPECIES, *D. bicornis*, occurs in most
parts of eastern and South Africa but is common
only locally. Still, it is the most numerous living species of rhino. The western limits apparently are in
the region of Lake Chad and eastern Nigeria. Thorn
bush country, with scattered streams and water holes,
is the typical habitat; but in Kenya rhinos abound in
dense mountain forest.

Head and body length is 3 to 3.75 meters; tail length
is about 710 mm.; shoulder height is 1.4 to 1.5 meters;
and weight is 1 to 1.8 metric tons. The anterior horn
is larger than the posterior horn, averaging about
50.8 cm. in length; sometimes the beginning of a
third posterior horn is present. Both this rhino and
the "white" rhino (*Ceratotherium*) are dark in color,
but the black rhino is slightly darker. Coloration in
Diceros is dark yellowish brown to dark brown. An
external feature more clearly distinguishing these two
genera is the upper lip; in *Diceros* it protrudes slightly
in the middle, and its tip is prehensile, whereas in
Ceratotherium it is squared.

In contrast to the square-lipped rhino, the black
rhino is less sociable and more aggressive. It is
sometimes solitary; a female may be accompanied by
her single young. Studies indicate that the male will
take over and defend a given area. The female and
the young also may be present in this area, but strange
rhinos are apparently not tolerated. It is uncertain
whether this area represents a breeding station for the
male or the usual home range. Dung heaps, urination
spots, and rubbing sticks presumably serve as area
markers. The rubbing sticks carry the body scent of
the animal and also may carry the scent of the secretion of the characteristic sores on the flanks. The
black rhino is unpredictable and can be a dangerous
animal, sometimes charging a disturbing sound or
smell. It has tossed men in the air with the front
horn, and regularly charges vehicles and camp fires.
Catching the scent of man, it usually crashes off
through the brush and runs upwind at speeds of up
to 45 km. per hour, sometimes for several kilometers,
before stopping.

This is a browsing animal that feeds on twigs and
leaves. During the heat of the day it lies in scrub
thickets.

Black rhinos seem to breed throughout the year.
The gestation period is 530 to 550 days; sexual maturity is attained in about five years.

Somalis value the hide, using it for their shields.
The hide also has been used for whip handles. Some
natives eat the flesh. The horns have figured in the
aphrodisiac trade to China, which seems to be the
most important present-day factor leading to the
decimation of this species. As in the square-lipped
rhino, reserves are deemed essential for the survival
of this animal.

Square-lipped or White Rhinoceroses (*Ceratotherium simum*), photo from Societe Royale de Zoologie d'Anvers through Walter Van den Bergh.

SQUARE-LIPPED OR WHITE RHINOCEROSES; WITRE-NOSTER.

THE SINGLE SPECIES, *C. simum*, is apparently now known in South Africa only from the Zululand reserves, where the present population is estimated at 600 animals and Kruger National Park, into which it has been reintroduced. This species also is found in the southern Sudan, Uganda, and adjacent parts of the Congo. Like the other species of rhinos, this animal has been greatly reduced in numbers, although now through effective protection, it is increasing in South Africa. Habitats are savannahs and brushy areas.

Next to the elephant, this is probably the largest living land mammal. Head and body length is 3.6 to 5 meters; shoulder height is 1.6 to 2 meters; and weight is usually 2.3 to 3.6 metric tons. Coloration is yellowish brown or slaty grayish. This mammal is naked except for the ear fringes and the tail bristles. Hairs are present in the skin but do not protrude. The front horn averages about 0.6 meter in length but can attain a length of more than 1.5 meters.

External features distinguishing the white rhino from the black rhino are as follows: Usually lighter coloration; a squared upper lip with no trace of a proboscis; elongated and pointed ear conchae with a few bristly hairs at the tips, compared to rounded conchae with hair edges in the black rhino; more sloping, less sharply defined forehead; a shoulder lump; and less conspicuous skin folds on the body.

This rhino is more sociable and less aggressive than the black rhino. Pairs and family units of three and four animals are common, and family groups of six or seven may congregate in a favorable feeding area. The white rhino seems to have a more loosely defined home range and territory than the black rhino. The dung heaps of the white rhino may serve as a sort of "family bulletin board," chronicling the whereabouts of the group, as well as a sort of territorial marker. There are only a few records of attacks on hunters.

White rhinos are mainly grazers, feeding on grasses and low shrubs rather than on the leaves of trees.

They seem to breed throughout the year. The single young is born after a gestation period of 17 to 18 months and is sexually mature at 4 to 5 years of age. A female young gained about 400 kg. in weight (from about 50 to 450 kg.) over an 18-month period and was believed to have eaten its droppings for a short period until it began to eat more solid food.

Order: ARTIODACTYLA

THE EVEN-TOED HOOFED MAMMALS (UNGULATES)—PIGS, PECCARIES, HIPPOPOTAMUSES, CAMELS, CHEVROTAINS, DEER, GIRAFFES, OKAPIS, PRONGHORN ANTELOPES, SHEEP, GOATS, CATTLE, AND ANTELOPES.

THIS ORDER of 9 Recent families and 82 genera occurs throughout the world except in Australia, New Zealand, Antarctica, and some isolated islands. A great variety of structural types is demonstrated in the order Artiodactyla, but a general unity of anatomy exists throughout the group. This order contains many graceful as well as ungainly creatures, and some of man's most useful animals.

Artiodactyls range in size from a mousedeer (*Tragulus*—length of the head and body, 460 to 560 mm.) to a giraffe (*Giraffa*—shoulder height about 3.5 meters) and a hippo (*Hippopotamus*—weight about 4.5 metric tons). The principal distinguishing feature of the members of this order is the foot, which has an even number of well-developed digits (except in some members of the family Tayassuidae, in which the hind foot has three digits); the main axis of the limb passes between these digits (the third and fourth). The body weight is borne by the median digits. The first digit occurs only in certain fossil species, and the lateral digits (the second and fifth) are more slender than the third and fourth, or are vestigial or absent. In the two-toed or "cloven-hoofed" forms, the central wrist or ankle bones are fused to form a "cannon bone" and the lateral wrist or ankle bones are absent. The humerus is usually shorter than the forearm, with some few exceptions, and the radius and ulna are separate or fused. The ankle bone, or astragalus, has a rolling surface above the joint and a pulley surface below, giving free movement to the ankle. The fibula articulates with the heel bone and is usually slender or incomplete, in some cases it is fused with the tibia.

The mammae are few and in the region of the groin or they are numerous and on the abdomen.

The upper incisors are reduced or absent, and the canine teeth are usually reduced or lost, although in some species they are enlarged and tusk-like. The space between the front teeth and the cheek teeth is largest in the ruminants or "cud-chewers." The molars, which are more complex than the premolars, are low-crowned with cusps, generally two pairs, in the pigs, peccaries, and hippos, or they are high-crowned with crescents, two pairs, in the other members of this order—the ruminants. Frontal appendages, i.e., bony outgrowths of the skull, occur in some forms. The nasal bones are not expanded posteriorly as they are in the order Perissodactyla.

The stomach, in the families Suidae, Tayassuidae, and Hippopotamidae, is two- or three-chambered and non-ruminating; in the families Camelidae and Tragulidae it is three-chambered and ruminating; and in the remaining families, the so-called true ruminants, (Cervidae, Giraffidae, Antilocapridae, and Bovidae), it is four-chambered and ruminating. All the ruminants, or "cud-chewers," crop or graze quantities of vegetable food, such as grasses and woody material, in which there is a relatively low amount of nutri-

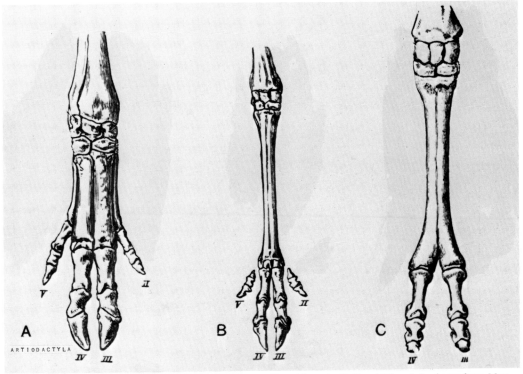

Bones of the fore feet of three artiodactyls, A. Hog (*Sus*); B. Deer (*Cervus*); C. Camel (*Camelus*); photos from *Mammalia*, Beddard.

ments. They swallow the food rapidly with little chewing and then retire to some secluded spot to digest it more thoroughly. In the true ruminants, when the food is first swallowed, it enters the rumen or paunch and, after undergoing a softening process there, it is regurgitated into the mouth, where it is chewed again and further mixed with the salivary juices. The food is then swallowed a second time, entering the second compartment of the stomach (the reticulum or honeycomb bag). It then progresses to the third stomach (the manyplies or psalterium), and then to the fourth stomach or digesting chamber (the reed or abomasum), where the greatest digestive activity takes place. In this manner, cud-chewing animals can quickly consume a large quantity of low-grade food and, when no danger threatens, impart to it the thorough grinding and chemical treatment necessary to convert it to their use. Bacterial action is also involved in the breakdown of food by a ruminant.

Because most artiodactyls are massive and have large bones which resist decay and other destructive forces, there exists a good record of fossil forms, as is the case with the perissodactyls. The order Artiodactyla includes 16 extinct families of about 130 genera; other fossil genera which belonged to Recent families are discussed under the respective family accounts; that is, those genera known from the Pleistocene of the Old World. The Old World was the apparent region of evolution of the artiodactyls, whereas the perissodactyls flourished mainly in North America. The earliest members of the evolutionary line of the Artiodactyla apparently had the full complement of teeth (a total of 44), four distinct digits on each foot with distinct foot bones, no frontal appendages, and a simple, non-ruminant stomach. Separation into bunodont and selenodont dentition lines seems to have taken place at an early period, and there is evidence that intermediate forms existed. Currently the family Bovidae is the dominant group in the order Artiodactyla.

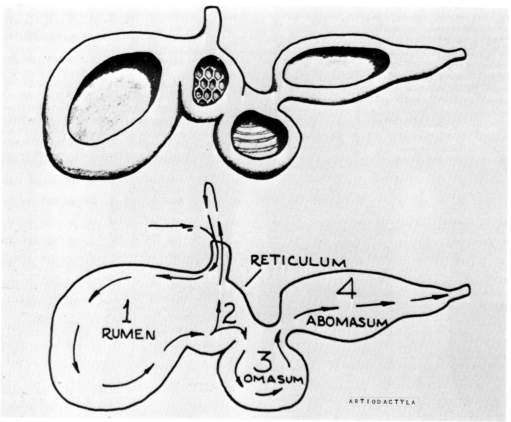

Diagrams of the complicated four-compartmented stomachs of ruminants (the Cervidae, Bovidae, and Antilocapridae). The lower diagram shows the route traversed by the food from the time it is first swallowed until it is returned to the mouth for further mastication and then swallowed again to go into the second chamber and the remainder of the digestive tract. The camels (Camelidae) also ruminate or chew their cud, but their stomachs are slightly different, and the Tragulidae have only three compartments. Photo from *Detroit Zoo Guide Book.*

PIGS OR HOGS; BABIRUSAS, CERDOS, SOOR, INOSISI (local vernaculars).

THIS FAMILY of five genera and approximately nine species is native to the Old World, living south of 58 degrees N. latitude throughout Eurasia, and in Africa, Madagascar, Japan, Formosa, the Philippines, and Indonesia. Hogs have been introduced into several regions, such as New Guinea, New Zealand, the British Isles, and parts of North America. They generally live under dense cover in forests and woodlands.

Suids are medium-sized mammals with long, pointed heads, short necks, and barrel-like, stocky bodies. The mobile snout is truncated terminally, with a disk-like cartilage in the tip. This cartilaginous snout, used for turning up surface soil, is strengthened by an unusual bone, the prenasal, situated below the tip of the nasal bones of the skull. Grooving of the snout occurs in only one genus, *Babyrousa*. The nostrils are terminal, the eyes are small, and the ears are fairly long, often with a tassel of hairs near the tip. Some members of this family have warts or ridges on the face, which are skin growths without a bony support or core. The fore legs are half as long as the height at the shoulders. The foot bones are separate (not fused), and the feet are narrow. Each foot has four toes; the middle two (the third and fourth) are flattened and have hooves, whereas the other two toes (the second and fifth) are located higher up on the limb and do not reach to the ground in the ordinary walking position and have smaller hooves than the third and fourth toes.

The length of the head and body is approximately 700 to 1,900 mm.; and the tail is 35 to 320 mm. Adult suids weigh as much as 275 kg. The thick skin is usually sparsely covered with coarse bristles or bristly

hairs, and some suids are almost naked. A mane occurs on some forms, and the tail has bristly hairs at its tip. The young are striped (except in *Babyrousa* and domestic *Sus*). The female animals in most genera have three or six pairs of mammae (only one pair in *Babyrousa*). Suids have a two-chambered, simple, non-ruminating stomach.

The dental formula is i 3/3, c 1/1, pm 4/4, m 3/3 = 44, except in *Babyrousa* (2/3, 1/1, 2/2, 3/3 = 34) and the wart hog *Phacochoerus* (1/3, 1/1, 3/2, 3/3 = 34). The upper incisors decrease in size from the first to the third, and the lower incisors are long, narrow, set closely together, and almost horizontal in position. The incisors and the canines have sharp lateral edges. The large upper canines grow outward and backward, and the lower canines grow upward and backward, tending to form a complete circle. Usually, however, the canine teeth wear against each other, thus producing the sharp edges. These tusks, which are most prominent in male suids, reach their greatest development in *Babyrousa*; in this genus the upper canines are directed upward through the skin, never entering the mouth, and curve backward and downward, often touching the forehead. The cheek teeth are cuspidate, and the upper premolars are simpler in structure than the molars. With age the enamel wears away and all the teeth disappear except for the canines and the back molars. The third molars of wart hogs, which are often the only cheek teeth in this genus, are unlike those of any other mammal; they are composed of a number of closely-set cylinders of dentine embedded in cement. The most striking feature of the skull in the family Suidae is the elevation and backward slope of the occipital crest, formed by the union of the supraoccipital and parietal bones.

Suids are usually gregarious, ranging in bands of

Wart Hog (*Phacochoerus aethiopicus*), photo by P. F. Wright of skull in U.S. National Museum.

A. European Wild Hog (*Sus scrofa*), mother and young, photo by Eric Parbst through Zoologisk Have, Copenhagen.
B. Domestic Hog (*S. scrofa*), photo by Roy Pinney.

40 to 50 individuals, although wart hog boars often live alone. The members of this family are sure-footed and rapid runners; the wart hog, for example, is capable of speeds of 18.5 km. per hour. They are good swimmers and are fond of mud baths. When cornered or wounded, they are courageous and frequently will fight back. There are authentic reports of *Sus* attacking and killing camels and even tigers. In such battles, their tusks are the deadly weapons. Boars of the forest hog genus (*Hylochoerus*) sometimes charge without actual warning or provocation, presumably to protect the band. Suids shelter in tall grass or reed beds and in burrows, which are self-excavated or are abandoned by other animals.

These hoofed mammals are active mainly at night, particularly if man is around to molest them. Some forms use their snouts and a few use their tusks to dig for food; pigs are omnivorous. They eat fungi, leaves, fruits, roots, bulbs, and tubers but also take snails, earthworms, reptiles, young birds, rats, and the eggs of vertebrates. Some forms include carrion in their diet. Wart hogs, when feeding, drop on their padded knees and frequently shuffle along in this position. A wild pig, contrary to popular ideas, will rarely overeat.

The gestation period is 112 to 175 days, and the litter size is 2 to 14. In *Sus* the boars leave after the female is no longer in heat. Hogs live almost 20 years.

Domestic pigs are derived from the wild hog (*Sus*). Some members of this family are hunted for sport, as a source of food, or because of the damage they inflict on cultivated crops.

The geological range of the family Suidae is from the lower Oligocene to the Recent in Europe, the lower Miocene to the Recent in Africa, and the upper Miocene to the Recent in Asia.

African Water or River Hogs (*Potamochoerus porcus*), A. Photo by Bernhard Grzimek. B. Photo from New York Zoological Society of immature animal.

AFRICAN BUSH PIGS; RED-RIVER HOGS; AFRICAN WATER OR RIVER HOGS.

THE SINGLE SPECIES, *P. porcus*, inhabits all of Africa south of the Sahara, and Madagascar. It is found in all types of country.

The head and body length of one specimen, an adult male, was 1300 mm. and the tail length was 316 mm. The average shoulder height is 585 to 965 mm., and weight is about 75 to 130 kg. Coloration varies from reddish brown to black, often with a heavy mixture of white or yellowish hairs, and some individuals are almost white or mottled white and black or brown. The young are longitudinally striped with pale yellow or buff on a dark-brown ground color. The long, pointed ears, in many instances, have long tufts or streamers of hairs at the tips, and there is a pronounced light-colored mane along the top of the neck and back.

The average upper tusk length is 76 mm., and the lower tusk measures from 165 mm. to 190 mm. The upper tusks point downward and wear against the lower ones. The male has warts in front of the eye, and although they protrude 40 mm., they are frequently not conspicuous as they are often concealed by facial hair. The female has three pairs of mammae.

This genus resembles *Phacochoerus* and *Sus;* it differs from the former genus in having more hair and a greater number of teeth, and from *Sus* in having ears that are more tufted.

These animals are most active at night, resting during the day in tall, dense grass, reed beds, and other similar cover in which they burrow out tunnels. They are gregarious and usually travel in family parties of 4 to 20. An old boar is often accompanied by a half-grown boar, a habit reported to occur also in the European boar (*Sus scrofa*); in France the young boar is called the "page" of the old one. When cornered or wounded, they exhibit considerable courage and frequently attack. They are swift on foot and good swimmers. These animals are wary of traps; when a trap is discovered, the animals will avoid that particular area for many weeks.

The diet consists principally of roots, berries, and wild fruit; reptiles, eggs, and occasionally young birds also are eaten. They use their snouts in feeding as ploughs to "root" up subsoil vegetation, and in a short period of time a herd can do extensive damage to native crops.

The young, two to eight per litter (ten in one instance), are born in December and January.

In captivity these animals seldom live over 10 years, but one individual lived in the London Zoo for 14 years and 8 months. Other records indicate that the potential longevity is about 20 years.

European Wild Hog (*Sus scrofa*), photo by Ernest P. Walker and William J. Schaldach, Jr.

WILD BOARS, HOGS, PIGS; VARKENS, CERDOS, SOOR AND KALAJARAWUR, INOSISI, BABI HUTON, SANGLIER, WILDSCHWEIN, EBER, VARKEN, WILD ZWIJN, EVERZWIJN, BALI UTAN. (Included are vernaculars used in other countries.)

THIS GENUS is found in Europe, northern Africa, Asia, Japan, and the Malayan islands, and it also has become established in the United States. The number of species is still doubtful, but at least five seem to exist. Domestic pigs have been derived from the wild hogs.

The species *S. salvanius* is separated subgenerically as *Porcula* because of its small size (shoulder height 28 cm.; tail length about 3 cm.) and because of the presence of only three pairs of mammae, as compared with six pairs in the other species of *Sus*. Head and body length in the larger species is as much as 1.8 meters; tail length is about 0.3 meter; shoulder height is about 1.0 meter; and the weight is about 75 to 200 kg. in males and 35 to 150 kg. in females. Coloration is dark gray to black or brown. The body is covered with stiff bristles and usually some finer fur, but the body covering often is quite scant, and the tail is only lightly covered with short hairs. Many individuals have side whiskers and a mane on the nape. The young are striped. Hogs have four continually-growing tusks, two in each jaw.

The habits of all wild pigs are similar. Not only are they quick-footed on the ground but they also are good, strong swimmers. They wallow in mud and will do so for hours if the opportunity affords. Individuals construct crude shade-shelters by cutting grass and spreading it over a given area. They crawl under the grass and then raise themselves to lift the grass mat, which then attaches to uncut grass and forms a canopy. Wild pigs usually do not attack unless molested but are dangerous when aroused.

They travel in bands of 6 to 50 and are most active in the evening and early morning. During the night they may travel great distances in their search for roots, nuts, grains, and plant stems. Although they are mainly vegetarians, they occasionally eat carrion and often eat large quantities of various insect larvae.

In the large species, the young number 3 to 12 per litter and are born 112 to 115 days after mating. The sow is in heat about every 21 days, and the duration of heat is 2 to 3 days. The piglets are raised by the sows, as the boars leave after the female is no longer in heat. Sexual maturity is reached at about 1½ years. They are fully grown at 5 or 6 years of age. The life span is generally 15 to 20 years, occasionally up to 27 years.

Sus has been hunted for hundreds of years in Europe for sport, as a food source, and because of its destruction to crops.

The type species of the genus is *S. scrofa*, Linnaeus.

Wart Hog (*Phacochoerus aethiopicus*), photo from New York Zoological Society.

WART HOGS; VLAKVARKS.

THE SINGLE SPECIES, *P. aethiopicus*, inhabits most of Africa, the greatest concentration being in the east and south. It usually inhabits savannah and light forests.

The head and body length of one specimen was 1055 mm., and the tail length was 205 mm. The shoulder height is usually 635 to 732 mm., and the weight of an average individual is 75 to 100 kg. The males have upper tusks 255 to 635 mm. in length, while the upper tusks of the female are 152 to 255 mm. The hair covering consists of a long, thin mane of coarse hair from the nape to the middle of the back, where it is broken by a bare space, and continued again on the rump. The remainder of the body is covered with bristles. The color of both the skin and hair is dark brown to blackish. The immature are reddish brown. A long, ridge-like fold on the cheek bears white hairs. The warts, which are prominent only on the males, are skin growths and have no bony support or core; they are located on the side of the head and in front of the eye.

When the animals move slowly, the tail hangs limply, but when they run it is carried in an upright position with the tufted tip hanging over. Although the eyesight of the wart hog seems to be poor, the senses of smell and hearing are acute.

These animals are usually diurnal, as opposed to the bush pig, except in sections where they are mo-lested, where they have become almost nocturnal. They travel about singly, in pairs, or small "sounders," consisting of family parties of one or two sows accompanied by their latest offspring. The boars frequently travel alone.

While of ferocious appearance, they are usually inoffensive but will defend themselves when cornered and can inflict severe wounds with their tusks. Frequently these animals will seek cover or temporary refuge by backing into burrows dug by aardvarks (*Orycteropus*). They enjoy mud baths like any other hog. They are capable of attaining speeds of up to 47 km. per hour.

Wart hogs feed on grass, roots, berries, the bark of young trees, and occasionally carrion. Their tusks are used in digging up roots, etc., as opposed to the rooting method of *Potamochoerus* and *Sus*. While feeding, these animals drop on their padded knees and frequently shuffle along in this position; wart-hogs also grunt when rooting about but otherwise are rather silent.

Litters of two to four are born from October to November. The gestation period is 171 to 175 days. An individual lived in the London Zoo for 12 and a half years.

The flesh of the wart hog is very tasty; because of this it is widely sought by natives. These hogs are much less destructive to native crops than are the other African pigs.

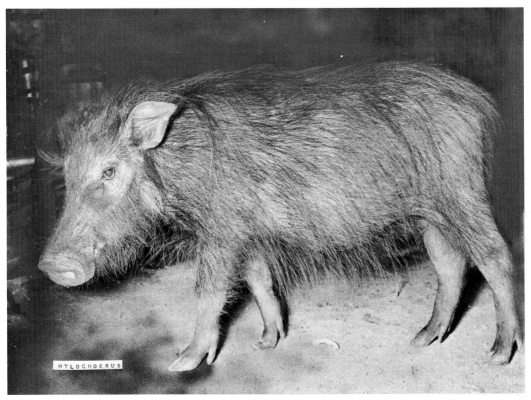

Giant Forest Hog (*Hylochoerus meinertzhageni*), photo by Bernhard Grzimek.

GIANT FOREST HOGS.

THE SINGLE SPECIES, *H. meinertzhageni*, inhabits thick forests and bamboo jungles in equatorial central Africa.

Shoulder height is 762 to 965 mm.; head and body length is 150 to 190 mm.; and tail length is about 30 mm. Weights are 160 to 275 kg. The pelage is long, coarse, and black, becoming sparse with age; the skin is blackish gray. The skin in front of each eye and on the upper part of the cheek below the eye is almost naked. Below and behind each eye there are two moveable cutaneous thickenings or facial excrescences. One of these forms a wide ridge on each naked area of skin. *Hylochoerus* seems to be the only genus of Suidae with a facial gland; a preorbital gland is present, marked externally by a slit on the naked area of the face in front of each eye. There are no facial protuberances, as in the wart hog, and the upper canines are set horizontally, not at an angle as in the wart hog.

The large skull of *Hylochoerus* contains a depression in the roof "capable of containing nearly a cup full of water."

Forest hogs usually travel in groups or sounders of 4 to 20 individuals. Natives seem to fear these animals more than the bush pigs (*Potamochoerus*); male forest hogs will often charge without warning and without provocation, presumably to protect the sounder. *Hylochoerus* wallows in water and in swamp, makes runs and bedding-down places, seldom uses or constructs holes in the ground but often digs a hole at the base of a tree for a latrine and resorts to salt licks. Forest hogs feed mainly on shrub and tall, lush grass, and do not dig or grub appreciably for food. They sometimes raid native shambas at the forest edge and cause much destruction. From two to six young are born in the bedding-down place after a gestation period averaging 125 days.

Certain tribes, such as the Terekis, make war shields from the hides of these hogs.

Babirusa (*Babyrousa babyrussa*), photo from New York Zoological Society.

BABIRUSAS; HIRSCHEBER, HERTZWIJN, ULANGIO, KALAWATAN (local vernaculars).

THE SINGLE SPECIES, *B. babyrussa*, is native to North Celebes, Togian Islands, the island Buru (N. Moluccas), and the Sula Islands. It prefers a habitat of moist forests, cane brakes, and the shores of rivers and lakes.

The head and body length is usually 875 to 1,065 mm. The tail is 275 to 320 mm. long and has no tuft on the tip. The shoulder height is 650 to 800 mm., and weight is as much as 90 kg. The legs are relatively long. Almost devoid of hair, the skin is rough and brownish gray or smooth, sparsely covered with short whitish-gray to yellowish hairs. The underside of the body and inner sides of the legs are sometimes lighter than the rest of the body. Frequently this whitish color extends alongside the sides of the upper lip. The skin usually hangs in loose folds. In most wild swine the tusks grow from the side of the jaw, but in babirusas the upper tusks grow through the top of the muzzle and then curve backward toward the skull between the eyes, so that they are of little use as weapons. Even the lower tusks are of little use as weapons, since they are not kept sharp by wearing against the upper pair. The exaggerated tusks are not known to serve any particular function but, promi-nent only in the males, probably are a sexual adornment. According to a native legend, these hogs hang themselves by their tusks from a tree limb at night.

These pigs are nocturnal and travel about in small parties, rooting in the ground and revealing their presence by low grunting moans. It is interesting to note that the males do most of the digging; the females and young follow along behind to chew on the things unearthed. Babirusas are swift runners and often swim in the sea to reach small islands. Their senses of smell and hearing are acute. Their food consists of roots, berries, grubs, and the like.

The young are born in the early months of the year, and are not striped like the young of most pigs. Two usually constitute a litter, and the sow has only one pair of mammae. The gestation period is 125 to 150 days. They have lived for over ten years in captivity.

Babirusas are frequently captured young and tamed by the natives. The natives hunt them regularly for meat, erecting an inclosure of poles and nets into which the animals are driven and then killed by spearing. The species is officially protected but is threatened with extinction. The natives say the tusks are like the antlers of a deer, hence the name "babirusa," meaning "pig-deer."

Collared Peccary and young (*Tayassu tajacu*), photo from New York Zoological Society.

COLLARED AND WHITE-LIPPED PECCARIES, JAVE-LINAS; JABALIS, AK, CUY, CUYAM, CITAM, KEN-KEN, COCHE DE MONTE, WARREE, PECARIS, CHAN-CHOS DE MONTE, BAQUIROS, COCHES DE MONTE, PUERCOS DE MONTE, PORCOS DO MATO, MUSK HOG, PECARI, PEKARI, NABELSCHWEIN, NAVEL-ZWIJN. (Included are vernaculars used in other countries.)

IN THIS FAMILY is included a single Recent genus, *Tayassu*, with two species distributed as follows: *T. tajaçu*, the collared peccary, from Texas, New Mexico, and Arizona southward to Patagonia, and *T. pecari*, the white-lipped peccary, from southern Mexico to Paraguay. The first species is common in deserts, arid woodlands and rain forests; the white-lipped peccary occurs primarily in humid tropical forests.

These pig-like animals have long, slim legs, with four toes on the fore feet and three toes (two in some fossilized forms) on the hind feet. The hooves are small. The third and fourth foot bones (completely separate in the pigs, Suidae) are united at their proximal ends, as in the ruminants. The snout is the same as in Suidae: elongate, mobile, and cartilaginous, with a nearly naked terminal surface in which the nostrils are located. The ears are ovate and erect. Both species have a musk gland on the back about 20 cm. in front of the tail; this gland is approximately

7.5 cm. in diameter and 1.25 cm. thick. When the animal is excited, the hairs on the neck and back bristle and the dorsal gland emits a musky secretion, the odor of which can be detected for many meters. The females have four mammae. Peccaries have a two-chambered, non-ruminating stomach, but it is more complex than that of the Suidae.

The length of the head and body is 750 to about 1,000 mm., and the length of the tail is 15 to 55 mm. Peccaries have only 6 to 9 tail vertebrae, compared with 20 to 23 in Suidae. The height at the shoulders is 440 to 575 mm., and adult specimens weigh 16 to 30 kg. The white-lipped species averages considerably larger in size than the collared species. The pelage is bristly, with a mane of long, stiff hairs on the mid-dorsal line from the crown to the rump. The white-lipped peccary is dark reddish brown to black, with white on the sides of the jaw, whereas the general coloration of the collared peccary is dark gray with a whitish collar on the neck. The young of the latter species are reddish with a blackish stripe along the back.

The dental formula is as follows: i 2/3, c 1/1, pm 3/3, m 3/3 = 38. The upper canines form tusks, but these are directed downward, not outward or upward as in the Suidae, and are smaller than those in pigs (the average tusk length in peccaries is about 4 cm.). There is a space between the canines and the premolars. The premolars and the molars form a continuous series of teeth, gradually increasing in size from the first to the last. The last premolar is nearly as complex as the molars; the true molars have square crowns with four cusps.

Collared peccaries usually travel in bands of 5 to 15 animals, whereas the white-lipped species tends to associate in groups of 50 to 100 or more. Both males and females of all ages mingle in these bands. There is no apparent leadership; it has been suggested that the scent of the musk gland helps to co-ordinate the herd's movement. If unmolested, these animals ordinarily do not bother human beings, but if a member of the band is wounded or pursued, the entire herd may counterattack. The speed, agility, and group defense of these mammals renders them more than a match for dogs, coyotes, and even bobcats. Peccaries often clash their canine teeth together when alarmed or angry, a warning to stay at a safe distance. When peccaries flee danger, they move with a fast running gait.

The usual resting area is in a thicket or under a large boulder, with limestone caves often serving as winter quarters in some areas. Javelinas are fairly sedentary; they do not seem to travel far from their birthplace. The territorial range of the collared peccary, for example, is usually less than 5 km.

Peccaries, like pigs, are not "dirty" animals; on the contrary, they are quite clean. The habit of pawing sand against the belly with their front feet is believed to be a cleansing action.

These hoofed mammals are most active in the cooler hours of the day and at night. They have poor vision and fair hearing. Their sense of smell is keen enough to enable them to locate a small covena bulb 5 to 8 cm. underground before the new shoots are visible. These animals grub for food with their snouts. Javelinas are mainly vegetarians, feeding on cactus fruit, berries, tubers, bulbs, and rhizomes; they also consume grubs and, like most of the pigs in the family Suidae, do not seem to be harmed by rattlesnake bites; snakes and other vertebrates are occasionally eaten. Waterholes are frequented by both species, but the tropical peccaries stay near running rivers.

Breeding appears to take place during most of the year, although most births occur during the summer. The gestation period is 142 to 148 days in the collared peccaries, and the litter size for the genus is one to four, usually two. Some females probably have two litters per year. The young are born in a thicket, hollow log, cave, or a burrow dug by some other animal. Young peccaries can run in a few hours and accompany their mother in a day or so after birth when she rejoins the herd. Collared peccaries nurse for six to eight weeks; the milk of this species is lower in fat and total solids than that of the domestic sow. Young peccaries, at least in the collared species, reach the teats from the rear of the sow instead of standing parallel to her side. The youngsters, which except for a mid-dorsal stripe are not striped as most pigs, remain with the mother for two or three months. The life expectancy is about 20 years.

Peccaries are hunted for their meat and hide, but the musk gland must be removed before the flesh can be eaten. Although the adults are sometimes unpredictable, a pet kept in captivity at the U.S. National Zoological Park in Washington, D. C., would come to the fence when it recognized a friend and enjoyed being scratched as much as any domestic pig. It knew its name and would come promptly when called.

The name "javelina" is derived from the Spanish "javeline," javelin or spear, and refers to the spear-like tusks of these animals.

The geological range of this family is the lower Oligocene to the upper Miocene in Europe, the lower Pliocene in Asia, the Pleistocene to the Recent in South America, and the lower Oligocene to the Recent in North America.

The type species of the genus is *T. tajaçu* (Linnaeus).

HIPPOPOTAMUSES.

THIS FAMILY of two Recent genera, each with one species, occurs in Africa, north to Khartoum and west to Sierra Leone. The big hippo, *Hippopotamus*, prefers a river habitat, whereas the pygmy hippo, *Choeropsis*, generally lives in dense, swampy forests.

These large mammals have a broad snout, large mouth, a short barrel-like body, and short, stocky legs. The belly is carried only a short distance above the ground. The eyes are protruding in *Hippopotamus*, and the ears (up to 100 mm. long) are set high up and far back on the head. The nostrils are located on top of the snout and can be closed. The sparsely-haired body contains special pores which secrete a pinkish substance known as "blood sweat"; this material is thick, oily, and protective in nature, allowing the animal to remain in water or in a dry atmosphere on land for extended periods. The skin contains a layer of fat which in *Hippopotamus* is 5 cm. thick. The short tail (150 to about 560 mm. long) is rather bristled. The foot bones are separate. All four toes on each foot support the body weight; the two lateral digits are nearly as well developed as the median digits. The terminal digital bones have nail-like hooves. Hippos have a complex, three-chambered, but non-ruminating stomach. The females have two mammae.

In the big hippo the length of the head and body is 3.75 to 4.5 meters and the weight is 3 to 4.5 metric tons, whereas in the pygmy hippo the length of the head and body is 1.5 to 1.75 meters and the weight is 160 to 180 kg.

The dental formula is as follows: i 2-3/1, c 1/1, pm 4/4, m 3/3 = 38 to 42. The incisors and canines are tusk-like and grow continuously. The incisors are rounded, smooth, and widely separated; the upper incisors are quite short and project downward, and the lower ones are longer, especially the inner pair (in *Hippopotamus*), and project forward and only slightly upward. The lower canines, which are the largest of the tusk-like teeth, project upward and outward. The premolars are usually single-cusped, although this condition may vary even on opposite sides in the same animal; two pairs of cusps are developed in the molars, except in the third molar, which has three pairs. These cusps wear down to various trefoil, figure-eight, or dumbbell-shaped enamel patterns. The large skull has an elongated facial area although the brain pan is small.

These amphibious mammals are good swimmers and divers. *Hippopotamus* occurs singly, in pairs, in groups of half a dozen, or sometimes in groups of 30 individuals, whereas *Choeropsis* usually lives alone or in pairs. When frightened, the pygmy hippo usually runs for the forest, but the big hippo generally heads toward water. The bulls, at least in *Hippopotamus*, habitually fight one another; the chief weapons in such encounters are their large lower canines. Hides of mature bulls invariably exhibit numerous scars. Hippos have a good sense of smell but only fair vision.

These mammals generally remain in the water during the day, emerging at night to feed on land, and often range over many kilometers during their nocturnal wanderings. They consume vegetation, which is cropped with the heavy front teeth and the lips.

The big hippo has a 3-day rut, an hour-long mating act, and breeds again from 12 to 16 days after the baby is weaned. In *Hippopotamus* the gestation period is 227 to 240 days, and the single baby weighs 27 to 45 kg. at birth. In *Choeropsis* the gestation period is somewhat shorter, 201 to 210 days, and the offspring

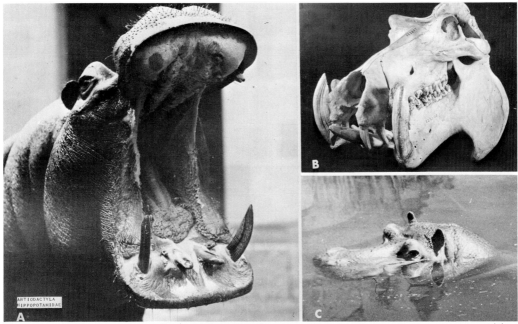

Hippopotamus (*Hippopotamus amphibius*), A. Photo from New York Zoological Society. B. Photo by P. F. Wright of specimen in U.S. National Museum. C. Photo from Castle Films through U.S. National Zoological Park.

weighs 3 to 4.5 kg. at birth. Young hippos can swim before they can walk, and they nurse under water. The cow is devoted to her calf; the youngster of the big hippo scrambles onto the mother's back and suns itself while she is floating on the surface. This may afford some protection against crocodiles. A subadult of the big hippo weighed 250 kg. at the end of its first year of life. The big hippos are sexually mature at 3 years of age (captivity records).

Hippopotamus is hunted because of its abundant fat (approximately 90 kg.); its flesh, which is highly prized by the native people (the flesh of *Choeropsis* is said to taste like that of the wild pig, *Sus*); its thick hide, which, when made supple, is used as a whip in South Africa; its teeth, which yield a superior ivory; and because it damages crops during its nocturnal ventures on land.

The geological range of this family is the middle Pliocene to the Pleistocene in Asia, including Ceylon; the Pleistocene in Europe and Madagascar, and the middle Pliocene to the Recent in Africa. *Hexaprotodon*, an extinct genus known from the middle Pliocene to the Pleistocene in Asia, can be recognized by the uniform size of the six incisors.

Hippopotamus (*Hippopotamus amphibius*), photo from New York Zoological Society.

HIPPOPOTAMUSES; SEEKOIE, NYLPAARDEN.

THE SINGLE SPECIES, *H. amphibius*, was formerly found throughout Africa in all rivers and streams with deep water. Through man's destruction it is now restricted to the river areas south of 17 degrees north latitude. Hippos prefer a river habitat with areas of marshes and reed beds.

Head and body length is 3.75 to 4.6 meters; tail length is about 560 mm.; and shoulder height is about 1.5 meters. The weight varies from 3 to 4.5 metric tons. The body is so scantily covered with short, fine hairs that it appears naked. The usual color of the skin is a slaty copper-brown shading to dark brown above and purplish below. The upper canines are as much as 230 mm. or more in circumference, and the lower canines are about 0.6 meter long and weigh as much as 3 kg. The skin is glandular and exudes droplets of moisture which contain red pigment; light reflected from the skin through these droplets appears red, thus giving rise to the statement that hippos "sweat blood."

When submerging, hippos close the slit-like nostrils and the ears. If they wish to see and breathe without exposing themselves, they can keep the protruding eyes and nostrils out of the water and remain submerged. They normally stay under water for three to five minutes but can stay under longer, perhaps a half-hour. Due to their specific gravity they can walk about on the bottom. While not naturally vicious, hippos on occasion attack small boats or strange objects that they think may endanger them.

These animals travel singly (usually old bulls), in pairs, or small "schools" of up to a half dozen; only occasionally do groups number as many as 20 to 30. They are equally at home in salt water or in fresh water. Hippos spend practically the entire day sleeping and resting in or near water, but when molested they will lie in deep water in reed beds. At night they may cover 33 km. of water in search of food; they seldom venture farther than 0.3 km. from the water, however. Their diet consists mostly of grass. Sometimes they enter cultivated fields where they do extensive damage both by eating and trampling crops. They do not remain long in any one area but move to new grounds after a few days.

Hippos appear to breed at all times of the year; the female becomes sexually mature between five and six years of age. A single calf, rarely two, is born at a time. The gestation period is 227 to 240 days. The weight at birth is 27 to 45 kg. One individual weighed 250 kg. at the end of the first year. Records indicate that in captivity both sexes are sexually mature at an age of three years. Potential longevity is 40 to 50 years.

The hippo has been hunted for its abundance of fat (90 kg.) and its flesh and thick hide. The flesh is highly prized by the natives, and the hide makes excellent soup. The teeth are composed of a superior ivory.

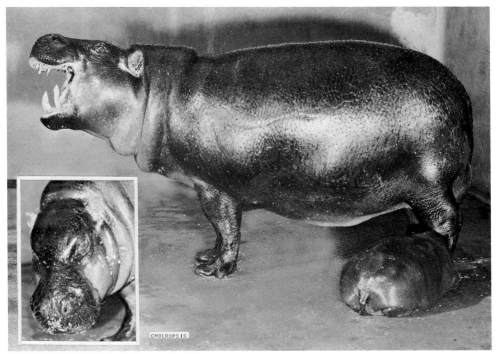

Pygmy Hippopotamus (*Choeropsis liberiensis*) and 23-day old young, photos by Ernest P. Walker.

PYGMY HIPPOPOTAMUSES, SEA-COWS, WATER-COWS.

THE SINGLE SPECIES, *C. liberiensis*, is known only from the Ivory Coast, Liberia, and the adjacent parts of Sierra Leone. It is found in streams, wet forests, and swamps, and is less aquatic than the larger hippo.

Head and body length is 1.5 to 1.75 meters; the tail length is 156 mm.; the shoulder height is 0.75 to 1.0 meter; and adults attain weights of 160 to 240 kg. The body is without hair except for a few bristles on the lips and tail. The color above is a slaty greenish-black, the sides are more gray, and the under parts are grayish white to yellowish green. At a superficial glance this animal appears to be a miniature of the well-known hippo (*Hippopotamus*), but there are notable structural differences. The head is rounder and not as broad and flat, the nostrils are large and almost circular, the eyes are set on the side of the head and do not protrude, and the toes have sharp nails and are well separated. In addition, pigmy hippos usually have only one pair of upper incisors as compared to two pairs in the large hippos. The exudation from the pores of the skin of the pigmy hippo is a clear, viscous material that makes the animal sleek to the touch. In certain lights the reddish-brown tone of the skin is reflected in the beads of secretion which then look almost blood-red. Erroneously, many people believe the animal to be "sweating blood."

This species is little known. One may travel for days within its range and see no signs of it. When frightened it will run for the forest, whereas the big hippo will invariably head toward the water. Pygmy hippos are not unduly vicious animals, but when disturbed they can be dangerous. They are usually found singly or in pairs, sleeping by day and wandering about during the night among the forests seeking tender shoots, leaves, and fallen fruit.

A single young, weighing 3 to 5 kg., is born 201 to 210 days after the parents have mated. Pigmy hippos have a life-span of 17 to 40 years.

Except for their flesh, pigmy hippos are of no economic value. The flesh is prized by the natives and is said to taste like that of the wild pig (*Sus*). Specimens are in great demand for exhibition in zoological gardens because of their limited numbers and restricted range. In captivity these animals easily become adjusted and some breed well. Because of their scarcity, they were accorded complete protection by the London Conference of 1933.

CAMELS, GUANACOS, LLAMAS, ALPACAS, AND VICUÑAS.

THIS FAMILY of three Recent genera and six species is known in the wild state at the present time in South America (guanacos, *Lama guanacoe;* vicuñas, *Vicugna*) and the Gobi Desert in Mongolia (the two-humped camel, *Camelus bactrianus*). The one-humped camel (*C. dromedarius*), most two-humped camels, the llama (*Lama peruana*), and the alpaca (*L. pacos*) exist only in the domesticated state. Camels have been introduced at various times into southern Europe, Australia, and North America; their present domesticated range is from northern Africa through Central Asia to Mongolia. Llamas and alpacas occur in South America. The wild forms inhabit semiarid to arid plains, grasslands, and deserts; the vicuña ranges in the Andes to above 5,000 meters elevation.

These are artiodactyls with two digits (the third and the fourth) on each foot (in the Recent forms). The proximal digital bones are expanded distally; the middle digital bones are wide, flattened, and embedded in a broad, cutaneous pad which forms the sole of the foot; and the distal digital bones are small, not flattened on their inner surface, and not encased in hooves, bearing nails on the upper surface only. The digits are spread nearly flat on the ground. The feet are broad in *Camelus* and slender in *Lama* and *Vicugna*. The foot bones are united to form a cannon bone; in one genus (*Vicugna*) glands are associated with the cannon bone of the hind limb. In the forearm the ulna is reduced distally and in the shank the fibula is reduced. The knee joint is low in position due to the long femur and its vertical placement. All the limbs are long. The forelimbs have naked callosities in the guanaco, and prominent knee pads are present in camels.

The head is small, and the neck is long and thin. The slender snout bears a cleft upper lip. The ears are small in *Camelus* and long and pointed in *Lama* and *Vicugna*. The Recent forms have one hump on the back (*C. dromedarius*), two humps (*C. bactrianus*), or no humps (*Lama* and *Vicugna*). The hind part of the body is contracted. The length of the head and body is 1.2 to 3 meters, that of the tail is 120 to about 550 mm. (short in *Lama* and *Vicugna*, long and tufted in *Camelus*), the height at the shoulder is .75 to 2.1 meters, and adult camelids weigh from 45 to about 500 kg. The hair is soft, fine, and woolly on the one-humped camel; well developed on the top of the head, neck, humps, and the forearm in the two-humped camel; up to 50 cm. long on the body of the alpaca; and silky (40 to 60 mm. long at the base of the neck) in the vicuña. Camelids have a three-chambered, ruminating stomach.

The members of the family Camelidae differ from all other mammals in the shape of their red blood corpuscles, which are oval instead of circular.

ARTIODACTYLA
CAMELIDAE

The head of a Bactrian camel (*Camelus bactrianus*), showing the closable, slit-like nostrils and the heavy eyebrows and eyelashes, which provide valuable protection in severe sandstorms. The slightly divided upper lip is also shown. Photo by Ernest P. Walker.

The dental formula in *Camelus* is i 1/3, c 1/1, pm 3/2, m 3/3 = 34, and in *Lama* and *Vicugna* it is i 1/3, c 1/1-0, pm 2/2-3, m 3/3 = 30 to 34. The premaxillary bones of the skull bear the full number of incisors in the young, but only the outer incisor (in the upper set) persists in the adult; the incisors, which are spatulate, are located in a forward, somewhat upward position. The lower incisors of *Vicugna* are

Front foot of Bactrian Camel (*Camelus bactrianus*), showing the hard ends of the toes and the broad foot with soft pads which is well adapted to traversing soft sands, from color photo by Constance P. Warner.

unique among Recent artiodactyla—ever-growing, with the enamel on only one side. The nearly erect and pointed canines are present in both jaws or absent in the lower jaw. The front premolars are simple, usually separated from the other cheek teeth, and the molars have crescentic ridges of enamel on their crowns. The skull is low and elongate, and antlers or horns are absent.

Camels and the members of the genus *Lama* run with a swinging stride, due to the front and hind legs moving in unison on each side of the body. Guanacos can run as fast as 55 km. per hour. Some of the adaptations of camels to conserve water in the stomach are discussed in the generic account of *Camelus*. The members of this family are gregarious, the herds often consisting of a male (the leader) and several females; camels in the wild state usually associate in groups of four to six individuals, whereas vicuñas and the wild forms of *Lama* generally mingle in larger groups. Camelids lay down to rest and sleep and have the habit of spitting the contents of their stomach at annoying objects, including incautious zoo visitors.

These mammals are diurnal. They are grazers, feeding on many kinds of grasses, although camels, when extremely hungry, will eat a wide range of food.

The female camelid comes into heat several times a year. The gestation period in *Lama* and *Vicugna* is 10 to 11 months, and in *Camelus* it is 370 to 440 days. The number of offspring is one, rarely two. In camels the life expectancy may exceed 45 years, and in *Lama* and *Vicugna* it is about 20 years.

The geological range of the family Camelidae is the upper Eocene to the Pleistocene in North America, the Pleistocene in Europe and northern Africa, and the Pleistocene to the Recent in South America and Asia. The camel family originated and developed in the Americas.

A. Camel (*Camelus bactrianus*), the unusually ragged appearance is due to spring shedding of its winter coat, photo by Fritz Grogl. B. Camel (*C. dromedarius*), photo from U.S. National Zoological Park. Inset: *C. bactrianus*, photo by Ernest P. Walker.

CAMELS; KAMELEN, CAMELLOS, CHAMEAUX. (Included are vernaculars used in other countries.)

THE TWO SPECIES are *C. dromedarius*, the one-humped camel, whose exact range probably will never be known since it now exists only in the domesticated state and has been transferred to various parts of the world, but it probably originally inhabited Arabia; and *C. bactrianus*, the two-humped camel, which is native to Chinese Turkestan and Mongolia. The habitat of the Bactrian (two-humped) camel is the Gobi steppe along rivers; however, as soon as snow falls it moves to the desert.

The head and body length of *C. bactrianus* is about 3 meters; the tail length is about 530 mm.; the shoulder height is 1.8 to 2.1 meters; and the weight is 450 to 690 kg. Elongated hairs (255 mm.) are thickest on the head, neck, hump, thighs, and the tip of the tail; the remainder of the body is covered with dense, shaggy wool about 50 mm. in length. Camels shed their winter coat so rapidly that it comes off in large masses, giving the animal the ragged appearance shown in the photograph of the Bactrian camel. Camels vary in color from deep brown to dusty gray.

The Bactrian camels have shorter legs than the one-humped camels and therefore are not as tall. They also have harder and shorter feet, are more docile, easier to ride, and are slower.

Both species have a long head and neck. The feet have two toes and undivided soles; the long, slender legs have prominent knee pads. The tail is short, the eyes have heavy lashes, the ears are haired, the nostrils closable, and the sight is keen. The sense of smell is extremely good. The upper lip is deeply divided, and the slit-like nostrils can be closed to keep out dust and sand. There is a groove from each nostril to the cleft upper lip so that any moisture from the nostrils can be caught in the mouth. The stomach is comprised of three chambers; however, contrary to popular belief, there are no valid accounts to support the legend of water storage in the stomach. Although these animals are remarkably adapted for the conservation of water, they cannot store quantities of water and go for long periods without drinking except at the expense of great loss of weight and strength. When camels are well fed, the hump is erect and plump, but when they do not have adequate food, the hump shrinks, and often leans to one side. The red blood corpuscles are oval-shaped, whereas those of other mammals are disk-shaped. The skin has almost no sweat glands.

Over a four-day period a camel is able to carry 170 to 270 kg. at a rate of about 47 km. per day and 4 km. per hour. The camel is very shy in its habits. The wild camel is seen alone and in pairs, but the general rule is for a troop of four to six individuals to associate together. Troops of 12 to 15 are extremely rare. The characteristic rolling gate of the camel is accomplished by its ability to simultaneously bring up both legs on the same side. The maximum speed is about 16 km. per hour. Camels are cabable of withstanding extreme heat and cold and are said to be good swimmers. They can and will drink brackish and even salt water. In drinking as many as 57 liters of water, camels restore the normal amount of body moisture. They eat practically any vegetation that grows in the desert or subarid regions. If forced by hunger, they will eat fish, flesh, bones, and skin. They thrive on salty plants that are wholly rejected by other grazing mammals. Camels are said to need halophytes in their diet and will lose weight if they are lacking.

A single calf, rarely two, is born after a gestation period of 370 to 440 days. The calf has soft fleece, utters a gentle "bah," and lacks the knee pads of the adult. By the end of the first day it can move about freely. At four years the young camel becomes wholly independent. Full growth is attained at 5 years. A female may breed every alternate year and produce 12 young in a lifetime. Life expectancy is 17 to 50 years.

These animals are well known as beasts of burden; in addition, they supply milk, meat, wool, hides, sinews, and bones. Chemicals can be extracted from their dung and urine. The milk is fermented to produce kumiss, a common intoxicating liquor.

In the middle of the nineteenth century, camels were introduced into the southwestern United States as a potential source of efficient transportation. Enthusiastic advocates even predicted that because of their versatility camels would supplant beef cattle in the southwest. However, due to the building of railroads and many other factors, the experiment was a failure.

The type species of the genus is *C. dromedarius*, Linnaeus.

A. Alpaca (*Lama pacos*), photo by Ernest P. Walker. B. Llamas (*L. peruana*), photo from the U.S. National Zoological Park. C. Leg of Llama; D. Guanaco (*L. guanacoe*).

Suri Alpacas at livestock fair, Arequipa, Peru, 1952. This is the best wool breed of alpacas. Photo by Hilda Heller.

Guanacos, Llamas, Alpacas.

THREE SPECIES are recognized: *L. guanacoe*, the guanaco, a wild form; and *L. peruana* (the llama) and *L. pacos* (the alpaca), both of which were found only in domestication when the Spanish first reached their range in South America. All species are found in southern and western South America from sea level to elevations of 5,000 meters in a semidesert habitat.

The guanaco has a head and body length of 1.2 to 1.75 meters, a tail length of about 250 mm., a shoulder height of .9 to 1 meter, and a weight of 48 to 96 kg. The erythrocyte life span is about 235 days, the longest of all mammals. The woolly coat is longest on the flanks, chest, and thighs. Coloration is dark fawn-brown above with white under parts; the face is blackish. The limbs and neck are slender and the body is trim. This species is distinguished from *Vicugna* by the callosities on the inner side of the forelimbs. Also, the vicuña has a bib of white or yellowish red, but the guanaco does not.

Guanacos are usually found in small herds of four to ten females led by a single male. In the mountains they prefer the high pampas and plateaus. Since this is open country, their safety depends upon their speed (up to 56 km. per hour) and alertness. They enjoy standing and even lying in mountain streams and are said to be good swimmers. When about to lie down, they first go down on the front knees, collapse the

hindquarters, and then drop onto the chest, with the legs tucked under the body. These creatures display a great sense of loyalty. It is said that if the male leader of a herd is shot, the females will not run, as would be expected, but will nudge the dead leader with their noses in an effort to get him to his feet. These animals are grazers, their diet consisting almost wholly of grasses from mountain slopes. When fighting, the male emits a high-pitched scream which changes to a low growl.

Adults mate in August and September, and 10 to 11 months later one young is normally born, although the female has four teats. Females bear young every other year. Immediately after birth the young are able to run with surprising endurance. The youngster is nursed for 6 to 12 weeks. As the young males develop, they are eventually driven from the herd by the adult females. Life expectancy is about 20 years.

Guanacos are usually gentle and can become good pets, although as adults they can be aggressive.

The llama has a head and body length of about 1.2 meters, a tail length of about 15 cm., and a shoulder height of about 1.2 meters. The weight is 70 to 140 kg. The body has fairly long, dense, fine wool, and the hair on the head, neck, and limbs is shorter than elsewhere on the body. Coloration is brown to black or even white, usually irregularly blotched with these colors.

The structural features, habits, and biology are similar to those of the guanaco. Guanacos and llamas are both graceful in their movements. The llama has been under domestication for a thousand or more years and is used primarily as a beast of burden. It is capable of carrying a load of 96 kg. at a speed of 26 km. per day over rugged mountain terrain at elevations of 5,000 meters, where other animals cannot move efficiently under loads. At the time of the Spanish conquest, 300,000 llamas were being used at the silver mines. The llama is the only native beast of burden domesticated by the peoples of the New World.

It is easy to realize the importance of the llama to the Indian, as he utilizes it almost 100 per cent, from its smallest hairs to its most insignificant droppings. Jerked llama meat nourishes the Indian; its woven fleece keeps him warm; its hide is made into the crude sandals with which he is shod; its tallow is used in making candles; braided, the long hairs serve him as rope; and the excrement, dried, constitutes a fuel which helps him ward off the penetrating chill of his treeless, high-altitude home.

The alpaca, somewhat smaller than the llama, is selectively bred for its wool, the quality of which can be matched by no other animal. Its wool is much longer than that of the llama. Formerly it was woven into robes that were worn by the Inca royalty; today a coat made from these fine hairs costs over $1,000.

All forms resemble camels in certain structural features and habits. Fossils found in the western United States indicate that the animals of this genus and the camel apparently had a common ancestry in the United States, one migrating southward into South America (*Lama*) and the other going northward across Asia and southward (*Camelus*). In *Lama*, as in *Camelus*, we find a three-chambered stomach, the peculiar habit of simultaneously lifting the feet on the same side when running, and the unpleasant habit of spitting when angry.

Certain excretion sites are used by llamas, as is indicated by dung heaps up to 2.4 meters in diameter and about 31 cm. deep, composed of small, dry pellets. It is interesting to note that, in contrast to other animals, the hemoglobin of *Lama* has a much greater affinity for oxygen and the blood contains more red corpuscles. This partly accounts for the ability to satisfactorily survive high altitudes.

At least sixteen fossil genera of the camel-llama-vicugna-guanaco-alpaca group have been described from North American formations, and at least one genus of fossils has been described from South America.

Whether or not the so-called species *L. peruana* (the llama) and *L. pacos* are true species is open to question. The matter may never be settled, as they have been domesticated and bred for certain characters for so long and they may have lost or acquired so many characters, that it may never be possible to verify or disprove their distinct specific status.

The type species of the genus is *L. pacos* (Linnaeus).

Vicuña (*Vicugna vicugna*), photo by C. B. Koford.

VICUÑAS.

THE SINGLE SPECIES, *V. vicugna*, is native to an area about 2,080 kilometers in length between the latitudes of 10 degrees and 29 degrees south in the South American Andes. Vicuñas inhabit semiarid rolling grasslands and plains at elevations between 3,500 and 5,750 meters.

Head and body length is 1.45 to 1.6 meters; tail length is about 152 mm.; shoulder height is 760 to 860 mm.; and weight is 35 to 65 kg. The woolly coat is longest on the brisket and sides, and the coloration is a tawny brown with a white or yellowish-red bib. The vicuña resembles the guanaco in general form but is about one-fourth smaller, paler in coloration, and lacks the dark face. The forelimbs have no callosities. The lower incisors are unique among living artiodactyls—they are rodent-like, that is, evergrowing with enamel on only one side.

Vicuñas travel in bands of 5 to 15 females, normally led by the male. In time of danger the male warns the females with an alarm trill, interposing himself between the source of alarm and the females as they retreat. Vicuñas defecate and urinate on communal dung piles. The characteristic spitting of these animals is accomplished by a quick forceful expulsion of air and saliva. They are capable of running 47 km. per hour at elevations of 4,500 meters. To dust their fleece and scratch their bodies, vicuñas paw and then vigorously roll on the ground. Of the senses, the best developed is sight, hearing is only moderately acute and the sense of smell is poor. Vicuñas are exceedingly graceful in their movements, perhaps surpassing any other hoofed mammal in this respect.

Juveniles often graze while lying prone, their legs tucked under the body, and both young and adults chew cud while resting. Vicuñas are grazers, the diet consisting almost entirely of low perennial grasses. Territoriality is exhibited and its extent depends largely on food abundance.

The single young is usually born in February, 11 months after the parents have mated. The young can stand and walk about 15 minutes after birth. The young sleep by the side of the mother until they are at least eight months old. They nurse several times a day until they are at least ten months old. Life expectancy is about 15 to 20 years.

Legal protection of vicuñas has been ineffective due to lack of law enforcement. The vicuña population would probably respond well to wildlife management and could produce a large annual harvest of young males for meat and exquisite wool.

CHEVROTAINS, MOUSE DEER.

IN THIS FAMILY are two Recent genera: *Hyemoschus* for a single species from central Africa, and *Tragulus* for approximately six species from southeastern Asia. Chevrotains or mouse deer inhabit tropical forests and mangrove thickets, often near water.

Although these small, graceful animals somewhat resemble deer, they belong to a group of artiodactyls which seems to be more closely related to camelids (Camelidae) and pigs (Suidae) than to deer (Cervidae). Chevrotains actually look like agoutis (Rodentia: Dasyproctidae). The head is small and the snout is pointed; the narrow, slit-like nostrils are located in the naked nasal surfaces. There are no facial or foot glands. The legs are long, thin, and delicate, about the size of a lead pencil. In *Tragulus* the pairs of metacarpal and metatarsal bones in the limbs are united into single bones, known as cannon bones, but in *Hyemoschus* cannon bones are not formed until old age. Each foot has four well-developed digits, although *Hyemoschus* is reported to stand on the tips of its toes, so that the lateral toes do not touch the ground. The female tragulid has four mammae. These animals ruminate, but the stomach has only three distinct compartments, the third chamber is vestigial.

The length of the head and body is about 0.5 to 1 meter, the tail about 55 mm., and the height at the shoulders is 205 to 355 mm. The adults weigh from 2 to 5 kg. The hair is appressed and arranged in groups. The coloration above is rich brown, with white spots and stripes in most species, and below it is generally white.

Chevrotains lack horns or antlers. The dental formula is as follows: i 0/3, c 1/1, pm 3/3, m 3/3 = 34. The upper canines are well developed (especially in the males), protrude below the lips, and are narrow, curved, and pointed; the lower canines look like incisors. All the premolars, except the last, function in cutting the food; there are no premolars that resemble the canines. The molars bear crescentic ridges of enamel on their crowns. All the cheek teeth are arranged in a continuous series.

Mouse deer (so called because of their small size and superficial resemblance to deer) are shy and wary. They are solitary and nocturnal and, consequently, seldom receive detailed treatment in scientific publications. They are rapid runners, darting through the brush like rabbits. Some forms are semiaquatic, and the African chevrotain is said to climb a sloping tree in order to sun itself or to escape a predator. They utter rather weak bleating sounds.

These ungulates are essentially vegetarians, feeding on fallen fruit and various aquatic plants; a captive African chevrotain ate insects.

Chevrotains in Asia mate in June and July or throughout the year. The gestation period in the different genera varies from about 120 to 155 days. The offspring number one or two and are often born at the end of the rainy season, when vegetation is more lush and abundant.

The geological range of this family is the upper Miocene to the lower Pliocene in Europe; the Pleistocene to the Recent in Africa, and the upper Miocene to the Recent in Asia.

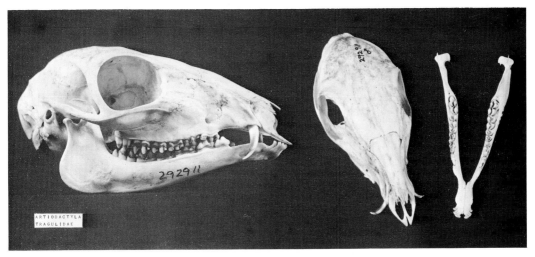

Asiatic Mouse Deer (*Tragulus* sp.), photos by P. F. Wright of specimen in the U.S. National Museum.

Water Chevrotains (*Hyemoschus aquaticus*), photo by Ernest P. Walker.

WATER CHEVROTAINS; VION, ZWERGMOSCHUSTIER, WASSERHIRSCHFERKEL, WATERMUSKUSDIER, DWERGMUSKUSDIER (local vernaculars).

THE SINGLE SPECIES, *H. aquaticus*, is found in Africa along watercourses in dense forests from Gambia and Sierra Leone in the west to the Ituri Forest at the eastern border of the Congo Basin and southward to the Cameroons.

The length of the head and body is about 1 meter, and the height at the shoulders is 305 to 355 mm. Coloration is a rich brown, marked along the body with several longitudinal rows of white spots which become fused to form broken lines on the flanks. A white stripe runs along the edge of the jaw and the sides of the neck; the underside of the tail is white. The color and the arrangement of the spots are not constant. Water chevrotains have small heads, pointed snouts, short tails, and high bodies set on long, slender legs. Neither sex has antlers, but the upper canines of the male are developed into tusks similar to those of the musk deer (*Moschus*). These animals differ from deer, which they somewhat resemble, in that each foot bears four well-developed digits.

In *Tragulus*, the other genus of chevrotains, the pairs of metacarpal and metatarsal bones in the limbs are united into single bones, called cannon bones. Cannon bones are not formed in *Hyemoschus* until old age.

Little is recorded of the habits and general biology. It has been observed that when disturbed, water chevrotains usually plunge into the water and vanish, only to come up under the cover of overhanging vines and bushes farther upstream. They stand on the tips of their toes, so that the lateral toes do not touch the ground. When they are tired they tuck in both front legs and sit on them. They are said to occasionally climb sloping or vine-covered trees to sun themselves or to try to escape predators. Water chevrotains are solitary except in the mating season, and they are most active by night, when they come out to feed on grass, water weeds, and lily roots. Captives feed readily on fish, small crustaceans and insects. Their stomach is only three-chambered.

The gestation period is reported to be 120 days. Natives, their chief enemy, have over-hunted these small animals in many areas with dogs, snares, and long nets, although water chevrotains do not seem to be in danger of extermination. However, the fact that they are the modern survivors of an ancient group of primitive hoofed animals makes their preservation a matter of interest. Water chevrotains are difficult to maintain in captivity. One survived in the London Zoo for only one year.

Dorcatherium, a closely related and similar but extinct form, which inhabited Europe and Asia during the upper Miocene to the lower Pliocene, became known to the scientific world before living *Hyemoschus* specimens were recorded from Africa.

A. Asiatic Mouse Deer or Chevrotain (*Tragulus javanicus*), photo by Ernest P. Walker. B. Asiatic Mouse Deer or Chevrotain (*T. meminna*), photo by Bernhard Grzimek.

ASIATIC CHEVROTAINS, MOUSE DEER; KANTJIL, BENKURANG, PELANDOK (native names).

ABOUT HALF A DOZEN SPECIES are found from India through southeastern Asia to the East Indies, including Balabac. They generally live among undergrowth and herbage on the edges of heavy lowland forests. Seldom, if ever, are they found far from water.

Head and body length is 455 to 560 mm.; tail length is usually 25 to 125 mm.; shoulder height is 204 to 330 mm.; and the weight is generally 2.5 to 4.5 kg. Short, even, close hair covers the body, even shorter on the head and under parts. All species are colored some shade of brown with whitish under parts. The white expanse of the chin and throat is variously though symmetrically cut by patches of brown. Certain species have longitudinal rows of spots or stripes of white or buff on the back and sides.

These small deer-like animals have a moderately robust body and limbs about the size of an ordinary lead pencil. They lack horns, but have canines in both jaws; these teeth are especially developed in the upper jaw and enlarged in the males into tusks. There are four fully developed toes. At a casual glance they have the appearance of miniature deer but differ in that the stomach has only three divisions. They are more closely related to the hogs (Suidae) and camels (Camelidae) than to the deer (Cervidae).

These little animals are present in relatively large numbers and are therefore well known to most natives. However, being essentially shy, retiring, and nocturnal, they are seldom seen. They are solitary except during the mating season. Customarily they traverse tiny tunnel-like jungle trails like fleeting shadows. The mouse deer's diet consists chiefly of grass, the leaves of low bushes and seedlings, and fallen jungle fruit and berries.

Mating may take place in June and July or throughout the year, depending on the locality. One, rarely two, young are born in some secluded nook or crevice amongst a jumble of rock, 150 to 155 days after the parents have mated. The female has four mammae.

These animals are preyed upon by a large number of carnivores and snakes and are also widely sought by the natives for food. They tame readily and make good pets but are very delicate creatures. In Malay folklore the mouse deer plays the same role as the red fox in European folklore.

The type species of the genus is *T. javanicus* (Osbeck).

DEER.

THIS FAMILY of 17 genera and about 53 species occurs in North America, south to 40 degrees latitude in South America, northwestern Africa, Eurasia, Japan, the Philippines, and most of Indonesia. Deer have been introduced in New Guinea, Australia, New Zealand, and the Hawaiian Islands, and reintroduced in Great Britain where they lived originally but were exterminated. The extremely varied habitats include

A. Central American White-tailed Deer (*Odocoileus virginianus truei*); B. Père David's Deer (*Elaphurus davidianus*); photos by Ernest P. Walker. C. Red Deer (*Cervus* sp.), photo by Erna Mohr. D. Père David's Deer (*Elaphurus davidianus*) showing deep preorbital lachrymal pits, photo by Ernest P. Walker.

forests, arctic tundra, dry desert, open brush country, and swamps.

These slim, long-legged artiodactyls are best characterized by the presence of antlers, which are lacking in only two genera—musk deer, *Moschus*, and Chinese water deer, *Hydropotes*. Antlers are borne only by the males, except in caribou and reindeer (*Rangifer*); in the latter genus both the males and the females have antlers. The male deer is illustrated more than the female in these volumes inasmuch as the antlers are the principal external character by which the genera can be distinguished. Antlers are appendages of the skull, composed of a solid bony core and supported on permanent skin-covered pedicels. In the temperate zones the antlers begin to grow early in the summer during which time they are well supplied with blood. They are soft and tender and are covered with a thin skin which bears short fine hairs and has the appearance of velvet. By late summer the antlers have attained their maximum size. The blood then gradually recedes, and the thin skin with the velvety hair dries, loosens, and is rubbed off. Before the velvet is shed, all circulation of blood has ceased and, when shedding takes place, there is no bleeding and probably not even discomfort to the animal. After the velvet is rubbed off, the antlers serve as sexual ornaments and weapons. The antlers are shed each year between January and April, following the mating season. The species in temperate climates complete the shedding process in two to three weeks. In a single deer both antlers are usually shed within several hours or days of each other. At least some of the tropical deer do not have a fixed breeding season and these forms do not shed their antlers at any certain time. Deer grow their first set of antlers when one or two years old, and these first-year horns are generally short, almost straight spikes. The antlers become larger and acquire more points in succeeding years until the animal is mature, when the antlers attain the shape typical of the species. Normal antler growth is largely dependent upon an adequate diet, for if certain minerals or vitamins are lacking, the antlers may be stunted or dwarfed. (Note stages in development of antlers in photographs on p. 1382.)

Female deer are generally slightly smaller and more delicately built than males; their necks in particular are not so full as those of the males during the rutting season and the hair on the neck is not so heavy. The length of the head and body is .75 to 2.9 meters, the tail is short, and adult deer weigh from 9 to 800 kg., musk deer being the smallest members of the family and moose (*Alces*) the largest. The coloration is brownish; the young are usually spotted and the adults are spotted in some species. The winter coats are darker than the summer coats, at least in those species in temperate latitudes.

Nearly all deer have facial glands, located in a depression in front of the eye; the pit is lined with a continuation of the skin of the face. Glands also occur on the limbs. There is a cannon bone which is formed by the fusion of the two main foot bones. The ulna and the fibula are reduced. Each foot has four digits, i.e., the third and fourth, which are well developed, and the second and fifth, which are small. Female deer usually have two pairs of mammae (only one pair in musk deer). The stomach is four-chambered and ruminating, and a gall bladder is absent, except in musk deer.

The dental formula is as follows: i 0/3, c 0-1/1, pm 3/3, m 3/3 = 32 or 34. The upper canines are saber-shaped and enlarged in the antlerless species and absent in most others; the lower canines resemble the incisors. The low cheek teeth bear crescentic ridges of enamel on their crowns.

Most deer associate in groups; a few, such as *Alces*, are solitary, at least during the non-mating season. The stags typically gather a harem during the breeding season. Deer are usually good swimmers, some species being semiaquatic. Some (for example, *Rangifer*) migrate seasonally. Members of the family Cervidae are herbivores, feeding on grass, bark, twigs, and the young shoots of trees and other plants.

The stags of a single species often fight among themselves for the possession of a harem; their antlers sometimes become locked in these combats. Deer in tropical areas may come into heat several times during a year, whereas those in a more temperate climate have a definite mating season in the late fall or winter. The gestation period ranges from 160 days in musk deer to approximately 10 months in roe deer (*Capreolus*); the latter genus is the only deer known to have delayed implantation. The number of young is usually one or two, but three and four sometimes are born.

The geological range of this family is the lower Oligocene to the Recent in Asia; the upper Oligocene to the Recent in Europe; the lower Miocene to the Recent in North America, and the Pleistocene to the Recent in South America. Specimens of *Metacervulus*, the red deer of the later Pleistocene period, have been found in Asia and Japan. This genus became extinct prior to the invasion of the wild boar and the accompanying modern fauna. These deer had three-tined and fairly advanced antlers. *Eucladocerus* is a deer known from the Pleistocene of England and is characterized by intricately branched antlers. Many complete skeletons of *Megaloceros* have been reconstructed from remains found in peat bogs in Ireland and are dated as Pleistocene. The male had antlers measuring as much as 3 meters from tip to tip.

Musk Deer (*Moschus moschiferus*), photo by Bernhard Grzimek. Inset: Photo from *Guide to the Great Game Animals*, British Museum (Natural History).

MUSK-DEER; KASTURA, LAWA, JAKO-ZIKA (native names).

THE SINGLE SPECIES, *M. moschiferus*, is found in central and northeastern Asia from China, Manchuria, Korea, and Sakhalin Islands to the Amur region and through Siberia to western Mongolia. It prefers forests and brush land at elevations of 2,600 to 3,600 meters.

Head and body length is about 1 meter; tail length is 38 to 51 mm.; shoulder height is 510 to 610 mm.; the rump is about 50 mm. higher; and adults weigh approximately 9 to 11 kg. The body is covered with long, thick, bristly hairs which are usually white at the base; they are pithy and protect the animal from the severe weather encountered at high elevations. Coloration appears to be quite variable, possibly as a result of age and season, but generally it is rich dark brown, mottled and speckled with light gray above and paler beneath. The chin, inner borders of the ears, and insides of the thighs are whitish, and occasionally there is a spot of white on each side of the throat. Although horns are lacking, the upper canine teeth are developed as tusks in the male, about 75 mm. in length. Those of the female are smaller. A musk gland in the abdomen of the male (three years of age or older) secretes a brownish wax-like substance; about 28 grams of this secretion can be obtained from a single male. Unlike other Cervidae, musk-deer have a gall bladder.

Musk-deer are generally solitary, more than two or three almost never are found together. They are most active in the morning and evening and sleep in "forms" like a hare (*Lepus*) during the daytime. They are shy, timid creatures and do not like to be molested. Their diet consists of a variety of vegetation such as grass, moss, and tender shoots. In winter they necessarily feed on twigs, buds, and lichens.

Mating usually takes place in January, and the birth of one young, rarely two, takes place 160 days later. The young are spotted, and sexual maturity is attained in about one year. The female has two mammae.

The substance obtained from the gland of the male is one of the musks used extensively in the manufacture of perfume and soap. Because of the small quantity of musk obtained per animal a high price is paid for this product, thus making the musk-deer much sought after by natives and European hunters. Also the pouch in which the musk is stored is highly valued. Many females and young that do not produce musk are captured in the traps. Because hunters trap so many, it is surprising that these animals are not extinct; perhaps they owe their survival to their small size and secretive habits.

Muntjac (*Muntiacus muntjak*), photo by Ernest P. Walker. Inset: Photo from *Guide to Great Game Animals*, British Museum (Natural History).

MUNTJACS, BARKING DEER, RIB-FACED DEER; KAKAR, KIJANG, KIDANG (native names).

ABOUT HALF A DOZEN SPECIES are found from Nepal, the Indian Peninsula, and Ceylon, east to Sumatra, Java, Borneo, and some small adjacent islands, and north to southern China and Formosa. They are usually found in areas of dense vegetation and hilly ranges from sea level to medium elevations.

Muntjacs are rather small, slender deer, with a head and body length of 800 to 1,000 mm., a tail length of 110 to 185 mm., a shoulder height of 450 to 580 mm., and adult weights of 14 to 18 kg. The body is covered with short, soft hairs, except for the ears, which are sparsely haired. Coloration varies from deep brown to yellowish or grayish brown with creamy or whitish markings. In one species the head is decidedly lighter than the body. Antlers are carried only by the males and are shed annually, dropped in May in southern Asia. They rarely exceed 125 to 152 mm. in length and are carried on long, bony, hair-covered pedicels. The upper canine teeth of the males are elongated into tusks which curve strongly outward from the lips; they are thus capable of inflicting considerable injuries to dogs and other animals. The females have small bony knobs and tufts of hair where the antlers occur in the male. The tusks of the females are smaller. When alarmed, or during the mating season, muntjacs produce a bark-like noise. If they sense a predator in the area, they will "bark" for an hour or more; hence the origin of the common name "barking deer."

They are chiefly nocturnal except in sparsely settled areas, where they are active during the morning. These animals are not gregarious and are generally found alone or in pairs not far from water. Barking deer are dainty little creatures; when walking, they lift their feet high, always on the alert. Their diet consists mainly of grasses, low-growing leaves, and tender shoots.

It is believed that mating occurs throughout the year, perhaps more frequently, however, in January and February. One or occasionally two young are born about 180 days after the parents have mated. The young are usually born in dense jungle growth where they remain hidden until they can move about with the mother. At birth the young weigh about 550-650 grams. Life expectancy is probably about 10 years.

Barking deer are hunted for their meat and skins by the natives. They thrive well and breed freely in captivity; therefore they are generally found in most zoos. They are considered a nuisance in some areas because they destroy trees by ripping off the bark. Their most important natural enemies are the tiger and the leopard.

The type species is *M. muntjak* (Zimmermann).

Tibetan Muntjac (*Elaphodus cephalophus*), photo from *Deer of All Lands*, Lydekker.

TUFTED DEER, TIBETAN MUNTJACS; CHINESISCHER SCHOPFHIRSCH, KUIFMUNTJAK, KUIFHERT.

THE SINGLE SPECIES, *E. cephalophus*, is found in southern China and northern Burma at elevations of 900 to 2,600 meters. Tufted deer are said always to be found near water.

These dainty deer are somewhat larger than muntjacs (*Muntiacus*), having a head and body length of about 1,600 mm., a tail length of 70 to 120 mm., a shoulder height of 500 to 700 mm., and adult weights of 17 to 23 kg. The body is covered with coarse, almost spine-like hairs which give a shaggy appearance. The general color on the upper parts is deep chocolate-brown, the under parts are white, and the head and neck are gray. In some cases a pale streak extends forward from the pedicel and above the eye, and the tuft on the forehead is blackish brown. There are white markings on the back tips of the ears and on the underside of the tail.

Tufted deer are very similar to muntjacs. Although the canines are comparable in size, the antlers are much smaller, frequently completely hidden by the tuft on the forehead. Other distinguishing characteristics are that the bony pedicels on which the horns grow are shorter than those of the muntjac, do not form heavy ridges on the forehead, and converge at the tips.

Both the male and the female "bark" during the mating season or when suddenly alarmed.

Tufted deer are usually found singly, but occasionally they travel in pairs. When feeding they carry their tails high; the tails flop with every bounce, displaying the white underside much in the same fashion as the Virginia deer (*Odocoileus*). Tufted deer feed on grasses and other vegetation.

The mating season is during April and May, followed by a gestation period of about six months, after which one or two young are born. The young are colored like their parents but have a row of spots along each side of the mid-line of the back. One lived for seven years in the London Zoo.

Fallow Deer (*Dama dama*), A. Male in spring pelage, photo from Zoological Society of London. B. Female in winter pelage, photo from New York Zoological Society.

D. dama: FALLOW DEER, DAMHERT, *D. mesopotamica:* PERSIAN FALLOW DEER; TAKBOKKA, DAIM, DAMHIRSCH. (Included are vernaculars used in other countries.)

TWO SPECIES are recognized. The one is *D. dama*, whose range was originally the Mediterranean region of southern Europe and Asia Minor. It has been widely introduced and is now found in the wild state throughout most parts of western Europe, the western Ukraine, the Baltic countries, Great Britain, and in a few areas in the United States. The other is *D. mesopotamica*, which is native to Persia and Iraq. The latter species is now extremely rare in the wild; there are a few in captivity.

Head and body length is 1.3 to 1.6 meters; tail length is 160 to 190 mm.; shoulder height is about 1 meter; and adults weigh from 40 to 80 kg. The most common summer coloration, which is acquired in May, is a bright fawn with white spots above and whitish under parts. The winter coat, which is acquired in October, is grayish fawn without spots, and the under parts are lighter. There is also a dark race which has a blackish-brown summer coat without spots and a similar, but slightly lighter, winter coat. There are also albino strains.

Only the males have antlers; their peculiar shape is the basis for placing these deer in a genus distinct from *Cervus*. The antlers are flattened and palmate with numerous points. The males develop a single unbranched horn the second year, and each succeeding year the horns are larger and have more points until the fifth or sixth year. The antlers are generally shed in April and the new ones are full grown and free of velvet in August. The front outer curve of the antlers is 635 to 940 mm. and the tip-to-tip measurement is 305 to 762 mm. There are no upper canines or tusks.

Domesticated, these animals are gregarious, but in the wild they travel in small groups. Usually the females and young stay together, and the males range separately except during the mating season. Fallow deer have feeding habits similar to most members of this family, feeding mainly on grasses during the morning and evening.

Mating occurs in September or October, during which time the bucks assemble the does in groups and fight off rivals. Throughout the mating season the buck does a dance-like ritual and bellows in a deep voice, which presumably attracts the female. The fawns, which are slightly darker than the adults and spotted with white, are usually born in June and July, about 230 days after mating; the usual number is one. The life span is about 15 years.

Fallow deer are among those most commonly kept in herds on estates and in parks.

The type species of the genus is *D. dama* (Linnaeus).

Axis Deer or Chital (*Axis* sp.), photo from San Diego Zoological Garden.

CHITAL, SPOTTED DEER, AXIS DEER, AXISHIRSCH, AXISHERT (*A. axis*), HOG DEER, SCHWEINHIRSCH, VARKENSHERT (*A. porcinus* and *A. calamianensis*).

FOUR SPECIES are recognized: *A. axis*, native to Ceylon and India; *A. calamianensis*, known only from the Calamian Islands in the western portion of the Philippines; *A. kuhli* of Bawean Island; and *A. porcinus*, native to India, Indo-China, and Thailand, and introduced into Ceylon. These animals frequent open grasslands and light jungle, seldom penetrating into heavy forests.

Head and body length is 1.0 to 1.75 meters; tail length is 128 to 380 mm.; shoulder height is 0.6 to 1 meter; and weight is usually 27 to 45 kg. *A. porcinus* is the smallest of the three species. The hair is coarse and longest on the flanks. There is no mane on the throat or neck. Coloration varies not only among the species but also from season to season. The general color is a bright rufous-fawn or yellowish brown to brownish. During part of the year the upper parts of *A. axis* are beautifully marked with small white spots. All species have a dark dorsal stripe, white under parts, and a whitish tail under-surface. *A. axis* and *A. calamianensis* are slender and graceful and of medium body build, whereas *A. porcinus* is stocky and has shorter legs. The antlers are carried on pedicels and are three-tined, the brow tine nearly forming a right angle with the beam. Upper canines are usually absent, and the tail is usually relatively long and slender.

Although hog deer do not generally congregate in herds, more than two or three rarely being found together, the spotted deer is the most gregarious of all Eastern deer. Herds of up to 100 or more animals composed of both sexes and all ages sometimes assemble. Normally they are diurnal, resting during the heat of the day and moving about in the morning and late afternoon; however, when molested they become nocturnal. The spotted deer stags (*A. axis*) may stay with the herd all year but frequently retreat to the jungle to shed their antlers, usually in August, and to grow a new set, after which they majestically return to the herd. All the species readily take to water and are said to be good swimmers. They are grazers, although they occasionally browse and are fond of various fallen flowers and fruits of forest trees.

The mating season varies among the species and localities but is usually in April or May, although fawns of all ages and sizes can be found at all times. After a gestation period of seven to eight months, usually two young, but not uncommonly one or three, are born in dense cover. The mother feeds nearby and nurses the infant until it has sufficient strength to roam with the herd. The life span is 10 to 15 years.

Axis deer do well in captivity and are common in zoos and parks. Strains of albinos have been developed.

The type species of the genus is *A. axis* (Erxleben). *Hyelaphus*, Sundevall, 1846, is recognized as valid subgenerically for the hog deer, *A. porcinus*.

RED DEER, WAPITI, CERFS, HIRSCHE, CIERVOS, VENADOS, POSU, HERTEN. (Included are vernaculars used in other countries.)

ABOUT 15 SPECIES are found in North America, Great Britain, Europe, Asia, the East Indies, and the Philippine Islands. The two best known species, the red deer (*C. elaphus*) of Europe and the wapiti (*C. canadensis*) of North America, are herein discussed separately, followed by some general remarks on the other species.

The red deer has a head and body length of about 1.65 to 2.5 meters; a tail length of about 120 to 150 mm.; a shoulder height of about 1.2 to 1.5 meters; and weights of 100 to 250 kg. The general body color is reddish brown with light under parts and a light patch on the buttocks; frequently there is a dark dorsal stripe.

Red deer are gregarious, each group remaining in a definite territory from which it does not normally stray. Most of the year the sexes remain in separate herds. Like most deer, red deer usually graze and browse during the morning and late afternoon; foliage from deciduous trees makes up a considerable part of their diet. After the stag sheds its velvet in August or September, the herds break up for the mating season and the stags gather their harems. During this time they emit a deep, powerful bellow. After a gestation period of 230 to 240 days, normally one spotted calf is born. The usual life span is 15 to 18 years.

The wapiti has a head and body length of 2.25 to 2.5 meters, a tail length of 125 to 200 mm., a shoulder height of 1.4 to 1.5 meters, and weights of 200 to 350 kg. The general body color is grayish brown, with dark chestnut along the back and mane. There is a yellowish-white rump patch. The adult males possess a magnificent set of antlers that are effective weapons of defense; they measure about 1.75 meters along the beam.

A. Thamin or Eld Deer (*Cervus eldi*), photo by Hans-Jurg Kuhn. B. Luzon Deer (*C. philippinus*), photo from U.S. National Zoological Park. C. Schomburgk Deer (*C. schomburgki*), photo from *Proc. Zool. Soc. London*. D. Thorold Deer (*C. albirostris*), photo by Joseph F. Rock. E. Sambar (*C. unicolor*), photo from City Public Works of Pematangsiantar, Indonesia, through Tiar Hulman Hoetabarat.

Wapitis are not specialized feeders, as they graze and browse on grasses, twigs, leaves, and other green vegetation. Cows breed when they are about 28 months old and usually produce one calf after a gestation period of 249 to 262 days. The calf weighs 14 to 18 kg. at birth, stands quickly, follows the cow in three days, grazes at four weeks, and is weaned and loses its spots at three months. Life expectancy is about 22 years.

Until recently wapitis were hunted extensively for their teeth, which were used as emblems in a fraternal order.

The remaining species are quite variable. Some have a shoulder height of only 0.6 meter and are found singly and in groups of varying size from mountain country to lowland swamps. In like manner the coloration, habits, and biology vary with the species. The stag is hunted for the stately antlers.

The type species of the genus is *C. elaphus*, Linnaeus. The genus has been divided into a number of subgenera.

1. *Cervus*, for the species *C. elaphus* and *C. canadensis*.
2. *Rusa*, H. Smith, 1827, for the sambar, *C. unicolor*.
3. *Rucervus*, Hodgson, 1838, for the barasingha, *C. duvauceli*.
4. *Thaocervus*, Pocock, 1943, for Schomburgk's deer, *C. schomburgki*.
5. *Panolia*, Gray, 1843, for the thamin, *C. eldi*.
6. *Sika*, Sclater, 1870, for the sika, *C. nippon*.
7. *Przewalskium*, Flerov, 1930, for Thorold's deer, *C. albirostris*.

A. American Elk (*Cervus canadensis*), photo from U.S. Fish & Wildlife Service. B. European Red Deer (*C. elaphus*), photo by Hans-Jurg Kuhn. C. Swamp or Barasingha Deer (*C. duvauceli*), photo from Zoological Society of London. D. Sika (spotted form) (*C. nippon*), photo by Alwin Pedersen. E. Sika (unspotted form) (*C. nippon*), photo by Ernest P. Walker.

Père David's Deer (*Elaphurus davidianus*), photo from Cleveland Zoological Society.

PÈRE DAVID'S DEER; MI-LU, DAVIDHIRSCH, CERF DU PÈRE DAVID, PÈRE DAVID'S HERT. (Included are vernaculars used in other countries.)

THE SINGLE SPECIES, *E. davidianus*, is believed to have originally inhabited the alluvial plains of northern China, and may have been an inhabitant of swampy reed-covered marshlands. It is now known only from the descendants of the herd formerly kept in the Imperial Hunting Park, Peking, China. Père David's deer were named after Abbé Armand David who procured two skins from the imperial herd in 1865 by bribing sentinels. There are now about 400 individuals in zoological parks throughout the world. The genus would probably not exist now if the Duke of Bedford had not brought some from China to his estate, Woburn Abbey, in England about 1900. The last specimen of this imperial herd died in 1920, almost 20 years after the Boxer Rebellion. The Duke's herd is the nucleus from which those now in China and other parts of the world are descended. They were reintroduced in China from Woburn Abbey in 1960.

The Mi-lu stands about 1,143 mm. at the shoulder. The summer pelage, reddish tawny mixed with gray, is much shorter and thinner than the grayish buff winter pelage. A mane is present on the neck and throat, and the fawns are spotted. The antlers have a single long straight tine pointing backward, while the main beam extends almost directly upward and usually forks only once. The hooves are large and spreading.

Although Père David's deer supplements its grass diet with water plants in the summer, it is essentially a grazing animal. The antlers are shed from October through December, and a new set begins to grow immediately, although it may take six months to mature.

Fawns are now born in Woburn Park, England, in April and May, and the rut begins in June. A stag, after joining his harem of hinds, fasts for several weeks; these males sire the earliest calves and are ousted and succeeded by other stags. This process continues until the rut ends in August. After leaving the harem, the stags begin feeding again and quickly regain weight. The hinds tend to bunch together in several groups in definite areas in Woburn Park during the mating season, and the stags defend these areas against intruding males. The master stag is often engaged in mock combat and in actual fights with rival stags for the possession of the harem. While fighting, Père David's deer will not only use its antlers and teeth but will also rise on its hind legs and box, much like the red deer (*Cervus elaphus*). Adult stags usually keep to themselves for about two months before and two months after the rut; the sexes are together for the remainder of the year. The gestation period is about 250 days, and the number of young is one or two. The life span is at least 20 years.

A. White-tailed Deer (*Odocoileus virginianus*), male in velvet, photo by Earl W. Craven of U.S. Fish & Wildlife Service.
B. White-tailed Deer (*O. virginianus*), two year old doe with fawn, photo by Rex Gary Schmidt of U.S. Fish & Wildlife Service.

WHITE-TAILED OR VIRGINIA DEER (*O. virginianus*), MULE DEER (*O. hemionus*); VENADOS.

THE TWO SPECIES and their distribution are as follows: *O. virginianus*, southern Canada and most of the United States southward to northern South America; and *O. hemionus*, western Canada and western United States southward into northern Mexico. They occupy a variety of habitats but prefer areas with enough vegetation for concealment.

Head and body length is 1.5 to 2.1 meters; tail length is 100 to 280 mm.; shoulder height is 0.8 to 1.1 meters; and weight is 48 to 145 kg. The fall and winter coat is a brownish gray with lighter under parts. In summer the coat is reddish brown, lighter below, and is then spoken of as "in the red." The hairs, particularly those of the winter coat, are tubular and somewhat stiff and brittle. For this reason the winter skins float in water and have at times been used as life preservers. In North America the antlers are shed from January to March and the new ones begin to grow about April or May, losing their velvet in August or September. The full size antlers are attained by the fourth or fifth year. The antler of the mule deer branches into two nearly equal parts, whereas the antler of the white-tailed deer has one main beam with minor branches.

Unlike many deer of the Old World and the wapiti (*Cervus*) of North America, these deer usually do not congregate in herds, although two to four may frequently be found together. The closest approach to herding is the occasional assembling in certain favored locations when the snow is deep and there is difficulty in obtaining food. A wide variety of vegetation such as grass, weeds, shrubs, twigs, mushrooms, nuts, and lichens are included in the diet.

Some mate at seven months, but the majority do not mate until the second year. Mating takes place in November and December, and 196 to 210 days later usually one fawn in the first litter, and two young thereafter (occasionally three and four), are born. At birth the fawn weighs 1.5 to 2.5 kg., is beautifully spotted, and is able to walk. The mother leaves her youngster in dense growth where it lies until she regularly (about every four hours) comes to nurse it. The young nibble on vegetation when only a few days old. They are weaned after about the sixth week. The young females may follow the mother for two years, but the males usually leave during the first year. Life span in the wild is about 10 years, but these animals have lived as long as 20 years in captivity.

These deer are popular game animals in many areas. Buckskin, a leather originally tanned by the Indians, is made from their skin. The meat, venison, is tender, juicy, and of excellent flavor.

Swamp Deer (*Blastocerus dichotomus*), photo of mounted group in Denver Museum of Natural History.

SWAMP DEER; VEADO GALHEIRO, CIERVOS DE LOS PANTANOS.

THE SINGLE SPECIES, *B. dichotomus*, inhabits the Guianas, Brazil, Paraguay, and Uruguay. Swamp deer prefer wet savannahs with high grass and wooded islands, and damp forest edges. *Edocerus*, Ávila-Pires, 1957, is a generic name favored by some mammalogists for these animals.

These are the largest of the South American deer: the height at the shoulders is about 1.1 meters and large individuals weigh as much as 100 kg. The coat is long and coarse. In summer the coloration is bright rufous-chestnut; in winter it is brownish red, becoming lighter on the flanks, neck, and chest. The lower legs are black, and the tail is yellowish rusty red above and black below. The antlers of adults are usually doubly forked, that is, each of the two branches has a single fork for a total of four points. The hoofs can be spread widely and are bound by a strong membrane in the inner part of the divergence point. This represents an adaptation against sinking into soft ground.

Swamp deer, as the name suggests, enter water frequently. In spite of their size, they are quite timid. They wander in groups of two to five or more, and are often found in the same areas as livestock, especially horses. They remain in seclusion most of the day and come out into clearings during the evening and through the night to feed. The diet consists of grass, reeds, and numerous aquatic plants.

Newborn fawns have been noted at various times of the year. The gestation period is about nine months, and a single young is usually born. It has been reported that the males do not fight for possession of the females, and that there is not a definite season when the antlers are dropped.

The skins are used by natives but the meat is not desirable. Natives prepare several kinds of medicines from the antlers, especially from the spikes. Among medicines prepared are an aphrodisiac and a concoction given to pregnant women to ease delivery.

Pampas Deer (*Blastoceros campestris*), photo of mounted group in Denver Museum of Natural History.

PAMPAS DEER; CICRUOS DE LAS PAMPAS.

THE SINGLE SPECIES, *B. campestris* (= *Cervus bezoarcticus*, Linnaeus), inhabits dry, open plains from Brazil, Paraguay, and Uruguay to Argentina and northern Patagonia. It is occasionally found in wooded country. The generic name, *Ozotoceras*, Ameghino, 1891, is favored by some mammalogists who hold that the name *Blastoceros* is too similar to *Blastocerus* and leads to confusion.

The shoulder height is 0.6 to 0.75 meter. The prevailing color of the upper parts and limbs is reddish brown or yellowish gray, the face is somewhat darker, the under parts are white, and the tail is dark brown above and white below. Fawns are spotted. The lower or front prong of the main fork of the antler is not divided, but the upper or posterior prong is. The usual number of tines is three.

This deer originally used tall pampas-grass for cover, but with increasing settlement and cultivation, it has had to live more in the open and has thus become quite wary. Pampas deer travel in pairs, in small parties of three or four, and in small herds. They tend to live alone or in pairs during the winter, and in larger groups in the spring. Bucks are often solitary for most of the year and have glands on the posterior hoofs that emit a strong odor capable of being detected at a distance of 1.5 km. Pampas deer graze in the evening, resting during the day in any shelter they can find. When startled, they bound off at considerable speed.

Published information indicates that in some parts of their range pampas deer breed during the end of the summer. The young are said to be born in April on the Argentine plains. In other areas there does not seem to be a definite breeding season; in Paraguay, for example, newly born young have been noted in May, June, October, and in a winter month (probably January). The number of young is usually one. When a mother with a young is surprised by hunters, she may remain motionless until the young has managed to conceal itself. The mother may then move off slowly, occasionally with a limping gait, to focus attention on herself and away from her young.

A. Andean Deer with antlers in velvet (*Hippocamelus antisensis*); B. Andean Deer (*H. antisensis*); photos by Heinz-Georg Klos through the Zoological Garden Berlin-West.

GUEMALS, HUEMULS, ANDEAN DEER; TARUGA, CIERVOS ANDINOS.

THE TWO SPECIES and their distributions are as follows: *H. bisulcus*, the Andes of southern Chile and Patagonia; and *H. antisensis*, the Andes of Ecuador, Peru, Bolivia, and northern Chile. Their habitat is grassy hills and dense forests at elevations of 3,300 to 5,000 meters.

Head and body length is 1.4 to 1.65 meters; tail length is 115 to 130 mm.; shoulder height is 775 to 795 mm.; and weights are 45 to 65 kg. The fur is coarse and brittle, longest on the forehead and tail. Each individual hair has a whitish base. Generally the speckled yellowish-gray-brown coloration of *H. antisensis* is uniform during all seasons and in both sexes. This species has a dark-brown tail with a white undersurface, and there is a black, Y-shaped streak on the face. *H. bisulcus* is similarly colored but lighter beneath; this species has a brown spot on the rump, and its tail has a brown underside. The males of both species possess small, simple antlers which usually branch only once, the front prong being the smaller. Both sexes of both species have large canine teeth similar to those of the musk deer (*Moschus*) and the Chinese water deer (*Hydropotes*), but the tusks of the guemals do not project beyond the lips. Metatarsal glands are absent.

Huemuls commonly associate in groups of two to eight individuals. During the day they are not active; they frequently hide in caves and dense foliage until evening, when they move about, feeding on lichens, mosses, and other vegetation. They tend to live at higher elevations in the summer, moving down the mountains in the fall and spending the winter in forests and valleys.

The type species of the genus is *H. bisulcus* (Molina).

Brocket Deer (*Mazama americana?*), photo of mounted group in Denver Museum of Natural History.

BROCKET DEER; CORZUELAS, TEMAZATES, SUIT-SIZIL, SUISIZIL, CALOROS, CABROS DE MONTE, MATACANES, LOCHOS (South American vernaculars).

THIS GENUS of about ten species ranges from southern Mexico to Paraguay. The species normally inhabit wooded tropical areas and forested hillsides near running water from sea level to elevations of 5,000 meters.

These little deer have a head and body length of .9 to 1.3 meters, a tail length of 50 to 200 mm., a shoulder height of 430 to 685 mm., and a weight of 16 to 21 kg. The hair on the face radiates in all directions from two whorls. The pelage of the adult is generally uniformly colored, with the species varying in color from light to dark brown. Usually the body color is bright reddish brown above and lighter below, and the underside of the tail is white. Some species are especially light-colored. The body is stout with slender limbs, and the back is arched. Although the antlers vary in size, they lack a brow tine and are usually simple spikes in all the species. The upper canines may be present or absent, the metatarsal gland is absent, and there are four mammae.

Brocket deer are usually solitary or associate in pairs.

It is interesting to note that at least one species seems to inhabit an area of only a few hundred meters in circumference. These deer are seldom seen, owing to their shyness, protective coloration, and their habit of "freezing" when danger is sensed. Nevertheless, if they are flushed, they frequently scamper a short distance and stop to look back at the pursuer. They enjoy water and are good swimmers. Brockets are diurnal, most active during the early morning and at dusk, at which time they forage about in search of numerous species of plants, preferring grasses, vines, and tender green shoots.

Breeding appears to occur throughout the year in some areas. The one or rarely two young are spotted with white.

The timidity and wariness of brocket deer protect them to some extent from their many enemies, such as the jaguar, puma, and the larger snakes (anacondas and boas). They are hunted by the natives for food and because they frequently damage bean and corn crops. Brocket deer do not seem to have the endurance of some other deer, as a common dog will often overtake one and kill it. The native hunter sometimes finds that his dogs have killed and eaten the animal before he can secure it.

The type species of the genus is *M. pita*, Rafinesque.

Pudu (*Pudu pudu*), photo of mounted specimen in Field Museum of Natural History.

PUDUS.

THIS GENUS consists of two species: *P. pudu*, distributed through Bolivia and Chile, southward along the coast nearly to the Straits of Magellan; and *P. mephistophiles*, distributed throughout Ecuador. The former species appears to favor temperate forests from sea level to moderate elevations in the Andes, while the latter has been taken at elevations of 3,000 to 4,000 meters. *Pudu mephistophiles* has also been placed in the genus *Pudella*, Thomas, 1913.

In *P. pudu* the length of the head and body is 775 to 825 mm.; the length of the tail is 25 to 35 mm.; the height of the shoulder is 375 to 415 mm.; and the weight of adults is about 9 kg. In *P. mephistophiles* the total length is about 650 mm. and the height of the shoulder is 320 to 355 mm. The hairs of the coat are long, coarse, and rather brittle.

The general coloration in *P. pudu* ranges from rufous to dark brown or gray. The legs and feet are generally tawny. The fawns in this species have three rows of spots running from the shoulder to the base of the tail, plus additional spots on the shoulders and flanks. *P. mephistophiles* has a generally rich brown body coloration. The face and legs are nearly black; long white hairs line the short ears; and the inner sides of the legs and the abdomen are covered with long yellow hairs.

Both species possess short, spike-like antlers; tusks do not occur in the upper jaw; and an external tail is practically lacking. Members of this genus are the smallest native American deer. *P. mephistophiles* differs from *P. pudu* in the following features: hoofs narrow and pointed; rhinarium smaller; preorbital glands absent; and the premaxillary bones of the skull do not reach the nasals.

The following information applies only to *P. pudu*. The animals are seldom seen due to their apparent limited numbers and extreme shyness. They are hunted by the natives in the following manner: After having put a pack of dogs on the trail, the natives wait in a nearby river in a boat. When the animal is pursued, it generally heads for the water to escape; not a strong swimmer, it is soon overtaken by the waiting hunters.

Although the young animals are said to be easily tamed, adults do not take readily to captivity. Adults continue to struggle for their freedom, often until they die from exhaustion.

Alaska Moose (*Alces alces*), photo by Tom Scott of mounted group in Royal Scottish Museum.

MOOSE IN NORTH AMERICA; ELK IN EUROPE; ELCH, ÉLANS OR ORIGNALS, ELANDEN. (Included are vernaculars used in other countries.)

THE SINGLE SPECIES, *A. alces*, inhabits most of the timbered regions of Alaska and Canada and part of northwestern United States along the Rocky Mountains. In the Old World it is found in Norway, Sweden, and eastward across Russia and Siberia to Manchuria and Mongolia. Its favorite habitat is a moist area with abundant willows and poplars.

Moose are the largest members of the deer family,

having a head and body length of 2.5 to 3 meters, a tail length of 50 to 76 mm., a shoulder height of 1.4 to 1.9 meters, and a weight of up to 825 kg. The summer pelage is dark above, varying from black to dark brown, reddish brown, or grayish brown, and the under parts and lower legs are lighter; the winter pelage is grayer. The young are reddish brown and, unlike most immature members of this family, are not spotted. This stately mammal is easily identified by its broad overhanging muzzle, massive antlers, heavy mane, and the characteristic pendulant flap of skin beneath the throat known as the "bell."

Although vision is poorly developed, the senses of hearing and smell are acute. Generally these animals do not collect in herds and, although they do not shun company, they act independently. Their trotting speed is about 25 km. per hour, but if closely pursued they can travel as fast as 35 km. per hour.

Moose frequent marshy and timbered regions in search of shrubs and trees on which they browse. They also feed on water vegetation by wading into lakes and streams, often submerging entirely to obtain the roots and stems of plants on the bottom. By necessity, they eat the bark of trees, twigs, and paw through the snow for small plants in winter.

Mating occurs in September or October. During this time the bulls fight for a given cow, and the victorious bull may stay with the cow until the calf is ten days old, at which time he leaves. After a gestation period of 242 to 250 days, one to three (normally two) calves are born. The female moose is a good mother and for the first few days keeps her calf well hidden. When the calf is about ten days old, it follows the mother about and may remain with her for two years. The females are sexually mature at two to three years. The life span is about 20 years.

For the Indians and early pioneers, moose furnished meat, leather, and bone. Because of this these animals were heavily hunted. Fortunately, however, public sentiment for their protection is growing and their numbers are increasing, at least in North America.

North American Moose (*Alces alces*), juvenile, photo by Eugene Maliniak.

Caribou (*Rangifer tarandus*), photo of mounted group in Field Museum of Natural History.

CARIBOU, REINDEER; RENNE, RENTIERE.

THE SINGLE SPECIES, *R. tarandus*, is native to the Arctic regions of the world. Caribou are found in the New World and the Siberian region. The reindeer is native to the Old World and Greenland. Because reindeer are more readily domesticated than caribou, they were introduced into Alaska about 1900 and considerable interbreeding with caribou has occurred.

Head and body length is 1.2 to 2.2 meters; tail length is 10 to 21 cm.; shoulder height is 1.1 to 1.4 meters; and adults weigh as much as 318 kg. As protection against the rigorous climate, reindeer have a heavy coat of woolly underfur protected by straight, stiff, tubular guard hairs. Coloration varies widely but most individuals are predominantly brownish or grayish with white or light under parts, inner legs, and buttocks; the winter pelage is somewhat lighter. Some are dark brown or almost black and some are quite light, while the Peary caribou is almost white.

This is the only genus of the deer family in which both sexes are antlered. Although there is great diversity in the shape of the antlers, they are usually long sweeping beams with forwardly-projecting brow tines. The broad, flat, and deeply cleft hoofs aid in walking on soft ground and snow. When walking, a clicking noise is produced by a tendon slipping over a bone in the foot.

Caribou and reindeer are highly gregarious, although during certain periods they are sexually segregated. They formerly assembled in herds of hundreds or thousands of individuals for their fall migration from the treeless tracts to timbered areas. On these migrations they swam rivers and lakes and followed quite a definite course, traveling about 160 km. per day. In the spring they strayed back in smaller groups. Through a combination of circumstances, the herds were greatly reduced between 1930 and 1955.

Caribou and reindeer are spirited, exhibiting both shyness and curiosity. When alarmed, adults snort, rutting bucks roar, and fawns bawl. The diet consists chiefly of grasses, sedges, leaves of willows and birches, lichens, and mosses.

In the fall, bulls savagely fight for a harem of 5 to 40 cows. The one or two unspotted young are born about 240 days later on the summer grounds. The youngster is able to walk in about two hours, nurses for two months, and then joins the herd in the fall migration. Males breed at one and one-half years, and the life span is about 15 years.

To natives, these animals are important. Their flesh is excellent, the skins are valuable for warm garments or leather, and the bones, sinews, and antlers are also used. The leather has the property of shrinking when wet, and for this reason is prized for snowshoe lacing.

Chinese Water Deer (*Hydropotes inermis*), photo by Ernest P. Walker. Insets: Head, photo by Erna Mohr. Fawn, photo from New York Zoological Society. Skull, photo from *Guide to the Great Game Animals*, British Museum (Natural History).

CHINESE WATER DEER; KIBANORU, GASHA.

THE SINGLE SPECIES, *H. inermis*, is found in China on the islands and along the shores of the Yangtze River, and in Korea, usually among tall reeds and rushes. It also frequents the tall grasses of mountainsides and cultivated fields.

Head and body length is 775 to 1,000 mm.; tail length is 60 to 75 mm.; shoulder height is 450 to 550 mm.; and weight is 9 to 11 kg. The hair is generally thick and coarse, longest on the flanks and rump. The top of the face is grayish to reddish brown, the chin and upper throat are whitish, and the back and sides are usually a uniform yellowish brown finely stippled with black. The under parts are white. Both sexes lack antlers, but the upper canine teeth, especially in the males, are enlarged, forming fairly long, slightly curved tusks. There is a small inguinal gland present on each side in both sexes; this is the only instance known of such glands in the Cervidae.

Chinese water deer rarely congregate in herds. When disturbed, they "hump up" their backs and travel by a series of leaps similar to that of rabbits (*Lepus* and *Sylvilagus*). They feed on reeds, coarse grasses, and vegetables.

Chinese water deer generally give birth to more young than any other members of the deer family (Cervidae). Litter size is usually four to seven, although the female has but four mammae. The young are born in the spring and are marked with white spots and stripes.

Formerly the Chinese did not kill or eat them, probably because of superstition. The Koreans believe that the deer's bite is fatal. The scientific name means "unarmed water-drinker."

The Zoological Society of London has had excellent success in establishing breeding colonies at their zoos, and other zoos have also had them breed in captivity. Many of these deer escaped from the Duke of Bedford's Woburn Park, and now in parts of England the Chinese water deer is one of the local game animals.

Roe-deer (*Capreolus capreolus*), female with fawn born in the spring, and male with winter coat and antlers, photos from the Zoological Garden Berlin-West.

ROE-DEER; REHE, CHEVREUIL, REE. (Included are vernaculars used in other countries.)

THE SINGLE SPECIES, *C. capreolus*, is widely distributed throughout the Eurasian region except in the extreme north and in India. It is found in almost any area that furnishes a reasonable amount of cover and is able to live in park-like places between very dense human populations. Generally roe-deer avoid thick forests, preferring sparsely wooded valleys and the lower slopes of mountains usually not exceeding 2,400 meters in elevation.

Head and body length is 950 to 1350 mm.; tail length is about 20 to 40 mm.; shoulder height is 650 to 775 mm.; and the weight of adults ranges from 15 to 30 kg. Coloration varies with the season: the summer coat is reddish above, with blackish ears and white under parts; while the winter pelage is buff or dark brownish, the face, chest, and legs are tawny with white throat and rump patches. Roe-deer are small, graceful animals. The antlers are slightly roughened at the base, only about 230 mm. long, erect, and seldom more than three-tined. The tail is inconspicuous.

These animals usually associate in family groups, each group generally consisting of a doe and its latest offspring. Bucks live with the does only in mid-summer. In the early morning and late evening they emerge from cover and seek open grasslands, where they graze. These deer are shy yet curious and have well developed senses. They are excellent swimmers. When disturbed, roe-deer bark like dogs.

Roe-deer reach sexual maturity at about a year and four months. Mating takes place in July and August, and the fawns, usually one but occasionally two, are born in March or June. Twins are not born or suckled at the same spot, but usually 10 to 20 meters apart from each other. The long gestation period consists of an interval of about four and one-half months during which the fertilized egg lies dormant in the uterus; after this, development proceeds as usual. *Capreolus* is the only deer known to have delayed implantation. Unlike most other deer, the bucks usually have only one female and will savagely fight any intruding male. When about to bear her young, the doe chases away the young of the previous season and then retires to the forest, returning in about ten days with the new family. The young have three longitudinal rows of white spots.

During the mating season, males often chase females in circles, leaving a track often referred to as "witch circles." Even out of season this chasing in circles is frequently practiced, sometimes between individuals of the same sex.

Roe-deer utter a barking sound when frightened. Females call fawns with a typical screeching sound. The same sound is also uttered by females during the breeding season.

In captivity roe-deer are delicate. The average life span of 11 specimens kept at the London Zoo was 40 months; the maximum was 7 years. Normal life span in the wild is from 10 to 12 years, and may be 17 years.

GIRAFFES AND OKAPIS.

THIS FAMILY of two Recent genera, each with a single species, lives over most of Africa south of the Sahara. Giraffes (*Giraffa*) prefer dry savannahs, whereas okapis (*Okapia*) choose dense forests in areas not inhabited by lions.

These large, long-legged artiodactyls have large eyes and ears, long and thin lips, and long and extensible tongues. Giraffes may be 3.5 meters high at the shoulders, and the bulls weigh approximately 1.9 metric tons and the females, 550 kg. The long neck, which is maned with short hair, has the usual seven vertebrae. The legs are long, and the tail (tufted terminally) is long. The back inclines upward from the loins to the withers. Giraffes can close their nostrils at will. The coloration is light tan with brown splotches. Okapis are about 1.5 meters high at the shoulders, and the neck and legs, although quite long, are short in comparison with those of the giraffe. The body in *Okapia* is short and compact. The short tail is tufted terminally. Okapis have a color pattern of rich dark brown and white; the hindquarters are striped with black and white.

The feet are large and heavy, with two hoofed digits, the third and the fourth; the lateral digits are not developed. Females have two or four mammae. The four-chambered stomach is ruminating, and a gall bladder is not present.

The horns in the Giraffidae are unlike those in any other mammal. They are present at birth as cartilaginous knobs which rapidly ossify and grow slowly throughout life, consisting of a bony core which is at first separate from, but later fuses with, the skull. In the giraffe they arise over the anterior part of the parietal bones behind the eyes, the forward base growing over the frontal-parietal suture; whereas in

Front foot of a Giraffe (*Giraffa camelopardalis*), from color photo by Constance P. Warner.

the okapi they arise on the frontals above the orbit. They are covered with skin and hair throughout life; the hair is worn away from the apex but not the skin as is commonly supposed. Horns occur in both sexes, but growth is less vigorous in the female. The giraffe also bears a median horn on the fore part of the frontal bones and the back of the nasal bones which develops to a greater or lesser extent and is identical in its mode of growth with the posterior horns. The skull of the giraffe is characterized by large pneumatic sinuses above the nasal bones and cranium; these are developed to a much less extent in the okapi and do not extend back over the cranium.

The dental formula is as follows: i 0/3, c 0/1, pm 3/3, m 3/3 = 32. The low-crowned molars are characteristically rugose in all giraffids, unlike any other mammal in which the enamel is always smooth; the upper molars lack inner accessory columns.

Okapis are usually solitary and secretive. They are browsers, feeding mainly on leaves. Giraffes, on the other hand, generally live in family groups or in large herds. The tallest of all living mammals, giraffes are alert and swift as well as keen sighted. A panicky movement indicates danger. They are browsers, existing mainly on legumes, with a preference for prickly acacias; they feed by taking branches in their mouths and tearing off the leaves by pulling their heads away. Giraffes may chew their cud at any time of day. As in many other animals, feeding also seems to act as a "displacement activity" when the animals are disturbed or fighting, in the sense that they may nibble momentarily when alarmed or before resuming battle.

Giraffes have a courting procedure, apparently also common in domestic cattle, of "urine testing." The male lays his head on the flanks of the female, the female urinates, and the male collects the urine in his mouth. He then curls his lips in a characteristic fashion and ejects the urine from his mouth in a thin stream. A young giraffe begins to browse when two or three weeks old. Female giraffes seem to have a fairly weak maternal instinct; they may not let their calves suckle and may show apathy when the bulls herd the calves away. A single birth is usual in the Giraffidae, but occasionally there are twins.

The geological range of this family is the lower Miocene to the Pleistocene in Asia, the lower Pliocene in eastern Europe, and the Pliocene to the Recent in Africa. *Sivatherium* was a large, heavily-built member of this family known from the Pleistocene of southern Eurasia and Africa. The male often developed a variety of large horns—frequently four in number and greatly branched. These creatures were more bovine in appearance than the Recent giraffe, both the neck and legs of *Sivatherium* were shorter than those of *Giraffa*. *Indratherium*, another giraffid described from the Pleistocene of the Old World, may actually represent the female of *Sivatherium*; it is a smaller animal than *Sivatherium*; and, although there are skull differences between these two forms, the dentition is the same.

Nubian Giraffe (*Giraffa camelopardalis*), photo from San Diego Zoological Garden.

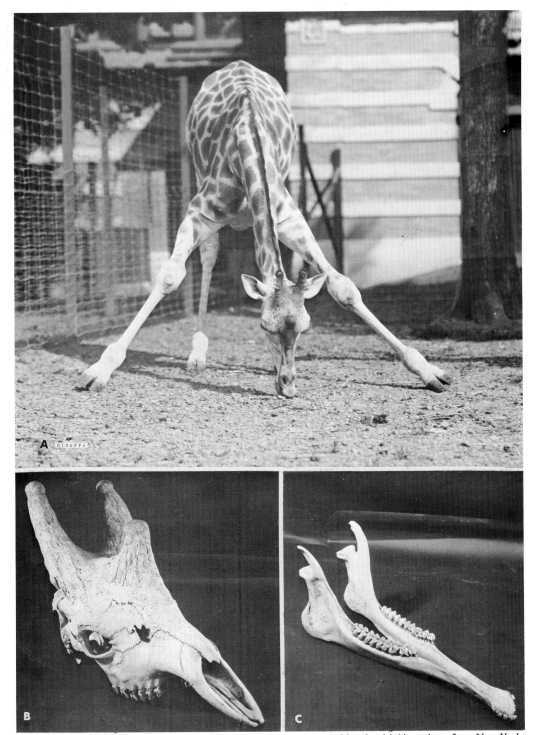

A. Giraffe (*Giraffa camelopardalis*) with legs spread in a characteristic position for drinking, photo from New York Zoological Society. B. & C. Skull (*G. camelopardalis rothschildi*), photos by P. F. Wright of specimen in U.S. National Museum.

GIRAFFES; KAMEELPERDE, GIRAFFEN.

THE SINGLE SPECIES, *G. camelopardalis*, with several subspecies, inhabits Africa south of the Sahara. It is usually associated with scattered acacia growth.

Head and body length of one specimen, an adult male, was 4 meters, and the tail length was 860 mm. Shoulder heights are 2.5 to 3.7 meters and weights range from 550 to 1800 kg. The color scheme varies considerably in pattern but consists essentially of dark-reddish to chestnut-brown blotches of various shapes and sizes on a buff ground color. The under parts are generally light and unspotted. The coloration darkens with age.

Giraffes have seven neck vertebrae, like most other mammals, but these vertebrae are greatly elongated. Both sexes possess two to four blunt, short, horn-like structures on top of the head. There is another protuberance, sometimes only a knob, in some forms situated more or less between the eyes. This is why some people refer to such a giraffe as five-horned. The lower canine teeth are peculiarly flattened and deeply grooved at right angles to the plane of flattening. The tongue is long, capable of being extended as much as 456 mm., flexible, and is used in plucking leaves from trees. The lips are prehensile and hairy. The feet are large and heavy. Scent and hearing are acute. Giraffes are believed by some people to be voiceless, but they have been known to utter low moans or bleats. The eyes are large, dark brown, and shaded by long black lashes; probably this animal has the keenest sight of any African big-game animal, and its height gives it the greatest range of vision of any terrestrial creature. The height of this animal requires a series of valves to regulate the flow of blood to the head.

Giraffes are shy, timid animals, naturally quiet, silent, and inoffensive. They are gregarious, wandering about in herds of as many as 70 animals, but most herds consist of about 12 to 15 individuals. A herd consists of an adult male leader, cows, calves of various ages, and some adolescent males not yet sufficiently mature to compete with the herd bull. It is the females that keep the most diligent watch; they are generally the first to detect danger. Some of the old bulls are solitary or roam in pairs, although they sometimes join a herd.

Over moderate distances a good horse can scarcely overtake giraffes. If they are not crowded, they can lope for long distances without tiring. Maximum speed is about 47 km. per hour. While running, the hind feet are swung forward of the fore feet, the head and neck swing widely almost in a figure eight, and the tail is raised over the back. While walking,

however, both feet on a side are carried forward simultaneously. Although the giraffe has large feet, it is able to walk only on hard firm earth, since in supporting such a heavy body, the long legs would soon become bogged down if the animal attempted to cross swampy terrain. As a result, large rivers are usually barriers.

When forced to defend themselves, giraffes kick with their fore feet. In addition, the head is frequently used to give blows, particularly to another giraffe. Competition between bulls for the possession of cows consists of fighting with their heads and necks.

Usually giraffes sleep standing up, but they occasionally sleep lying down. In real sleep a giraffe rests its head on the lower part of one hind leg, its neck forming an impressive arch. While dozing, which is more common, it rests on its withdrawn legs; but the neck remains out-stretched, the eyes are half-closed, and the ears continue twitching. In order to drink or to pick food from the ground, the fore legs are spread widely and well to the front or are bent at the knee until the head can reach the ground or water level. The evenings and early mornings are spent searching for food; giraffes rest during the heat of the day.

Giraffes are browsers and cud-chewers, feeding almost entirely on leaves from acacia, mimosa, and wild apricots. If water is available, they will take occasional drinks (about two gallons a week). They are able to do without water for many weeks, if not months, at a time.

Mating takes place from July to September in some parts of Africa, and the young, weighing from 47 to 70 kg. and standing from 1.7 to 2 meters, are born 420 to 450 days later. The number of young is almost always one, although twins have been known. The youngsters are able to stand on their wobbly legs about 20 minutes after birth, begin to nurse within one hour, and continue to nurse for about nine months. It is believed that when the young reach a certain age they are looked after by a few adults, not necessarily their parents. Records in captivity indicate that both sexes are sexually mature at an age of three to four years. The life span is usually about 15 to 20 years, although one individual lived 28 years in captivity.

Giraffes are vulnerable to lion predation when they are lying down, ground feeding, or drinking. Man is their only other enemy, although leopards may attack the young. Pioneers killed the animals in great numbers for their hide, which was used in making traces, long reins, whips, etc. Natives secure the animals by snares and pitfalls. They use the strong sinews for bow strings, musical instruments, and the thick hide for covering their shields. The meat, although tough, has a good flavor.

Okapis (*Okapia johnstoni*), photo by Ernest P. Walker and William J. Schaldach, Jr.

OKAPIS.

THE SINGLE SPECIES, *O. johnstoni*, inhabits the eastern equatorial rain forests of the Congo in Africa. Dense and damp forests are preferred.

The head and body length of one individual, an adult female, was 2 meters; the tail length was 419 mm.; and the shoulder height was 1600 mm. The body is covered with short sleek hair; the sides of the buttocks and upper portion of the limbs are conspicuously transversely barred with black and white stripes of varying width. The shanks are white to maroon; the general overall body appearance is purplish, deep reddish, or almost black, and the facial markings are light. The okapi has large dark eyes, relatively big ears, a long neck, and long limbs. The males have small hair-covered horns. Okapis have such long tongues that they can wash or clean their eyes with them.

Okapis are diurnal, wandering about singly, in pairs, or in small family parties, but never in herds. Normally they travel on well-trodden paths that weave through the dense vegetation of their remote haunts. They are extremely wary and retiring, dashing through the forest at the least suspicion of danger. They especially fear man, leopards, and snakes. Hearing is the best developed of the senses.

The diet consists of leaves, fruit, and seeds of many plants.

The young are born from August to October (the period of the most rainfall), and the gestation period is about 440 days. The newborn stand about 790 mm. at the shoulder and nurse in 6 to 12 hours. An adult female weighing 210 kg. that arrived at the Bronx Zoo in 1956 gave birth to a calf, approximately 16 kg. in weight, in 1959.

It is interesting to note that the okapi was unknown to the scientific world until 1900, although it seems to be common over its range. The pygmy, who also claims the forest as his home, has killed and eaten them for centuries.

Pronghorn Antelopes (*Antilocapra americana*), A. Winter coat has been shed from the legs exposing the powerful tendons in the hind legs and other details that are usually hidden by the hair. Photo by Ernest P. Walker. B. One-day-old twins in the typical hiding position in which they remain for a few days after birth until they have gained sufficient strength to accompany their mother. Even though the vegetation may be scant, lying flat on the ground saves them from many enemies. Photo by W. D. Parker through U.S. Fish & Wildlife Service.

PRONGHORN ANTELOPES, PRONG BUCKS, AMERICAN ANTELOPES.

THIS FAMILY contains a single Recent genus, *Antilocapra*, for the species *A. americana*, the pronghorn antelope. These artiodactyls are native to deserts and grasslands in southwestern Canada, the western United States, and northern Mexico.

Antilocapra is not a true antelope but is the only living representative of a group of ungulates that arose and developed in North America. Both sexes carry horns which consist of a permanent, laterally flattened bony core covered with a sheath of fused hairs which is shed annually after each breeding season. The new sheath grows upward under the old sheath. The horns are erect, backwardly-curved at the tips, and approximately 25 cm. in length. A short branch directed forward (actually part of the sheath) arises from the upper half of the horn. Pronghorns have large eyes (approximately 5 cm. in diameter) and long, pointed ears. Only two digits are developed, the third and the fourth; the lateral toes are lacking, hence there are no "dew-claws." The hooves, especially those of the fore feet, are supplied with cartilaginous padding.

The length of the head and body is 1 to 1.5 meters; the tail is 75 to 100 mm.; the height at the shoulders is 810 to 1,040 mm.; and adult antelopes weigh from 36 to 60 kg., the females being smaller than the males. The woolly undercoat is overlaid with fairly long, straight, coarse, pithy, and brittle guard hairs. By flexing certain skin muscles, the pronghorn can maintain its pelage at different angles. Cold air is excluded when the hairs lie smooth and flat, but the hairs may be erected in the desert sun to allow air movement to cool the skin. The upper parts are reddish brown to tan, the neck has a black mane, and the under parts, the rump, and two bands across the neck are white. In the male the face and a patch on the side of the neck are black, the horns are longer than the ears, and the nose is pointed downward slightly when running. In the females the mask and patch are lacking or nearly so, the horns seldom exceed the ears in length, and the nose is held more nearly horizontal when running. The female pronghorn has four mammae.

The dental formula is as follows: i 0/3, c 0/1, pm 3/3, m 3/3 = 32. The high-crowned cheek teeth are supplied with crescentic ridges of enamel.

Antilocapra is the swiftest mammal in the New World, able to run as fast as 65 km. per hour, not 95 km. per hour as is commonly reported, on hard ground with 3.5 to 6 meter leaps. Its cruising speed is approximately 48 km. per hour. Fast runs of 5 to 6 km. are common, but then exhaustion occurs rapidly; pronghorns shake the body after a fast run. The front feet carry most of the weight while running.

These ungulates roam in small scattered bands throughout the summer but congregate in herds which may number up to a hundred or more individuals in the winter. Strong group leadership is evident in the herds. Old bucks are occasionally solitary. Pronghorns shift from one area to another several times in a year (or change elevation) to seek water or food, but the does usually remain with the kids at lower altitudes. The daily feeding range of a pronghorn may be as much as 5 square km., with occasional side trips to obtain water.

Pronghorns can see objects several kilometers away and are curious animals; if they do not scent an object and it does not move suddenly or otherwise alarm them, they will often approach it. Mature animals of both sexes reveal their anger or anxiety by forcefully expelling air through their nostrils. The hairs of the white rump patch are raised when danger is sensed, a conspicuous warning signal to other pronghorns. The white flash can be seen by man for a distance of at least 4 km. Pronghorns allow the lower lip to sag to one side, giving an unusual appearance. They are good swimmers.

These mammals feed during the day and night on a wide variety of vegetation including shrubs, grasses, and weeds. They use their front feet for digging food buried under snow and also to scratch depressions for the deposit of their droppings. If water is available they will drink freely, but if necessary they can derive sufficient moisture from plants.

The bucks fight for harems late in the summer. There may be 15 does in such a group, with the actual mating season lasting only two or three weeks. The expectant mother seeks solitude, after a gestation period of 230 to 240 days, to give birth in rolling country with low vegetation. She usually has a single offspring at the first birth, and twins, rarely triplets, thereafter. At birth a pronghorn weighs from 1.8 to 2.5 kg. and has a beautiful, wavy, grayish pelage. The mother's milk is extremely rich in solids. At an age of four days the young antelope can outrun a man; at three weeks it is nibbling at vegetation; and before three months it has acquired its first adult-like pelage. The does mate when 15 or 16 months old, whereas the bucks probably do not begin to mate until they are about two years old. Both sexes apparently mate throughout life, which seems to be from seven to ten years in most individuals.

Man has greatly reduced the numbers and range of pronghorn antelopes, but as a result of carefully planned conservation practices, these animals are now on the increase. Pronghorns are hunted for sport, trophy, and meat. Generally, they do not damage the range as do sheep and cattle when they forage.

The geological range of the family Antilocapridae is the middle Miocene to the Recent in North America.

BUSHBUCKS, KUDUS, BONGOS, ELANDS, BUFFALOS, BISON, CATTLE, DUIKERS, ANTELOPE, WILDEBEESTS, GAZELLES, GOATS, SHEEP, BOSBOKS, NILGAIS, WATERBUCKS, ORYXES.

THIS FAMILY of 49 genera and about 115 species occurs from Greenland southward through North America to northern Mexico as well as in Africa, eastern Europe, Asia, Japan, the Philippines, and most of Indonesia. Its members have been introduced in New Guinea, New Zealand, Australia, and the surrounding islands. The family Bovidae is mainly Old World in variety and number of forms. Most bovids inhabit grassland, scrubby country, or desert, but some forms live in forests, swamps, or the arctic tundra. Goats and sheep generally occur in rocky, mountainous areas.

The body form differs widely: it is graceful in most antelopes, slight in goats, and stout in oxen and sheep. Water buffalos (*Bubalus*) and bison (*Bison*) are approximately 1.9 meters high at the shoulders, whereas the pygmy antelope (*Neotragus pygmaeus*) has a shoulder height of only 255 to 305 mm. One genus (the dik-diks, *Madoqua*) is unusual because it has an elongated snout. The pelage varies from smooth and sleek to rough and shaggy. The ulna and the fibula are reduced, and the main foot bones are fused into a cannon bone. The front and hind feet are not the same in length. The lateral toes, digits 2 and 5, are small, forming the so-called "dew-hooves" or "dew-claws," or are absent. The female bovid has one or two pairs of functional mammae.

The stomach is four-chambered and ruminating, and a gall bladder is usually present.

Horns, which vary in size and shape, occur in both sexes in most genera (only the males are horned in nine genera). *Tetracerus* is unique among the Bovidae in having four horns; all the other horned members of this family have two horns. The horns are composed of a bony core (which is attached to the frontal bones of the skull) and a hard sheath of horny material. The lower incisors project more or less forward, and the cheek teeth are low-crowned or high-crowned, with crescentic ridges of enamel on the crowns. The dental formula is as follows: i 0/3, c 0/1, pm 3/3, m 3/3 = 32.

Most forms are gregarious, associating in herds of various sizes for protection against their natural enemies (the carnivores), but some bovids live alone or assemble in small groups, finding protection either in their agility or in the cover of their habitat. Glands on the hooves of the gregarious species release a sub-stance onto the ground having a characteristic scent which an isolated animal can follow back to the herd. These glands are lacking in the solitary species. Some members of the family Bovidae, such as impalas (*Aepyceros*) and springbucks (*Antidorcas*), have unusual leaping and springing ability. The top running speed for the family is about 56 km. per hour.

Bovids are grazers or browsers and ruminants, that is, they chew the cud. The food is brought up from the first compartment of the stomach and chewed when the animal is at leisure, before being swallowed a second time for thorough digestion. These ungulates feed by twisting grass, stems, or leaves around the tongue and cutting them off with the lower incisors.

Some forms gather harems, but others appear to be monogamous. A number of bovids breed in the fall, but some have no definite breeding season. The gestation period varies from 4 months in duikers (*Cephalophus*) to 11 months in African buffalos (*Syncerus*), and the number of young is generally one to three (domestic forms may have more than three offspring). The potential life span may be 20 years or more.

Domestic cattle, sheep, and goats have all been derived from Eurasian species; the domestication of sheep and goats probably began in southwestern Asia between 8,000 and 9,000 years ago. In addition to their many economic uses, man hunts some of the wild bovids for sport, meat, hides, or as trophies. The flesh of an African antelope is generally dry and coarse in comparison with the flesh of deer (*Cervidae*).

The geological range of this family is the lower Miocene to the Recent in Europe; the lower Pliocene to the Recent in Asia and Africa, and the Pleistocene to the Recent in North America. Many fossil genera are known from the Pleistocene of the Old World. These include: *Duboisia*, *Pelorovis*, *Proboselaphus*, *Leptobus* (similar to *Bos*), *Hemibos*, *Bucapra* (a genus with a massive skull and body), *Platybos*, *Bularchus* (distinguished by the untwisted, closely-set horns), *Vishnucobus* (known from only one specimen), *Indoredunca* (known from the Punjab and resembling the Recent *Redunca*), *Gangicobus* and *Sivadenota* (resembling kobs, subgenus *Adenota*, genus *Kobus*), *Sivacobus*, *Sivatragus*, *Sivoryx*, *Damalops*, *Parmularius*, *Palaeotragiscus*, *Spirocerus*, *Phenacotragus*, *Myotragus* (resembling Recent sheep and goats in most features), *Boopsis* (resembling the Recent genus *Ovibos*, the musk-oxen), *Sivacapra* (the earliest true goat known), *Pultiphagonides* (a genus of unknown affinities), *Thaleroceros*, and *Vishnumeryx*.

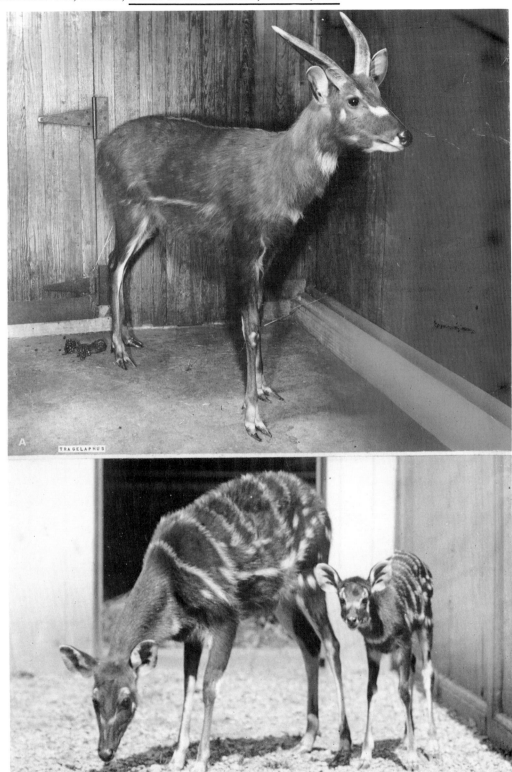

A. Sitatunga (*Tragelaphus spekii*), photo by Ernest P. Walker. B. Bushbuck or Harnessed Antelope (*T. scriptus*), photo from U.S. National Zoological Park.

BUSHBUCKS; BUSCHBOCK, BOSBOK, GUIB, AN-
YIHA, NGULUNGO, NKWAI, IMBABALA, NYALAS,
NYALA ANTILOPE, NYALA BOSBOK, INYALA, KU-
DUS, KOEDOE, GOMA OR NGOMA, TODO, CHAIB,
MPULUPULV, GODIR, KUNGO, LISHONGOLOLO,
IMGANKLA, SITATUNGAS, WATERBUCKS, MARSH-
BUCKS, WATERKOEDOE, KAWE, MBURI, NAKONG,
WASSERBOCK, WATERBOK, NZOHE. (Included are
vernaculars used in other countries and by native
tribes.)

MEMBERS OF THIS GENUS inhabit Africa south of the
Sahara. There are about six species of such widely
different body form, horn shape, and other anatomical
characters that some of the species have been placed
under three other generic names in the past: *Strepsiceros*, *Limnotragus*, and *Nyala*. In recent years,
however, there has been a tendency to consider the
first two as subgenera, and *Nyala* as a synonym of
Tragelaphus, because of certain characters which are
common to all the species. Since the animals are so
different from each other and since certain of the
species have habits very different from those of the
other species, we treat each separately.

The bushbuck, *T. scriptus*, inhabits Africa south
of the Sahara at least as far south as George in Cape
Province. At least 20 geographical subspecies are
currently recognized in this wide range. The description given here, however, is valid for most, if not all,
of the named forms. Head and body length is approximately 135 cm. Adult males range in size from 660 to
1,092 mm. at the shoulders, with horns 350 to 635 mm.
long in a straight line. The horns have pronounced
keels in front and back and are twisted into spirals.
The females are smaller than the males and are
generally without horns. The colors of the back and
sides range from light tawny or reddish in females to
dark brown or almost black in the males, with the
under parts usually slightly darker than the sides or
back. There are a variety of white markings, mainly
white patches, on the throat and lower neck, and there
is a line down the middle of the back and stripes or
rows of dots vertically on the sides. In some forms
there is a pronounced mane the full length of the back.
There is, however, wide variation; and the proper
status of many of the forms remains to be determined.

The general habits are much like those of the North
American white-tail deer (*Odocoileus*) and the form
is similar. Bushbucks are rarely found far from water;
they frequent forested or brushy areas and are adept in
going through tangles of interwoven vines and shrubbery in the jungle and brush. Some observers dwell
at length on the skill with which these animals follow
small, overgrown tunnels through the jungle in which
a man must proceed in a crouched or crawling posture.
Also they commonly frequent swamps. They feed
mainly at twilight or at night upon leaves and twigs of
shrubbery and trees, but they also graze.

These animals give a call so closely resembling the
barking of a dog that stories are told of people
following the sound to find the dog. The necks of
males often have marks on the sides as though they
had been wearing collars. Such marks are made by
the tips of the horns when the animals throw them
back onto the neck when going through brush.

Their principal enemies are probably leopards and
wild dogs (*Lycaon*). The young are sometimes taken
by *Lynx*. The female does not find herself gravely
handicapped by the lack of horns, as Theodore
Roosevelt discovered when one charged a line of his
native beaters and knocked one flat. Wounded
animals or males at bay have been known to attack
and kill men and dogs.

The gestation period is about 220 days. They
appear to breed all the year round, but there may be
regional variations since, in general, the inland-living
forms appear to favor the summer months. The life
span in captivity is about ten years.

There are two species of nyala, *T. angasi* and *T.
buxtoni*. Recent studies of cranial characters show
that they may not be as closely related to each other
as *T. angasi* is to the sitatunga (*T. spekii*) and as *T.
buxtoni* is to the kudus (*T. strepsiceros* and *T. imber
bis*). *T. angasi* is restricted to southeastern Africa:
Natal, Transvaal, Nyasaland, and the Rhodesias.
T. buxtoni is found only in southern Ethiopia. In
T. angasi the shoulder height ranges from about 965
to 1,065 mm.; the weight from 112 to 127 kg., and the
record horn length is 835 mm. In *T. buxtoni* the
shoulder height is about 1,345 mm., the weight ranges
from about 200 to 225 kg., and the record horn length
is 1,187 mm. *T. angasi* differs from other species of
Tragelaphus by a fringe of long pendant hairs which
form a line around the lower neck, lower shoulders,
sides of the belly, lower thighs, and back of the thighs.
The color is grayer than in most of the other species.

The nyala is little known, probably because it
haunts the most impenetrable and fever-infested areas.
Rams live singly or associate together, while does and
immature rams form separate herds. The doe is
found alone only when she has a newly-born fawn.
Herds number from 8 to 16. The cry is a sonorous
bark, deeper toned than that of the bushbuck. The
meat of the nyala is said to be excellent.

The greater kudu, *T. strepsiceros*, ranges over most
of Africa south of the Zambesi River, westward to
Angola and east and northward to Ethiopia. The
lesser kudu, *T. imberbis*, inhabits Somalia and the
eastern regions of East Africa. Male greater kudus
stand 1,270 to 1,320 mm. at the shoulders. The head
and body length is about 2,100 to 2,450 mm., and the
tail is 400 to 450 mm. The weight is about 270 kg.
These kudus range in color from reddish to pale slaty
blue-gray with white markings. The horns measured
about 1,016 mm. in a straight line and 1,320 mm.
along the curves. In one instance they measure
1,816 mm. in a straight line. The hairs of the neck are
short and scant in number. The females are similar
in color but are smaller and lack horns.

Males of the lesser kudu stand about 1,016 mm.
at the shoulders and are of a deep yellowish gray,
although some individuals are darker. They lack
the throat mane of the greater kudu but have two
white patches on the throat like some of the bushbucks
(*T. scriptus*), which they resemble. The vertical body
stripes vary from 11 to 14, and the horns measure
about 610 mm. in a straight line. The females are
smaller, without horns, and possess a similar pattern;
but the general color is fawn. The young are still
more reddish and strongly marked with white.

Among the African antelopes, the greater kudu is

A. Nyala (*Tragelaphus angasi*); B. Greater Kudu (*T. strepsiceros*); photos from San Diego Zoological Garden.

second in size to the eland (*Taurotragus*). These kudus live in rugged brush or timber-clad hills where they hide by day in secluded spots in dark ravines, grazing and browsing in the late evenings and early mornings. Some, however, live on the thorn-grown plains. Their hearing is acute, and all observers agree that their extreme wariness makes them difficult to approach. They have the often fatal habit, however, of stopping after a short run to look back. Mature males usually live in separate groups of 6 or 7, but may be solitary; females and young are usually seen in family groups including subadult bulls, but a female may be alone with her calf when it is very young. As in some of the Cervidae, kudu bulls often fight to a mutual death as a result of their horns being inextricably interlocked during combat. Their ability to leap is marvelous, one writer describes a leap of 9.2 meters by a lesser kudu, in which it went over the top of a bush 1.5 meters high and 1.8 meters in diameter. Another writer says the greater kudus clear bushes 2.5 meters high with ease.

The gestation period is about 212 days.

The sitatunga, *T. spekii*, is divided into three subspecies and inhabits three separate areas in central Africa: the vicinity of the Niger River, the headwaters region of the Congo and Zambesi Rivers and south to northern Bechuanaland, and in and around Lake Victoria and north to the southern Sudan. This remarkable antelope varies from 915 to 1,016 mm. in height at the shoulders, and the weight is about 125 kg. Heavy horns, about 508 to 924 mm. long, are possessed by the males only. The general color is a dull grayish brown with two whitish areas on the throat, one near the head and one near the chest. There are whitish marks on the face, ears, cheeks, body, legs, and feet. The females are slightly more brownish than the males, generally chestnut. The young are the color of the mother. The hair is much more shaggy than in other antelopes. The great elongation of the hooves and the peculiar flexibility of the joints at the feet (pasterns), which are bare and rest on the ground, are striking structural characters adapted to walking on boggy and marshy ground in the swamps where they dwell.

During the day they spend their time quietly in the papyrus swamps, often in water 1.2 meters or more in depth, and at night they go onto adjacent marshy lands to feed on sedges and swamp grasses. Many of the swamps they inhabit have exceedingly soft bottoms, matted with roots and decaying vegetation. Indeed, the bottom is a semifloating area; but here the animals find almost perfect security from enemies, although they are preyed upon by leopards and perhaps lions. They often submerge entirely when feeding in the water, and if hard pressed for shelter they are said to hide under water with only the nose out. The natives often spear them when thus hidden.

The gestation period is 245 to 258 days. The life span is about 20 years.

The type species of the genus is *T. scriptus* (Sparrman). The other subgenera are arranged as follows:

Strepsiceros, H. Smith, 1827, with type species *T. strepsiceros*, Pallas.

Limnotragus, Pocock, 1900, with type species *T. spekii*, Sclater.

Bongo (*Boocercus eurycerus isaaci*), female, photo from New York Zoological Society.

BONGOS, BROAD-HORNED ANTELOPES, HARNESSED ANTELOPES; TROMME, GUIN, N'DONGORO, SIROYA, MBANGANA, KENGE, ELK, BANGANA (native names).

THE SINGLE SPECIES, *B. eurycerus*, inhabits central Africa from Sierra Leone to Kenya. Within its wide range, however, it is restricted to dense, humid forests with thick undercover at altitudes of 2,000 to 3,000 meters on the mountainsides. These forests are misty

and cool throughout the year. During the dry season, they seek the higher altitudes of wooded mountains and bamboo forests; in the rainy season they go to lower elevations.

Both sexes have horns. Bongos are so similar in general form of body, horn shape, presence of a tail tuft, and coloration to the kudus (*Strepsiceros*) and elands (*Taurotragus*) that they have been placed in these groups by many mammalogists. However, the differences in body form, including a complete absence

1417

of the dewlap and of inguinal glands, and the very different forest-living habit of the bongos, seem sufficient to warrant generic distinction.

Bongos have short hair and an erect mane from the shoulder to the rump. These antelopes are among the most beautiful of bovids. The color is a bright chestnut-red on the back and sides, with a black belly. A pure white "chevron" crosses the forehead, and other white patches are located on the sides of the head. The breast bears a large white crescent. There are usually 11 to 12 narrow, vertical white stripes on the sides of the body. Apparently the number of stripes on each side is rarely the same. Females are usually brighter-colored, and old males may become much darker, the chestnut-red turning dark mahogany-brown and the body stripes becoming buffy. A dark dorsal stripe is present and the tail tuft is dark maroon or black. The outside of the legs is dark or blackish, with a black chevron above white knees and a white patch above the hooves. The inside of the legs is white. The horns have yellow or buffy tips.

An adult male may stand as high as 1.4 meters at the shoulders. Adults weigh about 220 kg., although a female shot in the Aberdare Forest of Kenya was estimated to weigh 155 kg. The ears are large and noticeable. The longest horns on record are listed as 1,002 mm. along the front curve and were borne by a Kenya male, but the average horn length is about 835 mm. The horns spiral in one complete twist, and those of the female are usually smaller than those of the male.

Bongos live in the densest, most tangled parts of the forests. They are apparently diurnal, but most activity is carried on during the morning and afternoon. At midday they usually rest in heavy cover while ruminating. Old bulls are usually solitary. These antelopes do not congregate in herds but are somewhat social in that young males, cows, and calves travel in family parties of as many as 20 animals. They depend more on their sense of hearing than on sight or smell. When startled, they can disappear "almost like magic," according to hunters' accounts. Bongos are very shy and fleet-footed. They run gracefully through even the thickest tangles of lianas and brush at full speed, laying their heavy, spiralled horns back on their backs so that the brush cannot impede their flight. So common is this habit that most older animals have bare, rubbed patches on their backs where the horn-tips rest. Also, the front surfaces of the horns of older animals are often much worn and frayed due to the friction caused by their rapid passage through the heavy undergrowth. They prefer to go under or around obstacles rather than over them, even though leaping would take less exertion. They like to wallow in mud puddles and then rub off the mud against a tree, at the same time polishing their horns.

Bongos do not make a variety of sounds but occasionally omit a sound similar to that of the eland and to that of a domestic calf. The food is varied; but, in general, bongos are browsers. They eat the tips, shoots, and trailers of many plants and, like brushbuck and nyala, show a marked preference for the tender bush herbage which grows around the bases of trees. Roots, bamboo leaves, cassava and sweet-potato leaves are also preferred items in their diet. They sometimes raid coco yam farms for the tender leaves. They often uproot saplings with their horns in order to eat the roots. Like many other browsing animals, they can rear up on their hind legs, bracing their fore legs against a tree-trunk, and reach leaves and twigs as high as 2.5 meters above the ground. Bongos are said to eat earth at times and also to chew and swallow pieces of burned wood from lightning-killed forest trees, apparently to obtain salt.

They are said to have more than one young at each birth, but a captive gave birth to only one young. The cows are said to drop their calves about December or January in the wild, and three captive animals gave birth in December; but others gave birth in August and April. The young have the same color pattern as the adults but are a rich tawny shade and much lighter. The young are preyed upon by leopards and pythons. The life span is probably about 18 or 20 years.

Eland (*Taurotragus oryx*), photo by C. A. Spinage through East Africa Wildlife Society.

ELANDS; ELANDE, ELAND ANTILOPE, IMPOFO, POFU, SIRUWA (native names).

THE TWO SPECIES and their distribution are as follows: *T. oryx*, the common eland, central and southern Africa; and *T. derbianus*, the Derby eland, central Africa. Elands prefer plains or moderately rolling country with brush and scattered trees.

Head and body length is 1.8 to 3.4 meters; tail length is 0.3 to 0.6 m., shoulder height is 1.0 to 1.8 meters; and weight is about 900 kg. *T. oryx* is a fairly uniform grayish fawn in color. *T. derbianus* is a rich fawn in color; its head is lighter than its body and its neck is black with a white band at the base. The horns of *T. derbianus* are longer and more massive; the record horn length is 1.2 meters. Both species have whitish or creamy vertical stripes on the upper parts.

Elands have a short mane on the nape with longer hairs on the throat. They are characterized by their ox-like massiveness, rounded hoofs, and the heavy spiral horns which are carried by both sexes.

Elands are gregarious, occurring in groups of a few individuals to herds of up to 100 or more. Although the bulls are usually associated with the herd, they occasionally are solitary. When alarmed, the herds trot off, usually in single file, up wind, with the old bulls in the rear. Although alert, keen of sense, and thus difficult to approach, elands are slow-moving creatures and can be run down rather easily. They prefer to lie in some shelter during the heat of the day. In the morning and evening they seek more open country where they browse upon leaves, bushes,

1419

and succulent fruits. When feeding in desert tracts they can exist for months at a time without drinking, deriving sufficient moisture from leaves and ground bulbs. Elands, despite their size, are good jumpers and can take a 1.5 meter fence with ease.

Apparently there is no fixed breeding season. The usual number of young is one, born about 250 to 270 days after breeding. Sexual maturity is reached at four years in eland males, and at three years in females. Fifteen to 20 years is the life expectancy.

There are several reasons why the elands have become reduced in numbers: they are easily captured and killed; they yield large amounts of tender meat; the quality of the thick hide is excellent; and rinderpest has depleted herds in various areas.

Some elands have been tamed and it is possible that they might be domesticated profitably.

The type species of the genus is *T. oryx* (Pallas).

Nilgais (*Boselaphus tragocamelus*), A. Female; B. Male; photos from New York Zoological Society.

NILGAIS, BLUEBUCKS, BLUEBULLS, BUSHCOWS; NILGAU, ROZ, NILGAIE OR NYLGHAIE.

THE SINGLE SPECIES, *B. tragocamelus*, is found in peninsular India, more concentrated in the central section than in the north and extreme south. It is not found in Ceylon. Nilgais frequent forests, low jungles, and occasionally open plains.

Head and body length is 2 to 2.1 meters; the tail length is 456 to 535 mm.; the shoulder height is 1.2 to 1.5 meters; and the adults weigh about 200 kg. The nilgai is the largest antelope native to India. The hair on the body is short and wiry. Although in both sexes the neck is ornamented with a mane, only the bulls develop a tuft of hair on the throat. The male is iron gray, but the lower surface of the tail, stripes inside the ears, rings on the fetlocks, and under parts are white; the head and limbs are tawny and the throat tuft and the tip of the tail are black. The females are more lightly colored. The fore legs are somewhat longer than the hind ones, and the head is long and pointed. Short horns are carried only by the male.

Although the old bulls prefer a solitary existence during at least part of the year, they occasionally collect in small parties; the cows, on the other hand, are usually associated in herds along with their calves. This species is diurnal, but it also rests during the day. Nilgais browse as well as graze; they are fond of fruits and sugar cane and do considerable damage to the latter crop.

It is believed that there is no definite mating season in the wild, although March and April are more generally preferred. The bulls are said to fight each other on their knees. Mating takes place immediately after the cow has dropped her offspring; one, or more commonly two, calves comprise a normal litter. The gestation period is about 245 days. The life span is about 15 years.

Nilgais, because of their insignificant trophies and poor-tasting meat, are not much sought after by the modern hunter. The Hindus regard these animals as close relatives of the sacred cow. Consequently nilgais enjoy immunity from molestation and display remarkable unconcern at the presence of man. They are rather docile for such a large animal and it is said that they tame easily; they thrive and breed in captivity. Leopards and tigers are their chief enemies and are responsible for reducing their numbers.

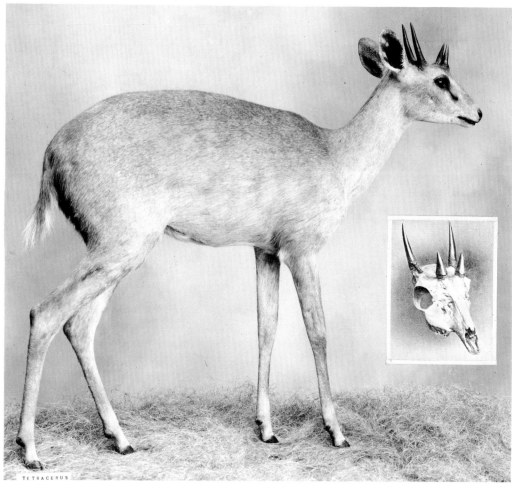

Four-horned Antelope (*Tetracerus quadricornis*), photo from Field Museum of Natural History. Inset: Photo from *Guide to Great Game Animals*, British Museum (Natural History).

CHOUSINGHAS, FOUR-HORNED ANTELOPE; GUN-TADA, VIERHORN-ANTILOPE, VIERHOORN-ANTILOPE.

THE SINGLE SPECIES, *T. quadricornis*, is native to peninsular India, although it is not found east of the Bay of Bengal nor in Ceylon. It is found most frequently in open forests, avoiding dense wooded growth.

Head and body length is about 1 meter; tail length is about 126 mm.; shoulder height is about 0.6 meter; and adults weigh only 17 to 21 kg. The short, thin, coarse hair is a uniform brownish bay above, lighter on the lower sides, and white on the insides of the legs and middle of the belly; the muzzle, outer surface of the ears, and a line down the front of each leg are blackish brown. The horns are short, conical, and smooth and are usually four in number. The posterior pair of horns are 80 to 100 mm. long, while the front pair are often small, about 25 to 38 mm. long but sometimes represented by only a slightly raised area of black hairless skin. In this respect—the presence of four horns in adult males, the females being hornless—chousinghas are unique among the Bovidae.

The hoofs are small and rounded in front.

This species differs from all other Indian antelope not only in structural features but also in habits. Chousinghas are not gregarious and rarely are more than two individuals found together. These little creatures are shy and swift, dashing into dense cover at the first sign of danger. Although in the brush some observers confuse this animal with the hog deer (*Axis porcinus*), it can be readily distinguished by its peculiar jerky manner of walking or running. They drink regularly, are seldom found far from water, and are grazers.

Mating takes place during the rainy season and the young, one to three in number, are born in January or February; the period of gestation is about 183 days.

Despite the small size of the horns, the presence of two pairs makes these animals much sought after as trophies. Some say the meat is dry, while others like its taste. Most agree, however, that it is not as good as that of some of the other antelope. When captured young, chousinghas are easily tamed. They are apparently quite delicate. One lived nearly four years in the London Zoo.

Asiatic Water Buffaloes (*Bubalus bubalis*), photo by R. Van Nostrand through San Diego Zoological Garden.

WATER BUFFALOES OR CARABAOS; BUFFLES, WAS-SERBUFFEL, WATERBÜFFEL OR KARBOUW, KERBO, ARNI. (Included are vernaculars used in other countries.)

THE SINGLE SPECIES, *B. bubalis*, is widely domesticated from Egypt to the Philippines and is also said to be found in the wild in Nepal, Bengal, and Assam, although some naturalists think that these are feral animals. They prefer dense grass and reed growth in moist areas.

The water buffalo has a head and body length of 2.5 to 3 meters, a tail length of 0.6 to 1 meter, and a shoulder height of 1.5 to 1.8 meters. It has an average weight of 726 to 816 kg. The hair is moderately long, coarse, and sparse and is directed forward from the haunches to the head. There is a tuft on the forehead, and the tip of the tail is bushy. Coloration is ash-gray to black. In the Celebes a preferred white coloration is produced by selective breeding. Water buffaloes are large, clumsy beasts with a long, narrow face, large splayed hoofs, and comparatively small ears. Horns, carried by both sexes, are heavy at the base and normally curve backward and inward; they are somewhat triangular-shaped and conspicuously marked with cross wrinkles. The spread of the horns, up to 1.2 meters along the outer edge, exceeds that of any other living members of the family Bovidae.

These are gregarious animals, assembling in herds of various sizes and feeding during the morning, evening, and night, while spending the greater part of the day chewing cud or sleeping. They are pestered by insects, and as a means of protection they wallow in the water and soil. Thus they frequently are completely caked by a layer of mud through which insects cannot penetrate. They also escape from insects by submerging in the water with only the nostrils exposed. Unless harassed or wounded, they seldom attack man. Lush grass and vegetation growing in or beside rivers and lakes are their favorite foods. They may do considerable damage to crops.

During the mating season, a bull leads off several cows to form a small harem. About ten months later one or two calves are born. The calf is born in the vicinity of the harem, and it follows the mother as soon as it is able. The life span is about 18 years.

Domesticated cows of the water buffalo yield milk of good quality. The flesh is not especially good. The leather made from the skins is of superior quality. Water buffaloes are also used as beasts of burden. They are docile and tractable with persons to whom they are accustomed but are ill-natured toward strangers.

A. Tamaraus (*Anoa mindorensis*), photo from "Saugethiere vom Celebes- und Philippinen- Archipel," Adolf B. Meyer, *Abh. Zool. anthrop.-ethn. Mus. Dresden.* B. Anoas or Dwarf Water Buffaloes (*A. depressicornis*), photo from San Diego Zoological Garden.

ANOAS, DWARF WATER BUFFALOES, TAMARAUS; ANOA, ANOA OR GEMSBUFFEL, ANOEANG, SAPI OETAN, BOEOELOE TOETOE.

THIS GENUS comprises three species: *A. depressicornis*, which is native to the lowland forests throughout most of Celebes; *A. anoa*, which prefers the forested mountains of western Celebes; and *A. mindorensis*, the tamarau, which inhabits the dense grass and reed growth in moist areas as well as the bamboo jungles of mountain forests on Mindoro Island in the Philippines, where they are rare—probably no more than 200 or 250 are still living. Some authors classify the tamarau as a species of *Bubalus*. At the present time there is controversy as to whether *A. anoa* ranks a specific standing.

In anoas, the shoulder height is 690 to 1,060 mm., and the tail length is 180 to 310 mm. The head and body length is about 1,600 to 1,720 mm. Although the young are thickly covered with yellowish-brown woolly hair, the skin of old individuals of both species is almost bare. Coloration of adults varies from dark brown to blackish with frequent blotches of white on the face, nape, throat, and lower limbs; the under parts are usually light brown. The white areas are quite variable. Males are generally darker than females. Their hide is of exceptional thickness. Anoas are the smallest of the buffaloes; the limbs are rather short, the body plump, and the neck thick. Their horns are short, the maximum size being about 380 mm. along the outer curve; they are ringed and triangular at the base.

The tamarau is about 1 meter high at the shoulder. It has more hair on its body than the water buffalo (*Bubalus*) and is dark brown to grayish black. The horns are stout and short, only about 355 to 510 mm. long.

Little is known about the habits and general biology of these animals because of their wary nature, secluded environment, and restricted range. They apparently associate in pairs rather than in herds, except when the cows are about to give birth; and some individuals are reported to enjoy water and wallowing in mud. Hediger (*Zeitschr. Saugetierk.*, vol. 30, No. 4, pp. 249–53, 1965), however, found that *A. mindorensis* dislikes water pronouncedly, and when it rains will at once seek cover in thick vegetation. It neither bathes nor wallows. During the morning members of this genus feed alone, but in the afternoon they gather and seek refuge under shade trees. It is said that they feed chiefly upon young cane shoots and various water plants. Their gait is a trot, but at times they make clumsy leaps.

The gestation period is 276 to 315 days, there is generally only one young, and life expectancy is probably about 20 to 25 years.

The flesh, especially of calves, is tender and well flavored. Anoas are steadily decreasing in numbers because they are hunted for their hide, horns, and meat. The decrease is also probably caused by the advancement of civilization. Natives use the hide, tanned with the tail attached, as a dancing costume.

Although exceedingly rare in zoos, they do well and even reproduce in captivity. They are said to be somewhat aggressive and pugnacious in captivity.

The type species of the genus is *A. depressicornis* (Smith).

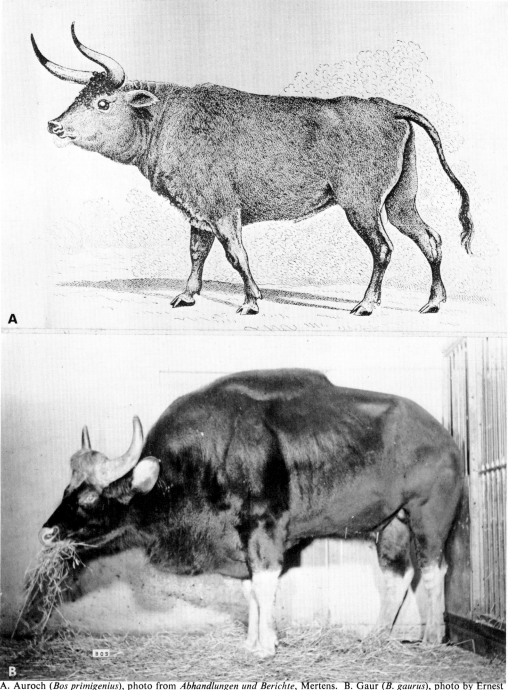

A. Auroch (*Bos primigenius*), photo from *Abhandlungen und Berichte*, Mertens. B. Gaur (*B. gaurus*), photo by Ernest P. Walker.

A. Gayal (*Bos frontalis*); B. Scotch Cattle (*B. taurus*); photos by Ernest P. Walker.

A. Zebu (*Bos indicus*), photo by R. Pucholt. B. Ankole Cattle (*B. taurus*), photo by C. A. Spinage.

TRUE CATTLE; GANADOS, RUNDEREN, ZEBOE, RINDER, BOEUF, AUROCHS, ZEBUS, BRAHMAS, YAKS, GAUR, SELADANG, GAYAL, MITHAN, BANTENG, TSAING, SAPI UTAN, KOU PREH OR KOUPREY, NGAVA PO, CAMBODIAN FOREST OX, HIGHLAND CATTLE OR SCOTCH CATTLE, BRITISH PARK CATTLE, CHARTLEY CATTLE. (Included are vernaculars used in other countries.)

THIS GENUS of about seven living species is distributed as follows: *B. taurus*, cattle, have probably been domesticated since the beginning of written history or even earlier and are worldwide. *B. indicus*, the zebu or Brahma, is native to India and now widely introduced. *B. grunniens*, the yak, is native to Kansu in China, Tibet, and Ladak in India, the domesticated form living in the high plateaus and mountains of central Asia. *B. gaurus*, the gaur, had an extensive range in the last century from all the hilly, forested country of the Indian Peninsula through Nepal, Assam, and Burma to Indo-China and down the Malay Peninsula to Perak, but it is now much reduced in range and numbers. *B. frontalis*, the gayal, is restricted to the Chittagong Hills of India, Assam, and northern Burma (Tenasserim). *B. banteng*, the banteng, formerly ranged from Burma and Thailand to Indo-China and down the Malay Peninsula as far as Java; it is now extremely scarce or exterminated over most of its former range. *B. sauveli*, the kouprey, is native to Cambodia (Indo-China).

Although the origins of domestic cattle are uncertain, it seems likely that the long-horned wild auroch (auerochse, ur [German], boeuf sauvage [French], oeros, oerrund [Dutch]), *B. primigenius*, is one of the ancestors of modern cattle (*B. taurus*). The auroch was referred to by Julius Caesar in his writings and was found throughout the forests of North Africa, Europe, and southwestern Asia until it became extinct about 1627. A second, short-horned form, which has been described as *B. longifrons* and which may have occupied much the same range, actually may represent the females of *B. primigenius*. Regardless of their disputed ancestry, cattle were probably first domesticated in southwestern Asia and have since been widely bred. Experiments have been made by Heck of Munich and others to establish a race of cattle closely resembling the phenotype of the extinct aurochs by crossing primitive breeds of cattle (reversed selection). A breed is a group of animals within a species with a common origin and particular characteristics which have become fixed through generations of selection and are passed on to successive generations.

Domesticated cattle (*B. taurus*) usually have a shoulder height of 0.9 to 1.1 meters and weigh 450 to 900 kg. The body is covered with short hair, and coloration depends upon the breed, ranging from whitish to black with shades and blotches of red, brown, and buff. Cattle graze approximately eight hours a day, spending the remaining time resting and chewing their cud. Instead of upper incisor teeth, *Bos* has a thick layer of the hard palate which is called the dental pad. During an eight-hour day a cow will eat about 70 kg. of green grass. Mating takes place throughout the year, and one young (occasionally twins) is born after a gestation period of 277 to 290 days. Females begin to mate at 18 months of age and remain fertile for about 12 years. The life span may be more than 20 years. Cattle have a variety of uses: they provide dairy products, meat, medicines, fertilizers, fat, glue, soap, leather, sandpaper, and other items of economic importance and are sometimes used as beasts of burden.

The origin of the so-called "white wild cattle" enclosed in the British parks of Chillingham and Chartley is unknown. The Chillingham herd has been fenced since about 1220 and thus has been inbred for nearly 750 years. The only change, at least in external appearance, in this herd over the centuries has been a slight decrease in size. The herd is an absolute monarchy, the "king" bull being the only male mating with the females. He usually reigns for two or three years or until he is deposed by another bull. The male of the Scotch highland cattle which is pictured is probably of a domesticated breed that was particularly well adapted to the climatic conditions of the region in which it lived, and it is possible that it may represent a strain of a primitive form.

Zebus (*B. indicus*) are frequently called humped cattle because of the characteristic hump over the shoulder; they also have drooping ears and a large dewlap. Their coloration is pale fawn, bay, gray, or black. They no longer exist in the wild state. Zebus are used mainly as draft animals, and as they are the "sacred cattle" of India, they are allowed to roam the streets and villages without molestation. Of the 30 or more breeds of zebus, each of which originated in a province of India, four main strains have been introduced into the United States. Although not of the same species as cattle, they will breed with them and produce valuable hybrids. The advantageous features of zebus and their hybrids are the ability to resist heat, ticks, and insects. One of the most recent breeds of *Bos* to gain official recognition is the Santa Gertrudis, recognized in 1940. This breed was established on the King Ranch in Texas by breeding zebu bulls with the stock that developed from Texas longhorns, Herefords, and shorthorns.

The yak or grunting ox (*B. grunniens*) inhabits elevations up to 6,100 meters, living among desolate surroundings. These animals do not thrive in the lower and warmer parts of Asia. The wild yak bull is nearly twice as large as the domesticated variety, and may stand as high as 2 meters at the shoulder. Yaks weigh about 525 kg. and are long, low, and massive in appearance. The large black horns curve upward and forward in the males. Long hairs that reach almost to the ground form a fringe around the lower part of the shoulders, the sides of the body, and the flanks and thighs. The tail also has long hairs. Wild yaks are blackish brown in color, and the domesticated individuals are red, mottled, brown, or black. During most of the year the bulls roam in groups of two or three individuals, while the cows and calves associate in large groups. In spite of their awkward appearance, yaks are expert climbers, surefooted, and sturdy. In Tibet these animals have been domesticated for centuries, are quite docile, and are used as beasts of burden and as sources of meat and milk.

The gaur (*B. gaurus*) frequents altitudes of 750 to 1,800 meters and prefers rocky, forested hills, with

A. British Park Cattle (*Bos taurus*), photo by Ernest P. Walker. B. Yak (*B. grunniens*), photo from U.S. National Zoological Park.

open, grassy tablelands at the summits. These are large animals. A large male had a head and body length of almost 3 meters, a tail length of 865 mm., and a shoulder height of 2.2 meters; it was estimated to weigh more than 1 metric ton. An average cow has a head and body length of 2.1 meters, a tail length of 610 mm., and a shoulder height of 1.8 meters. The color is quite distinctive. Gaurs are dark, almost blackish brown to dark reddish brown, with white stockings. Gaur range in herds of 5 or 6 to as many as 20 animals, occasionally more. They feed in the early morning and again in the evening. The heat of the day drives them to rest and chew their cud in grassy areas in the thick forest. They are not excessively wary animals but can be dangerous when wounded or pursued too closely. They mate during the cold months (the dry season in tropical areas). The single calf is dropped in August or September, when the torrential monsoon rains have replenished the region with tender new grass and herbage. A whistling snort is their alarm note, but they also bellow and "moo" like domestic cattle. When startled, they crash off through the jungle at high speed, and the sound of the herd's progress can be heard for a considerable distance.

The gayal (*B. frontalis*) is considered a domesticated form of gaur by many zoologists, but there are some constant and striking differences between them. The gayal, however, has apparently never been found truly wild. Gayals have a different horn and skull shape from those of the gaur, and they are smaller animals. A bull had a head and body length of 2.8 meters, a tail length of 800 mm., and a shoulder height of 1.5 to 1.6 meters. A cow stood 1.4 meters at the shoulder. One bull from Assam was estimated to weigh 540 kg. Gayals are blackish brown, often with a bluish cast, with white stockings and tail tufts.

The banteng (*B. banteng*) prefers forested, hilly country up to 2,000 meters in altitude. The species *B. sondaicus* is conspecific with *B. banteng*. Bantengs are smaller than gaur. A large bull had a head and body length of 2 meters and a tail length of 850 mm.; it stood 1.5 meters at the shoulder. The coloration is similar to that of the gaur but tends to be more blue-black, with white stockings and a white rump patch. Bantengs are found in herds of 10 to 30 animals, but often solitary bulls are encountered, presumably having been driven away from a herd. These lone bulls tend to be larger than usual. Bantengs feed continuously through the night, with many pauses for rest and cud-chewing in shady thickets. They lie in dense thickets by day. They can live in drier districts than the gaur, as they apparently do not need to drink as often. In Burma, gaur and bantengs occur together in the same forests. They are extremely wary and shy. During the monsoon season, bantengs leave the lowlands and drift up into the hill forests where they feed on tender new herbage, including bamboo shoots. In the dry season, they return to the valleys and more open wooded districts, where they feed on grass. They mate during the dry season, and the single calf is born during August or September.

The kouprey (*B. sauveli*) was discovered as recently as 1936, when a young animal was captured and brought to the Paris Zoo. In 1940 the total population was estimated at only about 1,000 animals. With the recent wars in Indo-China, it is feared that the species may be nearly or quite extinct. F. E. Blanc suggests that this species may be a hybrid between the banteng and either the gaur, water buffalo, or domestic cattle. Bulls attain a shoulder height of 1.9 meters and are thus comparable to gaur in size. Old bulls are blackish, with whitish stockings. The horn shape differs considerably from all the other Asiatic wild cattle, being cylindrical, widely separated, recurved in old bulls and lyre-shaped in the cows. These horns, in some old bulls, are frayed at the tips, producing a shaggy appearance. Almost nothing is definitely known about the habits of these vanishing wild cattle.

The type species of the genus is *B. taurus*, Linnaeus. The yak has been separated subgenerically from *Bos* under the name *Poëphagus*, Gray, 1843. Likewise the gaur, gayal, banteng, and kouprey have been separated subgenerically from *Bos* under the name *Bibos*, Hodgson, 1837, with type species *B. subhemachalus*, Hodgson = *B. gaurus*, H. Smith.

African Buffaloes (*Syncerus caffer*), photo from San Diego Zoological Garden. Inset: Photo from U.S. National Zoological Park.

AFRICAN BUFFALOES; AFRIKAANSE BUFFELS, MBOA (native names).

THE SINGLE SPECIES, *S. caffer*, lives in Africa, south of the Sahara. It is usually found near water, grass, and sufficient cover.

The head and body length is 2.1 to 3 meters, tail length is 0.75 to 1.1 meters, shoulder height is 1.1 to 1.5 meters, and the weight of adult bulls has been estimated at about 600 to 900 kg. The body is thickly covered with hair on young individuals and sparsely covered on adults; old animals have little, if any, hair. Coloration is brownish to black. The African buffalo is characterized by its bulky ox-like form, massive head and limbs, and by the horns, which spread outward, downward, then upward in some and out and back in others, the bases almost meeting in the middle of the forehead. The breadth of the chest is great, and the relatively large, drooping ears are fringed by soft hairs.

The African buffalo is often considered the most dangerous big-game animal of Africa, for old bulls, usually those that have been previously wounded, will sometimes stalk a victim and attack without provocation; also, an injured animal will lie in wait for the hunter and charge viciously. If the charge is not successful, it will often seek the enemy.

These animals can run 57 km. per hour. They are such powerful and deadly fighters that they have little to fear, although in Northern Rhodesia buffaloes are often the main prey of lions; but the latter do not always succeed in killing the buffalo or even in getting away unscathed. They are gregarious, the herds ranging in size from a dozen to several hundreds usually led by an old female. Herds of 1,000 to 2,000 can still be seen at certain seasons in Kruger National Park and Gorougoza Game Reserve, near Beira. They enjoy splashing about in water and wallowing in mud. They go to drink usually in the evening and morning and feed during the early part of the night. Later in the night they usually rest and chew their cud. They usually retire to the shade of the forest during the heat of the day. The African buffalo is a grazer, but it also browses on leaves and bushes.

Mating appears to be affected by climatic conditions, but in southern Africa the mating season is from September to March, and in Northern Rhodesia throughout the year, but mostly in the dry season. The single reddish or blackish-brown young is born about 11 months later, showing few indications of the powerful animal it will eventually become. The stronger mature bulls drive the older bulls from the herd, the latter then associate in groups of two to five individuals. Life expectancy is about 16 years.

African buffaloes are hunted commercially for game and by the natives for food. Thus their numbers have been greatly reduced. They are also subject to rinderpest.

American Bison (*Bison bison*), photo from U.S. National Zoological Park.

AMERICAN BISON, EUROPEAN WISENT, BISONTES.

THIS GENUS comprises two species: *B. bison*, the American bison, which formerly occupied most of North America; and *B. bonasus*, the European wisent, which inhabited nearly all the European continent. Both species inhabit prairies and open woodlands, but the American variety prefers prairies, and the European species, the woodlands. Today bison are found only in protected herds, and the wisents have been reduced to only several hundred individuals.

Head and body length is 2.1 to 3.5 meters; tail length is 0.5 to 0.6 meter; shoulder height is 2.6 to 2.8 meters; and adults weigh 450 to 1,350 kg. The pelage on the head, neck, shoulders, and fore legs is long, shaggy, and brownish black; there is usually a beard on the chin. The remainder of the body is covered with short, lighter-colored hairs. Young calves are reddish brown. Bison are unmistakable in appearance with their short and broad forehead, heavy head, short neck, high, humped shoulders, and tufted tail. The horns, borne by both sexes, are short, upcurving, and sharp. The voice is a bellow. The American bison has longer and more luxuriant hair on the neck, head and forequarters, giving the animal the appearance of larger size. The body is lower, the pelvis smaller, and the hindquarters are less powerful than in the European bison, although the body of the former is on the whole more massively built. The horns of the American species are shorter and more curved, the front of the head more convex, and the tail is shorter and less bushy.

The herd size is variable, ranging from a family group of a bull, a cow, and their offspring to herds of thousands of individuals. Usually the cow is the leader in the family group. Frequently bison wallow in dust or mud and then rub against boulders, tree trunks, and other objects to rid themselves of parasites. They feed mostly in the morning and evening and rest during the day. American bison feed mostly on grasses, while the European species feeds on leaves, twigs, and bark of trees. American bison formerly made seasonal migrations of hundreds of kilometers to find better feeding areas.

The bulls fight each other during the mating season (July to September). The gestation period is about nine months, and the cow is solitary when its calf is born. As soon as the youngster is able to stand, it and its mother join the herd. The calf is protected by the bull, the cow, and frequently the entire herd. Nursing takes place for nearly one year, and the calf usually stays with the mother until it is three years old, at which time it usually mates and becomes independent. The life span is 18 to 22 years.

The reduction of bison almost to extinction is a tragedy of natural history. Fifty million *B. bison* once roamed over North America; by 1889, however, there were only 541 individuals. Through the efforts of a few public-spirited persons, interest was aroused in their preservation, and the few remaining animals were carefully saved and bred until they now appear safe from extermination. The European bison has had a similar history. Some Indian tribes were so dependent upon the North American bison that their entire societies were based on them.

The type species of the genus is *B. bison* (Linnaeus).

DUIKERS, MAXWELL'S OR FOREST DUIKERS, BLOU-DUIKERS; PAA NUNGA OR PAA.

ABOUT TEN SPECIES comprise this genus which inhabits Africa from the southern border of the Sudan southward. Some species prefer open country with scattered trees and brush, whereas others are partial to the dense growth of the jungle. *Philantomba* is regarded by some zoologists as a subgenus of *Cephalophus*.

There is considerable variation in the size of duikers: the length of the head and body ranges from 550 to 900 mm., the length of the tail, from 90 to 140 mm., and the height of the shoulders from 357 to 457 mm. The weights range from about 5 to 65 kg. The body is covered with fairly soft hair, which is longest on the rump and forehead. Coloration varies from almost buffy above and white below, through shades of brown to almost black above and only slightly lighter below. Most forms have a stripe along the middle of the back which differs in color from the remainder of the back. One species, *C. zebra*, has a pronounced pattern as the bright orange coat is marked with dark vertical stripes.

All the species are similar in form and are characterized by their medium to small size, short legs, pointed hoofs, and arched back. The horns, possessed by both sexes, are short, project backward from the skull, and are frequently hidden by a long tuft of hair on the crown.

This genus resembles *Sylvicapra*, differing from it in that the horns are usually carried by both sexes and project straight back in a line with the dorsal profile of the head. *C. silvicultor* is larger than *Sylvicapra*.

Duikers are not gregarious and usually move about singly or in pairs. Although these antelopes are quite numerous, they are seldom observed owing to their shyness, largely nocturnal habits, and inaccessible habitats. When alarmed, they dart away with great speed into the protection of dense vegetation; hence the origin of the common name, duiker, which means diving buck. They are sturdy, active, and fleet-footed. The horns serve several purposes, such as defense against enemies and battling other individuals of their own kind. They feed on grass and leaves and at times scramble upon logs or climb vine-entangled shrubs to

A. Black-fronted Duiker (*Cephalophus niger*), photo by Ernest P. Walker. B. Striped-backed Duikers (*C. zebra*), photo by Bernhard Grzimek. C. Light-backed Duiker (*C. silvicultor*), photo by Bernhard Grzimek.

obtain choice leaves and fruit. In Kruger National Park, they have been observed to eat insects and carrion.

Apparently one young is the usual number per birth. The gestation period is about 120 days. Young ones tame readily and become pleasing pets. In zoos they have survived as long as nine years.

Although duikers are game animals, they are not sought after by sportsmen as their heads do not make showy trophies. Natives kill them for food and to add strength to their "hunting medicine" trees.

The type species of the genus is *C. silvicultor* (Abzelius). *Philantomba*, Blyth, 1840, is used as a subgenus to include the forest duikers; *Cephalophella*, Knottnerus-Meyer, 1907, is similarly used for Peter's duiker, *C. callipygus*.

Gray Duikers (*Sylvicapra grimmia*), photo from New York Zoological Society.

GRAY DUIKERS OR DUIKERBOKS, GEWONE DUI-KERBOKKE.

THE SINGLE SPECIES, *S. grimmia*, ranges from Senegal to east, central, and southern Africa, usually in regions with suitable shrub and grass cover. This hardy and adaptable antelope lives at higher elevations than any other hoofed mammal in Africa. The gray duiker is reported as common in alpine meadows in equatorial Africa.

The shoulder height is 570 to 670 mm.; head and body length is .9 to 1.1 meters; tail length is 110 to 180 mm.; and weight is 14 to 17 kg. Females are usually larger than males. Coloration is grayish, yellowish, or reddish yellow. Females are usually hornless, but occasionally carry small, stunted horns, and horned females seem to be more common in some localities than in others. This genus is distinguished from *Cephalophus* in that the horns are usually present in the male only, are sharply pointed, and rise above the plane of the face; and in its pointed rather than rounded ears.

Gray duikers usually travel singly or in pairs, have great speed and stamina, and are usually able to out-distance dogs. They rest during the day in scrub or grass, often in favorite hiding places, and come out to browse and graze in the evening. The diet is an extremely varied one, as almost any green plant material seems to be a potential food item at some time. Captive specimens often kill fowl in the same enclosure, pulling off the head of their prey and lapping the blood. If a salt lick is supplied, this behavior usually ends. There is some indication that these animals kill birds in the wild. Gray duikers have been noted in association with guinea fowl, although the birds actually may be sentinels for the mammals.

Males probably fight among themselves for possession of the females. Duikers seem to mate all year, although there are evidently peak periods of lambing. The gestation period is not definitely known; one record places it at four months and another at seven months. One young (occasionally two) is the usual number. Individuals have lived to an age of nine years in zoos.

The Bakete tribe in the Congo will not kill or eat these animals, for they believe their teeth will fall out if they do.

Lechwe Antelope or Waterbuck (*Kobus lechee*), photo from New York Zoological Society.

WATERBUCKS, KOB, LECHWES; PUKU, TSHITONDA-BASHI, TSHIHIMBI, SING-SING, KRINGAAT, KURU, BALANGO, DEFASSA (native names).

THIS GENUS of about six species inhabits most of Africa south of the Sahara, and the Nile valley. These animals are seldom found far from water and usually remain in swampy tracts where they frequent reedbeds and shrubby growth. *Adenota*, Gray, 1847, and *Onotragus*, Gray, 1872, are herein regarded as subgenera of *Kobus*. The members of the subgenus

Onotragus, the lechwes, are entirely restricted to the flood plains and adjacent ground, while those of the subgenus *Adenota*, the kobs, inhabit the dambos, sometimes flood plains, and the margins of the adjacent light woodlands. Despite the name waterbuck, members of the subgenus *Kobus* are less confined to wet areas than the other subgenera, though they are always within reach of water; they range farther into woodlands than *Adenota*.

The length of the head and body varies from 1.4 to 2.1 meters, the length of the tail, from 190 to

350 mm., the height of the shoulders, from 760 to 1,340 mm., and the weight is up to about 272 kg. The hair is long and coarse, longest on the throat and the tip of the tail. There is considerable color variation among the species; some are yellowish brown and others range to almost black. Some species have white markings on various parts of the body. *K. ellipsiprymnus*, for example, has an elliptical white ring on the buttocks which extends downward to the thighs, and *K. defassa* has a large white patch on the lower part of the buttocks. The horns are long and, although variously shaped, all are normally carried only by the males, curve forward at the tips, lie at an angle slightly above the level of the face, and have transverse corrugations. The horns usually measure from 510 to 1,020 mm. along the front from base to tip. The hooves vary in size and shape, but usually the false hooves are conspicuous. The lechwes have the back of the pasterns bare, an adaptation to their swampy habitat.

Members of the genus *Kobus* are gregarious, associating in herds of 10 to 50 individuals, although often in separate groups, and occasionally solitary. Waterbucks are graceful in their movements and run swiftly. Like most antelopes, these animals are most active in the morning and evening. During the heat of the day, however, some species wander far from water to seek the cool higher ground, only to return to the swamps and rivers at night; others seldom stray from their swampy haunts. The lechwes in particular are fond of wading and swimming and travel by a series of leaps in water that is too shallow for swimming. Their diet consists chiefly of aquatic plants and grasses upon which they frequently nibble while wading.

The breeding habits of these animals are not well known, although it is believed that bucks fight for harems and that the young (most frequently one) are usually born from August to December after a seven- to eight-month gestation period. The life span is about 16 years.

Hunters prize the heads and horns of waterbucks as trophies, but the meat is said to be coarse, strong, and unpalatable.

The type species of the genus is *K. ellipsiprymnus* (Ogilby). The type species of the subgenus *Adenota* is *K. kob*, Erxleben. The type species of the subgenus *Onotragus* is *K. lechee*, Gray.

Chanler's Mountain Reedbuck (*Redunca fulvorufula chanleri*), photo from New York Zoological Society.

REEDBUCKS; REITBOKS, NAGOR, BOHOR, KABASHI AND NTOLE, LUFUMBU OTETELA, NGHOLIGATA, SUWALA (native names).

THE THREE SPECIES, *R. arundinum*, *R. fulvorufula*, and *R. redunca*, inhabit the African continent south of the Sahara. They frequent rolling grasslands, mountain plateaus, thin open forests, and reedbeds, usually near water.

The length of the head and body ranges from 1.1 to 1.4 meters; that of the tail is from 165 to 300 mm.; the height of the shoulder is 685 to 960 mm.; and weight is from 23 to 91 kg. The body is covered with short, stiff hair, which varies from bright fawn to grayish above; the under parts are light and the underside of the tail is white. These animals have a thin neck, moderate body, long, slender legs, and a bushy tail. The hairy coat of the young is woolly. Horns, carried only by the male, are large at the base, prominently ringed, and are usually 203 to 254 mm. in

length. They point backward, diverge in a graceful upward curve, and the tips curve sharply forward. There is a conspicuous bare glandular patch below each ear. Female reedbucks have four mammae.

Although these animals are social, they are not strictly gregarious, usually foraging about singly, in pairs, or in family groups. *R. fulvorufula*, however, sometimes associates in herds of up to 20 individuals. *R. arundinum* may rarely be found in groups of about a dozen individuals. When scared, these animals scatter singly rather than running off in a group, except for members of *R. arundinum*, which run off together. The tails are held upright in flight, exposing the white undersurface. They are perhaps the least wary of riverside antelopes, and, once set to flight, they seldom go far before stopping to glance back. If suddenly alarmed, they crouch close to the ground. A characteristic shrill whistle is given as a signal of alarm. Although they live near water, they do not enter it freely; even when pursued, they will travel out of their way to avoid crossing a stream, preferring to take refuge in brush. They graze early in the morning and evening, eating grass and tender shoots of reeds, although they frequently move about throughout the night on fairly open ground. The diet consists almost wholly of grass.

Information regarding the breeding habits of these animals is meager. The young are born over a considerable period of the year, and the gestation period is about 232 days. One specimen lived in the London Zoo for nine years.

Most hunters agree that reedbucks are one of the tamest and easiest of antelopes to approach and kill in southern Africa. However, they have maintained their population better than most large game of Africa. The meat is considered a delicacy by some but is said to be scarcely palatable by others.

The type species of the genus is *R. redunca* (Pallas).

Rhebok (*Pelea capreolus*), photo by Herbert Lang through J. Meester.

RHEBOKS; VAALRIBBOKS, VAAL RHEBOK, ILIZA, PEELI (native names).

P. capreolus, the only representative of this genus, inhabits South Africa. It lives among rocks and tangled growth or mountain sides and also on plateaus, but, where protected, it will venture to grassy valleys. It probably frequented such valleys regularly before extensive human activities drove it out of these areas.

The length of the head and body is 1.1 to 1.2 meters; the length of the tail is 110 to 140 mm.; the height of the shoulder is 71 to 78.7 cm.; and adults weigh 20 to 23 kg. The body is covered with hair that is woollier and curlier than in other antelope. Color-ation is brownish gray, and the tips of the hairs are buff; the face and the lower legs are yellowish, and the under parts of the body and tail are white. Rheboks may be readily distinguished from other ante-lopes by their slender build, woolly hair, straight, upright horns 20 to 25 cm. in length, long, pointed, erect ears, and the absence of a bare patch below the ear. The females are hornless. A naked area around the nostrils extends to the top of the nose and is swol-len; it becomes studded with moisture when the an-imal is excited. The females have four mammae.

These animals consort in family parties and small groups and occasionally combine to form herds numbering as many as 30 individuals. The herd is usually led by a mature buck. Old bucks are fre-

Beisa (*Oryx beisa beisa*), photo from New York Zoological Society

ORYXES AND GEMSBOKS.

THE FOUR SPECIES and their distribution are as follows: *O. leucoryx*, the oryx of Arabia and Iraq; *O. tao*, the scimitar-horned oryx of the Libyan and Sahara deserts; *O. beisa*, the beisa oryx of eastern Africa; and *O. gazella*, the gemsbok of southern Africa. Most species now exist only locally and are rare as they have been hunted intensively, although the beisa is still fairly abundant in parts of Kenya, and the gemsbok is still common in the Kalahari. The Arabian oryx, however, is nearly extinct in the wild, where it has been hunted with machine guns from jeeps. The Phoenix Zoo is attempting to establish a breeding colony to preserve this species.

These animals usually live in arid plains and deserts, but they also inhabit rocky hillsides and thick bush-forest in some areas.

The height at the shoulders is 1.0 to 2.2 meters. Both sexes have long horns ranging from 0.6 to 1.2 meters in length; those of the females are usually longer and more slender than those of the males. The mature animals occasionally weigh as much as 210 kg. The color of adults varies from cream to grays and browns, with striking markings of black and brown; the young are brownish, with markings only on the tail and knees. Externally the genus is characterized by straight horns directed backward from the eyes (except in *O. tao*), a tuft of hair on the throat of the males, a mane which extends from the head to the shoulder, fairly short ears which are broad and rounded at the tips, and slightly tufted tails.

Oryxes usually range in bands of two to a dozen, occasionally as many as 60 are noted together. They are described as alert, wary, and keen-sighted. All the species of this genus are hunted for their strikingly marked heads bearing rapier-like horns which make choice trophies. When injured or brought to bay, oryxes will attack with the head lowered so that the sharp horns point forward. Such attacks can be quite dangerous, and oryxes also defend themselves in this manner from their natural enemies, which include lions. These large antelopes feed on grasses and shrubs and go to streams and waterholes to drink. When free water is not available, they obtain moisture from such sources as melons and succulent bulbs.

The bulls fight one another during the rutting season. The gestation period in *O. beisa* is 260 to 300 days, with a single offspring the usual issue. The young of *O. beisa* and of *O. gazella* are born from September through January. The maximum life span appears to be about 20 years.

The ringed horns are so sharp that the tips are often used by the natives for spear points, and the thick, tough skin of some species is used for shield coverings. The meat is said to be excellent.

The type species of the genus is *O. gazella* (Linnaeus).

Addaxes (*Addax nasomaculatus*), photo from New York Zoological Society.

ADDAXES, ANTILOPE ADAXES, MENDESANTILOPE.

THE SINGLE SPECIES, *A. nasomaculatus*, lives throughout the Sahara desert from Senegambia and Algeria eastward to the Sudan. Hunters have greatly reduced the range and numbers of this antelope.

Addaxes measure 1.0 to 1.1 meters at the shoulder, and adult males weigh about 120 kg. The head and body length is about 2 meters, and the tail length is 150 to 200 mm. The body and neck are grayish brown in winter, but in summer the body coloration becomes sandy to almost white. The legs, hips, belly, ears, and marks on the face are white, and the tuft on the forehead is black. Both sexes possess horns similar to those of the oryxes (*Oryx*), but with a spiral twist of one and a half to almost three turns. The horns measure 762 to 890 mm. along the curves. The widely splayed hooves are an adaptation for traveling on desert sands.

Little is known about the habits and biology of these animals, but apparently they travel in herds of 5 to 20 individuals, led by an old male. They probably would have been exterminated long ago had it not been for the difficulty of human travel in the immense wastelands which they inhabit. Addaxes live most of their lives without drinking, deriving sufficient moisture from the plants upon which they feed. They travel great distances in their search of the scant vegetation of the Sahara, and, in spite of the adverse conditions of their habitat, they are said to always appear in good condition.

Only one young is born at a time, in the winter or early spring.

This antelope is heavily built and does not attain a great speed, as a result it is easy prey to the natives with their camels, horses, dogs, and modern weapons. Both the meat and the skin are prized by the natives; the skins are used for shoe and sandal soles. This is the white antelope seen by American soldiers in World War II and which they described to their families, who called zoos to learn where such animals lived in order that they might know where their sons were.

It is noted that no game reserves exist for the protection of these splendid animals, and they are now on the way to extinction.

TOPIS, BLESBOKS, BLESBUCKS; SASSABY OR TSES-
SEBY, BASTERHARTBEESTE, BONTEBOCKS, BLES-
BOKKE, BONTIBOKKE (native names).

THIS GENUS is composed of about six species which
inhabit grasslands, sparsely timbered regions, and
arid sections of the African continent. Some of the
species are greatly reduced and survive only in
protected areas.

The length of the head and body is 1.3 to 1.8 meters;
the length of the tail is 177 to 450 mm.; the height of
the shoulder is 880 to 1,200 mm.; and adults weigh
114 to 136 kg. The hair is generally soft, with an
iridescent sheen, but on some animals there is a
mixture of soft and coarse hairs. All species have
quite characteristic markings. The colors range from
shades of gray and reds, with a white mark between
the eyes, to rich brown with black or white markings
on the face, legs, and hips, to almost black. This genus
is distinguished by its angular and curved horns,
which are situated behind the orbits, its slightly convex
forehead, and its somewhat elongated muzzle (nose).
The horns, which average about 375 mm., are borne
by both sexes and lack pedicels.

Early observers recorded herds of thousands of
these beautiful animals grazing on the plains, but
indiscriminate slaughter has reduced all species to
remnants of the original stock, although topis are
still abundant in parts of east Africa. The bontebock,
in particular, is on the verge of extinction. Like most
other antelopes, these are preyed upon by lions.

When suddenly alarmed, *Damaliscus* will often
jump over each other's backs in their haste to escape.
D. lunatus is said to be the fleetest of South African
antelopes, but its normal gait is a lumbering canter.
Before these antelopes were so seriously depleted
and the settlers appropriated much of their range,
some of the animals would migrate north and south
with the seasons.

The strongest bulls drive the other males from the
herd, and the latter in turn form small bands of their
own; old bulls often live alone. The gestation period
is 225 to 300 days, and the mating season appears to

Blesbok (*Damaliscus albifrons*), photo from New York
Zoological Society.

be variable geographically, although there is a limited
season of birth in each particular area. A single calf
is usually born, but twin births have been recorded.

The heads are prized as trophies by hunters, and
the flesh is considered excellent. The blesbok thrives
so well in semicaptivity that domestication is taking
place in South Africa, and marketing of the meat is
now a general practice.

The type species of the genus is *D. pygargus* (Pallas).

Coke's Hartebeests (*Alcelaphus buselaphus cokii*), photo by C. A. Spinage.

HARTEBEESTS; NGONDO, NKONZE, KONDIKONDI, SIG (native names).

THIS GENUS of two species, *A. buselaphus*, the red hartebeest, and *A. lichtensteini*, Lichtenstein's hartebeest, occurs from Senegal, the Sudan, and Somaliland to southern Africa. Hartebeests inhabit open plains or areas of scattered scrubs.

The length of the head and body is 1.5 to 2 meters; the length of the tail is about 0.3 meter; the height of the shoulder is 1.2 to 1.5 meters; and adults weigh 160 to 180 kg. The body hair is about 25.4 mm. in length and is particularly fine-textured. Coloration ranges from fawn through brownish gray to chestnut. The red hartebeest has prominent white patches on the hips and black on the forehead, muzzle, shoulders, and thighs. Lichtenstein's hartebeest has a chestnut area along the back. Both sexes have horns which unite or rise from a single pedicel; average length is 255 to 380 mm. The horns have heavy encircling rings. The rump is lower than the shoulders, the head is long, and the legs are slender; the tail is tufted at the end. The large glands below the eyes are conspicuous.

Hartebeests are gregarious, often roaming about with roan antelopes, zebras, waterbucks, and wildebeests. They wander about in herds of 6 to 20 with members of their own species. In areas where they have not been molested by human beings they are not wary, but persecution has caused them to become quite cautious. For example, the herd usually has a sentinel posted upon a nearby summit to warn the others of danger. When alarmed, they gallop off in single file. Owing to the difference in height of the fore- and hindquarters, their gait is clumsy, although they attain speeds of up to 64 km. per hour. Hartebeests are silent and non-aggressive; and even when they are wounded or at bay, they seldom if ever fight with their horns. When attacked, it is said that they drop to their knees to defend themselves. These animals are diurnal, eat grass during the morning and late afternoon, and rest in shade during the heat of the day.

Normally, one young is born after a gestation period of 214 to 242 days; the calving period is seasonal. The female has two mammae, and the life span is 11 to 20 years.

Formerly quite numerous, the extreme northern and southern races of *A. buselaphus* are now rare or locally extinct, but in Northern Rhodesia at least, *A. lichtensteini* is still widely distributed and, in the favorable parts of its habitat, often the commonest of large antelopes. Although they are often sought by big-game hunters for their heads, the head of *A. lichtensteini* is often described in hunter's accounts as an uninspiring trophy. In Northern Rhodesia, they have never been particularly sought as trophies, though often as meat for the safaris.

The type species of the genus is *A. buselaphus* (Pallas).

Hunter's Antelope (*Beatragus hunteri*), photo from *Proc. Zool. Soc. London.*

HUNTER'S ANTELOPES; HEROLA.

THE SINGLE SPECIES, *B. hunteri*, inhabits a fairly small area in Kenya and Somaliland. This antelope lives on grassy plains and in areas of scattered shrubs and thorny bushes. Some zoologists include this species in the genus *Damaliscus*.

The shoulder height of *Beatragus* is about 1.1 meters; head and body length is about 1.1 meters; and tail length is about 0.3 meter. The animal is rufous-colored, with whitish under parts; it has no markings except for a white line passing from one eye to the other across the forehead, which is its distinguishing external feature. The characteristic horns start upward at the base, then curve down and out, then they spread apart and curve evenly forward so that the terminal halves point upward. The horns are ringed from the base for most of their length and are developed about equally in males and females, that is, from 510 to 660 mm. in length along the curve.

Hunter's antelopes feed and travel in bands of 6 to 40 or more individuals (usually 10 to 25) and seem to be fairly numerous within their restricted range. The gait is a heavy gallop, like that of the hartebeest (*Alcelaphus*). Lions are their main enemy. Hunter's antelopes were quite wary when first discovered, and, since the natives do not hunt them extensively, their wildness is probably a natural trait rather than a habit acquired through fear of human molestation.

Young of these little-known antelopes have been seen in October and November.

White-bearded Gnu (*Connochaetes taurinus*), photo from New York Zoological Society. Inset: White-tailed Gnu (*C. gnou*), photo from Zoological Society of London.

GNUS, WILDEBEESTS, WILDBEESTE, GNOES.

TWO SPECIES comprise this genus: *C. gnou*, the black wildebeest or white-tailed gnu, which is almost extinct, only a few protected herds remaining; and *C. taurinus*, the blue wildebeest, brindled gnu, or white-bearded wildebeest, which occurs from Tanganyika and Kenya southward. These animals prefer a habitat of open grassy plains with a near-by water supply. *Gorgon*, Gray, 1850, is herein regarded as a subgenus of *Connochaetes* to include the species *C. taurinus*.

The length of the head and body is 1.5 to 2 meters; the length of the tail is 350 to 550 mm.; the height of the shoulder is 1 to 1.3 meters; and adult males attain weights of 230 to 275 kg. The coloration of *C. gnou* is buffy brown to black; tufts of long, black hair protrude from the muzzle, throat, and between the fore legs. The mane is upright and the tail is white. *C. taurinus* is grayish silver with brownish bands on the neck, shoulder, and to the middle of the body. The face, mane, beard, and tail are black,

except in the subspecies *C. t. albojubatus*, in which the beard is white. Both sexes possess horns which arise separately and are usually heavy and recurved. The ox-like head and horns, with bristly facial hair, and the general body form give these animals a ferocious appearance which is misleading.

Gnus gather in herds of 5 to 15 animals, occasionally assembling in large herds of 100 or more individuals. The small herds are usually led by a single bull, but the large herds appear to have several domineering males. Old bulls that have been driven from the herd form small independent groups or roam alone. When disturbed, gnus begin curious antics: they prance about, paw the ground, probe their horns into the earth, and thrash their tails. If man approaches too close (about 500 meters), they snort and dash off a short distance, wheel about to face the intruder, and then resume the curious ritual. *C. gnou*, in captivity, has attacked and killed its keeper; *C. taurinus* appears to be less aggressive. These African antelopes forage during the morning and evening, searching for karroo bushes, succulents, and grasses; during the heat of the day they relax in the shade.

Mating takes place about June, and generally one young is born after a gestation period of eight to nine months. The youngster nurses for seven to eight months but eats grass when one week old. Cows mate before their second year, and females have four mammae. The life span of *Connochaetes* is about 16 years.

The flesh is coarse, dry, and hard; the skins make good leather; and the silky tails are used for chowries (fly whisks used in Africa and the East as a symbol of rank).

The type species of the genus is *C. gnou* (Gmelin).

Klipspringer (*Oreotragus oreotragus*), photo from San Diego Zoological Garden.

KLIPSPRINGERS OR KLIPBOKKIES; UM DIGDIG, ALAKUD (native names).

THE SINGLE SPECIES, *O. oreotragus*, inhabits rocky hills and mountains in southern and eastern Africa, northward to the Sudan and Somaliland. The klipspringer is also found in northern Nigeria.

The shoulder height is 0.45 to 0.6 meter; head and body length is 770 to 920 mm.; tail length is 50 to 100 mm.; and weight is 11 to 16 kg. The horns, ringed at the base and usually borne only by the males, are from 75 to 153 mm. in length. The pelage has a yellowish-olive gloss and is speckled with yellow and brown or orange, shading to white below. The coat harmonizes with the background of rocks. The texture of the bristly hair has been variously described as moss-like and grass-like; the thick, pithy hair lies like a mat on the body to cushion the animal against bumps and bruises in its rocky environment.

This little "cliff-springing" antelope might be likened to the chamois (*Rupicapra rupicapra*) or the mountain goat (*Oreamnos americanus*) in its mode of life among the rocks, where it makes rapid progress without apparent suitable footholds. It walks and stands on the tips of the relatively round hoofs; it can jump onto a rocky projection the size of a silver dollar and land on it with all four feet. Klipspringers travel in pairs or in groups of three to eight. The call is a shrill whistle, mainly given when these animals are curious or slightly alarmed; when frightened, they flee into the rocks. These small African antelopes browse and graze, resting at intervals under overhanging cliffs or bushes. Apparently they do not drink water regularly.

The mating season is probably an extended one, but most of the young appear to be born from September through January. The gestation period is about 214 days.

Skins are used by the hill tribes to make bags for carrying bread. The meat is excellent. Because of its elasticity and lightness, klipspringer hair was once in demand for stuffing saddlebags.

Oribi (*Ourebia ourebia*), photo by Bernhard Grzimek.

ORIBIS, OORBIETJIES.

A SINGLE SPECIES, *O. ourebia*, comprises this genus, which inhabits Africa south of the Sahara, usually where there is a sufficient growth of shrubs and trees to offer protection.

The length of the head and body is about 1 meter; the length of the tail is 100 to 150 mm.; the height at the shoulder is 0.5 to 0.7 meter; weight is 14 to 21 kg. The hair is fine and silky, and the general body color is bright sandy rufous to tawny above, with white on the under parts, on the chin, and the underside of the tail. The females usually bear a dark crown patch. Typical characteristics of this genus are the horns, which are carried only by the male, and are 75 to 125 mm. long, set at an angle of about 45 degrees to the plane of the face, and ringed at the base. Both sexes have tufts of long hair on the knees; beneath the ears there is a bare glandular area which is usually dark and conspicuous. Oribis have a short, bushy, black tail, large ears, and slender legs. Females have four mammae.

Oribis usually live in pairs or in small parties. They customarily shelter in tall grass and do not attempt to escape until an intruder is within a few yards. When flushed, they bound along, leaping above the grass. While fleeing, they conspicuously display the tail, which acts as a warning signal to other *Ourebia*. They are capable of traveling at a considerable speed. A loud, shrill whistle may be uttered when alarmed. These small antelopes are active both day and night, lying in thickets during the heat of the day and emerging in groups of three to five in the morning and evening to graze and browse. They are often associated with reedbucks, duikers, or wildebeests, and sometimes feed among domestic goats.

Births occur from September to December; the young are born after a gestation period of about 210 days. The life span is usually 10 to 12 years.

The flesh of these animals is said to be excellent and they are hunted extensively. Although their population has been greatly reduced, they apparently are not in danger of immediate extinction. Oribis are relatively easy to raise and are said to make delightful pets.

Steinbok (*Raphicerus campestris neumanni*), photo of mounted group in Milwaukee Public Museum.

STEENBOKS; GRYSBOKS; VLAKBOKKIES, INGAMA, DONDORO (native names).

THIS GENUS is comprised of three species, *R. campestris*, the steinbok; *R. melanotis*, the grysbok; and *R. sharpei*, Sharpe's grysbok. Members of this genus inhabit stony, hilly, and grassy areas scattered with scrubs, from Kenya and Tanganyika southward to southern Africa.

The length of the head and body is 700 to 850 mm.; the length of the tail is 40 to 80 mm.; the height of the shoulder is about 500 mm.; and the weight is from 7 to 14 kg. The hair is rather coarse. The color of the grysbok is tawny rufous to chocolate-red, speckled with white, with dark markings on the crown; the steinbok is reddish fawn to brown or gray. The underside of the body and tail of all three species is white. In contrast to *Ourebia*, there are no bare patches below the ears, no tufts on the knees, and the straight horns are not conspicuously ridged, but rather smooth. *R. campestris* and *R. sharpei* do not have false hooves, but small ones are present in *R. melanotis*. The males have horns that are 25 to 127 mm. in length, but the females are hornless. The ears are long and narrow, the tail is short, and the legs are slender.

These animals are usually solitary, but occasionally two or three will live together, especially a mother with her fawn; they are not gregarious. Instead of running when danger threatens, these small antelopes hide in the grass, lying flat against the ground with outstretched neck; they do not dart away until nearly trodden upon. Their gait is unlike that of *Ourebia*, being a swift, less bounding run, and it takes a good dog to run one down. It is said that when hard pressed they will seek retreat in burrows of the aardvark (*Orycteropus*). Although generally silent, they utter a loud bleat when seized by a carnivorous predator. During the evening they begin grazing on grasses and tender shoots, occasionally browsing on leaves when the grass has dried up. They travel widely in their quest for food, and, although they will drink if water is convenient, they do not seem to require free water.

At the onset of the rainy season, although perhaps also at times in the dry season, one, or rarely two, young are born. The gestation period is about seven months and the female has four mammae.

Their flesh is palatable but somewhat dry. It is claimed that they do some damage to crops.

The genotype is *R. campestris* (Thunberg).

Zanzibar Antelope (*Nesotragus moschatus*), photo from *The Book of Antelopes*, P. L. Sclater and Oldfield Thomas.

ZANZIBAR ANTELOPES; SUNI, SOENIE, PAA (native names).

ALTHOUGH TWO SPECIES, *N. moschatus* and *N. livingstonianus*, have been named and described, it is possible that only one species exists, the earliest name being *N. moschatus*. These animals range from Kenya through Tanganyika to Northern Rhodesia and Mozambique, including Zanzibar. Their distribution appears to be limited to areas of tangled underbrush within this range.

The length of the head and body is 580 to 620 mm.; the length of tail is 115 to 130 mm.; the height at the shoulder is 300 mm.; and the weight is 8 to 9 kg. The rather short hair is brownish gray to chestnut above and rufous on the sides. The underside of the body and tail is white. These antelope are small and slender, the legs lack knee tufts, and the feet have no false hooves. This genus is characterized by the small horns (65 to 90 mm. in length), which are heavily ringed for at least three-fourths of their length and slope backward at about the same angle as that of the plane of the face. Females of the species do not have horns.

These animals are not gregarious but prefer to range by themselves. Their coloration harmonizes with their surroundings and they are generally not seen until almost underfoot, when they bound away with considerable speed, dodging and twisting about the underbrush, then quickly disappearing. They sleep in the shade during the heat of the day; as evening approaches they move toward open glades, where they feed on grass and shrubs. They are almost independent of free water, apparently deriving sufficient moisture from vegetation.

Little is recorded on the breeding habits of these timid animals. The young, however, are usually born from mid-November to mid-December and are somewhat darker than the parents.

Although supposedly protected in several game preserves, these animals are being rapidly depleted through illegal killing. Owing to their tiny, delicate structure, they are easily killed and are preyed upon by pythons and other forest predators. Their meat is of mediocre quality.

Pygmy Antelope (*Neotragus pygmaeus*), photo from *Proc. Zool. Soc. London.*

ROYAL, PYGMY, OR DWARF ANTELOPES; SANGA.

THE TWO SPECIES of *Neotragus* are distributed as follows: *N. pygmaeus* is found in the forests of West Africa from Sierra Leone and Liberia east into Nigeria, and *N. batesi* lives in the village clearings and forests east of the Niger River in Nigeria and Cameroon. The latter species has also been known as *Hylarnus batesi*.

The height of the shoulder of *N. pygmaeus* is 250 to 305 mm., whereas in *N. batesi* it is about 355 mm. In *N. pygmaeus* the horns are 12 to 25 mm. long and black in color, whereas in *N. batesi* they are 38 to 50 mm. long and usually brown and/or fawn in color. The smooth horns occur only in males. The tuft and underside of the tail is white in *N. pygmaeus* and usually dusky in *N. batesi*. They also differ in cranial characters. With the exception of some individuals of *Tragulus*, *N. pygmaeus* is the smallest hoofed mammal. The length of the head and body in this species is about 500 mm., and the length of the tail about 75 mm. Coloration in both species is cinnamon to russet above and white below. The females of *N. pygmaeus* have four mammae.

Little is known about these small ungulates. Observers and writers have confused *Neotragus* with other genera, notably with *Nesotragus*. These animals usually occur singly or in pairs. They are shy and secretive and flee from danger with long bounds and leaps. Jumps of 2.8 meters have been credited to *N. pygmaeus*. The species *N. batesi* often feeds on the tops of peanut plants and is caught in nooses set around peanut patches. There is some indication that there is a definite breeding season, but this has not been proved.

This species, in Liberian folklore, replaces our "Br'er Rabbit" for quickness and sagacity.

The genotype is *N. pygmaeus* (Linnaeus).

1454

Dik-dik (*Madoqua phillipsi*), photo by J. Meester. Inset: Dik-dik (*M. kirkii*), photo by C. A. Spinage.

DIK-DIKS.

ABOUT SIX SPECIES have a discontinuous distribution. One population lives from Somaliland and Ethiopia southward through Kenya and Tanganyika, and another lives in South West Africa and Angola. Animals of this genus usually frequent somewhat dry areas with scattered brush and vegetation. *Rhynchotragus* is herein regarded as a subgenus.

The length of the head and body is 520 to 670 mm.; the length of the tail is 35 to 55 mm.; the height of the shoulder is 305 to 405 mm.; and the weight of adults is 3 to 5 kg. The texture of the hair is soft and lax. The coloration varies from yellowish gray to reddish brown above and grayish to white below. Horns, possessed only by the males, are ringed, stout at the base, somewhat longitudinally grooved and are occasionally partially concealed by a tuft of hair on the forehead. A characteristic feature of this genus is the elongated snout. The accessory hooves are small and the tail is not conspicuous.

Dik-diks live alone, in pairs, or in small family parties, but sometimes they congregate in larger groups in thorn thickets. When startled they may dash off in a series of erratic, zigzag leaps, uttering a call resembling "zik-zik" or "dik-dik," hence the origin of the common name. They are shy and elusive animals and usually stay in dense vegetation, but they utilize definite paths. They generally live in definite areas and appear to have habits that are quite predictable. They browse on such shrubs as acacias and may emerge in the evening to feed on lower land. Although at least one species inhabits streambanks regularly, others seem to live for months without moisture except that obtained from dew and the vegetation they consume. The young are probably born during and at the end of the rainy season. A dik-dik of the species *M. kirkii* has lived in captivity nine years and two months.

Sportsmen dislike these little animals as they flush and warn the larger game. Many forms are protected by law. The Bushmen do not kill these little antelopes, probably because of some superstition. The Bakete tribe in the Congo will not kill or eat the rather common dik-diks (*M. guinie*) because they believe their teeth will fall out if they do. In the Ituri Forest, pygmies net and kill them in large numbers and sell them by the roadside, hanging them on sticks like rabbits.

The genotype is *M. saltiana. Rhynchotragus*, Neumann, 1905 is currently used for the Damara dik-diks or long-snouted dik-diks, *M. damarensis*, *M. guentheri*, and *M. kirkii*.

BEIRAS.

THE SINGLE SPECIES, *D. megalotis*, inhabits stony hills and hot, dry plateaus in the mountains of Somaliland and Ethiopia.

The length of the head and body is 76.2 to 86.5 cm.; the length of the tail is 51 to 76 mm.; the height at the shoulder is 500 to 760 mm.; and the weight is from 9 to 11 kg. The hair is thick and coarse, the coloration is reddish gray above and white below, the head is yellowish red, and the legs are fawn-colored. There are white areas around the eyes and a distinct dark line occurs along each side from the lower shoulder to the flanks. Only the males have horns, which are 76 to 102 mm. long, upright, straight, spiked, and spaced widely on top of the head. The ears are large, about 152 mm. long and 76 mm. wide, and are curiously marked inside with white hairs. The short body, long legs, short bushy tail, and short, padded hooves are typical characters of the genus *Dorcatragus*.

Information regarding this little antelope is limited. It appears to be goat-like in its habits, leaping from rock to rock with great agility. It associates in herds of four to seven individuals, made up of one or two males with females. Hunters report that it is extremely difficult to shoot or to obtain these animals because of their protective coloration, extreme wariness, and swift speed when alarmed. These factors may account for the few specimens that have been killed and their rarity in museums. These antelopes eat shrubbery and herbaceous plants, and from these they derive enough moisture to live without additional water.

Beira Antelope (*Dorcatragus megalotis*), photo from Zoological Garden of Naples, Italy. Inset: Photo from *The Book of Antelopes*, P. L. Sclater and Oldfield Thomas.

Blackbucks (*Antilope cervicapra*), photos from New York Zoological Society and San Diego Zoological Garden.

BLACKBUCKS, INDIAN ANTELOPES; KALJAR, HIRSCHZIEGENANTILOPE, HERTANTILOPE, HERT-GEITANTILOPE (local vernaculars).

THE SINGLE SPECIES, *A. cervicapra*, inhabits West Pakistan and India from Sind, Kathiawar, and the Punjab eastward to Bengal and southward to Cape Comorin. It lives on open plains and avoids hilly and forested areas.

The length of the head and body is about 1.2 meters; the length of the tail is about 178 mm.; the height of the shoulder is about 812 mm.; and the average weight of an adult is 37 kg. The blackbuck is one of the few antelopes in which the coloration of the male differs from that of the female. The buck is rich dark brown above, on the sides, and on the outside of the legs, whereas the doe is yellowish fawn on the head and back. In both sexes the under parts, inside of the legs, and an area encircling the eyes are white. The males gradually become darker with age. Blackbucks are medium-sized antelopes of graceful and slender build. Only the males have horns, which are 456 to 685 mm. long, ringed at the base, and twisted spirally up to five turns. The narrow muzzle is sheep-like, the tail is short, and the hooves are delicate and sharply pointed.

Although this animal occasionally lives in herds of several hundred members, it more often associates in groups of 15 to 50. These smaller herds are attended by a single buck. As the young males approach maturity, they are driven from the herd and form small groups among themselves. The alert females usually are the first to warn the herd of approaching danger. When blackbucks are first alarmed, a single member will bound into the air to a surprising height and is soon followed by others until the whole herd is in motion. These bounds are continued for a few strides, after which the herd settles down to a regular gallop. Indian antelopes are particularly fleet, and even a greyhound is seldom able to catch them. Indians train the cheetah (*Acinonyx*) to capture blackbucks on command.

Although they feed throughout the day, the herd enjoys a rest in shade during the hottest part of the afternoon. The short grass, typical of the plains of India, and the various cereal crops are the chief food supply of *A. cervicapra*.

The mating season is February or March, during which time the male will protect its harem against rival bucks or man. One or two young are born after a gestation period of about 180 days. The life span is almost 15 years.

The blackbuck forms one of the constellations of the Indian zodiac. The shooting of blackbucks is one of the favorite sports in India, as this animal is prized for its meat and as a trophy.

Impalas (*Aepyceros melampus*), A. Male, photo by Dick Wolff through the Wildlife Protection Society of South Africa. B. Female, photo from New York Zoological Society.

IMPALAS, PALAS, ROOIBOKKES; SCHWARTZFERSEN ANTILOPE, SWALA.

THE SINGLE SPECIES, *A. melampus*, is native to central and southern Africa, from Kenya and Uganda to South Africa. It inhabits open woodlands, sandy bush country, and acacia savannahs. Apparently waterholes are needed by this species, unlike certain of the other antelope genera.

The length of the head and body is 1.1 to 1.5 meters; the tail length is 250 to 400 mm.; the height at the shoulder is .775 to 1 meter; and the weight is 65 to 75 kg. The hair is sleek and glossy. The coloration is dark fawn or reddish above, but lighter on the thighs and legs. A distinct vertical black streak lies on each side of the hindquarters. The underside of the body and tail, the inside of the upper fore leg, the upper lip, and the chin are white. This genus is also distinguished by the horns, which occur only in the males and are 50 to 75 cm. long and lyrate, with ridges confined to the front surface. The hoofs lack clefts, and there are glandular tufts of black hair on the cannon bones of the hind legs.

During the dry months, male and female impalas associate in large herds, sometimes numbering hundreds of animals which later break up into smaller groups of about 15 to 25 females led by a single male. The weaker males then form herds among themselves. When alarmed, impalas make prodigious leaps seemingly without effort, often jumping over each other, over bushes, and even springing high into the air when there is no obstacle to clear. Their speed is considerable; when running, they have been known to make successive leaps of 8, 5, and 9 meters. Although the gazelles (*Gazella*) and the hartebeests (*Alcelaphus*), with which they often graze, run away on the open plains when disturbed, the impala seeks shelter in shrubbery and forests. Impalas are active both night and day, alternately feeding and resting. They graze on grass and browse on the leaves of bushes and trees, drinking at least once a day.

Bucks fight desperately during the mating season (April and May) and frequently utter loud, hoarse grunts. Following a gestation period of about 171 days, one (rarely two) young is born.

Lions, leopards, and wild dogs prey on impalas.

Dibatags (*Ammodorcas clarkei*), photo of mounted group in Field Museum of Natural History.

DIBATAGS, CLARK'S GAZELLE.

THE SINGLE SPECIES, *A. clarkei*, is native to Somaliland, where it inhabits the eastern part of the arid Haud plateau. Dibatags frequent sandy regions with scattered growths of thorn trees and grass.

The length of the head and body is about 1.17 meters; the tail is about 355 mm. long; the height of the shoulder is 762 to 890 mm.; and the weight is 27 to 34 kg. The dark upper parts are purplish rufous, the under parts are white, the buttocks are light and lack a dark band on the flank. The streak down the middle of the face is rich chestnut, and the tail is black. The peculiar purplish tint of the rufous coat blends so well with the surroundings that dibatags are difficult to see.

Dibatags are excessively slender creatures with the essential body characteristics of a gazelle (*Gazella*) and the horns of a reedbuck (*Redunca*). The neck and tail are long, the skull is flat, and the hooves are small. The horns, which are absent in the female, are 150 to 250 mm. long; the basal half is ringed and curved backward and the terminal half is smooth and curved forward. The genus *Ammodorcas* can be distinguished from *Litocranius* by the ears; dibatags have rounded ears, whereas gerenuks have pointed ears.

The dibatag generally travels singly or in small family parties of three to five. It is not readily seen in its natural habitat as it conceals its body behind vegetation and peers over the top. The neck is so slender, the head so pointed, and the coloration so closely resembles the natural cover that the animal is practically invisible. It remains motionless until discovered.

Although *A. clarkei* resembles the gerenuk (*Litocranius*), it can readily be distinguished by its gait as the dibatag bounds away with the head arched back and the tail thrown forward, whereas the gerenuk runs with head and tail outstretched in line with the body. When browsing on shrubs, the long necks of dibatags enable them to reach to considerable heights, reminding one of miniature giraffes. Dibatags often stand on their hind legs with the fore feet in the trees to reach as high as possible. Their long upper lip also facilitates browsing.

Because dibatags live far from water, they probably can exist without free water like many other antelopes.

Although little is recorded concerning their breeding habits, it is believed that the females have their offspring in October and November, after a gestation period of about 12 months.

In addition to man, the principal enemy of *Ammodorcas* is the leopard.

Gerenuks (*Litocranius walleri*), A. Photo by Hans-Jurg Kuhn. B. Photo by Reginald Bloom showing characteristic browsing pose.

GERENUKS, WALLER'S GAZELLE, GIRAFFE GAZELLE, GUGUFTO, NANJAAT.

THE SINGLE SPECIES, *L. walleri*, inhabits eastern Africa from former British Somaliland to Kenya in desert areas where the thorn and shrub growth is sparse.

The length of the head and body is about 1.5 meters; the length of the tail is about 230 mm.; the height of the shoulder is .9 to 1 meter; and the weight ranges from 43 to 50 kg. The general coloration is reddish fawn, with a broad, dark-brown band running down the back and along the upper third of the sides; the front of the neck and under parts are white. Gerenuks are characterized by their long, slender legs; elongated muzzle; giraffe-like neck, which is only 180 to 255 mm. in circumference; wide, flat skull and wedge-shaped head; and the horns. The latter, developed only in the male, are about 355 mm. in length and are comparatively massive. They curve backward and upward and finally hook forward near the end.

Gerenuks travel singly, in pairs, or in groups of six or seven females led by a single male, which is rather closely guarded and protected by the females. When gerenuks see a strange object, they usually stand motionless, hide behind bushes or trees, and then look over or around their cover by means of their long neck. When frightened, they usually leave in a stealthy, crouched trot with the neck and tail carried horizontally, in marked contrast to the erect carriage of the neck and tail of the dibatag (*Ammodorcas*), which somewhat resembles the gerenuk and shares parts of the same range. The gerenuk is not a speedy animal as compared with other antelope genera. It is active throughout the day.

Those individuals living near water occasionally drink, but gerenuks far from a water supply may not drink at all. Their eating habits are much like those of the giraffe (*Giraffa*), for their diet consists largely of acacia leaves which they pluck with their long upper lips and long tongues. To reach the food, they often stand upright on their hind legs, with the body practically vertical. They then place their fore legs against a tree to reach for branches from which they eat the highest and most succulent leaves. Often their food is wilted or dried leaves or twigs.

The young are usually born in time to browse on the tender new leaflets which appear with the rains.

The Somalis refuse to eat the meat of gerenuks as they believe that these animals are relatives of the camel. They believe that if gerenuks are destroyed, a sickness would develop which would kill their camels. Paintings of these animals have been discovered in Egyptian tombs dating from 5600 B.C.

Gazelle (*Gazella subgutturosa*); photo by R. Pucholt.

GAZELLES, CHINKARA.

ALTHOUGH NUMEROUS FORMS of gazelles have been named and described, there are perhaps only about a dozen valid species. Members of this genus inhabit northern and eastern Africa, Arabia, Israel, Syria, central Asia from Turkey to the Gobi Desert of Mongolia, and the plains of India. Most gazelles frequent plains or somewhat treeless areas; the genus ranges from sea level to about 5,750 meters elevation.

Gazelles are medium-sized antelopes. The length of the head and body is 1 to 1.2 meters; the length of the tail is 120 to 140 mm.; the height of the shoulder is 510 to 890 mm.; and the weight ranges from 14 to 75 kg. The back and sides vary in color from rich brown through fawn and gray to white. In many species a dark band extends along the sides, immediately above the light area of the belly, and frequently there is a light band above the dark one. Most of the species have white areas around the base of the tail and on the back of the thighs. The muzzle is normal and is not expanded as in *Pantholops* nor elongated as in *Saiga*; the neck is not long as in *Litocranius*; and the back lacks evertible folds as in *Antidorcas*. Both sexes of most species possess horns which are smaller and more slender in females. One exception is *G. subgutturosa*, in which horns usually occur only

in the males. Well-developed horns measure from 150 to 760 mm., but generally average 255 to 355 mm., and all are strongly ringed. Many gazelles have lyre-shaped horns, but there is considerable variation in the shape of horns among the various species.

The name gazelle has come to suggest grace and beauty for all the species are dainty, alert, and graceful. Although the herd size differs greatly, it is usually fairly constant within a given species, ranging from single animals and small family groups to hundreds of members. The usual size of the group is five to ten, however. The largest herds assemble in the fall among species that migrate to lower elevations and new feeding grounds.

The young are usually born from April to June and in a few days they have sufficient strength to follow the mother. Within a week they are able to run almost as rapidly as their sires. The life span is about 10 to 12 years.

The Bedouins and some sportsmen hunt gazelles with falcons and dogs. The falcon strikes its prey about the head and so annoys or injures it that it is readily overtaken by the dogs. The flesh of some of the species is excellent, while that of others is strong, coarse, and dry.

The genotype is *G. dorcas* (Linnaeus).

Springbucks (*Antidorcas marsupialis*), photos from San Diego Zoological Garden.

SPRINGBUCKS, SPRINGBOKS, SPRINGBOKKE, TSIPI.

THE SINGLE SPECIES, *A. marsupialis*, is native to the treeless velds of the Kalahari Desert, Angola, and South Africa.

The length of the head and body is 1.2 to 1.4 meters; the length of the tail is 190 to 275 mm.; the height at the shoulder is 730 to 870 mm.; and adults weigh 32 to 36 kg. The springbok is cinnamon-fawn above with a dark reddish brown horizontal band extending from the upper fore leg to the edge of the hip, separating the upper color from the white underside; the inside of the legs, the back of the thighs, the tail, and a patch extending onto the rump are also white. Both sexes have black, ringed horns. False hoofs are present and there are no tufts of hair on the knees. The general external appearance is very similar to that of the gazelle (*Gazella*). Springboks were separated generically from gazelles because of their teeth; in the springbok, there are five pairs of grinding teeth in the lower jaw, two premolars and three molars, in contrast to six pairs of grinding teeth in gazelles. The one peculiar and striking external difference of *Antidorcas* is the fold of skin extending along the middle of the back to the base of the tail. This fold is covered with hair, much lighter in color than the rest of the back, and when the animal becomes alarmed it opens and raises this fold so the white hair shows as a conspicuous crest along the back. At the same time the white hairs on the rump are erected.

Springboks are highly gregarious and at one time migrated across southern Africa in herds numbering over a million. These migrations were caused by drought which forced the animals to seek new pastures. They were so numerous and closely packed that it would take days for the herd to pass a given point. These migrations were so ruinous to crops that the government issued firearms in an effort to destroy the springboks. In addition to slaughter for "crop protection," they were depleted by poachers for biltong. Today springboks are very rare and exist only in one or two state parks in South Africa and on a few adjacent farms.

Antidorcas is the national emblem of the Republic of South Africa. The name springbok arose from their habit of leaping 3 to 3.5 meters into the air when startled or at play. In springing the body is curved, the legs are held stiff and close together, and the head is lowered; as soon as the animal hits the ground, it rebounds again with no apparent effort. *A. marsupialis* is suspicious of roads and wagon paths and clears these hurdles at a bound. These animals thrive on karroo shrubs and grass and are able to get along well without water, although they will drink if a supply is available.

Single births are usual and occur most frequently in November and December after a gestation period of about 171 days.

Springbucks are easily tamed and thrive well in captivity and as a result they are seen in most zoological parks. The meat is considered excellent.

Mongolian Gazelle (*Procapra gutturosa*), drawing by Adolf Kleinschmidt through Staatl. Museum für Naturkunde. Inset: (*P.* sp.), photo by Howard E. Uible of skull in U.S. National Museum.

MONGOLIAN GAZELLE OR ZEREN (*P. gutturosa*); TIBETAN GAZELLE OR GOAS (*P. picticaudata*); MONGOLISCHE GAZELLE, TIBETGAZELLE, TIBETAANSE GAZELLE.

THE TWO SPECIES are distributed as follows: *P. gutturosa*, on grassy plains in Siberia, Mongolia, and Kansu, China; and *P. picticaudata*, in Tibet, parts of China, and southern Mongolia. In the southern part of its range, the latter species lives on plains up to 5,750 meters in elevation.

The Mongolian gazelle has a head and body length of 1 to 1.3 meters; a tail length of 85 to 115 mm.; a shoulder height of about 760 mm.; and weighs about 20 kg. This gazelle is orange-buff in summer, with pinkish cinnamon sides and white under parts; but the winter pelage is paler. The Tibetan gazelle has a shoulder height of 0.6 meters, a weight of about 20 kg., and is brownish gray in summer and paler in winter. The under parts are white. The horns are present only in male *Procapra* and are 255 to 355 mm. long. In the species *P. picticaudata*, they have a pro-

nounced backward curvature, whereas in *P. gutturosa* the deflection is not so conspicuous.

The Mongolian gazelle migrates northward in spring to better pastures and to drop the young. They have been seen in migratory herds of 6,000 to 8,000 individuals in June. On reaching the summer pasture in June, the sexes separate and the young are born. Within a few days the young can keep up with the parents, and the adult males and females remain apart until the rutting season late in the fall. Buck Mongolian gazelles have swollen throats during the breeding season. The rutting season in the Tibetan gazelle begins in December and lasts for about a month; the young are born the following May. Both species commonly have one young per birth, but occasionally two are born. *P. picticaudata* travels singly, in pairs, and in small groups; it is a wary and swift animal that scrapes out its bedding places and feeds in areas of scant vegetation.

These gazelles, particularly the Mongolian species, are hunted for their flesh and skin.

The type species of the genus is *P. gutturosa* (Pallas).

CHIRUS, TIBETAN ANTELOPE, ORONGO; TSU (MALE), CHU (FEMALE), TSÖ (native names); ORONGO-ANTILOPE, TIBETANTILOPE, TIBETAANSE ANTILOPE.

THE SINGLE SPECIES, *P. hodgsoni*, inhabits the plateaus of Tibet and Ladak between 3,700 and 5,500 meters elevation.

The length of the head and body is 1.3 to 1.4 meters; the length of the tail is about 100 mm.; the height at the shoulder is 790 to 810 mm.; and the weight is 40 to 50 kg. The hair is short, dense, and woolly. The back and sides are pale fawn with a pinkish suffusion, the face and front of the legs are dark, and the under parts are white. Slender black horns, carried only by the males, are 510 to 710 mm. in length, ridged in front, and rise almost vertically from the head. The nose is swollen at the tip, the legs are slender, and the tail is short.

Chirus are quite wary and live usually singly or in small groups of four or five individuals; occasionally they form larger herds of 40 to 200 members. Except for the mating season, they are said to occur in herds of one sex only. Their call is a sharp bleat, and the gait is a trot which can be rapid enough to outdistance dogs and wolves. When in motion, the horns are held high, greatly enhancing the appearance. At rest chirus often lie in shallow depressions that they have excavated to a depth of about 300 mm., and thus sheltered from the wind and hidden, they watch for enemies. They graze and perhaps browse along the glacial streams on barren plateaus in the morning and evening.

They breed in November and December, and the young are born in May. During the rutting season the adult males eat little and are in a state of great excitement. The buck forms a harem of 10 to 20 does which he jealously guards. As soon as he sees an adversary, he lowers his saber-like horns and rushes to attack. These battles are fierce. The long sharp horns inflict terrible wounds and sometimes both die as a result. If a doe attempts to leave the harem, the

Tibetan Antelopes or Chirus (*Pantholops hodgsoni*), photo from *Mammals of the Second Yarkland Mission*, Blandford.

buck tries to drive her back. Meanwhile, the other does may take advantage of the bucks' absence and desert him, for there appears to be no bond of union between the buck and his does.

Apparently no living specimens have ever been exhibited far outside their native haunts. The meat of these animals is considered tasty. The chiru is considered sacred by the Mongols and Tangutans who claim that the blood possesses medicinal values and who predict the future by the rings on the horns. This animal is believed by some to be the basis for the story of the unicorn, for when viewed from the side and at a distance, the two horns appear as one.

Saiga Antelopes (*Saiga tatarica*), photo from Dierenpark "Wassenaar," Wassenaar, Holland.

SAIGAS, SCHAFSANTILOPE.

THE RANGE of this genus at one time extended from Poland to the Caucasus and the Caspian, but the species, *S. tatarica*, presently exists only in the area from the lower reaches of the Volga River across Kazakhstan to Zungaria. Even in this area its distribution is not continuous. In addition, a smaller form has recently been named from Mongolia, *S. mongolica*. Saigas prefer treeless plains.

The length of the head and body is 1.2 to 1.7 meters; the length of the tail is 76 to 100 mm.; the height of the shoulder is about 750 to 800 mm.; and the weight is usually 36 to 69 kg. The coat is heavy and wool-like, with a fringe of long hairs extending from the chin to the chest. In summer, the coloration is cinnamon-buff above, the nose and sides of the face are dark, the crown is grizzled, and the rump patch, the under parts of the body, and the tail are white. In winter the coat is longer and thicker and is uniformly whitish. The horns, possessed only by the males, are 203 to 255 mm. in length, irregularly lyrate, heavily ridged, and pale amber in color.

A remarkable feature of this genus is the inflated and proboscis-like nose with downwardly-pointed nostril openings, and with unusual developments and peculiar structures within: the bones of the nose are greatly developed and convoluted; the nasal openings are lined with hairs, glands, and mucous tracts; and in each nostril there is a sac lined with mucous membranes which appears in no other mammals but the whale. The inflated nose and associated structures may be an adaptation for warming and moistening inhaled air. The exceptionally keen scent also may be related to the nostril development.

During the fall, saigas collect in large herds and migrate southward to warmer grassy valleys. In April they split up into groups of two to six members and later they again congregate in herds on the summer range. In the spring the males go north first and are soon followed by the does. In their shambling gait, whether walking, trotting, or galloping, they carry the head down. Their speed has been measured to reach 60 km. per hour. They feed principally on low-growing shrubs and grasses and they are able to exist for long periods without water if their food contains sufficient moisture.

The young, one to three in number, are usually born in May after a gestation period of about five months. Although the young begin to nibble on grass at four weeks, they continue to nurse until fall.

The reduction of the once numerous herds is due largely to the fact that the horns, when ground into powder, are, or were, a prized ingredient in the Chinese pharmaceutical trade. A pair of horns brings up to $250. The meat is said to be tender and well flavored. It is difficult to keep these animals in captivity.

Saigas have been under strict protection since 1920. There are now over a million saigas in the wild, and with a yearly increase of about 7,000, at least 5,000 have to be cropped to prevent overpopulation.

Goral (*Naemorhedus goral*), photo by R. Pucholt.

GORALS; HIMALAYAN CHAMOIS; CHOSEN KAMO-SICA.

THE TWO SPECIES are distributed as follows: *N. goral* occurs from southeastern Siberia southward through Manchuria, Korea, Mongolia, and most of China to northern India and Burma; *N. cranbrooki* lives in parts of Tibet, Assam, and Burma. There seem to be no records of *N. goral* from the area occupied by *N. cranbrooki*. These animals are mountain dwellers and prefer rugged, grassy hills and rocky ground near forests at elevations of from 1,000 to 2,500 meters.

The length of the head and body is .9 to 1.3 meters; the length of the tail is 76 to 203 mm.; the height at the shoulders is 584 to 711 mm.; and the weight ranges from 22.5 to 32 kg. The body is covered by a short, woolly undercoat, which is protected by long, coarse guard hairs; the body covering looks shaggy and the male has a short, semierect mane. Coloration in *N. goral* is from buffy gray to dark brown above and paler below. There is a black stripe on the fore leg, a white patch on the throat, and a dark stripe down the middle of the back. In *N. cranbrooki* the coloration is bright foxy red to tawny buff, with a blackish dorsal stripe from the back of the neck nearly to the base of the tail. The general appearance of the goral resembles that of the serow (*Capricornis*), but gorals may be distinguished by their smaller size, absence of facial glands, and shorter horns. The horns, which are carried by both sexes, are conical in form, 127 to 178 mm. in length, curve backward, and are marked by small irregular ridges. The facial profile is concave, the back is somewhat arched, and the limbs are stout and long, well adapted to climbing and jumping.

Gorals usually range in family groups of four to eight members, although old bucks generally live alone most of the year. When one animal is seen, others are almost certain to be near. When frightened, gorals utter a hissing sound. They are most active during the early morning and late evening when they feed, but on cloudy days they roam throughout the day. After eating in the morning, they usually drink water, then they retire to a sunny rock ledge to stretch out and rest until evening. They are quite difficult to recognize, even though they are in full view, for they lie motionless and their color blends with that of the rocks.

The single young, rarely two, is born in May or June among crags and rocky recesses of the mountains. The gestation period is about six months, and the female has four mammae.

Although their heads do not make showy trophies, they are frequently hunted for sport.

The genotype is *N. goral* (Hardwicke).

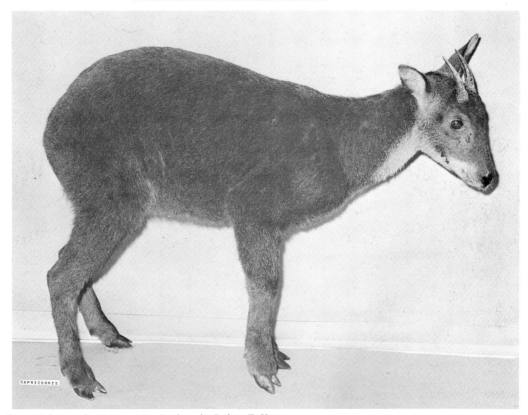

Formosa Serow (*Capricornis crispus*), photo by Robert E. Kuntz.

SEROWS; KAMING UTAN.

THIS GENUS comprises two species which are distributed as follows: *C. sumatraensis* from northern India eastward to central and southern China and southward through Burma, Indo-China, Thailand, and the Malay States to Sumatra; and *C. crispus*, native to Formosa and Japan. These animals inhabit bush or forest country on rugged rocky ridges from 600 to 2,700 meters elevation.

The length of the head and body is 1.4 to 1.5 meters; the length of the tail is 80 to 120 mm.; the height of the shoulder is 850 to 900 mm.; and the weight is 100 to 140 kg. The individual hairs on most of the upper parts have light-colored bases and black tips, giving a blackish appearance; the hairs along the spine, however, are completely black, forming a black dorsal stripe. The mane ranges in color from white to black, and the under parts are whitish. These animals are similar to the gorals (*Naemorhedus*) but differ from that genus in the larger preorbital glands and in skull character. Serows possess eye glands that produce a substance similar to that of the eye glands of duikers (*Cephalophus*). The serow has a straight facial profile, whereas the profile of the goral is concave. In the serows, the ears are long, narrow, and pointed; the rhinarium is naked; and the slightly-curved horns, which are carried by both sexes, are marked with narrow transverse rings in their basal three-fourths; and the horns are 152 to 255 mm. in length. The short hooves are solid, and the tail is moderately bushy.

Serows usually travel singly or in small groups of about six members. The gait is clumsy and not particularly rapid, but they are sure-footed in descending steep, rocky slopes. These animals are usually hunted with dogs and, when brought to bay, they defend themselves with deadly effect by attacking with their horns. Their call, which they utter when alarmed, angry, or wounded, is a peculiar combination of a snort and a screaming whistle. They eat grass and leaves in the shelter of thickets and on grassy ridges during the early morning and late evening. During the day they return to favorite resting places, often under the shelter of overhanging rocks and cliffs.

Little is recorded regarding their breeding habits. One or usually two young are said to be born in Burma in September or October, after a gestation period of about eight months.

Some natives capture them in snares and pitfalls. They are hunted by the Chinese natives for medicinal purposes, as serows are believed to have great healing properties. Their meat is mediocre in quality.

The genotype is *C. thar* (Hodson) = *C. sumatrensis thar* as currently arranged. *Capricornulus*, Heude, 1898 is often used for the species *C. crispus*.

North American Mountain Goat (*Oreamnos americanus*), photo from New York Zoological Society.

NORTH AMERICAN MOUNTAIN GOATS.

THE SINGLE SPECIES, *O. americanus*, lives in the Rockies and coastal ranges of North America from Cook Inlet, Alaska, and the eastern Yukon border, south to western Montana, central Idaho, and northern Oregon. *Oreamnos* was introduced into the Black Hills of South Dakota in 1924. The mountain goat, actually a goat-antelope and not a true goat, occurs in rocky areas at and above timber line.

The head and body length is 1.3 to 1.6 meters; tail length is 150 to 200 mm.; and weight is 75 to 140 kg. The conical and unbranched horns are black in color and 203 to 305 mm. long; they occur in both sexes. The pelage is white or a yellowish white, and the underfur is thick and woolly. The hair is long and stiff along the mid-line of the neck and shoulders, forming a ridge or hump. A beard is also present. The hooves have a hard, sharp rim, enclosing a soft inner pad, and are well suited to climbing over rocks and ice.

Some of the climbing and jumping feats of mountain goats are remarkable, although they lack the grace and daring of mountain sheep. Mountain goats climb with sure-footed ease but move quite slowly unless pressed. They graze on grasses, sedges, and lichens, and browse on shrubs and trees; *Oreamnos* may travel several miles through timber in summer to reach alkaline salt licks. Deep snow may force them to sea level along the coastal range, for their survival depends upon wintering in areas where the snow is not too deep. They sometimes shelter in caves in severe weather. Cougars, wolves, bears, and golden eagles may sometimes kill young mountain goats, but deep snow and snowslides are probably the chief cause of mortality.

The mating season is in November and the one or two young are born from April to June. "The kids can stand in 10 minutes, nurse in 20 minutes, jump in 30 minutes, and at 2 days stand 80 cm. high and weigh 3 kg." (E. Laurence Palmer, *Fieldbook of Mammals* [New York, 1957], p. 238). The mountain goat is probably monogamous, and the male, female, and young may remain together throughout the summer, but the females and the young usually stay together and the males live alone or in small bands of two or three.

This species is classified as a legal game animal in some areas.

Chamois (*Rupicapra rupicapra*), photo by Fritz Grögl.

CHAMOIS; GEMZEN, REBECOS, GEMSE, GAMS, ISARD, CAMOSCIO, CAMUZA. (Included are vernaculars used in other countries.)

THE SINGLE SPECIES, *R. rupicapra*, inhabits the mountain ranges in Europe and Asia Minor.

The length of the head and body is .9 to 1.3 meters; the tail length is 30 to 40 mm.; the height at the shoulder is 760 to 810 mm.; and the weight is 24 to 50 kg. The hair is stiff and coarse, that of the summer coat is only about 40 mm. in length and tawny brown in color, whereas the blackish brown winter coat is 100 to 200 mm. in length, with a thick, woolly undercoat. The under parts are light and the throat patch is white. The chamois is distinguished by the structure of its horns: they are set close together, rise almost vertically, and then abruptly bend backward to form a hook. Horns are borne by both sexes, are slender, black, and are 152 to 203 mm. long. The pad of the hoof is slightly depressed and somewhat elastic, giving them a sure foothold on uneven, slippery terrain.

They normally consort in herds of 15 to 30 females and young, but the old males live rather solitary lives for the greater part of the year.

During the rutting season, which is in the autumn, the adult males join the herds. During this period they drive the young males from the herd, and occasionally kill them. The usual number of young is one,

although twins and triplets sometimes occur. The offspring are born among a shelter of grass and lichens after a gestation period of 153 to 210 days. The chamois kids are able to follow their mother almost immediately after birth and readily improve their leaping abilities within the first few days. If the female is killed, the other chamois take care of the young; this undoubtedly plays a part in saving the species from extinction. The life span is about 22 years.

This beautiful animal is nimble, agile, daring, and graceful. The herd is said to post a sentinel to warn others of approaching danger by stamping its feet and uttering a sharp, high-pitched, whistling note. When alarmed, the chamois flees to the most inaccessible places, often making prodigious leaps. Their senses are acute. During the summer months, the diet consists chiefly of herbs and flowers, but in winter chamois descend to a lower elevation and eat young shoots of pine, lichens, and mosses. When the snows become too deep for securing food, they have been known to fast for two weeks and survive. However, chamois herds are periodically decimated by the "gamsraüde," a kind of scabies.

The chamois skin is soft and is made into "shammy" leather for cleaning glass, and the flesh is prized as venison. The winter hair from the back is used to make the "gamsbart," the brush of Tyrolean hats.

Golden Takin (*Budorcas taxicolor*), photo from New York Zoological Society.

TAKINS.

THE SINGLE SPECIES, *B. taxicolor*, is native to Mishmi, Bhutan, and northern Burma; the states of Szechuan and Shensi, and probably into southern Kansu China. Takins prefer dense thickets near the upper limit of tree growth, i.e., about 2,400 to 4,250 meters elevation.

The length of the head and body is about 1.2 meters; the length of the tail is about 100 mm.; the height of the shoulder is 760 to 1,070 mm.; and the weight of adults is 230 to 275 kg. This animal is heavily built and clumsy in appearance: the front limbs are stout, the lateral hooves (dew claws) are large, the profile is convex, and the muzzle is hairy. The genus *Budorcas* is most readily distinguished by its horns, which arise near the mid-line of the head, abruptly turn outward, sweep backward, and then upward. The horns are fairly massive, transversely ribbed at the bases, up to 635 mm. in length, and are carried by both sexes. Coloration of the shaggy fur varies from yellowish white through straw-brown to blackish brown. There is a dark stripe along the back. *Budorcas* exhibits physical characteristics of cattle, muskoxen, and goat-antelopes.

Takins gather in herds of considerable size near and above the tree line during the summer, but in winter they disperse into smaller bands and migrate to grassy valleys at somewhat lower elevations. The old bulls usually are solitary, but during August and September cows and bulls are often seen together. When alarmed, a warning cough is given to alert the others of the herd, at which time the animals quickly dash for the safety of dense underbrush. Takins make narrow paths through this thick growth which they use regularly in their passage to and from grazing areas and salt licks. They spend the day in thickets from which they emerge in the evening to feed. On cloudy or foggy days they remain active throughout the day. In summer they eat grasses and other tender mountain vegetation, but in winter the principal diet is bamboo and willow shoots.

They mate in July and August and the birth of usually a single young takes place in March or April. Within three days, the kid is able to accompany its mother almost anywhere.

Natives capture the takin for its flesh, which they highly esteem, by means of deadfalls, spear-traps, and snares. Europeans, however, usually regard the meat as of inferior quality.

ARTIODACTYLA; BOVIDAE; **Genus: OVIBOS, Blainville, 1816**

A. Musk Oxen in defensive position (*Ovibos moschatus*); B. Four-year-old Musk Ox Bull (*Ovibos moschatus*); photos from U.S. Fish & Wildlife Service.

MUSK OXEN; BOUEFSMUSQUES, MOSCHUSOCHSE, MUSKUSOSSEN.

THE SINGLE SPECIES, *O. moschatus*, is presently limited to northern Canada and Greenland. During the Pleistocene, *Ovibos* inhabited Siberia, the plains of Germany and France, parts of England, and the United States. In Eurasia, its bones have been found in river deposits with those of reindeer, mammoth, and woolly rhinoceros. It is believed that the fossil remains of musk oxen in Europe, Asia, and North America are identical with living species. In Europe and Siberia, *Ovibos* had been exterminated in prehistoric times.

The length of the head and body is 1.9 to 2.3 meters; the length of the tail is 90 to 100 mm.; the height at the shoulder is 430 to 510 mm.; and the weight is 320 to 410 kg. The coat has two parts: the dark-brown, coarse guard hairs, reaching nearly to the ground, which shed rain and snow and take the wear; and an inner coat of fine, soft, light-brown hair which is so dense neither cold nor moisture can penetrate it. The front and under parts are black, and the legs are light. The general form of this animal is robust, with a slight hump at the shoulder; the neck, legs, and tail are short. Although the musk ox appears to be clumsy, it moves about with surprising ease and agility. The horns, which are broad and curve downward, nearly meet in the mid-line of the skull to form a broad frontlet.

The musk ox is gregarious, and herds occasionally number 100 members. In the days before firearms, gregariousness contributed toward their survival, for when attacked, the herd forms a defensive circle with the calves inside. This is adequate protection against wolves, but it renders the shooting of an entire herd an easy matter for the "sportsman," since the animals do not attempt to escape.

1471

As the young bulls approach maturity, they are driven out by the herd masters. These young bulls often unite until they are old and strong enough to overpower a leader, who is then ousted from the herd and thereafter leads a solitary life. During the battles against other bulls to gain mastery over a herd of cows, bulls give off a strong scent. They are so jealous during the rutting season that they even chase birds which alight too near their cows. Mating takes place in August, and birth of a single calf occurs the following May. The young at birth weighs about 7 kg. and stands about 460 mm. at the shoulder. The calf follows its mother in one or two hours. Cows first breed when 5 years old and produce a calf every alternate year. The maximum life span is about 20 years.

Musk oxen feed entirely on plant life, regularly pawing through snow to obtain grasses, lichens, and mosses; they also eat willow and pine shoots. These animals are so well adapted to the arctic that they have been introduced on Nunivak Island, Alaska, where they are a source of food for the inhabitants. At one time the skins were used for robes, and the horns were made into bows.

Tahrs (*Hemitragus jemlahicus*), photo from New York Zoological Society.

TAHRS, KRAS, JAGLA.

THIS GENUS comprises three species, whose names and distribution are as follows: *H. jemlahicus* (the Himalayan tahr), the Pir Panjal Mountains, Kashmir, Punjab, Kumaon, and Nepal to Sikkim; *H. jayakari* (the Arabian tahr), the Oman district of Arabia; and *H. hylocrius* (the Nilgiri tahr), the Nilgiri hills south to Travancore and southern India. The typical habitat of this genus is tree-covered mountain slopes.

The length of the head and body is about 1.1 meters; the length of the tail is about 90 mm.; the height of the shoulder is 610 to 1,060 mm.; and weight is up to 100 kg. The body covering and coloration varies within each species. The Himalayan tahr has a shaggy mane around the neck and shoulders which extends to the knees; it is reddish to dark brown in color. The Arabic tahr is covered with shaggy, brittle, short hairs which are grayish to tawny brown. The Nilgiri tahr is dark yellowish to brownish and has a grizzled area across the back. Although the general appearance of these animals is similar to that of true goats, they differ in a number of respects. In this genus the males lack beards, the muzzle is naked, the feet have glands, and

the horns are not twisted but are somewhat laterally flattened. In *H. hylocrius* the female has two mammae, but females of the other two species have four.

Their habits are essentially similar to those of goats. Tahrs are gregarious and usually travel in herds of as many as 30 to 40 individuals. These animals are wary and difficult to approach, particularly from below, as they post a sentinel to keep watch for enemies and look downhill for danger. However, they do not watch as closely the hillside above them. It is surprising with what ease and security they scamper about their uneven rocky haunts. Tahrs eat almost any plant life available.

The breeding season appears to be variable but may have a peak in winter. The normal number of young per birth is one or two, the gestation period is about 180 to 242 days, and the life span is 16 to 18 years.

Tahrs are not as plentiful as they once were. They have some economic value as food for the natives. The hillmen consider the flesh an excellent medicine for fever and rheumatism. These creatures are seen in zoological gardens as they adjust well in captivity.

The genotype is *H. jemlahicus* (Smith).

Cretian Agrimi Goat (*Capra aegagrus cretensis*), photo by Ernest P. Walker.

GOATS, IBEXES, MARKHORS, TURS; STEINBÖCKE, BOUQUETINS, CABRAS, STEENBOKKEN. (Included are vernaculars used in other countries.)

THIS GENUS comprises five species that inhabit an extensive range from Spain eastward to India and northward to Mongolia and Siberia. Their range also includes Egypt, the Sudan, Ethiopia, Arabia, and the Greek islands. They are usually found in rugged mountain country, rocky crags, and meadows just below the snow line, although some occur on lowlands and plains. Goats seem to prefer an environment where the ground is broken and rough.

The length of the head and body is about 1.3 to 1.4 meters; the length of the tail is 120 to 150 mm.; the height of the shoulder is 600 to 850 mm.; and the weight in females is 50 to 55 kg. and in males, 75 to 120 kg. The coloration is shades of brown or gray; some are almost white beneath and others are dark brown practically throughout the coat. Goats are similar to sheep (*Ovis*), but among the differences are the following: goats possess beards, the males are odorous, the feet lack scent glands, and the forehead is convex, not concave, as in sheep (*Ovis*).

Members of the genus *Capra* generally gather in herds of 5 to 20 individuals, and the groups are usually led by an old female. There is a rather definite seasonal migration for some of the mountain forms. In spring they move upward to new areas for feeding, and in winter they leave the deep snows and severe weather to seek lower levels. These animals become active in the afternoon and may feed throughout the night. They graze and browse.

Mating, in at least some of the species, appears to take place in the fall, when the males join the bands of females. The young are born after a gestation period of 147 to 180 days. The mother protects her young by fighting with her horns or by decoying the intruder. The young mature in 8 to 12 months, and the life span is 10 to 18 years.

Present evidence indicates that the earliest domestication of the goat took place in the open-forest hills of southwestern Asia between eight and nine thousand years ago.

The type species of the genus is *C. hircus*, Linnaeus. A number of generic and subgeneric names have been proposed in the past for the various species. Currently, only *Orthaegoceros*, Trouessart, 1905, is used, for the markhor, *C. falconeri*.

Blue Sheep or Bharals (*Pseudois nayura*), photo by Ernest P. Walker.

BHARALS, BLUE SHEEP, BURRHELS, NAHURS; BLAUSCHAF, BLAWSCHAAP.

THE SINGLE SPECIES, *P. nayaur*, is native to the mountainous range which includes Kansu, Szechuan and Shensi, China; it also occurs north to Mongolia, and from Nepal to Kashmir. This animal prefers a habitat between 3,600 to 5,000 meters in elevation in areas where there is rich and abundant grass; it almost never enters bush country.

The length of the head and body is 1.3 to 1.4 meters; the length of the tail is 130 to 200 mm.; the height at the shoulder is 700 to 890 mm.; and the weight is 55 to 73 kg. The coloration of the head and upper parts is brownish gray with a tinge of slaty blue, and the under parts and the inside of the legs are white. The coloration blends well with the blue shale, rocks, and brown grasses of the open hillsides. In structure and habits the bharal holds a place intermediate between the sheep and the goat, but it is closer to the goat. The genus *Pseudois* is distinguished by the peculiar shape of the horns, which are rounded, smooth, and curve backward over the neck. Horns are borne by both sexes, and the maximum horn length is about 820 mm.

During the summer months, bharals usually associate in herds of 10 to 50 individuals, although as many as 200 may assemble at times. The groups are made up of both males and females. In the summer the old males prefer high elevations, but they rejoin the herd in September, at which time the large herds break up into smaller groups consisting of one ram and his harem. Sentinels are often stationed amid jagged rocks where they may obtain a good view of approaching danger, while the remainder of the herd rests or feeds. Because of their protective coloration and in the absence of any brush in which to hide, these animals remain motionless when approached. However, when they discover that they have been seen, they take to the precipitous cliffs, ascending to the most difficult and inaccessible places. These animals feed and rest alternately throughout the day on the grassy slopes of mountains.

Little is recorded of the breeding habits of these shy animals. They mate in September, and one or two young are born in the spring; the female has two mammae. The life span is about 20 years.

These animals do well in captivity but apparently do not cross breed with domestic sheep. The flesh is considered excellent by local tribesmen and hunters.

Barbary Sheep or Aoudads (*Ammotragus lervia*), photo by Ernest P. Walker.

AOUDADS, ARUI, BARBARY SHEEP; NAGOT, EDDA, MÄHNENSCHAF, MANENSCHAAP (native names).

THE SINGLE SPECIES, *A. lervia*, is native to northern Africa from the Atlantic Coast to the Red Sea and southward to the Sudan and the north bend of the Niger River. Rough, rocky, barren, waterless tracts are the chief habitats of the aoudad. This is the only wild sheep indigenous to Africa.

The length of the head and body is 1.3 to 1.9 meters; the length of the tail is about 250 mm.; the height of the shoulder is 915 to 1,000 mm.; and the weight is 50 to 115 kg. The coloration is a uniform rufous tawny; the inside of the ears, the chin, a line on the under parts, and the inside of the legs are whitish. This genus is distinct from all other wild sheep, the most unique feature being the mane of long, soft hairs on the throat, chest, and upper part of the fore legs. The horns sweep outward, backward, and then inward; they are rather heavy, wrinkled, and measure up to 840 mm. in length. The horns of the female are also large.

Aoudads generally associate in small family groups consisting of an adult male and female, with their offspring of various ages. Males frequently stand facing one another 10 to 15 meters apart, then walk rapidly toward each other, gradually gaining speed, and finally break into a run shortly before they collide. Just before impact the heads are lowered. A male will not attack, however, if the other is off balance or unprepared. The almost total absence of vegetation large enough to conceal these animals has resulted in their developing exceptional ability to hide by remaining motionless whenever danger threatens. Within their range, bodies of water are few and far between, but these desert creatures appear to be able to obtain sufficient moisture from green vegetation and the dew which condenses on leaves during the cold desert nights. Grass, herbaceous plants, and stunted bushes comprise their diet.

In captivity females are monestrous. The gestation period is 154 to 161 days, and the number of young is one or two. The life span of *Ammotragus* is about 15 years.

The aoudad herds decrease sharply during periods of drought. Desert natives take heavy toll of this large animal, which is an important source of meat, as well as hide, hair, and sinews, all of which are valuable in a desert economy. In captivity aoudads like water and enjoy taking a bath. Aoudads have been introduced into the southwestern United States. They have been crossed successfully with domestic goats in 1957 at Halle, East Germany; and offsprings of such crossings have been recrossed with ibex.

A. Mountain Sheep (*Ovis canadensis*), photo of mounted group in Denver Museum of Natural History. B. Mouflons (*O. musimon*); C. Barbados Sheep (*O. aries*); D. Young Dall Mountain Sheep (*O. dalli*), photos by Ernest P. Walker.

SHEEP, MOUNTAIN SHEEP, BIGHORNS, DALL SHEEP, MOUFLONS, SCHAPEN, DUEJAS, URIAL, SHAPU, NYAN, ARGALI, MARCO POLO'S SHEEP, WILDESCHAPEN.

THE SIX SPECIES are distributed as follows: In North America, *O. canadensis* (bighorn sheep) occurs in the western part north to British Columbia and Saskatchewan, Canada, and east to the Black Hills of North Dakota, Nebraska, Colorado, and New Mexico. *O. dalli* (Dall sheep) occurs in northwestern Canada (British Columbia, Yukon Territory and Mackenzie District) and Alaska (southeast to the Brooks Range and Kuskokwim River). In the Old World *O. ammon* (Argali or Marco Polo sheep) occurs in the mountains of central and eastern U.S.S.R., east to Shansi in western China, and south to Ladak and Nepal. *O. orientalis* (Asiatic mouflons, red sheep, urial, or shapu) occurs in the mountains of southern and western U.S.S.R., Iran, Afganistan, Cyprus, Kashmir, Pakistan, and Baluchistan. *O. laristanica* (Laristan sheep) occurs in the Laristan region of southern Iran. *O. musimon* (mouflons) occurs on Sardinia and Corsica and has been introduced widely in Europe at various times. These animals prefer fairly dry upland and mountain areas, often occupying the roughest and most precipitous parts there.

The length of the head and body is 1.2 to 1.8 meters; the length of the tail is 70 to 150 mm.; the height of the shoulder is about 1,000 mm. in males; and the weight is 75 to 200 kg. Some males possess a fringe of long hair down the front of the neck, but they do not have a beard. Coloration varies from creamy white through gray and brown, and some have light-colored markings.

Narrow noses and pointed ears are characteristic of this genus. The gland at the base of the tail that is present in all goats is lacking. The males have massive spiral horns, but the females have only slightly curved horns a few centimeters long.

During the summer the males associate in groups by themselves, while the females live with their young. Sheep generally confine their wanderings to limited areas which include places in which to feed, water, and rest—resting places are preferably under an overhanging ledge that commands a full view of the area below. Adults snort at danger and, when alarmed, bound away over jagged rocks with surprising speed and agility. Wild sheep feed several hours in the morning, then they rest during the heat of the day. They resume feeding in the evening and occasionally continue into the night. Grasses, flowers, young plants, and leaves make up the chief part of the diet.

In the late fall and early winter the older rams engage in combat for mastery of harems. In these battles they select a level spot, back away from one another, and then rush together with such heavy impact that occasionally one is killed.

Gestation periods vary from 150 to 180 days, after which one to three young are born. The female selects the privacy of the most dangerous and inaccessible crags to give birth. When the young is born, she becomes a careful and vigilant mother, keeping it close by her side and watching for potential foes. Puberty is reached at two and a half to three and a half years, and the life expectancy is 15 to 20 years.

The earliest domestication of sheep is believed to have taken place in southwestern Asia. The domestic sheep has the name *Ovis aries*. No wild animals of this species have come to the attention of zoologists, and it is possible that the species may have become extinct in the wild. Bones of *O. aries* have been found in excavations of human settlements dating as far back as 5,000 B.C. The fact that no wild living *O. aries* have been found and that no fossil remains of them have been found outside of early human settlements suggests that perhaps domestic sheep have been derived from one or more species of *Ovis* still surviving in the wild, but through domestication they have become so changed that their ancestry cannot be determined.

None of the wild sheep have a woolly coat comparable to that of the domestic sheep, although the European mouflon (*O. musimon*) has a woolly underfur in winter; but this is well hidden by the coarse, heavy coat. No other wild sheep are recorded that have such a woolly coat. It has been reported that when domestic sheep revert to the wild, they gradually lose much of their woolly coat and develop a coat of coarse hairs approaching the type worn by other members of the genus.

INDEX

Order, family, and generic names used by us as valid are in boldface type. Synonyms of valid generic names are so numerous that we did not feel justified in listing all of them under each genus, together with the explanations that would often be necessary, but many are listed here, in Roman type, as clues for persons accustomed to other books which use the synonyms as valid. Vernacular names in many languages, including tribal and aboriginal names, are also listed in Roman.

S

Designed by Edward D. King
Composed in Times Roman and Times New Roman by Monotype Composition Company, Inc.
Printed by Universal Lithographers, Inc., on Warren's Offset Enamel Gloss
Bound by L. H. Jenkins, Inc., in Columbia Pyroxylin Buckram
1500

U.S. Customary to Metric		*Metric to U.S. Customary*	

—— Length ——

To convert	*Multiply by*	*To convert*	*Multiply by*
in. to mm.	25.4	mm. to in.	0.039
in. to cm.	2.54	cm. to in.	0.394
ft. to m.	0.305	m. to ft.	3.281
yd. to m.	0.914	m. to yd.	1.094
mi. to km.	1.609	km. to mi.	0.621

—— Area ——

sq. in. to sq. cm.	6.452	sq. cm. to sq. in.	0.155
sq. ft. to sq. mi.	0.093	sq. m. to sq. ft.	10.764
sq. yd. to sq. m.	0.836	sq. m. to sq. yd.	1.196
sq. mi. to ha.	258.999	ha. to sq. mi.	0.004

—— Volume ——

cu. in. to cc.	16.387	cc. to cu. in.	0.061
cu. ft. to cu. m.	0.028	cu. m. to cu. ft.	35.315
cu. yd. to cu. m.	0.765	cu. m. to cu. yd.	1.308

—— Capacity (liquid) ——

fl. oz. to liter	0.03	liter to fl. oz.	33.815
qt. to liter	0.946	liter to qt.	1.057
gal. to liter	3.785	liter to gal.	0.264

—— Mass (weight) ——

oz. avdp. to g.	28.35	g. to oz. avdp.	0.035
lb. avdp. to kg.	0.454	kg. to lb. avdp.	2.205
ton to t.	0.907	t. to ton	1.102
l. t. to t.	1.016	t. to l. t.	0.984

Abbreviations

U.S. Customary	*Metric*
avdp.—avoirdupois	cc.—cubic centimeter(s)
ft.—foot, feet	cm.—centimeter(s)
gal.—gallon(s)	cu.—cubic
in.—inch(es)	g.—gram(s)
lb.—pound(s)	ha.—hectare(s)
l. t.—long ton(s)	kg.—kilogram(s)
mi.—mile(s)	m.—meter(s)
oz.—ounce(s)	mm.—millimeter(s)
qt.—quart(s)	t.—metric ton(s)
sq.—square	
yd.—yard(s)	

SCALES FOR COMPARISON OF METRIC AND U.S. UNITS OF MEASUREMENT

WEIGHT

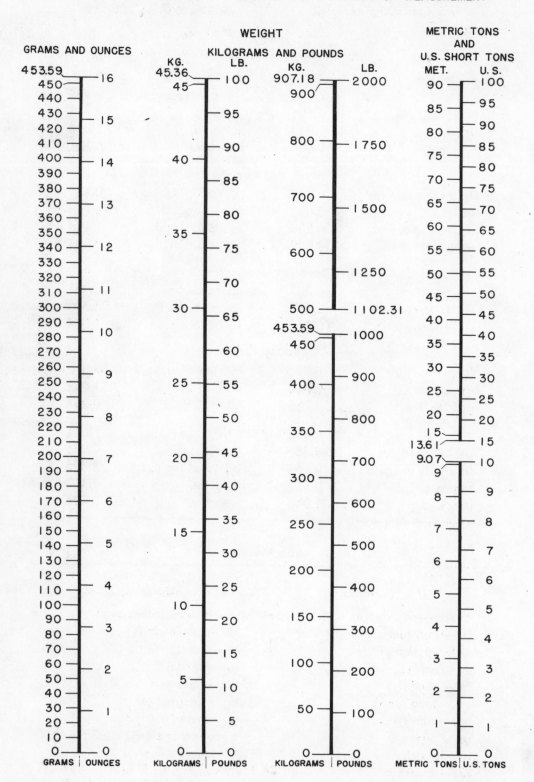

GRAMS AND OUNCES | KILOGRAMS AND POUNDS | METRIC TONS AND U.S. SHORT TONS